Table of contents

2. Methods for rock stress measurement

3. Interpretation of rock stresses

4. Application of rock stress measurements in mining

5. Application of rock stress measurement in underground construction

VIII

FOREWORD

The International Symposium on Rock Stress and Rock Stress Measurements was held in Stockholm, Sweden in September 1-3, 1986. The Symposium was organized within the Swedish National Group of ISRM by the Swedish Rock Engineering Research Foundation – BeFo and the Division of Rock Mechanics at the Luleå University of Technology.

The purpose of the Symposium on Rock Stress and Rock Stress Measurements was to contribute to the overall understanding of the state of stress in the earth crust, methods to determine the stresses and the application of rock stresses and measurements in mining and civil engineering. Technical sessions under the following headings were presented and published in this proceedings:

- State of stress in the earth crust
- Methods for rock stress measurement
- Interpretation of rock stresses
- Application of rock stress measurements in mining
- Application of rock stress measurements in underground construction.

The Organizing Committee wishes to sincerely thank the authors for their valuable contributions and hopes that the information relayed with this volume will be of use to the scientists and engineers who are concerned with rock stresses and measurements of rock stress.

No project like the arrangements of a symposium and producing this document is possible without the assistance of many. Tuula Kyräs at Centek/Congress and Annica Nordmark at BeFo made an outstanding job in preparing the circulars, arranging registrations and administrating the participants. Terje Höiseth, Agnetha Burström and Gun-Britt Överby at Centek/Publisher made an outstanding job in preparing the final proceeding in time for the Symposium. We would like to express our thanks for their unrelenting efforts.

The International Symposium on Rock Stress and Rock Stress Measurements was sponsored by:

- International Society for Rock Mechanics
- Swedish Nuclear Fuel and Waste Management Company
- Swedish State Power Board
- City of Stockholm
- National Swedish Board for Technical Development.

We like to express our sincere thanks for their kind efforts.

Stockholm, August 1986

Sten Bjurström
Chairman of the Organizing Committee

Ove Stephansson
Editor

Honorable lecture

Proceedings of the International Symposium on Rock Stress and Rock Stress Measurements/Stockholm/1-3 September 1986

In-situ stress determination – an appraisal of its significance in rock mechanics

C. FAIRHURST
Department of Civil and Mineral Engineering, University of Minnesota, Minneapolis, Minnesota, USA

ABSTRACT

This paper comments generally on the inherent difficulties of interpreting in-situ stress determinations. These difficulties arise primarily from geological complexity and the localized significance of individual measurements. Frequently the stress state information is sought as input for excavation design studies. In such cases, greater emphasis should be placed on assessing the effect of in-situ stresses, and stress variations, in combination with several other factors (rock strength, excavation geometry, ...) which influence design. Observation of the overall response of the rock mass to the combined effect of these variables is then more important than the specific determination of stress state.

RESUME

Ce rapport offre des remarques en general sur les difficultes inherents d'interpreter les determinations des contraintes 'in-situ' dans les roches. Ces difficultes arrivent primitivement a cause du complexite geologique, et le caractere ponctuel des essais individuels.
Frequemment, on se sert de l'information qui concerne des contraintes pour dessiner les excavations. Dans tels cas, plus d'effort doit etre attacher au jugement des effets des contraintes in-situ, aux variations des contraintes de point a point, en combinaison avec des autres facteurs (la resistance des roches, la geometrie de l'excavation...)qui peuvent influencer le dessin.
Les mesures de la reponse en total du massif rocheux aux effets integrals de ces variables sont encore plus important que la mesure specifique de la contrainte in-situ.

ZUSAMMENFASSUNG

Dieser Beitrag ist uber die innliegenden Schwierigkeiten in der Ausdeutung des Messungen der "in-situ" Spannungen. Diese Schwierigkeiten kommen erstens von der Geologischen Complexitat und von der lokaler Wichtigkeit der einzelnen Messungen. Die Information an den Spannungszustand wird oft gesucht als Eingabe zu den Aushohlung Entwurf Studien. In diesen Fallen sollte ein grosseres Gewicht gelegt sein an die Auswertung der "in-situ" Spannungen und an die Spannungs wechseln, welche, in Kombination mit anderen Einflussen (Gebingsfestigkeit, Form der Hohle u.s.w) den Entwurf beinflussen. Die Besichtigung der uberall Reaktion der Gebirgsmasse zu dem kombinierten Effekt dieser Variablen ist dann wichtiger als die spezifische Messungen des Spannungszustandes.

1. INTRODUCTION

Study of the deformation and failure of rock masses has relied traditionally on concepts of continuum mechanics. These concepts are powerful and can provide valuable insights for rock engineering. It is important to appreciate, however, that continuum mechanics, and engineering design procedures based on continuum mechanics, developed within the context of a concern for engineering materials and/or situations quite different from those often encountered in rock engineering. Care must be taken, therefore, to ensure that these design procedures are not applied inappropriately to rock.

In many classical design problems (e.g. design of buildings, bridges, pressure vessels, air frames ...) the applied loads are known and remain constant independent of the displacements (so called 'following loads'). The energy available to propagate rupture continuously exceeds the energy that can be stored or absorbed within the structure (Fig. 1(a)). In this case, onset of rupture, (at load F_a) is synonymous with collapse. It is important, therefore, to ensure that at no point in the structure does the applied load (or stress state) exceed the resistance (i.e. strength) of the structural material. Classical stress analysis is possible; the structural material adequately satisfies the requirements of homogeneity, continuity, and elasticity. The dimensions and locations of all components are well defined. Material properties (deformability, anisotropy, strength) can be determined reliably from laboratory tests on specimens of a size comparable to the prototype structure (or at least to components of it), and taken from the same material; strength variability can be determined and, together with other uncertainties in the analysis, can be accounted for by an appropriate "safety factor" in the analysis, thus assuring that loads in the structure are everywhere well below the limit (F_a) i.e., everywhere on the rising portion of the load-deformation curve.

2. IN-SITU STRESS DISTRIBUTION IN ROCK MASSES

Rock engineering problems are much less well defined than those described

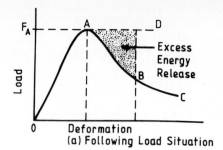

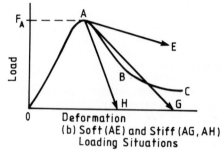

Fig.1 – Effect of Stiffness of Applied Loads on the Deformation Stability of the Structure

above. The rock mass has usually been subjected to numerous epochs of loading throughout geological time, producing fracture and faulting of systems of different orientations in space, resulting in a 3-dimensional network of interconnected blocks. The scale of fractures or joints is such that direct laboratory testing of a "representative volume" of the rock mass is impossible. Groundwater influences the pressure distribution in the rock mass. Undulating topography will also affect both vertical (gravitational) and lateral load distributions. In many rock engineering projects (tunnels, dam foundations, mine excavations, ...) the scale of the structure and the region affected by it are comparable to the scale of the rock mass jointing.

In some cases, (e.g. dam foundations, rock slopes) the applied loads have a "following" character. Here it is important to ensure that discontinuities are not so loaded (both by solid and fluid forces) that alone or in combination (e.g. as a wedge or connected planes) they begin to slide and, hence, collapse. Although more qualitative than for problems involving fabricated materials, design procedures and options for such problems are relatively well established (Hoek and Bray 1981).

For the case of rock masses at depth, the applied loads and spatial load distributions are unknown. The outer boundary of an underground excavation or series of excavations is often essentially infinite, so that loads initially concentrated close to the face of the excavation tend to be redistributed into the solid rock mass as the rock near the face starts to disintegrate; i.e. the load on this region decreases as the rock disintegrates. Thus the load, or stress, on the disintegrating or 'slipping'(in the case of rock masses with joints or discontinuities) rock mass has a stiff or 'non-following' character. [Lines AG, AH in Fig.1(b)] The energy output of the load on the failing rock may be less than the energy that the disintegrating rock can absorb(Line AH). In this case, the rock will not disintegrate, and will stabilize, still supporting some load. The existence throughout the earth's crust of faults, folds and fractures in geological structures that have not totally disintegrated clearly indicates that stable redistribution of loads and stresses, and hence heterogeniety of stress distribution, is a pervasive feature in rock masses. Given the usual inhomogeneities such as folded and faulted rock formations of differing compressibility, and discontinuities such as faults, joints, bedding planes, it is clear that the in-situ gravitational and tectonic forces will be distributed more or less non-uniformly through the rock mass.

Fig. 2 indicates several simple hypothetical examples of the influence of discontinuities and inhomogeneities on the in-situ stress distribution in rock masses.
It is clear from these examples that the in-situ stress distribution is likely to vary considerably throughout a rock mass. [Note that this comment applies also to the vertical normal stress (σ_{zz}), often assumed to be constant (equal to the "lithostatic pressure" $\sigma_{zz} = \rho g z$, where ρ is the average mass density of the overlying rock, g is the gravitational acceleration, z is the depth below surface.]
It also seems likely that as depths increase and discontinuities are subjected to higher normal stresses,

they will become stiffer both in the normal and shear directions. The discontinuities, especially smaller scale features with relatively little shear displacement across them, will tend to have a reduced influence on the in-situ stress distribution which in turn, will become more uniform. The data shown in Fig. 3 (reproduced from Brady and Brown (1985), p. 149) exhibits this trend. Depth does not entirely eliminate the influence of discontinuities, especially large scale features. Mature faults with wide gouge zones, for example, oriented so as to be subjected to high shear stress along the discontinuity, will distort the stress field for a considerable distance away from the fault even at depths of many kilometers. Earthquakes, i.e. unstable slip along faults, are recorded with epicenters of the order of 20 Km.
Excavations within the rock mass will intensify the stress differences due to inhomogeneities and discontinuities and may lead to instability and ground control problems around the excavations. If there are regions of relatively massive rock of considerable extent (from several excavation diameters to batholith-scale) within a more fractured or jointed environment, then stresses tend to be concentrated in the massive region, which acts as a "high modulus" inclusion (see Fig. 2) within the jointed rock. Excavations within the massive rock can produce brittle spalling of the exposed rock, and in extreme cases, rockbursts.

Overall, therefore, unless the geological conditions are simple and the rock homogeneous, it is to be expected that in-situ rock stress conditions will vary from place to place within the rock. Computation of the detailed stress distribution within a rock mass on the scale of isolated excavations is, in general, impossible. Facing this difficulty, and a belief that in-situ stresses have an important influence on the design of engineering projects in rock (e.g. the stability of excavations, directions of hydraulic fractures in oil well stimulation, etc.) experimental determination of in-situ stresses has become a prominent topic of study in rock mechanics.

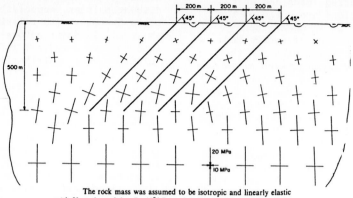

The rock mass was assumed to be isotropic and linearly elastic
with Young's modulus $E = 10^7$ kPa and Poisson's ratio $v = 0.2$, and the
joint stiffness parameters were taken as $K_s = 0$ and $K_n = 10^7$ kPa/m. *(p.219.)*

(a) Influence of discontinuities on stress distribution (after
    Crouch and Starfield)
    This example illustrates the influence of planar discontin-
    uities on stress magnitude and orientation.

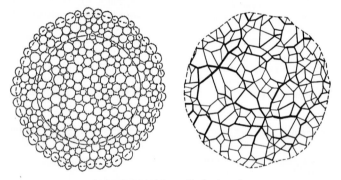

A computer-generated assembly of grains and
intergranular forces

(b) Non-uniformity of load distribution in heterogeneous mater-
    ials (after Cundall and Strack)
    The thickness of the lines indicates the magnitude of the
    forces transmitted through the assembly of particles. Note
    the decidedly non-uniform load distribution. Although a more
    severe case than is typical of rock masses, non-uniformity
    of loads in rock masses can be expected.

Fig.2 Examples of the effects of discontinuities and hetero-
      geneities on stress distributions.

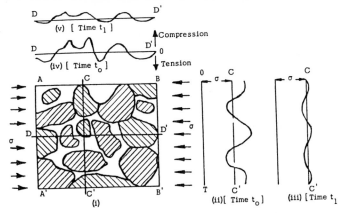

Stress Changes with Time in Rock Grains and Matrix.

(c) Strain relaxation (after Fairhurst)
This illustrates schematically the existence of grain to
grain variation in tension/compression stresses. The sum
of such stresses must be in equilibrium with loads at the
external boundaries - but the stored strain energy (proportional to the square of the stresses and hence always
positive) will tend to decrease with time, as the magnitudes of tension/compression alternations also decay. This
process can explain strain relaxation in recently unloaded
rock, such as cores.

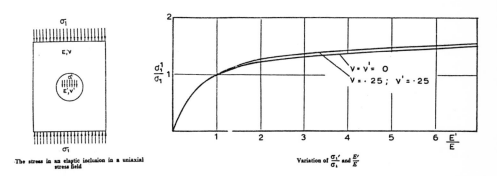

The stress in an elastic inclusion in a uniaxial
stress field

Variation of $\frac{\sigma_1'}{\sigma_1}$ and $\frac{E'}{E}$

(d) Stress concentrating effect of high modulus inclusions
(after Leeman)
It is seen that stresses may increase by fifty percent
or more in the high modulus inclusion, depending on the
ratio of inclusion modulus to host modulus. Note that
stress directions are unchanged. The analysis assumes that
there is continuity, i.e. no slip, at the inclusion-host
interface.

Fig.2 Examples of the effects of discontinuities and heterogeneities on stress distributions.

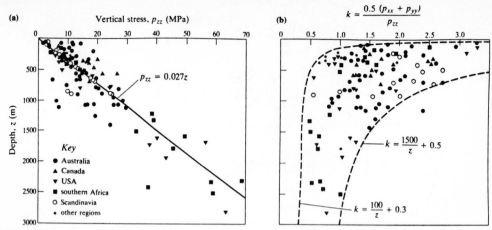

Fig.3 Variation with depth below surface of (a) measured values of vertical in-situ stress, Pzz, and (b) ratio of the average measured horizontal stresses to the vertical stress (after Brown & Hoek 1978)   [Brady and Brown]

3.IN-SITU STRESS DETERMINATION TECHNIQUES

Although a variety of methods have been used in attempts to determine in-situ stresses in rock masses, (see, for example, Leeman 1964-65, Fairhurst 1968), the two most popular currently are:

    i) borehole overcoring
    ii) hydraulic fracturing

Each of these methods relies on the fact that drilling of a circular hole into the stressed rock induces stress (and strain) concentrations and associated displacements in the wall of the hole. Assuming that the rock in the immediate vicinity of (i.e. $5 \approx 10$ borehole radii around) the hole is isotropic and linearly elastic, the induced stresses and displacements are as shown in Fig. 4. Strains induced in the borehole wall may be derived from the induced stresses (see e.g. Brady and Brown (1985) p. 141).

In borehole overcoring, transducers (e.g. the U.S. Bureau of Mines (USBM) deformation gauge; the Commonwealth Scientific and Industrial Research Organization (Australia) (CSIRO) traixial strain cell) are inserted into the borehole in order to detect minute changes in the dimensions of the borehole when the hole is relieved from the in-situ stresses by drilling (overcoring) a larger diameter annulus around the borehole. The

assumption of linear elasticity for the rock allows one to assume that the relief strains or relief displacements measured upon over-coring are of exactly the same magnitude, but opposite in sign, to the strains or displacements produced around the hole by application of the in-situ stresses. In order to determine all components of the stress tensor (σ_x, σ_y, σ_z, τ_{xy}, τ_{xz}, τ_{yz}), it is necessary to observe either

    i)   in a single borehole: radial displacements at several orientations (ϕ) around the borehole, <u>and</u> axial displacements at diametrially opposite points across the borehole, or

    ii) in several boreholes (each over-cored): radial displacements at several orientations around each borehole. The borehole measurement regions need to be fairly close to each other since it is assumed that the pre-existing in-situ stress field is the same in the vicinity of each borehole. The multiple borehole approach is sometimes used with the USBM gauge since this instrument measures radial deformations only. In special situations, e.g. near the free face of an excavation, where some stress

8

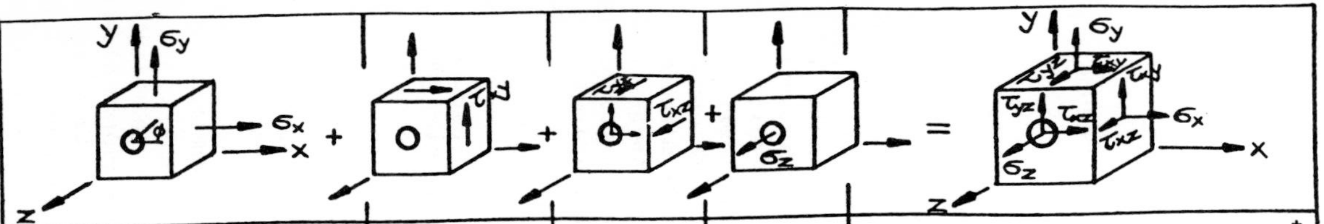

Stresses applied at infinity / Stresses at wall of hole (r = a)	σ_y, σ_x (x)	τ (xy)	τ_{xz}	σ_z	=
σ_ϕ	$\sigma_x + \sigma_y - 2(\sigma_x - \sigma_y)\cos 2\phi$	$4\tau_{xy}\sin 2\phi$	0	0	$\sigma_\phi = s_1 + s_2 - 2(s_1 - s_2)\cos 2(\phi - \alpha)$ *
$\sigma_z{}'$	$-2\nu(\sigma_x - \sigma_y)\cos 2\phi$	$-4\nu\,\tau_{xy}\sin 2\phi$	0	σ_z	$\sigma_z{}' = \sigma_z - 2\nu(s_1 - s_2)\cos 2(\phi - \alpha)$
$\tau_{\phi z}{}'$	0	0	$2(\tau_{yz}\cos\phi - \tau_{xz}\sin\phi)$	0	$\tau_{\phi z}{}' = 2(\tau_{yz}\cos\phi - \tau_{xz}\sin\phi)$
Displacements at wall of hole u_r	$\dfrac{a}{E}\left[(\sigma_x + \sigma_y) + 2(1 - \nu^2)(\sigma_x - \sigma_y)\cdot\cos 2\phi\right]$	$\dfrac{4a}{E}\,\tau_{xy}\sin 2\phi$	0	$-\dfrac{a\nu\sigma_z}{E}$	$u_r = \dfrac{a}{E}\left[\,(s_1+s_2) + 2(1 - \nu^2)(s_1 - s_2)\cos 2(\phi - \alpha) - \nu\sigma_z\,\right]$ ‡
v_ϕ	$-\dfrac{a(1 - \nu^2)}{E}(\sigma_x - \sigma_y)\sin 2\phi$	$\dfrac{2a}{E}(1-\nu^2)\tau_{xy}\cdot\cos 2\phi$	0	0	$v_\phi = \dfrac{-a}{E}(1-\nu^2)(s_1 - s_2)\sin 2(\phi - \alpha)$
w	$-\dfrac{\nu z}{E}(\sigma_x + \sigma_y)$	0	$\dfrac{4a(1+\nu)}{E}\big[\tau_{xz}\cos\phi + \tau_{yz}\sin\phi\big]$	$\dfrac{\sigma_z z}{E}$	$w = \dfrac{1}{E}\left\{[\tau_z - \nu(\sigma_x + \sigma_y)]\,z + 4a(1+\nu)(\tau_{xz}\cos\phi + \tau_{yz}\sin\phi)\right\}$

Stress and Displacement Components at Wall of Hole

(Positive as shown)

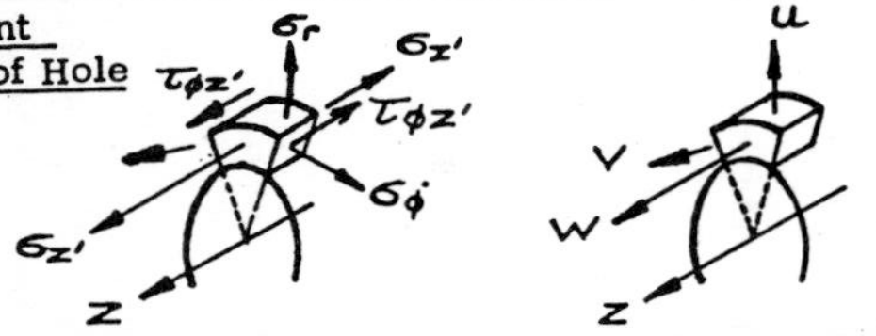

* Definitions of s_1, s_2, α as used above

$$\left.\begin{array}{c} s_1 \\ s_2 \end{array}\right\} = \sigma_x + \sigma_y \pm \frac{1}{2}\sqrt{(\sigma_x - \sigma_y)^2 + 4\tau_{xy}{}^2}$$

$$\alpha = \frac{1}{2}\tan^{-1}\left(\frac{2\tau_{xy}}{\sigma_x - \sigma_y}\right)$$

‡ $u_r = U/2$

U = diametral displacement

NOTE

Fig. 4 — Stresses and Displacements at the Wall of a Circular Hole in an Isotropic Elastic Medium

Fairhurst 1968

9

component directions are known, measurements in a single borehole may suffice.

iii) in a single borehole: radial and axial displacements can be detected by the strains introduced into a "low modulus cylindrical inclusion" containing strain gauge rosettes. The inclusion (e.g. CSIRO cell) is cemented into the borehole prior to overcoring.

3.1 Overcoring

There are two main limitations with respect to overcoring techniques:

1.   the very localized nature of the measurement. The stresses and strains induced by the borehole decay as the square of the ratio of borehole radius (a) to radial distance (r) (i.e., at 5 borehole radii from the axis of the borehole, the stresses are perturbed by $(1/5)^2 = 4\%$ only from the pre-borehole value); radial displacements decay inversely as the ratio (a/r).

2.   the difficulty of obtaining the required precise measurements under field conditions. This refers not only to the need for experienced personnel when using a particular technique, but also to the need for intact (isotropic elastic) rock at the measurement site. While this is not a serious restriction in some rock masses, care is needed in interpretation of the results if the intact rock is essentially a relatively high modulus inclusion in a lower modulus (e.g. fractured) mass. As Fig. 2 indicates, the stresses in the high modulus inclusion can be appreciably higher than those in the surrounding mass. [Obviously, a similar stress amplification will result for biaxial, and triaxial loading.]
Discontinuities within the zone of influence of the borehole may go undetected during the measurement, and can result in erroneous results due to inelastic slip either on boring of the original hole or during overcoring.

In summary, it is neither a simple nor inexpensive matter to make reliable determinations of in-situ stresses by overcoring. A robust instrument, used with care by experienced personnel aware of the theoretical limitations of the technique are all prerequisite to successful overcoring measurements. Several series of tests at different locations are needed before reliable conclusions can be drawn concerning the state of stress within a region of engineering interest. Such a program is both expensive and time-consuming.

3.2 Hydraulic Fracturing

Although overcoring methods are being adapted to facilitate their application in deep boreholes, hydraulic fracturing is still the preferred technique for use at depths greater than some tens of meters from the mouth of the borehole.

In hydraulic fracturing, a region of the borehole usually 10 borehole diameters or more in length is isolated by 'packers', and the packed-off interval subjected to progressively increasing radial fluid pressure, until a fracture develops in the borehole wall, propagating away from the hole, driven by penetration of the pressurized fluid into the crack. It is assumed that the fracture

(i) initiates when the internal fluid pressure (p_i) is sufficient to overcome the minimum tangential compression around the borehole wall, plus the tensile strength (K_ϕ) of the rock, i.e. from Fig. 4

$$\sigma_{\phi\ min} = 3S_2 - S_1$$
$$\sigma_i = \sigma_{\phi\ min} + K_\phi = 3S_2 - S_1 + K_\phi \quad \text{Eq. 1}$$

(ii) propagates away from the borehole in a plane normal to the minimum principal stress i.e. least compression, (σ_3) and, when pumping is stopped and the pressure system closed, or "shut-in", then the 'instantaneous shut-in pressure' (p_f) will be equal to σ_3.

$$P_f = \sigma_3 \qquad \dots\dots \text{Eq.1(b)}$$

If it is further assumed that the borehole axis is a principal stress direction [Boreholes from the surface are more or less vertical and it is frequently assumed (with little justification) that in-situ principal stresses are vertical and horizontal.] and that the minimum compression σ_3

acts horizontally, then S_1 and S_2 become $(\sigma_{max})_{horizontal}$ and σ_3 respectively. By recording the fluid pressure p_i and p_f we may solve the above Equations 1 for the maximum and minimum (principal) stresses acting in the horizontal plane at the depth of the test.

Using the fracture trace to indicate principal stress directions can lead, however, to substantial error. It is important to note that the shear stresses (τ_{xz}, τ_{yz} in Fig. 4) acting parallel to the borehole (anti-plane shears), produce an anti-plane shear stress ($\tau_{\phi z}'$) at the borehole, where

$$\tau_{\phi z}' = 2(\tau_{yz} \cos\phi - \tau_{xz} \sin\phi). \quad \text{Eq. 2}$$

The effect of the shear ($\tau_{\phi z}'$) is to change the direction of the two principal stresses in the borehole wall, such that they are not parallel and perpendicular to the axis of the borehole. The normal to the borehole wall [i.e. radial direction] remains, of course, a principal direction. The effect of the anti-plane shears is shown for a particular case in Fig. 5. It could be anticipated that fracture initiation in hydraulic fracturing would occur normal to the minimum compression [i.e. crack opening along the plane inclined at δ to the direction of the borehole axis (Fig. 5)]. Experiments (Leonard, 1985) reveal that:

(i) the increasing tangential compression suppresses propagation of the crack at the angle δ as the initiated fracture attempts to extend around the hole,

(ii) the cylindrical geometry of the borehole in effect "stacks" potential fracture initiation loci (each inclined at δ) above each other parallel to the axis of the hole],

(iii) the stress concentration at the borehole of the antiplane shears is weak relative to the in-plane stresses (see, for example Fig. 5).

These factors combine to constrain the fracture to extend parallel to the borehole wall, even though this may not

be a principal stress direction. The fracture does however, re-orient itself to become normal to the minimum compression principal stress as the fracture propagates away from the wall of the hole. Hydraulic fracturing experiments using a spherical cavity cast into "Hydro-Stone" (a gypsum

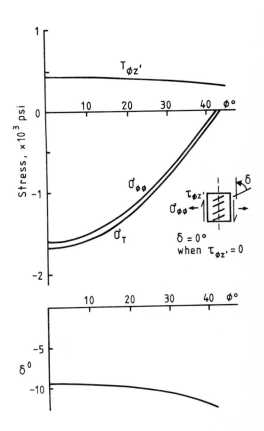

Fig.5 Variation of
(i) maximum tensile stress (σ_T),
(ii) hoop tensile stress ($\sigma_{\phi\phi}$),
(iii) anti-plane shear stress ($\tau_{\phi z}'$)
(iv) the angle (δ) as a function of the borehole radial angle (ϕ) for the case where the borehole is inclined 30° to the vertical in the y,z plane:

Hydraulic Fracturing Conditions
Pz = vertical principal stress
=1500 psi compression,
Py = horizontal principal stress
= 1000 psi compression,
Px = horizontal stress
=2000 psi; and
borehole pressure, Pb = 3000 psi.

11

cement) test specimens show that fractures do initiate and propagate normal to the minimum in-situ compression stress when the cylindrical geometry constraint is removed. Thus, in general,

1.   The existence of an axial fracture trace in the wall of a hydraulically fractured borehole is not prima facie evidence that the in-situ stresses are parallel and normal to the borehole axis, since the fracture is essentially unaffected by the anti-plane shear components of the stress tensor.

2.   The orientation of the fracture plane in the plane normal to the borehole axis does indicate the direction of the minimum (S_2) and maximum (S_1) secondary principal stresses.

Uncertainty as to interpretation of the fluid pressure-flow behavior during crack initiation and propagation, (e.g. the effects of changing fracture path, and changing permeability and fluid penetration into the rock as the hole is pressurized) result in an associated uncertainty in the calculation of the maximum and minimum in-situ stresses by hydraulic fracturing. Thus, while the technique is valuable because it allows estimates to be made of in-situ stresses at considerable depth, hydraulic fracturing is probably most reliable as an indicator of the directions of maximum and minimum stress (i.e. the "secondary" principal stresses) in the plane normal to the borehole. Good correlation has been found between these directions, as observed in boreholes across North America and those predicted from finite element models of 'ridge-push' plate tectonics for North America.

Figure 6 (after Pine and Cundall 1985), shows the results of a computer modeling exercise using the program FRIP (Fluid-Rock Interacting Program), in which discontinuities (joint sets) are explicitly modeled. The program simulates a geothermal field experiment in Cornwall, England in which fluid was injected from a borehole into a more or less vertically jointed granite at a depth of almost 2000m. In-situ stress determinations by overcoring in mines and quarries in the vicinity suggested

that the maximum horizontal stress direction (here denoted σH) at that depth was as shown in Fig. 6. Presumably, a small scale hydraulic fracture initiated in a borehole in solid rock would have indicated this minimum stress direction. It is seen, however, that as the pressurized fluid penetrates into the rock mass, the anisotropy in both rock strength and stress distribution causes the fluid to flow preferentially via the existing joints in an overall direction that is significantly different from that expected in an isotropic medium (i.e.in the direction of σ_H, normal to the minimum compression). Records of seismic signals generated by joint slip during fluid injection tended to confirm the model predictions both with respect to the general direction of the fluid penetration and with the shear-slip motion when joints subjected to shear stress (i.e. joints inclined to a principal stress direction) open under fluid pressure. This example illustrates a difficulty of extrapolating from small-scale borehole observations to larger scale situations. Note, however, that careful modeling of rock mass taking discontinuities into account did result in good agreement with observations.

Hydraulic fracturing tests have also been suggested as a means of measuring the ability of a pressure tunnel in a given rock mass to sustain internal hydraulic pressures. Although there are obvious similarities between these situations, the large differences in scale can be of considerable importance. Thus, while it is not unusual, in a hydraulic fracturing test, to locate the pressurized interval (e.g. 0.5m length in a 0.05m diameter borehole) entirely within intact rock, it is very unlikely in many geological conditions to find a corresponding length (i.e. 50m in a 5m diameter tunnel) of unfractured rock along a tunnel.

The discrepancy can be alleviated in several ways;
1. using the "fracture re-opening pressure/flow" observations, rather than the initial "fracture breakdown pressure/flow" observations, as an indicator of the pressure containment capability of the tunnel. This, in effect, starts the test with a pre-

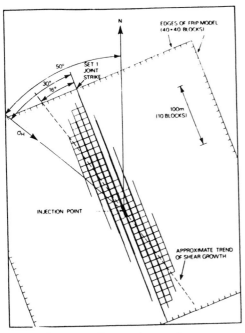

Fig. 6 Plan view of hydraulically stim- ulated joint network from FRIP model; 2:1 horizontal stress ratio.(Pine & Cundall)

existing fracture (generated during the first cycle of loading)i.e. the value of K_ϕ in Eq. 1 is zero). Alternatively, efforts can be made to include natural fractures or joints within the pressurized region.

2.   By continuing the re-opening pressurize cycle until sufficient fluid is injected to pressurize (and open) joints over a larger region, and observing the pressure-flow trends as the fractures extend. This is not possible in shallow holes, since the fluid tends to flow in fractures towards the free surface.

3.   If sufficient information on joint-set orientations and properties is available, it is informative to conduct discontinuum modeling simulations of the (large volume injection) small-scale hydraulic fracturing tests similar to those described above in Cornwall.

In summary, although in-situ rock stress determination techniques to date have helped develop a qualitative

understanding of the state of stress in the shallower regions (approaching 4 km in mines) of the earth's crust, their detailed application on projects is subject to considerable uncertainty with respect to the (excavation scale) heterogeneity of the state of stress in the rock, (i.e. the "general" signficance of a small number of measurements), the restrictive assumptions concerning rock isotropy and measurement accuracy constraints imposed by field testing conditions. Given these difficulties, it is important to give serious consideration to the purpose of the stress measurement program before it is undertaken.

4. PRACTICAL SIGNIFICANCE OF IN-SITU STRESS DETERMINATIONS IN ROCK

Information on in-situ rock stresses is valuable in numerous disciplines including tectonophysics, seismology, mining engineering, petroleum engineering, and underground construction. Given the unknown and probably locally heterogeneous distribution of in-situ stress, plus the difficulty and expense of conducting programs comprehensive enough to identify local heterogeneities (it is important to examine the need for direct knowledge of the local stress state before embarking on a program of measurements.

For the geosciences,much of the interest in in-situ stress determination is usually centered on regional estimates of the stress state at depth for correlation with theoretical models of plate tectonics, earthquakes and other deformation processes in the earth's crust. 'Direct" techniques such as overcoring and hydraulic fracturing have been limited to depths (see Fig. 3) that are relatively shallow in geo-science terms

'Indirect' techniques can also provide valuable qualitative information . These include a. Borehole 'breakout' or spalling. Borehole logging (e.g.by caliper) can identify ellipticity of the borehole, resulting from fracture (and loss of the broken material) due to a relatively high stress(concentration)- low rock strength combination at that location in the hole. The major and minor axes of the ellipse are taken to indicate the directions of the minor and major secondary principal stresses normal to the axis of the borehole.

b. Core discing. In-situ stresses in rock induce tensile stress concentrations that maximize in the center of the plane through the bottom of the bit, during coring. In high in-situ stress regions, the tensile stresses cause core discing, i.e. breakage of the core into "poker chips" during coring. The thickness of the chips decreases with increase of the in-situ stress level.

c. Differential Strain Analysis. As discussed with respect to Fig. 2, isolation of a core from in-situ stresses during coring may give rise to "grain scale" internal stresses in the core, and to time-dependent deformations. It is contended that the relative magnitude of these deformations in different orientations in the core are proportional to the pre-coring three-dimensional stresses acting on the core. Strain gauges are placed on the cores as they are received at the surface to obtain an indication of the down-hole principal stress orientations in space.

d. Fault-plane solutions. Analysis of seismic signals from earthquakes, and rockbursts and tremors in mines, are used to estimate the "stress drop,"or change in shear stress acting along the rupture plane due to dynamic slip. (See, for example, Spottiswoode 1984)

Assembly of all available data together with detailed geological information from both 'direct' and 'indirect' observations can provide considerable insight into the regional stress state. It is important to recall however, that the state of stress is 3-dimensional in nature, and 2-dimensional analysis may be misleading (see Fairhurst and Cundall, 1985). Study of in-situ stresses for petroleum engineering problems is somewhat akin to that of the geo-sciences in that borehole or seismic signal information is available.but there is no access to large openings at depth.

Much of the effort in stress determination by overcoring and hydraulic fracturing has been made in the context of underground mining and civil engineering excavations, where the need is felt to determine the in-situ stress on the more local scale of the excavation. Here we recall the comments earlier on the use of stress analysis in engineering design. The fundamental concern is with energy changes, i.e. an interaction of loads and deformations, and to ensure that the design does not "fail." This usually implies that energy changes during performance of the engineering structure, machine or system...do not result in undesired unstable energy states. As discussed earlier [with respect to Figs.1(a)(b)] it is usually possible, in the design of structures using man-made materials, to reduce the consideration of these changes to a criterion based on stress-analysis.

With underground structures in rock, loads and resistances are so ill-defined that design emphasis must remain directly concerned with an analysis of energy changes. Observation of excavation convergence as a function of time is probably the most valuable indicator of stability;it is at the same time probably the simplest measurement to make.

Fig. 7 illustrates the classical "ground reaction curve" used to discuss interaction between the inward deformation (convergence) of a point P on the periphery of an excavation and a support installed to ensure that the excavation does not collapse.

The support pressure pi required for static equilibrium tends to decrease because, as the rock deforms into the tunnel so the tangential stress T increases, tending to inhibit further inward deformation. (Note that the rate of decrease of pi with convergence differs for different locations around the tunnel) The resistance offered by the support will increase with inward deformation of the rock. Thus, for a given deformation, (Fig.7) Ul at P.,it is the difference (Fr - Fs) that is accelerating the associated deforming rock mass into the opening. As the difference declines towards the static equilibrium points F1,F2,F3 (for various support types) the rate of inward deformation will decline continuously. Inadequate support and/or disintegrating rock will exhibit acceleration of deformation as the rock mass and support curvews diverge. The convergence-time curves corresponding to these situations is shown in Fig. 7(b). Developing instability can be detected and remedial action taken (e.g. additional support).

The area under the rock resistance and support curves are proportional, respectively, to the energy released by the rock and the energy absorbed by the support. The magnitudes of the forces and pressures shown in Fig. 7 are usually not well defined in practical situations. For practical design purposes, however, the primary concern is that the excavation reach long term static equilibrium within an acceptable limit of deformation. Calculations (or estimates)can be made of the support probably required for given rock types and depths [See, for example Brady and Brown(1984) Chapter 11, 260-291], but convergence-time observations provide essential field assurance of a suitable

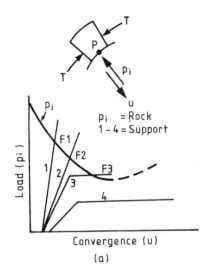

p_i = Rock
1 – 4 = Support

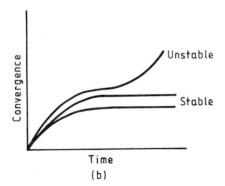

Fig.7 Typical Ground-reaction and Convergence-Time Curves for Excavations in Rock.

design. Extensometer systems and in-situ stress determinations are useful aids to help define the nature of situations requiring special attention, but observation of the overall behavior as described is the more valuable field measurement in excavation design.

It is interesting to recall the considerable activity in in-situ stress determinations in South Africa in the 1960's, stimulated by a desire to understand the causes of rock bursts, a serious problem in the deep gold mine.(e.g.Leeman 1964-65). Despite this activity, relatively little advance was made towards amelioration of the problem until the classical work by Cook (1967) who concentrated attention on the underlying energetic principles involved. Treating the planar reef excavations (2m or less in height) at depths in excess of 3000 m in brittle quartzites, as thin slits in an elastic medium, Cook computed from simple elastic theory the energy releases when a unit area of reef was "removed."If this energy exceeded the amount of energy that could be absorbed in crushing (Ec) of the rock then the excess energy release (Er-Ec) would cause violent disintegration. Again, as in the discussion of the ground reaction curve (Fig.7) above, the value of Ec was essentially unknown. Assuming Ec to be constant(albeit unknown) Cook reasoned that the potential for violent rockbursting would be minimized if the (areal) pattern of reef extraction were such that the value (Er-Ec) remained as close as practically possible to a constant value for each stage of reef extraction. The total energy released elastically due to a given change in the shape (plan area) of the reef excavation is independent of the geometrical sequence of intermediate excavations, but the proportion of the total released at any given step does depend on the sequence.

The concept of reef design based on computation of the Energy Release Rate (ERR) is now well established in rock-burst prone mines world-wide. Practical correlations have been established between rockburst violence or damage (Fig 8) and ERR, and substantial improvement in mine design has resulted since the use of the ERR concept. A more detailed discussion of ERR procedures is presented in Brady and Brown(1985)Chapter 10.

The conclusion to be drawn from these examples is, again, that the nature of many rock engineering problems is such that the approach to their solution should proceed from direct consideration of the energy principles involved and qualitative examination of interaction between various components. Following this approach, in-situ stress determinations sometimes tend to become of secondary importance in mining and underground excavation problems. The availability of computer programs that allow specific consideration of discontinuities represents a potential for advance in approaches to design in jointed and fractured rock masses - a situation frequently encountered, and in which design difficulties arise. It is now possible with such programs to examine, inexpensively(and graphically) the predicted consequences of changes in various initial conditions(stress magnitude, orientation, joint or fracture properties, fluid pressures...)on the response, for example, to excavation design or support alternatives. Such exercises can be very valuable in developing understanding of the 'critical' measurements that should be made in the field.It is probable that determination of in-situ stresses at specific locations will be desirable to aid in defining design variables. Undertaken on such a basis, in-situ stress determination can be very informative. It is also true, of course, that there are situations where the need for stress determinations is clear without computer modeling, or any sophisticated analysis. All too frequently, however, it seems that programs of rock stress determination are undertaken without a clear recognition of their limitations in resolving design issues.

5. SUMMARY AND CONCLUSIONS

In-situ stress determinations in rock are often undertaken with the intention of obtaining information specifically on the in-situ stress state, as a separable component in problems of engineering design in rock. Difficulties of interpreting the in-situ measurements, especially in the practically important situations where discontinuities and inhomogeneities in the rock mass have a significant, but uncertain, influence, make the focus on

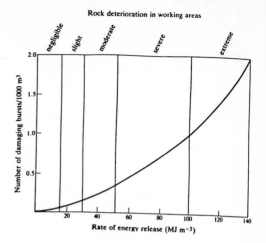

Fig.8 Relation between frequency of rock bursts, local ground conditions, and energy release rate in longwall mining of gold reefs (after Cook 1978)[Brady & Brown]

stress-determination unrewarding.

A more effective design strategy is to give greater emphasis to the overall effects of interaction between stress states, rock mass properties and excavation geometry. The design approach is then to develop
1. an understanding of the probable causes of observed field behavior
2. effective practical construction responses to the field observations.

Convergence measurement is the primary example of such an integrated effect; supplementary shotcreting and rockbolting used in response to observations of excessive convergence rates is an example of an effective construction response. The increasing availability of computer programs, useable on personal computers, that allow consideration of discontinuities, and testing of alternative hypotheses or assumptions(e.g. with respect to the in-situ stress state) and explanations of observations make this indirect approach to consideration of the in-situ stress now realistic.

6. REFERENCES

Brady, B.H.G. and E.T.Brown 1985. Rock Mechanics for Underground Mining. George Allen and Unwin, London.

Cook, N.G.W. 1967. The Design of Underground Excavations. In C. Fairhurst (ed) Failure and Breakage of Rock, Amer. Inst. of Min. and Metallurgy, New York. 167 -193 [See also Brady and Brown (1985) Chapter 10, esp. p. 257].

Crouch, S.L. and A.M.Starfield 1983. Boundary Element Methods in Solid Mechanics. George Allen and Unwin, London.

Cundall, P.A. and O.D.L.Strack 1979 A Discrete Numerical Model for Granular Assemblies, Geotechnique 29; 47-75.

Cundall, P.A. and O.D.L.Strack 1983 Modeling of Microscopic Mechanisms in Granular Materials. In J.J. Jenkins and M.Satale (ed) Materials: New Models and Constitutive Relations. Elsvier, Amsterdam; 137-149.

Fairhurst, C. 1968 Methods of Determining In-Situ Rock Stresses at Great Depths. Technical Report 1-68. U.S. Army Corps of Engineers, Omaha, Nebraska.

Fairhurst, C. and P.A.Cundall 1985 Correlation of Discontinuum Models with Physical Observations - An Approach to the Estimation of Rock Mass Behaviour. Geomechanics Colloquium, Salzburg, October (to appear in a special issue of Felsmechanic Springer Verlag. Vienna).

Hoek, E. and J.W.Bray 1981 Rock Slope Engineering #rd Edition Inst. Mining and Metallurgy, London.

Leeman, E.R. 1964-1965 The Measurement of Stress in Rock. Parts 1-4. Jour.So. African Inst. Mining and Metallurgy, Johannesburg Vol. 65 Nos 2,4;7,12. Vol. 66 No.3 (also reprinted in Fairhurst, 1968).

Leonard, G. 1985 Fracture Mechanics Analysis of the Validity of Hydraulic Fracturing as a Technique of In-Situ Stress Determination. Ph.D.Thesis. University of Minnesota, Minneapolis.

Pine, R.J. and P.A.Cundall 1985 Applications of the Fluid-Rock Interaction Program (FRIP) to the Modeling of Hot Dry Rock Geothermal Energy Systems. Proceedings Intl. Symp. on Fundamentals of Rock Joints, Bjorkliden, Sweden. 293-301.

Spottiswoode S.M. 1984. Source Mechanisms of Mine Tremors at Blyvooruitzicht Gold Mine. 29-37, in N.C. Gay and E.H. Wainwright (eds) Rockbursts and Seismicity in Mines. South African Inst. of Mining and Metall. Johannesburg.

7. NOTE ON DISCONTINUUM MODELING PROGRAMS.

UDEC(Universal Distinct Element Code), 3 DEC (3- Dimensional Version of UDEC).

Details of these programs and their availability in both main frame and IBM personal-computer versions, may be obtained by writing to Itasca Consulting Group Inc., P.O. Box 14806 Minneapolis, Minnesota 55414 U.S.A. Telephone (612)623-9599.

The principles of the Distinct Element Method are briefly described in Brady and Brown 1985 pp.180-182

1. State of stress in the earth crust

Proceedings of the International Symposium on Rock Stress and Rock Stress Measurements/Stockholm/1-3 September 1986

State of stress in Fennoscandia

O. STEPHANSSON
Division of Rock Mechanics, Luleå University of Technology, Luleå, Sweden

P. SÄRKKÄ
Laboratory of Mining and Metallurgy, Helsinki University of Technology, Espoo, Finland

A. MYRVANG
Department of Mining, Norwegian Institute of Technology, Trondheim, Norway

ABSTRACT: Rock stresses have been measured in Finland, Norway and Sweden for more than three decades. In this contribution a historical review of rock stress measurements conducted in these three countries is presented. A Fennoscandian Rock Stress Data Base (FRSDB) for stress measurements in the Baltic Shield and the Caledonides has been established. The data format is described, maps are plotted and results of almost 500 entries from 102 sites are presented. The data strongly indicates a large scatter in the direction and magnitude of stresses versus depth. The increase in stresses versus depth for different measuring techniques is also presented.

RÉSUMÉ: Les tensions des roches ont été mesurées en Finlande, Norvège et Suède il y a près de trois décennies. Dans cette étude, il a été procédé à l'historique des mesurations des tensions des roches dans ces trois pays. Il a été établi une Base Informatique pour les Tensions des Roches en Fennoscandinavie (FRSDB) pour les mesurations des tensions dans le bouclier baltique et dans le plissement calédonien. La disposition informatique est décrite, des cartes sont relevées et les résultats de presque 500 inscriptions en provenance de 102 sites sont présentés. Les données indiquent fortement und grande dispersion dans l'orientation et l'ampleur des tensions par rapport à la profondeur. L'accroissement des tensions par rapport à la profondeur pour les différentes techniques de mesuration est également présenté.

ZUSAMMANFASSUNG: Seit drei Jahrzehnten werden die Gesteinsspannungen in Finnland, Norwegen und Schweden gemessen. In diesem Beitrag wird ein geschichtlicher Überblick über die Gesteinsspannungsmessungen in diesen drei Ländern gegeben. Eine skandinavische Gesteinsspannungsdatenbank (FRSDB) für Spannungsmessungen im Baltischen Schild und in den Kaledoniden wurde gegründet. Das Datenformat wird beschrieben, mit graphischen Darstellungen auf Karten und den Ergebnissen von rund 500 Angaben aus 102 Anlagen. Die Daten deuten stark eine erhebliche Streuung in der Richtung und Grösse der Spannungen im Verhältnis zur Tiefe an. Der Bericht enthält auch eine Beschreibung des Anstieges der Spannungen im Verhältnis zur Tiefe bei Anwendung verschiedener Messverfahren.

1   INTRODUCTION

An understanding of the in situ state of stress within the Earth's crust prior to excavation is a vital requirement for the design of mines and underground excavations. Knowledge of the in situ stress regime also provides insight into the applicability of crustal dynamics such as plate tectonics, seismic risk evaluation and earthquake prediction. As a result, numerous measure-

ments of in situ stress have been conducted throughout the world during the past 30 years, both for specific mining and civil engineering projects as well as for research programmes.

Many compilations of in situ stress measurements made in various parts of the world have been published. One of the very first presentations of stresses over large areas was presented by Hast (1958). This publication demonstrated the existence of large, horizontal stresses in the Earth's crust. Ten years later Hast (1969) presented new results of rock stress measurements which further supported the idea of large horizontal stresses outside Fennoscandia, from Spitzbergen in the nort to Zambia in the south. Myrvang (1976) presented a compilation of rock stresses in Fennoscandia.

More recent compilations of rock stresses from various parts of Europe are, given by region: Alpine-Mediterranean region, (Greiner and Lohr 1980), Western European, (Schmitt, 1981), SW-German block, (Rummel et al, 1983) and most recently Western Europe, (Klein and Barr, in this volume).

Zoback and Zoback (1980) have prepared a map of horizontal stress orientations for the contiguous United States, inferring principal stress directions from geological data, focal mechanisms, and in situ stress measurements. They found stress orientations quite uniform within a given province. A normal and an extreme population has been observed by Herget (1986) in the Canadian Shield after the analysis of 54 ground stress tensors.

The Nordic countries have a long tradition in rock stress measurements. This paper therefore presents a historical review of in situ stress measurements in Finland, Norway and Sweden. Due to the large number of stress measurements conducted in these countries it was possble to enter the data into a Fennoscandian Rock Stress Data Base (FRSDB). The database was started in 1986 to provide a comprehensive collection of stress measurement for the area. The main objectives of the database are to to locate data on in situ rock stress measurements made within Fannoscandia and to determine any systematic variation with respect to geological structures, strength and elastic parameters etc. as well as attempting to establish whether any regional trends in the stress regime exist and whether any of the previously observed features of stress fields occur within the Baltic Shield. The database also acts as a foundation for further research.

2   HISTORY OF ROCK STRESS MEASUREMENTS IN FENNOSCANDIA

The overcoring method for rock stress measurements has a long tradition in the Nordic countries. At the time of this symposium it is exactly 35 years since the first "rock pressure" measurements were conducted in the Grängesberg Mine of Central Sweden (Hast, 1958). A few years later the magnetostriction method of overcoring by Hast was introduced in Norway and Finland. In the following sections we present a brief history of the rock stress measurements in Sweden, Norway and Finland.

2.1   Sweden

Measuring rock stress by the overcoring method with the magnetostrictive cell was first conducted in 1951 in the mines of Trafikaktiebolaget Grängesberg-Oxelösund at the Grängesberg iron ore mine, Central Sweden by Nils Hast. A preliminary report on the subject was presented as a lecture to members of the Swedish Mining Association and later published in a Swedish journal.

After completion of stress measurements in six mines in Sweden and Norway, Hast published the classical paper "The measurement of rock pressure in mines" (Hast, 1958). In a number of successive papers, Hast described additional results of his measurements around the world, see Hast (1974) for a complete list of references. His results, in particular the measured excess of horisontal stresses in the upper part of the Earth's crust, were controversial to the earth scientists of the late fifties.

One of the very first tests to test the feasibility of gluing strain gauges on rock surfaces in order to determine the state of stress was conducted by Gustavsson and Wirstam (1951). They applied a technique consisting of strain gauges combined with overcoring to determine the pillar load in sandstone pillars in the Laisvall lead mine, Northern Sweden. Following the development by Leeman (1964) the Swedish State Power Board (SV) developed the two-dimensional doorstopper method, (Hiltscher, 1969) and later the three-dimensional overcoring method with strain gauges. In 1979 the group at SV completed stress measurement in a 500 m deep vertical borehole (Hiltscher et al , 1979).

In 1976 the Leeman triaxial strain cell was introduced at the Division of Rock Mechanics, Luleå University of Technology (Carlsson, 1978 and Leijon et al, 1981). The original Leeman cell was modified by B Leijon. Improvements have been made in the hole-cleaning technique, the installation tool, the readout equipment and four-component strain gauges (Leijon, 1986).

For several years, the Stripa mine in Central Sweden has been the site for rock mechanical field testing, in order to evaluate the feasibility of storing radioactive waste in granitic rocks. In 1981/82 Doe et al (1983) carried out a programme of in situ stress measurements by hydrofracturing in combination with a variety of overcoring techniques. This was the first test of hydraulic fracturing and overcoring in the same deep borehole and the very first hydraulic fracturing stress measurement in Sweden. In 1982 the Division of Rock Mechanics at Luleå University of Technology built its first version of the hydrofracturing field unit, (Stephansson and Ångman, 1986). A later version of the hydrofracturing instrumentation was completed in 1985. Altogether, testing has been conducted at five sites in Fennoscandian bedrock (Bjarnason et al, 1986). Hydraulic fracturing rock stress measurements for the Swedish Hot Dry Rock Project have been conducted as a joint project between the University of Bochum and the Department of Geology of Chalmers Institute of Technology (Sundqvist, 1985).

The latest development in rock stress measurement techniques in Sweden is sleeve fracturing, (Stephansson, 1983). With this method a dilatometer is allowed to expand in the borehole. Simultaneous recording of the pressure and volume changes of the pressurizing liquid allow the rock deformability and rock stress to be calculated.

2.2 Norway

The first stress measurements in Norway were carried out by professor Hast in 1958. The Mining Department of the Norwegian Institute of Technology (NTH) started their first test in 1964 with an early version of the USBM cell (Gelvold et al, 1967). This was to be followed by extensive development of the doorstopper method during the years 1965-67, (Li, 1967). A pioneer in connection with this was the late professor Bjørn Li, whose contributions to the field of rock mechanics in Norway were most important. The first tests with a triaxial rock stress measuring device were conducted in 1968, (Myrvang, 1970). The instrument used was a modification of the Leeman cell. Both this cell and the doorstopper are still in use at the NTH, but the devices have undergone continuous development throughout the years and are today reliable tools with reasonable accuracy for practical purposes.

Today the majority of mining companies in Norway use rock stress measurements and rock mechanics as important tools in mine planning and operation, (Myrvang and Grimstad, 1981). Because the Norwegian mining industry is small, NTH in cooperation with SINTEF (The Foundation of Scientific and Technical Research at the Norwegian Institute of Technology) act as a central rock mechanics laboratory for the mines. During the last 10 years rock stress measurements have become increasingly important in civil engineering projects. As many tunnelling projects in Norway are affected by high stresses with associated spalling and rock burst problems, the determination of the in situ stress field is important. Predictions, based on the interpretation of early rock stress problems, can be made, as demonstrated by Myrvang (1984). In many Norwegian hydroelectric power plants unlined pressure shafts are used. A very important criteria here is that the minor principal stress in the rock mass is greater than the water pressure. In this connection rock stress measurements are vital before the final decision is made, both as general information and as the most important input in numerical modelling. During recent years a combination of triaxial stress measurements by SINTEF and simple hydraulic fracturing by The Norwegian Geotechnical Institute (NGI) has been carried out.

For the time being, storage of natural gas under high pressure in unlined caverns is seriously discussed in Norway, (Roald et al, 1986). In this case, as well as before, knowledge concerning rock stresses is vital.

The first measurements of the state of stress in Finnish bedrock were conducted in Lohja Co's Tytyri limestone mine by professor Hast's measurement team in 1961. After further experiments the company bought Hast's equipment in 1964.

In the sixties, Lohja Co's stress measurement group was the only one conducting stress measurements in Finland. It performed about 60 measurements at 9 different mines. The results were used mainly in mine planning. In 1970 a Leeman device modified by the Norwegian Institute of Technology (NTH), Trondheim, was purchased by the company for true triaxial measurements.

In 1971 all equipment and contracts were transferred to a state-owned mining company, Suomen Malmi OY Finnprospecting. In the seventies interest in stress determinations increased, mainly due to better possibilities of utilizing the results in computerized stability calculations.

Some tests were done in 1977-1979 by the Helsinki University of Technology, Laboratory of Mining Engineering, with a soft-inclusion device. The method was technically successful, but not commercially applicable (Särkkä, 1978).

In the eighties measurements of the state of stress became a standard test for all major underground projects, both in mining and in civil engineering. The main method used employs the Leeman-NTH device. A compilation of all Finnish stress measurements until 1981 was presented by Matikainen 1981.

Today there is an increasing need for the determination of stress at depths of 200 to 300 m and in some cases down to 1000 m. Several new methods have been tested. Among these are hydraulic fracturing and the Leeman-Hiltscher (Swedish State Power Board) method. One method that remains to be tested is differential strain analysis (DSA), which allows stresses to be measured in the laboratory.

As of the summer of 1986, 170 measurements have been done at 45 different locations in Finland. These are mainly restricted to the mining districts, major cities, and industrial areas for underground storage facilities.

Rock stress data for Finland, Norway and Sweden have been compiled as a computer data base entitled Fennoscandian Rock Stress Data Base (FRSDB). The data base was started in early 1986 as a joint project between the mining departments in Helsinki (Finland), Trondheim (Norway), and Luleå (Sweden) to provide a comprehensive collection of stress measurement for the area of concern.

3.1   Technical aspects of the data base

A computer data base is a short-lived product intended to disseminate its information widely and rapidly. Therefore we decided to choose a general data handling software package for micro computers. The rock stress data base was designed and implemented using KNOWLEDGEMAN, version 1.07, which is widely used and can be implemented on most modern personal computers. A copy of the data base is available by subscription to K Bergström Division of Rock Mechanics, Luleå University of Technology, S-951 87 Luleå, Sweden.

The FRSDB data base of rock stress measurements, as implemented, consists of 36 fields for entering, printing and plotting information. A listing of entry no 62 in the data base is shown in Figure 1. Some of the fields require further explanation.

Information in FRSDB has two access levels. Most of the information stored to today is freely accessible. Data can be implemented and extracted for each country separately and/or together. Input data for FRSDB has been collected separately by each of the research groups in Finland, Norway and Sweden. For Finland and Norway data were stored in one or two archives, whereas for Sweden data had to be collected from a number of sources. References to published data are always presented in FRSDB. Site co-ordinates are given as latitude in degrees north and longitude, of positive sign, indicating degrees east of Greenwich. Topography is presented according to a five digits scale, where 1 means flat and 5 steeply hilly. Stratigraphy of the measuring site is presented in accordance with the stratigraphic scheme of the geological map of the Baltic Shield, Figure 2. A list of

Output of entry #62

Country : SWEDEN   year : 1977
Site   : NÄSLIDEN
Measuring Group : DIVISION OF ROCK MECHANICS,UNIVERSITY OF LULEA
Method   : LEEMAN
Information given by :
UNIVERSITY OF LULEA AND SWEDISH ROCK ENGINEERING FOUNDATION,BEFO.
INPUT IN NRSDB BY OVE STEPHANSSON

References :
STRESS MEASUREMENTS IN NÄSLIDEN MINE.LEIJON,B.,CARLSSON,H.AND MYRVANG,A.
IN EDITOR O STEPHANSSON AND M JONES APPLICATION OF ROCK MECHANICS TO CUT
AND FILL MINING.IMM,LONDON.1981,P.162 - 168.
Measuring Station   : DRIFT TO BOTTOM OF STOPE 2 BH2
Coordinates   : X= 2257   Y= 1501   Z= 261   (32.8,44.4)
Vertical overburden (m) : 260
Topography   : SLIGHTLY HILLY
Direction of measuring hole (deg) :   5
Dip of measuring hole (deg)   :   0
Stratigraphy   : MAINLY FELSIC VOLCANICS (SVECOFENNIAN,KALEVIAN AND
                   OTHERS, 2000-1900 Ma)
Rocktype   : QUARTZITE
Major structure : SCHISTOSE direction (deg)= 110   dip (deg)= 70
Density (kg/m3) : 3000
Uniaxial Compressive Strength (MPa) :
Tensile Strength (MPa) :
Point Load Index:
Young's Modulus (GPa) : 68.1
Poisson's Ratio   : 0.22
Seismic Velocity (m/s) :
Magnitude and Direction of Principal Stress :
Sigma1 (MPa) = 22.2   Direction (deg) = 245   Dip (deg) = 25
Sigma2 (MPa) = 14.4   Direction (deg) = 156   Dip (deg) = 20
Sigma3 (MPa) = 5.8   Direction (deg) = 35   Dip (deg) = 80
Vertical stress (MPa)   :   6.0
Maximum Horizontal Stress (MPa) :   21.0
Minimun Horizontal Stress (MPa) :   14.0
Direction of Maximum Horizontal Stress (deg) : 245
Comments :
MEASUREMENTS WERE CONDUCTED VWITH THE LEEMAN OVERCORING INSTRUMENT FROM CSIR.
SIGMAH VARIES ACCORDING TO EQ.SIGH=6.1+0.045Z THE CORRELATION COEFFICIENT
BEEING 0.75.DATA WERE USED FOR FEM ANALYSIS FOR THE NÄSLIDEN PROJECT.
FIVE MEASURING POINTS ALONG THE BOREHOLE NOT FARE FROM THE SHAFT.

Figure 1.   Example of data entry to Fennoscandian Rock Stress Data Base (FRSDB).

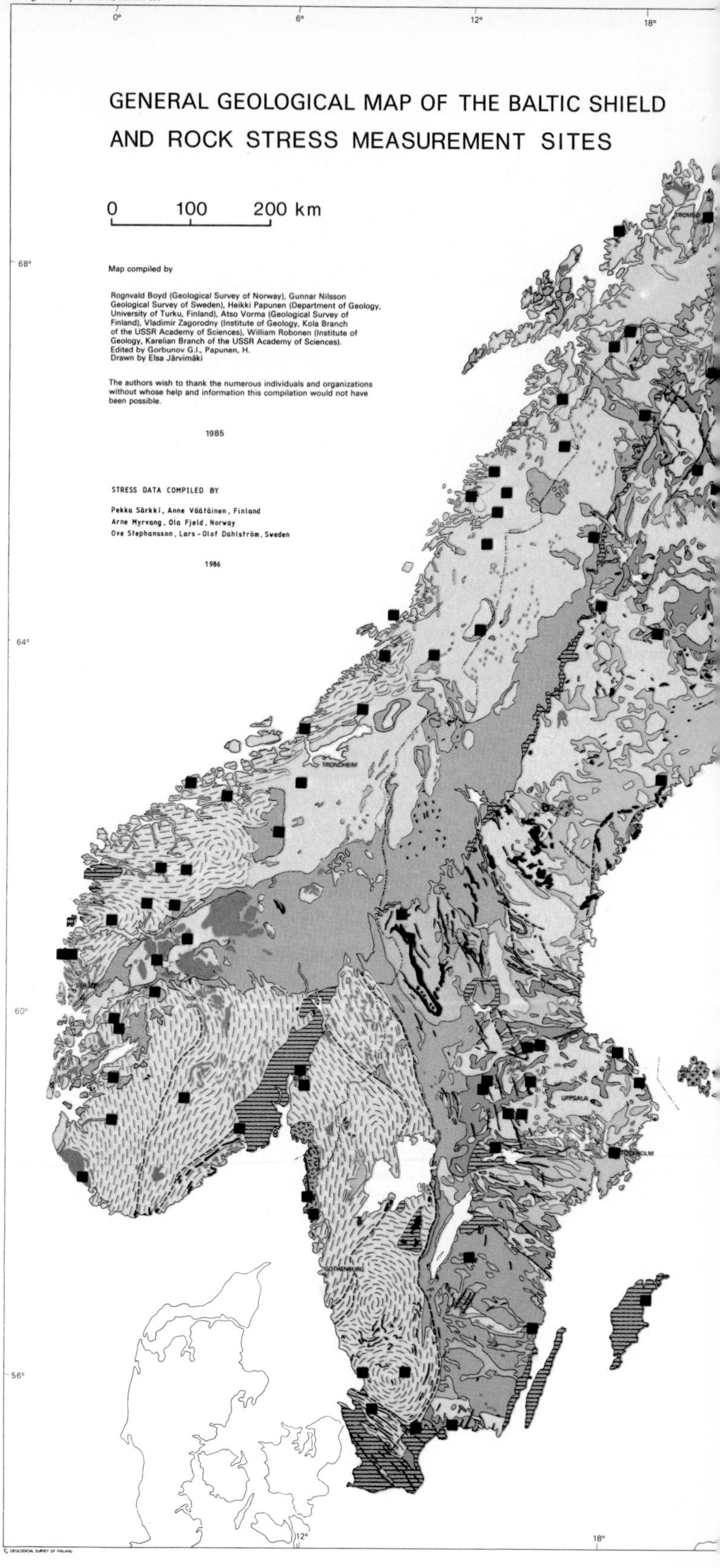

Figure 2. Geological map of the Baltic Shield and location of in situ stress measurements in Finland, Norway and Sweden.

Map 1

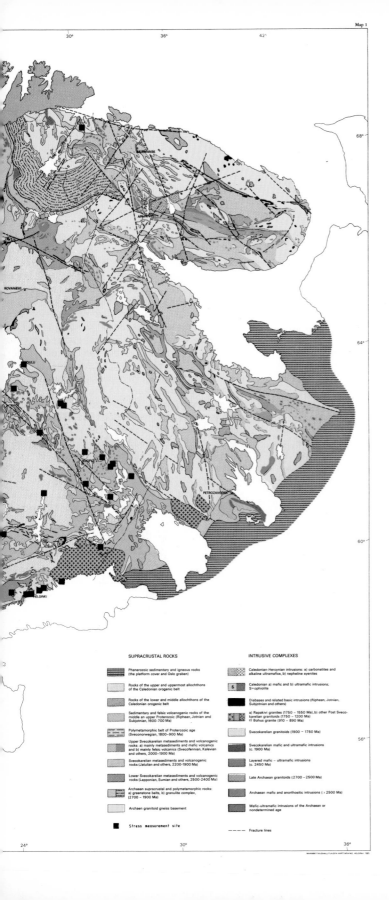

30°   36°   42°

68°

64°

60°

56°

24°   30°   36°

SUPRACRUSTAL ROCKS

INTRUSIVE COMPLEXES

Phanerozoic sedimentary and igneous rocks (the platform cover and Oslo graben)

Rocks of the upper and uppermost allochthons of the Caledonian orogenic belt

Rocks of the lower and middle allochthons of the Caledonian orogenic belt

Sedimentary and felsic volcanogenic rocks of the middle an upper Proterozoic (Riphean, Jotnian and Subjotnian, 1600–700 Ma)

Polymetamorphic belt of Proterozoic age (Sveconorwegian, 1800–900 Ma)

Upper Svecokarelian metasediments and volcanogenic rocks: a) mainly metasediments and mafic volcanics and b) mainly felsic volcanics (Svecofennian, Kalevian and others, 2000–1900 Ma)

Svecokarelian metasediments and volcanogenic rocks (Jatulian and others, 2200–1900 Ma)

Lower Svecokarelian metasediments and volcanogenic rocks (Lapponian, Sumian and others, 2500–2400 Ma)

Archaean supracrustal and polymetamorphic rocks: a) greenstone belts, b) granulite complex, (2700 – 1900 Ma)

Archaean granitoid gneiss basement

■ Stress measurement site

Caledonian-Hercynian intrusions: a) carbonatites and alkaline ultramafics, b) nepheline syenites

Caledonian a) mafic and b) ultramafic intrusions; S=ophiolite

Diabases and related basic intrusions (Riphean, Jotnian, Subjotnian and others)

a) Rapakivi granites (1750 – 1550 Ma), b) other Post Sveco-karelian granitoids (1750 – 1200 Ma) c) Bohus granite (910 – 890 Ma)

Svecokarelian granitoids (1900 – 1750 Ma)

Svecokarelian mafic and ultramafic intrusions (c. 1900 Ma)

Layered mafic – ultramafic intrusions (c. 2450 Ma)

Late Archaean granitoids (2700 – 2500 Ma)

Archaean mafic and anorthositic intrusions (> 2500 Ma)

Mafic-ultramafic intrusions of the Archaean or nondetermined age

- - - - Fracture lines

90 rock types together with a list of different geological structures are used to describe the geology of the test site. For a number of rock stress measurement sites rock testing has been done and these data are stored in the data base. Magnitude and direction of principal and horizontal stresses are presented as the last entry for each measurement. 5 lines of 76 characters each are allowed for comments to the entry.

3.2   Current state of FRSDB

The FRSDB database contained 487 entries from 102 sites as of June 1986. The location of the measuring sites and their stratigraphy is shown in Figure 2. The quality of recorded stresses can be specified only as a comment to the entry. Only results from measured in situ rock stresses are entries to FRSDB. Stress data ifluenced by underground structures such as mines, tunnels and excavations are omitted. Interpreted stresses from focal mechanism studies of earthquakes and mapping of geological structures are not entered in FRSDB.

Applied methods of rock stress measurements in Fennoscandia, the number of entries to FRSDB for each method and its maximum depth of measurement are shown in Table 1.

Table 1.   Current state of FRSDB

Method	Number of entries	Maximum depth (m)
Doorstopper	3	900
Leeman, NTH, LUT	142	1250
Hast	136	880
Leeman-Hiltscher	87	665
Hydraulic fracturing	120	501
Soft inclusion	1	570

3.3   Results

The development of output routines and statistics for FRSDB is in progress.

Results can be extracted from the database in a variety of fashions and combinations at this date. Principal stress versus depth for the Leeman triaxial overcoring methods is shown in Figure 3. Stress components are shown to increase with depth which has been demonstrated by many investigators. Of particular interest is the indication of slatter stress gradients at about 500 m depth in the Baltic Shield. This will have implications in relation to the location of a radioactive waste repository in Finland and Sweden.

Regression analyses of maximum and minimum horizontal stress versus depth for four different measuring methods are shown in Figure 4. The overcoring method of Hast gives by far the largest stress gradient and large stress values as intercepts in linear plots of stress versus depth as compared with other methods. The same conclusion was obtained by Berman (1977) in his compilation of rock stresses for the Swedish radioactive waste programme. Hydraulic fracturing gives the smallest stress gradients and intercepts, see Figure 4D. This is contrary to the final conclusion reached by Doe et al (1983) from the stress measurements at Stripa mine. They calculated the stresses according to the first breakdown method and added the pressure from the water head. All hydrofracturing stress data in FRSDB are calculated according to the second breakdown method.

The curves presented in this paper should be considered as a first attempt to demonstrate the large variation and scatter from ground stress determinations with different methods. Plotting of stress directions for one hundred meter depth intervals indicates a similar variation.

4   ACKNOWLEDGEMENTS

The work presented in this paper was funded by the Academy of Finland, Royal Norwegian Council for Scientific and Industrial Research, and National Swedish Board for Technical Development.

The authors are endebted to many mining companies, underground construction companies and governmental organizations who actively assisted in the task of determining rock stresses and made data available for the database and this paper.

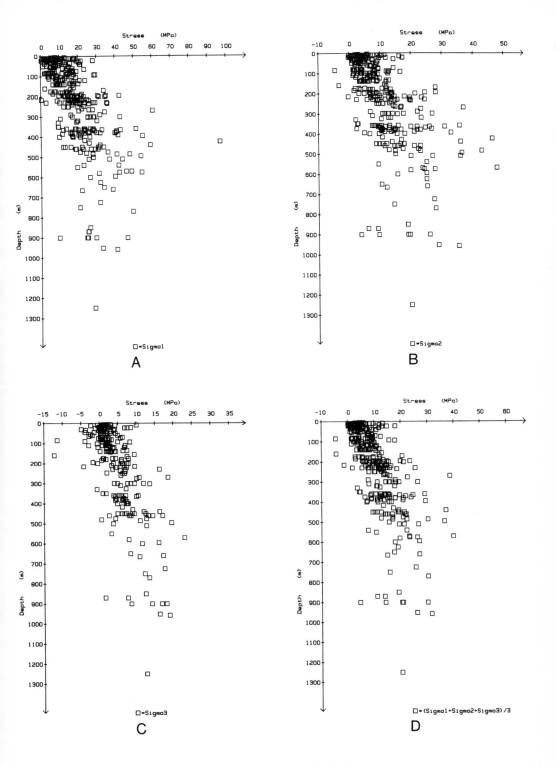

Figure 3. Principal stress versus depth for triaxial overcoring stress measurements by means of Leeman, Leeman-NTH, Leeman-LUT, and Leeman-Hiltscher methods. A) major principal stress; B) intermediate principal stress; C) minor principal stress; and D) mean principal stress.

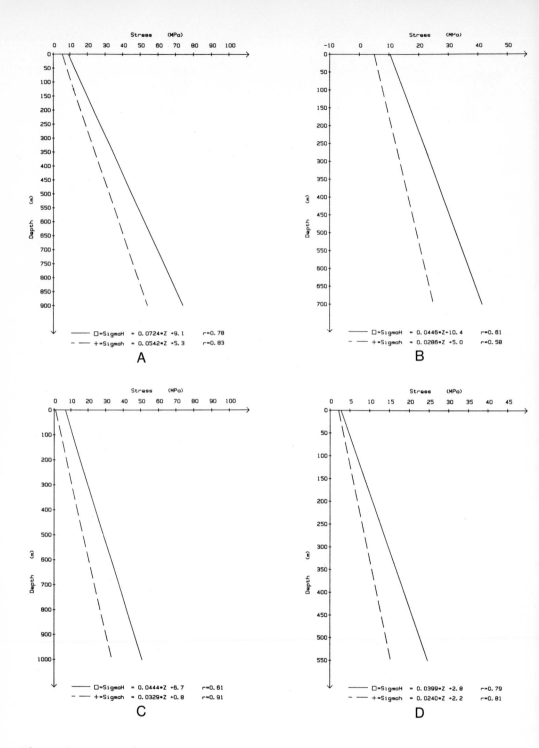

Figure 4. Regression analyses of maximum horizontal stress (SigmaH) and minimum horizontal stress (Sigmah) versus depth for four different rock stress measurement methods. A) Hast overcoring; B) Leeman-Hiltscher, Swedish State Power Board, overcoring; C) Leeman, Leeman-NTH, Leeman-LUT, overcoring; and D) hydraulic fracturing, LBL, CTH and LUT.

We are most grateful to Kjell Bergström
for the design and programming work for
FRSDB. Anne Väätäinen, Ola Fjeld and
Lars-Olof Dahlström entered most of the
data into the database and made valuable
comments regarding the design and output
routines for FRSDB.

We are grateful to the Director of the
Finnish Geological Survey for permission
to publish the geological map of the Baltic Shield.

5   REFERENCES

Bergman, S.G.A. 1977. Stress measurements
in Scandinavian bedrock - conditions,
precedent, results and evaluation.
Swedish Nuclear Fuel and Waste Management Company. Stockholm. Technical Report 64, 23 pp.

Bjarnason, B., Stephansson, O., Torikka A. and Bergström, K. 1986. Four
years of hydrofracturing rock stress
measurements in Sweden.

Carlsson, H. 1978. Stress measurements
in Stripa granite. Lawrence Berkeley
Laboratory Report, LBL-7078, SAC-04.

Doe, T.W., Ingervald, K., Strindell, L.,
Leijon, B., Hustrulid, B., Majer, E.
and Carlsson, H. 1983. In situ stress
measurements at Stripa mine, Sweden.
Lawrence Berkeley Laboratory Report,
LBL-15009, SAC44, 251 p.

Gjelvold, P., Moslet, R. and Myrvang, A.
1964. A rock mechanical investigation
of the Kjørholt limestone mine. M.Sc.
Thesis, NTH, Trondheim.

Greiner, G. and Lohr, J. 1980. Tectonic
stresses in the Northern Foreland of
the Alpine System Measurements and Interpretation in Scheidegger, A. Tectonic stresses in the Alpine-Mediterranean Region. Rock Mechanics Supplemen-
tum 9, p 5-15.

Gustavsson, G. and Wirstam, Å. 1951.
Metod att mäta bergtryck. Teknisk Tidskrift, April 14, 1951, 297-300.

Hast, N. 1945. Measuring stresses and
deformations in solid materials. Ingen-
jörsvetenskapsakademiens Handlingar,
No 178, Stockholm.

Hast, N. 1958. The measurement of rock
pressure in mines. Swedish Geological
Survey, Ser. C, No. 560, 183 pp.

Hast, N. 1969. The state of stress in
the upper part of the Earth's crust.
Tectonophyrics, vol. 8, 169-211.

Hast, N. 1974. The state of stress in the
upper part of the Earth's crust as determined by measurements of absolute
rock stress. Naturwissenschaften 61,
468-473.

Herget, G. 1986. Changes of ground
stresses with depth in the Canadian
Shield. Proceedings Rock Stress and
Rock Stress Measurements, Stockholm
(this volume).

Hiltscher, R. 1969. Beitrag zur Gebirgsspannungsmessung nach dem Bohrlochbo-
den - Entspannungsverfahren. Proc. Symposium on Determination of Stresses in
Rock Masses, Lisboa, 245-264.

Hiltscher, R., Martna, J. and Strindell, L. 1979. The measurement of triaxial rock stresses in deep boreholes.
Proceeding 4th Int. Congr. on Rock
Mechanics, Montreux, vol. 2, 227-234.

Klein, R.J. and Barr, M.V. 1986. Regio-
nal state of stress in Western Europe.
Proceedings Rock Stress and Rock Stress
Measurements, Stockholm (this volume).

Leijon, B., Carlsson, H. and Myrvang, A.
1981. Stress measurements in Näsliden
mine. In Application of Rock Mechanics
to Cut and Fill Mining. IMM, 162-168.

Leijon, B. 1986. Application of the LuH
triaxial overcoring technique in
Swedish mines. Proceeding of Rock
Stress and Rock Stress Measurements,
Stockholm (this volume).

Li, B. 1967. Rock stress in mines. Dr.
ing. Thesis, NTH, Trondheim.

Matikainen, R. 1981. Measurements of the
state of stress in Finland. Res. Rep.
A64. Finnish Association of Mining and
Metallurgy. Engineering, 123 p. (in
Finnish).

Myrvang, A. 1970. A rock mechanical investigation of the Rødsand iron ore
mine. Dr. ing. Thesis, NTH, Trondheim.

Myrvang, A. 1976. Practical use of rock
stress measurements in Norway. Symposium on Investigation of Stress in
Rock - Advences in Stress Measurements
Sydney, Aug. 11-13. 1976, p 92-99.

Myrvang, A. and Grimstad, E. 1981. Rock
stress measurements as a practical tool
in Norwegian Mining Engineering Practice. Proc. AIME, Annual Meeting, Chicago.

Myrvang, A. 1984. Coping with the problems of rockbursts in hard rock tunneling. Tunnels & Tunneling, July 1984.

Roald, S., Ustad, O. and Myrvang, A.
1986. Natural gas storage in hardrock
caverns. Tunnels & Tunneling, January
1986.

Rummel, F., Baumgartner, J. and Alheid, H.J. 1983. Hydraulic fracturing stress measurements along the
eastern boundary of the SW-German
block. In Hydraulic Fracturing Stress
Measurements National Academy Press,
Washington D.C., p 3-17.

Schmitt, T.J. 1981. The Western European stress field: new data and interpretation. J. Structural Geol., Vol 3,
No. 3, p 309-315.

Stephansson, O. 1983. Rock stress measurement by sleeve fracturing. Proceedings 5th Int. Congress of Rock Mechanics, Melbourne, vol. 2, F 129-F 137,

Stephansson, O. and Ångman, P. 1986.
Hydraulic fracturing stress measurements at Forsmark and Stidsvig, Sweden.
Bull. Geol. Soc. Finland, vol. 58,
part 1, 307-333.

Sundqvist, U. (Ed.) 1985. Berggrundsun-
dersökningar i samband med borrning
av ett 500 m djupt borrhål i Fjällbac-
ka, Bohuslän. Chalmers Institute of
Technology, Gothenburg. ISSN 0281-7845.

Särkkä, P. 1978. Soft inclusion stress
measuring cell - Tehory and practice.
Bergshanteringens vänner v 36, Nr. 2,
28-30.

Zoback, M.L. and Zoback, M. 1980. State
of stress in the conterminous United
States. J. Geophys. Res., vol. 85,
p 6113-6156.

Proceedings of the International Symposium on Rock Stress and Rock Stress Measurements/Stockholm/1-3 September 1986

Regional state of stress in Western Europe

R.J. KLEIN
British Petroleum Company p.l.c., Sunbury-on-Thames, United Kingdom

M.V. BARR
BP Petroleum Development Limited, Stavanger, Norway

ABSTRACT

The results of wellbore breakout analyses performed on orientated 4-arm caliper logs of near vertical wells drilled in the North Sea, the Atlantic Ocean and onshore Britain are presented. These results are supplemented by a compilation of previously published Western European in situ stress data, and together used to infer the regional orientation of the maximum horizontal principal stress across Western Europe.

Generally, within Central and Northern Europe, the North Sea, the British Isles and Northern Scandinavia, the regional direction of maximum horizontal stress is aligned approximately NW-SE. In Southern Scandinavia the maximum stress direction is approximately E-W. The consistency of the regional direction of maximum horizontal principal stress suggests that the orientation of the latter is dominated largely by tectonic plate boundary forces.

RESUME

Les résultats des analyses de la coulure du forage de puits, qui sont faites sur les bords orientés de 4-bras compas de calibre des puits presque verticals, qui sont forés dans la Mer du Nord, dans l'Océan Atlantique et dans la Grande Bretagne, sont présentés. Ces résultats sont supplémentés par une compilation des données publiées prévieusement de la contrainte en place de l'Europe Occidentale et tous les deux ont été utilisés d'inférer l'orientation régionale de la contrainte maximum principale horizontale dans l'Europe Occidentale.

En générale, dans l'Europe Centrale et du Nord, la Mer du Nord, les Îles Britanniques et la Scandinavie-Nord, la direction régionale de la contrainte horizontale est alignée approximativement nord-ouest à sud-est. Dans la Scandinavie-Sud la direction de la contrainte maximum est approximativement est-ouest. La consistance de la direction régionale de la contrainte maximum principale horizontale suggère que l'orientation de celui-là est dominée principalement par les forces de frontières des plateaux tectoniques.

ZUSAMMENFASSUNG

Die Ergebnisse der Analysen der Bruchproben des Bohrloches, die an orientierten 4-Ärme kalipersche Loge der fast aufrechten Bohren ausgeführt werden, die in der Nordsee, im Atlantischen Ozean und im Lande in Grossbritannien gebohrt werden, werden vorgestellt. Diese Ergebnisse werden durch einem Verzeichnis der vorhergehend in Westeuropa herausgegebenen in-situ Spannung-Daten supplementiert und benützten zusammen die örtliche Orientierung der grössten horizontalen hauptsächlichen Spannung quer durch Westeuropa.

In Zentral-und Nordeuropa, in der Nordsee, in der Britischen Inseln und in Nordskandinavien wird im allgemeinen die örtliche Richtung der grössten horizontalen Spannung umgefahr Nordwest-Sudost liniiert. In Sudskandinavien ist die grösste Richtung der Spannung ungefahr Ost-West. Die Konsistenz der örtlichen Richtung der grössten horizontalen hauptsächlichen Spannung vorschlägt, dass die Orientierung des Letzteres hauptsächlich durch tektonischen plattenförmigen Grenzenkräfte beherrscht wird.

1. INTRODUCTION

A knowledge of the prevailing in situ stress state within the Earth's crust is fundamentally important to the successful drilling and production of oil and gas wells and is a prerequisite for the rational design of any underground excavation in rock. In addition, it provides insight into the applicability of modern theories of plate tectonics and aids seismic risk evaluation and earthquake prediction.

The in situ stress regime within a rock mass either can be measured or it can be inferred from earthquake focal mechanisms, geological information and wellbore breakout analysis (wellbore elongation measurement). Measurement (either direct or indirect) may provide information on both the magnitudes and orientations of the principal stresses. Alternatively, earthquake focal mechanisms, recent geological structures and wellbore breakout analysis, at best, provide information solely on the possible orientations and relative magnitudes of the in situ principal stresses.

In this study, the results of wellbore breakout analyses performed on orientated 4-arm caliper logs of near vertical oil and gas wells drilled in the North Sea, Atlantic Ocean and onshore Britain are presented. These results are supplemented by a compilation of previously published in situ stress data within Western Europe. Horizontal and vertical principal stresses have been assumed. In situ stress measurements, earthquake focal plane solutions, geological stress indicators and wellbore breakout analyses have been included in the compilation and used, together with the breakout analysis results from the present study, to infer the orientation of the maximum horizontal principal stress across Western Europe.

2. WELLBORE BREAKOUT ANALYSIS

Measurement of the azimuthal frequency of wellbore elongation (defined here as breakout analysis) has been used by numerous workers to infer the orientations of unequal horizontal stresses in vertical and near vertical wellbores (e.g. Bell and Gough, 1979

and Blumling et al., 1983). Essentially, the technique assumes that wellbore elongation results from localised rock spalling following compressive shear failure of the wellbore wall in the regions of greatest induced circumferential compressive stress concentration. The latter occur at an azimuth perpendicular to the maximum horizontal stress direction in an assumed homogeneous isotropic linearly elastic rock formation (Figure 1). Wellbore elongation (breakout) forming in this way is termed true breakout.

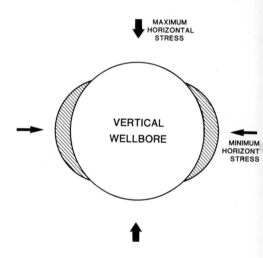

Figure 1. Assumed wellbore breakout mechanism in a vertical wellbore: hatched regions represent zones within which the induced shear stresses exceed the rock strength and which subsequently spall from the wellbore wall resulting in wellbore elongation perpendicular to the maximum horizontal stress direction.

Good agreement between maximum horizontal stress directions inferred from breakout analysis and other in situ stress data has been reported (Gough and Bell, 1981; Springer and Thorpe, 1982; Blumling et al., 1983; Cox, 1983 and Hickman et al., 1985). However, other potential sources of wellbore elongation exist. These include:

(1) Localised compressive shear failure (of the wellbore wall) similar to that described above accompanied by dilation of the sheared rock but un-

accompanied by spalling due to either or both the nature of the sheared rock (e.g. plastic shales retaining some cohesive strength) and the support offered by the drilling fluid over-balance pressure (wellbore fluid pressure minus formation pore fluid pressure). This will result in an under-gauge wellbore elongated parallel to the maximum horizontal stress direction.

(2) Elastic stress-induced well-bore deformation leading to elongation perpendicular to the maximum horizontal stress direction.

(3) Tensile stress-induced well-bore wall rock failure at an azimuth parallel to the maximum horizontal stress direction accompanied by spalling in the region of the tensile fracture.

(4) Keyseat formation in deviated wells (Babcock, 1978).

(5) Uneven drilling fluid erosion of the wellbore wall.

(6) Wellbore intersection with steeply dipping natural fractures (Babcock, 1978).

The general concensus of the most recently published results of breakout analyses, however, suggests strongly that wellbore breakout is usually stress related and aligned perpendicular to the maximum horizontal principal stress direction. Further, in a well investigated recently by Plumb and Hickman (1985), wellbore breakout has been demonstrated to be unassociated with natural fractures intersecting the well. The investigators conclude that the breakout is stress related.

2.1 Measurement of Wellbore Elongation

Wellbore elongation in vertical and near vertical (deviation from vertical not greater than 10°) wells within the study area was measured using dipmeter logs. The 10° deviation limit on the well logs analysed was chosen primarily to minimise the likelihood of keyseats being present and their possible confusion with stress-induced wellbore breakouts.

The dipmeter tool is designed to determine the strike and dip of bedding planes. It measures formation resistivity using four electrode pads, pressed against the wellbore wall by four orthogonally arranged caliper arms. The tool also records the orientation of two orthogonal wellbore diameters as a function of depth and therefore can be used to measure wellbore elongation azimuth. As the tool is winched up a circular borehole it rotates, normally in a clockwise direction, due to torque induced in the wireline cable (Schlumberger, 1981). Within elongated intervals, one of the caliper arm pairs tends to track the long axis of the wellbore, temporarily arresting normal tool rotation, and recording an increase in the wellbore diameter at that azimuth.

2.2 Data Analysis

To determine the mean azimuth of wellbore elongation within each well analysed and to facilitate identification of true breakouts, field dipmeter log prints were digitised at specified measured depth intervals, processed and replotted using a computer program developed from a prototype obtained from Karlsruhe University. The use of a computer allowed rapid processing of the dipmeter data and eliminated the subjectivity inherent in manual breakout analysis. Further, by digitising the dipmeter data at fixed intervals, small differences in orthogonal wellbore diameters insufficient to impede the normal rotation of the tool were not excluded from the analysis as can happen if cessation of tool rotation is adopted as a criterion for breakout selection.

An example of the replotted processed data is shown in Figure 2. The upper diagram is a frequency plot of wellbore elongation azimuth for which the difference between the diametral readings equals or exceeds a pre-selected value defined as the 'ellipticity threshold' (taken as 0.5 inches for this interval). A marked preferred elongation orientation between 040° and 060° is apparent. Below is plotted the wellbore deviation followed by both breakout azimuth and wellbore plane azimuth, each versus depth. Both breakout azimuth and wellbore plane azimuth are plotted to facilitate keyseat identification. In this example, keyseating can be dismissed as unlikely

since the mean breakout azimuth differs
from the mean wellbore azimuth by
approximately 70°, and the interval is
within 1.5° of vertical. Finally, the
lower diagram depicts the two caliper
arm pair readings versus depth. Thus,
divergence of the diametral readings is
indicative of wellbore elongation. The
azimuthal extent of wellbore elongation
within the most elongate sections between approximately 2990 and 3014 metres
and between 3160 and 3185 metres,
ranges from 040° to 060°. In the
former section, both caliper arm pairs
indicate overgauge hole (concurrence of
wellbore washout with wellbore breakout) while, in the latter section, the
smaller wellbore diameter is essentially in gauge.

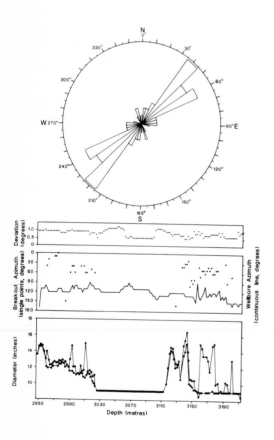

Figure 2. Well 84 replotted dipmeter
data. Data digitised at 2 metre intervals, bit size = 8.5 inches. Approximate well location is shown in Figure 5.

2.3 Results

Wellbore elongation azimuth frequency plots from a total of 19 wells
drilled in the North Sea (11 wells),
the Atlantic Ocean (2 wells) and onshore Britain (6 wells) are presented
in Figures 2 and 3. The plots were
generated using an ellipticity threshold of 0.5 inches. This empirically
derived value was found to be sufficiently small to allow detection of
wellbore elongation at preferred azimuths from dipmeter logs exhibiting
little apparent visual elongation while
at the same time being large enough to
eliminate the effect of hole geometry
irregularities thought to be related to
the drilling process.

The intervals analysed ranged in
depth from 240 to 1928 metres onshore
and 812 to 3970 metres offshore and
were drilled at nominal hole diameters
of 12.25, 8.5 and 6.0 inches. The
wells penetrated a variety of generally
near horizontally bedded sedimentary
rock types including sandstones, siltstones and mudstones. Wellbore elongation was manifest within all these
lithologies to a greater or lesser
degree. Within some zones one or both
orthogonal caliper arm pairs reached
the limit of their extension of 18
inches or more.

Typically, the elongation azimuth
frequency plots (Figures 2 and 3) exhibit a unidirectional preferred elongation orientation. The mean wellbore
elongation azimuth has been taken as
the bisector of the azimuthal extent of
the preferred elongation orientation.

The pronounced preferred unidirectional orientation of wellbore elongation exhibited by the majority of the
elongation azimuth frequency plots presented in Figures 2 and 3 is thought to
be stress induced and to result from
compressive shear failure and subsequent spalling of the wellbore wall at
an azimuth perpendicular to the maximum
horizontal in situ stress direction as
first proposed by Bell and Gough
(1979). Observations of the shape of
wellbore wall cavings to date provide
the only direct evidence of this compressive shear failure mechanism. The
arcuate shape of these cavings (Figure
4) is similar to that predicted by
Zoback et al (1985). The two sandstone
cavings shown in Figure 4 were recov-

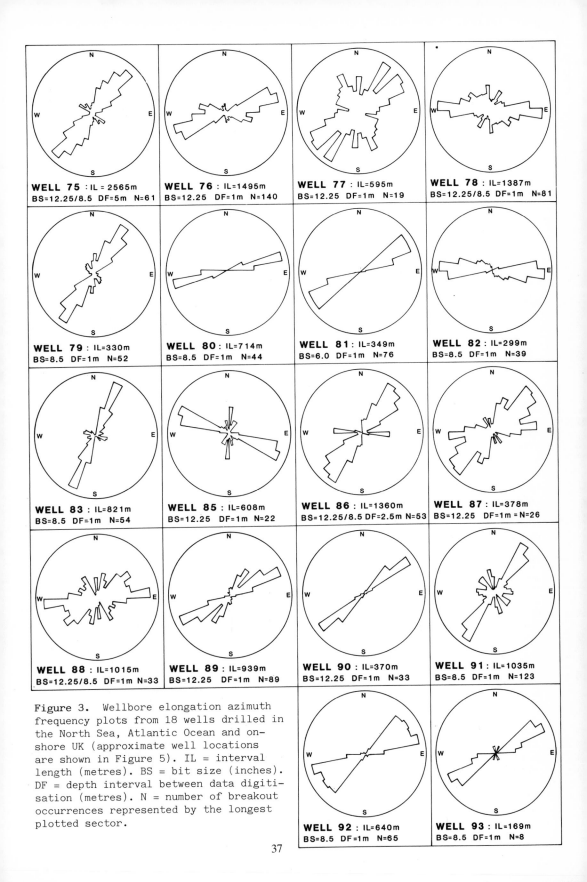

WELL 75 : IL = 2565m
BS=12.25/8.5 DF=5m N=61

WELL 76 : IL=1495m
BS=12.25 DF=1m N=140

WELL 77 : IL=595m
BS=12.25 DF=1m N=19

WELL 78 : IL=1387m
BS=12.25/8.5 DF=1m N=81

WELL 79 : IL=330m
BS=8.5 DF=1m N=52

WELL 80 : IL=714m
BS=8.5 DF=1m N=44

WELL 81 : IL=349m
BS=6.0 DF=1m N=76

WELL 82 : IL=299m
BS=8.5 DF=1m N=39

WELL 83 : IL=821m
BS=8.5 DF=1m N=54

WELL 85 : IL=608m
BS=12.25 DF=1m N=22

WELL 86 : IL=1360m
BS=12.25/8.5 DF=2.5m N=53

WELL 87 : IL=378m
BS=12.25 DF=1m N=26

WELL 88 : IL=1015m
BS=12.25/8.5 DF=1m N=33

WELL 89 : IL=939m
BS=12.25 DF=1m N=89

WELL 90 : IL=370m
BS=12.25 DF=1m N=33

WELL 91 : IL=1035m
BS=8.5 DF=1m N=123

Figure 3. Wellbore elongation azimuth frequency plots from 18 wells drilled in the North Sea, Atlantic Ocean and onshore UK (approximate well locations are shown in Figure 5). IL = interval length (metres). BS = bit size (inches). DF = depth interval between data digitisation (metres). N = number of breakout occurrences represented by the longest plotted sector.

WELL 92 : IL=640m
BS=8.5 DF=1m N=65

WELL 93 : IL=169m
BS=8.5 DF=1m N=8

37

ered from a depth of around 3000 metres
in a nominally 8.5 inches diameter
hole. The caving on the left of the
photograph shows the original concave
wellbore wall while the caving on the
right exhibits a typical convex compressive shear failure surface. The
ridge running parallel to the wellbore
axis at the centre of this caving is
thought to mark the intersection of two
conjugate curved shear failure
surfaces.

Figure 4. Arcuate sandstone cavings
from well 82.

In the majority of wells studied
most of the other previously mentioned
causes of wellbore elongation can be
dismissed as unlikely explanations of
the observed wellbore elongation by
close examination of the dipmeter data,
geological data and drilling data. In
addition, it is shown later that the
direction of maximum horizontal stress
inferred from the breakout analyses is
consistent with other regional in situ
stress data. Thus, the argument for
the assumed breakout mechanism also is
supported indirectly.

3. **MAXIMUM HORIZONTAL STRESS**
   ORIENTATION WITHIN WESTERN EUROPE

Stress provinces within which the
maximum horizontal stress direction is
reasonably constant already have been
delineated for several parts of the
globe (e.g. Zoback and Zoback, 1980 and
Gough et al., 1983). Besides using
breakout analysis, principal stress
orientations have been obtained from in
situ measurements, earthquake focal
plane solutions and recent geological
stress indicators. These methods of
determining principal stress orientations together with the major assump-

tions and inherent difficulties and
uncertainties associated with each
technique already have been discussed
fully by Zoback and Zoback (1980) and
others (e.g. Klein and Brown, 1983) and
need not be considered further.
Suffice to say, principal stress orientation data derived from all these
techniques may have large error bands
($\pm$ 20° or more), and wherever possible,
large numbers of data should be used to
infer regional principal stress
orientations.

In 1969, Hast published a compilation of in situ rock stress measurements made in boreholes predominantly within the Fennoscandian block.
In a later compilation which included
Hast's data, Ranalli and Chandler
(1975) concluded that within the
southern half of the Fennoscandian
block the maximum horizontal stress
trends approximately E-W while within
the northern half the trend is approximately N-S. Focal plane solutions in
Southern Norway (Bungum and Fyen, 1979)
indicated a direction of maximum horizontal stress between NW-SE and WSW-ENE
(strike-slip and dip-slip movements)
consistent with Ranalli and Chandler's
conclusions. The intraplate Meloy
earthquake sequence in Northern Norway
was analysed by Bungum et al (1979) and
Vaage (1980), each using different data
sets. Bungum et al obtained an oblique
dip-slip (normal) solution indicative
of a WSW-ENE maximum horizontal stress
direction while Vaage obtained a
strike-slip solution with a normal dip-
slip component indicative of a NNW-SSE
maximum horizontal stress direction
consistent with Ranalli and Chandler's
conclusions. The difference in solutions probably indicates variations in
the focal mechanisms occurring at
different times, but may also reflect
non-uniqueness of the respective
solutions.

Greiner (1975) found from a number
of overcoring in situ stress measurements in Southwest Germany that the
direction of maximum horizontal stress
trends approximately NW-SE. This NW-SE
trend was supported later by additional
Central European in situ stress measurement compilations (Greiner and
Illies 1977; Greiner and Lohr, 1980;
Froidevaux et al., 1980; Illies et al.,
1981 and Rummel et al., 1983). Focal
plane solutions in Central Europe are

consistent with these stress measurement results. Solutions in the Upper Rhine graben and the Swiss Alps show that strike-slip mechanisms dominate in these regions (Ahorner, 1975; Pavoni et al., 1980 and Becker et al., 1984). In the Upper Rhine graben, the relative motion direction is sinstral along fault planes striking parallel to the graben axis and dextral along fault planes perpendicular to it (Ahorner, 1975), indicative of a NW-SE direction of maximum horizontal stress. In the Lower Rhine graben, similar numbers of strike-slip and dip-slip earthquake mechanisms have occurred, the latter being normal in character (Ahorner, 1975). Most of Ahorner's Lower Rhine graben solutions are indicative of a NW-SE direction of maximum horizontal stress.

Compilations of Western European stress data from in situ stress measurements, earthquake focal plane solutions and geological stress indicators including data from within the British Isles (Klein, 1982 and Klein and Brown, 1983) suggest that the general NW-SE direction of maximum horizontal stress within Central Europe persists over the British Isles. These findings concur with fracture mapping in Southern England and Northern France by Bevan and Hancock (1986) who suggest that the NW system of mesofractures was initiated in the same regional stress field as that which reactivated the neotectonic faults of the Lower Rhine graben system. Further, within the Carnmenellis granite in Cornwall there are two major sub-vertical joint sets striking approximately 155°-335° and 75°-255° with an additional sub-vertical set trending 30°-210° (Pine et al., 1983). Since thermal brines in nearby deep active mines issue predominantly from the NNW-SSE trending fracture system, a present day direction of maximum horizontal stress of similar trend seems likely, and is supported by in situ stress measurements in this region (Pine et al., 1983 and Cooling et al., 1984).

Cox (1983) published results of three breakout analyses from individual wells within the North Sea which also indicate an approximately NW-SE maximum horizontal stress direction consistent with the Central European and British data. Further breakout analysis

results within the Carboniferous of Northern Germany and Eastern Holland (Draxler and Edwards, 1984) also yielded an approximately NW-SE maximum stress direction.

The data from the previously published compilations discussed above, together with other published Western European in situ stress orientation data and the results of breakout analyses from the present study, are summarised in Table 1 and presented in the form of a stress map of the direction of maximum horizontal stress (Figure 5).

The wellbore breakout data from the present study (Figure 5) confirms that the general NW-SE direction of maximum horizontal stress within Central Europe persists over the Southern, Central and Northern North Sea, with the inferred maximum horizontal stress direction generally varying between WNW-ESE and NNW-SSE. Of the two breakout analysis results west of the Shetland Islands in the Atlantic Ocean, one conforms to the NW-SE regional trend while the other indicates an approximately N-S maximum horizontal stress direction. Onshore within the British Isles all six of the breakout analysis results in Lancashire and the Midlands conform closely to the general NW-SE maximum horizontal stress direction observed within Central Europe and the North Sea. These data are thus in agreement with the majority of the in situ stress measurements made within the British Isles (Figure 5) and the North Wales focal plane solution. In situ stress orientation indicators within Northern England and Scotland are limited to two focal plane solutions (King, 1980 and Assumpcao, 1981) which both indicate an approximately N-S maximum horizontal stress direction.

To summarise, the direction of maximum horizontal stress determined from some seventy in situ measurements, forty breakout analyses, and sixty focal plane solutions within Western Europe is, in general, aligned between NNW-SSE and WNW-ESE. Exceptions to this general trend do exist, the most notable being the southern half of the Fennoscandian block in which both focal plane solutions and in situ stress measurements indicate an approximately E-W maximum horizontal stress direc-

TABLE 1 : SUMMARY OF IN-SITU STRESS DATA

MEASUREMENT NUMBER	LOCALITY	DEPTH	ROCK TYPE	METHOD OF MEASUREMENT	STRESS REGIME			REFERENCES
					σ_1	σ_2	σ_3	
					MAGNITUDE (MPa) (ORIENTATION, DIP/DIP DIRECTION)			
1	Camborne (B)	790	Granite	O.C.	45.6 (01/129)	19.8 (89/012)	12.9 (01/220)	Pine et al. (1983)
2	Dover (B)	48	Chalk	O.C.	1.3 (H/024)	0.8 (V)	0.3 (H/114)	Reid (1980)
								Maconochie (1977)
3	Dinorwic (B)	320	Slate	O.C.	17.6 (26/300)	8.0 (26/198)	6.4 (52/074)	Douglas et al. (1977)
4	Boulby (B)	1110	Potash	O.C.	30 (V)	15 (H)	15 (H)	Hebblewhite (1977)
5	Meadowbank (B)	144	Halite	O.C.	3.01 (52/285)	2.35 (19/169)	1.55 (31/066)	Miller et al. (1977)
6	(E)	200	-	O.C.	-(H/164)	(average H stress 17.2)		Ranalli & Chandler (19
								Hast (1969)
6a	Camlough (E)	195	Dolerite	O.C.	27.0 (13/027)	22.9 (08/295)	11.6 (74/165)	Seddon (1973)
6b	(B)	34	Granite	O.C.	7.4 (09/139)	3.9 (10/048)	-0.1 (77/269)	Cooling et al. (1984)
7	Choignes (F)	0	Limestone	F.J.	1.1 (H/148)	-0.2 (H/058)	-	Froidevaux et al. (198
8	Etrochey (F)	0	Limestone	F.J.	1.1 (H/149)	0.0 (H/059)	-	Froidevaux et al. (198
9	Ravieres (F)	0	Limestone	F.J.	2.2 (H/152)	0.5 (H/062)	-	Froidevaux et al. (198
10	Massangis (F)	0	Limestone	F.J.	2.4 (H/167)	-0.2 (H/077)	-	Froidevaux et al. (198
11	Terce (F)	0	Limestone	F.J.	5.1 (H/100)	1.4 (H/010)	-	Froidevaux et al. (198
12	Bonnillet (F)	0	Limestone	F.J.	0.9 (H/141)	0.2 (H/051)	-	Froidevaux et al. (198
13	Vilhonneur (F)	0	Limestone	F.J.	1.2 (H/139)	0.5 (H/049)	-	Froidevaux et al. (198
14	Hydrequent (F)	0	Limestone	F.J.	3.8 (H/170)	0.0 (H/080)	-	Froidevaux et al. (198
15	Hydrequent (F)	< 1.5	Limestone	O.C.	-(H/166)	-(H/076)		Froidevaux et al. (198
16	Nennig (FRG)	-	Limestone	O.C.	-(H/126)	-	-	Greiner & Illies (197
17	Auerbach (FRG)	ca. 140	Diorite	O.C.	-(H/125)	-	-	Greiner & Illies (197
18	Albersweiler (FRG)	-	Gneiss	O.C.	-(H/075)	-	-	Greiner & Illies (197
19	Wossingen (FRG)	-	Limestone	O.C.	-(H/140)	-	-	Greiner & Illies (197
20	Onstmetingen (FRG)	ca. 25	Limestone	O.C.	-(H/130)	-	-	Greiner & Illies (197
21	Hohenzollern (FRG)	ca. 35	Limestone	O.C.	-(H/152)	-	-	Greiner & Illies (197
22	Bolschwell (FRG)	-	Limestone	O.C.	-(H/153)	-	-	Greiner & Illies (197
23	Kleinkems (FRG)	-	Limestone	O.C.	-(H/176)	-	-	Greiner & Illies (197
24	Grimsel (Ch)	ca. 265	Granodiorite	O.C.	-(H/171)	-	-	Greiner & Illies (197
25	Luzern (Ch)	ca. 90	Sandstone	O.C.	-(H/ca. 104)	-	-	Gysel (1975)
								Greiner & Illies (197
26	Hochkonig Mts. (A)	ca. 750	Greywacke	O.C.	-(ca. 70/160)	-	-	Bruckl et al. (1975)
								Greiner & Illies (197
27	Mont Blanc (F)	ca. 1800	Schist, Granite	-	-(H/ca. 040)	-	-	Greiner & Illies (197
28	Lago Dello (I)	ca. 180	Gneiss	-	-(H/ca. 140)	-	-	Greiner & Illies (197
29	Val Camonica (I)	ca. 230	Phyllite	-	-(H/ca. 165)	-	-	Greiner & Illies (197
30	Felbertal (A)	70	Schist	O.C.	25 (54/115)	16(-)	5(-)	Kohlbeck et al. (1980)
31	Gleinalm (A)	800	Gneiss/Schist	O.C.	32 (45/162)	20(-)	13(-)	Kohlbeck et al. (1980)
32	Fohnsdorf (A)	1100	Sandstone	O.C.	54 (12/188)	25(-)	11(-)	Kohlbeck et al. (1980)
33	Bleiberg (A)	236	Limestone	O.C.	41 (20/310)	21(-)	7(-)	Kohlbeck et al. (1980)
34	Vorarlberg (A)	140-200	Sandstone	O.C.	-(H/092)	-	-	Innerhofer (1977)
35	Bacharach (FRG)	-	-	O.C.	-(H/151)	-	-	Greiner & Lohr (1980)
36	Nastatten (FRG)	-	-	O.C.	-(H/150)	-	-	Greiner & Lohr (1980)
37	Kamberg (FRG)	-	-	O.C.	-(H/133)	-	-	Greiner & Lohr (1980)
38	Hohenzollern (FRG)	25	Limestone	H.F.	2.4 (H/150)	1.5 (H/240)	0.65 (V)	Rummel & Jung (1975)
39	Stallberg (S)	900	-	O.C.	-(H/120)	(Mean H stress 49 MPa)		Ranalli & Chandler (19
40	Vingesback (S)	410	Granite, amphibolite	O.C.	44.1 (H/010)	11.0 (H/100)	-(V)	Ranalli & Chandler (19
41	Malmberget (S)	460	Granite	O.C.	35.2 (H/100)	10.8 (H/190)	-(V)	Ranalli & Chandler (19
42	Laisvall (S)	120	Granite	O.C.	24.5 (H/163)	12.8 (H/253)	-(V)	Ranalli & Chandler (19
43	Kiruna (S)	290	-	O.C.	-(H/163)	(Mean H stress 9.8 MPa)		Ranalli & Chandler (19
44	Malm (NO)	650	-	O.C.	-(H/162)	(Mean H stress 9.8 MPa)		Ranalli & Chandler (19
45	(NO)	380	-	O.C.	-(H/108)	(Mean H stress 27.5 MPa)		Ranalli & Chandler (19
46	(NO)	-	-	O.C.	-(H/091)	-	-	Ranalli & Chandler (19
47	(NO)	-	-	O.C.	-(H/086)	-	-	Ranalli & Chandler (19
48	(NO)	-	-	O.C.	-(H/114)	-	-	Ranalli & Chandler (19
49	(S)	-	-	O.C.	-(H/175)	-	-	Ranalli & Chandler (19
50	Mol-Rana (NO)	-	Mica-garnet schist	O.C.	-(H/025)	-	-	Ranalli & Chandler (19
51-67	(FRG)	40-450	Lmst,Sst,Slts, Ecologite, Granite	H.F.	Θ_H plotted on Figure 5 are representative of a number of measurements at each location			Rummel et al. (1983)
68	Mulhouse (F)	691-700	Salt	H.F.	23 (H/010) 13 (H/100)			Cornet (1983)
69	Vichy (F)	54-186	Granite	H.F.	-(H/053)			Cornet (1983)
70	Brotjorden (S)	ca. 60	Granite	O.C.	17 (H/315)	8.5 (H/045)	0 (V)	Bergman & Stille (1984
71	(Ch)	upto 2500	Sedimentary and basement	B.A.	Generally $\Theta_H = 160° \pm 10°$ in sedimentary trough, $140° \pm 10°$ in crystalline basement			Becker et al. (1984)
72	(FRG,N)	upto at least 1480	-	B.A.	$\Theta_H = 140° \pm 10°$			Draxler & Edwards (1984
73	(NS, F,I)	-	-	B.A.	Approximate Θ_H plotted on Figure 5.			Cox (1983)
74	Urach (FRG)	1900 to 3334	Crystalline basement	B.A.	$\Theta_H = 173° \pm 10°$			Blumling et al. (1983)
75-93	(NS,AO,B)	240 to 3970	Sedimentary	B.A.	See Figures 2 and 3 for details			This paper

Locality: A = Austria; AO = Atlantic Ocean; B = Britain; Ch = Switzerland; E = Ireland; F = France; FRG = Federal Republic of Germany;
I = Italy; N = Holland; NO = Norway; NS = North Sea; S = Sweden.
Measurement method: O.C. = overcore; H.F. = hydrofracture; F.J. = flat jack; B.A. = breakout analysis
Stress Regime: Θ_H = maximum horizontal stress azimuth; H = horizontal; V = vertical

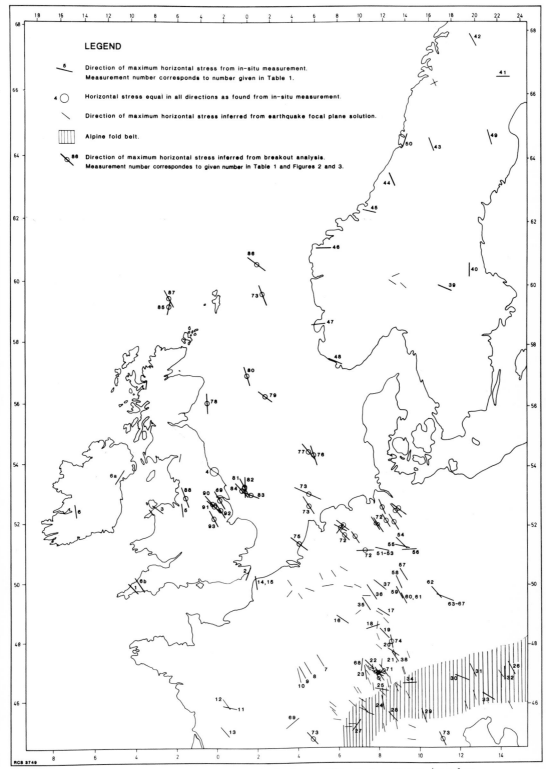

Figure 5. Orientation of maximum horizontal principal stress within Western Europe (based on Klein, 1982)

tion. Elsewhere, isolated data points contrary to the regional trend do exist, but generally can be explained in terms of either measurement errors, or local effects such as topography, geological structure, or nearby excavations which may mask the regional trend. Considering that the stress orientation data have been obtained using a range of different techniques, in a variety of geological rock types and structures, and at a variety of depths, it is remarkable that the results generally fall within such a narrow band. It is even more remarkable when one considers the enormous area from which the data derive, indicating a relatively uniform direction of maximum horizontal stress on a regional scale.

4. DISCUSSION AND CONCLUSIONS

The current state of in situ stress results from the combination of a number of natural sources of rock stress including: present boundary conditions such as gravitational stress (Terzaghi and Richart, 1952), tectonic stress (Le Pichon, 1968 and Bott and Kuznir, 1984) and thermal stress (Voight and St. Pierre, 1974); material properties (Prats, 1981); and previous stress history including residual stress (Voight, 1966 and Jaeger and Cook, 1979). Gravitational stresses arise from the overburden weight and alone are unable to explain the presence of regional anisotropic horizontal stresses in the absence of topographic features. While the latter can explain the (regional) stress conditions in the Western Alps (Baumann, 1981), the same does not apply to the persistent orientation of maximum horizontal stress from the Alpine foreland to the British Isles, North Sea and Atlantic Ocean. Similarly, thermal, residual and material property related stresses cannot explain the consistent direction of maximum horizontal stress over so extensive an area and range of depths, and encompassing widely varying rock types and rock structures of variable geological histories. Therefore, it is concluded that the consistent NW-SE orientation of the maximum horizontal in situ stress direction over Western

Europe is dominated largely by plate tectonic boundary forces (recently discussed by Bott and Kuznir, 1984) acting upon the Eurasian tectonic plate. These forces include plate edge forces such as compressive ridge push forces perpendicular to the Atlantic mid-oceanic ridge and forces perpendicular to the Eurasian/African continental collision zone as expressed by the Alps, as well as shear stresses exerted on the base of the lithospheric plates (whether mantle convection or asthenospheric drag).

ACKNOWLEDGEMENTS

The authors wish to thank British Petroleum plc for permission to publish this paper and their colleagues for assistance during its preparation, particularly Mr. K.J. Heffer and Dr. A.L. Ward.

REFERENCES

Ahorner, L. 1975. Present-day stress field and seismotectonic block movements along major fault zones in central Europe. Tectonophysics 29 (1-4) : 233-249.

Assumpcao, M. 1981. The NW Scotland earthquake swarm of 1974. Geophys. J.R. astr. Soc. 67 : 577-586.

Babcock, E.A. 1978. Measurement of subsurface fractures from dipmeter logs Amer. Assoc. Pet. Geol. Bull. 62 (7) : 1111-1126.

Baumann, H. 1981. Regional stress field and rifting in western Europe. Tectonophysics 73 : 105-111.

Becker, A., P. Blumling and W.H. Muller. 1984. Rezentes Spannungsfeld in der zentralen Nordschweiz. Nagra Nationale Genossenschaft fur die Lagerung radioaktiner Abfalle. Technischer Bericht 84-37.

Bell, J.S., and D.I. Gough. 1979. Northeast-southwest compressive stress in Alberta : Evidence from oil wells. Earth Planet. Sci. Lett. 45 : 475-482.

Bergmann, S.G.A. and H. Stille. 1984. Rock burst problems in a 2.6 million m^3 underground crude oil storage in granite. Proc. 5th Int. Congr. on Rock Mechs., ISRM, Melbourne 2 (D) : 301-314.

Bevan, T.G. and P.L. Hancock. 1986. A late Cenozoic regional mesofracture system in southern England and northern France. J.Geol.Soc.London 143:In Press.

Blumling, P., K. Fuchs and T. Schneider. 1983. Orientation of the stress field from breakouts in a crystalline well in a seismic active area. Physics of the Earth and Planetary Interiors 33 : 250-254.

Bott, M.H.P. and N.J. Kusznir. 1984. The origin of tectonic stress in the lithosphere. Tectonophysics 105 : 1-13.

Bruckl, E., K.H. Roch and A.E. Scheidegger. 1975. Significance of stress measurements in the Hochkonig Massif in Austria. Tectonophysics 29 (1-4) : 315-322.

Bungum, H. and J. Fyen. 1979. Hypocentral distribution, focal mechanisms, and tectonic implications of Fennoscandian earthquakes, 1954-1978. Geol. Foren. Forh. 101 (4) : 261-271.

Bungum, H., B.K. Hokland, E.S. Husebye and F. Ringdal. 1979. An exceptional intraplate earthquake sequence in Meloy, northern Norway. Nature 280 (5717) : 32-35.

Cooling C.M., L.W. Tunbridge and J.A. Hudson. 1984. Some studies of rock mass structure and in situ stress. ISRM Symposium on Design and Performance of Underground Excavations. Published by British Geotechnical Society, London : 199-206.

Cornet, F.H. 1983. Interpretation of hydraulic injection tests for in-situ stress determination. In Hydraulic Fracturing Stress Measurements, National Academy Press, Washington DC : 149-158.

Cox, J.W. 1983. Long axis orientation in elongated boreholes and its correlation with rock stress data. SPWLA 24th Annual Logging Symp. June 27-30.

Douglas, T.H., L.R. Richards and D. O'Neill. 1977. Site investigation for main underground complex - Dinorwic Pumped Storage Scheme. Field Measurements in Rock Mechanics, K. Kovari (ed.), A.A. Balkema, Rotterdam 2 : 551-567.

Draxler, J.K. and D.P. Edwards. 1984. Evaluation procedures in the Carboniferous of Northern Europe. Trans. 9th Int. Formation Evaluation Symp., Paris, 24-26 October.

Froidevaux, C., C. Paquin and M. Souriau. 1980. Tectonic stresses in France: in-situ measurements with a flat jack. J. Geophys. Res. 85 (B11) : 6342-6346.

Gough, D.I. and J.S. Bell. 1981. Stress orientations from oil-well fractures in Alberta and Texas. Canadian J. Earth Sci. 18 : 638-645.

Gough, D.I., C.K. Fordjor and J.S. Bell. 1983. A stress province boundary and tractions on the North American plate. Nature 305 : 619-621.

Greiner, G., 1975. In-situ stress measurements in southwest Germany. Tectonophysics 29 (1-4) : 265-274.

Greiner, G. and J.H. Illies. 1977. Central Europe: active or residual tectonic stresses. Pure and Appl. Geophys. 115 (1) : 11-26.

Greiner, G, and J. Lohr. 1980. Tectonic stresses in the northern foreland of the alpine system - measurements and interpretation. Rock Mechs., Suppl. 9, A.E. Scheidegger (ed.) : 5-15.

Gysel, M. 1975. In-situ stress measurements of the primary stress state in the Sonnenberg tunnel in Lucerne, Switzerland. Tectonophysics 29 (1-4) : 301-314.

Hast, N. 1969. The state of stress in the upper part of the Earth's crust. Tectonophysics. 8 : 169-211.

Hebblewhite, B.K. 1977. Underground potash mine design based on rock mechanics principles and measurements. Ph.D. Thesis, Univ. of Newcastle upon Tyne.

Hickman, S.H., J.H. Healy and M.D. Zoback. 1985. In-situ stress, natural fracture distribution and borehole elongation in the Auburn Geothermal Well, Auburn, New York. J. Geophys. Res. 90 (B7) : 5497-5512.

Illies, J.H., H. Baumann and B. Hoffers. 1981. Stress pattern and strain release in the Alpine Foreland. Tectonophysics 71 : 157-172.

Innerhofer, G. 1977. Stress measurements of the rock mass in the headrace tunnel Langenegg. Field Measurements in Rock Mechanics, K. Kovari (ed.), A.A. Balkema, Rotterdam 1 : 247-253.

Jaeger, J.C. and N.G.W. Cook. 1979. Fundamentals of Rock Mechanics, 3rd ed. Chapman and Hall, London.

King, G. 1980. A fault plane solution for the Carlisle earthquake, 26

December, 1979. Nature 286 (5769) : 142-143.

Klein, R.J. 1982. In-situ stresses in the British Isles, northern Europe and Scandinavia. MSc thesis (Imperial College), London University.

Klein, R.J. and E.T. Brown. 1983. The state of stress in British rocks. Rep. Dep. Environ. DOE/RW/83.8.

Kohlbeck, F., K.-H. Roch and A.E. Scheidegger. 1980. In-situ stress measurements in Austria. Rock Mechs., Suppl. 9, A.E. Scheidegger (ed.) : 21-29.

Le Pichon, X. 1968. Sea-floor spreading and continental drift. J. Geophys. Res. 73 (12) : 3661-3697.

Maconochie, D.J. 1977. Geotechnical studies for the Channel tunnel. Ph.D. Thesis, Univ. of Newcastle upon Tyne.

Miller, H.D.S., E.L.J. Potts and A. Szeki. 1977. In-situ stress measurements in halite in Cheshire, potash in north Yorkshire and slate at Dinorwic - part 2. Proc. Conf. on Rock Engineering, Univ. of Newcastle Upon Tyne : 257-274.

Pavoni, N. 1980. Crustal stresses inferred from fault plane solutions of earthquakes and neotectonic deformation in Switzerland. Rock Mechs., Suppl. 9, A.E. Scheidegger (ed.) : 63-68.

Pine, R.J., L.W. Tunbridge and K. Kwakwa. 1983. In-situ stress measurement in the Carnmenellis granite. 1 - overcoring tests at South Crofty Mine at a depth of 790m. Int. J. Roch Mech. Min. Sci. & Geomech. Abstr. 20 (2) : 51-62.

Plumb, R.A. and S.H. Hickman. 1985. Stress-induced borehole elongation : a comparison between the four-arm dipmeter and the borehole televiewer in the Auburn Geothermal Well. J. Geophys. Res. 90 (B7) : 5513-5521.

Prats, M. 1981. Effect of burial history on the subsurface horizontal stresses of formations having different material properties. Soc. Petr. Eng. J. 21 : 658-661.

Ranalli, G. and T.E. Chandler. 1975. The stress field in the upper crust as determined from in-situ measurements. Geol. Rundschau 64 (2) : 653-674.

Reid, A.G. 1980. Rock mechanics investigations relating to tunnelling in chalk. Ph.D. Thesis, University of Newcastle upon Tyne.

Rummel, F. and R. Jung. 1975. Hydraulic fracturing stress measurements near the Hohenzollern Graben Structure, SW Germany. Pageoph 113 : 321-330.

Rummel, F., J. Baumgartner and H.J. Alheid. 1983. Hydraulic fracturing stress measurements along the eastern boundary on the SW-German block. In Hydraulic Fracturing Stress Measurements, National Academy Press, Washington D.C: 3-17.

Schlumberger, 1981. Dipmeter Interpretation, Volume 1 - Fundamentals. Schlumberger Ltd. New York.

Schmitt, T.H. 1981. The West European stress field : new data and interpretation. J. Struct. Geol. 3 : 309-315.

Seddon, B.T. 1973. Rock investigations for Camlough Underground Power Station. Field Instrumentation in Geotechnical Engineering, Proc. Symp. British Geotechnical Society, Butterworths, London: 370-381.

Springer, J.E. and R.K. Thorpe. 1982. Borehole elongation versus in-situ stress orientation. Int. Conf. on In-Situ Testing of Rock and Soil Masses, Santa Barbara, California, January 4-8.

Terzaghi, K. and F.E. Richart. 1952. Stresses in rock about cavities. Geotechnique 3(2):57-90.

Turbitt, T. et al. 1985. The North Wales earthquake of 19th July 1984. J. Geol. Soc. London 142: 567-571.

Vaage, S. 1980. Seismic evidence of complex tectonics in the Meloy earthquake area. Norsk Geologisk Tidsskrift 60 (3) : 213-217.

Voight, B. 1966. Interpretation of in-situ stress measurements. Proc. 1st Congr. ISRM, Lisbon 3 : 332-348.

Voight, B. and H.P. St. Pierre. 1974. Stress history and rock stress. Proceedings of the 3rd International Congress of ISRM 2(A) : 580-582.

Zoback, M.L. and M. Zoback. 1980. State of stress in the Conterminous United States. J. Geophys. Res. 85 (B11) : 6113-6156.

Zoback, M.D., D. Moos and L. Mastin. 1985. Wellbore breakout and in situ stress. J.Geophys.Res.90(B7):5523-5530.

Lokale variation regionaler spannungsfelder an zwei beispielen aus SW-Deutschland und der Schweiz

H. BAUMANN
A. BECKER
University of Karlsruhe, Karlsruhe, Federal Republic of Germany

Abstract

In the area of the Hohenzollerngraben (SW-Germany) and in the Jura mountains East of Basel (NW-Switzerland) in situ stresses have been measured by the Doorstopper and the CSIR-triaxial cell. Additional data gathered from hydraulic fracturing, breakouts and from fault plane solutions have been used. Stresses obtained by these methods show detailed stress fields of the regions concerned. By these stress data, models of local stress changes are derivated.

Résumé

Dans la région du Hohenzollerngraben (Allemagne du sud-ouest) et dans le Jura, à l'est de Bâle (Suisse du nord-ouest) on a effectué des mesurages de contraintes in-situ selon le procédé Doorstopper et le procédé à cellule triaxiale (CSIR). De plus, on a eu des données à la disposition provenant de mesurages effectués selon le procédé 'hydraulic fracturing', de 'breakouts', et de mécanismes au foyer de tremblements de terre. De ces données résulte une image détaillée de l'orientation du champ de contraintes dans les régions examinées. On en dérive des modèles sur le mécanisme de changements locaux du champ de contraintes.

Zusammenfassung

Im Gebiet des Hohenzollerngrabens (SW-Deutschland) und im Juragebirge östlich von Basel (NW-Schweiz) sind in situ-Spannungsmessungen nach dem Doorstopper- und Triaxialzellenverfahren (CSIR) ausgeführt worden. Zusätzlich standen Daten aus Hydraulic-fracturing-Messungen, von Bohrlochrandausbrüchen und Herdflächenlösungen von Erdbeben zur Verfügung. Aus diesem Datenmaterial ergibt sich ein detailliertes Bild der Orientierung des Spannungsfeldes in den untersuchten Gebieten. Hieraus werden Modelle über den Mechanismus lokaler Änderungen des Spannungsfeldes abgeleitet.

1. EINLEITUNG

Spannungsmessungen, die seit Mitte der siebziger Jahre in Mitteleuropa durchgeführt werden, haben ein Feld divergierender Spannungstrajektorien im nördlichen Alpenvorland ergeben (Illies & Baumann 1982) und zwar derart, daß Trajektorien der größten horizontalen Hauptspannung etwa normal zum Verlauf der Alpen orientiert sind. Mit zunehmender Meßpunktdichte zeigte sich aber auch, daß dieses großräumige, einheitliche Spannungsfeld regionale, eigenständige Span-

nungsfelder einschloß, wie zum Beispiel das Rheinische Schiefergebirge, und die Ursachen hierfür in der besonderen geologisch-tektonischen Situation dieser Bereiche zu finden waren (Baumann 1982). Für uns war es daher naheliegend, in in räumlich kleineren Bereichen den Einfluß geologischer Strukturen auf das mitteleuropäische Spannungsfeld, das seine Ursachen wahrscheinlich in plattentektonischen Vorgängen hat, mit Hilfe von Spannungsmessungen zu untersuchen. Hierfür bot sich der Hohenzollerngraben mit seiner Tiefenstörung an, die dextralen

Schercharakter hat, oder auch der Faltenjura, der durch Abscherhorizonte vom unterlagernden Grundgebirge mechanisch entkoppelt ist und daher eine vertikale Änderung des Spannungsfeldes im Bereich dieser Entkoppelung erwarten ließ.

2. DAS SPANNUNGSFELD IM BEREICH DES HOHENZOLLERNGRABENS UND DIE SICH DARAUS ERGEBENDE GEBIRGSMECHANISCHE INTERPRETATION DER REZENTEN TEKTONIK.

Das Studium des lokalen Spannungsfeldes im Hohenzollerngraben verspricht interessante Ergebnisse zur Spannungsumlagerung an Störungen, beziehungsweise zur Frage, weshalb in der seismisch eher ruhigen Zone der Schwäbischen Alb konzentriert Erdbeben im Bereich des Grabens auftreten (Intra-Plattenseismizität). Wir haben daher sowohl in situ-Spannungsmessungen mit dem Doorstopper-Verfahren (Greiner, 1978) als auch mit Triaxialzellen durchgeführt. Zur Erfassung von zeitlichen Spannungsänderungen wurden von uns zwei Dauermeßstationen südlich des Grabens (Abb. 1; TRU) und im Graben (Abb. 1; ONST) installiert (Baumann, 1984). Eine dritte Meßstation wird zur Zeit nördlich des Hohenzollerngrabens (Abb. 1; RIN) aufgebaut. In dieser Arbeit werden ausschließlich die Daten der Absolutspannungsmessungen vorgestellt und eine tektonische Interpretation in Bezug zum Hohenzollerngraben gegeben.

2.1 in situ-Spannungsmessungen

Über die verwendeten Doorstopper- und Triaxialzellen-Meßverfahren wurde schon häufiger berichtet (Baumann 1982; Greiner 1978), so daß an dieser Stelle darauf verzichtet werden kann und auf diese Arbeiten verwiesen wird. Die für die Berechnung der Spannungen verwendeten Elastizitätsmoduli wurden in situ mit einer Goodmansonde im Bohrloch gemessen. Die Ergebnisse der Spannungsmessungen sind in Tabelle 1 zusammengefaßt. In diese Tabelle wurden ebenfalls die Daten einer Hydraulic-fracturing-Messung (Rummel & Jung 1975) aufgenommen. Die Raumlage der Hauptspannungen aus den Triaxialzellenmessungen (Truchtelfingen / Ringingen) ist in Abb. 1 in winkeltreuer Pollagenkugeldarstellung wiedergegeben.

Aus diesen Spannungsdaten der fünf Meßstellen läßt sich im Bereich des Hohen-

zollerngrabens ein eindeutiges Muster der Spannungsverteilung angeben. In größerer Entfernung, südlich des Hohenzollerngrabens, ist die gemessene Richtung der größten horizontalen Hauptnormalspannung (152° und 150°) identisch mit dem Mittelwert, der für das westliche Alpenvorland (146°) angegeben wird (Baumann & Illies 1983). Unmittelbar südlich des Hohenzollerngrabens und im Graben ist die größte horizontale Hauptnormalspannung um 20° in Grabenrichtung rotiert (127° und 130°). Nördlich des Grabens stellt sich dann wieder die 150°-Richtung für die größte horizontale Hauptnormalspannung ein.

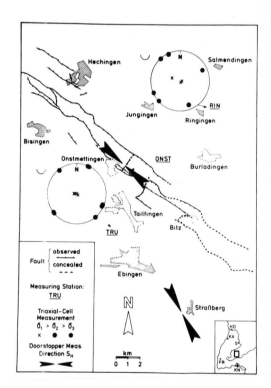

Abb. 1: Tektonische Übersichtskarte des Hohenzollerngrabens. Die Hauptnormalspannungsrichtungen der Triaxialzellenmessungen sind in winkeltreuer Pollagenkugeldarstellung (Projektion in die untere Halbkugel) weitergegeben. Die Richtungen der größten horizontalen Hauptnormalspannungen aus den Doorstopper-Messungen sind mit soliden Pfeilen markiert. Aus den in situ-Spannungsdaten wird deutlich, daß S_H bei den Meßpunkten Straßberg und Ringingen etwa 150° gerichtet ist, während unmittelbar südlich und im Graben S_H in Grabenrichtung eindreht.

46

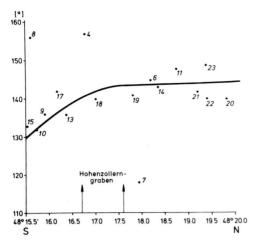

Abb. 2: Dargestellt ist die Richtung der P-Achsen von Herdflächenlösungen des Erdbebenschwarmes von 1978 (umgezeichnet nach Turnovsky & Schneider 1982). Es wurden nur die Beben verwendet, die nach diesen Autoren unverfälschte Richtungswerte lieferten. Die Erdbeben sind von Süd nach Nord aufgetragen und der Schnitt mit dem Hohenzollerngraben ist markiert. Die Nummern der Erdbeben entsprechen denen von Turnovsky & Schneider (1982).

Die Ergebnisse der Spannungsmessungen werden durch zwei weitere Argumente untermauert. Die Spannungsdaten wurden nicht nur mit drei verschiedenen Meß-

methoden ermittelt (Doorstopper, Triaxialzelle und Hydraulic-fracturing Verfahren), sondern auch von drei verschiedenen Meßgruppen gewonnen. Das stärkste zusätzliche Argument für das Eindrehen der größten horizontalen Hauptnormalspannung in Grabenrichtung liefern die seismischen Herdflächenlösungen des Bebenschwarms vom September 1978 (Turnovsky & Schneider 1982). In Abb. 2 sind die größten horizontalen Hauptnormalspannungsrichtungen, die aus diesen Herdflächenlösungen abgeleitet wurden, gegen die geographische Breite des jeweiligen Hypozentrums aufgetragen. Nicht berücksichtigt wurden in dieser Darstellung Daten, die Turnovsky & Schneider (1982) als richtungsmäßig verfälscht ansehen. Aus dieser Darstellung geht eindeutig hervor, daß die größte horizontale Hauptnormalspannung südlich des Hohenzollerngrabens mit 130° gerichtet ist und sich zum Nordrand hin zu Richtungswerten um 145° dreht. Das heißt, im dargestellten Bereich verhalten sich die horizontalen Hauptnormalspannungen sowohl nach in situ-Messungen als auch nach Herdflächenlösungen gleichsinnig.

2.2 Der Hohenzollerngraben - eine tiefreichende Störung oder seichter Graben?

Die beobachtete Spannungsrotation im Bereich des Hohenzollerngrabens muß loka-

Location	Straßberg-1	Straßberg-2	Truchtelfingen	Onstmettingen	Ringingen
N-Latitude	48° 10'	48° 10'	48° 14'	48° 17'	48° 21'
E-Longitude	09° 05'	09° 05'	09° 00'	09° 01'	09° 06'
Method	Doorstopper	Hydraulic-Fracturing	Triaxialcell	Doorstopper	Triaxialcell
Direction:					
S_V	----	----	±vertical	----	±vertical
S_H	152°	150°	127°	130°	150°
S_h	62°	60°	37°	40°	60°
Magnitude:					
S_V	----	----	+3,0 MPa	----	+4,9 MPa
S_H	+1,9 MPa	+2,4 MPa	+1,1 MPa	+1,9 MPa	+2,2 MPa
S_h	-0,2 MPa	+1,5 MPa	+0,5 MPa	-0,5 MPa	+1,7 MPa
Literature	Greiner 78	Rummel & Jung 75	this paper	Greiner 78	this paper

Tabelle 1: Bisher wurden im Bereich des Hohenzollerngrabens fünf in situ-Spannungsmessungen mit unterschiedlichen Meßverfahren durchgeführt. Mit Hilfe der Triaxialzelle ist es möglich, den vollständigen Spannungstensor zu bestimmen, wohingegen sich mit dem Doorstopper und durch das Hydraulic-fracturing nur ebene Hauptspannungen (S_H und S_h) erfassen lassen.

le tektonische Ursachen haben. Daher ist es notwendig, Klarheit über die heutige tektonische Position und Mechanik des Grabens sowie seines Störungsmusters zu erhalten. Aus der Grabengeometrie ergibt sich ein maximaler Tiefgang von ca. 2000 m (Baumann 1984), wahrscheinlich ist ein Tiefgang von 900 bis 1300 m. Die Kristallinoberkante liegt in benachbarten Bohrungen bei 950 bis 1100 m Teufe, so daß der Hohenzollerngraben das Kristallin vielleicht anritzt, sich als Grabenstruktur aber nicht in dieses fortsetzt. Eine Y-artige Fortsetzung der Hohenzollern-graben-Nordrandstörung in das tiefere Grundgebirge ist unstrittig (Illies, 1982; Illies & Greiner, 1976 und Schädel, 1976). Folgende Argumente werden angeführt:

1. Die Grabenabsenkung setzt aus geometrischen Gründen einen Zerrungsbetrag von ca. 150 m voraus. Diese Zerrung kann nicht über eine Sedimentmächtigkeit von 1000 m abgefangen werden und muß daher von einer tief in das Grundgebirge eindringenden Zerrstruktur begleitet sein.
2. Die Verteilung der Hypozentren der Erdbeben zwischen 1800 - 1978 (nach Turnovsky 1981) zeichnet den Verlauf einer sich zur Tiefe hin versteilenden Nordrandstörung nach.
3. Störungen der Bouguer-Schwere wurden von Jensch (1972) bevorzugt außerhalb und südlich des Grabens beobachtet.
4. In NW-Fortsetzung des Hohenzollern-grabens zeigen die seismischen Horizontalverschiebungen einen dextralen Charakter, der vielleicht auch im Rastatter Beben von 1933 seinen Ausdruck findet (Schneider 1971). Die Bernbach Störung bei Bad Herrenalb wird von Ortlam (1974) als paralleles, tektonisches Element des gleichen Spannungsfeldes angesehen (dextraler Gesamtversatz ca. 7 km).

Die rezenten Bewegungen im Hohenzollerngraben, die sich durch die Erdbeben dokumentieren, sind für den kartierenden Geologen, bedingt durch die schlechten Aufschlußverhältnisse, kaum zu erkennen und führen daher auch zu widersprüchlichen Interpretationen. Stellrecht & Moelle (1980) beobachteten vor allem konjugierte Scherflächen in 10° (dextral) und 125° (sinistral). Hoffers (1974) erkennt ebenfalls zwei, wahrscheinlich junge Scherflächenrichtungen mit 30° und 110°. Allerdings ordnet er der 110°-Richtung einen dextralen Bewegungssinn zu. Bankwitz et al. (1979) und Kronberg (1977) beschreiben aus dem Satellitenbild eine dominierende NNE-Richtung, aber auch

Hohenzollerngraben-parallele Fotolineationen, und ordnen diesen Scherflächencharakter mit einem Bewegungssinn entsprechend Hoffers (1974) zu. Illies & Greiner (1976) halten aus felsmechanischen Gesichtspunkten die Hohenzollerngraben-parallelen Störungen für das hauptsächlich aktive, dextrale Scherelement. Illies (1982) wiederum sieht die NNE-gerichteten, sinistralen Scherflächen vor allem aufgrund der Herdflächenlösungen des Mikroerdbebenschwarms von 1978 als die rezenten Bewegungsbahnen an, betrachtet aber die Tiefenstörung des Hohenzollerngrabens als das auslösende Strukturelement (Abb. 3).

In seismisch aktiven Gebieten, wie dem Hohenzollerngraben, können Herdflächenlösungen helfen, die rezente Bruchmechanik zu erkennen. Herdflächenlösungen haben aber den grundsätzlichen Nachteil, daß ohne die Kenntnis zusätzlicher seis-

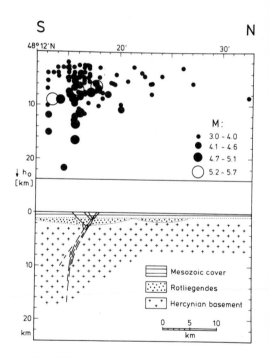

Abb. 3: Die Verteilung der Hypozentren der Erdbeben von 1800-1978 (Turnovsky 1981) im Nord-Süd Herdtiefenschnitt im Bereich des Hohenzollerngrabens zeichnen die Tiefenstörung des Hohenzollerngrabens bis in ca. 20 km Teufe nach. Deutlich wird auch, daß die flache Grabenstruktur nicht Ursache der Intraplattenseismizität sein kann, sondern daß diese ihre Ursache in der die Grabenstruktur bedingenden Tiefenstörung hat.

mischer Parameter und Geländebeobachtungen der aktiven Bewegungsflächen immer ein mögliches Bewegungsflächenpaar resultiert. Es kann also nicht zwischen Herdfläche und Hilfsfläche unterschieden werden. Für den 1978-Bebenschwarm berechneten Turnovsky & Schneider (1982) zwei dominante Bewegungsflächenpaare, und zwar 7° (97°) und 22° (112°). Vor allem aus der Anordnung der Epizentren schließen diese Autoren, daß die N-S beziehungsweise die NNE-SSW gerichteten Flächen die Herdflächen sind. Diese Interpretation ist sicher auch aus geologischen Gründen zutreffend für die Beben nördlich des Hohenzollerngrabens sowie südlich von Truchtelfingen. Im Bereich des Grabens, beziehungsweise unmittelbar südlich desselben, werden zumindest zusätzlich die von Turnovsky & Schneider (1982) als Hilfsflächen bezeichneten Flächen als Herdflächen genutzt. Dies zeigt deutlich das Beben 15 (aus Turnovsky & Schneider, 1982), das nach Daten des Institut de Physique du Globe in Straßburg berechnet wurde. Die Bevorzugung dextraler und grabenparalleler Herdflächen im unmittelbaren Bereich des Grabens zeigt ebenfalls die Anordnung der Epizentren des Bebenschwarmes von 1969 (Schneider 1971).

Die geologischen sowie die seismischen Daten machen wahrscheinlich, daß im Hohenzollerngrabenbereich rezente dextrale Scherbewegungen stattfinden. Wobei noch einmal darauf hingewiesen wird, daß als Ursache für diese Bewegungen nicht der flache Graben verantwortlich gemacht wird, sondern die unterlagernde Tiefenstruktur, die sich nach oben wahrscheinlich in der Hohenzollerngrabennordrandstörung fortsetzt. Diese Störung ist wahrscheinlich auch für die tertiäre Grabenbildung verantwortlich und wird heute als dextrales Scherelement genutzt. Die im folgenden beschriebene Modellvorstellung zur Erklärung der beobachteten Spannungsrotation im Hohenzollerngraben wird im rekursiven Schluß die Annahme einer dextralen Scherbewegung bestätigen.

2.3 Modell zur Erklärung der beobachteten Rotation des Spannungsfeldes im Bereich des Hohenzollerngrabens

Die lokalisierende Wirkung des Hohenzollerngrabens und seiner Tiefenstörung auf die erhöhte Seismizität dieses Raumes wurde von Illies (1982) betont. Dieser Autor erklärt die Seismizität durch die Blockierung N-S-gerichteter Scherlamellen durch die Hohenzollerngraben-Nordrandstörung und deren Fortsetzung in der Tiefe. Voraussetzung hierfür ist, daß diese Störungszone eine höhere mechanische Festigkeit hat als das umgebende Gestein. Die erhöhte Festigkeit dieser Störungszone könnte zum Beispiel dadurch gegeben sein, daß diese durch hydrothermale Lösungen zementiert und verfestigt wurde. Die Spannungsverteilung im Kontaktbereich der N-S Scherlamellen mit der tiefreichenden Fortsetzung der Nordrandstörung nahm Illies (1982) analog dem Modell von Chinnery (1966a) für die Spannungsverteilung am Ende von Blattverschiebungen an. Entsprechend den Annahmen von Illies (1982) würde in diesem Modell eine Rechtsrotation des Spannungsfeldes erfolgen. Aus den Spannungsmessungen sowie aus den P-Achsen der Herdflächenlösungen kann aber im Bereich des Hohenzollerngrabens eindeutig eine Linksrotation des Spannungsfeldes abgeleitet werden. Die gemessene Spannungsrotation läßt

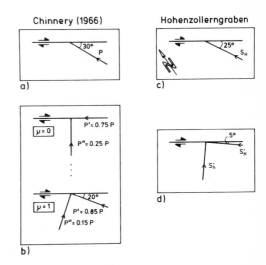

Abb. 4: 4b gibt das Modell zur Spannungsverteilung im zentralen Bereich einer Blattverschiebung wieder, auf die eine mit 30° gerichtete Spannung (P) wirkt (4a). In 4b ist der Winkel der Spannungsrotation in Abhängigkeit vom Winkel der Inneren Reibung (μ) wiedergegeben und zwar für die Grenzfälle μ=0 und μ=1. Die mechanischen Verhältnisse der Hohenzollerngraben-Tiefenstörung (siehe 4c) entsprechen 4a. Die Wirkung dieser Situation ist entsprechend 4b für den Hohenzollerngraben in 4d dargestellt. Die horizontalen Hauptnormalspannungen drehen in Grabenrichtung ein.

sich daher mit dieser Modellvorstellung nicht erklären.

Es konnte oben gezeigt werden, daß der Hohenzollerngraben und die seine rezente Bewegung bedingende Tiefenstörung dextralen Schercharakter haben und somit ähnlichen Bewegungssinn zeigen wie viele andere Schwächezonen in Schwarzwald und Schwäbischer Alb sowie in deren Vorland. Von dieser geologischen Situation ausgehend, erklärt die nachfolgende Modellvorstellung die gemessene Rotation des Spannungsfeldes im Gegenuhrzeigersinn zwanglos.

Diskontinuitätsflächen im Gestein können lokal eine Änderung des tektonischen Spannungsfeldes hervorrufen. Chinnery (1966b) untersuchte analytisch die Wirkung einer tiefreichenden Blattverschiebung auf das lokale Spannungsfeld für den Fall, daß eine Kompressionsspannung (P) unter einem Winkel von 30° zu dieser Blattverschiebung angreift (Abb. 4a). Er weist nach, daß die Komponente P' dieses Spannungstensors im zentralen Bereich der Blattverschiebung in deren Richtung eindreht. Der Winkel zwischen Blattverschiebung und P' ist abhängig vom Reibungskoeffizienten (μ). Für die Grenzfälle $\mu=0$ ist P' in Richtung der Blattverschiebung orientiert, für $\mu=1$ bildet P' mit der Blattverschiebung einen Winkel von 20° (Abb. 4b). Im Hohenzollerngrabenbereich liegt eine ähnliche mechanische Situation vor. Das tektonisch aktive Element ist eine tiefreichende dextrale Scherzone, zu der die größte horizontale Hauptnormalspannung (S_H) regional einen Winkel von ca. 25° bildet (Abb. 4c). Im Bereich des Hohenzollerngrabens und seiner Tiefenstörung dreht die gemessene größte horizontale Hauptnormalspannung in Störungsrichtung ein und bildet mit dieser einen Winkel von 5°-10° (Abb. 4d). Berechnet man aus diesem Winkel von 5°-10° den zugehörigen Reibungskoeffizienten, so hat dieser einen Wert von ca. 0,3 und damit eine realistische Größe. Die beobachtete Spannungsrotation läßt sich daher mit diesem Chinnery-Modell erklären und dessen Randbedingungen sind widerspruchsfrei zur geologisch-tektonischen Situation im Bereich der Tiefenstörung des Hohenzollerngrabens.

3. IN SITU-SPANNUNGEN IM ÖSTLICHEN JURA-GEBIRGE

Im Tafel- und Faltenjura der Nordschweiz ist der in situ-Spannungszustand mit dem Doorstopper- und dem Triaxialzellenverfahren in 6 Meßlokationen bestimmt worden. Beide Meßverfahren wurden in vertikalen Bohrlöchern in Tiefen zwischen 2 und 20 m unter Geländeniveau eingesetzt. Zusätzliche Informationen über den tektonischen Spannungszustand in der Erdkruste der Nordschweiz ergaben die Untersuchungen von Bohrlochrandausbrüchen in 5 Tiefbohrungen sowie der Herdflächenlösungen von Erdbeben.

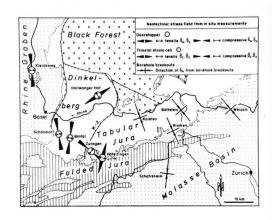

Abb. 5 Neotektonisches Spannungsfeld im mesozoischen Deckgebirge aus in situ-Spannungsmessungen und Bohrlochrandausbrüchen in der Nordschweiz.

Die Ergebnisse der oberflächennahen in situ-Spannungsmessungen zeigt die Abb. 5. Dargestellt sind die Richtungen der horizontalen Hauptspannungen. Mit Ausnahme der Meßlokationen Zunzgen im Tafeljura und Hollwanger Hof im Dinkelberg, die einen Einfluß der tiefreichenden, neotektonisch aktiven Wehratal-Zeininger Bruchzone wiedergeben, stellte sich angenähert eine N-S-Richtung der größten horizontalen Hauptspannung ein. Diese in der Umgebung von Basel gemessene Richtung weicht signifikant von der für SW-Deutschland und E-Frankreich charakteristischen NW-SE-Ausrichtung der größten horizontalen Hauptspannung (S_H) ab (Baumann 1981, 1982). Die hieraus zu konstatierende lokale Beeinflussung der regionalen S_H-Richtung läßt sich nicht auf eine Beeinflussung des tektonischen Spannungsfeldes durch die Struktur des Oberrheingrabens zurückführen (Becker 1985), sondern ist Ausdruck einer noch andauernden neotektonischen Aktivität des Faltenjura.

Eine N-S-Orientierung der größten horizontalen Hauptspannung S$_H$ zeigen auch die Richtungen der Bohrlochrandausbrüche in den mesozoischen Sedimenten der Bohrung Kaisten im mittleren Tafeljura (Abb. 5). Zum E' Ende des Juragebirges schwenkt die S$_H$-Richtung im mesozoischen Deckgebirge jedoch zusehends in die für weite Gebiete SW-Deutschlands und E-Frankreichs charakteristische NW-SE-Richtung ein, die schließlich in der Bohrung Weiach erreicht wird. Von besonderem Interesse ist die Bohrung Schafisheim, 5 km S' des Faltenjura im Molassebecken. Dort wurden im mesozoischen Deckgebirge oberhalb des triassischen Muschelkalks Bohrlochrandausbrüche beobachtet, die eindeutig eine N-S- Orientierung (N7°E) für S$_H$ erkennen lassen, wohingegen in Teilen des Muschelkalkes, und vor allem im kristallinen Grundgebirge, eine NW-SE-Orientierung vorherrscht (Abb. 6). Die hier zu beobachtende NW-SE-Orientierung für S$_H$ im kristallinen Grundgebirge zeigt sich ebenfalls in den Bohrlochrandausbrüchen der Kristallinabschnitte der anderen Tiefbohrungen im Taeljura (Abb. 6). Auch die Herdflächenlösungen von Erdbeben in der Umgebung von Basel (Abb. 6) zeigen eine generelle NW-SE-Orientierung von S$_H$ im kristallinen Basement bis zu 20 km Tiefe an.

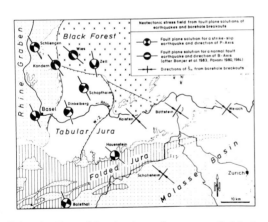

Abb. 6 Neotektonisches Spannungsfeld im kristallinen Grundgebirge aus Herdflächenlösungen von Erdbeben und Bohrlochrandausbrüchen.

Zusammenfassend ergibt sich aus diesen Daten das folgende Bild für den Spannungszustand der oberen Erdkruste des östlichen Juragebirges: Aus den in situ-Spannungsmessungen und den Bohrlochrandausbrüchen in Tiefbohrungen ergibt sich

im mesozoischen Deckgebirge des W' und mittleren Taeljura angenähert eine N-S-Ausrichtung für S$_H$, die zum E-Ende des Juragebirges in die für SW-Deutschland charakteristische NW-SE-Richtung einschwenkt. Im kristallinen Grundgebirge herrscht hingegen eine NW-SE-Richtung für S$_H$ vor, unbeeinflußt durch tiefreichende Strukturen, wie dem Oberrheingraben oder der Wehratal-Zeininger Bruchzone.

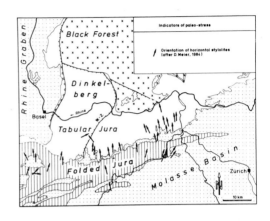

Abb. 7 Richtungen der Horizontalstylolithen im östlichen Juragebirge (nach Meier 1984).

Der Faltenjura ist eine oberflächennahe Struktur. Von der Faltung sind nur die Schichten oberhalb der Abscherhorizonte des Mittleren Muschelkalkes und des Gipskeupers (Trias) betroffen. Die abweichende Orientierung des Spannungsfeldes ober- und unterhalb des Muschelkalks, die in der Bohrung Schafisheim direkt nachzuweisen ist, wird zurückgeführt auf eine noch andauernde neotektonische Aktivität des Faltenjura und die Abscherhorizonte zwischen Deckgebirge und Grundgebirge. Die Annahme einer noch bis in die Gegenwart fortdauernden tektonischen Aktivität des Faltenjura wird durch den Vergleich des rezenten oberflächennahen Spannungsfeldes im mesozoischen Deckgebirge mit dem entsprechenden Paläospannungsfeld gestützt. Das Paläospannungsfeld kann durch Horizontalstylolithen erschlossen werden. Horizontalstylolithen sind Drucklösungssuturen, deren Zapfen parallel zur Richtung der größten horizontalen Hauptspannung während ihrer Entstehung orientiert sind (Buchner 1981). Die Richtungen der Horizontalstylolithen im Juragebirge nach Meier (1984) zeigt die Abb. 7. Die dargestellten Richtungen der Horizontalstylolithen sind ein direkter Ausdruck des während der Jurafaltung (vor allem im Mio-/Pliozän vor 10-4 m.a.) herrschenden Spannungsfeldes (Meier 1984). Der Vergleich des rezenten oberflächennahen Spannungsfeldes (Abb. 5) mit dem mio-/pliozänen Paläospannungsfeld (Abb. 7) zeigt, daß das rezente tektonische Spannungsfeld oberhalb der Abscherhorizonte die direkte Fortsetzung des Paläospannungsfeldes ist, das zur Entstehung des Faltenjura geführt hat. Demnach ist die tektonische Entwicklung des Faltenjura nicht abgeschlossen, sondern setzt sich bis in die Gegenwart fort. Eine Erklärung für die unterschiedliche Orientierung des Spannungsfeldes in den Sedimenten des Deckgebirges und im Grundgebirge gibt die von Buxtorf (1907) und Laubscher (1961) entwickelte Fernschubhypothese, die für die untersuchte Region eine N-S gerichtete größte horizontale Hauptspannung über den mesozoischen Abscherhorizonten postuliert.

Dieses Beispiel aus dem Juragebirge zeigt, daß in jungen Konvergenzzonen, wie z.B. dem Juragebirge, den Alpen oder den Karpaten, bereits in geringen Tiefen (im Jura i.a. 1000 m Tiefe) mit signifikant unterschiedlich orientierten Spannungsfeldern zu rechnen ist. Eine Extrapolation oberflächennaher Spannungsdaten in die Tiefe bzw. von Daten aus großer Tiefe in Oberflächennähe kann aus diesen Gründen äußerst problematisch sein.

4. SCHLUSSBEMERKUNGEN

Mit in situ-Spannungsmessungen konnte gezeigt werden, daß lokale Anomalien des regionalen Spannungsfeldes kartiert werden können. Dabei zeigt sich, daß diese Spannungsmessungen im Fall des Hohenzollerngrabens nicht nur das oberflächennahe Spannungsfeld sondern auch das tiefere Spannungsfeld im Tiefenbereich der Hypozentren der Erdbeben erfassen. Die oberflächennahen Spannungsmessungen können im vorliegenden Beispiel die Aussagen von Herdflächenlösungen dadurch verbessern, daß verschiedene Modelle zur Spannungsumlagerung und zum Spannungsabbau zumindest qualitativ getestet und an Hand der Spannungsdaten überprüft werden können und damit wiederum die räumliche Orientierung von Bewegungsflächen festgelegt werden kann. So ergänzen sich in situ-Spannungsmessungen und Herdflächenlösungen trefflich und führen zu einem konsistenten gebirgsmechanischen Modell

des Spannungsabbaus.

Andererseits wird durch das Beispie[l] der NW-Schweiz gezeigt, daß ein Span[n]ungsfeld sich in der Vertikalen schnel[l] verändern kann. Dort zeigten die in situ Spannungsmessungen sowie die breakout[s] flacher als ca. 1000 m eine etwa N-[S] Orientierung von S_H, wohingegen di[e] breakouts tiefer als 1000 m und die Herd[-] flächenlösungen eine NW-SE Ausrichtun[g] von S_H zeigten. Diese vertikale Änderun[g] des Spannungsfeldes läßt sich durch di[e] Modellvorstellung eines Abscherungshori[-] zontes zwischen Deckgebirge und Grund[-] gebirge erklären, der eine mechanische Entkoppelung beider Stockwerke beding[t] und damit den Aufbau von zwei Spannungs[-] stockwerken ermöglicht.

Die Fallbeispiele Hohenzollergrabe[n] und NW-Schweiz zeigen, daß neben Aussage[n] zur horizontalen Spannungsverteilung auc[h] Anhaltspunkte über ein vertikales Span[-] nungsprofil notwendig sind, um die rezen[-] te Tektonik zu verstehen und zu Modell[-] vorstellungen für junge Bewegungen z[u] gelangen. Mit den Beispielen soll abe[r] auch daraufhingewiesen werden, daß ers[t] durch die Einbeziehung von geologische[n] Faktoren in Modellvorstellung diese sinn[-] voll werden.

5. LITERATUR

Bankwitz, P., Bankwitz, E. & Frisch-butter, A. 1979. Fototektonische Interpretation von Mitteleuropa nach Aufnahmen der sowjetischen Wettersatelliten Meteor 25 und 28. Akad. Wiss. DDR, Zentralinst. Physik der Erde, 61: 37-60.

Baumann, H. 1981: Regional stress field and rifting in western Europe. Tectonophysics, 73: 105-111.

Baumann, H. 1982. Spannung und Spannungsumwandlung im Rheinischen Schiefergebirge. Numismatischer Verlag G.H. Forneck, Koblenz: 232 pp.

Baumann, H. 1984. Aufbau und Meßtechnik zweier Stationen zur Registrierung von Spannungsänderungen im Bereich des Hohenzollerngrabens - Erste Resultate. Oberrhein. geol. Abh., 33: 1-14.

Baumann, H. & Illies, J.H. 1983. Stress Field and Strain Release in the Rhenish Massif. In: K. Fuchs, K. von Gehlen, H. Mälzer, H. Murawski and A. Semmel (Editors), Plateau Uplift, Springer-Verlag, Berlin: 178-185.

Becker, A. 1985: Messung und Interpretation oberflächennaher in situ-Spannungen am Südost-Ende des Oberrhein-grabens und im Tafeljura. Diss. Univ. Karlsruhe; 221 pp.

Becker, A., Blümling, P. & Müller, W.H. 1984. Rezentes Spannungsfeld in der zentralen Nordschweiz. Nagra, Techn. Bericht 84-37: 35 pp.

Buchner, F. 1981. Rhinegraben: Horizontal stylolites indicating stress regimes of earlier stages of rifting. Tectono-physics, 73: 113-118.

Buxtorf, A. 1907: Zur Tektonik des Kettenjura. Ber. Versamml. oberrhein. geol. Ver., 30/40: 29-38.

Chinnery, M.A. 1966a: Secondary Faulting. I. Theoretical Aspects. Canad. J. Earth Sciences, 3: 163-174.

Chinnery, M.A. 1966b. Secondary Faulting. II. Geological Aspects. Canad. J. Earth Sciences, 3: 175-190.

Greiner, G. 1978. Spannungen in der Erd-kruste - Bestimmung und Interpretation am Beispiel von in situ Messungen im süddeutschen Raum. Diss. Univ. Karls-ruhe: 192 pp.

Hoffers, B. 1974. Horizontalstylolithen, Abschiebungen, Klüfte und Harnische im Gebiet des Hohenzollerngrabens und ihre Altersverhältnisse. Oberrhein. geol. Abh., 23: 65-73.

Illies, J.H. 1982. Der Hohenzollerngraben und Intraplatten-Seismizität infolge Vergitterung lamellärer Scherung mit einer Riftstruktur. Oberrhein. geol. Abh., 31: 47-78.

Illies, J.H. & Baumann, H. 1982. Crustal dynamics and morphodynamics of the Western European Rift System. Z. Geo-morph. N.F., Suppl.-Bd. 42: 135-165.

Illies, J.H. & Greiner, G. 1976. Regiona-les Stress-Feld und Neotektonik in Mitteleuropa. Oberrhein. geol. Abh., 25: 1-40.

Jensch, A. 1972. Die Entwicklung eines ALGOL-Programms für zweidimensionale Schweremodelle - mit Berechnungsbei-spielen zu gravimetrischen Längsprofi-len aus dem Hohenzollerngebiet. Diss. Univ. Stuttgart: 157 pp.

Kronberg, P. 1977. Die regionale und überregionale Bruchtektonik Mittel-europas, Bestandsaufnahme und Inter-pretation. Geotekt. Forsch., 53: 7-41.

Laubscher, H.P. 1961: Die Fernschubhypo-these der Jurafaltung. Eclogae geol. Helv., 54 (1): 221-282.

Meier, D. 1984: Zur Tektonik des schwei-zerischen Tafel- und Faltenjura (regio-nale und lokale Strukturen, Kluft-genese, Bruch- und Faltentektonik, Drucklösungen). Clausthaler Geowiss.

Diss., 14: 75 pp.; Clausthal-Zellerfeld.

Ortlam, D. 1974. Die Tektonik des nörd-lichen Schwarzwaldes und ihre Beziehung zum Oberrheingraben. In: J.H. Illies & K. Fuchs (Editors), Approaches to Taphrogenesis, Schweizerbart, Stutt-gart: 160-166.

Rummel, F. & Jung, R. 1975. Hydraulic fracturing stress measurements near the Hohenzollern-Graben-structure, SW-Ger-many. Pageoph., 113: 321-330.

Schädel, K. 1976. Geologische Karte von Baden-Württemberg 1:100.000, C 7918 Ebingen mit Erläuterungen. Freiburg i.Br., Geol. Landesamt Baden-Württem-berg: 85 pp.

Schneider, G. 1971. Seismizität und Seis-motektonik der Schwäbischen Alb. Ferdi-nand Enke Verlag, Stuttgart: 79 pp.

Stellrecht, R. & Moelle, H.R. 1980. Bruchtektonisch-genetisches Modell des Hohenzollern- und Lauchertgrabens/ Süddeutschland. Jber. Mitt. oberrhein. geol. Ver., NF 62: 229-250.

Turnovsky, J. 1981. Herdmechanismen und Herdparameter der Erdbebenserie 1978 auf der Schwäbischen Alb. Diss. Univ. Stuttgart: 109 pp.

Turnovsky, J. & Schneider, G. 1982. The seismotectonic character of the Septem-ber 3, 1978, Swabian Jura earthquake series. Tectonophysics, 83: 151-162.

On virgin stress state of a rock mass in mobile folded areas

I.T. AYTMATOV
Academy of Sciences of Kirghiz SSR, Frunze, USSR

ABSTRACT

Virgin stress of rock masses of folded areas is a result of tectono-magmatic history of a region. The upper parts of the Earth's crust in folded areas acted upon by horizontal tectonic forces have under-gone through considerable deformation and fracture. Consequently, rock masses within mining depths of deposits (2-3 km) are in post-failure stress-strain state. It explains the fact, that horizontal stresses in seismically active folded areas at equal depths below surface have 1,5-2,0 times smaller values than in the rock masses of the ancient stable consolidated shields (Baltic, Canadian, Indian).
A comparison of stress measurement data obtained by various workers in different folded areas of the world showed close agreement with the data obtained from mountain areas of Tian-Shan and Pamir.

RESUME

Cette communication présente l'état de contraintes naturelle des mas-sifs rocheux de régions plissées qui est une consequence de l'histoire magmatique tectonique de la région. Les forces tectoniques horizontales ont provoqué des déformations et des ruptures de parties supérieures de l'écorce terrestre dans les régions plissées. En conséquence, dans la profondeur d'exploitation de gisements (2-3 km) les massifs rocheux sont à l'état de contraintes et de déformations hors-limite. Cela ex-plique le fait qu'à la profondeur égale à partir de la surface ter-restre les contraintes horizontales des zones séismiques plissées sont inférieures (de 1,5 à 2 fois) à celles des massifs rocheux de bouc-liers consolidés stables anciens (baltique, canadien, indien).
Les contraintes mesurées par de différents auteurs pour de différentes zones plissées du globe sont conformes aux contraintes que nous avons reçues dans des régions montagneuses du Tian-Chan et du Pamir.

ZUSAMMENFASSUNG

Der natürlich angespannt-formveränderten Zustand des Berggesteins in den Gebirgsfalten Gebieten ist die Folge der tektonisch-magmatischer Geschichte des Regions. Im Einfluss den horizontal-tektonischen Kraf-ten haben die Oberflächen des Erdrindes den Gebirgsfalten Gebieten wesentliche Deformationen und Zerstörungen erduldet, wegen dessen sich die Bergmassiven in den Tiefen beim Abbau von Bodenschatzen (2-3 km) im übergrenzenden angespannt-formveränderten Zustand befinden. Dieses erklärt die Tatsache, dass in den gleichen Tiefen von der Oberfläche die horizontale Spannungen in den seismisch-aktiven Gebirgsfalten Gebieten kleinere Werten (um 1,5-2,0 Mal) als in den uralten stabilen konsolidierten Schilden (Baltischen, Kanadischen, Indischen) haben.

Eine Vergleichung den Endergebnissen bei Messungen von Gespannungen, die verschiedene Wissenschaftler in mehreren Gebirgsfaltenen Gebieten des Erdballs erhalten haben mit entsprechenden Angaben, die wir in den Berggebieten Tien-Schan und Pamir erhalten haben zeigten auf die gute Übereinstimmung.

Natural stress field in the upper parts of the Earth's crust has global character. The effect of gravitational, tectonic, thermal and other (at large depths) forces is the main cause for stress-strain state of rock masses.

An analysis of in-situ stress measurements in rock masses in different parts of the world carried out by workers in the USSR and other countries (Kropotkin 1973, Bulin 1971, 1972, 1973, Vloch 1979, Markov 1983, Turchaninov 1978, Ranalli 1975, Blackwood 1979) showed the inhomogeneity of the global stress field in the upper parts of the Earth's crust. The inhomogeneity of natural stress field is directly associated by many researchers with mechanical inhomogeneity of rock structure. More rigid elements are considered to undergo higher stresses. However, this assumption only partly explains the given fact since tectonic structure formation history is completely disregarded and a rock mass model is identified in practice with some solid under deformation with given physical inhomogeneity subjected to external forces. In fact, this approach suggests the following:

1. Rock masses are characterized by definite natural conditions of mechanical and structural inhomogeneity;

2. These inhomogeneous rock masses are acted upon by gravitational and modern tectonic forces;

3. A hard rock mass subjected to the mentioned forces are in elastic stress-strain state;

4. More rigid and stronger parts and elements of a rock mass undergo higher loads and, correspondingly, higher stresses.

The testing of all core material taken from boreholes used for the relief technique shows that in cases, when a rock mass seems to be homogeneous (e.g. a homogeneous granite section), its strength and deformation parameters in different parts can significantly differ from each other, too. Thereby, some periodical changes of mechanical properties of rock in space is observed (Fig.1). In an externally more homogeneous rock mass this change is apparently of sinusoidal character. For moderately and poorly fractured rock the wave length of property variation comprises about 0,5-4,0 m and the maximum/minimum ratio of mechanical parameters exceeds 2-4. This periodicity of the properties is typical of magmatic as well as metamorphic and sedimentary rocks.

Generally, the wave-like spatial variation of mechanical properties in a rock mass reflects its block structure. A single rock block confined by natural joints is mechanically inhomogeneous itself. Consider a case when a number of rock samples (e.g. 10-20) is taken from different parts of a 0,5x0,6 m rock block and appropriate mechanical tests are carried out. Then, even in relatively homogeneous rocks, e.g. granite and marmorized limestone, the coefficient of variation of the modulus of elasticity ranges from 15% to 25%. Thereby the edge parts of the blocks display minimum strength and modulus of elasticity values, whereas the middle parts their maximum values.

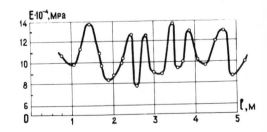

Fig.1 Modulus of elasticity variation along a borehole

A plane idealized model of an elastic blocky rock model was used to investigate the influence of mechanical rock inhomogeneity on the inhomogeneity of its stress state. In this model the Young's modulus varies in space according to the ordinary sinusoidal law. The problem was simulated by means of FEM using different ratios of vertical and horizontal loads, maximum and minimum Young's modulus and also Poisson's ratio values. The results of the numerical solution of the given problem allowed to draw the following conclusions. Stress distribution in mechanically inhomogeneous elastic body acted upon by external forces exhibits inhomogeneous character and depends on the Young's modulus and Poisson's ratio distribution in the discussed range of values: the parts of the body with higher elastic characteristics can be affected by higher stresses.

A comparison of calculated and measured stress data shows that actual stress inhomogeneity in a real rock mass results not only from its mechanical inhomogeneity. Some other natural factors considerably affect the natural stress field as well.

It is well known that in the process of tectonic structure formation of folded areas the rock masses markedly undergo deformation and generate numerous discontinuities. Particularly, the rock masses are deformed and fractured in the near-surface parts of the crust. However, in many theoretical works on geomechanical problems concerning stress-strain state of rocks a rock mass model is considered as some homogeneous elastic half-space with externally applied forces irrespectively of the tectonic disturbance degree of a rock mass, i.e. irrespectively of the tectonic structure type. Therefore, for a long time engineers and researchers in their stress state calculations during the exploitation of various deposits had to use the well-known conceptions (Heim 1878, Dinnik 1925) as universal techniques for determining natural stresses at any site of the world. But numerous experiments carried out in different parts of the world evidenced that in most cases (65-70%) horizontal stresses exceed vertical ones. This discrepancy between such stress distribution and the above mentioned models many workers explain by the influence of modern tectonic movements on the state of a rock mass. It implies that in presence of tectonic forces a rock mass in the upper parts of the Earth's crust acts as an elastic body which results in higher values of horizontal stresses than those of vertical ones.

In such a case it may be assumed that in tectonically active areas stresses in the upper parts of the crust should be higher than in rock masses of the stable areas. However, the results of experimental in-situ stress measurements in different types of tectonic structures showed that horizontal stresses in the upper parts of mobile folded areas, other conditions being equal, are lower than in rocks of the stable shields and platform fundaments (Fig.2).

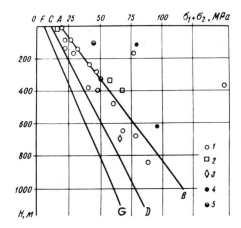

Fig.2 Variation of the sum of horizontal stresses with depth 1-Scandinavian mines; 2-Canadian mines (the Canadian schield); 3 - USA mines; 4,5-Khibin apatite mines, USSR. AB-within the stable schields;CD-in strong rocks; FG-in moderate strength rocks.

In pure elastic deformation of the crust under gravitational and tectonic forces, stresses located at different absolute altitudes, but at equal depths below surface, should differ. The results of in-situ stress measurements based on the relief technique in rock masses of various mobile folded areas show that at equal depths in such regions stresses are found to be equal or similar to each other even at completely different absolute altitudes of measurement points.

The results of in-situ stress measurements also show that a linear dependence exists between horizontal stress values and the depth in all the areas. In the folded seismically active areas the inclination tangent of this dependence curve to the depth axis is more significant than the corresponding curve value of the stresses distributed in the rock mass according to hydrostatic law. This condition also cannot be explained if the usual gravitating elastic model of a rock mass is used. Hence, a model of rock mass state available in the upper parts of the crust cannot be reasonably suggested as of some stress state, which was formed not in the process of rock mass formation and its tectonic structure, but as of state caused by external forces applied to naturally unstressed body.

Regional mechanical behaviour of upper parts of the crust in folded areas can be explained only by their post-failure state: thereby the formation of fault-fold structures and their upheaval occur in the process of orogenesis, and rock masses are greatly deformed and disintegrated and essentially reduce their overall strength and consolidation inherent in rocks in deeper parts of the crust. Obviously, if the upper parts of the crust were effected by tectonic forces as a simple gravitating body was (not yet fractured and quasi - plastically deformed), the horizontal stresses would change with depth, 1) as they do in accordance with the Dinnik's model, and 2) in different folded areas these stresses and the general stress level substantially differ from each other, since it is practically impossible that all folded areas at the same time (during the last 15-20 years, when measurements were taken in different parts of the world) remain at the same level of the pre-failure, mainly elastic deformation. At the same time, as the results of numerous investigations show, in several mobile areas the stress-depth relationship in the upper parts of the above mentioned tectonic structures follow the same regularities.

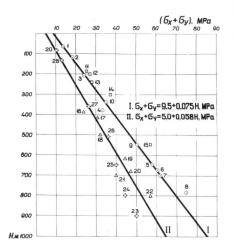

Fig.3 Variation of the sum of horizontal stresses with depth: 1,2 - Turangly,Tadjikistan,USSR; 3-Uluu-Too,Kirghizia,USSR; 4 - Kuru-Sai,Tajikistan,USSR; 5-Tekeli, South East Kazakhstan,USSR; 6-Kuru-Sai,Tadjikistan,USSR; 7-Tekeli, South East Kazakhstan, USSR; 8-Kansai, Tajikistan,USSR; 9-Tashtagol,Gornaya Shoriya, Sayany,USSR; 10-Temirtau,Gornaya Shoriya,USSR; 11-New South Wales, Australia; 12-Lago Maggiore,Alps Italy; 13-Piedmont,Italy; 14-Malaysia; 15-New South Wales,Australia; 16-Kuru-Sai,Tajikistan, USSR; 17-Tashtagol,Gornaya Shoriya,USSR; 18-Kuru-Sai, Tajikistan,USSR; 19-Kuru-Sai; 20-Kuru-Sai; 21-Sumsar,Kirghizia,USSR;

22-Tekeli,USSR; 23- Japan; 24 -

Ohio,USA; 25-Queensland, Australia; 26-New-York, USA; 27-Cobar, Australia; 28-California,USA; 29-Lucern, Switzerland.

There are practically equal stresses (Fig.3) in rocks with similar strength irrespectively of their location in terms of depth. Such condition may be observed only when the stress-strain state of a rock mass corresponds to the third (flat) portion of the full deformation diagram, where the remaining horizontal stress level depends on the rock mass strength properties and on depth below surface. Obviously, the residual (post-failure) strength of rock masses influenced by tectonic and gravitational forces would depend on "initial" strength and depth below surface, but not on when and where such a process occurs. As a matter of course, the subsequent geological history can somehow alter the post-failure stress-strain state of the rock mass, but in the areas of recent active seismo-tectonic processes, the upper parts of the crust would maintain the stress state level and the residual strength created earlier due to the mentioned processes. Thus the fact that various modern mobile folded areas practically do not differ from each other in terms of stress level in rock masses of the upper parts of the crust is explained. In such a case, strong rocks, other conditions being equal, have higher stresses than weak ones, due to more intensive tectonic deformation of the latter in comparison with the former. Continuing orogenesis provides evidence for the influence of active tectonic forces on rock masses of a region in modern period.
As a whole it may be stated that horizontal stresses in folded areas generally involve three main horizontal components:
1) residual stress component after rock deformation and failure during orogenesis;
2) stress component resulted from recent tectonic processes;

3) rock load stress component. Thus, the suggested model of stress state of a rock mass in the upper parts of the Earth's crust in the mobile folded areas takes account of the consequences of seismo-tectonic processes and demonstrates the unity of geomechanical nature of the discussed areas.

REFERENCES

Blackwood, R.L. 1979. An Inference of Crustal Rheology from Stress Observations. Proc. 4th Int. Congr. ISRM. 1.
Bulin,N.K. 1971. Modern Stress Field in the Upper Part of the Crust. Geotekhtonika (3) (in Russian).
Bulin, N.K. 1972. Modern Stresses in Rocks as Measured in Underground Openings of the USSR mines. Geologia i fizika (8) (in Russian).
Bulin, N.K. 1973. Some Conclusions Drawn from an Analysis of Natural Stress Measurement in Underground Mine Openings. In: Napryazhyonnoe sostoyanie zemnoi kory. Nauka, Moscow (in Russian).
Dinnik, A.N. 1925. On Rock Pressure and Circular Shaft Support Design. Inzhenernyi rabotnik (7)   (in Russian).
Heim, A. 1878. Mechanismus der Gebirgsbildung. Bale.
Kropotkin, N.P. 1973. Tectonic Stresses in the Earth's Crust as Determined from in-situ Measurement. In: Napryazhyonnoe sostoyaniye zemnoi kory. Nauka, Moscow (in Russian).
Markov, G.A. 1983. On Origin and Regularities of Horizontal Compression Stress in Rock Masses of the Upper Part of the Crust. Geotekhnika (3)   (in Russian).
Ranalli,G.and T.E.Chandler. 1975. The Stress Field in the Upper Crust as Determined from in-situ Measurement. Geol.Rundschau. 64 (2).
Turchaninov,I.A.et.al.1978. Tectonic Stresses in the Crust and Openings Stability. Nauka, Leningrad (in Russian).

Proceedings of the International Symposium on Rock Stress and Rock Stress Measurements/Stockholm/1-3 September 1986

Changes of ground stresses with depth in the Canadian shield

G. HERGET
CANMET, Energy, Mines and Resources, Ottawa, Canada

Abstract:
        In the Canadian shield a "normal" and an "extreme" population has
been observed during the analysis of 54 ground stress tensors. For the
"normal" population the vertical stress components are close to
overburden load, whereas the "extreme" population shows vertical
stresses far in excess of those derived from overburden load. For the
"normal" population the increase of the average horizontal stress with
depth is as follows:

$$0-800\text{m}: \quad \sigma_{Ha} = 0.0581 \text{ MPa/m depth}$$

$$800-2200\text{m}: \quad \sigma_{Ha} = 35.79 \text{ MPa} + 0.0111 \text{ MPa/m depth}$$

For the "extreme" population the following function was found for
the increase of the average horizontal stress with depth:

$$\sigma_{Hae} = 14.45 \text{ MPa} + 0.0563 \text{ MPa/m depth}$$

The ratio of measured horizontal stress to measured vertical
stress changes consistently with depth as follows:

Maximum horizontal stress/vertical stress = (367/depth (m)) + 1.46
Average horizontal stress/vertical stress = (267/depth (m)) + 1.25
Minimum horizontal stress/vertical stress = (167/depth (m)) + 1.10

RESUME:
        Lors d'un échantillonnage du bouclier canadien, on a observé un
groupe d'échantillons "normal" et un groupe d'échatillons "extrême"
pendant l'analyse des données de 54 capteurs de contraintes de terrain.
Les composantes de la contrainte verticale pour le groupe d'échantillons
"normal" sont proches de la charge de couverture, alors que le groupe
d'echantillons "extrême" indique des contraintes verticales qui
dépassent de beaucoup les contraintes provenant de la charge de
couverture. L'augmentation des contraintes de terrain en profondeur est
decrite dans le rapport.

ZUSAMMENFASSUNG:
        Die Analyse on 54 Druckspannungsmessungen ergab "normale" und
"extreme" Werte für den kanadischen Schild. Die "normalen" Werte
besitzen Vertikalkomponenten, die sich in etwa aus dem
Überlagerungsgewicht erklären lassen, während die Extremwerte weit
darüber liegen. Die Zunahme der Druckspannungen mit der Tiefe wird
in der Arbeit beschrieben.

INTRODUCTION

When the first stress gradients were published in Canada based on North American data only, the database was rather small and some of the results from ground stress determinations were of questionable quality.

In the last decade a number of Canadian mining companies, government agencies and consulting groups have made significant contributions to the database. The paper provides an update to previously published compilations of results of stress determinations (Herget 1973, Brown and Hoek 1978, Herget 1982).

The data have been obtained primarily at mining locations in Ontario, Manitoba and Quebec. Most of the sites are located in the Superior and Southern Tectonic Province of the Canadian Shield, which consist of Archaen and Proterozoic rocks comprising volcanics, metamorphosed sediments and granites. The youngest orogenic deformation occurred during the Grenville Orogeny (955 million years ago).

INSTRUMENTATION

Ground stress determinations in mines were carried out by overcoring methods, using biaxial instruments, (e.g., the USBM meter and CSIR doorstopper), and triaxial instruments, [e.g., the triaxial strain cell developed by the CSIR (South Africa) and that developed by the CSIRO (Australia)].

Fortunately the rock material in the Canadian shield is generally very strong. This is important because the maximum ground stress which can be determined with such instrumentation depends on the stress range in which the rock material behaves elastically. This has permitted the determination of ground stresses up to a magnitude of 130 MPa at a depth of 2100 m.

Discing of drill core can make overcoring difficult at such rock stress magnitudes and the possibility exists that full strain recovery is not measured (Hast 1979). It has been observed that the doorstopper method has been used successfully in highly stressed ground, where methods requiring the overcoring of an Ex annulus fo 30-50 cm were not successful.

Overcoring methods have been ver successful when used in fine-grained, isotropic, unfractured rock material a within 10 to 20 m of excavation bounda ries. For measurements in drill holes beyond this depth, overcoring procedur are less successful and become time co suming and very costly.

In most of the locations where strain recovery was measured by overcoring, a redundancy of strain recover data was available for each tensor determination, so that error determinations were possible with the method of least squares. Errors of ± 10-15% for stress components are common. Details of overcoring methods, quality testing to obtain a high degree of reliability and determination of physical paramete are described elsewhere, (Leeman 1969 Gray and Barron 1969, Herget 1973).

INCREASE OF VERTICAL STRESS WITH DEPTH

Many investigators have observed that the vertical stress component (S_V) increases linearly with depth and that the increase is related to overburden weight. The density for rocks rich in quartz and feldspar is about 2650 kg/m^3 and for basic and ultrabasic rocks 3300 kg/m^3. This results in a ve tical stress gradient of 0.0260 to 0.0324 MPa/m depending on the density of the rock formations involved.

Figure 1 shows that many of the results obtained in the Canadian Shield conform closely to these gradients, but some plot well outside this range.

In general high magnitude values were obtained at sites where at the time of testing, nothing noteable was observed in regard to the local geological setting. With the benefit of hin sight however, in some cases the follow ing possibly perturbing conditions were present: an unusual frequency of quart veins, a nearby shear-zone (50 m), or an adjacent well cemented contact zone between formations with large differences in elastic modulus (20%). In other cases nothing offered an explanation for the higher than usual strain recovery.

Generally, all stress determinations should be treated with caution where the calculated vertical stress component exceeds substantially the vertical stress component derived from overburden load. This is especially important if such a measurement is to be considered representative of a large area.

From statistical analysis of earlier data on vertical stress component variation with depth, a standard deviation of ±0.00278 MPa/m was established for the regression coefficient of a typical population (Herget 1973). For three standard derivations this value increases to 0.00834 MPa/m. The upper limit of rock densities in the earth crust is 3300kg/m^3 which would provide a vertical gradient of 0.03240 MPa/m. Thus any determined vertical stress component requiring a gradient exceeding (0.03240 + 0.00834) MPa/m cannot be explained on the basis that vertical stress is the result of overburden weight. The dashed line in Fig. 1 indicates vertical stress as a function of depth on the basis of this maximum gradient (0.04074 MPa/m).

These higher than usual values are shown in Fig. 1 as full circles and they follow a straight-line relationship going through the origin, with:

$$S_{Ve} = 0.0602 \text{ MPa/m depth} \qquad \text{Eq. 1}$$

with an approximate standard error of 0.0035 MPa/m

The regression yielded a correlation coefficient of 0.97. At one mine in Northern Ontario vertical stresses with this steep gradient were observed over three levels covering an interval of 250 m.

From observations of seismic activity around large hydro dams and isostatic adjustments due to melting ice sheets, it appears that the earth's crust is maintaining a delicate balance in the vertical direction and will adjust to changes in vertical loading of 0.5 to 1.0 MPa for large areas (Artyushkov 1971). On this basis the high values in Fig. 1 are considered localized stress anomalies which are not very extensive.

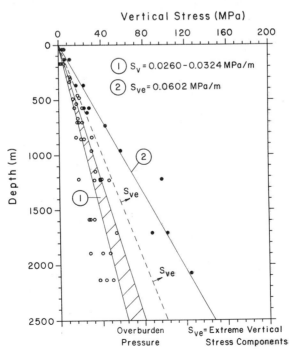

Fig. 1 - Change of vertical stress components with depth

INCREASE OF AVERAGE HORIZONTAL STRESS WITH DEPTH

It has been shown earlier that stresses can be found in the earth's crust where the average horizontal stress component is either equal, larger or smaller than the overburden load (Herget 1973). Around 1970, the majority of stress determinations showed the average horizontal stress component (S_{Ha}) to exceed the stress calculated from overburden weight, and a mean horizontal stress gradient of 0.0399 MPa/m provided a good fit to data.

Since then, additional information that has become available from measurements made in the Canadian Shield clearly shows that a constant straight-line increase of the average horizontal stress with depth does not occur beyond a depth of about 800 m.

Figure 2, a plot of the average horizontal stress component with depth, shows a rather large range of average horizontal stress values. It is interesting to note that ground stress tensors with higher or anomalous vertical stress components also had high average horizontal stress components. These are shown as full circles and conform to the following straight-line relationship:

$$S_{Hae} = 14.45 \text{ MPa} + 0.0563 \text{ MPa/m} \qquad \text{Eq.}$$

with an approximate standard error for the intercept of 4.36 MPa and for the regression coefficient of 0.0049 MPa/m and with a correlation coefficient of 0.95. It is interesting to note that for the extreme stress tensors both the vertical gradient and the horizontal gradient are similar.

For the purpose of obtaining the "normal" average horizontal stress gradient with depth, the extreme values were rejected. As the remaining values do not support a uniform gradient between 0 - 2200 m, two straight lines were fitted to the remaining values, with a break at 800 m. This break in the gradient was determined by adding and subtracting average horizontal stress components to the two populations until the best fit was obtained.

This provided the following linear relationship between average horizontal

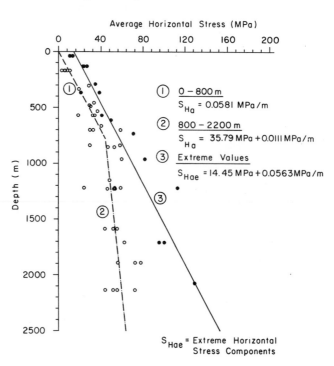

Fig. 2 - Change of average horizontal stress components with depth

stress S_{Ha} and depth (m).

$$S_{Ha} = 0.0581 \text{ MPa/m} \qquad \text{Eq. 3}$$
(0-800 m)

with an approximate standard error of 0.0100 MPa/m and a correlation coefficient of (r) = 0.85

An intercept of about 10 MPa was obtained in earlier attempts to arrive at an assessment of the change of the average horizontal stress with depth. This intercept disappeared in the present analysis because tensors with extreme vertical components were removed from the population.

Below 800 m the following relationship between average horizontal stress S_{Ha} and depth (m) was found to apply:

$$S_{Ha} = 35.79 \text{ MPa} + 0.0111 \text{ MPa/m} \qquad \text{Eq. 4}$$
(800-2200 m)

For the calculation of stress magnitudes the selection of the correct elastic modulus for the rock material is just as important as the measurement of the correct strain recovery. The effect of possibly incorrect moduli on determining stress change with depth

can be removed by calculating the ratio of the measured horizontal stress components to measured vertical stress components and plotting this ratio with depth.

Such a presentation has considerable merit from the point of view of designing underground excavations, especially if the ratios are not only calculated for the average horizontal stress component but also for the maximum and minimum horizontal stress components. In the Canadian Shield the majority of the principal stresses are aligned with the horizontal plane. Thus in nearly all cases, the ratio of maximum horizontal stress to measured vertical stress represents the ratio of the maximum principal compressive to the minimum principal compressive stress.

A number of functions were explored to obtain a reasonable fit to the available data. As the physical significance of these trends are not fully understood, the simple functional relationship between σ_H/σ_V and inverse depth (1/m) was selected for study.

The problem is however that an inverse relationship (hyperbola) is rather

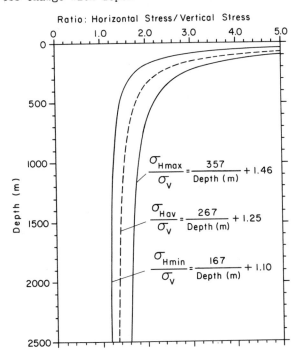

$$\frac{\sigma_{Hmax}}{\sigma_V} = \frac{357}{\text{Depth (m)}} + 1.46$$

$$\frac{\sigma_{Hav}}{\sigma_V} = \frac{267}{\text{Depth (m)}} + 1.25$$

$$\frac{\sigma_{Hmin}}{\sigma_V} = \frac{167}{\text{Depth (m)}} + 1.10$$

Fig. 3 - Change of ratio of horizontal stress/vertical stress with depth

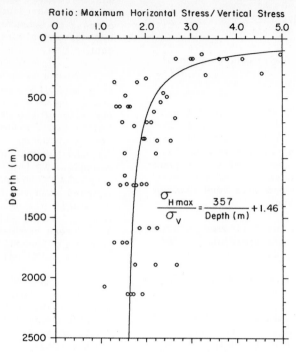

Fig. 4 - Change of ratio of maximum horizontal stress/vertical stress with
depth

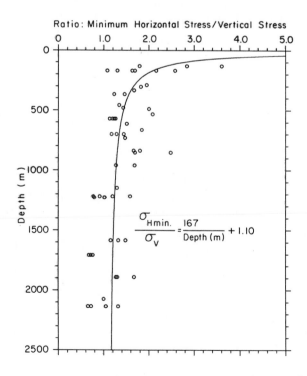

Fig. 5 - Change of ratio of minimum horizontal stress/vertical stress with
depth

rigid. With the asymptote of the depth values at zero, it was found that for the present data set any values at a depth of less than 50 m had a very profound affect on the position of the asymptote for the ratio values during regression analysis. Therefore it was decided not to admit data which were obtained at a depth less than 50 m.

The following results were obtained:

$$\sigma_{Hmax}/\sigma_V =$$

$$\frac{(357 \pm 36)}{depth(m)} + (1.46 \pm 0.11) \qquad Eq. 5$$

correlation coefficient (r) = 0.85

$$\sigma_{Hmin}/\sigma_V =$$

$$\frac{(167 \pm 28)}{depth(m)} + (1.10 \pm 0.08) \qquad Eq. 6$$

correlation coefficient (r) = 0.63

$$\sigma_{Hav}/\sigma_V =$$

$$\frac{(267 \pm 29)}{depth(m)} + (1.25 \pm 0.08) \qquad Eq. 7$$

correlation coefficient (r) = 0.79

The obtained family of curves is shown in Figure 3. Figures 4 and 5 show the datapoints used to develop equations 5 and 6. Figure 6 shows the results of the regression for the ratio of the average horizontal stress/vertical stress with depth. The dashed lines are the boundaries of the range of σ_{Hav}/σ_V ratios compiled by Brown and Hoek 1978, based on available world data. It shows clearly that the Canadian Shield results agree with these boundaries only to a depth of about 1000 m.

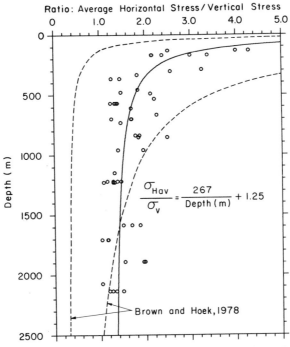

Fig. 6 - Change of ratio of average horizontal stress/vertical stress with depth

DISCUSSION

The data which have been compiled in this presentation show very clearly that near the surface, horizontal stress components exceed the stress values derived from overburden load.

A number of explanations have been offered in literature to explain the high horizontal stresses found during stress determinations, such as tectonic forces and processes of uplift and denudation. Such possible explanations are not easily verified because they require an assessment of loading conditions and a knowledge of material properties in the earth's crust on a long-term basis. Considering the slowness of changes in the earth's crust, the inhomogeneity of rock materials and the rather crude and cumbersome methods for stress determinations, the developing and testing of models to explain high horizontal stresses in the Canadian Shield is not conclusive at the present time.

The curves presented in this paper should be considered as an attempt to consolidate the results from ground stress determinations which are presently available.

ACKNOWLEDGEMENTS

The author is endebted to many mining companies who actively assisted in the difficult task of determination of ground stresses at their properties or made data readily available from their own stress determination programs. J. Folta and D. Dugmore prepared the drawings.

REFERENCES

Artyushkov, E.V., 1971. Rheological properties of the crust and upper mantel according to data on iso-static movements. Geophysical Research 76(5):1376-1390.

Brown, E.T. and Hoek, E., 1978. Trends in relationships between measured in-situ stresses and depth. Int J Rock Mech Min Sci & Geom Abstr 15: 211-215.

Gray, W.M. and Barron, K., 1969. Stress determinations from strain relief measurements on the ends of boreholes: planning, data evaluation and error assessment. Proc Int Symp Determination of Stresses in Rock Masses, Lisbon, Portugal.

Hast, N., 1979. Limit of stress measurements in the earth's crust. Rock Mechanics 11:143-150.

Herget, G., 1973 - a. Variations of rock stresses with depth at a Canadian iron mine. Int J Rock Mech Min Sci 10:37-51.

Herget, G., 1973 - b. Variations of rock stresses with depth at a Canadian iron mine. Int J Rock Mech Min Sci 10:37-51.

Herget, G., 1980. Regional stresses in the Canadian Shield. 13th Canadian Rock Mechanics Symposium, CIM Spec 22:9-16.

Herget, G., 1982. High stress occurrences in the Canadian Shield. Issued in rock mechanics, Proceedings 23rd Symposium on Rock Mechanics, Ed. R.E. Goodman and F.E. Henze, chapter 2:203-210.

Leeman, E.R., 1969. The 'doorstopper' and triaxial rock stress measuring instruments developed by the CSIR. J. South African Inst Min Met 69: 05-339.

In situ stress measurements, stress state in the upper crust and their application to rock engineering

FANGQUAN LI
Institute of Crustal Dynamics, State Seismological Bureau, Beijing, China

ABSTRACT: In situ stress measurement is one of the important methods for studying the recent tectonic stress field and the stress state in upper crust. Based on the data of in situ stress measurements, the author analyses the characteristics of recent tectonic stress field within China mainland and the stress state in upper crust. Meanwhile, the stress measurements and their application to rock engineering are also discussed.

RESUMÉ: Des mesures in situ des contraintes constituent une méthode importante pour les études du récent champ des contraintes tectoniques et de l'état des contraintes de la croûte terrestre supérieure. Sur la base des données au sujet des mesures in situ des contraintes, l'auteur a annalysé les caractéristiques du récent champ des contraintes tectoniques sur le continent chinois, les mesures des contraintes, l'état des contraintes de la croûte terrestre superieure et leur application en ingenieurie de roche.

ZUSAMMENFASSUNG: Die in situ Spannungsmessung ist eine wichtige Method, sich in dem heutigen tekonischen Spannungsfeld und dem Spannungstatus der oberen Erdkruste zu studieren. In verbindung mit den Daten der in situ Spannungsmessungen diskutiert der Autor über die Eigenschaft des heutigen tektonischen Spannungsfeldes in chinesischen Meistland, Die Spannungsmessungen, den Spannungstatus der oberen Erdkruste und ihre Anwendungen zur Steintechnik.

1. INTRODUCTION

In recent years great advances have been made in the field of in situ stress measurements. It attracted so much attention of the scientists in rock mechanics and geophysics, as well as of the engineering experts. From the in situ stress measurements we have obtained many valuable data for basic theoretical research of geodynamics and earthquake genesis. At present, the stress measurements are playing more important role in the practice related to designing of the mine tunnels and other underground constructions, nuclear waste treatment, oil-gas field exploitation, geothermal energy extraction, and determination of stability of water conservancy as well as hydropower facilities etc..

A series of in situ stress measurements have been carried out in various regions within China mainland by use of stress relief and hydrofracturing methods in the past decade. As a result, we have got preliminary knowlege of the stress state in the upper crust of China mainland, which is not only of tremendous interest in the theoretical researches of tectonic stress field and geodynamics, but also is of great significance in the practice regarding engineering projects, especially underground constructions (Li and Wang, 1979; Li et al, 1982).

2. STRESS MEASUREMENT TECHNIQUE

We have developed a piezomagnetic stress gauge for stress measurements in using the overcoring technique (i.e. stress relief method). The overcoring technique is suitable to the stress measurements in the near surface and the short drilling holes in tunnels, usually at depth ranged in several tens of meters, and its probable error in the better case is about 10% (Wang et al, 1981).

Since 1980 we have conducted stress measurements by using hydrofracturing technique. The main advantage of this technique is simplicity in operation, so that it does not need sophisticated downhole equipment and can be used for stress measurement in deeper part of the earth's crust (Li et al, 1983).

The data at the depths below 100 meters discussed in this paper are mostly obtained by hydrofracturing technique except for 6 groups of data which were measured at various depths in Jinchuan Mine, Northwest China, with the stress relief technique.

3. THE CHARACTERISTICS OF THE STRESS STATE IN UPPER CRUST WITHIN CHINA MAINLAND

In accordance with the data of stress measurement the essential characteristics of the stress state in the crust of China mainland can be described as follows:

3.1 The horizontal and the vertical principal stresses increase with depth

A lot of measurements made either in China or in other countries have shown that in most cases one of the three principal stresses is not exactly vertical but it is only inclined to the vertical less than 30 degrees. So it is still reasonable to recognize that one of the three principal stresses is vertical and the rest are horizontal. The vertical principal stress is related to the overburden weight and the horizontal stresses represent the regional tectonnic stresses.

The horizontal principal stress increasing with depth is not only several times greater than the weight of overburden but far exceeds the horizontal stress deduced from the lateral restriction.

The gradients of the variation of horizontal principal stresses with depth indefferent regions are not the same. For instance, in Northwest and Southwest China they are as follows:

$\sigma_{Hmax} = 1.48 + 0.067$ H (MPa),
$\sigma_{Hmin} = 0.62 + 0.032$ H (MPa),

where σ_{Hmax} is the maximum horizontal principal stress, σ_{Hmin} is the minimum one and H is the depth in meter.

However in Yixian, Hebei province, North China, they are expressed as the following:

$\sigma_{Hmax} = 3.92 + 0.032$ H (MPa),
$\sigma_{Hmin} = 2.88 + 0.029$ H (MPa).

In Xinyi, Jiangsu province, East China,

$\sigma_{Hmax} = 0.22 + 0.043$ H (MPA),
$\sigma_{Hmin} = 0.33 + 0.029$ H (MPa).

Obviously, the gradients of variations of the principal horizontal stresses with depth in Northwest and Southwest China are greater than those in North and East China (Figure 1).

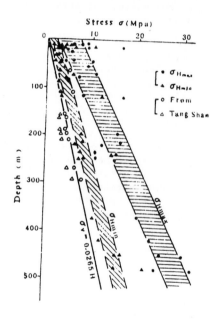

Fig. 1 Variation of the principal stresses with depth (The open circles and triangles represent the results obtained from Tangshan region)

3.2 The horizontal principal stress is characterized by strong directivity

Strong directivity is the another feature of the horizontal stress. It means that two horizontal principal stresses are scarcely equal to each other. According to the observations of ours, seventy per cent of the ratios between the minimum and the maximum horizontal principal stresses in the crust

70

of China mainland are in the range from 0.3 to 0.7. That is to say, the maximum horizontal stress is 1.4 to 3.3 times as great as the minimum horizontal stress. Such a ratio seems to have the regional difference. For instance, it is about 0.7 in Tangshan and Yixian, North China, 0.77 in Xinyi, Jiangsu Province. Whereas it is about 0.52 in Northwest and Southwest China.

3.3 Less variation of the direction of maximum horizontal principal stress with depth

If there were no topographic and other effects, the variation of direction of the maximum horizontal principal stress with depth would be slight. From the measurements obtained in Jinchuan Mine, Gansu Province, we have found out that while the stress value increased with depth, the direction of the maximum horizontal principal stress varied only a little, approximately between N30W and N20E, with an average direction about N10W (Figure 2). In addition to these, the hydrofracturing stress measurements at different depth in Xinyi of Jiangsu Province, Miyun of Beijing, Yixian of Hebei Province and Xiaguan of Yunnan Province also gave the same results. They coinside with the results obtained in USA and Germany (Haimson, 1980; Rummel, 1983).

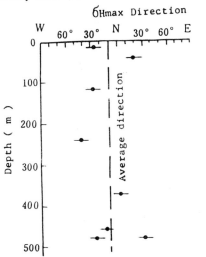

Fig. 2 Variation of directions of maximum horizontal principal stresses with depth in Jinchuan, Gansu Province.

3.4 Distribution of the maximum horizontal principal stresses and zoning of the stress state in China mainland

On the basis of the data so far obtained, we could not say that we have made enough researches on present tectonic stress field of China mainland, but we have got a brief understanding of this stress field in rough outline (Figure 3).

Taking the Mt Taihangshan as a boundary line, we can divide North China into two regions clearly different each to other in their stress state. To the east of the said Mt., in the North China plain and its surrounding areas, the axes of the maximum horizontal principal compressive stresses point to rearly E-W direction. And to the west of the said Mt., in the Shanxi Graben region, the axes of the above-mentioned stresses suddenly change into nearly S-N direction.

To the south of the East-west tectonic zone, in South China, the directions of the principal compressive stresses are considerably consistent with each other and point to NWW-NW.

It seems that the axes of the horizontal principal compressive stresses in Northeast China chiefly lie in NEE direction.

In West China the horizontal principal compressive stresses mostly extend in NNE direction and in some places they have turned to nearly S-N direction.

The tectonic stress field in Southwest China is relatively complicated. Nearby the Xiaojiang fault at the eastern side of the NS tectonic zone, the maximum principal compressive stresses run to nearly EW. To the west of this fault, including the fault block region which lies to the south of the Xianshuihe fault and to the north of the Lancangjiang fault, they have gradually turned to NNW direction. In the region to the south of of the Lancangjiang fault most of them act in NNE or nearly NS direction.

Xinjiang and Xizang regions are almost the gaps in stress measurement. only in 1982 some in situ stress measurements were done in Wushi Prefecture of Xinjiang, where the observed directions of the compressive horizontal principal stresses were N53W. These results agree with those obtained from the focal mechanism solution and the current tectonic movement over there

(Yan et al, 1979).

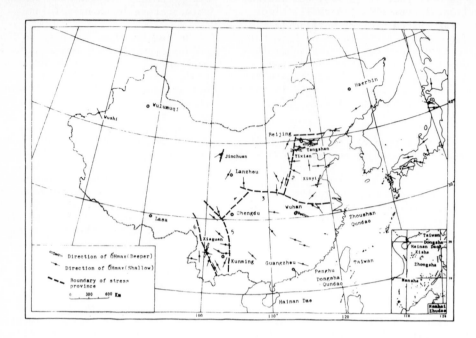

Fig. 3. Distribution of the direction of maximum horizontal principal stresses
in China mainland and Japan (The data of in situ stress measurements in Japan
are given by Yutaka Tanaka et al, 1979).
(In the figure: 1. Yinshan Tectonic Zone; 2. Taihangshan Tectonic Zone; 3.
Qinling-Dabieshan Tectonic Zone; 4. Longmenshan Fault Zone; 5. Xianshuihe-
Xiaojiang Fault Zone; 6. Lancangjiang Fault Zone.)

3.5 Variations of average horizontal
principal stresses with depth

Illustrated in Figure 4 are the average horizontal principal stresses,
$\bar{\sigma}_{Hav} = \frac{1}{2}$ ($\bar{\sigma}_{Hmax} + \bar{\sigma}_{Hmin}$), as a function of depth. Their values can be app-
roximately expressed by a linear relation as follows:
$\bar{\sigma}_{Hav} = 0.72 + 0.041$ H (MPa),
where H is depth in metre.
The result obtained by N. Hast in
the ancient Scandinavian (Hast, 1973)
is:
$\bar{\sigma}_{Hav} = 9.31 + 0.05$ H (MPa).
The result obtained by N. K. Bulin
in the overburden sedimentary rocks within the middle Asia platform (Bulin,
1971) is:
$\bar{\sigma}_{Hav} = 2.5 + 0.013$ H (MPa).
The result of stress measurements in
Japan reported by Y. Tanaka (Tanaka et
al, 1981) is:
$\bar{\sigma}_{Hav} = 5.8 + 0.015$ H (MPa).

It could be seen that the gradients
of variations of the average horizontal
stresses with depth in China mainland
are less than those observed by N. Hast
but greater than those reported by N. K
Bulin and Y. Tanaka et al. The stresses
measured in China mainland are of high
level (Figure 4).

3.6 Variation of the ratio between aver
age horizontal stress and vertical
stress with depth

Summarizing the stress measurement
data worldwide, Brown and Hoek (Brown
and Hoek, 1978) have developed an empirical formula which indicates that at
the shallow depths in the earth's crust
the ratio of the average horizontal
stress to the vertical stress, K, is
greater than 1, but in the deeps it is
smaller than 1 and approaches to a constant.

72

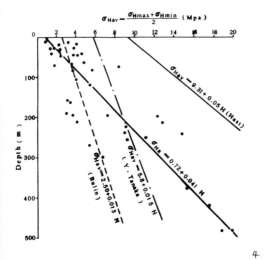

Fig. 4 **Variations of the average horizontal principal stresses.**

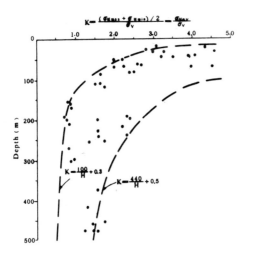

Fig. 5 Variation of K with depth (According to the data from China).

According to the data graned from the stress measurements in China it could be seen that the value of K at the depths less than 100m is scattered widely and approximately ranges from 1.5 to 5; however, at the depths below 100 m it varies from 0.5 to 2 (Figure 5). Its lower limit is:

$$K = 100/H + 0.3,$$

where H is the depth in metre. And the upper limit can be expressed as:

$$K = 440/H + 0.5.$$

Here we can see that the lower limit is coincident with the result reported by Brown and Hoek (1978).

3.7 Variation of the maximum horizontal shear stresses with depth

Figure 6 shows the variations of the maximum horizontal shear stresses with depth, $\tau = \frac{1}{2}$ ($\sigma_{Hmax} - \sigma_{Hmin}$). We can see that the rational difference is well demonstrated in the gradients of variations of maximum shear stresses with depth.

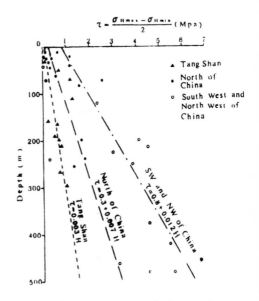

Fig. 6. Variations of the maximum horizontal shear stresses with depth.

In accordance with the real observations the variation of the maximum horizontal shear stress with depth in Southwest and Northwest China can be expressed as:

$$\tau = 0.8 + 0.012 \ H \ (\ MPa \ ),$$

where H is the depth in meter.
While in Northern China the

$$\tau = 0.3 + 0.007 \ H \ (\ MPa \ ).$$

And in Tangshan the

$$\tau = 0.003 \ H \ (\ MPa \ ).$$

4. APPLICATION OF IN SITU STRESS MEASUREMENT TO ROCK ENGINEERINGS

The determination of in situ stress is quite important in rock mechanics and engineerings. The essential task of rock mechanics is to study the mechanical behavior of rocks and rock mass at a static or dynamic loading. This must be concerned with the stress and strain measurements.

Up to now some people still ignore the existence of the high horizontal stresses in the earth's crust, though a lot of data of stress measurements have been accumulated. The very high horizontal stress may cause the wall stripping and drift deformation, even the rockburst and tunnel collapse. If an excavation is properly oriented with a reasonable section, the tensile stress along its boundaries and the concentrated compressive stress can be reduced to a minimum for keeping its stability. As to the stability of a tunnel or a drift, the state of stress in rocks should be considered as an important factor in choosing their location and direction, as well as the geometric configuration of their sections and the spans of their roofs.

4.1 Relationship between the stability of rock wall around an excavation and the in situ stress state

The stability of wall rock around an excavation depends mainly on the ratio between the horizontal and vertical stresses perpendicular to the axis of the excavation and their absolute values.

When the horizontal stress is greater than the vertical stress, the major axis of the excavation should be chosen in the direction of the maximum horizontal principal stress. When the vertical stress is greater than the horizontal stress, the major axis of the excavation must be chosen in the direction of the minimum horizontal principal stress. For example, a horse-shoe tunnel was excavated at depth of 450 m in Jinchuan Mine and the shaft lining was built with precast concrete blocks. Sometime a longitudinal tensile crack appeared seriously in the middle part of the upright wall and the roof of the tunnel had been squeezed into the shape of a peach. Thus the mine exploitation and underground construction were once obstructed. Afterwards, the geometric configuration of the section and the direction of winning were redesigned in accordance with the in situ stress

measurements. It was from then on that the tunnel which had been difficult to build for years were perfectly opened up and almost did not suffer from deformation any more (Liao and Shi, 1983).

4.2 Stability and bearing capacity of wall rocks around high pressure tunnel

In designing a high pressure tunnel, it's not only necessary to consider the deformation of rock mass, but also to study the its bearing capacity. In order to determine the magnitude of bearing capacity, we have to make analysis on stress and its intensity.

The observations from a hydropower station in Yunnan Province have shown that the wall rock around the tunnel withstood the major part of the internal water pressure in spite of that the overburden layer at the testing site is relatively thin and the rocks have been broken. The results of the test confirmed a great bearing capacity of the rock mass around the tunnel. As seen from the observation data on deformation of steel pipes and change of tunnel diameter, the pressure borne on the rock mass amounted to 11.5 to 12.0 MPa, i.e. 83-86 % of the total, while the internal water pressure was 13.9 MPa. The results obtained from hydraulic pressure tests and stress measurements formed a sound basis for designing the tunnel, on which we were able to save the steels, simplify the working process, speed up the construction and economize on funds. It is clear that in tunnel building and pipe laying the analysis of wall rock strength and crustal stress is of great significance in the practice related to tunnel lining (Jin and Wu, 1976).

4.3 Relationship between the in situ stress and the stability of rock mass within a slope

Redistribution of stress fields in rock mass in a slope is due to the composite action of the natural stress field and the stress field formed by unloading in rock mass. So that the stress state in rocks may have influence on stability of rock mass in slope. To what extent the redistribution of stresses in a slope would be affected by the state of the natural stresses? It mainly depends on the correlation between the strike of slope and that of stresses, as well as on the ratio between the horizontal and vertical stresses. While the vertical stress is the minimum principal one and the two horizontal stresses are perpendicular and parallel to the strike of slope respectively, the ratio between the horizontal principal stress perpendicular to the strike of slope and the vertical stress increases, and the shear stress parallel to the slope increases too. Such a case is unfavorable for the stability of the slope. Thus, if the maximum horizontal principal stress is parallel to the strike of the slope, it will be helpful to the stability of slope.

4.4 Crustal stress and stability of rocks under a dam

During the construction of a concrete dam, as the result of excavation, the unloading may simultaneously cause the rebound and rise of rock mass under the fundation pit as well as the radial displacement of the pit wall. If the vertical stress is the minimum principal stress and the horizontal principal stress is a greater one, and a nearly horizontal weak plane exists in the rock mass at the same time, the deformation of the rock mass will be very clear and produce a nearly horizontal dislocation of the pit wall along the weak plane. Firstly, as the result of rebound, rise dislocation and displacement, the permeability of the foundation will be increased and its mechanical properties will be worse. And then, as the dislocation or the displacement is a process necessary to go through, if such a process does not come to an end after the contact part of the building with the rock mass, owing to the further dislocation or displacement of rock mass, the building must be effected by an extra stress, even deformed and fractured, and loses its stability.

4.5 Stress state and treatment of nuclear waste

With the development of nuclear power station and nuclear industry the problem regarding treatment of nuclear waste becomes more and more important. In order to make the mixture of nuclear waste and cement solidified and sealed up in rock strata for permanent safekeeping, it's necessary to use the hydrofracturing technique for forming large horizontal fracture planes in rock strata. Whether the horizontal fracture planes can be formed by hydrofracturing, it depends on the state of stress in the strata. If the vertical stress is the minimum principal one, the cracks will extend along the horizontal strikes, otherwise along the vertical ones. It is worth notice that if the cracks link up with the underflow, our living environment will be polluted and this is harmful to mankind. For this reason, before the treatment of nuclear waste we must get knowledge about the state of in situ stress. In addition, during the construction of the nuclear waste storage we must take the crustal stress into account as an important factor for designing.

4.6 Stress state and regional stability

The characteristic and intensity of current tectonic movement in any regions are closely associated with the stress state and the mechanical properties of rocks. From the view-point of engineering geology, earthquake is one of the most important tectonic motions.

In certain regions owing to the building of large-scale reservoir the original state of in situ stress was changed and the earthquakes were induced. The investigations show that the occurrence of induced earthquake is related to the seismic and geologic conditions, particularly to the state of in situ stress. The sum of the values of shear stress and shear strength which had been reduced by the water storage in reservoir vary only in the range of tens Kg/cm^2, though the water storage in the reservoir had caused an increase of pore pressure in rock strata and a decrease of effective normal stress along the faults in the reservoir region and its vicinity, and heightened the shear stress responsible for dip-slip motion of the faults around the reservoir. Consequently, we can say that the occurrence of an earthquake in reservoir mainly depends on the seismic and geologic conditions in this region, especially on the original state of the in situ stress.

Meanwhile, if there is a fault near by the nuclear power station, the data on stress state are also needed for studying activity of this fault.

5. CONCLUSIONS

To study the state of in situ stress is of great significance in the practice related to the engineering constructions. As to the large and medium sized projects, we must take the in situ stress measurements as a requisite work to do, so that we can use the favorable and avoid the unfavorable aspects of the stress state in making reasonable designs.

The stress measurements have demonstrated that the characteristics of the in situ stress state in China mainland are as follows: The horizontal stresses are not only greater than the lithostatic pressure, but far exceed the theoretical horizontal stress calculated from the lateral restriction. The horizontal stress is characterized by its strong directivity and the direction of the maximum horizontal principal stress in some large areas is relatively stable and has a certain regularity in its distribution, being associated with the geological structure and the current crustal movement. According to the real measurements, the ratio of the minimum horizontal principal stress to the maximum horizontal principal stress and the gradient of variation of the maximum shear stress with depth have regional distinction. The depth gradient of the maximum horizontal shear stress in West China almost twice as great as that in East China. The horizontal stress in West China increases with depth at a higher speed than that in East China. All these phenomena probably reflect the differences in geological tectonic environment within various regions.

When we study the layout or plan of a construction and carry out the work at the building site, we must take the state and characteristics of the stresses into full account and adopt them as a basis for our considerations. The characteristics of the stress described here are just the statistic results. They are inadequate to meet the demand. Since the geologic structure and the properties of the rock are very complicated. If the conditions are avaliable, we'd better to do the in situ stress measurement.

REFERENCES

Brown, E. T. and E. Hoek 1978. Trends in Relationships between Measured In-Situ Stresses and Depth. Int. J. Rock Mech. Min. Sci. & Geomech. Abstr. 15 (4): 211-215.

Bulin, N. K. 1971. The Current Stress Field in the Upper Part of the Earth's Crust. Geotectonics 3: 133-139.

Haimson, B. C. 1980. Near-Surface and Deep Hydrofracturing Stress Measurements in the Waterloo Quartzite. Int. J. Rock Mech. Min. Sci. & Geomech. Abstr. 17: 81-88.

Hast, N. 1973. Global Measurements of Absolute Stress. Phil. Trans. R. Soc. Lond. A 274: 409-419.

Jin, H. and M. Wu 1976. Significance of In Situ Stress Studies for Design of High Pressure Tunnel. Collected Papers and Notes on Geomechanics 3: 170-176.

Li, F. and L. Wang 1979. Stress Measurements in North China. Acta Geophysica Sinica 22 (1): 1-8.

Li, F. et al 1982. In Situ Stress Measurements in North China and Tancheng-Lujiang Fault Zone. Chinese Journal of Rock Mechanics and Engineering. 1 (1): 73-86.

Li, F. et al 1983. Experiments of In Situ Stress Measurements Using Stress Relief and Hydraulic Fracturing Techniques. Hydraulic Fracturing Stress Measurements. National Academy Press. Washington, D. C. 130-134.

Liao, C. and Z. Shi 1983. In Situ Stress Measurements and Their Application to Engineering Design in the Jinchuan Mine. Proceedings of 5th ISRM Congress. Melbourne D 87-89.

Rummel, F. et al 1983. Hydraulic Fracturing Stress Measurements along the Eastern Boundary of the SW-Germam Block. Hydraulic Fracturing Stress Measurements. National Academy Press. Washington, D. C. 3-17.

Tanaka, Y. and Y. Oka 1979. Generation Mechanism of Rock Bursts and Water-Induced Earthquakes under the Tectonic Stress Field. Rock Mechanics in Japan 3: 71-73.

Tanaka, Y. et al 1981. The Crustal Stress Field in the Japanese Islands-- A general view of the results of in situ stress measurements--. J. Geod. Soc. Japan 27: 322-326.

Wang, L. et al 1981. Principles and Applications of Ground Stress Measurement. Publishing House of Geology.

Beijing. 48-142.

Yan, J. et al 1979. Some Features of
the Recent Tectonic Stress Field of
China and Environs. Acta Seismologica
Sinica. 1 (1): 9-24.

Twenty years of experience on in-situ stress measurements in China

LI GUANGYU
BAI SHIWEI
LIU JIGUANG
Institute of Rock & Soil Mechanics, Academia Sinica, Wuhan, China

ABSTRACT Various typical results are introduced of *in-situ* stress measurements by overcoring tests during last two decades. The cases can be divided into three types: *in-situ* stress in lower strength rocks, *in-situ* stress in higher strength rocks, *in-situ* stress in high stress region. The deepest borehole is 90m in depth. The measured highest and the lowest (tensile) natural stresses are 64.6MPa and 1MPa. Some general laws of natural stress in the shallow earth crust are drawn from the above results. The relationship between natural stress and Young's moduli of rocks and the influence of natural stresses on rock engineering are discussed.

RESUME On donne les différents résultats typiques des mesures des contraintes in-situ obtenues par l'essai de surcarottage pendant les dernières deux décades. Les cas se divisent en trois catégories: les contraintes in-situ dans le massif rocheux avec base resistance, celles dans le massif rocheux avec haute resistance, et celles dans les régions de hautes contraintes. Les contraintes naturelles maximale et minimale sont 64.6MPa et 1MPa (tension). Quelques lois sont decouvertées concernant la distribution des contraintes naturelles dans la partie superficielle de la croûte terrestre. Le rapport entre les contraintes naturelles et les modules d'elasticité et l'influence des contraintes naturelles sur le génie géomechanique sont discutés dans ce papier.

ZUSAMMENFASSUNG Im vorliegenden Beitrag werden die typische Ergebnise während der letzten Jahrzehnten von den verschiedenen *in-situ* Spannungsmessungen mittels der Uberkernnungstechnik berichtet und in den 3 Arten: die *in-situ* Spannung in klein-Festigkeit Felsen, die *in-situ* Spannung in groß-Festigkeit Felsen und die *in-situ* Spannung in groß-Spannung Bereiche sich teilt. Die Teufe der tiefsten Bohrung beträgt 90m. Die höchste und niedrigste Spannung sind 64.6MPa und 1MPa. Aus den obigen resultate wird die allgemeine Gesetze für Primärspannung in der oberflächlichen Erdrinde formuliert. Anschließend werden die Beziehung zwichen der Primärspannung und des E-Moduls des Felsen und der Einfluß der Primärspannung auf Felsbau disskutiert.

INTRODUCTION

In-situ stress measurements have been carried out in our institute since 1964. Some kinds of methods and instruments have been employed, such as partial stress relief, stress recovery, overcoring technique and strain gauge, vibrating wire, borehole deformeter, etc.. After a great mass of lab and field tests, overcoring technique with a borehole deformeter and bioaxial apparatus has been selected as the better one. The details about it can be found elsewhere (Zhu 1985). This method has successfully been adopted by many institutes and engineering departments in about twenty sites in China (Fig.1). The examples introduced in this paper are mainly abstracted from the tests which were carried out by the authors.

Fig.1 Project locations where *in-situ* stress measurements were carrid out.

The terminology and explanation used to describe *in-situ* stress are various, some are similar and some are different. The terminology quoted here comes from Bielenstein & Barron's suggestion (Bielenstein & Barron, 1971), as follows.

They classified *in-situ* stresses into two groups, i.e., natural one and induced one, the latter is artificial stress components due to removal or addition of materials. It is superposed on the former one which exists prior to any excavation. The natural stress field can be composed of gravitational stresses (due to the mass of overburden), tectonical stresses and residual stresses. Tectonic stresses may be active tectonic stresses and remanent tectonic stresses (due to post tectonic events which have only been partially relieved by natural processes).

IN-SITU STRESS IN ROCKS WITH LOWER STRENGTH

It is impossible to accumulate higher stress in rocks with lower strength. Hence the influence of natural stress in soft rock on the geotechnical engineering is always neglected. As a matter of fact, although *in-situ* stress is lower in soft rocks, the deformation of the rock engineering would probably large and lead to failure due to its lower modulus of deformation and creep behaviour.

During the construction of the Gezhouba Hydropower Station, large universally dislocations along the weak intercalations of rock were found after several months of excavation of the deep foundation pit by extensive observations and monitoring (Tseng et al, 1978) The dislocations have the following characteristics, their directions are neither perpendicular to the slope of the pit nor along the dipping of the weak intercalation, but intersect the axis of an angle of 58° (NE51°); Their orders are big, the biggest one is 80mm ; their influence is relatively wide and deep (300m away from the excavation line) and the dislocations lasted about two years. The above phenomenon could hardly be explained by the reasons of gravitational stress relief, rock swelling and the effect of blasting. However, most of engineers *in-situ* did not believe existing tectonic and residual stresses there at the biginning, because the valley is very wide (over 2000m), the elevation difference between the bottom and both banks of the river is only 100-150m, rock formation is weak and soft (siltstone and sandstone), occurrence is gentle (NE20-40°/SE 6°), weak intercalations are numerous, but joints and cracks do not develop.

In order to demonstrate, *in-situ* stress measurements were carried out in 1977. Three boreholes were drilled for overcoring tests, of which No.1 was located at the stage of upstream, No.2 at the bottom of the foundation pit, No.3 at the river bed of downstream 500m away from the axis of the pit to avoid the influence of excavation. All of the results are shown in Table 1 and Fig.2.

The results indicate that *in-situ* stress in the upper parts of borehole No.1 and No.2 are quite lower due to the rockmass failure caused by stress concentration and rock strength dropping . Therefore the stress concentration zones transfer into the deeper parts of the ground, encountering a sandstone formation with higher strength and modulus at the elevation of about -10 meter and forming a new band of stress concentration. With the further increase in depth, *in-situ* stress tends to becoming more or less stable

80

Table 1 *In-situ* measured stresses at the Erjiang dam of Gezhouba

borehole No.	point No.	depth (m)	σ_1 (kg/cm^2)	σ_2 (kg/cm^2)	ϕ	remarks
1601	1	3.3	16.7	13.3	NW27°	* midium-grained fine sandstone, great differentiation of elastical modelling tests, probably producing higher calculated stress.
	2	5.1	16.1	13.4	NE28°	
	3	6.6	7.2	3.8	NW49°	
	4	13.3	11.3	8.9		
	5	16.9	12.4	9.3	NE43°	
	6*	23.2	55.3	38.0	NE55°	
	7	26.7	22.6	17.2	NW45°	
	8	32.0	22.6	19.0	EW	
	9	35.4	26.5	22.3	NE48°	
1602	1	4.8	7.8	4.8	NE22°	ditto
	2	5.8	8.8	6.1	SN	
	3	6.4	9.5	7.5	NW12°	
	4*	11.1	27.2	22.2	NW47°	
	5*	16.5	33.8	24.5	NE47°	
	6	18.2	12.9	10.2	NE64°	
	7	22.9	20.8	14.8	NE49°	
	8	27.9	13.3	10.5	NE50°	
1603	1	16.8	20.0	17.2	NW48°	the average value of point 6,7,8: $\sigma_1 = 30.7$ $\sigma_2 = 23.4$ (unit:kg/cm^2)
	2	17.3	17.0	8.7	NE49°	
	3	21.6	9.9	8.5	NW22°	
	4	27.4	20.9	15.2	NE60°	
	5	30.2	24.8	9.6	NE32°	
	6	34.2	29.9	17.4	NE12°	
	7	37.2	31.5	26.5	NE62°	
	8	39.4	30.7	26.2	NE26°	

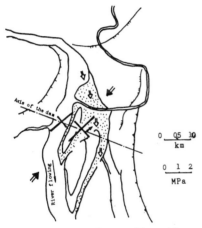

Fig.2 ➡ Tectonic stress direction
→ Dislocation direction of pit
+ Measured natural stresses

linear FEM calculation were carried out. Both results show that the horizontal stress should be about 2.5MPa when the dislocation of the side slope foot of the pit is 80mm. It approaches to the measured major principal stress. What is more interesting was that the orientation of the major principal stress conformed with those of displacement and neotectonic stress approximately(Fig.3). In 1982 other two boreholes were drilled at first channel to measure natural stress, the results are almost the same, as shown in Fig.2.

which may be considered as natural stress. If the last three sets of values in each borehole are taken out, then the average state of natural stresses $\sigma_1 = 2.34$MPa, and $\sigma_2 = 1.82$MPa, the azimath of $\sigma_1 = $ NE50°. This just conforms with the direction of the dislocations (NE51°) and closes to the direction of the tectonic stress (NE30-40°) determined by geomechanical investigation. In order to explain that the natural stress is the main source causing large dislocations, statical equilibrium analysis and non-

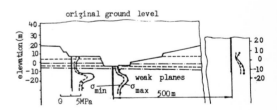

Fig.3 Distribution of *in-situ* stress in three boreholes

IN-SITU STRESS IN HIGHER STRENGTH ROCKS

It is quite possible for a high strength rockmass to accumulate a high natural stress in it, however

such is not the case with all high-strength rockmasses. The situation dependes upon such factors as the history of structural movements,especially the recent one and the topography in the region of interest, and the overburden depth.

To assess the stability of the underground opening with a large span,a series of *in-situ* tests for mechanical properties of rocks was carried out from 1973 to 1976, including a great number of extensive field stress measurements.

The working area is composed mainly of limestone strata belonging to Sinian , Cambrian and Ordovician Systems of Palaeozoic group, and exhibiting inversion from north to south. The strata have a strike of NW50-70° and a dip of 40-60°. The testing adit is in hard and competent but brittle thick dolomite strata with less developing stratification and developing cracks or joints (most are calcareously-cemented), i.e., the engineering geological condition is good.The compressive strength and the Young's module and the Poisson's ratio of the rock are 110-180MPa,105GPa and 0.26 respectively. The cross sectional sizes of the adit,with an average overburden depth of 120m,are 2.5×2.5m and its long axis direction is NE5°.

There were nine boreholes, each having a depth exceeding two times the adit's span, for stress relief method drilled in the testing adit to measure the natural stress of the rockmass which are not affected by the secondary stress of the opening periphery,and in the meantime to investigate the stress distribution rule at the periphery. The stress relief tests were step by step carried out towards depth. The stress distribution is illustrated in Fig.4. in which because of not very high natural stresses and of very high strength and higher Young's module, basically there is no plastic zone existing around the adit periphery and the factor of stress concentration is close to the calculated one according to elastic theory, say, about 2 . The measured stress at the place beyond the depth of 4m can be regarded as the natural stress . The average principal stresses are 15MPa for σ_1 and 30° for α , from which

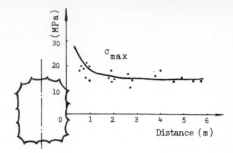

Fig.4 Max measured principal stress at the periphery of the prospecting adit

the stress distribution around the periphery can be derived. Owing to the horizontal stress, no tensile stress at the crown of the adit and by contrast, there is a compressive stress of 30MPa.A 78 meter deep borehole was drilled to check the above calculated results,at various depths of which the *in-situ* stress is measured . The measured and calculated stresses are shown in Fig.5, both of them are coincident with each other , which suggests that there exists a rather high compressive stress in the rock mass, quite benifiting the stability of surrounding rocks.

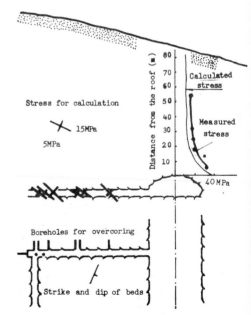

Fig.5 Comparison between the *in-situ* measured stresses and the calculated results

The calculation of the complete stress has shown that the orientation or direction of principal stresses are not obviously related to the structural trace but closely to the topography. The reason for this is that smaller overburden depth of measurements causes a greater boundary effect on the measured results. The following cases can show the same regulation as well.

The Shuikou Hydropower Station of the Minjiang River is located in the county of Minqing, Fujian province, the maximum dam height of the station is 100 m. The rockmass of the dam site comprises midium-grained granite of the Yanshan Period with less developing joints and cracks in it, the rock is fresh and hard and the Young's module is 65GPa. The *in-situ* measured stress distribution is illustrated in Fig.6, where the direction of the max principal stress closely relates the topography.

The Dayaoshan Railway Tunnel, being under construction, is the longest double-track railway tunnel in China, the max overburden depth

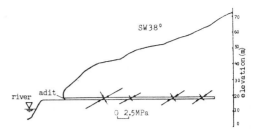

Fig.6 *In-situ* measured stresses at the prospecting adit of Shuikou Hydropower Station.

above it is 900m. The *in-situ* stress measurement result has shown that the stress due to dead weight, when the measured points are slightly buried(below 200m), is dominant; and its direction, at point 1 for example also governed by topography while in the case of heavily-buried points, the propotion of structure stresses increases a lot, and the direction of principal stresses is close to that obtained from geological investigation and geomechanical analyses (Fig.7).

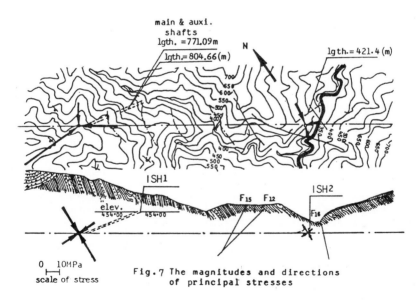

Fig.7 The magnitudes and directions of principal stresses

THE *IN-SITU* STRESS IN A HIGH STRESS REGION

The southwestern China is abundant in hydroelectric resources, making up about 75% of the total reserves in China. In a particular region of the Southwest, the rocks are very hard, so in explorating the dam site of a reservoir which will be built in the region, the rock-disking phenomenon more often than not occurred in boreholes and sometimes the rock-flake phenomenon took place in the prospecting adit. All this phenomenon did presage a very high natural stress existing in the rock mass, this is very unfavourable to the excavation of the dam foundation and slope and therefore to the stability of underground chambers or tunnels. The dam site of Ertan Hydropower Station of the Yalong River is one of the typical cases (Zhu et al 1985). The rock mass in the dam site consists mainly of basalt and syenite with a very high strength and a great elastic module. The river valley is an asymmetric "V" in shape, whose right bank with a slope of $25-40^0$ is about 500m high and left bank with a slope of $30-45^0$ is about 1000m in height. The Yalong River is only 100m in width. In prospecting, the rock-disking phenomenon was found in 84 boreholes of the total number of 200, among them 45 holes were located in the middle of the river bed. Besides in the prospecting adit parallel to the river bed, the rock-flake phenomenon was found, in particular, while preparing the test blocks for rock mechanical tests in the adit floor, the block surface desquamated with the increasing in grooving depth, it was unable to shape a complete or intact cubic block.

A great number of field tests of stress measurements have been carried out to ascertain the natural stress in this region, all together 45 boreholes with a total length of 450m were drilled. About 700 original data were obtained, the complete stress state at 12 testing points and the plane stress state at 6 points were determined, as shown in Fig.8(a),(b). It should be in particular pointed out that in testing in the vertical borehole at the right bank, when the overcoring reached the depth of 37.5m, a 30cm long rock core was fractured into 12 discks with the same thickness of 2.5cm. Fortunately, the four transducers of a probe were perfectly touched to the core central hole while disking and the four measured data can be checked each other $(u_0 + u_{90} = u_{45} + u_{135})$, the deformation curve was regular. The elastic module of the core *in situ* measured with two-way loading devices was conformable to those obtained on other specimens, thus the data measured by borehole deformeter can be considered reliable. The natural stresses were measured

$\sigma_1 = 63.7$MPa, $\sigma_2 = 28.5$MPa, the direction of σ_1 was NE34^0. The FEM regression analyses presaged a stress concentration zone beneath the river bed floor, this was quite coincident with the σ_1 of the measuring point (63.7MPa) and much more with that of the other point near the former (Fig.9).

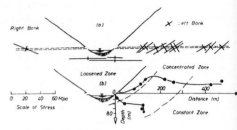

Fig.8 a) Principal stresses in cross section of the river. b) Three stress zone characterized by measured stresses

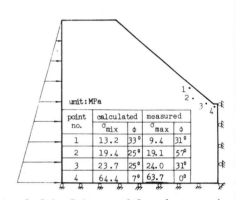

point no.	calculated		measured	
	σ_{mix}	ϕ	σ_{max}	ϕ
1	13.2	33^0	9.4	31^0
2	19.4	25^0	19.1	57^0
3	23.7	25^0	24.0	31^0
4	64.4	7^0	63.7	0^0

unit:MPa

Fig.9 Calculation model and comparison between calculated and measured results at four points.

Both measured and regressed results have indicated that this region is indeed the one with a high natural stress. The max average principal stresses of the rockmass in two banks are 20MPa for syenite and much higher (30MPa) for basalt, they are characterized by the followings:

(a) Their directions are governed by topography but not too related to the tectonic movements.

(b) because of unloading at the bank slope and the weathered rock surfaces, the stress values dre correspondingly and the stress concentration zone transfers to the deep parts, forming three various zones, i.e., stress relief, stress concentration and stress stability ones (Fig.8).

The success in field stress measurement in potential disking core region provides a good practical case for estimating *in-situ* stress from mechanical calculation. As an example, a symmetrical FEM analysis was carried out , the calculation model is shown in Fig.10, to simulate the drilling·procedure with a direction pointed by the downward arrow, after each calculation two elements of D/12 in length were elimilated and the next calculation was performed subsequently.

In Fig.11 shown are the axial stress distribution along the central axis and the longitudinal and

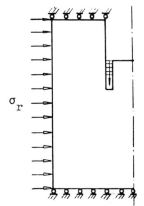

Fig.10 symmetrical calculation model

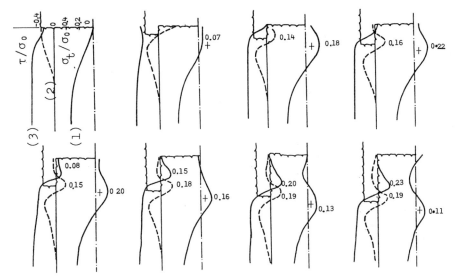

Fig.11 Diagram of the change with the drilling depths of the axial stress along the core nutral axis(1), shearing stress(2), and axial stress at the outer surface of the core (3).

tangential stress distribution of the external core surface for each drilling stage,"+" sign representing both tensile stress and counterclockwise shear stress.

In Fig.12 and 13 shown are the relationship between the tensile and shear stress at the borehole bottom and the overcoring depth. The max tensile stresses on the neutral axis , occurring at its length of D/4 ,are equal to 0.22 confinig pressure, on the contrary, when the drilling depth exceeds D/4, tensile stress drops instead. This indicates if no disking phenomenon

occurs within drilling depth of D/4 then the phenomenon will not occur afterwards . The thickness of rock disks in Ertan is nearly D/4,which is conformable with the calculated values . The tensile stress at the external surface of a core is extremely small; and this surface is still under compression while the tensile stress on the netural axis reaches its max value, therefore it is impossible for the core to be fractured from the external surface first,this is because the coefficient of the average tensile stress is below 0.11..The ratio of

85

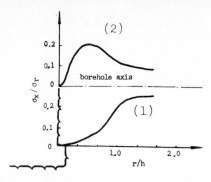

Fi:.12 Distribution of stress
    ratio vs. depth of overcoring.
    Max tensile stress on the core
surface(1) and in the axis (2).

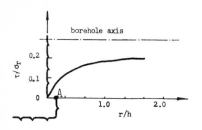

Fig.13 Shear stress at point A
    vs. depth of overcoring.

the shear stress can be great,say,
up to 0.2 times confining pressure
without axial force . In general,
although the coefficients of tensile and shear stresses are close
to each other , the shear failure
is less possible because the shearing strength is greater than the
tensile strength and the shearing stress on the neutral axis
is zero and the average one is only
0.1 confining pressure.

In the calculation above, the
axial stress is assumed to be zero,
further calculated result has shown
that with the increase in axial
stress, the tensile stress rapidly
drops linearly,i.e.,while existance of
an axial stress, a greater confining pressure is required to form
core-disks.

Some publications have pointed
out that through analysing the pattern
or configuration of disk-like fracture
of rock cores with a central hole , the
cracks on the external surface are much
more obvious than those on the internal
surface . This has been proved by

the disk cores obtained by the authors. The core was fractured into
12 disks superficially though,some
disks were not completely sepera-
ted from each other but two or even
three of them are still partly
connected together . The fractured
surfaces are rough with no scra-
ping traces and there are many minor
cracks parallel to the fractured
faces , all this can not be interpreted by the above calculation
results . For this reason, the authors carried out other numerical
analyses on the stress distribution
of the core with a central hole in
the course of being drilled. The
results indicate the tensile stress
on the internal surface of a core
is extremly small.The tensile stress
is shown in Fig.14 where one can see
the max axial tensile stress equals
to $0.163\sigma_r$, occurring at the place
of about 0.3D away from the drilling hole bottom, that is,the fracture does take place above the
drilling face rather than at the
bottom.

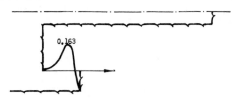

Fig.14 Tensile stress change on
    the surface of the core with
    pilot borehole vs. overcoring
    depth.

In the case of syenite in Ertan,
its average tensile strength is 8.7
MPa, the critical stress to produce
disks , σ_r, is equal to $R_t/0.163 =$
53.3 MPa, which is slightly lower
than the max in-$situ$ measured one.
Provided that the presence of the
axil stresses is taken into account
the above calculated σ_r is necessarily higher,thus the calculated and
the measured stresses are close to
each other . From the analyses and
calculation hereinbefore,it can be
known that disks should be attributed to the tensile stress imposed
on the core while overcoring other
than to shear stress . The mechanism of disk-like failure of cores,
can not,of course,be explained as simply
as it is stated here,it must be re-

lated to the local or micro structure , the drilling method and parameters etc.. For instance,at the place only 3m away from the diskcore in the same hole, in spite of slightly large stress, the disking phenomenon does not occur.In addition,according to the above analyses,the core without a centralhole seems to be fractured disk-like,but such is not the case. As stated above,this is because the external core surface is still under compressive stress.

A large hydropower station was planned to be built at Jinpingshan Mount., 120km away from Ertan but at its upper reach , and the *in-situ* stress measurement was carried out in the first half of 1966, the result is as shown in Fig.15 and 16. At that time only a single-borehole overcoring test was performed to obtain the natural stress with a direction parallel to the prospecting adit, nevertherless , because the borehole was basically parallel to the strata strike and the river flowing direction such stress could be considered as the one in the max major stress plane . The measured results have indicated that this area is located in a highlystresse region, where the orientation of the max principal stress is conformable with the bank slope, which shows the principal stress direction is governed by topography.

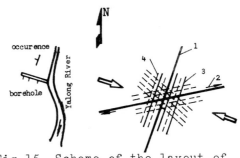

Fig.15 Scheme of the layout of the adit and strutural feature, 1,2 — faults, 3,4 — joints.

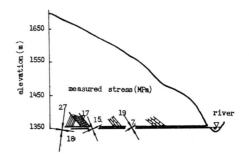

Fig.16 Measured *in-situ* stress at the Jinping project.

CONCLUSION

The practical cases mentioned previously have revealed a genaral rule that the natural stress in a rock mass should be grater than that due to dead weight even for the soft rocks with no developing tectonic movements , this excess part is a tectonic stress whose magnitude dependes on such factors as the mechanical properties , the history of tectonic movements and the depth of overburden.

The natural stress is generally of triaxial stress state , and its orientation is closely related to the topography and the tectonic movement direction. In the case of high mountains or valley region, topography is a dominant factor affecting natural stress whose direction of max principal stress is generally coincident with connecting line between the measuring point and hill-top , but rather, as concerns the smooth terrain,the orientation of tectonic movements is a main dominant factor.

Many writers have analysed or interpreted a great number of *in-situ* measured data and generalized many diagrams, tables and formulae.

A great number of diagrams and tables have shown that in the shallow parts of the earth crust,the ratio of horizontal stress to vertical one varies greatly, the results are scattered as well . This is because in statistical calculating, the mechanical characters of a rockmass are not taken into consideration . It is obvious that the higher the rock strength is,the greater the stress the rock bears could be and that the rockmass with a higher elastical module compared with others can,when subject to the same strain,accumulate higher energy in it.Following the basic concept above,the author(Li 1966) plotted max principal stresses against moduli of rock mass according to partial *in-situ* measured data(Fig.17). The relationship or curve has been proved by the data recently obtained still effective. This diagram more or less gives a reference to estimating the magnitude of a natural stress in engineering projects.

ACKNOLEGEMENTS

The authors wish to express their sincere thanks to Mr. Lin Shisheng and Mz. Wu Jiaxiu for their excellent FEM and regression calculation and analyses, and to Mr.Gu Zhimeng and Mr. Zhu Zuoduo for their help in performing field tests.

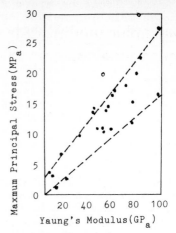

Fig.17   The relationship between σ_{max} and E (Young's modulus).

REFERENCES

Bielenstein H.V. & Barron K. 1971. *In-situ* Stresses. A Summary of Presentations and Discussions Given in Theme I at The Conference of Structural Geology to rock Mechanics Problems . Department of Energy, Mines and Resources, Mines Branch, Ottawa.

Li Guangyu, Bai Shiwei . 1979. *In-situ* Study on Stress in Rock Mass, Rock Mechanics (in Chinese).

Tseng Chao Min et al . 1978 Rock Mass Deformations in Gentle and Multiple Weakly — intercalated Bedrocks During Deep Excavation of the Foundation Pit . The Yongtze Valley Planning Office, China.

Weishen Zhu, Guangyu Li & Kejun Wang. 1985. Analyses of Disking Phenomenon and Stress Field in The Region of an Underground Powerhouse, Rock Mechanics and Rock Engineering, 18-15.

Topographic modification of in situ stress in extensional and compressional tectonic environments

H.S. SWOLFS
W.Z. SAVAGE
U.S. Geological Survey, Denver, Colorado, USA

ABSTRACT

States of stress in mountainous localities deduced from hydraulic-fracturing measurements or inferred from focal mechanisms are analyzed to examine the effects of topography on gravitationally and tectonically induced stresses. The results show that in extensional tectonic environments where gravity-induced stresses predominate ($S_V > S_H \geq S_h$), topography modifies this stress field to cause horizontal compressive stress components to exceed the vertical stress in the near surface and to retain finite, non-zero values along the surface. In compressional tectonic regimes where horizontal tectonic stresses predominate ($S_H > S_h$ and S_V), the stress fields induced by both gravity and plate tectonics are modified by topography to localize and enhance the stress conditions that favor recurrent faulting and seismicity along the axial portion of mountain ranges.

RESUME

Les états de contrainte dans des régions montagneuses déduits à partir d'essais de fracturation hydraulique ou de mécanismes focaux sont analyses pour examines les effets de la topographie sur les contraintes induites par la gravité et les contraintes tectoniques. Les resultats montrent que dans des environments tectoniques en extension dans lesquels les contraintes induites par la gravité sont dominantes ($S_V > S_H \geq S_h$), la topographie modifie cet etat de contrainte pour creer des contraintes horizontales en compression qui sont superieures a la contrainte verticale pres de la surface et qui ne sont pas egales a zero directement a la surface. Dans des environments tectoniques en compression dans lesquels les contraintes horizontales tectoniques sont dominantes ($S_H > S_h$ et S_V), les etats de contraintes induites par la gravite et la tectonique des plaques sont modifie par la topographie. Ceci resulte a creer une localisation et un accroissement de l'etat de contrainte favorisant la creation periodique de failles et une seismicite le long des axes des massifs montagneux.

ZUSAMMENFASSUNG

Um den Einfluss von Topographie auf Gravitätsstresse und tektonische Stresse zu untersuchen, werden die Zustände von Stress in Gebirgsgegenden von Messungen von hydraulischem Brechen deduziert oder von Fokalmechanismus vermutet. Die Resultate zeigen, dass in tektonischen Ausdehnungsgebieten, wo Gravitätsverursachte Stresse vorherrschen ($S_V > S_H \geq S_h$), die Topographie dieses Stressfeld derart verändert, das in der Nähe der Oberfläche die horizontalen Kompressionsstresskomponente grösser sind als die vertikalen, und das an der Oberfläche selbst endliche nicht-null Werte behalten werden. In kompressionalen tektonischen Gebieten, wo horizontale tektonische Stresse vorherrschen ($S_H > S_h$ und S_V), werden die Stressfelder, die durch Gravität und Plattentektonik verursacht sind, so durch die Topographie verändert, dass die Stressbedingungen lokalisiert werden und die sich wiederholenden Verwerfungsbewegungen und die seismische Aktivität entlang der Bergzugsaxen verstärkt werden.

1. INTRODUCTION

This paper is concerned with the topographic modification of gravitationally and tectonically induced stresses in mountainous terrains. In an extensional tectonic environment typified by normal faulting, gravity-induced stresses are assumed to predominate in the earth's crust. To determine the stress field at these mountainous localities, exact analytical solutions (Savage et al., 1985) are used for the gravity-induced stresses associated with ridges and valleys. The magnitude of these stresses is on the order of the characteristic stress, ρgb (where ρ is the density, g is the acceleration due to gravity, and b is the maximum relief of the topographic features). The effect of topography is to develop compressive horizontal stresses along the surface at or near the ridge crest (fig. 1A) that exceed the vertical stress, persist even when surface slopes are small, and decrease with increasing Poisson's ratio. In the central region of a ridge, a noticeable attenuation of the horizontal stress field develops because of gravitational spreading; this effect occurs at depths several times the ridge height (fig. 1A).

Horizontal gravity-induced tensile stresses develop along and just below the valley bottom (fig. 1B) that, with decreasing slope of the valley walls, spread upward along the walls, but decrease and become compressive with increasing Poisson's ratio. At depth below the valley bottom, compressive horizontal stresses concentrate due to gravitationally driven convergence of the material below the valley walls. At much greater depth and distance from both ridges and valleys, all stresses are compressive and approach the state of stress defined and constrained by the vanishing-displacement boundary condition (Savage et al., 1985; Savage and Swolfs, 1986).

To examine the topographic modification of the tectonically induced stresses in and near ridges and valleys, exact analytical solutions derived by Savage and Swolfs (1986) are used that obtain values for horizontal stresses that are on the order of a far-field uniaxial tectonic stress acting normal to the axis of a ridge or valley. The effect of topography

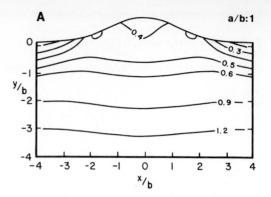

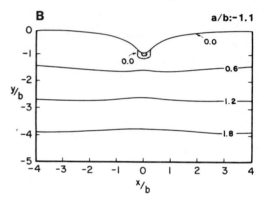

Fig. 1. Contour plots of the horizontal stress component, $S_{hn}/\rho gb$, normal to: A, a symmetric ridge where $a/b = 1$ and $\nu = 1/4$; B, a symmetric valley where $a/b = -1.1$ and $\nu = 1/3$.

reduces a regional tectonic compression in the crestal region of a ridge and, if the ridge is sufficiently steep, causes a stress reversal resulting in a small tension. Valleys, on the other hand, concentrate the far-field tectonic stress.

Any realistic appraisal of regional tectonic problems in the near-surface region of the earth must also consider the effects due to gravity. The superposition of the two analytical solutions for tectonically and gravitationally induced stresses results in an increase in horizontal compression at the crest of realistically shaped hills; whereas, at depth below the ridge the effects due to gravitational spreading are subdued but not entirely eliminated. As the ridge becomes steeper, the horizontal compressive stresses at the ridge crest will decrease but will not necessarily

come tensile. Gravitationally in-
ced tensile stresses below the bottom
 valleys are diminished in the pres-
ce of tectonic compression and, deep-
 below the valleys, the compressive
ress concentration is accentuated.

THEORY

e solution obtained by Savage et al.
985) for gravitational stresses in
mmetric ridges and valleys is based
 the Kolosov-Muskhelishvili method of
mplex potentials for plane elastic-
y. As shown in figure 2, a conformal
pping function is used to transform
 isolated symmetric ridge in x,y
ordinates into a half plane in u,v
ordinates in which the expressions
e derived for gravity-induced
resses in the ridge. The expressions
r horizontal, S_x, and vertical,
, total normal stresses and shear
ress, S_{xy}, in and away from the ridge
e of the form

$$ = \rho g b F_H(u,v,a,b,\nu) + \frac{\nu\rho g y}{1-\nu},$$

$$ = \rho g b F_V(u,v,a,b,\nu) + \rho g y,$$

d

$$_{y} = \rho g b F_S(u,v,a,b,\nu),$$

ere ρ is the bulk density, g is the
avitational acceleration, ν is the
isson's ratio, and F_H, F_V, and F_S are
mplex functions of u, v, a, b, and ν,
ich are defined in Savage et al.
985). Stresses given by these
juations satisfy the conditions of
anishing shear and normal tractions on
ie ridge surface, and the conditions
 plane strain parallel to the
idge. The stress state far from the
idge is given by assuming vanishing
ar-field horizontal displacements;
at is,
$_x= \nu\rho g y/(1-\nu)$, $S_y = \rho g y$, and $S_{xy} = 0$.
The expressions derived by Savage and
wolfs (1986) for the modified tectonic
tresses in symmetric topographic fea-
ures parallel those given above, but
 this case, are functions only of the
ar-field tectonic stress, N_1, and
ndependent of Poisson's ratio, ν. The
esulting stress fields satisfy the
onditions that shear and normal
ractions vanish on the surface of
idges and valleys, and that horizontal

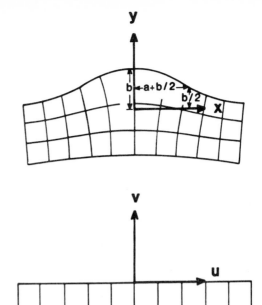

Figure 2. Conformal transformation for
a symmetric ridge in x,y coordinates
into a half plane in u,v coordinates
and the definition of the parameters
a and b, which describe the shape of
the ridge.

stresses away from these features approach the far-field tectonic stress,
N_1.
 Before use is made of the elastic
solutions by Savage et al. (1985) and
Savage and Swolfs (1986) to calculate
the gravitational and tectonic stresses
in a symmetric ridge or valley, the
parameters a and b, which describe the
shape of the ridge or valley (fig. 2),
must be determined. The required data
is obtained from a suitable topographic
map of the area of interest, and used
to construct a vertical relief section
perpendicular to the trend of the
ridge. The measured cross sectional
profile of a ridge, for example, is
then fitted to a smooth varying curve
for the surface of an isolated, symmetric ridge using the conformal transformation functions (Savage et al.,
1985, equations 11) for the case where
v = 0 (fig. 2):

$$x = u + \frac{abu}{u^2+a^2},$$

and

$$y = \frac{a^2 b}{u^2 + a^2} \; .$$

The ridge height, b, is the maximum relief of the ridge crest above an asymptotic baseline. When u = a, the horizontal and vertical coordinates of the inflection points on the flanks of the ridge are $\mp(a + b/2)$ and $b/2$, respectively (fig. 2).

In the following sections, specific cases will be discussed to illustrate these theoretical aspects. Stress measurements made in mountainous regions within extensional tectonic environments in the Western United States will be compared with the theoretical predictions. The effect of a far-field tectonic compression on a mountain range near a plate boundary will be considered to examine the localization of seismicity in the axial region of the mountain.

3. EXTENSIONAL ENVIRONMENTS

3.1. Fifth Water Ridge, Utah

Hydraulic fracturing measurements were made by Haimson (1981, 1984) and independently by Zoback (1981) and Zoback et al. (1981) in two adjacent boreholes spudded high on the flanks of Fifth Water Ridge. This site is located 20 km east of Provo, Utah, in a zone of seismicity that is part of the Intermountain Seismic Belt, a north-south trending region of diffuse and shallow seismic activity that extends from Arizona through Utah to western Montana (Smith and Sbar, 1974). The seismicity and Quaternary normal faulting in the area of central Utah suggest a general extensional stress field with the direction of the least horizontal stress component oriented generally east-west (Zoback, 1983).

Two boreholes, DH 101 and DH 103, were drilled a few hundred meters apart from one another by the U.S. Bureau of Reclamation in 1980-81 as part of a feasibility study for a hydroelectric powerplant site. In borehole DH 101, located 69 m below the crest of the ridge and drilled to a total depth of 581 m below the ridge flank, Haimson (1981) obtained hydraulic fracturing measurements at nine depth intervals between 458 and 570 m. Measured

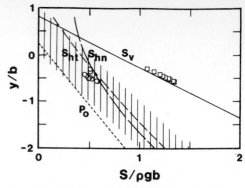

Fig. 3. Comparison between calculated and measured stresses in Fifth Water Ridge, Utah. Open symbols are data from hydraulic fracturing tests in drill hole DH 101 (Haimson, 1981). Solid and dashed lines are the predicted stresses associated with topography; the dotted line is the pore pressure gradient starting at the measured depth to the water table. Shaded region shows the range of S_h for the case of no topography, with the position of the flat surface varying from the crest (y/b = 1) to the base (y/b = 0) of the ridge.

magnitudes of the least horizontal and vertical stress components (normalized by $\rho g b$ = 10.9 MPa) are plotted in figure 3 against depth (normalized by the ridge height b = 426 m) below the crest of the ridge.

A cross section of Fifth Water Ridge is approximated by the conformal mapping function (Savage et al., 1985, equation 11); the shape parameters that fit the measured profile of the ridge are a = 456 m and b = 426 m. The predicted gravitational stresses associated with Fifth Water Ridge are calculated (Savage et al., 1984) using the following parameters: a/b ~ 1, Poisson's ratio ν = 1/3, bulk density ρ = 2.62 gm/cc. The predicted vertical stress, S_V, and the horizontal stresses, S_{hn} and S_{ht}, computed in this way are shown in figure 3, where S_{hn} is the horizontal compressive stress normal to the ridge trend and S_{ht} is parallel to it. Because plane-strain conditions are assumed to hold $S_{ht} = \nu(S_{hn} + S_V)$. Notice that both predicted horizontal stress components are larger than the vertical stress at the surface on the ridge flank.

The comparison between the measured or estimated stress magnitudes and the

edicted stress magnitudes is good,
though some discrepancies are appar-
nt. The vertical stress due to the
verburden reported by Haimson (1981)
s slightly overestimated because no
llowances were made for topography.
his discrepancy increases when the
osition of the drill hole approaches
he ridge crest, as is the case with
rill hole DH 103 (Zoback, 1981). The
easured least horizontal stresses
istributed in a narrow depth interval
n drill hole DH 101 agree with either
alculated horizontal stress compon-
nt. In this depth interval, the pre-
icted horizontal stress components are
early equal in magnitude, and as a
onsequence, provide no information on
nether the preferred orientation of
he least horizontal stress component
s either parallel or perpendicular to
he ridge trend.

In his discussion of the measured
alues of horizontal stress in drill
ole DH 101, Haimson (1981) suggested
hat they could be due to gravity load-
ng and given by $S_h = \nu S_V/(1 - \nu)$ using
value of 1/3 for ν. However, this
nalysis ignores the influence of topo-
raphy and assumes that the flat sur-
ace of the earth coincides with the
op of the drill hole at y/b = 0.84
fig. 3). The shaded region in figure
indicates the range of values for
h as the position of the flat surface
aries from the top to the base of the
idge. In the present case with the
lat surface keyed at y/b = 0.84, this
pproach would underestimate the hori-
ontal stresses in the ridge itself and
verestimate them beneath the ridge
cf., fig. 1A).

Hydraulic fracture orientations were
easured in drill hole DH 101 by
aimson (1981) using both impression
ackers and a borehole televiewer. The
verage direction of all but one of the
nduced near-vertical fractures was
. 75° W., which implies an orientation
or the least horizontal stress of
. 15° E. or about parallel to the
idge trend. From borehole televiewer
ogs obtained in drill hole DH 103,
ocated only 500 m away from DH 101,
oback (1981) detected several steeply-
ipping fractures in the zone (574 -
03 m) where several hydraulic-
racturing tests were attempted; the
verage orientation of these fractures
as N. 17° W. inferring a least hori-
ontal stress direction of N. 73° E. or

roughly normal to the ridge trend.
This discrepancy of 58° in induced-
fracture or stress orientation at the
same locality on Fifth Water Ridge may
not be readily resolved without additional evidence and, as mentioned
earlier, the computed topographically
induced stress distribution provides no
useful support because either orientation is theoretically possible at the
depth of interest.

Inspection of the fractures encountered in drill hole DH 103 and tabulated by Zoback (1981, table 1) reveal a
zone of near-vertical fractures at a
shallower depth interval between 480
and 528 m. These fractures range in
length between 3 and 17 m, parallel the
drill hole axis, and on the average
strike N. 64° W., which is in reasonable agreement with the induced-frac-
ture orientation observed by Haimson
(1981) in nearby drill hole DH 101. It
appears that these fractures may have
formed by inadvertent hydraulic fracturing during drilling, tripping, and
other pressure excursions in the
hole. The fractures observed and interpreted by Zoback (1981) as induced
by hydraulic fracturing deeper (574-603
m) in drill hole DH 103, may instead
represent pre-existing fractures that
were re-opened during testing and
inflation of the straddle packers.

The effects of adjacent ridges on the
stress distribution in Fifth Water
Ridge cannot be examined by the present
method. Instead, numerical schemes,
such as the finite-element method
(e.g., Sturgul et al., 1976), may be
used to model more complicated topographic terrains. Nevertheless, the
analysis presented here suggests that
the calculated stresses agree with the
observed ones, and that these latter
stresses are caused solely by the
weight of the ridge.

3.2. Yucca Mountain, Nevada

Yucca Mountain is a north-south-trend-
ing ridge of moderate relief located on
the western boundary of the Nevada Test
Site in southern Nevada. The site is
near the East-West Seismic Zone of the
southern Great Basin, a region of diffuse seismity; the regional stressfield orientation, as inferred from
focal mechanisms, is characterized by a
northwest-southeast directed least com-

pressive stress component (Rogers et al., 1983).

Eleven hydraulic-fracturing tests have been made to estimate the stresses beneath Yucca Mountain at depths from 646 to 1330 m (Stock et al., 1985; Stock and Healy, 1986) in the saturated zone below the static water table. Six of these tests were done in drill hole USW G-1 and two in drill hole USW G-2, both located on the flanks of the ridge where ridge topography is less pronounced. The three remaining tests were done in drill hole USW G-3 located on the crest of the ridge. These test results are shown in figure 4a to indicate the distribution of the least horizontal and vertical stress components as a function of depth measured from the surface. The average direction of the least horizontal stress components is approximately normal to the ridge trend. The stresses obtained in drill hole G-3 are smaller than those obtained at equal depth in drill hole G-1 and G-2 (Swolfs and Savage, 1985). To explain this observation, we use the method of Savage et al. (1985) to calculate the gravitationally induced stresses at various positions beneath Yucca Mountain.

East-west cross sections through Yucca Mountain incorporating drill holes G-1, G-2, and G-3 are approximated by the conformal mapping function (Savage et al., 1985, equations 11). For example, near drill hole G-3, the actual topographic cross section is modeled as an isolated, symmetric ridge that is 250 m high and 750 m wide between the inflection points on the flanks. The modeling parameters for Yucca Mountain are a/b = 1, ν = 0.32, and ρ = 2.14 gm/cc (Swolfs and Savage, 1985). Figures 4B and 4C show the calculated variations of the least-horizontal and vertical stresses (S_h and S_v) with depth below the baseline of the ridge as curves in the vicinity of drill holes G-1, G-2, and G-3.

The least-horizontal stresses determined by the hydraulic-fracturing method and estimated vertical stresses are shown as open and solid symbols, respectively, in figures 4B and 4C. Note that these measured or estimated values of stress as well as the calculated stress components are now plotted as a function of depth or elevation relative to a baseline; that is, a

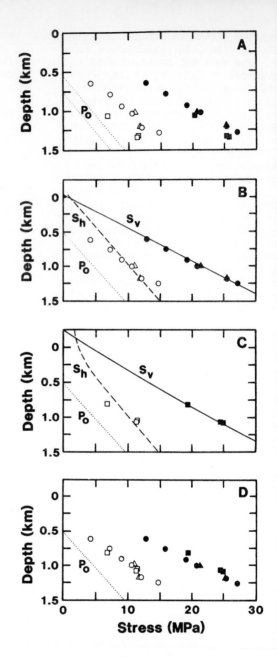

Fig. 4. A. Distribution of measured least-horizontal stress components (open symbols) and estimated vertical stresses (solid symbols) in drill holes USW G-1 (o), G-2 (Δ), and G-3 (□) as a function of depth below the surface. Vertical stresses in G-3 have been corrected for hole deviation. Dotted lines are the pore pressure gradients in drill holes G-1 and G-2 (shallower) and G-3 (deeper).

B. Comparison between the calcu-

94

ated and measured stresses in drill
holes G-1 and G-2, which are located
a few tens of meters above the
baseline.

C. Comparison between the
calculated and measured stresses in
drill hole G-3, which is located on
top of the ridge. Vertical stresses
have been corrected for topography.

D. Composite plot of all stress
measurements and pore pressure in the
saturated zone under Yucca Mountain
as a function of depth below the
baseline of the ridge.

rizontal surface that passes through
e base of the ridge. The elevations
 drill holes G-1 and G-2, located low
 the eastern flank of the ridge,
ount to only a few tens of meters
ove the baseline (fig. 4B), whereas
ill hole G-3 is located at the crest
 the ridge and elevated about 250 m
ove the baseline (fig. 4C). Because
 the distance from the ridge crest,
pography has little effect on either
e observed or calculated stresses in
ill holes G-1 and G-2 located near
e horizontal baseline.
The effect of topography on the
lculated stresses in drill hole G-3
neath the ridge summit is clearly
own in figure 4C, particularly at
allow depths just above and below the
seline. The topographically induced
crease in S_h along the ridge axis
own in figure 4C is consistent with
e predicted decrease in S_{hh} under the
dge at depths (y/b = -2) shown in
gure 1A. In figure 4C, the calcu-
ated stress component, S_h, shows
ttle tendency to increase with depth
r the first 200 m below the crest of
e ridge, whereas the calculated ver-
cal component of stress, S_V,
creases steadily with depth but at a
ightly lower rate than shown in
gure 4B. Below about 600 m from the
dge summit, both stress components
crease with depth at about the same
ate as shown in figure 4B.
Choosing the baseline rather than the
urface of the ridge as a reference
atum to compare the measurements made
n all three drill holes reconciles the
ifferences shown in figure 4A. This
s demonstrated in figure 4D which is
onstructed by superimposing figure 4B
n figure 4C such that their respective
aselines coincide. The observed mag-
itudes of the least-horizontal stress

component measured in all the drill
holes are in good agreement with one
another, but even at these depths beneath the ridge a small difference
remains in the values for the vertical stress. Due to the extra mass of
the ridge, the vertical stress directly
beneath it exceeds that below the
flanks by a few MPa.

It is worthwhile to observe that the
differences in the depths to the static
water table (fig. 4A) as measured in
drill hole G-3 at 752 m and in drill
holes G-1 and G-2 at 526 m and 575 m,
respectively, are due mainly to the
difference in surface elevation of the
drill holes above the baseline. With
reference to a common baseline (fig.
4D) the static water levels are now
found at a near constant depth of about
500 m below the base of the ridge.
This suggests a possible feedback relationship between the magnitude of the
horizontal stress component, S_h, and
the position of the water level. A
raise in the water table producing a
hydrostatic pressure on the order
of S_h would result in the reopening of
conductive fractures and a consequent
lowering of the water table to its
former level.

As demonstrated in the case of Fifth
Water Ridge presented earlier, the
measured stresses in Yucca Mountain are
predominantly of gravitational origin.
Except for the axial portion of Yucca
Mountain, the effect of topography on
the stresses is small at the depths
they were measured. The data distribution shown in figure 3D suggests
another aspect of the topographic effect that is of importance; the maximum
stress differences (S_V - S_h) are
greater in the axial portion of the
ridge than beneath its flanks. These
stress conditions would promote prefer-
ential failure in the axial region of
the ridge as suggested by the prepon-
derance of drilling-induced fracturing
in drill hole G-3 (Stock and Healy,
1986) over that observed in drill holes
G-1 and G-2.

4. COMPRESSIONAL ENVIRONMENTS

4.1. Hida Range, Japan

Information on the state of stress in a
region of concentrated seismicity has
been obtained in Japan by hydraulic-

fracturing (Tsukahara, 1983) and over-coring (Kanagawa et al., 1986) techniques. In this tectonically active region where the Eurasian, Philippine Sea, and Pacific plates converge, the data indicate that the greatest compressive stress component is horizontal and that its orientation may be understood in terms of the interaction between the three plates. In the vicinity of the Hida mountain range, a north-northeast-trending mountain system located 200 km northwest of Tokyo, Japan, the direction of greatest compression, deduced from focal mechanisms, is perpendicular to the mountain chain (Fukao and Yamaoka, 1983). The focal mechanisms of small magnitude earthquakes occurring as swarms beneath the mountain range, are of the strike-slip type, implying that the intermediate stress component is nearly vertical. These mechanisms, as well as their major orientations, are in agreement with the measured stresses and other focal mechanisms observed in the surrounding region of the Hida range. In particular, the direction of greatest compression coincides with the general east-west convergence direction of the Eurasian and Pacific plates (Fukao and Yamaoka, 1983).

The earthquake swarms, located in the axial portion of the Hida range since 1979, are of particular interest because of the inferences that may be drawn about the stress conditions beneath the mountain range. As before, we begin by approximating the cross section of the Hida range (see Fukao and Yamaoka, 1983, fig. 7) by the conformal mapping function (Savage et al. 1985, equations 11). The shape parameters, a and b, that fit the topographic profile of the Hida range are 15.2 km and 1.9 km, respectively. The modeling parameters used to calculate the stresses in the Hida range are $a/b = 8$, $\nu = 1/3$, and $\rho = 2.67$ gm/cc. The results are shown in figure 5A where the gravity-induced stresses, S_{hn}, S_{ht}, and S_V, in the axial plane of the mountains are plotted in dimensionless coordinates. The characteristic stress, ρgb, is about 50 MPa. About 60 percent of the earthquakes with strike-slip mechanisms observed in the Hida range occur in the depth interval from 0 to 5 km (Fukao and Yamaoka, 1983, Table 1). Hence, the gravity-induced stresses shown in figure 5A are not ap-propriate because the favorable stress field ($S_{ht}<S_V<S_{hn}$) is too shallow and the stress levels are too low. If a horizontal compressive tectonic stress (N_1) equal to the characteristic stress, ρgb, and directed normal to the trend of the mountain chain is added (Savage and Swolfs, 1986), then the depth interval in which the stress conditions for strike-slip faulting are favored is now below the baseline (fig. 5B), and the stress magnitudes are sufficiently large and consistent with the observed focal mechanisms. A doubling of the tectonic stress to about 100 MPa would enlarge the depth interval to about 6 km below the baseline.

As previously discussed, the maximum stress differences in the axial portion of a ridge or mountain tend to be larger than those in the surrounding region (fig. 4D). This topographic effect diminishes with increasing values of the ratio a/b and increasing tectonic stress, but is not entirely eliminated. Therefore, if stress conditions favoring the occurrence of earthquakes are present in the region surrounding a mountain range, then the mountain itself would enhance and localize the seismic activity. A similar situation in the southern Appalachian Mountains has been described by Long and Mareschal (1984).

5. CONCLUDING REMARKS

Several examples of the modification of gravitational and tectonic stresses by topographic features such as ridges and mountain chains have been presented. In extensional tectonic environments, the effects of topography modify the predominant gravity-induced stresses to depths several times the ridge height and, near the surface, produce horizontal stresses that exceed the vertical stress. The latter observation negates the commonly accepted interpretation that high horizontal stresses in the near surface are due largely to far-field tectonic loading. If the models presented here are a correct representation of the ambient stress fields in the vicinity of topographic features, then the stresses measured beneath Fifth Water Ridge and Yucca Mountain are due solely to gravitational loading of the ridges themselves.

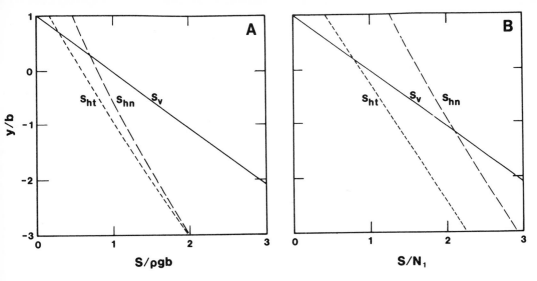

Fig. 5. Calculated stress distribution in the axial region of the Hida range:
A, gravitationally induced stress field; B, stress field due to the combined
effects of gravity and a far-field tectonic loading of about 50 MPa.

The topographic effects on the combination of gravitational and tectonic
loading, prevalent in tectonically
active compressional environments, may
be reflected in the localization of
seismic activity beneath mountain
ranges. This speculation is partially
supported by the models discussed in
this paper and by the data presented
elsewhere in the literature.

6. REFERENCES

Fukao, Y. and K. Yamaoka 1983. Stress
estimate for the highest mountain
system in Japan. Tectonics 2:453-471.

Haimson, B. C. 1981. Hydrofracturing
studies in drill hole DH-101, Fifth
Water underground powerplant site,
Diamond Fork power system -
Bonneville unit, Central Utah
project. Report to U.S. Bureau of
Reclamation 29 p.

Haimson, B. C. 1984. Stress measurements in the Wasatch hinterland
complement existing tectonic and
seismic data. Eos Transactions,
American Geophysical Union 65:1118-
1119.

Kanagawa, T., S. Hibino, T. Ishida, M.
Hayashi and Y. Kitahara 1986. In situ
stress measurements in the Japanese
islands - overcoring results from a
multi-element gauge used at 23 sites.
International Journal of Rock
Mechanics, Mining Sciences, and
Geomechanical Abstracts 23:29-39.

Long, L. T. and J. C. Mareschal 1985.
Lithospheric stresses and seismicity
in the southeastern United States.
Eos Transactions, American
Geophysical Union 66:380.

Rogers, A. M., S. C. Harmson, W. J.
Carr and W. Spence 1983. Southern
Great Basin seismological data report
for 1981 and preliminary data
analysis. U.S. Geological Survey
Open-File Report 83-669:240.

Savage, W. Z., P. S. Powers and H. S.
Swolfs 1984. RVT--a FORTRAN program
for the exact elastic solution for
tectonic and gravity stresses in
isolated symmetric ridges and
valleys. U.S. Geological Survey Open-
File Report 84-827:12.

Savage, W. Z., H. S. Swolfs and P. S.
Powers 1985. Gravitational stresses
in long symmetric ridges and valleys.
International Journal of Rock
Mechanics, Mining Sciences, and
Geomechanical Abstracts 22:291-302.

Savage, W. Z., and H. S. Swolfs 1986. Tectonic and gravitational stress in long symmetric ridges and valleys. Journal of Geophysical Research 91:3677-3685.

Smith, R. B. and M. L. Sbar 1974. Contemporary tectonics and seismicity of the western United States with emphasis on the Intermountain Seismic Belt. Bulletin of the Geological Society of America 85:1205-1218.

Stock, J. M., J. H. Healy, S. H. Hickman and M. D. Zoback 1985. Hydraulic fracturing stress measurements at Yucca Mountain, Nevada, and relationships to the regional stress field. Journal of Geophysical Research 90:8691-8706.

Stock, J. M., and J. H. Healy [in press]. Stress field at Yucca Mountain, Nevada. U.S. Geological Survey Circular.

Sturgul, J. R., A. E. Scheidegger and Z. Grinshpan 1976. Finite-element model of a mountain massif. Geology 4:439-442.

Swolfs, H. S. and W. Z. Savage 1985. Topography, stresses, and stability at Yucca Mountain, Nevada, in Research & Engineering Applications in Rock Proceedings of the 26th U.S. Symposium on Rock Mechanics 2:1121-1129.

Tsukahara, H. 1983. Stress measurements utilizing the hydraulic fracturing technique in the Kanto-Tokai area, Japan, in Hydraulic Fracturing Stress Measurements. Proceedings of a Workshop, December 2-5, 1981, National Academy Press, Washington, D.C. 18-27.

Zoback, M. D. 1981. Hydraulic fracturing stress measurements and fracture studies in hole DH-103, Fifth Water power plant site, Central Utah project. Report to U.S. Bureau of Reclamation 42 p.

Zoback, M. D., M. L. Zoback, J. Svitek and R. Liechti 1981. Hydraulic-fracturing stress measurements near the Wasatch fault, central Utah Eos Transactions, American Geophysical Union 62:394.

Zoback, M. L. 1983. Structure and Cenozoic tectonism along the Wasatch fault zone, Utah. Geological Society of America Memoir 157:3-27.

Influence of rock fabric on gravity–induced stresses

W.Z. SAVAGE
U.S. Geological Survey, Denver, Colorado, USA

B.P. AMADEI
University of Colorado, Department of Civil Engineering, Boulder, Colorado, USA

H.S. SWOLFS
U.S. Geological Survey, Denver, Colorado, USA

ABSTRACT

This paper presents four models for the stress distributions induced by gravity in anisotropic, stratified and regularly jointed rock masses. These rocks are assumed to be laterally restrained. It is shown that the nature of the stress field induced by gravity is strongly affected by rock mass structure. It is also found that a decrease in rock mass anisotropy and a stiffening of rock masses with depth can generate stress distributions comparable to empirical distributions proposed in the literature.

RESUME

Ce papier présente quatre modèles pour la distribution des contraintes induites par la gravité dans des massifs rocheux anisotropes, stratifiés et fracturés. La roche ne peut pas se déformer latéralement. On montre que l'état de contrainte induit par gravité est fortement relié à la structure du massif rocheux. On montre aussi qu'une diminution du caractère anisotrope et de la compressibilité des massifs rocheux avec la profondeur peuvent créer des distributions de contraintes comparables à celles proposées dans la litérature.

ZUSAMMENFASSUNG

Dieser Beitrag stellt vier Modelle vor für die Druckverteilung, die durch die Gravitation in anisotropischen, geschichteten und rissigen Felsmassen erzeugt wird. Es wird angenommen, daß der Fels seitlich fixiert ist. Es wird gezeigt, daß die durch die Gravitation erzeugten Druckverteilung stark von der Felsstruktur abhängt. Man kann darüberhinaus nachweisen, daß eine Abnahme in der Felsanisotropie und eine Versteifung der Felsmassen mit zunehmender Tiefe Druckverteilungen erzeugt die vergleichbar mit empirischen Verteilungen sind und in der Literatur vorausgesagt werden.

1. INTRODUCTION

In this paper, four models are proposed for the influence of anisotropy caused by rock fabric elements such as foliation, bedding or joints on gravity-induced stresses. At the outset, the constitutive relations for linear anisotropic elastic media and the thermodynamic constraints on the constants appearing in these relations are reviewed. Then, having established the general constitutive background, the four models are presented. The first and most general model describes gravity induced stresses in an anisotropic rock mass and provides a framework for the succeeding three models. The second and third models describe gravity-induced stresses in horizontally layered rock where layer thicknesses and elastic properties vary with depth. The last model describes gravity-induced stresses in a regularly jointed rock mass where joints are either parallel or normal to the ground surface. We conclude with a discussion of the implications of the results of each model with respect to measured stresses.

2. CONSTITUTIVE EQUATIONS

A general form for the constitutive relation of an anisotropic medium in an arbitrary x,y,z coordinate system can be written in matrix form as follows:

$$(\varepsilon) = (A)(\sigma) \qquad (1)$$

where (ε) and (σ) are respectively (6x1) column matrix representations of the strain and stress tensors in the x,y,z coordinate system, (A) is a (6x6) compliance matrix with components a_{ij} (i,j, = 1--6). Equation (1) is also known as the generalized Hooke's law and matrix (A) has, in general, 21 distinct components (Lekhnitskii, 1963).

For a material that is orthotropic in an x,y,z coordinate system, i.e. with planes of symmetry normal to the coordinate axes, equation (1) can be written as follows:

$$
\begin{bmatrix} \varepsilon_x \\ \varepsilon_y \\ \varepsilon_z \\ \gamma_{yz} \\ \gamma_{xz} \\ \gamma_{xy} \end{bmatrix}
=
\begin{bmatrix}
\frac{1}{E_x} & \frac{-\nu_{yx}}{E_y} & \frac{-\nu_{zx}}{E_z} & 0 & 0 & 0 \\
\frac{-\nu_{xy}}{E_x} & \frac{1}{E_y} & \frac{-\nu_{zy}}{E_z} & 0 & 0 & 0 \\
\frac{-\nu_{xz}}{E_x} & \frac{-\nu_{yz}}{E_y} & \frac{1}{E_z} & 0 & 0 & 0 \\
0 & 0 & 0 & \frac{1}{G_{yz}} & 0 & 0 \\
0 & 0 & 0 & 0 & \frac{1}{G_{xz}} & 0 \\
0 & 0 & 0 & 0 & 0 & \frac{1}{G_{xy}}
\end{bmatrix}
\begin{bmatrix} \sigma_x \\ \sigma_y \\ \sigma_z \\ \tau_{yz} \\ \tau_{xz} \\ \tau_{xy} \end{bmatrix}
\qquad (2)
$$

where E_x, E_y, E_z are Young's moduli in the respective x,y, and z directions, G_{xy}, G_{yz}, G_{xz}, are shear moduli in planes parallel to the xy, yz and xz coordinate planes respectively. Thus, the shear compliance $1/G_{xy}$ characterizes the shear strain, γ_{xy}, response to the shear stress τ_{xy}. The Poisson's ratios ν_{ij} characterize the compressive or tensile strain responses in the j direction to a uniaxial tensile or compressive stress acting in the i-direction. For example, ν_{xy} characterizes the extensile strain response in the y-direction to a compressive stress acting in the x-direction.

Of the twelve elastic constants entering into equation (2), only nine of them are independent due to the following symmetry conditions (Lekhnitskii, 1963)

$$\frac{\nu_{xy}}{E_x} = \frac{\nu_{yx}}{E_y} \; ; \; \frac{\nu_{xz}}{E_x} = \frac{\nu_{zx}}{E_z} \; ; \; \frac{\nu_{yz}}{E_y} = \frac{\nu_{zy}}{E_z} \qquad (3)$$

For a material that is transversely isotropic, only five independent elastic constants are needed to describe its deformational response. In this paper, these constants will be called E, E', ν, ν', and G' with the following definitions:

(1) E, E' are Young's moduli in the plane of transverse isotropy and in a direction normal to it, respectively,

(2) ν,ν' are Poisson's ratios characterizing the lateral strain response in the plane of transverse isotropy to a stress acting parallel or normal to it, respectively, and,

(3) G' is the shear modulus in planes normal to the plane of transverse isotropy.

Equation (2) also applies for a material that is transversely isotropic in one of the three coordinate planes of the x,y,z coordinate system. The elastic parameters entering into this equation can be expressed in terms of the five constants defined above. For example, if there is a plane of transverse isotropy parallel to the xy-coordinate plane, we have

$$E_x = E_y = E$$

$$E_z = E'$$

$$\nu_{xy} = \nu_{yx} = \nu$$

$$\nu_{zx} = \nu_{zy} = \nu'$$

$$G_{xz} = G_{yz} = G'. \qquad (4)$$

In addition, $G_{xy} = G = E/(2(1+\nu))$ and using equation (3)

$$\nu_{xz} = \nu_{yz} = \nu'\frac{E}{E'} . \qquad (5)$$

3. THERMODYNAMIC CONSTRAINTS

Consider a material that is orthotropic in a x,y,z coordinate system with a constitutive relation defined by equations (1) and (2). The strain energy per unit volume is equal to

$$U = \frac{1}{2} (\sigma)^t (A)(\sigma) . \qquad (6)$$

If this quadratic form is positive definite, as it must be for an elastic material (Love, 1927), the strain energy will be positive as required. A necessary and sufficient condition for the quadratic form to be positive definite is that all principal minors of matrix (A) (that is all minor determinants in the matrix having diagonal elements coincident with the principal diagonal of the matrix) are positive (Kreyszig, 1972). This leads to the following conditions on the elastic constants

$$E_x, E_y, E_z, G_{yz}, G_{xz}, G_{xy} > 0 \qquad (7)$$

$$1 - \nu_{yx}\nu_{xy} > 0 , \qquad (8a),$$

$$1 - \nu_{zy}\nu_{yz} > 0 , \qquad (8b),$$

$$1 - \nu_{zx}\nu_{xz} > 0 , \qquad (8c),$$

and,

$$1 - \nu_{zy}\nu_{yz} - \nu_{xy}\nu_{yx} - \nu_{xz}\nu_{zx} -$$
$$\nu_{yx}\nu_{xz}\nu_{zy} - \nu_{zx}\nu_{xy}\nu_{yz} > 0 . \qquad (9)$$

Substituting the symmetry requirements given by equations (3) into equations (8), it follows that:

$$-\sqrt{\frac{E_y}{E_x}} < \nu_{yx} < \sqrt{\frac{E_y}{E_x}} \ ; \ -\sqrt{\frac{E_x}{E_y}} < \nu_{xy} < \sqrt{\frac{E_x}{E_y}} \qquad (10a),$$

$$-\sqrt{\frac{E_z}{E_y}} < \nu_{zy} < \sqrt{\frac{E_z}{E_y}} \ ; \ -\sqrt{\frac{E_y}{E_z}} < \nu_{yz} < \sqrt{\frac{E_y}{E_z}} \qquad (10b),$$

$$-\sqrt{\frac{E_z}{E_x}} < \nu_{zx} < \sqrt{\frac{E_z}{E_x}} \ ; \ -\sqrt{\frac{E_x}{E_z}} < \nu_{xz} < \sqrt{\frac{E_x}{E_z}} . \qquad (10c)$$

The previous equations also apply if the material under consideration is transversely isotropic in one of the three coordinate planes of the x,y,z coordinate system. The results are summarized in Table 1.

	Plane of Transverse Isotropy Parallel to the:		
	xy-coordinate plane	yz-coordinate plane	xz-coordinate plane
Elastic Parameters	$E_x = E_y = E$ $E_z = E'$ $\nu_{xy} = \nu_{yx} = \nu$ $\nu_{zx} = \nu_{zy} = \nu'$ $G_{zx} = G_{zy} = G'$ and $G_{xy} = E/(2(1+\nu))$ $\nu_{xz} = \nu_{yz} = \nu'\dfrac{E}{E'}$	$E_y = E_z = E$ $E_x = E'$ $\nu_{yz} = \nu_{zy} = \nu$ $\nu_{xy} = \nu_{xz} = \nu'$ $G_{xy} = G_{xz} = G'$ and $G_{yz} = E/(2(1+\nu))$ $\nu_{yx} = \nu_{zx} = \nu'\dfrac{E}{E'}$	$E_x = E_z = E$ $E_y = E'$ $\nu_{xz} = \nu_{zx} = \nu$ $\nu_{yx} = \nu_{yz} = \nu'$ $G_{yx} = G_{yz} = G'$ and $G_{xz} = E/(2(1+\nu))$ $\nu_{zy} = \nu_{xy} = \nu'\dfrac{E}{E'}$
Thermodynamic Constraints on the Elastic Constants	$E, E', G', G > 0$ $-1 < \nu < 1$ $-\sqrt{\dfrac{E'}{E}}\,\dfrac{(1-\nu)}{2} < \nu' < \sqrt{\dfrac{E'}{E}}\,\dfrac{(1-\nu)}{2}$		

Table 1   Expression for the elastic parameters and the thermodynamic constraints for a material that is transversely isotropic in one of the three coordinate planes of the x,y,z coordinate system.

4.   STRESSES DUE TO GRAVITATIONAL LOADING OF AN ANISOTROPIC ROCK MASS

Consider the equilibrium of a flat-lying horizontal elastic rock mass of uniform density ρ under gravity alone. The rock mass is assumed to be laterally restrained and orthotropic in an x,y,z coordinate system such that the x and y-axes are horizontal and the z-axis is positive downwards with the plane z = 0 coinciding with the ground surface (Fig. 1). At each point in the rock mass, three planes of elastic symmetry exist, each plane being normal to a coordinate axis. The constitutive model for the rock mass is described by equation (2) where because of symmetry and lateral restraint γ_{xy}, γ_{xz}, γ_{yz}, ε_x and ε_y vanish.

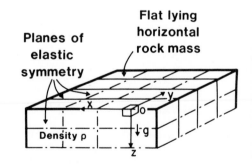

Fig. 1   Gravitational loading of an orthotropic rock mass. Block diagram shows the geometry of the problem.

Expressions for the stress distribution in an orthotropic rock mass under gravity alone which satisfy the equations of equilibrium, the boundary conditions at the ground surface ($\sigma_z = \tau_{xz} = \tau_{yz} = 0$) and which give strains satisfying the equations of compatibility (Timoshenko and Goodier, 1970) are

$$\sigma_x = \rho g z \frac{(\nu_{xz} + \nu_{yz}\nu_{xy})}{1 - \nu_{xy}\nu_{yx}} \qquad (11a)$$

$$\sigma_y = \rho g z \frac{(\nu_{yz} + \nu_{yx}\nu_{xz})}{1 - \nu_{xy}\nu_{yx}} \qquad (11b)$$

$$\sigma_z = \rho g z \qquad (11c)$$

(Amadei et al., in press). From equations (11) it can be shown that, unlike the isotropic case, unequal horizontal stresses can be induced under gravitational loading.

If the rock mass is transversely isotropic in planes parallel to the ground surface, i.e. plane xy, with the elastic parameters defined in equation (4) and (5), σ_x and σ_y are now equal to

$$\sigma_x = \sigma_y = \sigma_h = \rho g z \frac{\nu_{xz}}{1 - \nu} \qquad (12)$$

In this equation, ν_{xz} can also be replaced by $\nu' E/E'$. The domain of variation of σ_h defined above is controlled by the inequalities given in Table 1. From equation (12) and Table 1 we obtain for the domain of variation of σ_h,

$$0 \leq \frac{\sigma_h}{\rho g z} < \sqrt{\frac{E}{E'} \frac{1}{2(1-\nu)}} \qquad (13)$$

The variation of the stress ratio $\sigma_h/\rho g z$, with ν_{xz}, as given by equation (12), is shown in Fig. 2 for ν ranging between 0 and 1. For any fixed value of ν, the stress ratio is a linear function of ν_{xz} and has to satisfy inequality (13). The right hand side of this inequality is represented in Fig. 2 by three limiting curves, each one corresponding to a

fixed value of the ratio E/E'; e.g. E/E' = 0.5, 1 and 2.

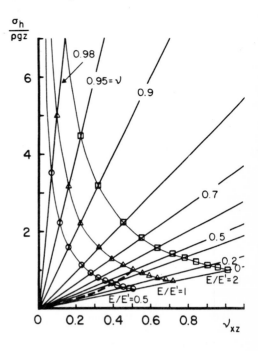

Fig. 2 Variation of the stress ratio $\sigma_h/\rho g z$ with ν_{xz} and ν for a horizontally transverse-isotropic rock mass. Limiting curves bounding thermodynamically admissible stress domains are shown for three values of E/E'. The isotropic solution is indicated by the dashed line.

If the rock mass is transversely isotropic in planes perpendicular to the ground surface, unequal horizontal stresses will be induced in the x and y directions. For planes of transverse isotropy parallel to the yz-coordinate plane, substituting the expression for the elastic parameters defined in Table 1 into equations (11a) and (11b) gives

$$\sigma_x = \rho g z \frac{\nu'(1+\nu)}{1 - \frac{E}{E'}\nu'^2} \qquad (14a)$$

$$\sigma_y = \rho g z \frac{(\nu + \frac{E}{E'} \nu'^2)}{1 - \frac{E}{E'} \nu'^2} \qquad (14b)$$

$$K_a = \frac{\sigma_x}{\sigma_y} = \frac{\nu' (1+\nu)}{\nu + \frac{E}{E'} \nu'^2} \qquad (14c)$$

The domains of variation of σ_x, σ_y and K_a depend on the constraints on E, E', ν and ν' defined in Table 1 and for $\sigma_x/\rho g z$ and $\sigma_y/\rho g z$ are

$$0 \le \frac{\sigma_x}{\rho g z} < 2 \sqrt{\frac{E'}{E} \frac{(1-\nu)}{2}} \qquad (15a)$$

$$\nu \le \frac{\sigma_y}{\rho g z} < 1 \qquad (15b)$$

Finally, if the rock mass is isotropic, all Poisson's ratios in equations (11) are equal to a same value, ν. Then, we obtain the familiar equation (Terzaghi and Richart, 1952)

$$\sigma_x = \sigma_y = \sigma_h = \rho g z \frac{\nu}{1 - \nu} \qquad (16)$$

The domain of variation of σ_h is now controlled by only one constraint; i.e. $-1 < \nu < 0.5$.

From this brief discussion of stresses due to gravitational loading of anisotropic elastic rock, it can be concluded that inclusion of anisotropy broadens the range of permissible values of gravity-induced horizontal stresses. In fact, as shown in Figure 2, it is thermodynamically admissible for the horizontal stress to exceed the vertical stress for certain ranges of anisotropic rock properties. Also, for vertical anisotropy, equation (14c) implies that horizontal stresses are no longer equal and the gravity induced stress state becomes truly triaxial.

5. GRAVITY STRESSES IN A HORIZONTALLY STRATIFIED ROCK MASS WITH DISCRETE LAYERS

The first model is limited to rock masses with uniform and homogeneous anisotropic properties. However, it can be generalized to include the heterogeneous character of a horizontally stratified rock mass. The rock mass consists of several horizontal strata; each one being thick enough to be regarded as homogeneous and transversely isotropic or isotropic and to have its thickness and deformability properties taken into account.

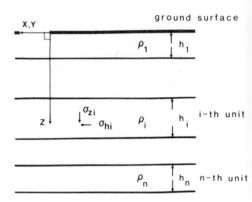

Fig. 3 Gravitational loading of a stratified rock mass consisting of transversely isotropic and/or isotropic mechanical units

Consider the equilibrium of a flat lying horizontal stratified rock mass under gravity alone. The rock mass consists of n horizontal mechanical units, each one being modeled as a linearly elastic, homogeneous continuum with planes of transverse isotropy parallel to the ground surface (Fig. 3). An xyz coordinate system is defined as in Fig. 1. The i-th rock unit has a thickness h_i and a uniform density ρ_i. Its deformability is defined by five elastic constants E_i, E_i', ν_i, ν_i' and G_i and its constitutive model is defined by equation (1) with the stress and strain components denoted by

σ_{xi}, σ_{yi},...,τ_{xyi} and ϵ_{xi}, ϵ_{yi},...,γ_{xyi}, respectively. The five elastic constants also satisfy the thermo-dynamic constraints in Table 1. If the i-th rock unit is isotropic, $E_i = E_i'$, $\nu_i = \nu_i'$, and $G_i = G_i' = E_i/(2(1+\nu_i))$ and ν_i varies over the domain $-1 < \nu_i < 0.5$. Within each unit in the rock mass, the stress components σ_{xi}, σ_{yi},....,τ_{xyi} satisfy the equations of equili-brium, and the strain components ϵ_{xi}, ϵ_{yi},...., γ_{xyi} are derived from a continuous displacement field with components u_i, v_i, w_i in the x,y,z directions, respectively. Continuity of the rock mass implies that at the interface between the mechanical units the stress components σ_z, τ_{zx}, τ_{zy}, the strain components ϵ_x, ϵ_y, γ_{xy} and the displacement component w must be continuous. Finally, it is postu-lated that for each rock unit under gravitational loading no lateral hori-zontal displacement takes place, e.g., $u_i = v_i = 0$ (for i = 1,n) and that the vertical displacement w_i is independent of x and y since planes of transverse isotropy are parallel to the ground surface.

Expressions for the principal components of the stress field induced by gravity in the i-th unit of the rock mass are (Amadei, et al., in press)

$$\sigma_{zi} = \rho_i gz + \sum_{j=1}^{i} (\rho_j - \rho_i)gh_j$$

$$\sigma_{hi} = \nu_i' \frac{E_i}{E_i'} \cdot \frac{1}{1 - \nu_i} \sigma_{zi}$$

(17)

For example, consider a rock mass consisting of a sequence of thick and thin mechanical units extending to a large depth. The thick rock units are all isotropic with constant Young's modulus E and Poisson's ratio ν. The thin rock units have a spacing S and a thickness t and are all transversely isotropic with Poisson's ratios ν_i, ν_i' equal to ν and Young's modulus in the

horizontal plane E_i equal to E. However, the ratio E_i/E_i' or E/E_i' decreases with depth simulating a decrease in the vertical compressibi-lity of the thin units. In other words, as depth increases the rock mass becomes more isotropic.

In this example, the Young's modulus E and Poisson's ratio ν are respectively equal to 4.0 10^4 MPa and 0.25. The unit weight, ρg, is constant in all rock units and is equal to 27 kPa/m. The ratio E/E_i' is assumed to vary with depth as follows:

$$\frac{E}{E_i'} = 1 + \frac{E}{a+bz_i}$$

(18)

where constants a and b were chosen equal to 10^4 MPa and 3.0 10^2 MPa/m to model a large variation of the vertical compressibility of the thin rock units over a depth of 1000 meters. The variation of the ratio σ_h/σ_z with depth for a spacing of 50 meters is shown in figure 4. For this spacing between the thin units, the stress distribution in the rock mass is mostly controlled by the isotropic character of the thick rock units despite the jumps in stress that take place across the thin units. For lower values of the spacing, the influence of the thin rock units and therefore the heterogen-eous character of the rock mass on the magnitude and distribution of gravity induced stresses should increase. As a limit, the stress distribution will approach the one that would develop if the whole rock mass was made out of rock with a vertical compressibility that varies continuously with depth according to equation (18) with z_i replaced by z. This limiting distribu-tion, shown by the dashed line in Figure 4 implies that a decrease in rock mass anisotropy and a stiffening of rock masses with depth, produce distributions for the ratio $k = \sigma_h/\sigma_z$ with depth that are very much compara-ble to the empirical ones proposed by Brown and Hoek (1978). This suggests that rock mass stiffening with depth may well be a major factor controlling the distribution of gravity induced stresses.

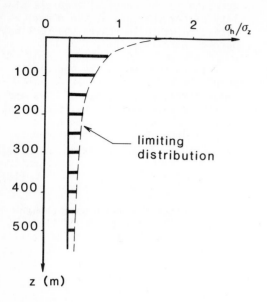

100

200

300 ———— limiting
distribution

400

500

z (m)

homogeneous transversely isotropic continuum (Salamon, 1968).

Consider m horizontal layers forming a representative sample of the rock mass of edge dimension L. If the thickness of the j-th layer is h_j, its relative thickness is $\phi_j = h_j/L$ with $\sum\limits_{j=1}^{m} \phi_j = 1$. The deformability of each layer is defined by five elastic constants E_j, E'_j, ν_j, ν'_j, G'_j in the xy coordinate system as introduced in the discrete model. As shown by Salamon (1968), the relationships between the six components of average stress and strain in the equivalent continuum can also be expressed by equations (2) and (4) with the following expressions for the compliance coefficients

$$\frac{1}{E} = \frac{\sum \dfrac{\phi_j E_j}{1 - \nu_j^2}}{\sum \dfrac{\phi_j E_j}{1 + \nu_j} \; \sum \dfrac{\phi_j E_j}{1 - \nu_j}}$$

$$\frac{\nu}{E} = \frac{\sum \dfrac{\phi_j \nu_j E_j}{1 - \nu_j^2}}{\sum \dfrac{\phi_j E_j}{1 + \nu_j} \; \sum \dfrac{\phi_j E_j}{1 - \nu_j}}$$

$$\frac{\nu'}{E'} = \frac{\sum \phi_j \dfrac{E_j}{E'_j} \dfrac{\nu'_j}{1 - \nu_j}}{\sum \dfrac{\phi_j E_j}{1 - \nu_j}}$$

$$\frac{1}{E'} = \sum \phi_j \left(\frac{1}{E'_j} - 2\nu'^2_j \frac{E_j}{E'^2_j} \cdot \frac{1}{1 - \nu_j}\right) +$$

$$2 \frac{\left(\sum \phi_j \dfrac{E_j}{E'_j} \cdot \dfrac{\nu'_j}{1 - \nu_j}\right)^2}{\sum \dfrac{\phi_j E_j}{1 - \nu_j}}$$

Fig. 4 Variation of the ratio σ_h/σ_z with depth in a stratified rock mass consisting of a sequence of thick and thin rock units with a spacing of 50 meters. The limiting distribution is shown by the dashed line.

6. GRAVITY STRESSES IN A HORIZONTALLY STRATIFIED ROCK MASS WITH MANY THIN LAYERS.

In the second model, the rock mass consists of several discrete horizontal mechanical units, each one being thick enough to be regarded as homogeneous and transversely isotropic or isotropic and to have its thickness and deformability properties taken into account. In this model, the overall rock mass or several of its units are thinly layered and the thickness and deformability properties of the horizontal layers vary appreciably with depth. In this case, the individual properties of all layers cannot be taken into account and the rock mass or its thinly layered units are replaced by an equivalent

$$\frac{1}{G} = \frac{1}{\sum \phi_j G_j}$$

$$\frac{1}{G'} = \sum \frac{\phi_j}{G'_j} \tag{19}$$

in which the summation from $j = 1$, m is implied. The shear modulus G is also equal to $E/(2(1 + \nu))$.

Equations (11c) and (12) also provide expressions for the vertical and horizontal stress components at any depth z in a stratified rock mass modelled as an equivalent homogeneous transversely isotropic continuum under gravity alone. No lateral displacement is permitted in all layers in the rock mass. ρ is the density of the equivalent continuum and can also be defined as the average density of the layers comprising the representative sample of the rock mass of edge dimension L. Thus,

$$\rho = \sum_{j=1}^{m} \phi_j \rho_j \tag{20}$$

Combining the expression for ν'/E', ν/E and $1/E$ in equation (19), the stress ratio $\sigma_h/\rho gz$ in equation (12) can be expressed as follows:

$$\frac{\sigma_h}{\rho gz} = \sum_{j=1}^{m} \phi_j \nu'_j \frac{E_j}{E'_j} \cdot \frac{1}{1 - \nu_j} \tag{21}$$

If all layers are isotropic, $E_j = E'_j$ and $\nu_j = \nu'_j$. Then, equation (21) becomes

$$\frac{\sigma_h}{\rho gz} = \sum_{j=1}^{m} \phi_j \frac{\nu_j}{1 - \nu_j} \tag{22}$$

Limiting the analysis to positive values for ν_j and ν'_j, each term $\nu'_j E_j/((1 - \nu'_j)E'_j)$ in equation (21) has an admissible domain of variation given by the inequalities in Table 1 with E, E', ν replaced by E_j, E'_j and ν_j. The ratio $\sigma_h/\rho gz$ in equation (21) can be larger than, less than or equal to unity. If all layers are isotropic

equation (22) implies that $\sigma_h/\rho gz$ can only vary between 0 and 1 as ν_j varies between 0 and 0.5.

The previous discussion dealt with a complete rock mass. It can also be used if only a mechanical unit i in the rock mass is thinly layered and for which a representative sample consisting of m layers j ($j = 1$, m) can be identified. The state of stress in that unit is given by equation (17) with

$$\nu'_i \frac{E_i}{E'_i} \cdot \frac{1}{1 - \nu_i} = \sum_{j=1}^{m} \phi_j \nu'_j \frac{E_j}{E'_j} \cdot \frac{1}{1 - \nu_j} \tag{23}$$

if some or all layers of the representative sample are transversely isotropic. If the layers are all isotropic, then

$$\nu'_i \frac{E_i}{E'_i} \frac{1}{1 - \nu_i} = \sum_{j=1}^{m} \phi_j \frac{\nu_j}{1 - \nu_j} \tag{24}$$

In both cases, the density of the i-th rock unit is given by equation (20).

As is the case with discrete layers, the induced horizontal stress in a horizontally transverse isotropic rock unit can, depending on the units elastic properties, be larger, equal to, or less than the vertical stress associated with the weight of the overlying materials. However, for a thinly layered unit, the horizontal stresses depend on the relative layer thicknesses and elastic properties. This indicates that depending on the distribution of deformability properties in a stratified rock mass, the nature of the stress field can vary widely with depth.

7. GRAVITATIONAL STRESSES IN A
    REGULARLY JOINTED ROCK MASS

The final model to be discussed is one presented previously (Amadei and Savage, 1985) for gravity stresses in jointed rock. Here the rock mass is modeled as being composed of two elements; elastic intact rock and a single regularly spaced joint set either parallel or normal to the ground surface. The joint deformability is given by a normal stress dependent stiffness and a constant shear stiffness.

The rock mass has the geometry of Fig. 1 and has one joint set with constant spacing S that is parallel to one of the three coordinate planes of the x,y,z coordinate system. The rock mass is modelled as an equivalent transversely isotropic continuum with a constitutive model defined by equation (1) in the xyz coordinate system. The elastic constants entering in this equation are related to E, E', ν, ν', and G' through the equations listed in Table 1. The values of some of the elastic constants in equation (1) depend on the normal stress level acting across the joints and will, in general, vary throughout the rock mass. The normal stress is σ_z, σ_x or σ_y if the joints are parallel to the xy, yz or xz coordinate planes, respectively.

Duncan and Goodman (1968) give for an equivalent transversely isotropic continuum

$$\frac{1}{E'} = \frac{1}{E} + \frac{1}{k_n S} \quad ; \quad \frac{1}{G'} = \frac{1}{G} + \frac{1}{k_s S}$$

$$\frac{\nu_{ns}}{E'} = \frac{\nu}{E} \quad ; \quad \frac{1}{G} = \frac{2(1+\nu)}{E}$$

(25)

where k_n and k_s indicate normal and shear stiffnesses. E, G, and ν indicate isotropic intact rock properties for the jointed rock mass and ν_{ns}/E' represents the Poisson effect associated with the joint set. Duncan and Goodman assumed that the joints have negligible thickness and create no Poisson effect; hence the equality $\nu_{ns}/E' = \nu/E$. They also assume shear and normal stiffnesses to be constant and independent of the initial and applied normal stresses acting across the joints.

Amadei and Savage (1985) relaxed both of these assumptions allowing the joints a Poisson effect and a stress dependent normal stiffness. Using the expression proposed by Bandis et al. (1983) for the secant normal stiffness

of a rock joint, an analytical expression for the horizontal stress component induced at depth z in a horizontally jointed rock mass modeled as an equivalent continuum was written as follows:

$$\sigma_h = \rho g z \frac{\nu}{1-\nu} \left(1 + \left(\frac{E}{S}\right) \frac{V_m}{V_m k_{ni} + \rho g z}\right) \quad (26)$$

where k_{ni} represents the initial normal stiffness and V_m is the maximum joint closure. ν_{ns} was also assumed to be equal to ν.

In equation (26), $\rho g z \cdot \nu/(1-\nu)$ is the isotropic solution for the horizontal stress and the second term in the parentheses represents the contribution of the joint set to the horizontal stress in the rock mass.

To illustrate equation (26), Amadei and Savage (1985) gave the following numerical example: (i) the intact component in the rock mass has a unit weight $\rho g = 0.027$ MPa/m, a Young's modulus $E = 4.10^4$ MPa and a Poisson's ratio $\nu = 0.25.$, (ii) the joint set spacing varies between 0.1 and 1 m, and (iii) the maximum joint closure V_m and the initial joint stiffness k_{ni} are equal to $0.091 \ 10^{-3}$m and $18.8 \ 10^3$ MPa/m, respectively (experimental test data on limestone joints by Bandis et al., 1983 measured with $\sigma_i = 1$ kPa).

Figure 5 shows the distribution of $\sigma_h/\rho g z$ with depth for the range of joint set spacings considered in this example. Stresses much larger than those associated with the isotropic solution are induced when S = 0.1 m. As the spacing increases, the stress distribution in the rock mass approaches very rapidly the one for the isotropic solution.

From Fig. 5, it appears that horizontal stresses larger than or equal to the vertical stress can be induced in the rock mass. In view of equation (26) this will particularly take place at shallow depth, for small values of the joint set spacing, and for joints with low initial stiffness, k_{ni}. Note that if the joints had

108

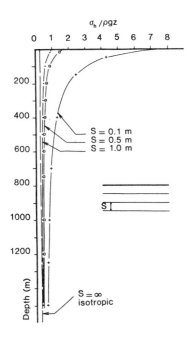

Fig. 5 Influence of joint set
spacing S on the variation
of the ratio $\sigma_h/\rho gz$ with
depth. Rock mass with
horizontal joints.

been assumed to create no Poisson's
effect, $\nu'E/E'$ would have been equal to
ν and equation (26) would be replaced
by the isotropic solution (equation
(16)).

A similar analysis for vertically
oriented joints (Amadei and Savage,
1985) leads to similar effects for the
two stress ratios $\sigma_x/\rho gz$ and $\sigma_y/\rho gz$
where the larger horizontal stress is
parallel to the joints. The variation
of the ratio of horizontal to vertical
stresses with depth for vertically and
horizontally jointed rock masses are
qualitatively similar to published
stress ratio with depth plots (Fig. 6)
based on stress measurements made in a
wide variety of rock types and locations (Brown and Hoek, 1978, Swolfs,
1984).

8. CONCLUDING DISCUSSION

The models in this paper show that
the nature of the stress field induced
in anisotropic rock mass under gravity
and vanishing horizontal displacements
depends on the type and magnitude of
the rock mass anisotropy and the orientation of the rock fabric with respect
to the ground surface. For stratified
rock masses, the induced stress field
also depends on the anisotropic character of the different mechanical units
comprising the rock mass, the thickness
of the layers within each unit and how
the deformability properties vary with
depth. Several ideas emerge from the
models presented in this paper. First,
the magnitude and orientation of the
stress field induced under gravity is
strongly affected by the rock mass
structure. Second, anisotropic models
create domains of variation for the
induced horizontal stress components
broader than that imposed by the isotropic model. Third, for rock masses
with vertical rock fabric the induced
stress field is multiaxial. Finally,
the gravity induced stress distributions predicted by the models assuming
a decrease in rock mass anisotropy and
a stiffening of rock masses with depths
are similar to stress ratio with depth
plots published in the literature.

9. REFERENCES

1. Amadei, B. and Savage, W.Z.
1985. Gravitational Stresses in
Regularly Jointed Rock Masses,
Proc. Int. Symposium on Fundamen-
tals of Rock Joints, Bjorkliden,
Stephansson, (Ed.),pp. 463-473.

2. Amadei, B., Savage, W.Z. and
Swolfs, H.S. In press. Gravita-
tional Stresses in Anisotropic
Rock Masses, Submitted to the
Int. J. Rock Mech. Min. Sci.

3. Amadei, B., Swolfs, H.S., and
Savage, W.Z. In Press. Gravity-
Induced Stresses in Stratified
Rock Masses, Submitted to Rock
Mechanics and Rock Engineering.

4. Bandis, S.C., Lumsden, A.C. and
Barton, N.R. 1983. Fundamentals
of Rock Joint Deformation, Int.
J. Rock Mec. Min. Sci, Vol. 20,
No. 6, pp. 249-268.

5. Brown, E.T. and Hoek, E. 1978. Trends in Relationships Between Measured in Situ Stresses and Depth, Int. J. Rock Mec. Min Sci, Vol. 15, No. 4, pp. 211-215.

6. Duncan, J., and Goodman, R.E. 1968. Finite Element Analysis of Slopes in Jointed Rocks, Corps of Engineers Rpt. No. CR. S-68-3.

7. Kreyszig, E. 1972. Advanced Engineering Mathematics. Third Edition, Wiley.

8. Lekhnitskii, S.G. 1963. Theory of Elasticity of an Anisotropic Elastic Body. Holden Day, Inc., San Francisco.

9. Love, A.E.H. 1927. A Treatise on the Mathematical Theory of Elasticity, Fourth Edition, Dover, New York.

10. Salamon, M.D.G. 1968. Elastic Moduli of a Stratified Rock Mass, Int. J. Rock Mech. Min. Sci., Vol. 5, pp. 519-527.

11. Swolfs, H.S. 1984. The triangular stress diagram - A graphical representation of crustal stress measurements. Geological Survey Professional Paper No. 1291, 19 pp, Washington.

12. Terzaghi, K. and Richart, F.E. 1952. Stresses in Rock About Cavities, Geotechnique, Vol. 3, pp. 57-90.

13. Timoshenko, S.P. and Goodier, J.N. 1970. Theory of Elasticity, Third Edition, McGraw-Hill, New York.

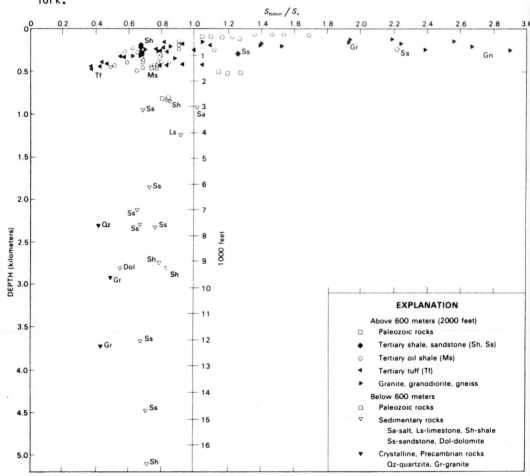

Fig. 6 Summary plot of the minimum horizontal to vertical stress ratio measured by hydraulic-fracturing techniques in sedimentary basins (Swolfs, 1984).

Evolution des contraintes naturelles en fonction de la profondeur et de la tectonique aux Houilleres du Bassin de Lorraine

L. TINCHON
US Technique Charbonnages de France, Freyming-Merlebach, France

Résumé
L'exploitation du gisement lorrain des Charbonnages de France s'approfondit très rapidement ce qui se traduit par une déformation plus importante des ouvrages. Il s'avère nécessaire de connaître l'état des contraintes in situ pour pallier cette situation. Trois techniques ont été utilisées jusqu'à présent aux Houillères du Bassin de Lorraine : le vérin plat, le surcarottage et la fracturation hydraulique. Les résultats obtenus montrent que la contrainte verticale tend à augmenter avec la profondeur mais elle est très sensible à la structure géologique du gisement - les contraintes horizontales ont une grande variabilité s'expliquant elle aussi par la géologie structurale.

1 - LES HOUILLERES DU BASSIN DE LORRAINE

Situé au Nord Est du pays (fig. 1) le bassin houiller lorrain est le prolongement en France du gisement sarrois.

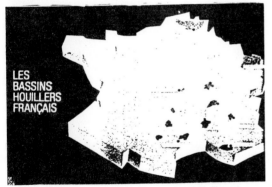

Figure 1

Affleurant en Sarre, les formations houillères plongent dans leur ensemble vers le Sud-Ouest sous une couverture de morts terrains aquifères qui s'épaissit vers le Sud-Ouest allant de 80 à 600 mètres. Entre les morts terrains essentiellement constitués de grès vosgiens et le houiller, un banc argileux et souple, le permier protège des venues d'eau.

Le gisement est constitué de 3 faisceaux distincts
- les flambants supérieurs
- les flambants inférieurs
- les gras.

La partie Ouest de la concession se caractérise par un gisement plat, peu dense (fig. 2), au contraire dans la partie Nord-Est. Le gisement est dense et il présente sous la couverture de grès triasique, une structure géologique compliquée avec succession de deux plissements déterminants (fig. 3), du Nord-Ouest au Sud-Est : l'anticlinal de Merlebach, le synclinal de Marienau et l'anticlinal de Simon.

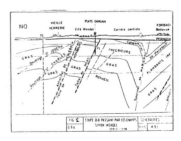

Figure 2

La proportion de couches pentées au-delà de 25° est donc importante et la mise en valeur de nouvelles réserves implique un approfondissement rapide.

2 - APPROFONDISSEMENT ET TENUE DES OU-VRAGES

Les nouveaux champs d'exploitation en cours de préparation sont situés entre 1 000 et 1 250 m de profondeur. C'est un fait universellement admis que la tenue des ouvrages devient plus difficile avec l'approfondissement. Les déformations sont plus importantes et les terrains se fracturent plus intensement.

En dehors du fait que la contrainte verticale en situation normale est proportionnelle à la profondeur, une exploitation statistique des mouvements enregistrés ne permet pas d'isoler de façon satisfaisante ce facteur profondeur, c'est pourquoi il semble préférable de rechercher l'état de contrainte dû à des conditions naturelles et leur influence non pas à travers leurs effets directs sur le comportement des ouvrages mais plutôt à travers les causes qui les déterminent, en d'autre terme l'état de contrainte initial.

La connaissance des diverses contraintes existant en un lieu ainsi que leur direction ne sont pas chose facile compte tenu des caractéristiques évolutives de la roche.

2 sites ont été étudiés aux Houillères du Bassin de Lorraine, le siège Vouters et le siège Simon.

3 - LA MESURE DES CONTRAINTES IN SITU

Trois techniques ont été utilisées jusqu'à présent aux Houillères du Bassin de Lorraine :
- le vérin plat
- le surcarottage
- la fracturation hydraulique.

3,1 - Le vérin plat

La figure 4 en rappelle le principe : une saignée est effectuée à la scie circulaire dans la roche sur une profondeur de 26 cm à partir de la paroi d'un ouvrage. La composante de la contrainte perpendiculaire au plan de cette saignée est ainsi "libérée" ce qui provoque le rapprochement de broches repères préalablement scellées dans le massif de part et d'autre de la saignée. La mesure de ce rapprochement est effectuée au micron près.

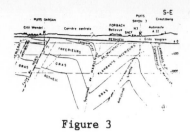

Figure 3

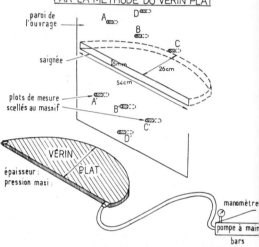

PRINCIPE DE LA MESURE DE CONTRAINTES PAR LA METHODE DU VERIN PLAT

Figure 4

Un vérin plat, constitué de deux tôles d'acier soudées, de même forme que la saignée, est alors introduit dans celle-ci puis gonflé jusqu'à ce que la distance entre les repères revienne sensiblement à sa valeur initiale. On suppose alors que la pression dans le vérin donne la valeur de la composante de la contrainte existant dans le terrain, en ce point, sur le plan de la saignée (à moins de 10 % près si cette dernière n'est pas contrainte principale.

Cette mesure n'a de sens que si le terrain qui subit la détente de la saignée et la remise en charge par le vérin admet un comportement réversible, ce qui est contrôlable en effectuant plusieurs cycles de charge-décharge avec le vérin plat. Mais bien entendu, cette technique n'est applicable que dans le cas d'un terrain dont les qualités mécaniques sont compatibles avec la succession de ces cycles de chargement-déchargement.

Pour une campagne de mesure sur un site donné, les saignées sont implantées suivant différentes orientations et en différents emplacements sur la périphérie de la galerie, comme dans l'exemple de la **figure** 5. Cette variété d'orientation est en effet nécessaire pour obtenir le tenseur complet des contraintes, comme nous le verrons plus loin.

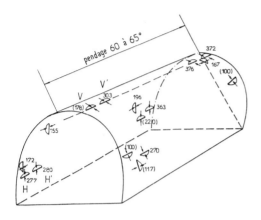

. (100) valeurs éliminées

Figure 5

Le nombre de saignées (16 dans ce cas) se justifie par l'obligation d'assurer des redondances. En effet, on constate **sur** cet exemple que deux saignées très voisines peuvent donner des résultats très différents (ainsi V et V'). Ceci tient presque toujours à la présence de fissures internes au massif observables par un examen endoscopique, mais que l'auscultation acoustique sommaire ou l'observation superficielle ne permettaient pas de déceler.
On voit ainsi, la nécessité de s'entourer de nombreuses précautions avant et après la réalisation des saignées, pour s'assurer que les pressions mesurées sont bien representatives de l'état de contrainte autour de la galerie.
Ces précautions sont :
- choix d'emplacement où la géométrie de la paroi est aussi régulière que possible
- Elimination des saignées implantées dans un massif affecté à proximité immédiate par des fissures ouvertes
- contrôle de la réversibilité du comportement du terrain lors de cycles de charge-décharge.

Mais la connaissance de ces pressions en différents points en bordure de la galerie ne fournit évidemment pas directement les valeurs des contraintes naturelles puisque le creusement même de la galerie a modifié le régime de contraintes.

Il importe donc de retrouver celui-ci à partir des résultats des saignées qui n'auront pas été éliminées, si elles restent assez nombreuses.
Une méthode de reconstitution du tenseur original des contraintes a été élaborée par le CERCHAR. Sur la base d'un modèle de calcul en déformation plane, ce qui revient donc à supposer qu'une des directions principales est parallèle à l'axe de la galerie, on détermine quel est l'état de contrainte naturelle qui s'accorde le mieux avec les résultats des mesures au vérin plat.
La figure n° 6 en présente les modalités pratiques.
A chaque pas du calcul, on compare la pression mesurée pour chaque saignée à la pression calculée à cet endroit suivant ce plan. On choisit le tenseur de contrainte naturelle qui minimise la somme de résidus carrés.
En toute rigueur, cette méthode d'estimation du tenseur des contraintes originelles ne peut avoir comme source d'erreur que :

1 - L'invalidité des hypothèses de base, qui sont, rappelons-le

- le comportement élastique linéaire de la roche, y compris à la paroi de l'ouvrage
- l'homogénéité du champ de contrainte initial
- la coïncidence de l'axe de la galerie avec l'une des directions de contraintes principales originelles.

2 - L'imprécision du calcul, conditionnée par :

- la finesse du maillage
- l'imprécision dans la connaissance de la géométrie de l'ouvrage (sa section)
- l'imprécision dans la connaissance des caractéristiques géomécaniques des terrains et leur homogénéité.

3 - L'incertitude sur les mesures elles-mêmes (à l'exclusion des mesures douteuses dont les critères d'élimination ont été expliqués plus haut)

- incertitude de mesure sur la pression

lue au manomètre (et sur la lecture des déformations, effectuée au mimicron)
- incertitude de mesure sur les orientations des saignées (lues sur l'éclimètre).

Si toutes les précautions sont prises, l'analyse de l'influence des diverses sources d'erreurs et d'incertitude montre qu'on peut très raisonnablement avancer des valeurs de contrainte originelles avec une précision inférieure à 20 %. La seule condition rédhibitoire pour l'application de cette méthode est que la roche accepte de se conformer à une loi de comportement de type élastique linéaire.

DÉTERMINATION DES CONTRAINTES PAR UNE SÉRIE D'ESSAIS AU VÉRIN PLAT - ORGANIGRAMME DE LA MÉTHODE DE DÉPOUILLEMENT

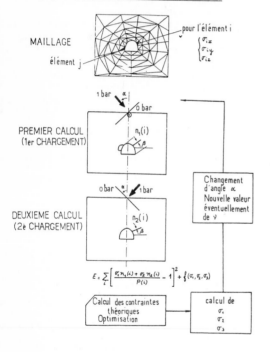

Figure 6

3,2 - Le surcarottage

La méthode du vérin plat a pour inconvénient de n'être représentative que de la surface de la paroi.
On est donc à la merci d'un biais introduit par des hétérogénéités très locales. La méthode est d'ailleurs

impraticable si le massif a été superficiellement altéré, ce qui sera toujours le cas en roche moyennement résistante à grande profondeur. Enfin le calcul interprétatif introduit une incertitude supplémentaire. La méthode du surcarottage pallie cet inconvénient en permettant de faire des mesures en profondeur.
La base de la méthode reste la même : on libère une contrainte et on détermine les déplacements ainsi induits. Connaissant les caractéristiques de la roche, on remonte à la contrainte naturelle.
Dans une première étape, on fore un trou de diamètre assez grand (210 mm) jusqu'à la profondeur à laquelle on veut mesurer les contraintes, (fig. 7A) On réalise ensuite un second forage concentrique au premier mais de diamètre plus petit (97 mm), (fig. 7B). La cellule de mesure est alors introduite dans ce petit forage, et les conditions initiales sont mesurées et enregistrées (diamètre initial du trou), (fig. 7C). Des cycles de mise en pression et de décharge de la cellule sont effectués, en vue de déterminer le module d'élasticité du massif. Une fois ces cycles terminés, le surcarottage proprement dit est exécuté ; les terrains autour de la cellule de mesure sont surcarottés en grand diamètre (210 mm) pendant que l'on mesure simultanément les variations de diamètre selon trois directions (fig. 7D). Dès la libération des contraintes et la stabilisation des mesures, six vérins courbes (fig. 7E - 8) ayant la forme circulaire du trou sont introduits dans la fente du surcarottage, une paire devant chaque paire de capteur (fig. 7E). La pression à l'intérieur des vérins est augmentée pour compenser les déformations mesurées et retrouver les conditions initiales enregistrées avant le surcarottage dans chaque direction.
En pratique les mesures sont faites à l'aide d'une cellule CERCHAR construite en coopération avec les Sociétés MAZIER et Cie et COYNE et BELLIER (fig. 9) - la figure 10 nous montre l'installation complète fond-jour.
La cellule se présente sous la forme d'un cylindre de 500 mm de longueur et de 95 mm de diamètre. Le corps en acier est enveloppé par une manchette de caoutchouc souple. L'étanchéité est assurée, à chacune des deux extrémités, par un manchon tronconique qui assure le

blocage de la manchette sur le corps métallique. Six capteurs de déplacement sont logés dans la partie centrale de la cellule, disposés en trois paires décalées de 120°. Un septième capteur bloqué est installé dans le corps de la cellule et sert de référence. Cette cellule peut fonctionner comme pressiomètre.

LA PROCEDURE DE SURCAROTTAGE

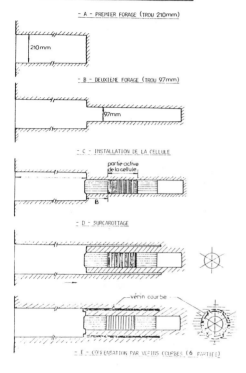

Figure 7

SCHEMA D'ENSEMBLE DES VERINS COURBES AVEC LE BLOC DISTRIBUTEUR

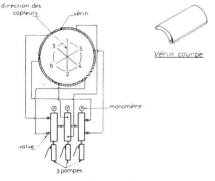

Figure 8

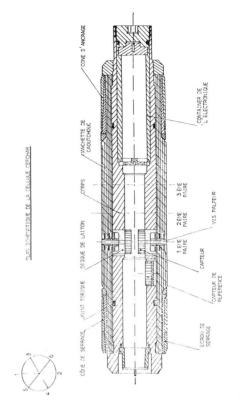

Figure 9

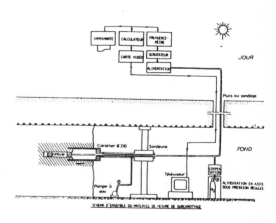

Figure 10

Les caractéristiques du matériau sont déterminées par des mesures in situ, complétées par des mesures en laboratoire. On sait déterminer de façon analytique les déformations d'un trou cylindrique induites par un état de contrainte quelconque, mais uniforme très

115

loin du trou. Il s'agit ici de faire le calcul inverse (fig. 11). La déformation d'un trou fournissant 3 paramètres et le tenseur de contrainte étant déterminé par six paramètres on pourrait penser que deux trous suffisent, en fait les six paramètres obtenus ne sont pas indépendants, il faut donc un troisième trou. Les données étant maintenant redondantes, on détermine le tenseur par un calcul des moindres carrés. Cette méthode de surcarottage est utilisable lorsque le massif en profondeur a un comportement élastique lui-même ou au moins réversible, ce qui couvre une large gamme de cas. Toutefois, elle est inopérante lorsqu'il est impossible de réaliser des carottes de longueur suffisante. Cela peut se produire dans des zones fortement contraintes où les carottes ont tendance à se disquer.

COURBE CARACTÉRISTIQUE DU SURCAROTTAGE D'UN
CHAMP DE CONTRAINTE TRIAXIAL

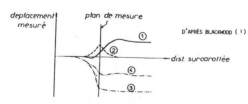

COURBE ④ EST LA SUPERPOSITION DE :
COURBE ① RÉSULTANTE D'UN CHAMP RADIAL SEUL
COURBE ② RÉSULTANTE DE LA CONCENTRATION DE CONTRAINTES DANS LE PLAN DU FOND DE SURCAROTTAGE, DUE À LA COMPOSANTE AXIALE
COURBE ③ RÉSULTANTE DE LA CONTRACTION RADIALE DE POISSON
(ICI : σ AXIALE $\gg$ σ RADIALE)

COURBE CARACTÉRISTIQUE DU SURCAROTTAGE D'UN
CHAMP DE CONTRAINTE TRIAXIAL

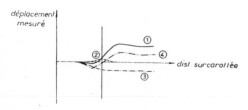

LA COURBE ④ EST LA RÉSULTANTE DE LA SUPERPOSITION DES
COURBES ① . ② LT ③

ICI σ AXIALE $\ll$ σ RADIALE

Figure 11

3,3 - La fracturation hydraulique

La méthode du surcarottage est très lourde en immobilisation de personnel et de matériel.

La fracturation hydraulique est moins contraignante et de ce fait peut s'avérer être la plus intéressante pour des mesures de contrainte à grande profondeur. Cette méthode consiste à isoler une portion de trou de foratio par deux obturateurs (fig. 12) et à remplir cette chambre de liquide jusqu'à une pression suffisante pour amo cer la rupture de la paroi, la pressi chute alors mais on poursuit le pompa ge pour propager la fissure. Lorsque cette dernière est de dimension suffi sante pour atteindre une zone non in fluencée, on arrête le pompage. On co tate alors que la pression se stabili à une valeur appellée "pression de fe meture". On peut poursuivre l'essai e réouvrant la fracture (fig. 13).

Ces différentes pressions ainsi que l'orientation de la fracture prise pa un "paker d'impression", cylindre en caoutchouc mou, permettant de remonte au tenseur des contraintes si l'on su pose que l'axe du sondage est parallè à une direction principale et que le massif est homogène et isotrope.

En fait, dans nos gisements, cette de nière condition n'est généralement pa vérifiée et de plus les terrains sont déjà fracturés ou présentent des plan de décollement. En revanche on a la possibilité de réaliser des trous de directions d'axe différents.

Si la chambre de fracturation est exe te de toute fracture initiale, la pre risation engendre une fracture longit dinale parallèle à l'axe du sondage q s'initie perpendiculairement à la plu faible des contraintes tangentielles à la paroi du sondage. Dans le cas de fractures naturelles, on a la possibi lité de réaliser des trous d'axe diff rents et en utilisant uniquement la pression de fermeture il faut pouvoir tester 6 fractures naturelles orienté différemment ; on exprime alors que la pression mesurée est égale à la compo sante de la normale au plan de fractu ration.

En pratique on ne dispose pas de six directions de fracturation naturelle, et on est alors amené à analyser les résultats obtenus provenant de fractu crées au cours de l'opération et de fractures naturelles.

L'interprétation se fait cas par cas. On cherche à conforter les résultats disposant de données redondantes.

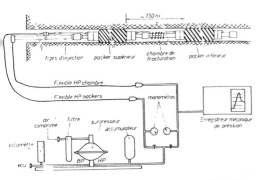

FIG. 11. SCHEMA DU MATERIEL DE FRACTURATION HYDRAULIQUE

tiges d'injection   packer supérieur   chambre de
fracturation   packer inférieur

F. exible HP chambre
F. exible HP packers   manomètres

Enregistreur mécanique
de pression

air   filtre   surpresseur
comprimé   accumulateur

volumètre

eau   BP   HP

EXEMPLE D'ENREGISTREMENT: PRESSION = f(TEMPS)

Pfr pression de fracturation 31 MPa
Pr pression de réouverture 20 MPa
Pfe pr de fermeture 15 MPa

Pfr   Pre   Pfe

Figure 12

a - Différentes phases d'un essai de fracturation hydraulique

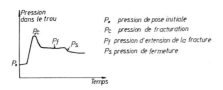

Pression
dans le trou

Pe pression de pose initiale
Pc pression de fracturation
Pf pression d'extension de la fracture
Ps pression de fermeture

Temps

b - Détermination des pressions de réouverture et de fermeture

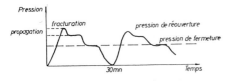

Pression

fracturation   pression de réouverture
propagation   pression de fermeture

30mn   Temps

Fig. 13 : Enregistrement de fracturation hydraulique

Figure 13

En conclusion, la méthode de la fracturation hydraulique permet dans nos exploitations, de réaliser des mesures de contrainte dans des situations où les méthodes par relachement de contraintes sont impraticables (discage de carottes) tout en étant plus écono-mique.

En revanche la détermination complète du tenseur de contrainte exige des terrains convenables où l'on puisse effectivement fracturer les roches, si cela n'est pas le cas, on peut cependant en espérer une indication sur le niveau général des contraintes et d'éventuelles anomalies sur l'orientation des directions principales.

4 - LES RESULTATS OBTENUS AUX HOUILLERES DU BASSIN DE LORRAINE

Les trois méthodes ont été testées en particulier au Siège Vouters et sur un même site on a pu vérifier la concordance des résultats.

Ce Siège qui exploite un gisement dense en dressants dont la structure géologique est celle d'un anticlinal schématisé (fig. 14), on relève les particularités suivantes :

- orientation N40 à 50E du pli constitué par deux faisceaux de couches : le faisceau des flambants supérieurs à l'Est (le plus dense) et celui des flambants inférieurs à l'Ouest. Entre les deux faisceaux un banc épais et hétérogène, le conglomérat de Merle-bach, contient les galeries principales d'infrastructure. Au toit du faisceau des flambants supérieurs, on trouve un conglomérat résistant : le conglomérat de Holtz.
- Découpage en trois compartiments par les failles Dora et Reumaux avec un compartiment central (contenant le puits Vouters), en butée sur le coeur de l'anticlinal sous l'effet de la contrainte de compression horizontale contemporaine.
- Plissement d'allure variable suivant les secteurs : la courbure des bancs régulière et continue dans la partie Nord, prend une forme plus saccadée dans la partie Sud-Ouest comme en témoigne le brutal changement de pendage bien connu entre les étages 600 et 800.

A l'étage 1250, on observe également des variations assez brutales de pendage dans certains bancs. Ces variations de pendage pourraient être interprétées comme le signe d'une nouvelle "flexure" dans le flanc du pli, dont l'importance et l'extension ne sont pas encore précisées, mais qu'il est tentant de mettre en parallèle avec le "changement de pendage" des étages supérieurs.

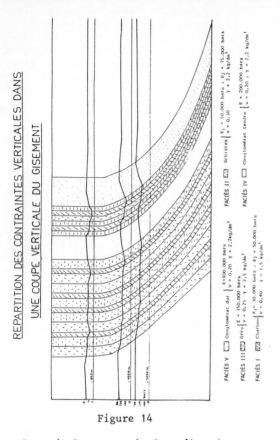

REPARTITION DES CONTRAINTES VERTICALES DANS
UNE COUPE VERTICALE DU GISEMENT

FACIÈS V ☐ Conglomérat dur { E = 600.000 bars ; γ = 2,2kg/dm³ ν = 0,20

FACIÈS III ☐ Grès { E = 150.000 bars ν = 0,25 ; γ = 2,5 kg/dm³

FACIÈS I ☒ Charbon { E₁ = 30.000 bars ; E₂ = 50.000 bars ν = 0,40 ; γ = 1,5 kg/dm³

FACIÈS II ▨ Schistes { E₁ = 50.000 bars ; E₂ = 75.000 bars ν = 0,10 ; γ = 2,2 kg/dm³

FACIÈS IV ☐ Conglomérat tendre { E = 200.000 bars ν = 0,20 ; γ = 2,2 kg/dm³

Figure 14

Les résultats acquis jusqu'à présent
sont représentés sur la figure 15.*

. Dans le conglomérat de Merlebach, on
dispose de mesures aux étages 747, 1036
et 1250 (les deux derniers points étant
situés au nord de la faille Dora et au
Sud de la faille Reumaux) : campagne 2,
3 et 4.
. Dans le conglomérat de Holtz, au toit
immédiat du faisceau de couches, on
dispose d'une seule mesure à l'étage
1036 (travers-banc, 1ère Nord-Est) au
Sud de la faille Reumaux, campagne 1.
On constate d'abord que les directions
principales diffèrent peu de la verticale et des directions horizontales
sensiblement perpendiculaires et
parallèles à l'axe de l'anticlinal.
Pour cette dernière, il faut noter que
c'est la conséquence d'une de nos hypothèses puisque les galeries qui ont
fait l'objet des mesures étaient le
plus souvant parallèles à l'axe de
l'anticlinal.

RESULTATS DES MESURES
DE CONTRAINTES A MERLEBACH

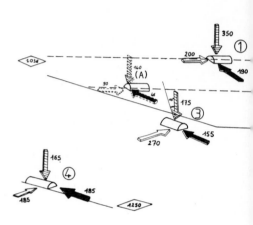

Figure 15

On remarque ensuite la grande variabilité des contraintes obtenues, verticales aussi bien qu'horizontales :

- L'amplitude de la contrainte verticale
  semble croître avec la profondeur dans
  un même type de terrain, en l'occurence le conglomérat de Merlebach. Mais
  la valeur trouvée à 1250 est plus faible que celle que l'on attendrait en
  extrapolant linéairement les résultats
  des étages supérieurs. D'autre part,
  on constate que le rapport de la contrainte verticale à la profondeur est
  inférieur à 0,2 dans le conglomérat de
  Merlebach, c'est-à-dire certainement
  inférieur à la densité des terrains
  susjacents. Ce rapport est au contraire supérieur à la densité (supérieur
  à 0,3) pour l'unique point de mesure
  du conglomérat de Holtz à l'étage 103.
  La comparaison des contraintes verticales pour cette même profondeur 1036
  fait donc apparaître une différence
  considérable suivant l'emplacement où
  elle est mesurée.

- Les contraintes horizontales n'évoluent
  pas de la même manière.

118

La contrainte horizontale parallèle à
l'axe de l'anticlinal est assez cons-
tante. Elle est toutefois plus faible
à 1036 dans le conglomérat de Merlebach
(point 3) peut être à cause de la proximité de la faille Dora (400 - 500 m).
La contrainte horizontale transversale
est beaucoup plus variable. On notera
la valeur particulièrement élevée au
point 3.
Cette variabilité, comme celle de la
contrainte verticale, étonne et mérite
réflexion. Elle dépasse largement l'or-
dre de grandeur de l'imprécision de la
méthode, que nous avons chiffrées, dans
les chapitres précédents, à 20 % du
résultat annoncé. Nous proposons les
éléments d'interprétation suivants :

. On peut trouver des causes d'hétérogénéité du champ de contrainte à grande
échelle. Un calcul simple, sur modèle
numérique par la méthode des éléments
finis nous a montré que dans un assem-
blage plissé de bancs pesants, aux caractéristiques mécaniques très contras-
tées (fig. 16), la contrainte verticale
sur un même horizon variait considéra-
blement (et n'était pas toujours direction principale).

Les contraintes verticales sont d'autant
plus élevées que les bancs sont minces
et rigides et elles ne sont qu'en
moyenne proportionnelles à la profondeur
et à la densité des terrains. Dans ce
modèle schématique, qui est inspiré
d'une coupe verticale transversale du
gisement de Merlebach, la contrainte
verticale varie de 1 à 3. Ce calcul
éclaire quelque peu la question de la
variabilité de la contrainte verticale.
La question de la variabilité de la
contrainte horizontale peut être abor-
dée de la même manière. On peut en effet
considérer que le compartiment géologique central délimité (fig. 17) par les
deux failles subverticales Dora et
Reumaux et soumis à la phase contemporaine de compression, constitue un
"poinçon" en butée sur le coeur de l'anticlinal. On imagine pour cela que les
compartiments Sud et Nord bénéficient
de possibilités plus grandes de mouvements, le long des plans de failles,
compte tenu de l'orientation de ces
dernières par rapport à la direction
supposée de la compression. Le compartiment central, au contraire, serait
logiquement soumis à des surcontraintes
horizontales importantes, surtout au
voisinage de la faille Dora.

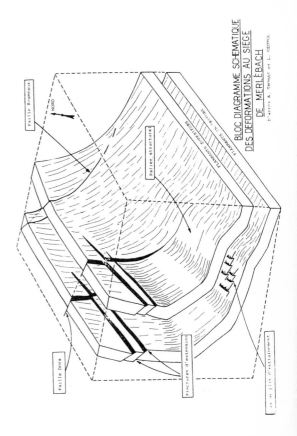

Figure 16

A défaut d'une vérification directe
(envisagée pour l'avenir), nous avons
cherché une justification de ce modèle
par l'étude statistique des convergences
en tailles montantes égides rassemblées
au cours de ces dernières années.
L'analyse est malheureusement rendue
difficile par le fait que la gamme des
valeurs de profondeur n'est pas toujours
comparable pour tous les compartiments.
Toutefois, on trouve au moins dans un
cas (celui du faisceau des flambants
inférieurs) une différence significative
entre les compartiments nord et centre :
pour des profondeurs comprises entre
700 et 800 m, les déformations sont
presque deux fois plus fortes dans le
compartiment central. On voit donc que
la structure discontinue et hétérogène
du gisement envisagée dans des plans
verticaux et horizontaux peut conduire
à des états de contraintes complexes.
Les hypothèses schématiques et les
calculs simples dont nous avons fait
état n'ont de valeur qu'indicative et
nos points de mesure sont trop peu

119

nombreux pour les valider complètement. Mais cet essai d'interprétation, motivé par des résultats a priori surprenants, a le mérite de mettre l'accent en la précisant, sur l'importance des conditions tectoniques dans la détermination de l'état de contrainte.

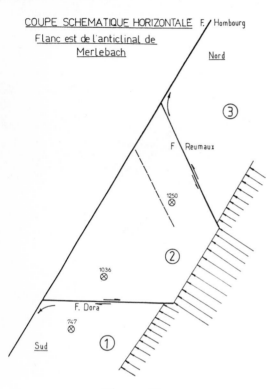

COUPE SCHEMATIQUE HORIZONTALE
Flanc est de l'anticlinal de Merlebach

Figure 17

5 - CONCLUSIONS

Les méthodes de mesure de contrainte in situ nous permettent d'annoncer des résultats avec une précision de ± 20 % dans la majorité des cas où les conditions du site le permettent.

Les résultats obtenus montrent :

- une tendance à l'augmentation des contraintes verticales avec la profondeur mais aussi une grande sensibilité de cette contrainte avec la structure géologique du gisement.
- Une très grande variabilité des contraintes horizontales interprétable elle aussi à partir de l'analyse géologique structurale.

L'ensemble de ces résultats, sont cohérents avec la connaissance que l'on a du comportement des ouvrages actuellemer voisins des sites instrumentés. En particulier l'apparition des phénomènes dynamiques paraît bien reliée avec l'existence d'états de contraintes particuliers.

En conclusion, cette recherche sur l'influence des facteurs naturels commencée avec l'accent mis sur le facteur profondeur, met en réalité en lumière la prépondérance de la tectonique (du moins en ce qui concerne les problèmes de pressio de terrains). Même si l'approfondissemer est une condition incontestablement aggravante pour le bon comportement des ouvrages, son effet ne peut être précisé que cas par cas, en étroite liaison avec le contexte géologique local et régional qui semble déterminant dans nos conditions de gisement.
Enfin, cette étude ouvre la voie à une utilisation nouvelle, quantitative, de la géologie structurale conjuguée aux méthodes de la mécanique des roches et des terrains.

---

* Les résultats en pointillé correspondent à une série de mesures peu nombreuses et à ce titre suspectées d'être peu représentatives (campagnes antérieures à la mise au point définitive de la méthode).

Bibliographie

L. GEORGES - Thèse Dr Ing. INPL Ecole des Mines de Nancy - Décembre 1981 Influence de la profondeur et des facteurs naturels sur le comportement des ouvrages miniers.

L. GEORGES - J.P. PIGUET - Rapport final CECA 7220-AC/303 - Influence de la profondeur et des facteurs naturels sur le comportement des ouvrages miniers

R. REVALOR - Octobre 1984 - Laboratoire de mécanique des roches - Ecole des Mine Nancy - Mesures de contraintes naturelle par surcarottage et fracturation hydraulique.

L. TINCHON - C. DAUMALIN - L. GEORGE - J.P. PIGUET - Septembre 1982 - Evolution des contraintes en fonction de la profondeur et des facteurs naturels.

Proceedings of the International Symposium on Rock Stress and Rock Stress Measurements/Stockholm/1-3 September 1986

Hydrostatic conditions in salt domes – a reality or a modeling simplification

L.G. ERIKSSON
Shannon & Wilson, Inc., Seattle, Washington, USA

A. MICHALSKI
The Earth Technology Corporation, Somerset, New Jersey, USA

Abstract: This literature-based study of in situ stress conditions in salt domes in the southeastern USA suggests that virgin in situ stresses within these structures are generally hydrostatic to within 2 MPa. Higher deviatoric stresses might occur locally within a dome in the presence of impure salt, geologic structures and other heterogeneities. The inferred near-hydrostatic stress condition in salt domes is based on detailed integrated analyses of six different types of evidence -- in situ stress measurements; deformational behavior on sample, borehole and mining scales; salt microstructures; regional stress field in the Gulf Coast; physical expressions of salt domes; and salt modeling results.

Résumé: Cette étude, basée sur documentation, des conditions de pression in situ dans les domes de sel dans le Sud-Est des Etats-Unis, suggère que les pressions vierges in situ à l'intérieur de ces structures sont géneralement hydrostatiques à 2 MPa pres. Des pressions déviatoriques plus élevées peuvent se produire localement à l'interieur d'un dome en présence de sel impur, de structures géologiques et autres éléments héterogènes. La conclusion de la condition de pression quasi-hydrostatique dans les domes de sel est basée sur de analyses détaillées et complètes de six différents types de preuves -- des mesures de pression in situ; un comportement altéré sur échantillons, des trous de sonde et sur des écailles de mines; des microstructures de sel; des champs de pression régionaux dans le "Gulf Coast"; des expressions physiques de domes de sel; et des résultats de modelages de sel.

Zusammenfassung: Diese auf schriftlichen Quellen basierte Studie über In-situ-Spannungsstände in Saltzdomen im Sudosten der U.S.A. behauptet der in-situ initialspannungen innerhalb dieser Strukturen im allgemeinen bis zu 2 MPa hydrostatisch sind. Höhere Deviatorspannungen könnte örtlich innerhalb der Dome eintreten, wenn unrein Salz, geologische Strukturen und andere Heterogenitäten vorhanden wären. Der gefolgerte fast-hydrostatische Spannungzustand in Salzdomen ergibt sich aus einer detaillierten, zusammenhängenden Analyse von sechs verschiedenen Beweistypen -- In-situ-Spannungsmessungen; charakteristische deformationen von Proben, von Bohrlöcher und Grubenanlagen; Salzmikrostrukturen; regionales Spannungsfeld in der "Gulf Coast"; physikalische Äusserungen der Salzdomen; und Resultate von Salzmodellen.

1 INTRODUCTION

Salt domes constitute a natural resource that can be mined and used for a wide variety of subsurface facilities. The virgin in situ stress conditions in salt domes constitute a critical design parameter for a cost-effective and safe design of salt openings and are also critical to credible performance assessments of underground salt openings. Frequently, design and modeling assumptions for underground openings in domal salt include hydrostatic stress conditions based on a single data set or, more often, because of lack of in situ stress data. The objective of this paper is to present and synthesize data on more than one in situ stress indicator to provide an overview and, possibly, a contemporary source document on virgin in situ stress conditions in salt domes.

This literature-based study of virgin in situ stress conditions in salt domes evaluates and synthesizes six different in situ stress indicators. The evaluation of data is limited to the values presented in the referenced source document(s) and does not include a critical evaluation of the validity of the referenced data. Only data available to the public were used to support the analyses and conclusions presented in this paper.

A major portion of the presented data were obtained in connection with a recent salt dome study performed in support of the U.S. Department of Energy's (USDOE's) Office of Civilian Radioactive Waste Management (OCRWM) Program. It should be noted that the analyses and conclusions presented here are solely the opinions of the authors, and may not concur with those of the USDOE or its staff. Because of the authors' active involvement in nuclear waste disposal studies, particular emphasis was placed on data from the United States (U.S.) Gulf Coast Region.

The following key questions related to the virgin in situ stress conditions in salt domes are addressed:

o Is the virgin in situ stress in salt domes hydrostatic, near-hydrostatic or of distinct anisotropic and heterogeneous character?
o If the virgin in situ stress in salt domes is anisotropic, what is the magnitude of the deviatoric stress?
o What is the virgin in situ stress distribution (magnitude and orientation) within the salt dome in relation to the internal dome structure and the external features?

The lack of adequate direct evidence on the virgin in situ stress in salt domes, such as true virgin in situ stress measurements, requires significant assumptions and interpretations to be made in addressing these questions. Therefore, the limited direct information on in situ stress conditions in salt domes has been supplemented by indirect data on virgin and mining-induced in situ stresses in domal salt including the following potential in situ stress indicators:

o Deformational characteristics of rock salt based on laboratory, borehole and mine data;
o Salt microstructures;
o Regional stress field and associated physical expressions (cross-sectional shapes) of salt domes in the Gulf Coast; and
o Modeling results.

A detailed discussion of all the data evaluated in support of the conclusions presented in this paper is precluded. All major data sources are, however, included.

In view of its fundamental importance to the understanding of virgin and mining induced in situ stress conditions in salt domes (as well as bedded salt) the discussion focuses on the direct information on in situ stress conditions in salt domes (in situ stress measurements). The inferred range in deviatoric stress at virgin in situ stress conditions in salt domes is presented to encourage an international discussion on this subject although the key issue is how to improve the state of the art of absolute in situ stress measurements in salt to enhance the confidence in measured values.

2 DIRECT INFORMATION ON IN SITU STRESS CONDITIONS IN SALT DOMES

2.1 In Situ Stress Measurements

Few in situ stress measurements have been performed in domal salt. Available in situ stress measurement results from three Gulf Coast salt domes and extrapolated maximum deviatoric and differential stresses are summarized in Table 1. Although not necessarily being the maximum deviatoric stress, the greatest stress difference that can be extrapolated from each data set in Table 1 is used in the continued discussion as a deviatoric stress indicator, because of the scarcity of credible absolute in situ stress measurement data in salt domes.

The maximum deviatoric/differential stress for the seven data sets in Table 1 ranges from 0.27 MPa to approximately 5 MPa. Prior to the discussion of these data, their relevance to virgin in situ stress conditions requires a brief discussion.

Two methods of stress measurement were used: overcoring and hydraulic fracturing

TABLE 1. Summary of In Situ Stress Measurements in Salt Domes

LOCATION	METHOD AND DEPTH	MEASURED OR CALCULATED PRINCIPAL STRESSES	SOURCE
Cote Blanche Salt Dome, Louisiana	"Minifrac" in an inclined hole, a few meters long and beneath a pillar DS = 490 m DG = Incomplete data (1 test at 0.3 m)	Greater stress beneath the pillar = 15.4 MPa Estimated lithostatic stress = about 10.4 MPa No direction Max. differential stress = about 5 MPa*	Thoms and Gehle 1982
Hockley Salt Dome, Texas	Overcoring in mine floor, 10 tests DS = 487.7 m DG = 0.2 - 1.2 m	Horizontal stresses = 7.24 MPa (N 58 E) and 7.03 MPa Vertical stress = 8.41 MPa Max. deviatoric stress = 1.38 MPa* - - - - - - - - - - - - Horizontal stresses = 7.93 MPa (N 58 E) and 5.31 MPa Vertical stress = 8.41 MPa Max. deviatoric stress = 3.10 MPa*	Lindner and Halpern 1978
Winnfield Salt Dome, Louisiana	Overcoring, 11 tests in horizontal holes DS = 244 m DG = 0.2 - 1.0 m	Horizontal stresses = 7.24 MPa (N 48 W) and 4.86 MPa Vertical stress = 6.21 MPa Max. deviatoric stress = 2.38 MPa* - - - - - - - - - - - - Horizontal stresses = 6.21 MPa (N 30 W) and 5.52 MPa Vertical stress = 6.21 MPa Max. deviatoric stress = 0.69 MPa*	Lindner and Halpern 1978
	Overcoring in mine floor DS = 270 m DG = No data	Average horizontal stress = 5.23 MPa Vertical stress = 5.50 MPa Max. differential stress 0.27 MPa*	Brown and Hoek 1978
	Overcoring in horizontal holes DS = 244 m DG = See Figure 1	See Figure 1 (Max. stress difference less than 15 percent)	Obert 1962

* = Inferred deviatoric/differential stress (not in the source document)
DS = Depicts depth below ground surface
DG = Depicts depth below borehole collar

(hydrofrac). The applicability of these methods to accurately measure in situ stresses in rock salt is subject to analytical constraints. Both methods rely on linear elastic solutions and an isotropic material to interpret the test data. Salt in general, and in particular at the reported test depths of between 244 m to 490 m, is a non-linear material, which reduces the confidence in the reported in situ stress data (Obert 1962, Lindner and Halpern 1978, Brown and Hoek 1978, and Thoms and Gehle 1982 and 1986).

At least four of the six data sets on in situ stress measurements were obtained in relatively shallow boreholes, less than 1.5 m deep, drilled from underground openings. Mining or other human activities such as induced thermal and ground-water flow fluxes are known to change the virgin in situ stress field some distance outside an underground opening. The virgin in situ stress field will respond to the change in the natural environment and zones of stress concentrations and stress relaxations will develop in the rock. The induced stress changes will vary in magnitude with time and distance outside the opening as a function of several factors, of which the geologic media and the change in the natural environment imposed by man are generally considered the most important.

For example, recent field data in bedded salt (Wawersik and Stone 1986) show that the maximum tangential stress loci, 200 percent of the lithostatic stress initially occurring at the borehole wall, moved outwards with time and reached its furthest distance from the borehole wall, approximately three borehole radii, between 30 and 165 days after drilling. Noticeably, the stress field at the maximum tangential stress loci was approximately constant between 55 and 165 days after drilling. The maximum tangential stress remained 117 to 118 percent higher than the lithostatic stress. The maximum tangential stress after 1100 days was close to the lithostatic stress; however, the lowest tangential stress, 65 percent of the lithostatic stress, occured at the borehole wall. The significant reduction in tangential stress at the borehole shows clearly that stress relaxation occurred at the borehole wall with time.

In view of the typically large dimensions of the rooms and the pillars in the mines at the measured sites, the data sets on in situ stresses in salt domes

(Table 1) are expected to be affected the presence of the opening(s) and obtained in the zone disturbed by mining induced stress changes.

Although the direct information on i situ stresses in salt domes is expecte be representative of contemporary rath than virgin in situ stress conditions, it is used in the subsequent discussio to bound the maximum deviatoric/differ tial virgin in situ stresss.

The highest deviatoric/differential stress that can be inferred from the d base on direct in situ stress measurements (Table 1) is about 5 MPa (Thoms Gehle 1982). This upper boundary data was obtained by hydrofracing underneatl and close to the perimeter of a mine pillar. The test location is clearly located in a zone governed by mining-induced increased stresses and was selected for the purpose of simulating cyclic loading rather than measuring virgin in situ stresses. This data set leads to the conclusion that the virgir in situ stresses, as well as the maximu deviatoric virgin in situ stress, were significantly lower than the measured mining-induced stress concentrations below the pillar.

Maximum deviatoric/differential stresses of 1.38 MPa and 3.10 MPa are inferred from the overcoring measuremen reported by Lindner and Halpern (1978) in the Hockley mine, Texas (Table 1). Two data sets were obtained in shallow (less than 1.2 m deep), vertical boreholes in the mine floor. The measuremen were clearly performed within the zone affected by the mine opening. The data sets are affected by a mining-induced stress increase and/or decrease. Hence, the maximum deviatoric virgin in situ stress could be higher or lower than th inferred maximum deviatoric stress of 3 MPa. The lithostatic vertical stress is the highest principal stress for this data set, suggesting that since the measured horizontal stresses are lower, the data were obtained in a zone affected by stress relaxation. This in turn suggests that the measured mining-induced stresses are lower than the virgin in situ stresses, hence the devia toric virgin in situ stresses should be less than the measured values (1.38 MPa to 3.1 MPa). If the stress relaxation is on the order of 65 percent, as reported for bedded salt (Wawersik and Stone 1986 the inferred maximum virgin deviatoric stress would be on the order of 2 MPa.

Maximum deviatoric stresses of 0.69 MPa and 2.38 MPa are inferred from two sets of overcoring measurements reported by Lindner and Halpern (1978) in the Winnfield mine, Louisiana (Table 1). The measurements were performed in shallow horizontal holes less than 1.2 m deep. Assuming a large opening and the boreholes being within reachable distance from the mine floor, these measurements were most likely performed in the zone governed by mining-induced stress increases. Consequently, the maximum virgin deviatoric stress value was less than the maximum deviatoric stress value inferred from the Winnfield mine data reported by Lindner and Halpern (1978) and the upper boundary for the maximum virgin deviatoric stress is lower than 2.38 MPa.

Obert (1962) also reports overcoring in situ stress measurement data from the Winnfield mine (Table 1 and Figure 1).

FIGURE 1. Overcoring Measurement Data Winnfield Salt Dome Mine (After Obert 1962)

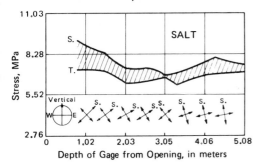

Explanation

Variation in magnitude and direction of the maximum (S) and minimum (T) stresses (normal to the axis of a horizontal hole) with respect to the distance from a room in the mine. Shaded area depicts inferred differential stress.

The maximum differential stress inferred from Figure 1 is on the order of 2.1 MPa. This data set was obtained in a shallow horizontal borehole approximately 5 m deep, collared at the end of a stope at the boundary of the mine. The opening was 15 m wide and 6 m high. The extraction rate in the room and pillar mine was 50 percent. This data set is clearly obtained from a zone disturbed by

the existing openings. Similar to the data reported from this site by Lindner and Halpern (1978), the maximum virgin deviatoric stress should be lower than the inferred value of 2.1 MPa. Obert's in situ stress data are based on linear elastic behavior of salt and measured deformations. The anticipated stress concentration outside the opening is not particularly well defined. The in situ stress measurements reported by Obert show a relatively even stress level with distance outside the opening without any pronounced stress concentrations (Figure 1). Figure 1 clearly supports the assumption of near-hydrostatic stress conditions in salt domes since there is an apparent lack of stress concentrations as well as low deviatoric stress outside the opening, in lieu of the relatively short distance between the measurements and the opening (Figure 1), and measured stress values are close to the calculated lithostatic stress value (Obert 1962).

A third data set on in situ stress conditions in the Winnfield mine is reported by Brown and Hoek (1978). This data set averages the horizontal stresses (Table 1) and the resulting low inferred differential stress (0.27 MPa) is not useful to the discussion of the maximum deviatoric stress and cannot be used to bound the maximum virgin deviatoric stress.

Although very little information on the size and shape of opening; prevailing geologic anomalies and structures; time between mining, drilling and measurement; and measuring location(s) are available in the reviewed literature, the review of the data sources on in situ stress measurements in salt (Table 1) and related bounding discussion, leads to the conclusion that the maximum virgin deviatoric stress is lower than 2.38 MPa and, possibly even lower than 0.69 MPa.

It is clear that current in situ stress measuring techniques are poorly adapted for quantitative stress determinations in salt. Overcoring techniques suffer from analytical and application constraints. The most apparent application constraint is the limited borehole depth that can be reached. Techniques and methods used in geologic media with deformational behavior closer to linear elastic theory, such as the Swedish State Power Boards device (Hiltscher, Martna and Strindell 1979), cannot be directly applied to salt without modification of system components and analytical solutions. Recent field and laboratory hydro-frac data (Wawersik and Stone 1985 and 1986, and Doe, Boyce and Majer 1985) suggest that hydrofrac is not a credible technique for quantitative stress deter-minations. However, hydraulic fracturing may be uniquely suited for qualitative stress inferences. Wawersik and Stone (1986) suggest that pressure-time curves with sharp contrasts between breakdown and fracture driving pressures are in-dicative of deviatoric stresses (Figure 2). Conversely, poorly defined pressure-time curves with little loss in pressure after primary breakdown as well as randomly-oriented fractures around the borehole wall suggest near-hydrostatic stress conditions. One distinct fracture set appears to require a minimum differential stress ratio in excess of 1.1 and possibly on the order of 1.5.

FIGURE 2. Predicted Shape of Pressure-Time Records for Hydrofracturing. in Salt under Hydrostatic and Anisotropic Far-Field Stresses. (After Wawersik and Stone 1986)

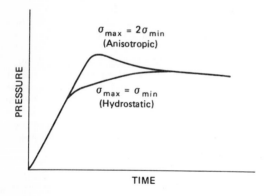

$\sigma_{max} = 2\sigma_{min}$
(Anisotropic)

PRESSURE

$\sigma_{max} = \sigma_{min}$
(Hydrostatic)

TIME

3 INDIRECT INFORMATION ON IN SITU STRESS CONDITIONS IN SALT DOMES

3.1 Deformational Characteristics of Rock Salt

The viscoplastic deformational behavior of salt will allow salt to respond to de-viatoric stresses by creep and associated equalizing stress redistribution. Field

observations (e.g. Baar 1977) suggest that creep-rates of salt are time depen dent, but very fast compared with rates of geological processes. Hence, salt ca relatively quickly dissipate distinct (high) deviatoric stresses imposed by natural processes and human activities through creep.

A characteristically low creep (yield limit of rock salt is generally accepte (e.g. Baar 1977, Gevantman 1981); how-ever, different values of the creep limit have been obtained from laborator tests, depending on loading rates and petrographic characteristics of salt samples. Baar (1977) assumed a creep limit of 1 MPa as typical of salt. Base on theory of plasticity, he also sugges-ted a maximum deviatoric stress of abou 2 MPa for the salt around underground openings.

Anhydritic salt, often referred to as "black salt" in the Gulf Coast mines, an sediment-bearing salt have higher creep limits and, therefore, are likely to sustain higher deviatoric stresses than pure rock salt (halite). Although salt domes in general are very pure and are comprised of more than 95 percent halite (NaCl), salt layering and the presence of anhydrite layers or other materials with dissimilar deformational behavior than salt are factors that may lead to stress heterogeneity in salt domes. Hence, distinct deviatoric stresses migh occur locally in salt domes, as suggeste by the typical subvertical banding in Gulf Coast salt domes, even though the mechanical behavior of salt suggests tha distinct deviatoric stresses dissipate with time. It is concluded, however, tha pure salt is unable to sustain distinct deviatoric stresses.

3.1.1 Borehole Closure

Closures of two approximately 1,500 m deep vertical boreholes in the Vacherie and Rayburn's domes, Louisiana, in the Gulf Coast Interior Basin, have been periodically measured over a period of about five years (Thoms and Mogharrebi 1979, Thoms 1981, and Thoms, Mogharrebi and Gehle 1982a and 1982b). Closures of the two boreholes were small and essen-tially of the same magnitude to a depth of approximately 790 m. Significant in-creases in borehole closure occurs below this depth. An elliptical configuration was measured in the upper portion of the borehole at the Rayburn's Dome; however it is not clear if this elliptical deformation was caused by an anisotropic stress field, fabric anisotropy or differences in other site-specific factors relative to the Vacherie Dome. Near-circular borehole cross sections are also evident in portions of the boreholes at Vacherie and Rayburn's domes. There is, however, a clear difference in the magnitude of borehole closure between the two domes. For example, at a depth of 1,510 m, the total diametric displacements at the last reported measurements were approximately 26 and 7 percent of the initial hole diameter for the Vacherie and Rayburn's domes, respectively. Thoms, Mogharrebi and Gehle (1982a) concluded that the difference in the virgin in situ stress field in the rock surrounding the salt dome (country rock) controlled the closure behavior of the two boreholes.

Other factors very likely contributed to the difference in deformation behavior of the boreholes at Vacherie and Rayburn's domes. The Vacherie dome borehole was reportedly slightly warmer and was drilled in salt with mechanical properties generally inferior to the Rayburn's domal salt. Both of these factors would tend to increase the closure of the borehole in the Vacherie Dome relative to the borehole in the Rayburn's Dome (Thoms, Mogharrebi and Gehle 1982a).

Moreover, as both boreholes were drilled near the center of the dome, respective local conditions related to the internal structure of salt stocks such as layering, folding, and material heterogeneity in the vicinity of the boreholes (not obvious from the cores) may have affected the dissimilar closure behaviour to a greater extent than far-field stress conditions imposed by the surrounding country rock.

It is not possible to estimate the stresses or their variations from the borehole closure data. Preliminary hydrofrac data were obtained at two depths in the borehole at the Rayburn's Dome in December of 1985 (Thoms and Gehle 1986). The preliminary data from the approximate measuring depths of 416 m and 438 m suggest that the horizontal stresses exceed the vertical lithostatic stress (calculated at 22.6 kPa per meter depth) and that the in situ tensile strength is twice the laboratory determined average value (1.35 MPa). Additional hydrofrac

tests down to a depth of 915 m are scheduled for 1986.

Interpretation of the borehole data from the Vacherie and Rayburn's domes are inconclusive at this time. However, the reported data suggest that stress conditions may vary within a salt dome as well as between salt domes. Conceivably, distance to and stress characteristics of the country rock may sustain deviatoric stresses close to the perimeter of the dome and affect the time required for stress equalization within the dome.

3.2 Salt Microstructures

The subgrain sizes and the free dislocation density in salt crystals are two microstructural features that are proposed to be a function of the applied differential stress (Carter, Hansen and Senseny 1982). Studies and analyses of these two features have been performed on etched cleavage chips of various types of salt by Carter, Hansen and Senseny (1982), Hansen and Senseny (1983), and Hansen (1985).

An inverse empirical equation has been proposed by Carter, Hansen and Senseny (1982) relating the applied stress difference and the subgrain sizes of experimentally deformed domal salt. This equation may allow the estimation of the maximum deviatoric stresses incurred during past deformational events, which may or may not coincide with the virgin in situ stress conditions. However, stresses calculated by this technique should provide an upper boundary condition for the virgin in situ stresses and associated deviatoric stresses.

Data on salt from seven locations, including two salt domes, are presented in Figure 3 (Carter, Hansen and Senseny 1982). From this relationship, the maximum stress difference for the domal salt samples from the Grand Saline Dome, Texas and the Avery Island Dome, Louisiana, were estimated to be 0.58 MPa and 1.1 MPa, respectively.

Free dislocation density has also been studied to infer deviatoric stresses in domal salt. The results are less consistent and do not corroborate the more extensive subgrain analyses (Hansen 1985). An empirical equation relating the free dislocation density to stress difference yielded untenably high stress differences for natural rock salt – one or two orders of magnitude higher than estimated from subgrain-size analysis. The reason for this inconsistency is not clear. The reported results of dislocation density studies imply that distinct deviatoric stress may occur in domal salt. Additional studies are required before the dislocation study results can be accepted because they appear to be contradictory to other studies and test results.

FIGURE 3. Subgrain Diameter-Differential Stress Relationship (After Carter, Hansen and Senseny 1982)

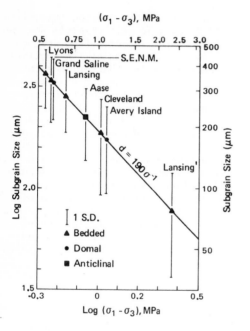

$(\sigma_1 - \sigma_3)$, MPa

d   Subgrain diameter
σ_1 Maximum principal stress
σ_3 Minimum principal stress

Explanation

Mean subgrain sizes and corresponding stress differences for seven naturally deformed bedded, domal, and anticlinal rock salts. Vertical bars show one standard deviation from mean subgrain diameter.

Based on the reported results of subgrain studies of domal salt, the estimated maximum deviatoric stress is equal to or less than 1.1 MPa. However, high deviatoric stresses may occur in portions of a salt dome containing impure salt as exemplified by one data set from Lansing, Michigan (Figure 3). Of eight data sets from seven locations, this data set experienced the highest deviatoric stress (2.34 MPa). The subgrain analyses indicated concentrations of stresses around anhydrite grains, which was proposed as the probable reason for the relatively high deviatoric stress relative to the other seven data sets (Figure 3).

3.3 Mining Experience

Earth Technology Corporation (1985) reviewed the performance of mined openings in salt. Numerous case histories on opening performance in domal and bedded salt and potash are reported by Baar (1977). Kupfer (1978) reports performance of underground openings in domal salt mines in Louisiana. Reported instances of roof stability problems in the Louisiana mines have been associated with arch bends in black beds of salt; roof instabilities appear to intensify near zones with extensive shearing of salt and/or the presence of sediments and fluids (Kupfer 1978). In general, underground openings in domal salt remain stable for decades.

Although stability problems are reported in domal salt mines, available data (observations) indicate that the performance of mined openings in salt is governed by mining-induced changes or by structural and lithological heterogeneities rather than virgin in situ stresses. The data on the performance of mined openings in domal salt do not support the existence of distinct deviatoric virgin in situ stresses. However, local occurrences of stiff and strong anhydritic and sediment-bearing salt can display abnormal stress concentrations viz. distinct deviatoric stresses (Golder Associates 1977).

3.4 Regional Stress Fields and Physical Expressions of Salt Domes in the Gulf Coast Region.

The regional stress field in the vicinity of a salt dome imposes far-field boundary stresses. Hence, an anisotropic regional stress field may be transmitted

128

to a salt dome from the surrounding country rock.

The regional stress field in the Gulf Coast Region is described by Zoback and Zoback (1980). Principal stress directions and stress regime data are derived from regional stress trends of active growth faults, focal mechanism solutions and in situ stress measurements. They concluded that the state of stress throughout the Gulf Coast stress province is quite uniform with the following general characteristics:

o The greatest principal stress is vertical
o The orientation of the least principal stress is perpendicular to the continental margin
o The magnitude of the least principal stress is 60 percent of the vertical stress

Most salt domes in the Gulf Coast Region exhibit near-circular horizontal cross sections (Halbouty 1979), implying isotropic horizontal stress. Some domes in the Gulf Coast Interior Basin (Vacherie, Richton, Rayburn's) have elliptical shapes that are aligned with the reported principal axes of respective regional stress field. Thoms, Mogharrebi and Gehle (1982a) suggested that the anisotropic regional stress field may have affected the emplacement (growth) of the domes and that the domes may still be subjected to an anisotropic regional stress transmitted from the country rock.

The suggestion of an anisotropic stress field in the salt stock caused by the stress state of the country rock is based on analyzing a salt dome as a geomechanical system that includes the country rock. Although rock salt is a plastic component of the system, the surrounding country rocks probably display elastic deformational characteristics. During domal growth, the salt stock is the most active component of the system while country rocks are the more passive components. The intruding salt might have imposed transformation of the adjoining sediments into the plastic state by pressurizing the sediments and the pore fluid in them. This is substantiated by the deformation of the sediments and the abundant presence of abnormal formation pressure at depth in the vicinity of salt stocks in the Gulf Coast Region. The zone of sediments in the plastic state outside a salt stock may still act as a geomechanical buffer to the intruding salt,

which may have preferentially used the preexisting regional stress anisotropy in the country rocks (as suggested by the elongate shape of the stock) to penetrate the sediments.

Conceivably, the prevailing regional stress field during the growth of a salt dome may affect the shape of a dome. The elongate horizontal cross section of a dome implies that the stress field adjacent to the dome at one time may have been, and perhaps still is, anisotropic. However, the existing data from the Gulf Coast Region do not provide conclusive evidence that the stress state in the interior of the dome is distinctly anisotropic thereafter. In this particular area the present does not hold the key to the past until credible methods are developed for absolute in situ stress measurements in the undisturbed portion of a salt stock.

3.5 Modeling Results

Various physical models, including scale-models with viscous media, have been used to simulate the formation and growth of salt domes (Parker and McDowell 1955, Ramberg 1963, Dixon 1975). These physical models were mostly concerned with the deformation and strain patterns produced during simulated, bouyancy-driven growth of model domes. Deformation patterns similar to those found inside and in the vicinity of salt domes were observed in the models. In general, hydrostatic stresses were assumed for physical models.

Earth Technology Corporation (1985) performed an axisymmetric, finite-element analysis of displacement and stress distribution during a simulated growth of an idealized salt dome. The objective was to evaluate whether unusual stress fields might develop during dome growth and, if so, where in the dome they could be expected. The model simulations showed that the change in stress imposed by dome growth would dissipate in a relatively short time. A maximum induced deviatoric stress of 4 MPa was seen after 13 years in one simulation – a substantial drop from the 50 MPa initially imposed by the discrete displacement at the base of the dome. All the simulations predicted that less than 10 percent of the induced stress remained after 100 years following a simulated dome growth.

The imposed stress for the model presents an extreme case when compared with estimates of differential (bouyant) pressure produced by the density contrast between the salt stock and surrounding sediments. Ode (1966) presented a cumulative curve of bouyancy-produced hydrostatic pressure difference at the bottom of the dome as a function of depth for the Gulf Coast Region. A maximum differential pressure of about 10 MPa was obtained, which is much lower than that imposed in the Earth Technology Corporation model.

The physical models assuming hydrostatic stresses and bouyancy-driven growth produced deformation patterns similar to internal structures seen in salt domes. Hence, hydrostatic stresses would not inhibit the development of the internal structures seen in salt domes. The numerical model shows a rapid dissipation of stresses. Therefore, under deviatoric stresses, rapid stress redistribution would occur according to the numerical model.

4 CONCLUSIONS

The reviewed direct and indirect information on the virgin in situ stress state in salt domes show certain consistencies. Based on these consistencies the following observations and conclusions are summarized:

1. The assumption of a near-hydrostatic state of stress appears to be a reasonable approximation of the virgin in situ stress conditions in salt domes, particularly at great depths. The assumption should be adequate for most mining applications. However, sensitive and long-lived facilities such as a high-level nuclear waste repository require credible absolute in situ stress data for the final design and performance assessment.

2. The maximum virgin in situ deviatoric stress in normal rock salt (halite), which generally makes up more than 95 percent of the domal salt mass, appears to be on the order of 1 to 2 MPa. This order of magnitude is indicated by the in situ stress measurement results in the domal salt mines in the Gulf Coast as well as recent data in bedded salt. It is also consistent with the postulated creep limit of salt, the deviatoric, stresses inferred from subgrain analyses mining experience and modeling results.

3. A higher deviatoric stress than 1 to 2 MPa may occur in association with the presence of impure rock salt, foreign salt materials and geologic structures.

4. Anisotropic regional stress conditions in the vicinity of a salt dome, although possibly governing the physical expression of the salt dome, appear to have little long-term effect on stress inside the dome. Regional stress conditions are not likely to impose a substantial anisotropic stress field within the dome. Relatively fast dissipation of imposed deviatoric stresses in rock salt is indicated by modeling data and geologic and mining observations.

5. The orientation of slightly anisotropic stress fields in salt stocks can probably be related to internal structures of the stocks (i.e., to features such as near-vertical layering, folding and sheared salt or included sediments, rather than the cross-sectional shape of the dome or the regional stress field.

6. The state of the art for absolute in situ stress measurments appears to be less applicable to rock salt than most non-evaporitic rock types. A current measuring error range of more than 1 MPa is not unrealistic.

5 DATA SOURCES

5.1 References

Baar, C.A. 1977. Applied Salt Rock Mechanics. Elsevier Scientific Publishing Co. Amsterdam.

Brown, E.T. and E. Hoek 1978. Trends in Relationships between Measured In-Situ Stresses and Depth. International Journal of Rock Mechanics, Mining Science and Geomechanics Abstracts. J15, N4:211-215.

Carter, N.L., F.D. Hansen and P.E. Senseny 1982. Stress Magnitudes in Natural Rock Salt. Journal of Geophysical Research. Volume 87(B11):8289-8300.

Dixon, J. 1975. Final Strain and Physical Deformation in Models of Diapiric Structures. Tectonophysics 28:89-124.

Doe, T., G. Boyce and E. Majer 1984. Laboratory Simulation of Hydraulic Fracturing Stress Measurements in Salt. Report prepared by Lawrence Berkeley Laboratory for Battelle Memorial Institute. Columbus.

Earth Technology Corporation 1985. A Study of Factors Affecting Rock Mass Conditions. Prepared for Battelle Memorial Institute. Columbus.

Gevantman, L.H. (editor) 1981. Physical Properties for Rock Salt. NBS Monograph 167. National Bureau of Standards (NBS). Washington.

Golder Associates 1977. Report to Gulf Interstate Engineering Company on the Geotechnical Study of the Cote Blanche Island Salt Mine. Prepared for U.S. Federal Energy Administration. Washington.

Halbouty, M.T. 1979. Salt Domes Gulf Coast Region, United States and Mexico. Gulf Publishing Co. Houston.

Hansen, F.D. 1985. Deformation Mechanisms of Experimentally Deformed Salina Basin Bedded Salt. BMI/ONWI-552. Prepared by Re/Spec Inc. for Battelle Memorial Institute. Columbus.

Hansen, F.D. and P.E. Senseny 1983. Salt Microstructures. RSI Publication No. 83-18. Prepared by Re/Spec Inc. for Solution Mining Research Institute. Woodstock.

Hiltscher, R., J. Martna, F.L. and L. Strindell 1979. The Measurement of Tri-axial Rock Stresses in Deep Boreholes and the Use of Rock Stress Measurements in the Design and Construction of Rock Openings. Proceedings 4th International Congress on Rock Mechanics. Volume 2:227-234.

Kupfer, D.H. 1978. Problems Associated with Anomalous Zones in Louisiana Salt Mines. Proceedings Fifth Symposium on Salt. Volume 1:119-134. Northern Ohio Geological Society Inc. Cleveland.

Lindner, E.N. and J.A. Halpern 1978. In-Situ Stress in North America, A Compilation. International Journal Of Rock Mechanics, Mining Science and Geomechanics Abstracts. Volume 15:183-203.

Obert, L. 1962. In-Situ Determination of Stress in Rock. Mining Engineering. Volume 14:51-58.

Ode, H. 1966. Review of Mechanical Properties of Salt Relating to Salt Dome Genesis. Diapirism and Diapirs. Geological Society of America Memoir 8:53-78. American Association of Petroleum Geologists. Tulsa (Oklahoma)

Parker, T.J. and A.N. McDowell 1955. Model Studies of Salt Dome Tectonics. Bulletin of the American Association of Petroleum Geologists. Volume 39(12):2384-2470.

Ramberg, H. 1963. Experimental Study of Gravity Tectonics by means of Centrifuged Modells, Geological Institution of Uppsala Bulletin 42:1-97

Tammemagi, H.Y., M.C. Loken, J.D. Osnes and R.A. Wagner 1981. Data Requirements for Site Characterization Repository Analysis. ONWI-369. Prepared by Re/Spec for Battelle Memorial Institute. Columbus.

Thoms, R.L. 1981. Borehole Closure in Salt Domes. Paper at the Solution Mining Research Institute's Fall Meeting.

Thoms, R.L. and R.M. Gehle 1986. Hydraulic Fracturing Tests in a Gulf Coast Salt Dome, A Progress Report On SMRI Project: Hydrofracture Gradients In Salt Domes. Spring Meeting Paper Technical Session: Hydrofracture Tests of U.S. Salt. Solution Mining Research Institute. Woodstock.

Thoms, R.L. and R.M. Gehle 1982. Experimental Study of Rocksalt for Compressed Air Energy Storage. Proceedings Rock Mechanics: Caverns and Pressure Shafts :991-1002. A.A. Balkema. Rotterdam.

Thoms, R.L. and M. Mogharrebi 1979. Borehole Closure in Salt Domes. Proceedings 20th U.S. Symposium on Rock Mechanics. Engineering Societies Library, New York

Thoms, R.L., M. Mogharrebi and R.M. Gehle 1982a. Borehole Closure in the Vacherie and Rayburn's Salt Domes. Prepared by the LSU Institute for Environmental Studies for Battelle Memorial Institute. Columbus.

Thoms, R.L., M. Mogharrebi and R.M. Gehle 1982b. Geomechanics of Borehole Closure in Salt Domes. Paper at the Gas Processors Association's Annual Meeting.

Wawersik, W.R. and C.M. Stone 1986. Stress Measurements in Rock Salt Using Hydraulic Fracturing. Spring Meeting Paper Technical Session: Hydrofracture Tests of U.S. Salt. Solution Mining Research Institute. Woodstock.

Wawersik, R.W. and C.S. Stone 1985. Application of Hydraulic Fracturing to Determine Virgin In Situ Stress State Around Waste Isolation Plant-In Situ Measurements. Sandia Report SAND85-1776. Sandia National Laboratories. Albuquerque (New Mexico).

Zoback, M.D. and M. Zoback 1980. State of Stress in the Conterminous United States. Journal of Geophysical Research. Volume 85(B11):6113-6156.

5.2 Bibliography

Abel, J.F. 1970. Rock Mechanics: Can It Pay Its Way? Proceedings Third Symposium on Salt. Volume 2:197-207.

Aughenbaugh, N.B. and M.W. Pullen 1970. Directional Hydrofracturing: Fact or Fiction? Proceedings Third Symposium on Salt. Volume 2:393-403.

Borchert, H. and R.O. Muir 1964. Salt Deposits: The Origin, Meatmorphism and Deformation of Evaporites. D. Van Nostrand Co. London.

Boucher, M., D. Boulanger, J.P. Saintives and P. Kuintz 1980. Lacunae and Inclusions in Halite from Valence and Bresse Saliferous Deposits. Proceedings Fifth Symposium on Salt. Volume 1:21-30. Northern Ohio Geological Society Inc. Cleveland (Ohio).

Bradshaw, R.L., F.M. Empson, W.J. Bogley Jr., H. Kubata, F.L. Parker and E.G. Struxness 1968. Properties of Salt Important in Radioactive Waste Disposal. Geological Society of America Inc. Special Paper 88:643-659.

Dix, R.O. and M.P.A. Jackson 1982. Lithology, Microstructures, Fluid Inclusion and Geochemistry of Rock Salt and of Cap Rock Contact in Oakwood Dome, East Texas. Texas Bureau of Economic Geology (TBEG) Report of Investigation No.120. Austin.

Doe, T. 1986. Laboratory Hydraulic Fracturing Experiments. Spring Meeting Paper Technical Session: Hydrofracture Tests of U.S. Salt. Solution Mining Research Institute (SMRI). Woodstock.

Flach, D., C. Frohn, B. Hente, M.W. Schmidt and E. Taubert 1984. Hydraulic Fracturing Experiments in Rock Salt with Seismic Fracture Location. Proceedings Field Measurements in Geomechanics. Volume 2:1331-1341. A.A. Balkema. Rotterdam.

Fossum, A.F. 1976. Structural Analysis of Salt Cavities Formed by Solution Mining: I. Method of Analysis and Preliminary Results for Spherical Cavities. Technical Memorandum Report RSI-0043. Prepared by Re/Spec Inc. for Oak Ridge National Laboratory. Oak Ridge.

Griswold, G.B. 1977. Solution Mining in Salt Domes of the Gulf Coast Embayments. PNL-3190. Prepared for Battelle Memorial Institute. Columbus.

Hoy, R.B., R.M. Foose and B.J. O'Neill Jr. 1962. Structure of Winnfield Salt Dome, Winn Parish, Louisiana. Bulletin of the American Association of Petroleum Geologists. Volume 46(8):1444-1459.

Jackson, M.P.A. 1985. External Shapes and Dynamics of Salt Structures. Prepared for Battelle Memorial Institute. Columbus.

Karably Jr., L.S., B.L. Jernigan, I.C. Petre and J.M. Sullivan 1983. Salt, Caprock, and Sheath Study. ONWI-355. Prepared for Battelle Memorial Institute. Columbus.

Kazemi, H 1963. Mechanism of Flow and Controlled Dissolution of Salt in Solution Mining. Ph. D. dissertation University of Texas. University Microfilms International. Ann Arbor.

Kovari, K (editor) 1983. Proceedings Field Measurements in Geomechanics. A.A. Balkema. Rotterdam.

Lamb, T.J. 1986. Stress Measurements in the Palo Duro Basin Texas Panhandle. Spring Meeting Paper Technical Session: Hydrofracture Tests of U.S. Salt. Solution Mining Research Institute. Woodstock.

Mullin, C.V. 1982. Salt Mineralogy and Geochemistry, Geology of the Caprock and Salt Stock of the Richton Salt Dome. Prepared for Battelle Memorial Institute. Columbus.

Nelson R.A. and J.E. O'Rourke 1986. Review of Hydraulic Fracturing Tests in Salt, Southeastern Utah, Compared to Other Recent Salt Testing Experience. Spring Meeting Paper Technical Session: Hydrofracture Tests of U.S. Salt. Solution Mining Research Institute. Woodstock.

Schwerdtner, W.M. and M.J. Morrison 1974. Internal-Flow Mechanism of Salt and Sylvinite in Anagance Diapiric Anticline near Sussex, New Brunswick. Proceedings Fourth Symposium on Salt. Volume 2:241-248. Northern Ohio Geological Society Inc. Cleveland.

Sellers, J.B. 1970. Rock Mechanics Instrumentation for Salt Mining. Proceedings Third Symposium on Salt. Volume 2:236-248. Northern Ohio Geological Society Inc. Cleveland.

Serata, S. 1983. Development of the Serata Stress-Measuring System for Application to Both Hard-Brittle and Soft-Ductile Grounds. Proceedings 24th U.S. Symposium on Rock Mechanics:249-279. Society of Mining Engineers. New York.

Wawersik, W.R. and D.H. Zeuch 1986. Modeling and Mechanistic Interpretation of Creep of Rock Salt Below 200 Degrees Celsius. Tectonophysics 121: 125-152.

Zoback, M.D. and B.C. Haimson (editors) 1983. Proceedings of a Workshop on Hydraulic Fracturing Stress Measurements. National Academy Press. Washington.

Features of tectonic stresses in rock masses and the rational location of openings

G.A. MARKOV
Polytechnical Institute of Higher Education, USSR

ABSTRACT

Tectonic stresses in rock masses are discussed. Analysis of 30000 measurements in mines is done, and four scale levels of space location of tectonically stressed rock masses are singled out. Independence of tectonic stresses from rock origin and absolute age of ore deposits is explained, a new approach to predicting stressed state and rock pressure is proposed.

RESUME

Sont envisagées les contraintes tectoniques des massifs rocheux. Sont examinées 30000 mesures séparées des contraintes dans les mines et sont mis en évidence quatre niveaux d'échelle de l'implantation dans l'espace des massifs en état de contrainte tectonique. On a fait des explications concernant l'indépendance de l'activité tectonique de la genèse des roches et de l'âge absolu des formations de minerai, on a présenté une nouvelle méthode des prévisions sur l'état de contrainte et la poussée des roches.

ZUSAMMENFASSUNG

Hieibei sind tektonische Beanspruchungen des Gebirges betrachtet, 30000 Einzelmessungen der Spannungen in Bergwerken ausgewertet und vier Maßstabsgrenzen der räumlichen Verteilung der tektonisch beanspruchten Massive festgestellt worden. Die Unabhängigkeit des tektonischen Spannungszustandes von der Genese der Gesteine sowie dem absoluten Alter der Erzbildungen ist geklärt und eine neue Methodik für die Vorhersage des Spannungszustandes und des Gebirgdruckes entwickelt worden.

This paper deals with tectonically stressed rock masses as ones characterized by the stressed state complicated by the effect of the stresses associated with the tectonic phenomena in the upper part of the Earth's crust, in addition to the stress caused by the sole weight of the overlying rock. The characteristics of the stress-strained state and rock pressure manifestation during excavation in such rocks differ from those in rock masses free from tectonic stresses.

.The characteristic feature of the tectonically stressed rock masses is the horizontal stresses (σ_h) exceeding the vertical ones (σ_v). This being true, in the general case the vertical stress (σ_v) agrees with the calculations from the bulk weight (γ) and with the height (H) of the overlying rock column. The rock pressure manifestation in workings driven in tectonically stressed rock masses takes place in the immediate vicinity of the surface (as if irrespective of the depth of the working), despite the high strength and solidity of the rock. Rock failure in excavations under high tectonic stresses takes on, as a rule, the form of rock bursts and bumps. The acting stresses are of the same order as the strength of the solid rock. Thus, the observations at a number of mines of the Kola peninsula showed that the rocks exhibiting the compressive strength ($\sigma_{compr.}$) in the samples up to 200 MPa failed actively, with rock bursts, under rock pressure during excavation. Rock pressure calculations with ordinary rock column weight showed that failures with bursts should occur at the depth about 2000 m below the surface (stress concentration around the working was not considered). Actually, such rock pressure manifestations were noted at the depth of 100 m below the surface, which means that the calculated values are twenty times as large as the actual ones. Further measurements in boreholes confirmed that relation.

The state of tectonic stress was discovered comparatively recently (in the late fifties - early sixties) as a result of measurements made in mines. Sine the effects of tectonic stresses are of great practical interest, this new trend in geomechanics has been rapidly developed. In 1973 in the USSR a special book was published by a body of authors, containing data which permitted the conclusion to be drawn as to rather extensive occurrence of rock tectonic stressed state. Among the generalizing works by foreign authors one can mark out the publications by Swedish researcher Hast, who was one of the first to begin stress measurements in a rock mass outside the zone of the excavation influence (Hast 1969).

At present it is proved and generally recognized that tectonic stressed state is characteristic of more than a half (60%) of all the mines situated in igneous rocks. In sedimentary, but highly metamorphic rocks this phenomenon has fewer occurrence and is observed in only 20% of the mines. In the remaining ones the stresses in rocks correspond to the weight of the overlying column. The theory and practice, however, still face important questions, such as what natural factors are related to the tectonic stress

phenomenon, and whether it is caused by the regional geotectonic state associated with the rock origin, structure, mechanical properties, depth, etc. More trustworthy answers to those questions will improve reliability of rock pressure prediction and efficiency of engineering solution when designing stable underground structures and supports.

The author of this paper has carried out such an analysis using the results of the measurements made by him in mines of the Kola peninsula, Middle Asia and East Europe, and those found in publications concerning stress determination in mines of these and other regions (Markov, Savchenko, 1984). About 30000 measurements have been analyzed. The analysis dealt with the connection of tectonic stresses with the following factors:

a) regional geotectonic condition of rock masses and mine field (shields and platforms with relatively quiet tectonic regime of the tectonically activated zones, tectonic movements of different signs, regions of strong blanket glaciation existing in recent geologic past, the absolute age of ore deposits);

b) peculiarities of mineral deposit location within large tectonic blocks, folds under tectonic movements of different signs (lifting, sinking, boundary and central zones of tectonic blocks, and folded structures close to and far from large geological faults);

c) geomorphologic conditions of the location of deposits and rock mass parts (in tops of mountains, above and below their bottoms, below valley floors, at similar and different absolute heights);

d) mechanical non-uniformity and difference in deformation of rock masses in correlation with difference in tectonic stress and depth below the surface.

The analysis of numerous results of determining stress and rock pressure manifestation enables one to single out several scale levels of tectonically stressed rock mass space location, with peculiar changes of value and direction (vertically and horizontally) and different rock pressure conditiones.

1. Regional geotectonic level with peculiar rock mass dimensions equal to hundreds and tens of kilometers.

2. Tectonic structural level of blocked type with peculiar dimensions of tectonic blocks and folds equal to kilometers and tens of kilometers.

3. Geomorphologic hilly structural level with peculiar dimensions equal to hundreds of meters and kilometers.

4. Local geomechanical level (rock masses with different physical and mechanical properties) with peculiar dimensions equal to meters, tens and hundreds of meters.

High horizontal stresses in a rock mass and "anomalous", rock pressure manifestations in excavations are in a regional plan assigned to the zones of rising Earth's crust movement irrespective of the rock origin, ore deposite age, tectonic type of the region (ancient shields, platforms, activation zones), and also irrespective of the existance of strong blanket glaciation in the geological past.

In tectonically stressed rock masses faults and expansion deformations are observed to develop according to three-dimensional grid in the horizontal and two vertical directions. The fault planes coincide (statistically) with those of the major principal stresses in the rock mass.

Within the geologically faulted zones consisting of crushed rocks and close to them tectonic stresses have minimum value.

In rock masses in the centre of rising tectonic structures high values of horizontal tectonic stresses are observed. Parts of rock masses with such high stresses are the nearest to the surface in the central zones of the rising tectonic blocks, while in the boundary zones of the blocks rock masses with high tectonic stresses are found at more considerable depth from the surface.

Accordingly, the boundary blocks are characterized by a high gradient of the change of horizontal stresses with depth, while the central zones - by a low one.

When the region is characterized by a hilly relief the highest horizontal stresses at the minimum depth are observed in rock masses below valley floors.

In the parts closer to the tops (higher local erosion bases) horizontal tectonic stress values are considerably smaller than those in the parts below the mountain bottoms. With this, the biggest horizontal compressive stress in the hilly parts is always parallel to the stretching mountain range irrespective of the direction of the biggest compression in the deep parts of the rock mass.

Parts with high horizontal stresses consist of the strongest elastic solid rocks. It is important to point out that the generalization of numerous experimental data obtained in tectonically stressed rock masses by various methods leads to the conclusion of higher values of the rock mass elastic parameters (such as modulus of elasticity, E, and elastic longitudinal wave propagation velocity, V_p) than the corresponding ones obtained in rock cores (the difference equals to 20-30%). That circumstance testifies of considerable potential energy accumulated in tectonically stressed rock masses.

Theoretical analysis shows that the stated experimental data and difference in tectonic stress fields are logically correlated effects of the model of tectonically stressed rock mass formation resulting from tectonic rising of the Earth's crust and denudation of the rising geologic structures.

Potential energy in the stressed rock mass of volume V at depth H depends on stresses σ_i and deformations E_i, which is expressed by the following:

$$P = \frac{1}{2} \int (v) \left(\sum_{i=1}^{6} \sigma_i E_i \right) d(v) \qquad (1)$$

With the Earth's crust rising, the rock mass moves to another level of gravitational stresses and is subjected to denudation. Due to those processes vertical stresses caused by the weight of rocks diminish. Potential energy P is realized in rock mass expansion, crack initiation, changes in rock properties. Irregularity and limitation of potential energy realization cause the conditions for formation of highly stressed (in relation to γ H) rock masses in the upper part of the Earth's crust. In those rock masses the horizontal components (σ_h) of the stress tensor can be much higher than the vertical ones (σ_v). Realization of those conditions depends on numerous factors: intensity of rising, time of stress relaxation in rock masses, structure of the rising blocks, hilliness of the relief, etc. According to geotectonics, time of relaxation of stresses accumulated deep in rocks ranges from tens of thousands to tens and hundreds of millions of years.

The analysis of these data shows that slow rising of the Earth's crust can with good reason be considered the source of energy of high horizontal stresses in rock masses.

That leads to the explanation of the independence of tectonic stresses from the rock origin and absolute age of ore deposits, which substantiates space assignment of tectonically stressed rock masses to the Earth's crust rising and definite regional division of mine fields according to the expected conditions of rock pressure manifestation. It must be emphasized, however, that in the zones with the Earth's crust rising there are also parts free from tectonic stress. From point of view of physics it can be explained by the difference in the conditions of stress relaxation between boundary and central parts of the blocks, between rock masses in the tops of mountains and below their bottoms and valley floors, as well as by the difference in rock viscosity.

Higher values of elastic parameters of tectonically stressed rock masses than those of rock cores also find explanation.

Both theoretical analysis and experimental data show that due to the realization of potential energy in tectonically stressed rock masses gradual (for geological time) expansion occur as well as opening of cracks according to three-dimensional grid corresponding to the planes of major horizontal and vertical stresses. The results obtained and the knowledge of tectonically stressed rock mass formation provided foundation for methods predicting stress state and rock pressure.

From rock pressure explanation was found for sharp differences conditions between:

a) neighbouring mines with deposits of the same origin situated at the same depth, but in different zones of tectonic blocks (central or boundary), the difference being 2-5 times;

b) neightbouring parts of the same deposit within the same minut differing in height: one situated in the hilly part above the erosion base, and the other below the valley floor, the difference amounting to several times with the depth change only in 50-100

c) neighbouring parts of the same mine horizon, where the difference in tectonic stresses with the change of rock mechanical properties is 2-3 and more times.

The information on tectonic stress distribution was successfully used in industrial experiments to test a number of deposits for reducing harmful rock pressure manifestation (Markov, Savchenko 1984). The tests proved that the axis orientation of long horizontal openings and chambers in the direction of the major horizontal stress results in increasing roof stability by 2-3 fold. For vertical openings the best is elliptical shape of the cross-section, providing the long axis of the ellipse is oriented in the direction of the asimuth of the major horizontal stress. In the case of the set of parallel vertical openings or the crossing of vertical and

horizontal ones the best is the
layout in the plane parallel to
the direction of the major horizontal stress.

REFERENCES

Hast, N. 1969. The State of Stresses in the Upper Part of the
Earth's Crust. Tectonophysics
8(3): 169-211.

Markov, G.A. and E.W. Kasparjan
1978. Erfassung der Strukturei-
genortigkeit und des Spanungszu-
standes des Felsgebiges bei Ermittlung der Standfestigkeit von
bergmännischen Hohlräumen. Rock
Mechanics 11: 43-49.

Markov, G.A. and S.N. Savchenko
1984. Napryazhennoye sostoyanye
porod i gornoe davlenie v struk-
turah goristogo relyefa."Nauka",
Leningrad.

Proceedings of the International Symposium on Rock Stress and Rock Stress Measurements/Stockholm/1-3 September 1986

Three-dimensional finite-element analysis of crustal stress field on a global scale

ZHANG XIAOPING, SHAO JIANGUO
Institute of Geomechanics, Chinese Academy of Geological Sciences, Beijing, China

ABSTRACT: Based on the linear elasticity theory, the three-dimensional finite-element method is used to calculate the crustal stress field. The three-dimensional nonuniformity not only along the earth's radius but also along the tangent of its meridian circle is considered in the calculation. The gravity (including the gravitation and the centrifugal inertial force) is taken for external load. As a result, the regularity that the horizontal and vertical stress varies with depth and latitude is known.

RESUME: La méthode d'éléments finis à trois dimensions, basée sur la théorie d'élasticité linéaire, a été appliquée, au calcul du champs des contraintes dans la croûte terrestre. Le résultat obtenu démontre la régularité de la variation des contraintes horizontales et verticales en fonction de la profondeur et de la latitude. Dans la calculation, la non-uniformité, existant non seulement au rayon de la Terre mais aussi à la tangente de la cercle de ses méridiens, a été prise en considération, la gravité (y compris la gravité terrestre et la force d'inerte centrifuge) et la température étant traitées en charges externes.

ZUSAMMENFASSUNG: Die Ungleichmäßigkeit der Erde hinsichtlich der Orientierung seines Radius und des Tangens seines Längenkreises erwogen, gilt die Effekt der Gravitation (einschließlich der Gravitation und Trägheit Kraft der Zentrifugal) und Temperatur als die externale Ladung. Auf Grund der linier-elastischen Theorie wird die Spannungsfeld der Krust mittls der Methods des drei-dimensionalen Finiteselements berechnet. Dadurch wird die Regal der horizontalen und vertikalen Spannung, die sich mit der Tiefe und Breite verändert, erhalten.

1. INTRODUCTION

Methods of studying crustal stress field are mainly as follows: in-situ measurement, seismic survey, mathematical simulation and approximation based on the results of geodetic survey and on lab data. They have their respective accuracy range and measuring-point effective depth within the nonuiform crust. In-situ method can only give the stress state at individual point within 5 Km below surface. Approximation method can only define the rough order of magnitude of the stress and, furthermore, their results are quite different (varying from 10 bars to 10 kbar) due to different models and assumptions used (Kanamori, 1980). Mathematical simulation is the most ideal method to get a general picture of the whole crustal stress field.

Considering that the earth is a nonuniform spheroid, the three-dimensional finite-element method is used to calculate the crustal stress field in this paper. Finally a general picture of the global stress state is given and its relation with plate tectonics is preliminarily explored.

2. CONSTRUCTION OF MODEL AND SELECTION OF DATA

The earth's crust is dominated by elastic deformation within 10^6—10^7 years (Murrell, 1976; Turcotte and Oxburgh,

1976; Wang Ren et al., 1982) and so a linear-elasticity mechanical model is used in this paper.

The earth is a complex spheriod acted upon by various forces. Considering the effects of the forces on the crust as a whole, it can be found that gravity load and temperature effect are two major factors causing tectonic stress and displacement (Hans, 1931; Beloussov, 1983; McNutt, 1980). This paper analyses the stress field under the influence of these two factors.

It is well known that the mass---geophysical field of the crust and mantle are not uniform not only along the earth's radius but also along the tangent of its meridian circle. This nonuniformity inevitably affects the stress field of the crust. We have considered the three-dimensional nonuniformity of the crust in the calculation.

A fix boundary condition is presumed, i.e. the displacement at the bottom of the crust is totally constrained. Assuming a thickness of 40 Km for the crust.

Consequently, what is dealt with in this paper is essentially a three-dimensional problem of nonuniform linear-elasticity mechanics, which can be solved only by the finite-element method. A standard finite-element equation is given by:

$$[K] \ [U] = [F] \qquad (1)$$

where $[F]$ is the matrix containing all loads acting on the structure given by:

$$[F] = [F_T] + [F_g] \qquad (2)$$

where $[F_T]$ is the thermal load. $[F_g]$ is the knot load transformed from gravity load on the basis of the principle of static equal effects. It includes F_1 and F_2:

$$F_1 = mg_p \qquad (3)$$

where g_p is the gravity acceleration at the two poles of the earth, it equals 983.22cm/s^2 (Fu Chengyi, 1976)

$$F_2 = mR\sin\phi \cdot \omega^2 \qquad (4)$$

where F_2 is the centrifugal inertial force. R is radius of the earth, it equals 6371 Km. ω is angular velocity of the rotation of the earth, it equals 7.29×10^{-5}/s (Fu Chengyi, 1976).

We have divided the whole crust into both seven geo-structure types (including ocean, continent, plateau area, mid-oceanic ridge, transform fault, sea-floor trench and triple junction; Fig. 1) along the tangent of the earth's meridian circle and two layers (including I Layer depths from 0 to 10 Km and II layer depths from 10 to 40 Km) along its radius. Parameters of them are listed in Table I. Mid-oceanic ridges, transform faults and sea-floor trenches are named abnormal zones, of which the dip angles are assumed to 90° except those of sea-floor trenches (presumed to be 45°), of which the widths are assumed to 0.2°.

Net of either of the layers is shown in Fig. 2. There are altogether 2158 real-body elements of hexahedron and pentahedron and 2985 knots. Each knot has three freedoms. Because the freedoms of knots at the bottom of the crust are all constrained, there are only 5970 freedom altogether.

3. STRESS STATE OF THE CRUST

43 pairs of real-body elements, corresponding above and below for each pair, have selected at random and their locations are shown in Fig.2.

Based on stress values of all the 86 elements and the results of in-situ stress measurement, the general trend of variation in stress is discussed below. All the equations given are derived by the leastsquares method. Tensile stress is taken negative and compressive stress is taken positive. 1 kbar is equal to 1×10^{2}MPa.

3.1 Tensile and Compressive Stresses

In-situ stress measurement suggests that the surficial layer of the crust is absolutely dominated by compressive stress (Hast, 1967, 1969), with tensile stress occurring only locally (near fracture or shatter zones). This verifies the results of our study and vice versa (Fig.3, 4, 5, 6, 7). It is inferred from geological data that on a global scale, tensile stress in the crust mainly occurs in rift and mid-oceanic ridge zones. The tensile stress in rift zones has been confirmed but that in mid-oceanic zones remains to be substantiated. Iceland

140

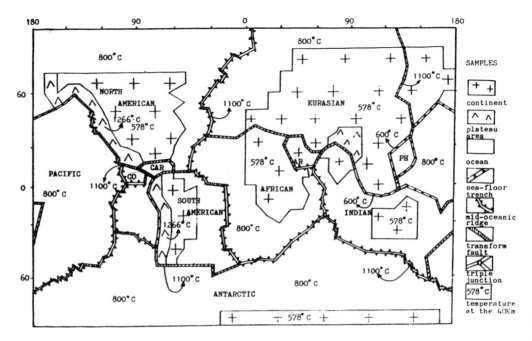

Abbreviations used in figure are: AR, Arania; CAR, Caribbean; CO, Cocos; PH, Philippine.

Fig.1. Geo-structure types in this study

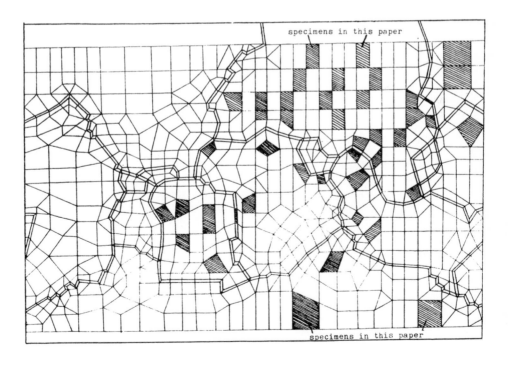

Fig.2. Finite element grid of either of the layers for the whole crust

Table I

Parameters in the computations

geo-structure types	0 Km	0 - 10 Km			10 Km		10 - 40 Km			40 Km	
	$T^{(1)}$ (°C)	P (g/cm³)	E (10¹⁰ dyne/cm²)	μ	$T^{(1)}$ (°C)	$\partial^{(3)}$ (10⁻⁵ °C⁻¹)	P (g/cm³)	E (10¹⁰ dyne/cm²)	μ	$T^{(1)}$ (°C)	$\partial^{(3)}$ (10⁻⁵ °C⁻¹)
ocean	0	2.840[2]	99.56[2]	0.260[2]	136	1.4	3.385[2]	93.34[4]	0.300[4]	800	1.4
mid-oceanic ridge	0	2.840	4.978[6]	0.260	272	1.4	3.385	4.667[6]	0.300	1100	1.4
transform fault	0	2.840	9.956	0.260	272	1.4	3.385	9.334	0.300	1100	1.4
triple junction	0	2.840	2.489	0.260	272	1.4	3.385	2.335	0.300	1100	1.4
sea-floor trench	0	2.900	4.978	0.260	69	1.4	3.500	177.3	0.264	600	1.4
plateau area	0	2.740	862.5	0.249	300	1.4	2.870	971.6	0.249	1266	1.4
continent	0	2.740[5]	86.25[5]	0.249[5]	150	1.4	2.870[5]	97.16[5]	0.249[3]	578	1.4

∂ : coefficient of thermal expansion

μ : Poisson's ratio

T : temperature

P : density

E : Young's modulus

(1)Fu Chengyi (1976)

(2)Press, F., Phys. Earth Inter., 3(1970), 3 - 22

(3)Chikuuchi Yoichiro (1977)

(4)Department of Gelogy and Geography, Beijing University (1982)

(5)Bolt, B.A. and Deer, J.S., Vista in Astron., 11(1969), 69 - 10

(6)$E_{mid-oceanic\ ridge} = 1/20\ E_{ocean}$ (Richardson et al., 1979)

is the only mid-oceanic ridge zones studied by in-situ stress measurement method. The measurement results suggest a comparatively high horizontal compressive stress within 600m below surface (Hast, 1967, 1969; Haimson and Voight, 1977; Haimson and Rummel, 1981), not a tensile stress as previously expected. Our calculation proves that tensile stress occurs extensively in mid-oceanic zones, up to hundreds of bars even at the depth of 25 Km. In areas outside mid-oceanic ridge zones, tensile stress only occurs locally at depth not exceeding 10 Km.

3.2 Vertical Stress

Fig. 3 shows the relation between vertical stress at different depths and latitude. In the upper crust, a linear increase of vertical stress may occur with the increase of latitude (Fig. 3). The linear regression equations for the relation of vertical stress at the depths of 2 and 10 Km to latitude are respectively as follows:

h = 2 Km $\delta_v = 0.468 + 0.007\varphi$

h = 10 Km $\delta_v = 1.768 + 0.030\varphi$

r = 0.172   s = 0.902   (5)

r = 0.582   s = 0.922   (6)

In the middle-lower crust, the magnitude of vertical stress is almost independent of latitude. The vertical stress at the depth of 25 Km is generally about 6.8 kbar.

Variation in vertical stress with latitude is related to the centrifugal inertial force caused by the earth's rotation. In the middle-lower crust, vertical stress almost does not change with latitude because the vertical stress associated with centrifugal inertial force is relatively low.

The dispersion of vertical stress(Fig.3) is related to the changes in geometrical and physical parameters of plate. The dispersion degree s reflects the magnitude of global additional vertical stress caused by changes in plate parameters, which is about 0.5-1 kbar.

In-situ stress measurements indicate that at the depths of 0-6 Km (depths of most measuring points being less than 2 Km), vertical stress increases with depth

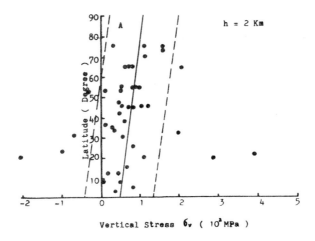

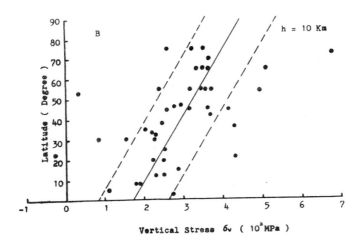

Fig. 3. The relation between vertical stress and latitude

A. at the depth of 2 Km
B. at the depth of 10 Km

and equals the load of overlying rocks, i.e.:

$$6_v = vh \qquad (7)$$

generally,

$$6_v = 0.27h \text{ (Brown and Hoek, 1978)} \quad (8)$$

Our calculation show that within the depth of 25 Km, vertical stress tends to increase in a linear way with depth. The linear regression equation is as follows:

$$6_v = 0.199 + 0.264h \quad r = 0.859$$

$$s = 1.510 \qquad (9)$$

Equation (9) is quite consistent with equation (8), indicating that in the middle-upper crust, vertical stress is mainly caused by the load of overlying rocks.

It shows that the relation between vertical stress and depth varies regularly with the change of latitude. The intercept a on 6_v axis in equation $6_v = a + bh$ increases and the slope b decreases from equator to the two poles (Fig. 4).

3.3 Latitudinal Horizontal Stress

This stress is not related to latitude and is about 0.513 kbar at the depth of 2 Km, about 1.833 kbar at the depth of 10 Km, about 2.878 kbar at the depth of 25 Km. The global latitudinal additional stress is 0.4 - 0.8 kbar caused by the changes in parameters of plate.

Like vertical stress, the latitudinal horizontal stress also tends to increase in a linear way with depth (Fig. 5). The linear regression equation is as follows:

$$6_\theta = 0.441 + 0.087h \qquad r = 0.703$$

$$s = 0.846 \qquad (10)$$

According to lateral constraint theory, horizontal stress is caused by the load of overlying rocks and controlled by lateral deformation, i.e.:

$$6_x = 6_Y = 6_z \qquad (11)$$
in which
$$\lambda = \frac{\mu}{1-\mu}$$

$$6_z = vh$$

Generally, μ is 0.25, v is 0.27, equation (11) thus may be changed as:

$$6_x = 6_Y = 1/3 \ 6_z = 0.09h \qquad (12)$$

Equation (12) is consistent with (10) and mainly related to the latitudinal horizontal stress in the middle-lower crust. The latitudinal horizontal stress in the middle-lower crust can be interpreted by the lateral constraint theory. The latitudinal horizontal stress in the upper crust is much greater than the stress value obtained from equation (12)

3.4 Longitudinal Horizontal Stress

Longitudinal horizontal stress is different from latitudinal horizontal stress. A horizontal stress associated with the earth's centrifugal inertial force must be related to latitude. In the upper crust, in contrast to the variation in vertical stress, longitudinal horizontal stress increases with the decrease of latitude (i.e. from the poles to the equator) (Fig. 6A,B). The linear regression equations at the depths of 2 and 10 Km are as follows:

h = 2 Km $\qquad 6_\phi = 1.172 - 0.010\phi$
h = 10 Km $\qquad 6_\phi = 3.953 - 0.030\phi$

r = -0.434 $\qquad$ s = 0.452 $\qquad$ (13)
r = -0.658 $\qquad$ s = 0.748 $\qquad$ (14)

In the middle-lower crust, longitudinal stress is almost independent of latitude, and about 2.7 kbar at the depth of 25 Km. The global longitudinal additional stress is 0.4 - 0.8 kbar caused by the changes in parameters of plate.

The longitudinal horizontal stress also tends to increase in a linear way with depth, the linear regression equation is:

$$6_\phi = 1.098 + 0.067h \qquad r = 0.525$$

$$s = 1.050 \qquad (15)$$

Equation (15) is basically consistent with (12). From this it can be seen that in the middle-lower crust, longitudinal horizontal stress is consistent with the lateral constraint theory. From the equator to the poles, a different relation between longitudinal horizontal stress and depth occurs (Fig.7) mainly represented by the decrease of intercept on 6_ϕ axis and increase of slope and of the correlation coefficient. At the two poles the relation between 6_ϕ and h is consistent with that between 6_θ and h.

It is notable that the longitudinal

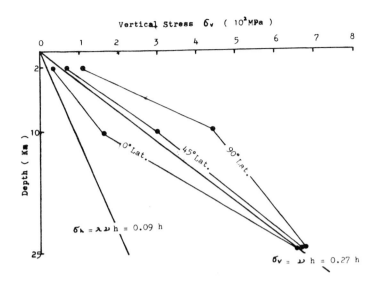

Fig. 4 The relation between vertical stress and depth below surface

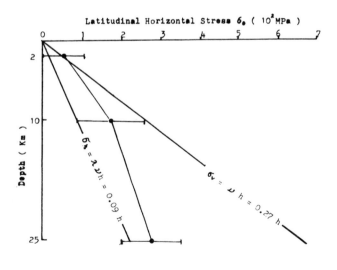

Fig. 5 The relation between latitudinal horizontal stress and depth below surface

145

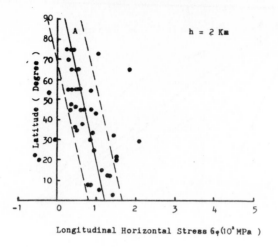

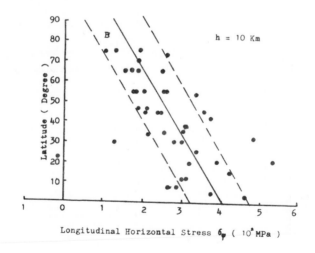

Fig. 6 The relation between longitudinal horizontal stress and latitude

A   at the depth of 2 Km
B   at the depth of 10 Km

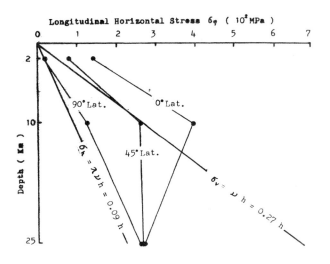

Fig. 7 The relation between longitudinal horizontal stress and depth below surface

horizontal stress in low–latitude areas is reversed, i.e. the longitudinal horizontal stress at the depth of 10 Km being greater than that at the depth of 25 Km. This implies a rather strong horizontal movement in the middle–upper crust in low–latitude areas.

4. CONCLUSIONS

A general picture of the crustal stress field is obtained through calculations by the use of a three-dimensional finite element method for a nonuniform spheroid. This stress field has the following characteristics:

1). Tensional stress occurs mainly in abnormal zones such as a mid–oceanic ridge area (occurring locally at the depth exceeding 25 Km) and its adjacent regions.

2). At the same depth, σ_v increases with the rise in latitude in the upper crust. At the same latitude, σ_v increases with the increase of depth.

3). At the same latitude, σ_h increases with the increase of depth. At the same

depth, σ_ϕ decreases with the rise in latitude in the upper crust.

4). In the upper crust, σ_h is far greater than the calculated values based on the lateral constraint theory, but σ_h corresponds to the calculated values in the middle–lower crust.

5). In the upper crust, high horizontal stress is widespread.

6). In the depth of the crust, no such static rock state as described by Heim exists. This state of stress occurs in particular portions in shallow crust and is related to tectonic stress.

ACKNOWLEDGEMENTS

The authors are particularly grateful to Prof. Pan Lizhou for the direction, to Mr. Ren Xiaohe for the help in calculation, and to Mr. Wang Lianjie for his support and encouragement to take up this work. Support for this compute was SAP6 current programme.

REFERENCES

Beloussov, V.V. (editor), 1983. Earth's Tectonosphere The Seisnological Press, Beijing. (in Chinese).

Brown, E. T. and E. Hoek, 1978. Trends In Relationships Between Measured In-Situ Stresses And Depth, Int. J. Rock Mech. Min. Sci. & Geomech. Abstr., 15 (4): 211 - 215.

Chikuuchi Yoichiro, 1977. Thermal Stress. The Science Press, Beijing. (in Chinese).

Department of Geology and Geography, Beijing University, 1982. Tectonic Stress Field (Section II). pp.59. (in Chinese).

Fu Chengyi, 1976. Ten Lectures on Earth. The Science Press, Beijing, pp. 58-93. (in Chinese).

Haimson, B.C. and B. Voight, 1977. Crustal stress in Iceland, Pure Apple.Geophys., 115: 153 - 190.

Haimson, B.C. and F. Rummel, 1982. Hydro-fracturing stress measurements in the IRDP at Reydarfjordur, Iceland, J.Geophys. Res., 87(B8).

Hans. R., 1981. Gravity, Deformation and the Earth's Crust. 2nd. Academic Press, London. pp. 20 - 28.

Hast,N., 1967. The State of Stresses in the Upper of the Earth's Crust, Eng. Geol., 2(1): 4-17.

Hast, N., 1969. The state of stresses in the Upper of the Earth's Crust, Tectonophysics, 8(3): 169 - 211.

Kanamori, H., 1980. Physics of the Earth's Interior. Italy, North-Holland Publishing Company, pp. 531 -554.

McNutt, M., 1980. Implications of Regional Gravity for State of Stress in the Earth's Crust and Upper Mantle, J.Geophys. Res., 85(B11): 6377 - 6396.

Murrell, S. A. F., 1976. Rheology of the Lithosphere --- Experimental Indication, Tectonophysics, 36: 5 - 24.

Richardson, R. M., S. C. Solomon and N. H. Sleep, 1979. Tectonic stress in the plate, Rev. Geophys. Space phys., 17(5): 981 -1019.

Turcotte, D. L. and E. R. Oxburgh, 19? Stress Accumulation in the Lithosphe? Tectonophysics, 35(1-3): 183 - 199.

Wang Ren and Ding Zhongyi, 1982. On the Possibility about the Variation of Earth's Rotation to Produce Tectonic Movements (a synopsis), Collection of Geomechanics, The Science Press, Beij (6): 193 -197. (in Chinese).

Proceedings of the International Symposium on Rock Stress and Rock Stress Measurements/Stockholm/1-3 September 1986

On ground stress measurement by borehole deformation method using a pre-pressed multiprobe unit of contact type

PAN LI-ZHOU
Shanghai Institute of Applied Mathematics and Mechanics, Shanghai, China

ABSTRACT

The use of a multiprobe unit for ground stress measurement is suggested in this paper. The working principle is analysed in detail and two fundamental formulas are derived therefrom, one for absolute and the other for relative stress measurements, which give the relationship between reduced displacements of contact points on the wall of a borehole and outputs of a physical quantity through probes of a measuring unit set in the borehole. Under certain assumptions the formulas are reducible to those rough ones which have long been adopted in the determination of ground stresses.

RESUME

Dans ce travail, l'utilisation d'unité de multisonde pré-pressée du type de contact pour mesurer la contrainte souterraine est proposée, le principe de fonctionnement est analysé en détail et deux formules fondamentales sont dérivées, l'une pour la mesure de la contrainte absolue et l'autre pour celle relative. Elles donnent la relation entre les déplacements réduits des points en contact avec le mur du forage et les valeurs de quantité physique donnée par sondes d'unité de mesure dans le forage. Avec certaines suppositions, les formules sont réduites en celles bien imprécises qui sont adoptées depuis longtemps à la détermination des contraintes souterraines.

ZUSAMMENFASSUNG

Ein vorgepreßtes Mehr-Kontaktpunkt Element zum Messen der Grundspannung wird hier empfohlen und dabei wird eine Analyse über dessen Funktionsweise in Detail ausgeführt. Daraus leiten sich zwei fundamentale Formeln ab: die eine für die absolute und die andere für die relative Messung der Grundspannung. Damit wird die Beziehung zwischen den reduzierten Verschiebungen der Kontaktpunkte an der Bohrungswand und den durch die Sonden des Messungselementes in der Bohrung ausgeführten Werten einer physikalischen Quantität gegeben. Unter gewissen Annahmen werden die seit langem in der Messungen der Grundspannung angewendeten ungenauen Formeln von diesen zwei Formeln reduziert.

1. INTRODUCTION

For determining ground stress by borehole deformation method, it is necessary to know three radial displacements u of three points of the borehole wall when no external force is acting on the wall. For this purpose, a measuring unit having three probes of contact type in different diametral directions is usually installed in the hole. The probes are essentially transducers, so each of them can take in a displacement u and give out a certain physical quantity L . The probes in the hole are pre-pressed so as to keep firmly in contact with the wall. They have well calibrated in advance so that we can use them to record three reduced displacements $S_i \equiv \eta u_i$, $i = 1,2,3$, where η is a reduction coefficient: $\eta = E/a$ when the measuring site in the hole is near the earth's surface, and $\eta = E/(1-\nu^2)a$ when the site is in the depth of the hole. Here a is the radius of the hole, and E and ν are Young's modulus and Poisson's ratio of the rock mass respectively. The magnitudes and directions of the ground stresses σ are calculated from the three recorded S_i, $i=1,2,3$, by using formulas drived from the theory of elasticity (Pan, 1980).

In order to diminish accidental errors and to get more reliable values of ground stresses, we had better record reduced displacements of as many points as possible of the wall in different directions and then apply data processing techniques. A multiprobe unit of contact type will serve the purpose.

It is common practice to ignore effects of contact pressures, overcoring diameter and intercoupling between probes as well as in rock mass. Obviously, that will introduce additional errors in the results. In a previous paper (Pan, 1984), we have considered the first two effects in the case of a single probe. The aim of this paper is to give a detailed analysis on the mechanics of a multiprobe unit, taking these three effects into account. Two fundamental formulas are derived, which reveal the proper relationship between the reduced displacements and the physical quantity outputs, and which are valid no matter whether the probes in the hole are placed on the same level or on different levels.

2. BASIC FORMULA FOR ABSOLUTE STRESS MEASUREMENT

Suppose we have an infinitely

large rock mass in uniform state of stress σ . Drill a hole of radius a in it, the stress at infinity being undisturbed by the hole according to the Saint-Venant's principle (Fig. 1). If the external forces at infinity be removed at that time, the rock mass would come to its stress-free state (Fig. 2). The radial displacement u of the borehole wall during the change of state from this shown in Fig. 2 to that shown in Fig. 1, multiplied

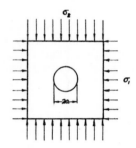

Fig. 1   Rock mass with a borehole

Fig. 2   Rock mass in stress-free state

by the reduction coefficient η , gives the required reduced displacement S . Put a measuring unit having n probes into the hole and pre-press them so that they are firmly in contact with the wall at n pairs of points denoted by 1-1, 2-2, ..., n-n as shown in Fig. 3. Their initial contact pressures are assumed to be $P_1^o, P_2^o, \cdots, P_n^o$ respectively and may be writter as a column vector

$$\boldsymbol{P}^o \equiv [\, P_1^o, P_2^o, \cdots, P_n^o \,]^T$$

called initial contact pressure vector. The symbol $[\ ]^T$ denotes

150

the transpose of the matrix $[\ \ ]$.

Outputs of a physical quantity L by the probes in response to contact pressures $P_1, P_2, \cdots, P_n$ are denoted by $L_1, L_2, \cdots, L_n$ respectively. They may likewise be written as column vectors:

$$\boldsymbol{p} \equiv [P_1, P_2, \cdots, P_n]^T$$

called contact pressure vector and

$$\boldsymbol{l} \equiv [L_1, L_2, \cdots, L_n]^T$$

called output vector. Without loss of generality, we shall reckon the output vector in response to the initial pressure vector as a zero vector.

The state shown in Fig. 3 can be reached in another way as follows: The lengths of the probes in the measuring unit are made to exceed the diameter $2a$ of the hole by amounts $2\delta_i$, $i=1,2,\ldots,n$, such that when the unit is forced into the hole in Fig. 1, there results a state which is exactly the same as in Fig. 3. Let the

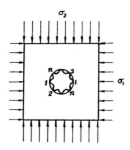

Fig. 3 A multiprobe unit in the borehole

radial displacements of the probes at the contact points in this state be u°_{ci}, $i=1,2,\ldots,n$, and those of the wall at the same points be u°_{wi}, $i=1,2,\ldots,n$. They may be written as column vectors:

$$\boldsymbol{u}^\circ_c \equiv [u^\circ_{c1}, u^\circ_{c2}, \cdots, u^\circ_{cn}]^T$$

and

$$\boldsymbol{u}^\circ_w \equiv [u^\circ_{w1}, u^\circ_{w2}, \cdots, u^\circ_{wn}]^T$$

Besides these vectors we introduce another column vector

$$\boldsymbol{\delta} \equiv [\delta_1, \delta_2, \cdots \delta_n]^T$$

called half-length excess vector.

From the theory of elasticity, we have

$$\boldsymbol{p}^\circ = -2\boldsymbol{K}_c\boldsymbol{u}^\circ_c \quad \text{or} \quad \boldsymbol{u}^\circ_c = -\tfrac{1}{2}\boldsymbol{K}_c^{-1}\boldsymbol{p}^\circ \quad (1)$$

and

$$\boldsymbol{p}^\circ = 2\overset{\infty}{\boldsymbol{K}}_w\boldsymbol{u}^\circ_w \quad \text{or} \quad \boldsymbol{u}^\circ_w = \tfrac{1}{2}\overset{\infty}{\boldsymbol{K}}_w^{-1}\boldsymbol{p}^\circ \quad (2)$$

where

$$\boldsymbol{K}_c \equiv [K_{cij}], \quad i,j = 1,2,\ldots,n,$$

is the stiffness matrix of the measuring unit, and

$$\overset{\infty}{\boldsymbol{K}}_w \equiv [\overset{\infty}{K}_{wij}], \quad i,j = 1,2,\ldots,n,$$

is the stiffness matrix of the rock mass that has been assumed to be infinitely large in size. The superscript -1 attached to a matrix indicates the inverse of the matrix.

The equations of compatibility for displacements at the contact points are

$$\boldsymbol{u}^\circ_w - \boldsymbol{u}^\circ_c = \boldsymbol{\delta} \quad (3)$$

From Eqs. (1), (2) and (3), we obtain

$$\boldsymbol{p}^\circ = 2(\overset{\infty}{\boldsymbol{K}}_w^{-1} + \boldsymbol{K}_c^{-1})\boldsymbol{\delta} \quad (4)$$

and

$$\boldsymbol{u}^\circ_c = -(\overset{\infty}{\boldsymbol{K}}_w^{-1}\boldsymbol{K}_c + \boldsymbol{I})^{-1}\boldsymbol{\delta} \quad (5)$$

where $\boldsymbol{I}$ denotes unit matrix.

For determining absolute ground stresses, we have to overcore the rock mass in Fig. 3 around the borehole with a core-drill. Suppose the coring diameter is $2b$ $(b > a)$. After overcoring, a tubelike rock core of inner radius a and outer radius b is isolated from the surrounding rock mass (Fig. 4) and then the measuring unit indicates that the physical quantity output vector is $\boldsymbol{l}^r$:

$$\boldsymbol{l}^r \equiv [L^r_1, L^r_2, \cdots L^r_n]^T$$

151

Fig. 4   Tubelike rock core
from overcoring

where L_i^r is the output given by the i-th probe, $i = 1, 2, \ldots, n$.

The state shown in Fig. 4 can be reached in the following way: If the measuring unit be removed from the rock tube, the tube would be in stress-free state and the distance between the i-th pair of points, $i-i$, would be $2(a - u_i)$, $i = 1, 2, \ldots, n$. The distances of all pairs of points 1-1, 2-2, $\ldots$, n-n may be expressed in matrix form $2(a\mathbf{I} - \mathbf{u})$. The lengths $2(a\mathbf{I} + \boldsymbol{\delta})$ of the probes in the measuring unit would then exceed these distances by amounts $2(\boldsymbol{\delta} + \mathbf{u})$. On forcing the measuring unit into the hole of the tube so that the i-th probe be made in contact with the i-th pair of points on the inner wall of the tube, $i = 1, 2, \ldots, n$, we would obtain the state of the system just the same as shown in Fig. 4.

Let the contact pressure vector between the probes and the inner wall in this state be

$$\boldsymbol{P}^r \equiv [P_1^r, P_2^r, \cdots, P_n^r]^T$$

and the radial displacement vector of the probes at the contact points be

$$\boldsymbol{u}_c^r \equiv [u_{c1}^r, u_{c2}^r, \cdots, u_{cn}^r]^T$$

Since this case is quite similar to that discussed above, we can make direct use of Eqs. (4) and (5), except for some modifications, to find $\boldsymbol{P}^r$ and $\boldsymbol{u}_c^r$ as follows:

$$\boldsymbol{P}^r = 2(\check{\boldsymbol{K}}_w^{-1} + \boldsymbol{K}_c^{-1})^{-1}(\boldsymbol{\delta} + \boldsymbol{u}) \qquad (6)$$

and

$$\boldsymbol{u}_c^r = -(\check{\boldsymbol{K}}_w^{-1}\boldsymbol{K}_c + \boldsymbol{I})^{-1}(\boldsymbol{\delta} + \boldsymbol{u}) \qquad (7)$$

where

$$\check{\boldsymbol{K}}_w \equiv [\check{K}_{wij}], \qquad i, j = 1, 2, \ldots, n,$$

is the stiffness matrix of the rock tube.

Suppose the probes in the measuring unit can convert their radial displacements $\boldsymbol{u}_c$ into physical quantity outputs $\boldsymbol{l}$ according to the law:

$$\boldsymbol{u}_c - \boldsymbol{u}_c^o = \boldsymbol{A}\boldsymbol{l}$$

or

$$\boldsymbol{l} = \boldsymbol{A}^{-1}(\boldsymbol{u}_c - \boldsymbol{u}_c^o) \qquad (8)$$

where

$$\boldsymbol{A} \equiv [\alpha_{ij}], \qquad i, j = 1, 2, \ldots, n,$$

is the matrix of conversion cofficients and the output vector in response to $\boldsymbol{P}^o$ and hence to $\boldsymbol{u}_c^o$ has been reckoned as a zero vector.

Since $\boldsymbol{l} = \boldsymbol{l}^r$ when $\boldsymbol{u}_c = \boldsymbol{u}_c^r$, on substituting into Eq. (8) we have

$$\boldsymbol{l}^r = \boldsymbol{A}^{-1}(\boldsymbol{u}_c^r - \boldsymbol{u}_c^o) \qquad (9)$$

From Eqs. (4), (5), (7) and (9), it follows that

$$\boldsymbol{u} = \frac{1}{2}(\check{\boldsymbol{K}}_w^{-1} + \overset{\infty}{\boldsymbol{K}}_w^{-1})\boldsymbol{P}^o$$
$$- (\check{\boldsymbol{K}}_w^{-1}\boldsymbol{K}_c + \boldsymbol{I})\boldsymbol{A}\boldsymbol{l}^r \qquad (10)$$

When multiplied by the reduction coefficient η, it yields the required basic formula

$$\boldsymbol{S} = \eta\left\{\frac{1}{2}(\check{\boldsymbol{K}}_w^{-1} + \overset{\infty}{\boldsymbol{K}}_w^{-1})\boldsymbol{P}^o - (\check{\boldsymbol{K}}_w^{-1}\boldsymbol{K}_c + \boldsymbol{I})\boldsymbol{A}\boldsymbol{l}^r\right\} \qquad (11)$$

where

$$\boldsymbol{S} \equiv [S_1, S_2, \cdots S_n]^T = \eta\boldsymbol{u}$$

called reduced displacement vector.

From this basic formula, it is seen that the reduced

displacements not only depend upon the physical quantity outputs but also upon the initial contact pressures, the coversion coefficients of the probes, and the stiffness matrices of the measuring unit, the rock mass and the rock tube.

3. BASIC FORMULA FOR RELATIVE STRESS MEASUREMENT

In determining relative ground stresses, we drill a hole in the rock mass, put a multiprobe unit into the hole and pre-press the probes as before, but we need not go on to overcore the rock mass. What we are necessary to do next is to record the physical quantity outputs of the probes at subsequent times. Without loss of generality, we shall reckon the time as time zero when the probes are pre-pressed under the initial contact pressures $\boldsymbol{p}°$.

Suppose the state of stress at infinity of the rock mass at time zero is $\boldsymbol{\sigma}$ and it becomes $\boldsymbol{\sigma}+\boldsymbol{\sigma}'$ at time t', where $\boldsymbol{\sigma}'$ represents a change in state of stress. Let the contact pressures at time t' be

$$\boldsymbol{p}' = [\, P_1',\, P_2',\, \cdots, P_n'\,]^T$$

and the radial displacements of the probes at the contact points be

$$\boldsymbol{u}_c' = [\, u_{c1}',\, u_{c2}',\, \cdots, u_{cn}'\,]^T$$

The state of the system at time t' can be reached in another way as follows: If at time t' the measuring unit be removed from the borehole, the distances of $\boldsymbol{n}$ pairs of points 1-1, 2-2, ..., n-n would be $2[a\boldsymbol{I}+\boldsymbol{u}(\sigma')]$, where $\boldsymbol{u}(\sigma')$ represents the radial displacements at points 1, 2, ..., n of the bore hole wall when the hole is empty and the external forces at infinity are such that the state of stress produced there is $\boldsymbol{\sigma}'$. The lengths $2[a\boldsymbol{I}+\boldsymbol{\delta}]$ of the probes in the measuring unit would then exceed the distances of all pairs of points 1-1, 2-2, ..., n-n of the wall by amounts $2[\boldsymbol{\delta}-\boldsymbol{u}(\sigma')]$. On forcing the measuring unit into

the hole so that the $\boldsymbol{i}$-th probe be made in contact with the $\boldsymbol{i}$-th point of the hole, we would obtain the state of the system shown in Fig. 4. Making direct use of Eqs. (4) and (5), except for some necessary changes, we obtain

$$\boldsymbol{p}' = 2(\overset{\infty}{\boldsymbol{K}}_w^{-1}+\boldsymbol{K}_c^{-1})^{-1}[\boldsymbol{\delta}-\boldsymbol{u}(\sigma')] \qquad (12)$$

and

$$\boldsymbol{u}_c' = -(\overset{\infty}{\boldsymbol{K}}_w^{-1}\boldsymbol{K}_c+\boldsymbol{I})^{-1}[\boldsymbol{\delta}-\boldsymbol{u}(\sigma')] \qquad (13)$$

Let the physical quantity output of the $\boldsymbol{i}$-th probe at time t' be L_i', $i=1,2,\ldots,n$. They may be arranged as a column vector, that is,

$$\boldsymbol{l}' \equiv [\, L_1',\, L_2',\, \cdots, L_n'\,]^T$$

From Eq. (8), noting that $\boldsymbol{l}=\boldsymbol{l}'$ when $\boldsymbol{u}_c=\boldsymbol{u}_c'$, we have

$$\boldsymbol{l}' = \boldsymbol{A}^{-1}(\boldsymbol{u}_c'-\boldsymbol{u}_c°) \qquad (14)$$

By substituting Eqs, (5) and (13) into this equation, we obtain

$$\boldsymbol{l}' = \boldsymbol{A}^{-1}(\overset{\infty}{\boldsymbol{K}}_w^{-1}\boldsymbol{K}_c+\boldsymbol{I})^{-1}\boldsymbol{u}(\sigma') \qquad (15)$$

Suppose at another time t"(>t'), the state of stress at infinity of the rock mass becomes $\boldsymbol{\sigma}'+\boldsymbol{\sigma}''$ and the physical quantity outputs become

$$\boldsymbol{l}'' = [\, L_1'',\, L_2'',\, \cdots L_n''\,]^T$$

In like manner, we can obtain

$$\boldsymbol{l}'' = \boldsymbol{A}^{-1}(\overset{\infty}{\boldsymbol{K}}_w^{-1}\boldsymbol{K}_c+\boldsymbol{I})^{-1}\boldsymbol{u}(\sigma'') \qquad (16)$$

Subtracting Eq.(15) from Eq.(16) and introducing $\Delta\boldsymbol{l}\equiv\boldsymbol{l}''-\boldsymbol{l}'$ called incremental outputs of the physical quantity and $\Delta\boldsymbol{\sigma}\equiv\boldsymbol{\sigma}''-\boldsymbol{\sigma}'$ callled incremental state of stress at infinity of the rock mass, we have

$$\Delta\boldsymbol{l} = \boldsymbol{A}^{-1}(\overset{\infty}{\boldsymbol{K}}_w^{-1}\boldsymbol{K}_c+\boldsymbol{I})^{-1}[\boldsymbol{u}(\sigma'')-\boldsymbol{u}(\sigma')] \qquad (17)$$

According to the theory of elasticity we know

$$u(\sigma'')-u(\sigma')=u(\Delta\sigma)$$

On substituting into Eq. (17), we obtain

$$\Delta l = A^{-1}(\overset{\infty}{\check{K}}{}_w^{-1}K_c+I)^{-1}u(\Delta\sigma)$$

or

$$u(\Delta\sigma)=(\overset{\infty}{\check{K}}{}_w^{-1}K_c+I)A\Delta l \qquad (18)$$

Multiplying both sides of this equation by the reduction coefficient η and introducing

$$\Delta S \equiv [\Delta S_1,\Delta S_2,\cdots,\Delta S_n]^T = \eta u(\Delta\sigma) \qquad (19)$$

called incremental reduced displacement vector, we obtain the basic formula

$$\Delta S = \eta(\overset{\infty}{\check{K}}{}_w^{-1}K_c+I)A\Delta l \qquad (20)$$

where ΔS_i represents the incremental reduced displacement of the i-th contact point of the wall, $i=1,2,\ldots,n$.

From Eq. (20), we can see that the incemental reduced displacements do not depend on the initial contact pressures, although they still depend on the incremental outputs of the physical quantity, the conversion coefficients of the probes and the stiffness matrices of the measuring unit and the rock mass.

4. SPECIAL CASES

If the probes in the measuring unit are mutually independent, then both the stiffness matrix K_c and the conversion matrix A reduce to diagonal matrices $D(K_{ci})$ and $D(\alpha_i)$ respectively , that is ,

$$K_c \equiv [K_{ij}] = D(K_{ci})$$

and

$$A \equiv [\alpha_{ij}] = D(\alpha_i)$$

where

$$K_{ci}\equiv K_{cii} \text{ and } \alpha_i\equiv\alpha_{ii}, \quad (\text{not summed}),$$
$$i = 1,2,\ldots,n$$

From linear algebra, it follows that

$$K_c^{-1} = D(K_{ci}^{-1})$$

and

$$A^{-1} = D(\alpha_i^{-1}), \qquad i = 1,2,\ldots,n$$

With probes of this kind, Fomulas (11) and (20) become

$$S = \eta\left\{\tfrac{1}{2}(\overset{\infty}{\check{K}}{}_w^{-1}-\overset{\infty}{\check{K}}{}_w^{-1})p^\circ\right.$$
$$\left.-[\overset{\infty}{\check{K}}{}_w^{-1}D(K_{ci})+I]D(\alpha_i)l^r\right\} \qquad (21)$$

and

$$\Delta S = \eta[\overset{\infty}{\check{K}}{}_w^{-1}D(K_{ci})+I]D(\alpha_i)\Delta l \qquad (22)$$

If, besides this, the coupling effects of the rock mass and the rock tube are neglected, then their stiffness matrices $\overset{\infty}{\check{K}}{}_w$ and $\check{K}_w$ reduce to diagonal matrices $D(\overset{\infty}{\check{K}}{}_{wi})$ and $D(\check{K}_{wi})$ respectively, that is ,

$$\overset{\infty}{\check{K}}{}_w \equiv [\overset{\infty}{\check{K}}{}_{wij}] = D(\overset{\infty}{\check{K}}{}_{wi})$$

and

$$\check{K}_w \equiv [\check{K}_{wi}] = D(\check{K}_{wi})$$

where

$$\overset{\infty}{\check{K}}{}_{wi}\equiv\overset{\infty}{\check{K}}{}_{wii} \text{ and } \check{K}_{wi}\equiv\check{K}_{wii},(\text{not summed}),$$
$$i = 1,2,\ldots,n,$$

Both the inverse of $\overset{\infty}{\check{K}}{}_w$ and that of $\check{K}_w$ are also diagonal matrices. They are

$$\overset{\infty}{\check{K}}{}_w^{-1} = D(\overset{\infty}{\check{K}}{}_{wi}^{-1})$$

and

$$\check{K}_w^{-1} = D(\check{K}_{wi}^{-1})$$

Under this condition, Formulas (21) and (22) reduce further to

$$S = \eta\left\{\tfrac{1}{2}[D(\check{K}_{wi}^{-1})-D(\overset{\infty}{\check{K}}{}_{wi}^{-1})]p^\circ\right.$$
$$\left.-[D(\check{K}_{wi}^{-1})D(K_{ci})+I]D(\alpha_i)l^r\right\} \qquad (23)$$

and

$$\Delta \mathbf{S} = \eta [\mathbf{D}(\overset{\infty}{\check{K}}{}_{wi}^{-1})\mathbf{D}(K_{ci}) + \mathbf{I}]\mathbf{D}(\alpha_i)\Delta \boldsymbol{l} \qquad (24)$$

which are equivalent to the following formulas in scalar quantities:

$$S_i = \eta \left\{ \frac{1}{2} (\check{K}_{wi}^{-1} - \overset{\infty}{\check{K}}{}_{wi}^{-1}) P_i^\circ \right.$$

$$\left. - \alpha_i (\check{K}_{wi}^{-1} K_{ci} + 1) L_i^r, \quad i = 1, 2, \dots, n \right. \qquad (25)$$

and

$$\Delta S_i = \eta \alpha_i (\overset{\infty}{\check{K}}{}_{wi}^{-1} K_{ci} + 1)\Delta L_i, \quad i = 1, 2, \dots, n \qquad (26)$$

By comparing these formulas with Formulas (11) and (20), it can be seen that these two sets of formulas are of the same structure, but they contain quantities of different type. The former set is in matrix form reflecting the coupling mechanism in the measuring unit as well as in the rock mass, while the latter is in scalar form which reflects that no coupling exists in them.

If one probe alone is considered, we would drop the superscript r and the subscript i , and thus we get two formulas that are consistent with those obtained in the previous paper (Pan, 1984)

If the effects of the initial contact pressures P_i°, $i = 1, 2, \dots, n$, are neglected, Formula (25) becomes

$$S_i = -\alpha_i (\check{K}_{wi}^{-1} K_{ci} + 1) L_i^r, \quad i = 1, 2, \dots, n \qquad (27)$$

If the probes are very compliant, then $K_{ci} = 0$ as well as $P_i^\circ = 0$, $i = 1, 2, \dots, n$, and therefore Formulas (25) and (26) become

$$S_i = -\eta \alpha_i \Delta L_i^r \qquad (28)$$

and

$$\Delta S_i = \eta \alpha_i \Delta L_i$$

These are two simplified and hence unaccurate formulas which have so far been used in ground stress or rock stress measurements.

5. DISCUSSION

If any two of the contact points are not far apart, the coupling effect of the rock mass is so significant that it must be taken into account. This is often the case in practice since the measuring borehole is usually small and there must be placed in it at least three probes.

The basic formulas (11) and (20) are also valid for the case when the borehole has an inner lining or when the measuring unit has an outer covering. In these cases, the only thing important is to use proper stiffness matrices of these systems, which can readily be calculated by the finite element method.

There are two methods for calibrating a probe: the one is due to Hast, the specimen being a rectangular rock block with a drill hole and under uniaxial compression (Hast, 1958), and the other has developed in China, the specimen being a rock tube under confining pressure. The rock tube is the very rock core left in the borehole in situ after overcoring. The author has drawn some conclusions by comparing both of the two calibration methods and has made a detailed analysis on the mechanics of the whole process of measuring ground stress including the procedure of probe calibration (Pan, 1981; 1984).

From the results obtained in this paper and the previous paper, it can be concluded that the rough formulas so far used in practical work are based on the following assumptions:

1. All contact points scatter mutually far apart.
2. The initial contact pressures are negligibly small.
3. The probes are very compliant and work independently from each other.
4. There is no coupling in the rock mass, that is, the responses of the rock mass to the contact pressures due to the probes are mutually independent.
5. The overcoring diameter is infinitely large.
6. The rock specimen for probe calibration is infinitely large in size.

155

7. The specimen in laboratory has the same elastic properties as the rock mass in the measuring site.
8. The measuring unit used in laboratory has the same performance as that used in the measuring site.

Obviously these assumptions will lead into the results considerable errors. The magnitudes of these errors can be estimated with the formulars obtained in the two papers.

The in-situ determination of elastic coefficients, E and ν, is of great importance to the ground stress measurement by borehole deformation method. Stephansson devised an equipment called sleeving fracturing system for this purpose (Stephansson, 1983). Pan suggested a method for the same purpose, using the same borehole, the same stress relief groove and the same apparatus at the same time when they were used for in-situ stress measurement (Pan, 1985)

How to determine the initial contact pressures $P°$ remains a problem to be solved.

In the inclusion techniques for measuring ground stresses (Duncan Fama,1979; Duncan Fama and Pender, 1980), the inclusion is essentially a coupled multiprobe measuring unit. It is a limiting case, for it can be imagined to be a unit having uncountably infinite number of probes.

We are coding computer programs for calculating the stiffness $\overset{\approx}{K}_w, \overset{\smile}{K}_w, \hat{K}_w, K_c$ and another stiffness $\hat{\beta}*$ that appear in this paper and the previous paper (Pan, 1984).

6. REFERENCES

Duncan Fama,M.E. 1979. Analysis of a solid inclusion in situ stress measuring device. Proceedings of the 4th international Congress on Rock Mechanics. Montreux. 2 : 113-120.

Duncan Fama, M.E. and M.J. Pender 1980. Analysis of the hollow inclusion techniques for measuring in situ rock stress. International Journal of Rock Mechanics and Mining Sciences & Geomechanics Abstracts 17: 137-146.

Hast, N. 1958. The measurement of ro pressure in mines. Sveriges Geolgiska Undersökning. Ser.C, Avhandlingar Och Uppsatser,No.560 Årsbok 52, No.3.

Pan, L.Z. 1980. On measurements of ground stress and strain component in a given direction. Mechanics and Its Practice 2(1): 20-26,33.

Pan,L.Z. 1981. Derivation of several formulas with their applications to in-situ stress measurements. in Principles and Applications of Ground Stress Measurements. Publishing House of Geology, Beijing: 163-203.

Pan, L.Z. 1984. On the mechanics of the whole process of measuring ground stress by the borehole deformation method using pre-press probes of contact type. Acta Geophysica Sinica 27 (6) : 548-561.

Pan, L.Z. 1985. In-situ determination of elastic coefficients of rock mass (Abstract). Proceedings of the 26th U.S. Symposium on Rock Mechanics, Rapid City: 869-871.

Stephansson, O. 1983. Rock stress measurement by sleeve fracturing. Reprints of the 5th International Congress on Rock Mechanics. Melbourne. Section F: 129-137.

Hydraulic fracturing stress measurements in anisotropic rocks: a theoretical analysis

M.G. KARFAKIS
Civil Engineering Department, University of Wyoming, Laramie, Wyoming, USA

ABSTRACT. The classical interpretation of hydraulic fracturing test results for in situ stress determination relies on a priori assumptions--assumptions that cannot always be justified. A brief description of the hydraulic fracturing stress measurement method is given, the assumptions made are critically examined, and the difficulties in the classical interpretation and analysis of the data are discussed. An alternative practice and analysis that makes use of existing fractures and takes into account the possibility of fractures initiating in any direction is proposed. Further, an example of the alternative analysis is given.

RÉSUMÉ. L'interprétation classique des resultats d'hydrofracturation pour la détermination des contraintes in situ compte sur des suppositions a priori. Ce sont des suppositions qui ne peuvent pɛs toujours être justifiées. On présente une description brieve de la méthode d'hydrofracturation pour la mesure des contraintes, les suppositions faites sont examiné d'une manière critique, et les difficultés de l'interprétation classique et l'analyse des données experimentales sont discuteés. On propose une procédure et une analyse alternative qui utilisent des fractures existantes et qui considèrent la possibilité des fractures qui commencent en n'importe quelle direction. En outre, on donne un example employant l'analyse alternative.

ZUSAMMENFASSUNG. Die klassische Deutung von Resultaten von Hydrobruch-messungen für in situ Stressbestimmungen ist auf a priori Annahmen aufgebaut, Annahmen, die nicht immer gerechtfertigt werden können. Eine kurze Beschreibung der Hydrobruchstressmessungsmethode wird gegeben, die Annahmen werden kritisch betrachtet, und die in der klassischen Deutung und Analyse der Daten enthaltenen Schwierigkeiten werden diskutiert. Ein alternatives Verfahren und Analysieren, die schon bestehende Brüchen gebrauchen und die Möglichkeit von in allen Richtungen beginnenden Brüchen in Kauf nehmen werden vorgeschlagen. Ferner ist ein Beispiel der alternativen Analyse gegeben.

INTRODUCTION

In situ stress in rocks arises both from actively applied forces and from stored residual-strain energy. The in situ state of stress is measured for two principal reasons: to predict rock response to changed loading conditions caused by construction or excavation, and to further understand tectonic processes. Included in construction and excavation are both traditional activities and new engineering procedures such as in situ extraction of geothermal power, in situ coal gasification, and storage of high-level radioactive waste. These are procedures that make use of the in situ stress field to guide the formation of fractures or their sealing as part of the design.

Values of the ambient state of stress are determined from measurements in two fundamentally different modes, active and passive (Hult, et al., 1966) In the active mode, the stress component is determined by eliminating stress-induced deformations with a counterbalancing force. In the passive mode, the stress components are inferred from measured displacements and are calculated using known elastic moduli. Among all the methods in use, the hydraulic fracturing stress measurement technique seems to be the most reliable one.

The fundamentals of the classic theory of hydraulic stress measurements were first presented by Hubbert and Willis (1957). The theory is based on the tangential stress distribution around a circular hole concept, first published by Kirsch (1898), and later confirmed by Hiramatsu and Oka (1962), Fairhurst (1964), and Hayes (1965) who also indicated its application to techniques for determination of the stress in rock. The use of the hydraulic fracturing method for in situ stress determination at depth has increased substantially in the past few years. Hydraufracturing stress measurements have been used to verify models of crustal dynamics in both seismically active areas and stable continental interiors (Haimson, 1978; Richardson, et al., 1979; Zoback and Zoback, 1980); in the design of underground structures such as pumped hydroelectric facilities, nuclear waste repositories, and coal mines (Haimson, 1981; Doe, 1983; Dischler and Kim, 1985; Enever and Wooltorton, 1983); and in the planning of massive hydraulic fracturing operations to increase the productivity of oil, gas, and geothermal energy recovery (Aamodt and Kuriyagama, 1983; Bowden, 1983; Gronseth and Kry, 1983). Although, the use of the hydraufracturing technique for stress determination is widespread, there still is considerable controversy over the correct interpretation of hydrofrac data and the validity of the assumptions on which the method is based. The following sections describe the classical hydraufracturing stress measurement technique, critically examine the assumptions made, and give an alternative analysis.

THE CLASSICAL HYDRAUFRACTURING STRESS MEASUREMENT TECHNIQUE

The hydraulic fracturing method consists of pressurizing a section of a drillhole, isolated by straddle packers, with fluid until inducing and extending a tensile fracture on the borehole wall. The fluid pressure required to generate, propagate, sustain, and reopen fractures in the rock at the test horizon is measured and is related to the existing stress field. Directions of principal stresses are obtained by observing and measuring the orientation of the hydraulically induced fracture plane.

In the first comprehensive analysis of the mechanics of hydraulic fracturing, Hubbert and Willis (1957) showed that the borehole pressure to hydraulically fracture a wellbore depends on the tensile strength of the rock and the in situ stresses. Subsequently, a number of authors (Scheidegger, 1962; Kehle, 1964; Haimson and Fairhurst, 1970) pointed out that the pressure-time records

obtained from a hydraufracturing operation could be used to determine the in situ stresses.

When a section of borehole isolated by a straddle packer is pressurized, the test will yield a pressure-time record as idealized in Figure 1. The pressure in the borehole first rises to a maximum value called fracture initiation pressure (P_f) or breakdown pressure. Then, as injection continues at a constant flow rate, the pressure drops and stabilizes at the extension pressure or pumping pressure (P). When pumping is stopped, a shut-in pressure (P_s) can be observed if the wellbore remains sealed off. If, after the borehole pressure is open to the atmosphere, a second cycle of pressurization is started, the borehole pressure will reach a second maximum (P_r) lower then P_f in the first cycle.

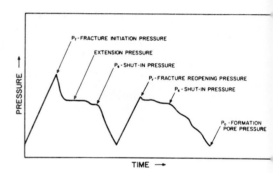

Figure 1. Idealized Hydraulic Fracturing Record

In order to derive the complete state of stress from such experiments certain assumptions must be made:

1. The rock is linear elastic, isotropic, and impermeable, not allowing the pressurizing fluid to penetrate into the rock.

2. One of the principal stresses is parallel to the borehole axis.

3. The hydraulic fracture is induced and propagates in a plane perpendicular to the direction of the least principal stress.

4. The critical fluid pressure (P_c) at fracture generation is the pressure sufficient to equalize the initial tangential stress and to overcome the rock tensile strength.

5. The pressure (P_s) to merely keep the induced fracture open corresponds to the principal

stress acting perpendicular to the fracture plane.

6. The pressure (P_r) to reopen the hydraulic fracture is the pressure sufficient to equalize the tangential stress on the borehole wall at the fracture.

Based on the above assumptions, Hubbert and Willis (1957) and Haimson and Fairhurst (1967) have derived the following formula:

$$P_f = 3\sigma_h - \sigma_H - P_o + T_o \qquad (1)$$

relating the fracture initiation pressure P_f to the horizontal principal stresses σ_h and σ_H, the formation pore pressure P_o, and the tensile strength T_o, that has to be determined from laboratory testings.

The minimum horizontal stress σ_h is determined from the shut-in pressure P_s which is the quasi-static equilibrium pressure required just to keep the hydraulic fracture open without further propagation or closure,

$$P_s = \sigma_h \qquad (2)$$

Bredehoeft et al., (1976) and Zoback et al., (1980, 1978) showed that the maximum horizontal stress could be determined without the knowledge of the tensile strength T_o by using the reopening pressure, thus eliminating the difficulty of determining accurate values of tensile strength.

$$T_o = P_f + P_r \qquad (3)$$

Replacing (3) in Equation (1),

$$P_r = 3\sigma_h - \sigma_H - P_o \qquad (4)$$

The magnitude of the principal horizontal stresses is determined from Equations (2) and (4). Since the induced fracture is assumed to propagate in a plane perpendicular to the minimum horizontal stress, the direction of the principal stresses can readily be obtained from the trace of the hydraulic fracture on the borehole wall. The orientation of this fracture is obtained either by an impression packer, which takes an imprint of the borehole wall in the pressurized section before and after the test, or by a borehole televiewer. Determination of in situ stresses using the hydraulic fracturing technique has not proved to be as straightforward as theory would predict. The following section discusses the controversy over the correct interpretation of the data and the validity of the assumptions given above.

DIFFICULTIES IN THE CLASSICAL ANALYSIS

The parrallelism prerequisite between hole axis and principal stress direction can be achieved by drilling vertical boreholes. This assumption is probably valid for most vertical drillholes, where the vertical stress given by the weight of the overburden is a principal stress. Various authors (Daneshy, 1973; Piner, et al., 1983; Hayashi, et al., 1985) have investigated the more general case where the borehole is not oriented parallel to one of the principal stresses. Richardson (1983) has given the most comprehensive treatment of the problem.

Equation (1) assumes the rock to be impervious to the pressurizing fluid. One major problem in this assumption is that in porous and permeable rocks, prior to fracture the pressurizing fluid may penetrate into the surrounding rock and, thus, perturb the stress field by reducing the fracture generation pressure. Haimson and Fairhurst (1967, 1969) have investigated the pore fluid permeation problem. When such permeation occurs, a so-called poro-elastic parameter can be incorporated into Equation (1) to compensate for the phenomena. In practice, however, the parameter is equal to unity, unless the rock is highly porous and permeable (Haimson, 1978). Fluid penetration into the rock matrix can be prevented if high pressurization rates or high viscosity fluids are used (Haimson and Fairhurst, 1969). Laboratory experiments have been conducted (Zoback, et al., 1977) to investigate the dependence of the breakdown pressure upon the rate of borehole pressurization and fluid viscosity. Increased injection rates and fluid viscosity were frequently observed to give increased breakdown pressure that did not coincide with crack inception. This was expained by fluid pressure loss in the propagating crack due to viscous drag, leaving the crack partially filled with a vacuum tip. If borehole pressurization is done at high rates or with high viscosity fluids, down-hole equipment, such as acoustic monitors (Ikeda, and Tsukahara, 1983) or a straddle packer borehole deformation gage (Dischler and Kim, 1985), must be used to detect the onset of the fracture and determine the fracture pressure. The use of Equation (4) instead of Equation (1) for σ_H determination will vitiate the effect of fluid permeation and pressurization rate on the fracturing pressure.

Equation (4) for σ_H estimation requires the determination of the fracture reopening pressure from subsequent pressurization cycles. Care must be taken with the test procedure to determine the fracture opening pressure accurately. Ideally, once the hydraulic fracture is formed during the first cycle, there should be no changes between fracture reopening pressures on subsequent cycles. However, in some instances, where breakdown is incomplete on the first cycle due to limited fracture extension (Zoback, et al., 1980; Hickman and Zoback, 1982), there would be a difference between the subsequent reopening pressures. To circumvent the possible influence of incomplete breakdowns, it was suggested to use the pressure at which the borehole pressurization rate in the third cycle deviates from linearity at the same flow rate prior to breakdown (Hickman and Zoback, 1982).

The minimum horizontal stress σ_h is inferred from the shut-in pressure obtained from the pressure-time records. In almost all hydraulic fracturing experiments, immediately after pumping has stopped the shut-in pressure shows a decrease as fractures are propagated. It is also observed that the shut-in pressure decreases with sequential pressurization cycles until it assymptotically approches a constant value (Enever and Wooltorton, 1983; Hickman and Zoback, 1982; Gronseth and Kry, 1983). It was suggested that this reductions in shut-in pressure magnitude is due to viscous pressure loss within the hydraulic fracture as it propagates (Hickman and Zoback, 1982). It was recommended that in order to obtain the best estimate for P_s, the value of the shut-in pressure must be determined after repeated pressurization of the fracture with a low viscosity fluid at relatively low flow rates, to minimize the viscous pressure loss and to insure that it reaches an asymptotic value. Only then will the shut-in pressure, determined at the inflection point on the pressure-time record after pumping is stopped, give the best estimate for σ_h.

One of the most constraining assumptions in the classical analysis is that hydraulic fractures initiate and extend perpendicularly to the minimum principal stress. The analysis assumes that the rock is free of fracture and that it is not notch sensitive in tension. Per definition, rocks or rock masses contain fractures

or cracks in the form of micro-crac or joints. In many instance anisotropic rock properties, due rock fabric, control the direction hydraulic fractures. This can be sho both by theory and analysis laboratory and field data (Zoback, al., 1977; Hanson and Towse, 198 Cornet, 1983; Haimson and Avasth 1975; Plumb, 1983). As a consequenc the initial azimuth of the fracture the borehole wall may not be indicati of the azimuth away from the hol Furthermore, the initial and fin. azimuth may not be normal to t' direction of the minimum horizont. principal stress. Based on the abov the measured initial shut-in pressu may not measure the minimum princip. stress, and the information obtaine from the classical analysis would I misleading. Abou Sayed and Brecht((1978) and Rummel and Winter (198: have suggested that fracture mechani(can be used to estimate the princip. horizontal stresses when pre-existing arbitrarily oriented cracks a pressurized. However, because there i considerable uncertainty in determinir the stress intensity factor and th length of the crack, the techniqu would have limited application. Corne (1983) has suggested a method c determining the state of stress whe pre-existing vertical joints do no align with the maximum horizonta stress. His analysis considers the tw horizontal principal stresses and th angle between the direction of th maximum stress and the fracture plan as unknowns. The three unknowns may b estimated if joints of differen azimuth can be tested.

The following section describes more general analysis for the hydrauli fracturing stress measurement method The analysis considers all field stres components, makes use of existin fractures, and takes into account th possibility of fractures initiating i any direction.

PROPOSED METHOD OF ANALYSIS

The boundary stress component around a pressurized borehole (Kirsch 1898) can be determined using th elasticity solution for a pressurize cylindrical cavity in an infinit isotropic elastic continuum. Th tangential stress σ_θ at a radius r fro the center of the borehole in terms o the system of cylindrical polar co ordinates r, θ, and z, as shown i Figure 2, is given by the expression:

160

$$\sigma_\theta = \frac{\sigma_x + \sigma_y}{2} \left(1 + \frac{a^2}{r^2}\right)$$

$$- \frac{\sigma_x - \sigma_y}{2} \left(1 + 3\frac{a^4}{r^4}\right) \cos 2\theta$$

$$- \tau_{xy}\left(1 + 3\frac{a^4}{r^4}\right) \sin 2\theta - P_i \frac{a^2}{r^2} \qquad (5)$$

where σ_x, σ_y, τ_{xy} = field stress
components along
an arbitrary global
axis;

P_i = borehole internal
pressure;

a = borehole radius;

r, θ = cylindrical polar
coordinates, from
the center of the
borehole and coun-
ter clockwise from
the x direction,
respectively.

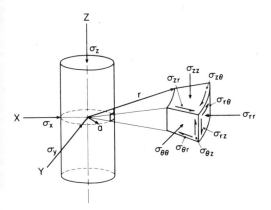

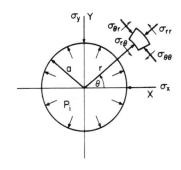

Figure 2. Notation of Stress
Components

Consider a borehole with a planar
fracture parallel to its axis oriented
at θ from the x direction. The
tangential stress on the borehole wall
($r = a$) normal to the fracture plane is
as follows:

$$\sigma_\theta = (1 - 2 \cos 2\theta)\, \sigma_x$$

$$+ (1 + 2 \cos 2\theta)\, \sigma_y$$

$$- \tau_{xy}\, 4 \sin 2\theta - P_i \qquad (6)$$

As the internal pressure P_i is
increased the tangential stress will
decrease. The fracture will open
(assuming no tensile strength across
the fracture) when the tangential
stress becomes tensile. At the onset
of fracture opening the internal
pressure is equal to the tangential
stress on the borehole wall normal to
the fracture plane, due to the field
stresses, and can be defied as the
reopening pressure P_r:

$$P_r = (1 - 2 \cos 2\theta)\, \sigma_x$$

$$+ (1 + 2 \cos 2\sigma)\, \sigma_y$$

$$- \tau_{xy}\, 4 \sin 2\theta \qquad (7)$$

If pore pressure P_o is present, P_r can
be replaced $P_{r_{eff}}$ in Equation (7) where

$$P_{r_{eff}} = P_r + P_o$$

is the effective reopening pressure.

We are required to determine
reopening pressure for three fractures
at different azimuth for the two
dimensional stress system to be
defined. These relations can be
expressed in the matrix form as:

$$\{P_r\} = [A]\ \{\sigma\} \qquad (8)$$

where $\{P_r\}$ = column matrix of
reopening pressures;

$[A]$ = 3x3 matrix of stress
component coefficients;

$\{\sigma\}$ = column matrix of field
stress components.

The solution for the stress
components gives:

$$\{\sigma\} = [A]^{-1}\ \{P_r\} \qquad (9)$$

If the planar fracture extends to
a distance away from the borehole, the
tangential stress normal to the
fracture at a distance $r \gg a$ is given
by:

$$\sigma_\theta = 1/2\,(1 - 2 \cos 2\theta)\, \sigma_x$$

$$+ 1/2\,(1 + 2 \cos 2\theta)\, \sigma_y$$

$$- \tau_{xy} \sin \theta - P_i \qquad (10)$$

where P_i is the internal pressure
acting on the fracture plane.

As the internal pressure is increased, the tangential stress normal to the fracture plane decreases until it vanishes. The internal pressure equalizing the tangential stress due to the field stress is defined as the shut-in pressure:

$$P_s = 1/2 \ (1 - 2 \cos 2\theta) \ \sigma_x$$
$$+ \ 1/2 \ (1 + 2 \cos 2\theta) \ \sigma_y$$
$$- \ \tau_{xy} \sin \theta \qquad (11)$$

When pore pressure is present, P_s can be written in term of effective shut-in pressure $P_{s_{eff}}$, where $P_{s_{eff}} = P_s + P_o$.

Here, also, P_s measurements for three differently oriented fractures must be made to define the two-dimensional stress system. In matrix form:

$$\{P_s\} = [A] \ \{\sigma\} \qquad (12)$$

where $\{P_s\}$ = column matrix of shut-in pressures.

The solution for the stress components gives:

$$\{\sigma\} = [A]^{-1} \ \{P_s\} \qquad (13)$$

Based on the above, hydraulic fracturing tests may be conducted either in intact and/or fractured rocks. The reopening and shut-in pressures data from induced and/or pre-existing vertical fractures can be used in the determination of the field stress components. Equations (8) and (12) require measurements in three different fracture orientations. Considering the scatter of induced fracture orientation from field measurements, three different orientations can be easily obtained for the two-dimensional stress system to be defined.

In hydraulic fracturing tests, the reopening and shut-in pressure for a given fracture are equalizing the normal tangential stress at two different locations on the fracture plane. These tangential stresses are generated by the same field stress components; consequently, Equations (8) and (12) can be combined to give:

$$\{P_i\} = [A] \ \{\sigma\} \qquad (14)$$

where $\{P_i\}$ = column matrix of effective internal pressures for reopening and shut-in;
$[A]$ = nx3 matrix of stress component coefficients

where n is the number of measurements.

For overdetermined systems where the number of measurements is greater then the number of unknowns, a least-squares approximation can be used. The solution for $\{\sigma\}$ in $\{P_i\} = [A] \ \{\sigma\}$, using a least-squares approximation, is:

$$[A]^T \ [A] \ \{\sigma\} = [A]^T \ \{P_i\}$$
$$[C] \ \{\sigma\} = [B]$$

where $\qquad [C] = [A]^T \ [A]$

and $\qquad [B] = [A]^T \ \{P_i\}$

hence $\qquad \{\sigma\} = [C]^{-1} \ [B] \qquad (15)$

Once the field stress components are known, the secondary principal stress values and their orientation can be readily determined by stress transformation formulas. The redundant observations may be used to determine a locally averaged solution for the ambient state of stress. Confidence limits for the various parameters defining the field stress may also be attached to the measured state of stress. An example of the application of the method is given in the Appendix.

CONCLUSION

The alternative analysis of the hydraulic fracturing experiments, described above, differs from the classical analysis in the following assumptions it makes:

1. Induced fractures can initiate and propagate in any direction;
2. The shut-in pressure is the pressure in the fracture necessary to equalize the tangential stress normal to the fracture plane at a distance at least three boreholes away, due to the local field stresses;
3. The reopening pressure is the borehole pressure that equalizes the tangential stress normal to the fracture plane on the borehole wall due to the local field stresses.

Since only reopening and shut-in pressures are required for the analysis, boreholes with pre-existing fractures can also be tested.

Problems in determining P_s and P_r from the pressure-time records will remain the same. Consequently, extreme care must be taken to minimize any effect that may alter the stress

concentrations around the borehole and
the pressure readings.

Best interpretation of hydraulic
fracturing data would be possible by
conducting repeated pressurization
cycles of progressively longer duration
and pumping at constant flow rates
throughout a test (Hickman and Zoback,
1982).

The stable shut-in pressure
attained after repeated pressurization
cycles should be used, since this will
minimize the effects of the viscous
pressure loss in the hydraulic fracture
on the shut-in pressure (Hickman and
Zoback, 1982; Gronseth and Kry, 1983).

The fracture reopening pressure
observed in the third pressurization
cycle must be used. This will
compensate the effect of incomplete
breakdown on the first cycle, minimize
the effect of fluid diffusion into the
surrounding rock during pumping and
shut-in, which may alter the stress
concentration around the borehole, and
will also minimize fluid infiltration
into the fracture prior to reopening.

When shut-in and reopening
pressure data are available for induced
or pre-existing fractures parallel to
the borehole axis, Equation (14) can be
used to determine the state of stress
around the borehole. For Equation (14)
to be valid in the case of pre-existing
fractures, these fractures must be
planar and intersect the borehole
diametrically. Otherwise Equation (8)
must be used instead.

Hydraulic fracturing measurements
must be made in different boreholes at
the same depths; or, if only one
borehole is available, the testing
interval must be kept relatively
small. An alternative would be to
assume that the horizontal stresses do
not vary with depth and that the
results obtained are average values for
the depth interval tested.

The proposed alternative analysis
of hydraulic fracturing measurements
would provide better estimates for the
magnitude and direction of the
horizontal principal stresses by
eliminating some assumptions made in
the classical analysis. Furthermore,
since pre-existing fractures can also
be tested, this would not restrict
testings to horizons of intact rocks
only.

REFERENCES

Aamodt, L. and M. Kuriyagama 1983.
Measurement of Instantaneous Shut-in
Pressure in Crystalline Rock. Proc.,
Workshop on Hydraulic Fracturing
Stress Measurements, U.S. Nat. Comm.
on Rock Mech., Washington, D.C., 394-
402.

Abou-Sayed, A. S. and C. Brechtel 1978.
In Situ Stress Determination by
Hydrofracturing: A Fracture
Mechanics Approach. J. of Geophysical
Research, Vol. 83, No. B6.

Bowden, W. F. 1983. Hydraulic
Fracturing in Alberta Tar Sand
Formations - A Unique Material for
In-Situ Stress Measurements. Proc..
Workshop on Hydraulic Fracturing
Stress Measurements, U.S. Nat. Comm.
on Rock Mech., Washington, D.C., 237-
275.

Bredehoeft, J. D., R. G. Wolff, W. S.
Keys, and E. Shutter 1976. Hydraulic
Fracturing to Determine the Regional
In Situ Stress Field, Piceance Basin,
Colorado. Geol. Soc. Am. Bull. 87,
250-258.

Cornet, F. H. 1983. Analysis of
Injection Tests for In-Situ Stress
Determination. Proc., Workshop on
Hydraulic Fracturing Stress
Measurements, U.S. Nat. Comm. on Rock
Mech., Washington, D.C., 414-443.

Daneshy, A. A. 1973. A Study of
Inclined Hydraulic Fractures. Soc.
Pet. Engng. J., Vol. 13, No. 2.

Dischler, S. A. and K. Kim 1985.
Determination of Rock Mass
Deformation Modulus during Hydraulic
Fracturing. Research and Engineering
Application in Rock Mechanics, Proc.
26th Symp. Rock Mechanics, (edited by
Ashworth, E.) 363-373, A. A. Balkema,
Boston.

Doe, T. W. 1983. Determination of the
State of Stress at the Stripa Mine,
Sweden. Proc., Workshop on Hydraulic
Fracturing Stress Measurements, U.S.
Nat. Comm. on Rock Mech., Washington,
D.C., 305-331.

Enever, J. R. and B. A. Wooltorton
1983. Experience with Hydraulic
Fracturing as a Means of Estimating
In Situ Stress in Australian Coal
Basin Sediments. Proc. Workshop on
Hydraulic Fracturing Stress
Measurements, U.S. Nat. Comm. on Rock
Mech., Washington, D.C., 62-102.

Fairhurst, C. 1964. Measurement of In
Situ Rock Stresses with Particular
Reference to Hydraulic Fracturing.
Felsmechanik und Ingehieurgeologic,
V. II, 3-4, 129-147.

Gronseth, J. M. and P. R. Kry 1983.
Instantaneous Shut-In Pressure and
Its Relationship to the Minimum In
Situ Stress. Proc., Workshop on
Hydraulic Fracturing Stress Measure-

ments, U.S. Nat. Comm. on Rock Mech., Washington, D.C., 147-166.

Haimson, B. C. 1978. The Hydrofracturing Stress Measuring Method and Recent Field Results. Int. J. Rock Mech. Min. Sci & Geomech. Abstr., Vol. 15, 167-178.

Haimson, B. C. 1981. In Situ Stress Measurements in Hydro Projects. Proc. Symp. on Large Hydro Projects, A.S.C.E., New York.

Haimson, B. C. and C. Fairhurst 1967. Initiation and Extension of Hydraulic Fractures in Rock. Soc. Petrol. Engrg. J., 7, 310-318.

Haimson, B. C. and C. Fairhurst 1970. In Situ Stress Determination at Great Depth by Means of Hydraulic Fracturing in Rock Mechanics--Theory and Practice. Proc. 11th Symp. Rock Mech. (edited by Somerton, W. H.), 559-584, A.I.M.E., New York.

Haimson, B. C. and J. M. Avasthi 1975. Stress Measurements in Anisotropic Rock by Hydraulic Fracturing. Applications of Rock Mechanics, 15th Symp. Rock Mech. (Ed. Hoskins), A.S.C.E., New York.

Haimson, B. C. and T. W. Doe 1984. State of Stress, Permeability and Fractures in the Precambrian Granite of Northern Illinois. J. of Geophysical Research, Vol. on the Illinois Deep Hole Project.

Haimson, B. C., and C. Fairhurst 1969. Hydraulic Fracturing in Porous-Permeable Materials. J. Petrol. Tech., Vol. XXI, July, 811-817.

Hanson, M. and D. Towse 1983. Studies of Earth Stress and Rock Properties and the Hydraulic Fracturing Process. Proc., Workshop on Hydraulic Fracturing Stress Measurements, U.S. Nat. Comm. on Rock Mech., Washington, D.C., 524-538.

Hayashi, K., T. Shaji, H. Niitsuma, T. Ito, and H. A. Abe 1985. A New In Situ Tectonic Stress Measurement and Its Application to a Geothermal Model Field. Proc. Geothermal Resources Council.

Hickman, S. H. and M. D. Zoback 1982. The Interpretation of Hydraulic Fracturing Pressure-Time Data for In Situ Stress Determination. Proc., Workshop on Hydraulic Fracturing Stress Measurements, U.S. Nat. Comm. on Rock Mech., Washington, D.C., 103-146.

Hiramatsu, Y. and Y. Oka 1962. Stress Around a Shaft or Level Excavated Ground with a Three-Dimensional Stress State. Mem. Fac. Engng. Kyoto, V, XXIV, Part 1, 56-76.

Hubbert, M. K. and D. G. Willis 1957. Mechanics of Hydraulic Fracturing. Trans. Am. Inst. Min. Engrs. 210, 153-168 (1957).

Hult, J., J. Kvapil, and H. Sundkvist 1966. Function and Scope of Stress Meters in Rock Mechanics. Int. J. Rock Mech. Min. Sci. & Geomech. Abstr. 3, 1-10 (1966).

Hyes, D. J. 1965. The In Situ Determination of the Complete State of Stress in Rock: The Principles of a Proposed Technique. CSIR Report MEG 404, Pretoria, South Africa.

Ikeda, R. and H. Tsukahara 1983. Acoustic Emissions Detected by Hydrophone during Hydraulic Fracturing Stress Measurements. Proc., Workshop on Hydraulic Fracturing Stress Measurements, U.S. Nat. Comm. on Rock Mech., Washington, D.C., 558-568.

Kehle, R. O. 1964. The Determination of Tectonic Stresses through Analysis of Hydraulic Well Fracturing. J. Geophys. Res. 69, 259-273.

Kirsch, G. 1898. Die Theorie der Elastizitat und die Bedurfnisse der Festigkeitslehre. Veit. Ver. Deut. Ing. 42, 797-807.

Piner, J., P. Ledingham, and C. M. Merrifield 1983. In Situ Stress Measurement in the Carnmenellis Granite - II, Hydrofracture Tests at Rosemanowes Quarry to Depths of 200 m. Int. J. Rock Mech. Min. Sci & Geomech. Abstr., Vol. 20, No. 2, 63-72.

Plumb, R. A. 1983. The Correlation between the Orientation of Induced Fractures and In Situ Stress or Rock Anisotropy. Proc., Workshop on Hydraulic Fracturing Stress Measurements, U.S. Nat. Comm. on Rock Mech., Washington, D.C., 596-623.

Richardson, R. M 1983. Hydraulic Fracture in Arbitrarily Oriented Boreholes: An Analytic Approach. Proc., Workshop on Hydraulic Fracturing Stress Measurements, U.S. Nat. Comm. on Rock Mech., Washington, D.C., 463-488.

Richardson, R. M., S. C. Solomon, and N. H. Sleep 1979. Techtonic Stress in the Plates. Rev. Geophys, Space Phys., 17, 981-1019.

Rummel F. and R. B. Winter 1983. Fracture Mechanics as Applied to Hydraulic Fracturing Stress Measurements. Earthq. Predict. Res., 2, No. 1, 33-45.

Scheidegger, A. E. 1962. Stress in the Earth's Crust as Determined from Hydaulic Fracturing Data. Geologie and Bauwesen, 27, H, 2, 45-53.

Zoback, M. D. and D. D. Pollard 1978. Hydraulic Fracture Propagation and the Interpretation of Pressure-Time Records for In-Situ Stress Determination. Proc. U.S. Rock Mech. Symp., Stateline, Nevada.

Zoback, M. D., F. Rummel, R. Jung, and C. B. Raleigh 1977. Laboratory Hydraulic Fracturing Experiments in Intact and Pre-fractured Rock. Int. J. Rock Mech. Min. Sci. & Geomech. Abstr., Vol. 14, 49-58.

Zoback, M. D., H. Isukahara, and S. Hickman 1980. Stress Measurements at Depth in the Vicinity of the San Andreas Fault: Implication for the Magnitude of Shear Stress at Depth. J. Geophys. Res., Vol. 85, 6157-6173.

Zoback, M. L. and M. D. Zoback 1980. State of Stress in the Conterminous United States. J. Geophys. Res., 85, 6113-6156.

APPENDIX

Hydraulic fracturing tests for stress measurements have been conducted for the Illinois Deep Hole Project (Haimson and Doe, 1984). In the 1600 m deep hole (UPH-3), a total of nineteen successful tests were performed. Only six of them gave an orientation for the induced hydraulic fractures. Table I gives the results for the six tests.

Table 1. Hydraulic Facturing Results in UPH-3 (Haimson and Doe, 1984)

Test #	Depth (m)	P_o (MPa)	P_r (MPa)	P_s (MPa)	Fracture Orientation
1	686	6.0	18.4	17.8	N 27° E
2	762	6.8	28.1	26.1	N 62° E
18	973	8.9	26.1	28.9	N 90° E
7	1186	11.0	29.6	28.9	N 15° E
8	1280	11.5	36.6	33.9	N 65° E
9	1449	13.6	41.1	38.3	N 27° E

Since reopening and shut-in pressures are available, Equation (14) is used. In the presence of pore pressure, P_r and P_s are replaced by the effective pressures $P_{r_{eff}}$ and $P_{s_{eff}}$.

$$\{P_{i_{eff}}\} = [A]\{\sigma\} \quad (A.1)$$

where $\{P_{i_{eff}}\}$ = column matrix of effective internal pressures for reopening and shut-in

$[A]$ = 12x3 matrix of stress component coefficients.

Taking East as the direction of x (Figure 3), Equation A.1 becomes

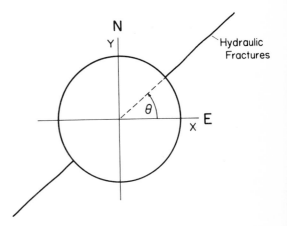

$$\begin{Bmatrix} 24.4 \\ 34.9 \\ 35.0 \\ 40.6 \\ 48.5 \\ 54.7 \\ 23.8 \\ 32.9 \\ 37.8 \\ 39.9 \\ 45.8 \\ 51.9 \end{Bmatrix} = \begin{bmatrix} 2.18 & -0.18 & -3.24 \\ -0.12 & 2.12 & -3.32 \\ -1.00 & 3.00 & 0.00 \\ 2.73 & -0.73 & -2.00 \\ -0.29 & 2.29 & -3.06 \\ 2.18 & -0.18 & -3.24 \\ 1.09 & -0.09 & -0.81 \\ -0.06 & 1.06 & -0.83 \\ -0.50 & 1.50 & 0.00 \\ 1.36 & -0.36 & -0.50 \\ -0.14 & 1.14 & -0.76 \\ 1.09 & -0.09 & -0.81 \end{bmatrix} \begin{Bmatrix} \sigma_x \\ \sigma_y \\ \tau_{xy} \end{Bmatrix}$$

Figure 3. Fracture Coordinate System

The least-squares approximation for $\{\sigma\}$ is

$$[A]^T[A]\{\sigma\} = [A]^T\{P_{i_{eff}}\} \quad (A.2)$$

$$\{\sigma\} = \left[[A]^T[A]\right]^{-1}[A]^T\{P_{i_{eff}}\} \quad (A.3)$$

Solving for $\{\sigma\}$, we obtain

$$\sigma_x = 29.80 \text{ MPa};$$

$$\sigma_y = 28.11 \text{ MPa};$$

$$\tau_{xy} = 4.76 \text{ MPa}.$$

Using the stress transformation equation

$$\sigma_1, \sigma_2 = 1/2(\sigma_x + \sigma_y)$$

$$\pm \left[1/4 \ (\sigma_x - \sigma_y)^2 + \tau_{xy}^2\right]^{-1/2}$$

we obtain:

$$\sigma_H = 33.86 \text{ MPa and } \sigma_h = 24.05 \text{ MPa}$$

for the maximum and minimum horizontal stresses. These values are average values for the depth interval tested. The direction of the principal stresses with respect to the x direction is given by:

$$\tan 2\,\alpha = 2\,\tau_{xy}/(\sigma_x - \sigma_y)$$

We obtain $\alpha = 40^0$; hence, the azimuth of the maximum horizontal stress is N 50° E. The average principal horizontal stress magnitudes obtained by the classical analysis were: $\sigma_H = 47.26$ MPa and $\sigma_h = 28.98$ MPa, with an orientation of σ_H of N 48° E.

Proceedings of the International Symposium on Rock Stress and Rock Stress Measurements/Stockholm/1-3 September 1986

Stress measurement schemes for jointed and fractured rock

B.H.G. BRADY
CSIRO, Division of Geomechanics, Mount Waverley, Victoria, Australia

J.V. LEMOS
P.A. CUNDALL
University of Minnesota, Department of Civil and Mineral Engineering, Minneapolis, Minnesota, USA

ABSTRACT

Determination of the state of stress in a jointed and fractured medium is complicated by the spatial heterogeneity of the stress distribution. In a discontinuous rock mass this is related to the current state of geologic loading, and the stress path defined by its geologic history. The stress path develops over geologic time from a variety of physical, chemical and mechanical changes, including processes such as fracture, and slip and separation on planes of weakness. The results of a stress measurement exercise, using a 1.81 m diameter borehole, are presented. They confirm the role of geologic structure in determining stress distribution in jointed rock. Computational analysis of generic models of jointed rock masses has been used to develop guidelines for the preferred number and location of stress measurement sites in such a medium, which can provide a reliable estimate of the average ·field stresses.

RESUME

La détermination de l'état de sollicitation d'un milieu fissuré et fracturé est compliquée par l'hétérogénéité spatiale de la distribution des contraintes. Dans le cas d'une masse rocheuses discontinue, celle-ci est relative à l'état courant de chargement géologique ainsi qu'à la trajectoire de contraintes définie par son histoire géologique. La trajectoire des contraintes se développe au cours du temps géologique d'une diversité de changements de nature physique, chimique et mécanique, y compris des procédés tels que la fracture, le'écoulement et la séparation suivant les plans de faiblesse. On présente les résultats d'un essai de mesure des contraintes en employant un trou de forage de 1.81 m de diamètre. Ils confirment le rôle de la structure géologique dans la détermination de la distribution des contraintes dans les masses rocheuses fissurées. On a fait appel à l'analyse de calcul de modèles génériques de masses rocheuses fissurées pour obtenir des indications du nombre préféré et de la location des sites pour la mesure des contraintes dans un tel milieu qui puissent aboutir à une appréciation sure des contraintes de champ.

ZUSAMMENFASSUNG

Die Bestimmung des Spannungszustandes bei einem geklüfteten und rissig gewordenen Gesteinssystem wird durch die räumliche Heterogenität der Spannungsverteilung kompliziert. Bei einem unterbrockenen Gesteinssystem ist diese mit dem augenblicklichen geologischen Beladungszustand sowie mit der von ihrer geologischen Vorgeschichte bedingten Spannungsrichtung verbunden. Die Spannungsrichtung entwickelt sich im Laufe der geologischen Zeit aus einer Vielzahl physischer, chemischer und mechanischer Veränderungen, einschliesslich Vorgänge wie Bruch sowie Fliessrutschung und Trennung an Schwachflächen. Die Ergebnisse eines Spannungsmessvorhabens unter Verwendung eines Bohrlochs mit einem Durchmesser von 1.81 m werden angegeben. Sie bestätigen die Rolle der geologischen Struktur bei der Bestimmung der Spannungsverteilung en einem geklüfteten Gesteinssystem. Rechneranalyse von allgemeinen Modellen geklüfteter Gesteinssysteme ist zur Entwicklung von Richtlinien betrefflich der vorzuziehenden Anzahl sowie Stellen der Spannungsmesspunkte bei einem solchen System, die eine sichere Auswertung der durchschnittlichen Feldspannungen liefern können, verwendet worden.

1. INTRODUCTION

In the design of underground excavations, reliable determination of the virgin state of stress is usually regarded as an essential component of site characterisation. Significant improvements have been made, in recent years, in instruments and techniques for determination of the average state of stress in a small volume of rock. The volume sampled using conventional borehole devices is typically 0.001 m^3, while the zone of influence of even a moderately sized excavation may exceed 100,000 m^3. Thus, the point determinations of the virgin state of stress will be adequate for design of the excavation only if the natural stress distribution in the medium is reasonably homogeneous throughout the zone of influence of the excavation.

It is inferred that the stress distribution in rock masses, particularly those that are fractured, faulted and jointed, is not homogeneous. This is concluded from the knowledge that, in its geologic history, a rock mass may be subject to episodes of tectonic and gravitational loading, fracturing, unloading, heating, cooling, water infusion, drainage and drying. Each of these physicochemical, thermal and mechanical processes may generate a highly heterogeneous state in the medium. It may also be inferred that the most recent geologic processes will be predominant in determining the current stress distribution. For the near-surface, these processes are erosion, current tectonism, fracture, and slip and separation on discontinuities.

It is notable that there has been comparatively little effort devoted to understanding the relation between structure and state of stress in a rock mass. Price (1966) asserted a relation between orientation of the major principal stress, and the orientation of the acute bisector of the dihedral angle defined by conjugate faults. Jamison and Cook (1980) examined limits on the state of stress in a rock mass defined by rock material strength and rock structure defined by faulting. Apparently, there has been comparatively little effort devoted to determining the stress distribution in a regularly jointed medium.

Model studies of discontinuous media, such as those reported by Chappell (1974), support the notion of a heterogeneous stress distribution in a discontinuous medium. Indeed, analysis of his model studies suggests that any single local determination of the stress tensor may have little relation to the average state of stress in the medium. It also suggests that, for some types of media, design analysis might best be conducted by first seeking to establish in the model a stress distribution compatible with the in-situ measurements. Development of the excavation causes some perturbation on the natural stress distribution, which then could be modelled explicitly. In other cases, it may be sufficient to determine some representative, average state of stress in the volume of rock of interest. The body of rock to be considered in any particular case logically needs to be comparable in scale with the excavations to be developed in the medium.

In this paper, attention is confined to the latter problem. The implicit assumption in the approach adopted is that, on the scale of the prospective zone of influence of an excavation, the stress distribution is variable on the scale of sub-regions within the zone. This means that, if the volume of the problem domain were increased, the average state of stress would not change significantly.

Some of the postulated issues concerning the variability and average state of stress in a jointed, fractured medium are demonstrated by reference to the results of a large-scale in-situ stress measurement exercise. Numerical analyses of some generic models of jointed and fractured assemblies are then used to establish some general principles for satisfactory determination of the average state of stress, from point observations of the stress tensor.

2. A LARGE SCALE MEASUREMENT OF THE FIELD STRESS TENSOR

2.1 Design of Experiment

A major rock mechanics programme, appropriately integrated with mine planning and operations, was established at the Mount Isa Mine, Australia, in

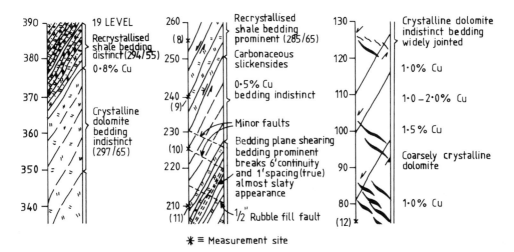

✳ ≡ Measurement site

Figure 1. Geology of sections of 1.81 m diameter borehole (north wall).

the mid 1960's. In early mine site characterisation, the reliability of in-situ stress measurements using techniques available at that time, including various types of strain cells bonded into core-drilled holes and subsequently overcored, was questioned. This led to the design of a stress measurement experiment in which the state of strain in a borehole wall could be determined using mechanical strain gauges. Such gauges have the advantage that they can be recalibrated easily and frequently when in use.

The design of the experiment, described by Brady et al. (1976), was proposed initially by Trollope (1970). The borehole was a 1.81 m diameter vertical excavation, developed with a raise boring machine between the No. 19 and 21 mine levels, 756 and 1072 m respectively below the ground surface. The test domain was outside the zone of influence of any nearby excavations. The borehole penetrated two rock types, coarse crystalline dolomite and bedded, recrystallized shale. Structural mapping revealed quartz and calcite filled tension gashes in the dolomite, and bedding plane shearing with carbonaceous slickensides in the recrystallized shale. Representative mapped sections of the borehole are shown in Figure 1.

To measure the state of strain in the borehole wall, 14 measurement stations were established at structurally suitable sites at various eleva-

tions in the excavation. Each station was designed as shown in Figure 2. It consisted of four strain rosettes, and each rosette consisted of 5 gauges, each formed from a pair of measurement pins located on a diameter of a 250 mm diameter circle inscribed on the raise wall. When a rosette was overcored, changes in gauge length of the gauges in the rosette could be measured directly using a Huggenberger demountable strain meter. Measured tensile strains corresponded to originally compressive strains in the hole wall.

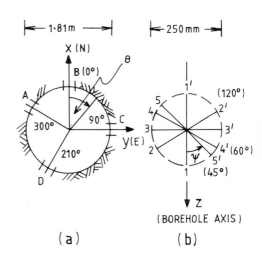

(a)   (b)

Figure 2. (a) Plan of borehole; (b) gauge configuration in strain rosettes.

169

The design of a measurement station and strain rosettes produced 20 strain observations for each station, compared with the 6 observations required to calculate the field stress tensor in an isotropic medium.

2.2 Measurement Procedure

To provide easy access and a working platform, Alimak raise climbing equipment was installed in the borehole.

In the strain rosettes, the measuring pins were 30 mm long, and manufactured from 12.5 mm diameter stainless steel rod. Each pin had two countersunk holes to accept the points of the Huggenberger gauge. Holes in the raise wall were drilled through a template, to produce the standard rosette shown in Figure 2(b), with a masonry drill. Pins were cemented in the holes, to a depth of 25 mm, with a quick setting polyester resin. Five initial readings of gauge lengths were made, for each gauge in a rosette.

Rosettes were overcored using a 360 mm diameter thin-walled diamond bit. In the initial stages, gauges were measured at each of 75, 150, 225, 300 mm depth of overcoring. When it was observed that strain relief was complete at a drilled depth of 150 mm, subsequent measurements were made only at 150 and 300 mm depth of overcoring.

The mechanical properties of the intact rock material were measured on cylindrical specimens of 55 mm and 275 mm diameter, taken from the test site. The mean Young's Modulus (E) and Poisson's Ratio (ν) were 83 GPa and 0.23, with no apparent size effect.

2.3 Analysis of Results

Suppose the reference axes for the borehole are X (North), Y (East), Z (vertical downwards), as shown in Figure 2(a). The location of any rosette on the borehole wall may be defined by the angle θ, measured in the X-Y plane clockwise from North. The orientation of any strain gauge A-A' on the borehole wall may be defined by an angle ψ measured counterclockwise from the Z axis. If P_{xx}, P_{xy} etc. are the components of the field stress tensor, the state of normal strain ε_A for a gauge A-A' defined by (θ,ψ) is given

by (Brady and Brown, 1985):

$$E\varepsilon_A = a_1 P_{xx} + a_2 P_{yy} + a_3 P_{zz} + a_4 P_{xy} + a_5 P_{yz} + a_6 P_{zx} \qquad (1)$$

where $a_i = a_i\,(\theta,\psi,\nu)$

Thus, if 6 independent strain observations are made, for various values of θ, ψ, 6 independent equations similar to equation 1 can be constructed to establish 6 independent simultaneous equations, i.e.

$$\underset{\sim}{A}\ \underset{\sim}{p} = \underset{\sim}{b} \qquad (2)$$

In this expression, the terms of the coefficient matrix A are determined explicitly by θ, ψ, the vector p lists the 6 components of the field stress tensor, and the vector b lists the measured strains, multiplied by the Young's Modulus of the rock. The simultaneous equations may be solved readily for the unknown field stress components.

In the current case, at any measurement station in the borehole, twenty strain observations were made. In theory, these could be used to obtain $20C_6$ (i.e. 38760) independent solutions for the stress tensor. In practice, some strain observations are consistent with others, and not all sets of equations are well conditioned. However, the high level of redundancy allowed methods of analysis to be developed to assess the reliability and consistency of independent solutions for the stress tensor. In the analysis, results from each station were treated as an independent data set, with the exception noted for the second method, discussed below.

Two methods of analysis were developed. In the first, the strain data set for any rosette was examined, by least-squares analysis, to identify observations not consistent with the set, or a set which was mutually inconsistent. Individual observations on the complete set were rejected on the basis of the magnitude of the least-squares residual. In the subsequent construction of sets of simultaneous equations defined by equation 2, tests were conducted on the coefficient matrix A to identify those sets most sensitive to small changes in the components of the b vector.

Table 1 – Summary of Measured Field Stresses Using First Method of Analysis

Station	No. of Solutions	Stress Magnitudes (MPa)			Stress Ratios		Orientations (Lower hemisphere projection)
		σ_1	σ_2	σ_3	σ_2/σ_1	σ_3/σ_1	
14	93	75	53	33	0.71	0.45	
5	892	83	28	4	0.34	0.05	
4	904	50	25	9	0.50	0.18	
6	904	51	32	19	0.62	0.36	
7	1012	36	22	14	0.62	0.38	
8	84	56	28	16	0.50	0.29	
9	318	66	46	29	0.69	0.44	
10	80	45	18	-1	0.41	-0.01	
12	1024	60	37	14	0.62	0.24	
3	1252	51	36	18	0.71	0.35	
13	276	60	38	21	0.63	0.36	
2	456	72	45	26	0.64	0.36	
1	1012	88	48	22	0.55	0.25	

The redundant strain observations allowed at least several hundred independent solutions for the field stresses, for which principal stress magnitudes could be displayed as histograms, and orientations contoured on a stereonet. A graphical summary of the results for Station 3 is shown in Figure 3. From the histograms, the mean values of the principal stresses can be estimated. From the stereoplots, the preferred orientations of the principal stress axes can be established.

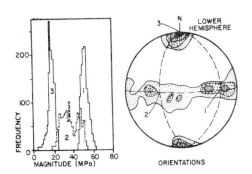

Figure 3. Field principal stresses at Station 3.

A summary of the solutions for the field stresses, for the 14 stations in the borehole, is given in Table 1. The results for Station 3 are close to the average for Stations 6, 4, 13, 2, 1, suggesting this may represent an average solution for the field stresses in the volume of rock constituting the zone of influence for the borehole.

In the second method of analysis, the acceptance tests for strain data were based on two criteria. These were that the rock behaved elastically on overcoring, as indicated by the shape of the strain-versus-overcoring depth plot, and that none of the results from the various gauges in a rosette differed greatly from the results in corresponding gauges in other rosettes in the raise. If either of these criteria was not satisfied, all strain observations for a rosette were rejected. Acceptable strain data were used to solve for the field stresses using techniques similar to that for the first method, described above. The results from this method of analysis showed orientations comparable with those from the first method, but the magnitudes of the principal stresses were lower. The principle of this method of analysis is that one of the strain acceptance criteria explicitly assumes homogeneous field stresses, and that local spurious stress concentrations can develop near the boundary due to the presence of joints. The results from this analysis are given in Table 2.

2.4 Discussion of Field Stress Determination

It is presumed that the first method of stress determination described above yields a representative value of the average state of stress in the volume of rock containing a measurement station. The relevant volume is about 100 m^3. The results in Table 1 suggest

Table 2 - Summary of Measured Field Stress Results Using Method 2

| Station | Stress Magnitudes (MPa) | | | Stress Ratios | | Orientations |
	σ_1	σ_2	σ_3	σ_2/σ_1	σ_3/σ_1	(Lower hemisphere projection)
5	61	20	10	0.33	0.16	
4	42	28	15	0.66	0.36	
6	57	45	29	0.78	0.51	
7	32	23	21	0.74	0.66	
8	41	35	20	0.86	0.47	
9	70	59	39	0.84	0.55	
10	54	41	27	0.75	0.50	
12	57	32	24	0.56	0.41	
3	50	39	19	0.78	0.38	

Stations 14, 13, 2 and 1 had insufficient accepted rosettes for analysis.

that, even allowing for error in any individual determination, the field stresses appear to vary non-systematically along the axis of the borehole. However, if the average of all stress determinations is considered, some individual solutions of the field stress tensor compare favourably with the average solution.

There are several possible explanations for the observed variation in the measured field stresses. The first of these posits that local rock structure determines the local state of stress in a rock mass. In the current case, this would suggest that bedding plane shears cause local variations in the stress tensor. This is supported by the differences between Stations 12 and 3, which were on opposite sides of a shear. However, these variations are apparently noise on a stable baseline state of stress. Average results from the upper part of the borehole, which was separated from the lower part by a 20 m band of bedding plane shears, were not distinguishable from those from the lower part.

A second explanation is that, even though the original state of stress is spatially homogeneous, excavation of the borehole in the jointed rock mass would generate boundary stresses inconsistent with the solution for the homogeneous, elastic, isotropic medium. This can be readily visualized from the local stress concentrations that could occur by slip on planes of weakness either intersecting, or close to, the boundary of the excavation.

Of course, a combination of these effects is possible, with the proviso that explanation 1 accepts the operation of the mechanism implied in explanation 2 as well, while mechanism 2 is sufficient in itself.

The second method of data reduction, yielding the results in Table 2, eliminated strain observations inconsistent with others along the borehole. It is therefore inferred that the results in Table 2 have been derived from strain observations in which local boundary stress concentrations developed by local joint action are excluded. Inspection of Table 2 shows a high level of variability for the field stresses along the hole axis. It is therefore concluded that the first explanation, i.e. spatial variability of the field stress tensor, is a likely explanation for the results of the stress measurement experiment.

Lithology did not appear to affect the stress tensor. Results obtained from the recrystallized shale could not be distinguished from those for the dolomite. However, the elastic properties of the materials were virtually identical, so that, mechanically, the different lithological domains are not distinguishable.

3. ANALYSIS OF "LOCKED-IN" STRESSES IN JOINTED ROCK

3.1 Problem Specification

The preceding discussion suggested that, in the jointed rock mass which

172

was host for the test borehole, the measured state of stress was spatially variable, and possibly related to proximity of measurement sites to structural features. The natural stress concentrations inferred from these measurements may arise from proximity to major faults (Lemos and Brady, 1983) or from differential, time-dependent effects. These phenomena depend on specific local geological conditions. Therefore, another effect that has more general statistical applicability has been studied: the irrecoverable movement that may be induced on existing joint planes during cycles of regional tectonic activity. An investigation has been made into the resulting locked-in stresses that could be introduced into a jointed rock mass by changes in the far-field stress tensor.

3.2 Method

The distinct element method (Cundall and Strack, 1979, and Lemos et al. 1985) was used to model an assembly of deformable rock blocks defined within a circular problem domain. Figure 4 illustrates the jointing pattern that was used in the numerical experiment reported here. It was found, by doing such experiments with several joint patterns, that almost no stress concentrations were introduced when all joints were continuous. In contrast, two of the three joint sets in Figure 5 consist of disconnected segments. Apparently it is this aspect of the fracture geometry that leads to

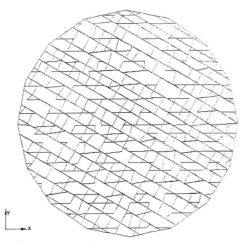

Figure 4. Jointing pattern used in numerical experiment.

locked-in stresses. In the analysis, the boundary blocks are coupled to a stiffness matrix that is generated by a boundary element model of a circular hole in an infinite continuum. That is to say, the blocks appear to be embedded in an infinite elastic continuum, which has the same average elastic properties as the rock mass. The formulation is similar to that described by Brady (1986).

Material properties for the test problem were as follows.

Young's modulus	50 GPa
Poisson's ratio	0.25
Joint friction angle	30 degrees
Joint normal stiffness	100 GPa/m
Joint shear stiffness	100 GPa/m
Radius of sample domain	25 m

Initially, the state of stress in the sample is hydrostatic and isotropic, and there is no gravity. Then the far-field stress ratio is increased from one to four, with the axis of major principal stress at 30 degrees to the X axis (see Fig. 4). Finally, the far-field stress ratio is decreased to unity again. During the period of increasing stress ratio, sliding occurs on some joints in the interior part of the sample. Joints near the boundary are prevented from sliding by the constraining action of the boundary element region, which is necessarily elastic. Although the boundary causes some non-uniformity, the effect is confined to a strip around the boundary. With either a constant-stress or a fixed boundary, the effect is much worse. Furthermore, the circular boundary was preferred in the analysis because it also reduces boundary effects compared to a rectangular boundary.

3.3 Results and Interpretation

The slip displacements that occur during the numerical test are illustrated in Figure 5 as variable-thickness lines, and the distribution of σ_{xx} in Figure 6 as contours. Similar patterns are observed in plots of the other stress components. Inspection of Figures 5 and 6 indicates that stress concentrations are introduced by the simulated tectonic activity wherever slipping joints

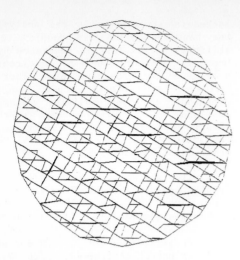

Figure 5. Slip displacements in
jointed medium, with magnitudes
denoted by line thickness.

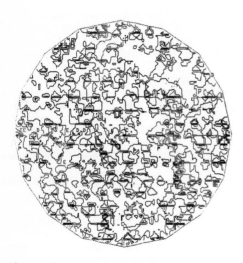

Figure 6.- Contours of σ_{xx} after cycle
of tectonic loading. Maximum contour
= 12 units, minimum 5 units.

terminate at another cross-joint. At
this point there is a stress jump
across the slipping joint. If slip is
towards the cross-joint, the compressive stress is increased; if slip
is away from the cross-joint, the
compressive stress is reduced. These
stresses are termed "locked in" since
they persist after the tectonic
activity has ceased.

In order to understand the nature
of the stress concentrations that are
induced around finite-length joints,
consider a single fracture exposed to

the same stress path. A closed form
solution exists for the case of a
uniform shear stress imposed on the
crack surfaces (Khott, 1973). Since
normal stress, σ_n, on the crack is not
changed by the imposed shear stress, a
uniform shear stress of $\mu\sigma_n$ will exist
on the crack whenever the far-field
shear stress, τ, exceeds this value.

Hence the shear stress drop due to slip
is $\tau - \mu\sigma_n$, where μ is the coefficient of
friction. Figure 7 shows contours of
σ_{xx} computed according to the exact
solution, for unit shear stress drop on
a crack of unit half-width. It is
observed that the contour of $\sigma_{xx} = 1$
extends transversely to the crack to a
distance equal to about the half-width
of the crack. If such locked-in
stresses occur naturally in the field,
there is a finite probability that a
stress-measuring device will encounter
areas in which the stress differs
markedly from the mean.

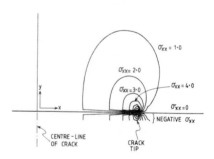

Figure 7.- Exact solution for σ_{xx}
around a shear crack.

The state of stress illustrated by
Figure 6 was sampled by a grid of
measurement points. For a large
sample, the standard deviation of σ_{xx}
was found to be 11% of the mean. It
was hoped that the same information
could be obtained approximately from
the exact solution of Figure 7 by
superimposing stresses due to many such
cracks. However, the area of stress
concentration around a crack is
influenced to a large extent by the
presence of neighbouring cracks, so
that a simple area summation is not
adequate.

A geostatistical analysis was
performed on the same data set
presented in Figure 6. The variogram
for σ_{xx} is recorded in Figure 8. The
values at neighbouring points are seen

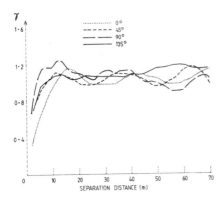

Figure 8.- Variograms of σ_{xx} for point-pairs at various angles to the X-axis.

to be correlated at separation distances in the order of 5 metres, which is equal to the mean joint spacing. This suggests that if the value of mean stress is important to a particular engineering project, then stress samples taken at spacings less than the mean joint spacing may be biased, and not representative of the overall mean stress. However, it should be noted that mean stress is not necessarily the most important stress measure. Stress gradients or maxima may also affect the mechanical behaviour of the rock, or the behaviour of contained fluid, in which case other conclusions may be drawn with respect to satisfactory field measurement schemes.

4. CONCLUSIONS

Results from a comprehensive programme of measurement of the state of stress in a jointed rock mass suggest that the measured field stress tensor may be spatially variable. The variability at the test sites was expressed by changes in both magnitude and orientation of the principal stresses, as particular structural features were transgressed. It appeared that stresses may be locally "locked-in" and concentrated by frictional locking on the joints. In an effort to elucidate the effect of rock structure on the local state of stress, numerical analyses of models of a jointed medium have been conducted. These show that rock masses containing sets of discontinuous joints may indeed be subject to locally varying field stresses. Statistical analysis of the state of stress in a model of a jointed medium indicated that, for a large

number of observations, the standard deviation of a stress component was 11% of the mean magnitude of that component. Geostatistical analysis suggested that, if field measurements of the stress tensor were made at spacings less than the mean spacing of joints, the results may not be representative of the average in the medium.

5. ACKNOWLEDGEMENT

Part of the work reported here was conducted in the course of a project funded by the U.S. National Science Foundation, Grant No. CEE-8212674, for which the authors record their gratitude. Several current and former staff of Mount Isa Mines Limited contributed to the research programme in the mine, in the early 1970's, including R. Blair, W. Phillips, K. Rosengren, and G. Talmage.

6. REFERENCES

Brady, B.H.G., 1986. Boundary element and hybrid methods for underground excavation design; In: Analytical and Numerical Methods in Engineering Rock Mechanics, ed. E.T. Brown, George Allen and Unwin (in press).

Brady, B.H.G. and E.T. Brown, 1985. Rock Mechanics for Underground Mining. George Allen and Unwin, London.

Brady, B.H.G., R.G. Friday and L.G. Alexander, 1976. Stress measurement in a bored raise at the Mount Isa Mine. Proc. Int. Soc. Rock Mech. Symp. on Investigation of Stress in Rock, 12-16, Sydney: Instn Engrs Aust.

Cundall, P.A. and O.D.L. Strack, 1979. A discrete numerical model for granular assemblies. Geotechnique 29:47-65.

Jamison, D.B. and N.G.W. Cook, 1980. Note on measured values for the state of stress in the Earth's crust. J. Geophys. Res. 85: 1833-1838.

Khott, J.F., 1973. Fundamentals of Fracture Mechanics, Butterworths, London.

Lemos, J.V. and B.H.G. Brady, 1983. Stress distribution in a jointed and fractured medium. Proc. 24th U.S. Symp. on Rock Mechanics, Texas A&M University: 53-59.

Lemos, J.V., R.D. Hart and P.A. Cundall, 1985. A generalized distinct element program for modelling jointed rock masses. Proc. Int. Symp. on Fundamentals of Rock Joints, Bjokliden, Lapland.

Price, N.J., 1966. Fault and joint development in brittle and semi-brittle rock. Oxford : Pergamon.

Stresses and tectonics of the upper continental crust – a review

F. RUMMEL
Ruhr Universität Bochum, Bochum, Federal Republic of Germany

Abstract: In the view of current deep continental drilling projects, the present knowledge on acting tectonic stresses is reviewed including both the constraints imposed by experimental rock mechanics as well as existing in-situ stress data from deep hydraulic fracturing borehole profiles. The in-situ data show that the maximum crustal shear stresses are given by the two horizontal principal stresses which favours strike-slip faulting on existing crustal fracture zones. Creep of granitic rocks sets an upper limit on high shear stresses. The peak shear stress seems to exist within the upper 10 km and may be determined by future deep measurements. Extrapolation and comparison of measured crustal stresses with crustal strength limits demonstrate that all faulting modes require extremely high pore pressures for above hydrostatic to reduce the effective normal stresses on existing fractures.

1. Introduction

Intracontinental earthquakes occur to crustal depth of about 20 km; the lower crust is essentially aseismic. This fact per se postulates stress anisotropy with sufficiently high shear stresses in the brittle upper crust and a decrease of shear stresses with greater depth due to ductile flow response of rocks to tectonic strain accumulation. At present, however, there is no consensus whatsoever among earth scientists about the magnitude of shear stress, its variation with depth or about the depth of brittle-ductile transition in crustal deformation behaviour. Stresses at depths greater than 3 km can only be estimated from empirical results of rock mechanics laboratory fracture and deformation studies, or by extrapolating existing stress data measured at shallow depth. Current ultra-deep continental drilling programs may provide an opportunity to conduct deep stress measurements in the near future and may even allow to study the nature of the brittle-ductile transition zone in-situ.

In the view of such drilling programs reviews on the present knowledge on the tectonic stress field and on the rheological response of crustal rocks to imposed tectonic deformation seem appropriate. They may contribute to the design of deep drilling schemes, the development of new drilling methods, to considerations about borehole stability at great depth, or may even stimulate new methods for measuring stresses at great depth.

2. Rheological Constraints

As suggested by various researchers (McGarr and Gay, 1978; Brace, 1979; Goetze and Evans, 1979; Brace and Kohlstedt, 1980; McGarr, 1980; Meissner and Strehlau, 1982; Kirby, 1983; Smith and Bruhn, 1984) the upper limits to crustal shear stresses can be estimated from the results of laboratory fracture and friction experiments. Such tests generally are carried out on intact, prefractured or saw-cut rock samples subjected to triaxial load with confining pressures ranging upto 1 GPa, to temperatures upto $900°C$, and deformed at strain rates of about $10^{-6} s^{-1}$. At these testing conditions most representative crustal rocks demonstrate brittle fracture behaviour with a defined peak strength. Probably best documented with respect to pressure and temperature is the fracture strength of intact granite. The numerous ecperimental data available in the literature (e.g. Rummel, 1982; Kirby and McCormic,

1984) can be fitted by a relation of the form

$$(\sigma_1 - \sigma_3)_c = A + B \, \bar{\sigma}_3^{1/2}, \qquad (1)$$

where $(\sigma_1 - \sigma_3)_c$ is the peak differential strength (in MPa), $\bar{\sigma}_3$ the effective confining pressure, and A and B are constants which only depend on the temperature:

$$A = A_o \left[1 - (T/T_m)^2 \right]^{1/2} \quad \exp \, (-kT/C_o) \qquad (2)$$

$$B = B_o (T_m - T) \qquad (3)$$

with $A_o = 305$ MPa, $C_o = 5.5 \cdot 10^{-20}$ Nm, $B_o = 5 \ 10^{-2}$ MPa$^{1/2}$, and T_m being the melting temperature. A_o characterizes the uniaxial strength at $T = 0$ K. The quantity C_o has the dimension of energy per atom; it is the work required to shear one atom or molecule in the lattice over another; assuming a mean molecular volume of $1.8 \cdot 10^{-28}$ m^3 the value of C_o yield an intrinsic lattice yield strength of 305 MPa; it is interesting to note that this value is the same as the value of A_o. For room temperature eq. (1) closely corresponds to the empirical strength relation for Westerly granite first published by Byerlee (1969).

Eq. (1) to (3) may be used to estimate the maximum differential stress an intact granitic crust can sustain at strain rates of the order of $10^{-6} s^{-1}$, if we replace the principal stress components σ_1 and σ_3 in eq. (1) by the crustal principal stress S_H and S_h, and take into account the variation of temperature with depth. The calculation can easily be carried out for two faulting modes normal ($\sigma_1 = S_v$, $\sigma_3 = S_h$) and thrust faulting ($\sigma_1 = S_H$, $\sigma_3 = S_v$). The result is given in Fig. 1 and shows the critical differential stress $S_H - S_v$ and $S_v - S_h$ as a function of depth assuming a rock density $\rho = 2.8 \cdot 10^3$ kgm^{-3}, the geotherm $T(z, \text{km}) = 298 + 33 \, z$ (km), and dry ($\bar{\sigma}_3 = \sigma_3$) as well as wet ($\bar{\sigma}_3 = \sigma_3 - P$, $P = \rho_{H_2O} \cdot g \cdot z$) conditions. The differential stress for strike-slip fault development cannot be specified since both S_H and S_h are unknown functions of depth.

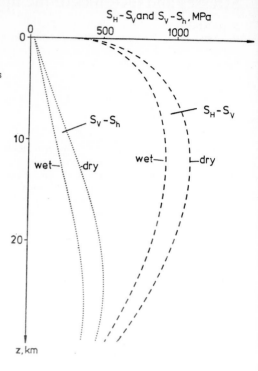

Fig. 1: Differential stresses required for normal ($S_v - S_h$) and thrust faulting ($S_H - S_v$) in an intact dry and wet graniti crust with normal temperature gradient.

The strength relation for intact rock used above is valid for laboratory strai rates. Tectonic strain accumulation certainly occurs at much smaller rates so that stresses may relax with time by roc creep. This effect can be taken into account by the empirical power law creep equation

$$(\sigma_1 - \sigma_3)_c = \left[(\dot{\varepsilon}/A) \, \exp \, (Q/RT) \right]^{1/n} \qquad (4)$$

with $\dot{\varepsilon}$ being the creeprate, Q the activation energy for thermally induced creep and A and n being constants. For the present creep strength estimation experimental data for dry and wet Westerly granite (Hansen and Carter, 1982; Kirby, 1983) are used:

	Q, kJ/mol	A, MPa^{-n}s^{-1}	n
dry	139	$2.5 \cdot 10^{-9}$	3.4
wet	137	$2 \cdot 10^{-4}$	1.9

The resulting differential strength is shown in Fig. 2 as a function of depth for strain rates 10^{-6}, 10^{-9} and $10^{-14}s^{-1}$, again assuming the above mentioned (rather high) geotherm. The curves indicate that for tectonic strain rates the strength of rocks rapidly decreases with depth which thus limits high shear stresses only to the uppermost crust.

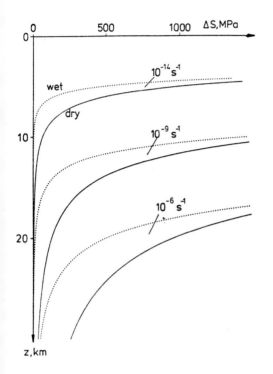

Fig. 2: Creep strength as a function of depth in a dry and wet granitic crust for various strain rates.

It is evident that most crustal earth-quakes are associated with slip along pre-existing fractures. Therefore, the fric-tional strength of rocks is a further con-straint on possible stress magnitudes. The critical shear stresses for a frac-tured crust may be estimated on the basis of Byerlee's (1978) empirical friction law which summarizes the results of lab-oratory friction experiments:

$$\tau_c = 0.85 \, \overline{\sigma} \qquad \text{for } \overline{\sigma} < 200 \text{ MPa} \qquad (5a)$$

$$\dot{\tau}_c = 50 + 0.6 \, \overline{\sigma} \qquad \text{for } \overline{\sigma} > 200 \text{ MPa} \qquad (5b)$$

where τ_c is the critical shear strength and $\overline{\sigma}$ the effective normal stress acting across the shear plane. The friction law seems to be relatively independent of the rock type, of temperature ($T < 400°C$) and strain rate ($\varepsilon < 10^{-7}s^{-1}$). Consider-ing again normal and thrust faulting on favourably oriented fault planes, the required differential stresses are shown in Fig. 3 for dry and wet conditions. The plot also includes the critical differ-ential stresses for strike-slip fault motion by taking into account the results of induced seismicity from controlled fluid injection experiments reported later in section 4. Again, rock creep will limit high differential stresses.

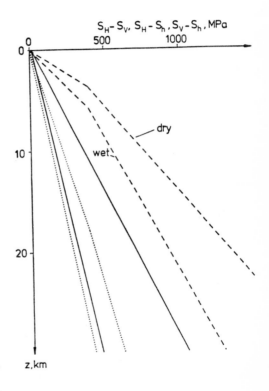

Fig. 3: Differential stresses required for slip along favourably oriented pre-existing faults for wet and dry condi-tions. Dashed: thrust faulting; dotted: normal faulting; full lines: strike-slip faulting.

3. In-situ Stress Data

Direct stress measurements presently reach to a depth of 5 km, however, only three data points exist below a depth of 3 km (Haimson, 1978). The most reliable stress data come from deep hydraulic fracturing stress profiles measured in boreholes drilled from surface. The existing published data are given in Table I in the form of dimensionless stress depth functions

$$S_{H,h}/S_v = (\alpha_{H,h}/z) + \beta_{H,h} \tag{6}$$

with

$\alpha_{H,h}, km = S_{H,h}(z=0)/\rho g, \quad \beta_{H,h} = (\partial S_{H,h}/\partial z) / g,$

and $S_{H,h}(z=0)$ being the horizontal principal stress components at $z=0$. Data sets for $z \geq 0.5$ km are given in Fig. 4a and b. At shallow depth we generally observe extremely high horizontal stresses with both S_H and S_h much greater than the calculated overburden stress S_v. With increasing depth horizontal stresses tend to approach the values $S_h = 0.5 \, S_v$ (the limiting value for normal faulting on wet faults) and $S_H = S_v$.

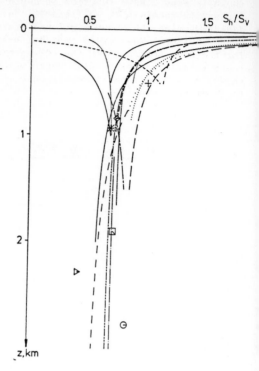

Fig. 4 b

Fig. 4: Measured horizontal stresses S_H(a) and S_h(b) normalized with respect to S_v for hydrofrac tests in boreholes with depth z 0.5 km. Data are taken from Table I.

Neglecting a few results from locations where evidently topography and local tec tonics dominate the stress field at shal low depth, the hydrofrac data yield the average normalized stress-depth relation

$$S_h/S_v = (0.15/z) + 0.65 \tag{7a}$$

$$S_H/S_v = (0.25/z) + 0.98. \tag{7b}$$

Horizontal stressed measured in the 2 km deep hot-dry-rock research drillhole in the Carrnmenellis granite in Cornwall (Batchelor, 1984) seem to represent an extreme case with a stress-depth functic of

$$S_h/S_v = (0.15/z) + 0.5 \tag{8a}$$

$$S_H/S_v = (0.58/z) + 1.06. \tag{8b}$$

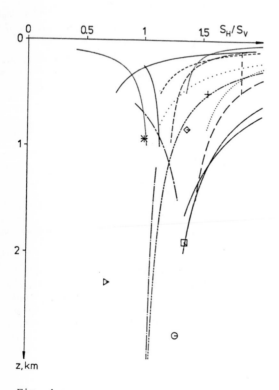

Fig. 4 a

In fact, water injection experiments at depth demonstrate that only a small increase of fluid pressure above hydrostatic triggers microseismicity and slip on existing vertical fractures at a depth below 2 km. This large scale experiment allows an assessment of the critical shear stress relation for strike-slip on favourably oriented vertical faults by inserting the principal stress-depth relations (eq. 8) into Byerlee's friction law (eq. 5). This results in the critical differential stress relation for strike-slip

$$(S_H-S_h)_c, \text{MPa}=13.9+(34.5-19.3k) \ z, \text{km}, \quad (9)$$

where k is the pore pressure ratio with respect to hydrostatic (k=1 : P_1=9.8 z). The critical differential stress-depth relation for strike-slip faulting (eq. 9) is shown in Fig. 5 for k-values k = 0,1 and 1.5, together with the measured differential stresses (average and for Cornwall)

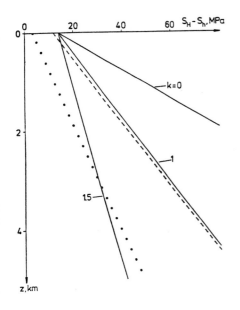

Fig. 5: Critical differential stresses for strike-slip faulting on favourably existing vertical fracture planes for various fluid pressure ratios k = P/P_o (P_o hydrostatic), in comparison with measured horizontal stresses (dashed: Cornwall; dotted: average).

$$(S_H-S_h)_{av}, \text{MPa} = 3.3. + 9.1 \cdot z, \text{km} \quad (10a)$$

$$(S_H-S_h)_{Cornw.}, \text{MPa}=11.8+15.4 \cdot z, \text{km} \quad (10b)$$

The plot indicate that the stress situation in Cornwall indeed is critical, while in the average case strike-slip requires pore pressures significantly higher than hydrostatic. Similar results can be derived from other controlled injection experiments in areas where stresses were measured and seismicity was artificially induced. Typical examples were injection tests in the Rangely oil field, Colorado (Raleigh et al., 1968) or waste disposal experiments in the Rocky Mountain Arsenal well near Denver, Colorado (Healy et al., 1968).

Using Byerlee's friction law the critical condition for normal faulting is given by

$$(S_v-S_h)_c, \text{MPa} = (21.7 - 7.8 \ k)z, \text{km} \quad (11)$$

while measured shear stresses are

$$(S_v-S_h)_{av}, \text{MPa} =-4.1 + 9.6 \cdot z, \text{km} \quad (12a)$$

$$(S_v-S_h)_{Cornw.}, \text{MPa}=-4.1+13.8 \cdot z, \text{km} \quad (12b)$$

The equations are plotted in Fig. 6 for k = 0,1 and 2. The plot demonstrates that normal faulting on favourably oriented faults in the upper crust again requires over-hydrostatic pore pressures.

Similarly, comparing the critical condition for thrust faulting on favourably oriented faults with measured stresses

$$(S_H-S_v)_c, \text{MPa} = (106 - 38 \ k) \cdot z, \text{km} \quad (13)$$

$$(S_H-S_v)_{av}, \text{MPa} = 7.4 - 0.55 \cdot z, \text{km} \quad (14a)$$

$$(S_H-S_v)_{Cornw.}, \text{MPa}= 16 + 1.7 \cdot z, \text{km} \quad (14b)$$

results in the situation illustrated in Fig. 7, where eq. (13) is plotted for k = 0,1,2 and 2.5. Accordingly, thrust faulting in dry or water-saturated rock is limited to extremely shallow depths. Deep thrust faulting requires crustal fluid pressures with k > 3.

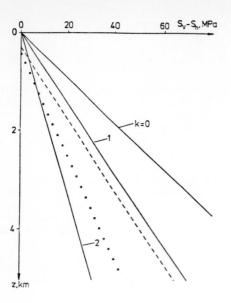

Fig. 6: Critical differential stresses for normal faulting on favourably oriented fracture planes for various fluid pressure ratios k = P/P_O, in comparison with measured horizontal stresses (dashed: Cornwall; dotted: average)

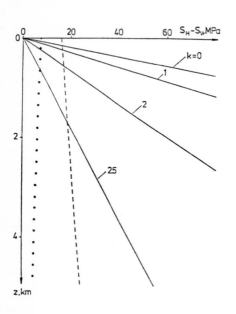

Fig. 7: Critical differential stresses for thrust faulting on favourably oriented fracture planes for various fluid pressure ratis k = P/P_O, in comparison with measured horizontal stresses (dashed: Cornwall; dotted: average)

4. Conclusions

In-situ stress measurements indicate that the maximum shear stress in the upper crust is determined by the two horizontal principal stresses, exept for the uppermost large where the maximum shear stress is given by $S_H - S_V$. Thus, strike-slip faulting is the dominant mechanism in a randomly fractured Earth crust, if the friction criterium (eq. ? is fullfilled. Generally, the acting shear stresses are not sufficient to activate dry faults (k=0), considerable fluid pressures within fault zones are necessary to reduce the acting effective normal stresses. The linear shear stress increase with depth is limited by stress relaxation due to rock creep at geological strain rates of the order of $10^{-14}s^{-1}$. Thus, we might expect a maximum in shear stress at a depth between 5 and 10 km depending on the fluid pressure at depth (Fig. 8). At greater depth shear stress must gradually diminish.

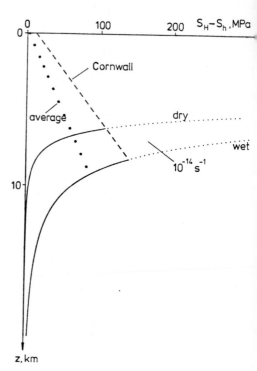

Fig. 8: Differential horizontal stress profile through the upper crust based on measured stresses (dashed for Cornwall, dotted for average data) and on tectonic creep (full lines).

Extrapolation of measured horizontal stress suggests that $S_H \approx S_v$ and $S_h \approx 0.5 S_v$ at a depth of a few kilometers. This also favours normal faulting as a dominant mechanism on fluid-pressurized faults if they are favourably oriented with respect to the principal stresses and favourably oriented vertical faults do not exist.

Thrust faulting on deep low angle faults is difficult to imagine without the presence of extremely high fluid pressures. Lystric faults as observed by deep reflexion seismics demand a progressive increase of fluid pressures with depth well above hydrostatic. At present, the existence of such high fluid pressures over geological times is not well understood unless one assumes deep-seated sources of constant fluid production.

Based on the present stress data for the uppermost 3 km, stress measurements in ultradeep drillholes may proof the existence of the postulated shear stress peak within the upper 10 km of the granitic crust. Another shear stress peak may exist in the lower ultramafic crust where stresses are not as rapidly released by rock creep. Estimates on the depth of such a second shear stress peak presently are not possible since reliable creep data of granulitic rocks are not available.

5. Acknowledgement

The work was stimulated by numerous discussions on the need of deep stress measurements within the German Deep Continental Drilling Project, and by a presentation of O.Stephansson during a seminar on stress measurements at Luleå, Sweden, in June 1985. Calculations and figures were supplied by Mrs. Möhring-Erdmann. In-situ stress data were collected by Mr. J. Baumgärtner. An early version of this paper is published in a Pageoph Special Issue on Physics of Fracturing and Seismic Energy Release (ed. by Waniek and Kozak, Liblice Conference, 1985).

6. References

Batchelor, A.S., Hot-dry-rock geothermal exploitation in the United Kingdom. Modern Geology. 9: 1-41, 1984.
Brace, W.F., Measured crustal stress compared with laboratory strength of rocks. Proc. Int. Research Conf. Intra-Continental Earthquakes, Ohrid, Yugoslavie: 11-13, 1979.
Brace, W.F., and D.L. Kohlstedt, Limits on lithospheric stress imposed by laboratory experiments. JGR. 85: 6248-6252, 1980.
Byerlee, J., Reply. JRG. 74: 5349-5350, 1969.
Byerlee, J., Friction of rocks. Pageoph. 116: 615-626, 1978.
Goetze, Ch., and B. Evans, Stress and temperature in the bending lithosphere as constrained by experimental rock mechanics. Geophys. J. Royal Astr. Soc., London. 59: 463-478, 1979.
Haimson, B.C., Crustal stresses in the Michigan Basin. JGR. 83: 5857-5867, 1978.
Hansen, F.D., and N.L. Carter, Creep of selected crustal rocks at 1000 MPa. Trans. Am. Geophys. Union, 63: 437, 1982.
Healy, J.H., W.W. Rubey, D.T. Griggs, and C.B. Raleigh, The Denver Earthquakes. Science, 161: 1301-1310, 1968.
Kirby, S.H., Rheology of the Lithosphere. Rev. Geophysics and Space Phys., 21: 1458-1487, 1983.
Kirby, S.H., and J.W. McCormick, Inelastic properties of rocks and minerals: strength and rheology. Handb. Phys. Prop. Rocks, Vol. III: CRC Press: 139-280, 1984.
Meissner, R., and J. Strehlau, Limits of stresses in the continental crust and their relation to the depth-frequency distribution of shallow earthquakes. Tectonics. 1: 73-89, 1982.
McGarr, A., and N.C. Gay, State of stress in the earth's crust. Ann. Rev. Earth Planet. Sci., 504-436, 1978.
McGarr, A., Some constraints on levels of shear stress in the crust from observation and theory. JGR. 85: 6231-6238, 1980.
Raleigh, C.B., J.H. Healy, and J.D. Bredehoft, Faulting and crustal stresses at Rangely, Colorado. Flow and Fracture of Rocks, Geophys. Monogr. AGU. 16: 275-284, 1972.

Rummel, F., Fracture and flow of rocks
and minerals. Landolt-Börnstein,
new Series, V, 1b (Phys. Prop. Rocks).
141-238, Springer, 1982.

Rummel, F., G. Möhring-Erdmann, and J.
Baumgärtner, State of stress in the
continental crust and crustal stability. Spec. Issue "Physics of
Fracturing and Seismic Energy
Release. (ed. L. Waniek), Pageoph,
in press.

Smith, R.B., and R.L. Bruhn, Intraplate
extensional tectonics of the Eastern
Basin-Range. JGR. 89: 5733-5762, 1984.

TABLE I
    In-situ stress data from deep hydraulic fracturing measurements.
    Data are presented according to eq. (7). For references see
    Rummel et al. (1986).

location	rock () density	depth, km () number of fracs	S_h/S		S_H/S		references	1(3)
			α_h	β_h	α_H	β_H		
Germany								
Falkenberg, SE Germany N 49 52'/E 12 12'	granite (2.65)	to 0.5 (35)	0.05	0.58	0.13	0.49	Baumgärtner et al., 1986	
average SE German block	--- (2.65)	to 0.5 (8120)	0.035	0.8	0.031	1.3	Rummel et al., 1983	
Konzen, Stavelot-Venn N 50 36'/E 06 16'	shales, silt- stones, granites (2.8)	0.1 - 0.5 (9)	0.034	1.06	0	1.82	Rummel & Baumgärtner, 198	
Sweden								
Stripa mine, central Sweden	granite (2.65)	to 0.38 (15)	0.08	1.04	0.13	1.54	Doe et al., 1981	
Fjällbäcka, Bohus granite massif, north of Gothen- borg N 58 20'/E 11 20'	granite (2.65)	to 0.5 (8)	-0.17	1.44	0.11	0.92	Baumgärtner & Rummel, 198	
United Kingdom								
CMS hole RH12, Carnmenel- lis granite massif, Corn- wall	granite (2.65)	to 2 (13)	0.15	0.5	0.58	1.06	Batchelor, 1984	

France   2(3)

Location	Rock type (density)	Depth range (n)					Reference
Le Mayet de Montagne, Vichy, NE Massif Central N 46 10'/E 03 30'	granite (2.7)	0.05 - 0.2 (7)	0.004	0.87	0.27	0.01	Cornet & Valette, 1984
Auriat sur Vige, Creux, NW Massif Central	granite (2.7)	0.24 - 1.0 (12)	-0.140	0.83	-0.045	1.18	Cornet, 1983
		0.1 - 1.0 (14)	-0.023	0.72	-0.068	1.09	Baumgärtner & Rummel, 1982
Echassieres, Vichy, N Massif Central	granite (2.65)	0.1 - 0.4 (8)	0.12	0.50	0.28	0.23	Baumgärtner & Rummel, 1986
		0.4 - 0.7 (6)	0.30	0.42	0.68	1.19	

Island

Location	Rock type (density)	Depth range (n)					Reference
Reydarfjördur, E-coast	basalt (2.75)	to 0.27 (16)	0.078	0.59	0.12	0.59	Haimson & Rummel, 1982

USA

Location	Rock type (density)	Depth range (n)					Reference
Auburn, N. Y.	paleozoic sediments (2.6)	0.6 - 1.5 (4)	-0.15	0.91	-0.38	1.55	Hickmann et al., 1985
Alma, N. Y.	--- (2.65)	to 0.503 (1)	---	1.0	---	1.54	Haimson, 1974
Ithaka, Michigan Basin	sediments (2.65)	1.2 - 5.3 (5)	0.04	0.69	0.13	1.00	Haimson, 1978
Darlington, Ontario	limestone (2.65)	to 0.21 (6)	0.30	0.15	0.46	0.15	Haimson & Doe, 1983
	granitic gneiss (2.65)	0.23 - 0.3 (4)	0.35	0.31	0.62	0.35	
UPH3, Illinois	granite (2.65)	0.65 - 1.65 (19)	0.33	0.73	0.79	0.88	Haimson & Doe, 1983
Great Lake Region	--- (2.65)	to 1.5	0.13	0.77	0.27	1.27	Haimson & Doe, 1983
Bad Creek, South Carolina	gneiss (2.65)	0.1 - 0.27 (7)	-0.12	3.08	-0.31	5.38	Haimson, 1981
Monticello, S-Carolina	granodiorite (2.7)	0.1 - 0.96 (11)	0.08	0.65	0.07	1.16	Zebach & Hickmann, 1982
Ira McCoy well 20403, Rome Basin, W-Virginia	devonian shale (2.69)	at 0.837 (1)	---	0.74	---	1.37	Abou-Sayed et al., 1978
Valders, Wisconsin N 44.1 /W 87.9	--- (2.65)	to 0.17	0.21	0.77	0.25	1.54	Haimson & Doe, 1983
Waterloo, Wisconsin N 43.2 /W 89.0	quartzite (2.65)	to 0.24 (13)	0.21	0.31	0.36	0.46	Haimson & Doe, 1983

continuation Table I

USA

Anna, Ohio	dolomite (2.65)	to 0.17 (43)	0.20	0.54	0.39	0.54	Haimson, 1982
Rangely, Colorado N 40.1 /W 108.9	sandstone	at 1.9 (1)	---	0.72	---	1.36	Haimson, 1979
Green River Basin, Wyoming N 42.5 /W 109	--- (2.31)	at 2.775 (1)	---	0.83	---	1.29	in: Haimson, 1977
Kellogg, Idaho N 47.33 /W 116.06	quartzite (2.77)	at 2.285 (1)	---	0.42	---	0.69	in: Haimson, 1977
LASL-HDR site, Jemes Mountain, New Mexico N 35.9 /W 106.8	granite (2.65)	0.76 - 3.0 (3)	0.29	0.45	---	---	in: Haimson, 1977
Farmington, New Mexico	(2.30)	at 0.93 (1)	---	0.69	---	1.00	in: Haimson, 1977
Nevada Test Site, Nevada N 37 /W 116	tuff (1.83)	to 0.25 (7)	-0.06	0.67	0.06	1.17	Haimson, 1981
Helms, Sierra Nevada	granite (2.75)	0.1 - 0.3 (9)	0.19	0.22	-0.024	1.30	Haimson, 1981
Kerckhoff -2, Sierra Nevada, Fresino, Cal. N 37 04'/W 119 3'	granodiorite (2.75)	to 0.1 (12)	0.13	0.74	0.26	0.81	Haimson, 1979
San Andreas Fault, Cal.	sediments	to 0.85	0.11	0.73	0.18	1.32	Zoback et al., 1980 McGarr et al., 1982
USA average	--- (2.55)	to 5 (Ø30)	0.080	0.640	0.30	0.96	Haimson, 1978

India

NGRI campus test hole, Hyderabad, Andra Pradesh N 17 25'/E 78 33'	granite (2.7)	to 0.15 (8)	0.10	0.94	0.10	1.69	Gowd et al., 1985

Japan

Kanto-Tokai area	various types (2.24)	0.1 - 0.8 (88)	0.15	0.64	0.25	0.82	Tsukahara & Ikeda, 1986

2. Methods for rock stress measurement

Proceedings of the International Symposium on Rock Stress and Rock Stress Measurements/Stockholm/1-3 September 1986

Low-cost monitoring of strain changes

F. KOHLBECK
A.E. SCHEIDEGGER
Technical University, Vienna, Austria

A low-cost automatic system based on the strain cell technique, suitable for the monitoring of strain (and stress) changes occurring in tunnels and mines over periods of up to several months, is described. Specific instances of the recording of the strain changes appearing in connection with the advance of stoping opera- tions and with the occurrence of rock bursts are presented.

Es wird ein billiges automatisches System zur Aufzeichnung von Dehnungs- (Spannungs-) aenderungen in Tunneln und Bergbauen beschrieben. Das System basiert auf der Dehnmessstreifen-Technik und ist fuer Langzeitmessungen ueber mehrere Monate ohne weitere Ueberwachung geeignet. Es werden Ergebnisse der Messung in Zusammenhang mit dem Fortschreiten eines Abbaues und dem Auftreten von Bergschlae- gen dargestellt.

Un systeme bon-marche est decrit qui est utile pour la determination des change ments des deformations et des contraintes dans un tunnel ou dans une mine pendant des periodes de quelques mois. On presente des cas specifiques de la determination des changements des deformations en connexion avec les operations mineres.

1 INTRODUCTION

It is desirable to know the stresses appearing in tunnels, dams, barriers and mines as accurately as possible. Knowledge of the rock stresses is also important for earthquake research and for research in the area of geodynamics. As it is difficult to measure stresses directly, one usually measures strains instead, and calculates the stresses from these. Absolute measurements of stresses in situ are generally not feasible because of the time and cost involved. In tunnels and mines convergence measurements are usually made by means of extensometers (Şchuermann, 1975; Siska, 1967) but usually only in one direction and manually. One hopes to automate the process in the near future (Olsen et al. 1977).

In mining operations the stability of slopes and the occurrence of rock bursts are serious problems. Because of the close relationship between micro- seismology and rock bursts, a knowledge of the stress field is important in establishing safety measures. Because of the technical difficulties in

measuring stresses, usually only seismic and seismoacoustic measurements are taken. Although dangerous areas can be located with those methods (Blake, 1971; Simone et al., 1981; Sibek et al., 1964) accurate statements regarding the size and slope of the stress changes can only be made by the use of direct measurements (Shepherd et al., 1981; Abel and Lee, 1973). The influence of active tectonics on rock bursts is not clear (Rainer, 1974).

A knowledge of the neotectonic stress field is also important for civil engineers because of the possible presence of large horizontal stresses which are not predictable without measurements (Gu et al., 1984). Exten- sometermeasurements in stopes (Bostrom, 1981) and measurements of deformations and stresses in the forefield of mine workings have been proven useful (Braeuner, 1974).It is desirable, how- ever, to monitor the entire mine, and therefore all mining-induced stress changes, with a network of automatically controlled instruments (Stillborg et al., 1983). The problem of measurements of stress changes has been discussed by AMADEI (1985), but no successful measurements of the long-term changes in stress fields referring to the complete stress tensor have been reported heretofore. This paper describes the development of a long-term stable system for measuring changes of the stress tensor.

2 REQUIREMENTS FOR A MEASURING SYSTEM

An instrument suitable for automatically monitoring a mine should fulfill the following requirements:
1) Only elastic changes should be measured in order to calculate the stresses. Accordingly, instruments with a base larger than 10cm appear to be unsuitable, as in the mountains longer distances usually contain joints.
2) All 6 components of the deformation tensor and additional components for control purposes should be measured.
3) All uncertainities in measuring strains should not exceed 10E-7. In comparison to this the slip rate on the San Andreas fault corresponds to strain rate of 10E-7/a to 10E-6/ (Thatcher,1983).Tidal strain reach 10E- (Bostrom, 1981) while nearby micro seismic events may involve strains up t 10E-6, but are more commony only aroun 10E-8. Strains induced by min excavations may reach values of 10E- just before fracture (Abel, 1973).
4) The measurements should be full automatic and should be made severa times during a day in order to registe short term events.
5) The instrument and its operatio should be inexpensive in order to permi installation at as many locations a posssible.

In order to keep costs as low a possible, the measurements are to b similar to those using triaxial cells c Leeman (1971) with strain gauges. I should be noted, however, that in thi case the accuracy requirements set for in paragraph 3 above can only be m with difficulty.

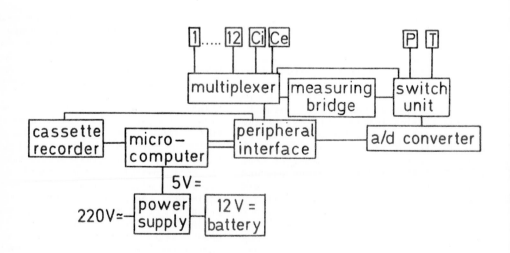

Fig. 1.   Block   diagram   of   monitoringsystem
          1...12   strain gauges
          Ci, Ce   internal and external references
          P,T   pressure and temperature gauges

3 MEASURING INSTRUMENTS

The basic design of the measuring system is depicted in Fig. 1. The central control of the installation is effected with a microcomputer board (with a 6502 microprocessor, in ROM Basic Module, 16 k RAM, serial I/0 port, cassette interface, monitor output and keyboard). The connection to the multiplex units which connect the external strain gauges (<1> ... <12>, <Ci> , <Ce>) to the measuring bridge, is made with a peripheral interface adapter (PIA). In addition, a temperature sensor and a pressure sensor are selected. All measurements are transmitted by an AC/DC converter and the PIA to the computer. The measurement values can be recorded on a cassette tape recorder. A battery supported network power supply unit (and a charging unit) provide the power for the computer even an eventual day-long power failure. The AC/DC converter operates according to the dual slope principle and by employing an integration time of about 0.2 seconds amply supresses high frequency disturbances. By the use of specialized technology, the carrier frequency measuring bridge requires no capacitive balance. The measured values can be recorded digitally to 0.1 m/m. The high accuracy is obtained by using full bridges which are switched by means of 3-position mercury relais where the errors that would otherwise normally be very large, are very small. In addition to the twelve active strain gauges <1> ...<12>, 2 resistance bridges Ci and Ce are connected. Ci is an internal reference consisting of interconnected precision resistors. This serves as the control of the measuring instrument. Ce is a further reference bridge located in the drill-hole near the active gauges. This bridge contains an active strip which is glued to a core of the drill hole. The bridge is sealed against water and permits the separate observation of the effects of temperature changes on the strain gauges. The measuring instrument runs virtually unattended. Only the cassettes must be changed every 2-4 weeks. The measurement and storage of the data are controlled by a "BASIC" program which greatly improves the quality of the data. The electrical current used for the strain gauges raises the temperature in the strips and consequently has an undesir-

able effect on the measured values. To eliminate this effect, each location is measured several times until three identical measurements are obtained (within a range of error). The average value is recorded. An upper limit for the number of measurements prevents undue lingering at any one location in the event of an error. A detailed description of the instrumentation has been given by Jaeger (1982).

4 MEASURING CELLS

The measuring cells present the greatest problem in the measuring system since standard strain gauges are not suitable owing to the diffusion of moisture into the devices. Measuring cells well tested in a damp medium, as for instance welded extension cells or vibrating wire gauges (Bordes and Debreuille, 1983; Di Biagio, 1983), only measure in one or at most in 3 directions. It was now attempted to protect the measuring cells from the humidity in the rock pores with metal foil (Al or Cu). Triaxial cells after Leeman made by Luwes instruments were only partially successful. The undesirable drift in the measuring cells caused by humidity amounted to 10 m/m/day (Kohlbeck and Scheidegger, 1983). Substantially better results were obtained with CSIRO hollow inclusion cells (Askew and Lee, 1982). These cells contain 9 strain gauges in an epoxy plastic cylinder with walls about 2 mm thick. The space between the cell and the interior surface of the drillhole is filled with an adhesive and is about 1mm thick.,
Thus, the construction permits mounting even in percussively drilled holes although rotary drilling is preferred. The electrical connections of the gauges are made with quarter bridges which make it difficult to compensate for the effect of temperature changes. A detailed description of the mounting of the cells has been given by Stillborg and Leijan (1982).
Vibrating wire gauges are much less sensitive to humidity than strain gauges. A stainless material must be used under wet conditions. A vibrating wire strain gauge of the firm Gage Technique was used. The two heads of the gauge are attached to the test body and have no further interconnection apart from the wire. With the exception of the

tension of the wire no additional forces act on the body when measuring displacements. For mounting in a borehole, a special device was developed where the gauge heads were clamped to the borehole walls. To test the measuring instrument and the clamping device, the wire strain gauge was mounted in a hollow rock cylinder in the labratory under in situ conditions. Four strain gauges were glued to the outside walls of the cylinder at the height of the vibrating wire gauge. The values of the instrument were compared in an uniaxial pressure experiment. There was an agreement of the strains within 1.E-6 which corresponds also to the resolution of the digital-display.

5 MEASURING AND RESULTS

The measurements were taken in various drives of the lead mine at Bleiberg, Carinthia, Austria. The rock was Triassic limestone, the depths ranged from 250 to 700 m below the surface. The diameter of the boreholes was 36 mm;they were approximately horizontal with a slight slant towards the mouth of the borehole in order to prevent water from collecting. The holes were between 1 m and 4 m deep, the rock was limestone; it

was completely saturated with water. T measuring installation has been operation for more than 3 years. Brea downs occurred only when the pow failed for more than one day, when t cassettes were not changed as order and when rock bursts caused damage the system.

The measurements with Leeman's CS cells proved that the measureme converter is significantly more accura than the cells and that temperatu variations in the drillhole were le than 0.1 C. As a result, the Australi CSIRO cells were not completed with fu bridges. A CSIRO cell was installed in drive in which stress phenomena we manifest about 20 m above a stopi operation. The outer surface of the ce was laminated with aluminium foil a then glued in. The first measurement taken every 2 hours, were made with minimum resolution of 1 μm/m. Fig. shows results for a measuring interv of 25 days (June 5 - 29, 1984). T apparent strain changes were attribut to the stoping operation which w advancing towards the installation sit No further evidence could be obtaine however, for showing that the measur values really correspond to stre changes.

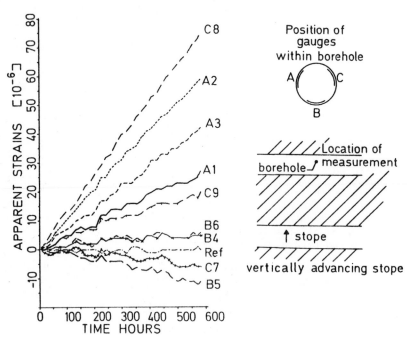

Fig.2. Measured strains with CSIRO strain cell and location of measurement with respect to the upward advance of the stoping operations

192

Consequently, a vibrating wire instrument was installed 1 m away from the CSIRO cell and these strain values were also entered into the microcomputer.

The sensitivity of the display of the strain gauge was raised to 0.1 μm/m. Fig. 3 shows the strain measurements recorded with reference to the first value of this measuring period. A shift in all values including those from the vibrating wire instrument occurred at the beginning of the period and on the 9th day. One can assume therefore that this is the result of a rockburst and not a measurement error. The increasing pressure of all gages can be interpreted as follows: The rock burst is equivalent of failing of one link of the natural tunnel lining. Therefore the remaining lining has to support more load. The occurrence on the rockburst was not preceded by any distinguishable changes in the strain values. This is in accordance with the substantially more accurate measurements of volume strains by McGarr et al. (1982) with a Sacks Everton strain measurement device that were performed at much greater cost elsewhere.

6 CONCLUSIONS

In conclusion it may be stated that it has been established that a primarily unattended recording of strain changes occurring within periods of months is possible with an inexpensive measuring instrument by using strain gauges. The simultaneous recording of 6 or more components of the strain tensor enabled us to study the strain changes appearing in connection with the advancing of drives or stopping operations and the stress changes connected with the occurrence of rock bursts.

7 ACKNOWLEDGEMENTS

The work reported here was supported by the Austrian Fund for the Advancement of Scientific Research (Oesterreichischer Fonds zur Foerderung der Wissenschaftlichen Forschung) under project number 4785. The calculations were performed through the courtesy of the Computing Center of the Technical University of Vienna. Much help with the experiments was also given by the mine management of the Bleiberger Bergwerks Union. The authors wish to acknowledge this support.

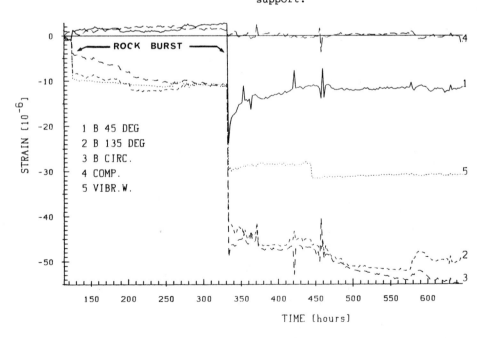

Fig.3. Sudden stress changes with rock burst. Negative values indicate pressure short peaks are instrumental noise.

8 REFERENCES

Abel, F.J. and Lee, F.T. 1973. Stress changes ahead of an advancing tunnel. Int. J. Rock Mech. Min. Sci. & Geomech. Abstr. 10: 673-697

Amadei, B. 1985. Measurement of Stress Change in Rock. Technical Note. Int. J. Rock Mech. Min. Sci. & Geomech. Abstr. 22(3): 177-182

Askew, J.E. and Lee, M.F. 1982. Field Manual C.S.I.R.O. HI Stress Gauge. Rock Instruments P.O. Box 209, Warwick QlD 4370, Australia: 1-33

Blake, W. 1971. Rockburst research at the galena mine, Wallace, Idaho. Bureau of Mines, U.S. Department of the Interior, Denver, TPR 39: 1-22

Bordes, J.L. and Debreuille, P.J. 1983. Borehole monitoring instrumentation for rock mechanics. Proc. Internat. Sympos. on Field Measurements in Geomechanics, Zuerich, 1: 31-48

Bostrom, R.C. 1981. Lithosphere Creep. J. Phys. Earth 29: 145-161 Braeuner, G., Baule, H. and Schluckebier, F. 1974. Spannungsaenderungen und seismische Aktivitaet im Vorfeld eines Strebes. Glueckauf 110(20): 825-830

Di Biagio, E. 1983. Instruments and instrumentation techniques used to monitor the performance of offshore structures. Proc. Interant. Sympos. on Field Measurements in Geomechanics, Zuerich, 1: 4 05-435

Gu Heng-Yue, Ai Nan-Shan, Zhu Hua-Ren and Chian Shan-Rung 1984. The macro and micro analysis of the environmental stressfield in tunnel engineering. Conference on low cost Road Tunnels, Oslo, Procee dings 2, Tapir: 609-624

Jaeger, F. 1982. Aufbau einer Anlage fuer langzeitstabile DMS-Messungen, Diplomarbeit, TU Wien, 60p.

Kohlbeck, F. and Scheidegger, A.E. 1983. Application of strain gages on rock and concrete. Proc. Internat. Sympos. on Field Measurements in Geomechanics, Zrich 1: 197-207

Leary, P.C. 1985. Near surface stre and displacement in a layered elast crust. J. Geophys. Res. 90: 1901-1910

Leeman, E.R. 1971. The CSIR "doo stopper" and triaxial rock stre measuring instruments. Rock Mech. 3: 2! 50

Mc Garr, A., Sacks, I.S., Linde, A.T Spottiswoode, S.M. and Green, R.W.] 1982. Coseismic and other short te strain changes recorded with Sack Everton strainmeters in a deep min South Africa. Geophys. J.R. Astr. Soc 70: 717-740

Nocke, H. 1972. Eine Gebirgsschla hypothese. Glueckauf-Forschungshe 33(1): 10-18

Olsen, A.J., Bryont, J.M., Pende M.J., Salt, P.E. 1977. Instrumentatic for Tunneling. Proc. Symp. "Tunneling i New Zealand", Hamilton, N.Z.; Instr Engrs., P.O. Box 12231, Wellington North 3(5): 14-25

Poskitt, T., Cuthbest, L. 198 Reliable instrumentation for fiel measurements on piles. Proc. Internat Sympos. on Field Measurements in Geome chanics, Zrich 1: 523-532

Rainer, H. 1974. Gibt es Zusammenhaeng zwischen Erdbeben und Gebirgsschlag haeufungen im Bergbau Bleiberg? Roc Mech. 6: 91-100

Schuermann, F. 1975. Das Messen vc Gebirgsbewegungen mit Langmeaanker Glueckauf 111(13): 625-631

Shepherd,J., Rixon,L.K. and Griffiths,L 1981. Outbursts and geologica structures in coal mines: A review Int J. Rock Mech. Min. Sci. 18: 267-283

Sibek, V., Simone, J. and Buben, J 1964. Methods of research int rockbursts in the Czechoslovak Socialis Republic. Internat. Conf. on Strat Control and Rock Mechanics, New York 422-433

Simone, J., Sklenor, J., Hribernigg, H., Kostelka, L. and Rainer H. 1981 Seismoakustische Untersuchungen zur Vorhersage von Gebirgsschlaegen, Berg- und Huettenmaenn. Monatsh.118 (12): 375-384

Siska, L. 1967. Der Konvergenzverlauf als ein Mass fuer die Gebirgschlaggeber, Glueckauf-Forschungshefte 28(2): 57-65

Stillborg, B. and Leijan, G. 1982. A comparative study of rock stress measurements at Loussavaara mine. Report FB 8217. Swedish Mining Research Foundation Box 814-981, 28, Kiruna, Sweden, 108p.

Stillborg, B., Pekkari, S., Pekkari, R. 1983. In: Advanced Rock Mechanics. Monitoring System. Proc. Internat-Sympos. On Field Measurements in Geomechanics, Zrich 2: 1215-1228

Thatcher, W. 1983. Nonlinear Strain Building and the earthquake cycle on the San Adreas Fault. J. Geophys. Res., 88: 5893-5902

Rock stress measurements performed by Swedish State Power Board

L. HALLBJÖRN
Swedish State Power Board, Stockholm, Sweden

Abstract

The Swedish State Power Board´s (SSPB) equipment for three-dimensional rock stress measurements in vertical boreholes was developed about 10 years ago. It is based on use of strain gauges and overcoring. Measurements have been performed in water-filled boreholes down to a depth of 500 m. The equipment has also been used in a 45° inclined borehole of 90 m length. A modified probe pushed by plastic pipes has been used from tunnels in horizontal and upwards inclined boreholes of up to 45 m length.

Résumé

L'équipement utilisé par la Direction nationale de l'énergie électrique de Suède pour la mesure tridimensionnelle des contraintes dans la roche dans des trous forés verticalement a été mis au point il y a 10 ans. Il est fondé sur l'emploi de capteurs extensométriques à fil résistant et la détente par trous cylindriques concentriques. Des mesures ont été effectuées jusqu'à des profondeurs de 500 mètres dans des trous de forage remplis d'eau. L'équipement a également servi dans des trous forés inclinés à 45° d'une longueur de 90 mètres. Une canne-jauge modifiée insérée dans le trou à l'aide de tubes en plastique a été utilisée à partir de tunnels dans des trous de forage horizontaux et inclinés vers le haut faisant jusqu'à 45 mètres de longueur.

Zusammenfassung

Die Ausrüstung der Schwedischen Staatlichen Kraftwerksverwaltung zur dreidimensionalen Gebirgsdruckmessung wurde vor zehn Jahren entwickelt. Sie gründet sich auf den Einsatz von Dehnungsmesstreifen-Gebern in Verbindung mit entspannendem Überbohren. In wassergefüllten Bohrlöchern wurden Messungen bis zu einer Tiefe von 500 m vorgenommen. Ferner wurde die Ausrüstung in Bohrlöchern von 45° Neigung und 90 m Länge eingesetzt. Eine mit Hilfe von Kunststoffrohr in das Bohrloch eingeschobene Sonde wurde, ausgehend von Tunneln, in bis zu 45 m langen, waagerechten und nach oben geneigten Bohrlöchern verwendet.

1. INTRODUCTION

Rock caverns and tunnels are being constructed in increasing numbers for a variety of purposes. The state of stress in the rock has influence on the stability and tightness of the rock mass. The stresses may therefore also influence the location, orientation and shape of rock chambers and on required strengthening and tightening measures.

There are considerable variations in the rock stresses between different places on the ground surface and also between different depths below the surface. The natural state of stress in a block of rock in situ can be considered as being the sum of three different states of stress: a) overall stress due to tectonic and gravitional forces under the assumption that the rock is homogeneous, b) variations from the above state due to the inhomogeneity in the rock mass, i. e. the influence of joints, fractured zones and local contact zones between blocks etc and c) residual stresses in each separate block.

The three-dimensional state of stress in a certain point in a block is characterized by three generally different principal stresses and their directions at right angles to each other. Each of the three above-mentioned states of stress has its own principal stresses with its own directions for each point in the block. As a rule no principal stress is exactly horizontal or vertical.

For judgement and calculation of rock stability and tightness knowledge about the overall stresses (a) above is desired. Local stress measurements in boreholes give the sum of the three influencing stresses and the desired separate overall stress can then be obtained only by taking the mean value from some measurements following each other. Local variations and residual stresses will then be neutralized.

For measurement of stresses in a rock mass prior to the start of construction a measuring probe is needed which can operate in deep water-filled boreholes. The main problems are how to get the strain gauges glued automatically to the borehole wall, how to glue the strain gauges under several hundred metres of water and how to measure from such a long distance.

For measurements around a rock cavern or tunnel a measuring probe is needed which can operate in holes in any direction i. e. also in holes inclined upwards and downwards.

2 THE SSPB-HILTSCHER ROCK STRESS MEASURING SYSTEM

The above-mentioned intention to realize three-dimensional rock stress measurements in great depths below ground surface and also around rock caverns and tunnels is fulfilled by the SSPB-Hiltscher rock stress measuring system. It is based on the use of strain gauges and overcoring.

The system developed for measurements in great depths was developed 10 years ago by Dr Rudolf Hiltscher. Measurements have been performed in water-filled boreholes down to 500 m depth. The equipment has also been used in a 45° inclined borehole of 90 m length. A detailed description of the measuring system has been published (Hiltscher, Martna, Strindell 1979). Only the main features will be mentioned below.

The original type of probe was later modified by Lars Strindell into a design which permits measurements around caverns and tunnels. Measurements have been performed in up to 45 m long horizontal and inclined boreholes.

3 MEASUREMENT PROCEDURE

The rock stress measurement procedure is illustrated in Fig 1. The small core is taken up to ground surface (step d) and inspected. Then it can be judged if the actual part of the rock is free from cracks and suitable for gluing the strain gauges. Gluing is done in step f and first rea-

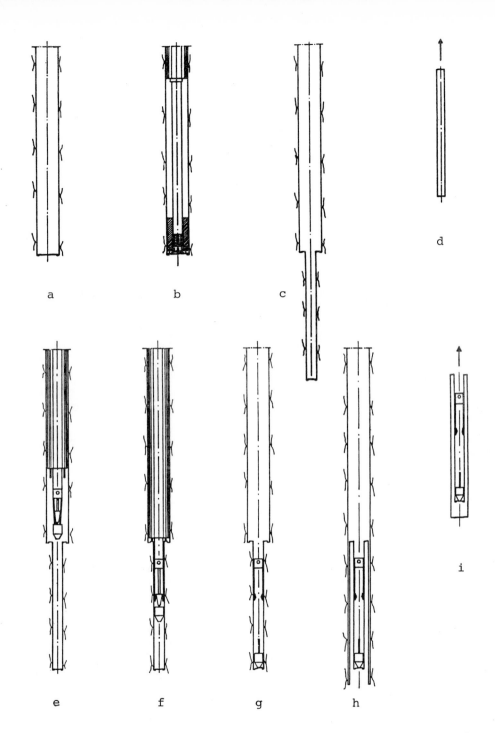

Fig 1. Procedure for cementing and measuring. a) Ø76 mm borehole.
b) Centering Ø36 mm bit. c) Ø36 mm borehole. d) Inspection of
small core. e) Probe before releasing the mechanism. f) Cementing gauges to the small borehole wall under pressure from
cone, first measurement. g) Release of the carrier and hoisting
of the probe. h) Overcoring. i) Second measurement.

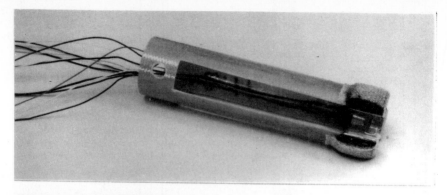

Fig 2. Strain gauge assemblies, for "vertical" probe
(top) and for "horizontal" or "inclined" probe
(bottom).

dings are done after a couple of
hours when the glue has hardened.
By overcoring (step h) the rock
hollow-core is stress-relieved
and zero-readings are done when
it has been taken up to the ground.
Three consecutive readings are
made before and after overcoring.
The hollow-core must be treated
in such a manner that least possible influence of temperature
variation occurs.

4 STRAIN GAUGE ASSEMBLY AND GLUE

The strain gauge assemblies are
shown in Fig 2. Each assembly has
three plastic tongues with a butyl-
rubber tape pad, strain-gauge
rosette and a layer of polyurethane foam. The tongues are 120°
apart and each rosette consists
of three strain gauges, one longitudinal, one transverse and one

45° in-between. The purpose of t
polyurethane foam is to hold a
sufficient amount of glue immediately before pressing the plasti
tongue with the strain gauge rosette against the borehole wall.

The glue is an acryl-resin,
metamethylacrylate monomer, with
catalyst, bensoylperoxide, and a
coupling agent. The glue must
have a certain viscosity and a p
life of about 20 minutes which i
attained by proper measures i. e
storing cold in a freezer, sometimes increasing the viscosity
by heat-treatment, mixing young
and old resin and test mixing be
fore measurements. If the weathe
is hot on the site when measurin
a cold box must be used.

5 MEASURING PROBES

The probes are shown in Figs 3

200

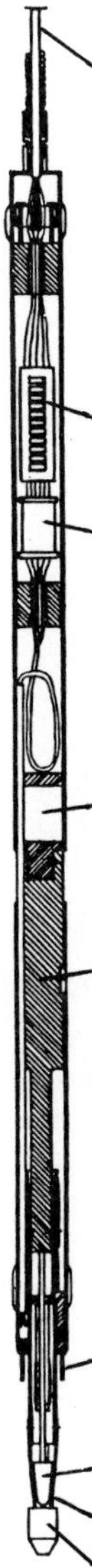

combined measuring
and carrying cable

electronic unit

passive strain
gauges

compass

weight

pins for releasing
the mechanism

cone

strain gauge carrier

glue pot with strain
gauges inside

and 4. The "vertical" probe, Fig 3,
hangs in a combined carrying and
measuring cable. The cable contains a carrying part of kevlar
and 12 conductors. The strain
gauges are submerged in glue in
a glue pot at the bottom end of
the probe. When the pinpoints
touch the bottom of the large
borehole the mechanism is released and the cone is pushed
downwards by the weight (including the upper part of the probe).
The glue pot sinks down to the
bottom of the small borehole and
the strain gauges are pressed to
the borehole wall by the cone.

During the glue hardening time
of two hours a pre-heated liquid
around the compass-needle, giving
the orientation of the probe,
solidifies by change of temperature. The liquid mix must be modified depending on the actual rock
temperature, from $+6^{\circ}C$ in northern
Sweden to, for instance, $+27^{\circ}C$ in
hot countries.

Measurements are made three
times from the ground surface
and the switching between the
strain gauges is made by the
electronic unit inside the probe
monitored from the ground surface.

When the probe is hoisted after
measurements have been made, the
carrier conductors are automatically disconnected. The carrier
with the strain gauges is left in
the small hole.

Fig 3 (left). Probe for rock
stress measurements in vertical
boreholes.

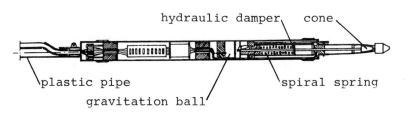

hydraulic damper   cone

plastic pipe

gravitation ball

spiral spring

Fig 4. Probe for rock stress measurements in horizontal and inclined boreholes.

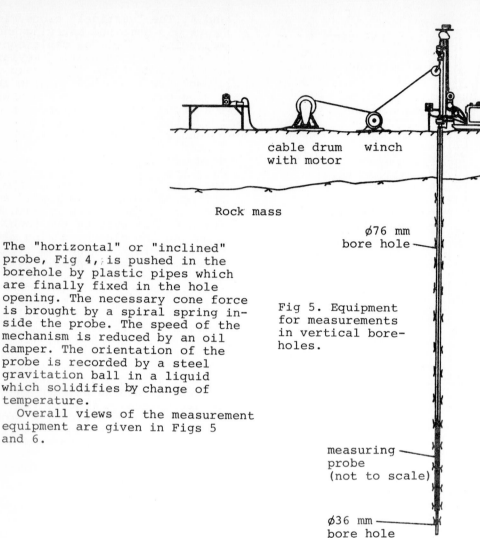

cable drum   winch
with motor

Rock mass

⌀76 mm
bore hole

The "horizontal" or "inclined"
probe, Fig 4, is pushed in the
borehole by plastic pipes which
are finally fixed in the hole
opening. The necessary cone force
is brought by a spiral spring inside the probe. The speed of the
mechanism is reduced by an oil
damper. The orientation of the
probe is recorded by a steel
gravitation ball in a liquid
which solidifies by change of
temperature.

    Overall views of the measurement
equipment are given in Figs 5
and 6.

Fig 5. Equipment
for measurements
in vertical bore-
holes.

measuring
probe
(not to scale)

⌀36 mm
bore hole

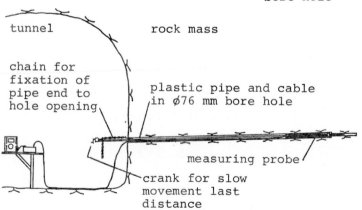

tunnel   rock mass

chain for
fixation of
pipe end to
hole opening

plastic pipe and cable
in ⌀76 mm bore hole

measuring probe

crank for slow
movement last
distance

Fig 6. Equipment for measurements in horizontal
and inclined boreholes.

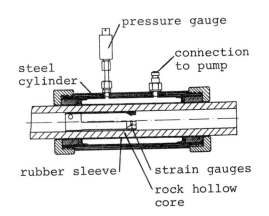

pressure gauge

connection to pump

steel cylinder

rubber sleeve

strain gauges

rock hollow core

Fig 7. Calibration of rock hollow-core with radial hydraulic pressure.

6 CALIBRATION

The rock hollow-cores are test loaded afterwards. In a device shown in Fig 7 a hydraulic pressure acts radially on the outer surface of the hollow-core. Strain gauge readings are taken at different load levels. From this it can be judged whether the strain gauges are properly cemented to the rock or not. In almost all cases they are so. From the readings Young's modulus (E) and Poisson's ratio (ν) are calculated.

When a hollow-core is too short to be calibrated in the calibration cylinder E and ν are usually taken from another hollow-core in the vicinity.

The hollow-cores and strain gauges can also be tested and calibrated by axial pressure.

7 RESULTS

The three-dimensional state of stress is calculated using a personal computer. To obtain a representative mean state of stress in a part of a rock mass usually three consecutive full measurements are performed. The mean state of stress is calculated from the mean values of the normal and shear stresses in a fixed x-y-z-coordinate system.

There is some difficulty in

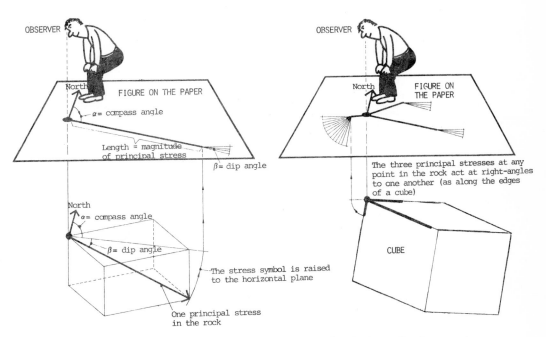

Fig 8. A way to show the three-dimensional state of stress in a two-dimensional figure.

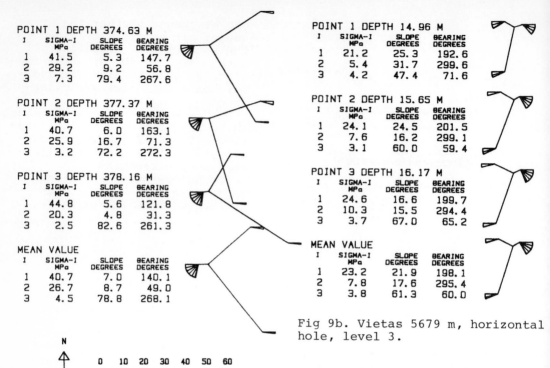

POINT 1 DEPTH 374.63 M

I	SIGMA-I MPa	SLOPE DEGREES	BEARING DEGREES
1	41.5	5.3	147.7
2	29.2	9.2	56.8
3	7.3	79.4	267.6

POINT 2 DEPTH 377.37 M

I	SIGMA-I MPa	SLOPE DEGREES	BEARING DEGREES
1	40.7	6.0	163.1
2	25.9	16.7	71.3
3	3.2	72.2	272.3

POINT 3 DEPTH 378.16 M

I	SIGMA-I MPa	SLOPE DEGREES	BEARING DEGREES
1	44.8	5.6	121.8
2	20.3	4.8	31.3
3	2.5	82.6	261.3

MEAN VALUE

I	SIGMA-I MPa	SLOPE DEGREES	BEARING DEGREES
1	40.7	7.0	140.1
2	26.7	8.7	49.0
3	4.5	78.8	268.1

N

0 10 20 30 40 50 60

SCALE OF STRESSES MPA

Fig 9a. Forsmark DBT-1, level 9.

POINT 1 DEPTH 33.96 M

I	SIGMA-I MPa	SLOPE DEGREES	BEARING DEGREES
1	15.0	0.1	228.2
2	8.2	13.5	138.2
3	5.8	76.5	318.5

POINT 2 DEPTH 34.64 M

I	SIGMA-I MPa	SLOPE DEGREES	BEARING DEGREES
1	11.8	4.2	58.2
2	7.2	28.3	150.5
3	5.3	61.3	320.5

POINT 3 DEPTH 34.94 M

I	SIGMA-I MPa	SLOPE DEGREES	BEARING DEGREES
1	16.9	5.1	236.9
2	11.2	15.7	145.5
3	7.3	73.5	344.5

MEAN VALUE

I	SIGMA-I MPa	SLOPE DEGREES	BEARING DEGREES
1	14.5	1.1	233.9
2	8.8	17.8	143.6
3	6.2	72.2	327.3

Fig 9c. Vietas 6029 m, level 2.

POINT 1 DEPTH 14.96 M

I	SIGMA-I MPa	SLOPE DEGREES	BEARING DEGREES
1	21.2	25.3	192.6
2	5.4	31.7	299.6
3	4.2	47.4	71.6

POINT 2 DEPTH 15.65 M

I	SIGMA-I MPa	SLOPE DEGREES	BEARING DEGREES
1	24.1	24.5	201.5
2	7.6	16.2	299.1
3	3.1	60.0	59.4

POINT 3 DEPTH 16.17 M

I	SIGMA-I MPa	SLOPE DEGREES	BEARING DEGREES
1	24.6	16.6	199.7
2	10.3	15.5	294.4
3	3.7	67.0	65.2

MEAN VALUE

I	SIGMA-I MPa	SLOPE DEGREES	BEARING DEGREES
1	23.2	21.9	198.1
2	7.8	17.6	295.4
3	3.8	61.3	60.0

Fig 9b. Vietas 5679 m, horizontal hole, level 3.

presenting the magnitudes and directions of the three principal stresses on paper because the state of stress is three-dimensional and the picture has only two dimensions. Fig 8 shows one possible method. The state of stress is seen from above, the stress vectors are turned vertically up to the horizontal plane and the dip angle is shown at the end of the line.

The results usually vary from point to point. Sometimes there are great local variations. Fig 9a-c shows measuring results from three places where the results from the different measuring points were quite uniform. Fig 9a shows the result from one level in the Forsmark 500 m-hole and Fig 9b-c shows results from the Vietas headrace tunnel. Note that the direction of the greatest principal stress in point 2, Fig 9c, seems to differ considerably from the others in direction, but that is not the case since the stress is almost horizontal in all three points.

Fig 10a-b shows horizontal and vertical stresses measured in a

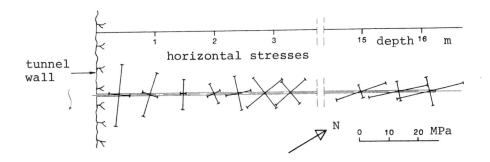

Fig 10a. Vietas headrace tunnel, 5679 m, horizontal stresses
measured in a horizontal borehole.

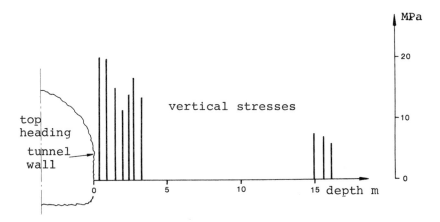

Fig 10b. Vietas headrace tunnel, 5679 m, vertical stresses
measured in a horizontal borehole.

horizontal borehole from the
Vietas headrace tunnel. The influence from the tunnel on the stresses in the vicinity can be seen.

During the ten years since 1976
three-dimensional rock stress
measurements with the described
SSPB-Hiltscher system have been
performed in many places in Sweden
and other countries. The method
has been used in connection with
hydropower stations and tunnels,
a subway station, ship-locks and
storage chambers for oil, gas,
hot water and nuclear waste. In
all measurements have been performed in some 360 points.

8 ACKNOWLEDGEMENTS

The author desires to express
his appreciation to Messrs

Lars Strindell, Kjell Ingevald,
Tage Öhman and Mats Andersson
for their development work in
the laboratory and field measurement work in Sweden and abroad.

9 REFERENCES

Hiltscher R, Martna J, Strindell L,
    1979. The measurement of tri-
    axial rock stresses in deep
    boreholes. Proceedings of the
    4. International Congress on
    Rock Mechanics, Montreux.
Martna J, Hiltscher R, Ingevald K,
    1983. Geology and rock stresses
    in deep boreholes at Forsmark
    in Sweden. Preprints, section F
    of the 5. International Congress
    on Rock Mechanics, Melbourne
    (Australia).

Hemispherical – ended borehole technique for measurement of absolute rock stress

K. SUGAWARA
Y. OBARA
K. KANEKO
T. AOKI
Faculty of Engineering, Kumamoto University, Kumamoto, Japan

Abstract
A hemispherical-ended borehole technique is presented to measure the complete state of in situ rock stress. The stress tensor is determined from 16 strains on the hemispherical bottom surface, in a single borehole. Details concerning an arrangement of strain gauges, observation equations and a continuous strain measurement system with the stress relief technique are presented and discussed. The usefulness of the present technique in the isotropic rock is verified by loading and unloading tests to the cubic rock specimens with an appropriately oriented borehole.

Resume
On propose la technique du trou percé anec un bout hemispherique pour mesurer l'état complet de la force du rocher. Le tenseur de tension est determiné par 16 distortions sur la surface hemispherique du fond dans un trou percé. On presente et traite de façon détaillé la disposition d'un jauge de tension, les equations d' observations et le système de mesure de la distorsion continue par la technique du soulagement de tension. L'efficacité de cette technique pour le rocher isotrope est verifiée par l'expérience de charge et decharge sur des specimens de roche cubique dont le trou percé est orienté de façon connenable.

Zusammenfassung
Zur Abmessung der vollstaendigen Spannungszustaende des liegenden Gebirges schlaegt man die Weise der Halbkugelbohrlochtiefsten vor. Die Spannungstensor wird durch sechzehnstueckige Beanspruchungen auf der Bohrlochtiefstenflaeche der Halbkugel im einzelnen Bohrloch entschieden. Die Einzelheit vom fortlaufenden Messungssystem der Beanspruchung durch Anordrung der Beanspruchungsgeraete, Messungsgleiche und Spannungsentlastungsweise wird vorgestellt und diskutiert. Die Wirksamkeit dieser Methode vom isotropischen Gebirge wird durch Be und-Entlastungspruefung der Gestein-Kubusprobe festgestellt, in der ein Bohrloch mit passender Richtung ist.

1. INTRODUCTION

Recent developments in rock engineering have required the improvement of the accuracy of the rock stress measurements in the field, and indicated the need for systematic stress measurements, e.g. systematic measurement of the stress distribution around rock caverns. In order to evaluate the complete state of stress at a certain point within a rock mass, the deformation of borehole, which is a function of the original stress, needs to be measured, by applying a stress relieving technique. Various types of device have been presented to measure the changes in length of borehole diameter, or to measure the changes in strain on the wall of the borehole. However, the methods which require two or more boreholes to determine the stress tensor are not desirable in consideration of the time, effort and costs involved.

A promising method is the stress tensor determination from the strains measured along the circumference of a single borehole, e.g. with three or more strain gauge rosettes (Leeman, 1968; Duncan and Pender, 1980; Amadei, 1984). However, it has been pointed out that, to adopt this method, the difficulty in direct bonding gages to the rock surface needs to be effectively resolved, and also that of obtaining an intact core with a sufficient length (Erer and Heidarieh-Zadeh, 1985).

In this paper, a hemispherical-ended boerhole technique is presented as a new approach to in situ stress measurements. Almost all of the strain measurements at the end of borehole have been performed on the flattened one, and a set of measurements in two or more boreholes, independent of each other, is necessary for determining the stress tensor, which can be only an average value over a considerable volume, (Hiramatsu and Oka, 1968 ; Sugawara and co-workers, 1985). The new method, presented in this paper, removes such a disadvantage by reforming the bottom into a hemispherical shape.

The theory of stress tensor determination from strains on the hemispherical bottom surface of a single borehole and the in situ strain measurement technique are presented. Additionally, the accuracy and sensitivity of the present method is examined by the laboratory borehole test.

2. THEORY

2.1 Strain on the Bottom Surface

As illustrated in Fig.1, the strains ε_θ and ε_ϕ on the hemispherical bottom of a borehole are measured to determine the original stresses, which exist prior to boring. For the analysis of the relation between the strain and the field stress, the cylindrical co-ordinates (r, θ, z), the spherical coordinates (ρ, θ, ϕ) and the Cartesian coordinates (x, y, z) are defined respectively, as shown in Fig.1, making the z-axis to coincide with the axis of borehole. Then the stress tensor at a certain point within the rock mass, existing prior to boring, can be represented by

$$\{\sigma\} = \{ \sigma_x, \sigma_y, \sigma_z, \tau_{yz}, \tau_{zx}, \tau_{xy} \}^T$$

referred to the Cartesian co-ordinates.

The strains ε_θ and ε_ϕ are related to the displacement components, u_ρ, u_θ and u_ϕ, referring to the spherical co-ordinates, as follows.

$$\varepsilon_\theta = \frac{1}{R} \cdot \frac{1}{\sin\phi} \cdot \frac{\partial u_\theta}{\partial \theta} + \frac{u_\rho}{R} + \frac{u_\phi}{R} \cdot \cot\phi ,$$

$$\varepsilon_\phi = \frac{1}{R} \cdot \frac{\partial u_\phi}{\partial \phi} + \frac{u_\rho}{R} , \quad (1)$$

where R is the radius of the borehole.

The displacement components in equation (1) are given by

$$u_\rho = u_r \cdot \sin\phi + u_z \cdot \cos\phi ,$$

$$u_\theta = u_\theta ,$$

$$u_\phi = u_r \cdot \cos\phi - u_z \cdot \sin\phi , \quad (2)$$

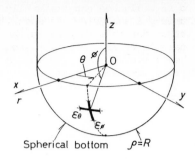

Fig.1 Strain components to be measured and the co-ordinates.

where u_r, u_θ and u_z are the displacement components referring to the cylindrical co-ordinates.

Assuming that the rock is a perfect-elastic body, u_r, u_θ and u_z, on the bottom surface of a borehole, can be represented by equation (3), in full consideration of the symmetry.

$$\begin{Bmatrix} u_r \\ u_\theta \\ u_z \end{Bmatrix} = \frac{R}{E} \cdot \begin{Bmatrix} S_0+S_2\cos2\theta, & S_0-S_2\cos2\theta, & P_0, \\ T_2\sin2\theta, & -T_2\sin2\theta, & 0, \\ U_0+U_2\cos2\theta, & U_0-U_2\cos2\theta, & W_0, \end{Bmatrix}$$

$$\left. \begin{matrix} R_1\sin\theta, & R_1\cos\theta, & 2S_2\sin2\theta \\ -Q_1\cos\theta, & Q_1\sin\theta, & -2T_2\cos2\theta \\ V_1\sin\theta, & V_1\cos\theta, & 2U_2\sin2\theta \end{matrix} \right\} \cdot \{\sigma\}$$

$$(3)$$

where E : the Young's modulus; S_0, S_2,..., U_2 : the displacement coefficients which are the functions of the Poisson's ratio and the co-ordinates r and z on the bottom surface.

By substituting equation (2) and (3) in the displacement-strain relationship, equation (1), the strains are re-written as follows,

$$\begin{Bmatrix} \varepsilon_\theta \\ \varepsilon_\phi \end{Bmatrix} = \begin{Bmatrix} A_{11}+A_{12}\cos2\theta, & A_{11}-A_{12}\cos2\theta, & C_1, \\ A_{21}+A_{22}\cos2\theta, & A_{21}-A_{22}\cos2\theta, & C_2, \end{Bmatrix}$$

$$\left. \begin{matrix} D_1\sin\theta, & D_1\cos\theta, & 2A_{12}\sin2\theta \\ D_2\sin\theta, & D_2\cos\theta, & 2A_{22}\sin2\theta \end{matrix} \right\} \cdot \{\sigma\}/E ,$$

$$(4)$$

where A_{11}, A_{12},..., D_2 are the strain coefficients which depend on the Poisson's ratio and the zenithal angle at the station of strain measurement.

Because no closed form solutions for the determination of the displacement at the end of a borehole are available, the displacement coefficients in eq.(3) have to be evaluated experimentally and/or by numerical analysis. The most widely used method for this purpose is the numerical analysis by FEM. The displacement coefficients evaluated by FEM analysis and the strain coefficients in equation (4) have been presented by Sugawara and coworkers (1985).

2.2 Observation Equation

When the measured strains, number of n, are denoted by
$$\{\beta\} = \{ \beta_1, \beta_2, \ldots, \beta_n \}^T,$$
the observation equation, namely the relationship between $\{\sigma\}$ and $\{\beta\}$, is given by the following matrix equation.

$$\{A\}\cdot\{\sigma\} = E\cdot\{\beta\} , \qquad (5)$$

where $\{A\}$ is an $n \times 6$ matrix, of which elements are computed according to equation (4). Therefore, they are depending upon the Poisson's ratio and the co-ordinates of the station for strain measurement.

The normalized form of eq.(5) is

$$\{B\}\cdot\{\sigma\} = E\cdot\{\overline{\beta}\} , \qquad (6)$$

where $\{B\} = \{A\}^T\cdot\{A\}$ and $\{\overline{\beta}\} = \{A\}^T\cdot\{\beta\}$, and the most probable stress tensor, $\{\overline{\sigma}\}$, is given as follows.

$$\{\overline{\sigma}\} = E\cdot\{C\}\cdot\{\overline{\beta}\} , \qquad (7)$$

where $\{C\}$ is the inverse matrix of $\{B\}$. Therefore it can be noted that the diagonal element of $\{B\}$ is propotional to the value of measured strain, and the diagonal element c_{ii} of $\{C\}$ is in inverse proportion to n. The variance of $\{\overline{\sigma}\}$ can be represented by $\{\xi_\sigma^2\} = \{ \xi_1^2, \xi_2^2, \ldots, \xi_6^2 \}$, and its component is given by the least squares method as follows,

$$\xi_i^2 = c_{ii}\cdot E^2\cdot\xi_\beta^2 , \qquad (8)$$

where ξ_β^2 is the variance of the measured strain.

By assuming that ξ_β^2 is constant, it can be concluded that the highest accuracy in the stress tensor determination is obtained by minimizing the magnitude of the diagonal element of $\{C\}$. The maximum variance ξ_{max}^2 of stress tensor can be estimated by replacing c_{ii} in equation (8) with the maximum value c_{max} of the diagonal element, as follows,

$$\xi_{max}^2 = c_{max}\cdot E^2\cdot\xi_\beta^2 . \qquad (9)$$

2.3 Suggested Gauge Arrangement

From comparing the size of c_{max}, the axisymmetric arrangement of strain gages along the circle of $\phi=130°$ has been proposed as the most suitable one (Sugawara and coworkers, 1985). Fig.2(a) shows the axisymmetric arrangement of eight single-gauges, and Fig.2(b) shows that of eight cross-gauges. As a matter of course, in the former case eight observation equations are set up and sixteen observation equations in the later case.

The elements of the matrix $\{A\}$ in eq. (5) can be determined with the strain coefficients in Table 1. These strain coefficients are evaluated by the FEM analyses mentioned previously. For the approximation of the strain coefficients corresponding to a certain value of Poisson's ratio, the linear interpolation for each section can be recommended.

2.4 Accuracy in Stress Determination

The value of c_{max} is in inverse proportion to the value of measured strain. Therefore, the product of n and c_{max} can be concluded to be rational parameter to choose the better of the methods.

(a)

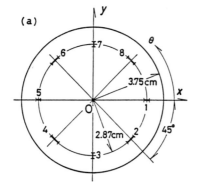

(b)

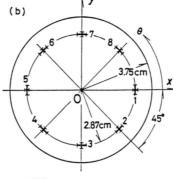

Fig.2

Suggested gauge arrangements,
(a): eight strain single-gauges,
(b): eight strain cross-gauges.

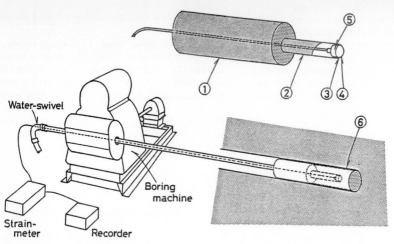

Water-swivel

Boring machine

Strain-meter   Recorder

(a)

(b)

Fig.3 Schematic view of in situ measurement, 1: large-diameter coring, 2: pilot-coring, 3: bottom polishing, 4: bottom cleaning, 5: bonding strain cell 6: over-coring operation.

Fig.5
Strain cell made
from epoxy resin.

Fig.4 Spherical diamond bits, (a): pilot borz crown, (b): spherical impregnated bit.

Table 1   Strain coefficients on hemispherical bottom of borehole at $\phi=130°$.

Poisson's ratio : ν	A_{11}	A_{12}	A_{21}	A_{22}	C_1	C_2	D_1	D_2
Evaluated by the FEM analysis:								
$\nu=0.1$	0.857	-1.360	0.223	0.629	-0.243	0.971	-0.053	2.311
$\nu=0.2$	0.830	-1.392	0.162	0.624	-0.333	0.939	-0.062	2.459
$\nu=0.3$	0.793	-1.386	0.107	0.598	-0.412	0.892	-0.069	2.570
$\nu=0.4$	0.751	-1.363	0.055	0.564	-0.487	0.837	-0.076	2.664
Evaluated by the laboratory borehole test:								
$\nu=0.27$	0.755	-1.449	0.125	0.682	-0.380	0.790	-0.020	2.699

Table 2   Comparison of $n \cdot c_{max}$ (Poisson's ratio : 0.25).

Method.	n	c_{max}	$n \cdot c_{max}$	Remarks.
Strain measurements on hemispherical bottom.	8	0.264	2.13	see Fig.2(a).
	16	0.1332	2.13	see Fig.2(b).
Strain measurements on cylindric wall of borehole.	9	0.280	2.52	with three strain gauge rosettes.

The values of $n \cdot c_{max}$ are summarized in Table 2, where the strain measurement along the circumference of a single borehole is given for reference, and the two types of method have been compared. The minimum value of $n \cdot c_{max}$ is given by the method presented in this paper. However, the difference between the two methods is comparatively small. Therefore, speaking of the theoretical accuracy and the sensitivity in determining the original stresses, these methods could hardly be compared.

3. IN SITU MEASUREMENT SYSTEM

Fig.3 shows the procedure of in situ measurement. First, a pilot borehole having diameter 180mm, or 146mm, is drilled to the stress measurement point. Then, a pilot coring, diameter of 75mm, is performed making the axis to coincide with that of the former. The bottom of the pilot borehole is formed into a hemispherical shape by the use of a borz crown bit in Fig.4(a), and the surface of which is ground smooth by a spherical impregnated bit in Fig.4(b). After the polishing and cleaning procedure, strain gages have to be bonded directly to the bottom surface in tight contact. In order to affix them at the appointed stations and in the designated direction, a special strain cell made from epoxy resin has been developed. As shown in Fig.5, this has eight cross-gauges on its spherical surface, to bond them directly to the rock surface under the arrangement in Fig.2(b). After that, the induced field stress around the bottom of borehole is relieved by the over-coring operation. During this operation, the changes in strain are measured. For this purpose, the cable is linked to the strain meter through the boring rods and the water swivel.

A series of changes in strain in Fig. 6 has been obtained with the continuous strain measurement system. In Fig.6, the transverse axis is the distance between the head of the over-coring and the centre of the hemispherical bottom. The influence of stress concentration appears when the over-coring approaches the bottom, but the changes in strain are rapid, in all cases, after over-coring reaches the bottom section. The strains existed on the bottom surface need to be determined after examining the convergence to a stable terminal value.

Such a monitoring of the changes in

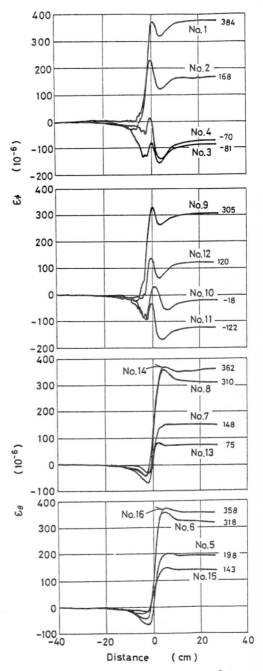

Fig.6 Strain changes measured during the over-coring operation.

strain with the over-coring operation by the continuous strain measurement system is indispensable to improve the reliability of measured strains, as well as the calibration test of the core obtained by the over-coring.

4. CALIBRATION PROCEDURE

In this method, homogeneity and iso-tropic elasticity must be assumed to compute the stress tensor. Then, variations of elastic modulus from one direction to another, or from point to point, may increase the uncertainty of the results obtained. Additionally, non-linear stress-strain relationship marked in some types of rock may also limit the usefulness of the stress tensor determination. To overcome these difficulties, the calibration procedure is indispensable.

Fig.7 shows an uni-axial compressive test of the core obtained by the in situ over-coring operation. The end-planes of the core must be cut correctly normal to the centre axis of the core. But, the advantage of this calibration test is that it can be carried out even if the length of the core is comparatively short. Additionally, such an axisymmetrical loading is convenient for the examination of the homogeneity and isotropy of the rock.

For the valuation of the Young's modulus and the Poisson's ratio of the rock, the relationships between the axial pressure and the elastic strains on the hemispherical bottom surface have to be measured by the repeat procedure of loading and unloading.

The strains ε_θ^* and ε_ϕ^*, on the bottom surface, which are estimated from the recovery behavior in the unloading process, can be written as follows,

$$\varepsilon_\theta^* = C_1^* \cdot \sigma_z / E \quad , \tag{10}$$

$$\varepsilon_\phi^* = C_2^* \cdot \sigma_z / E \quad , \tag{11}$$

where σ_z is the axial compressive stre the strain coefficients C_1^* and C_2^* depe on the Poisson's ratio and the outer d meter $2R_0$ of the core, as shown in Tab 3. The core of $2R_0=160$mm is obtained the over-coring having outer diameter 180mm, and $2R_0=118$mm corresponds to th of 146mm.

Eliminating the Young's modulus fr the eq.(10) and (11), the following fo mula is obtained.

$$\varepsilon_\phi^* / \varepsilon_\theta^* = C_2^* / C_1^* \quad . \tag{1}$$

This is useful for the valuation of t Poisson's ratio from the measured val of $\varepsilon_\phi^* / \varepsilon_\theta^*$, the procedure of that is ill trated in Fig.8. After that, the Young modulus can be estimated from eq.(10) .

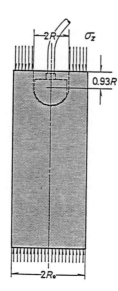

Fig.7
Axial loadin test using th boring core o tained by th in situ stres relief experi ment.

Table 3   Strain coefficients, C_1^* and C_2^*,

Poisson's ratio : ν	C_1^*	C_2^*	C_2^*/C_1^*
In the case of $2R_0=118.5$mm:			
$\nu=0.1$	−0.366	1.117	−3.05
$\nu=0.2$	−0.474	1.065	−2.24
$\nu=0.3$	−0.583	1.012	−1.738
$\nu=0.4$	−0.691	0.960	−1.388
In the case of $2R_0=160.0$mm:			
$\nu=0.1$	−0.297	1.040	−3.51
$\nu=0.2$	−0.392	0.996	−2.54
$\nu=0.3$	−0.488	0.952	−1.950
$\nu=0.4$	−0.584	0.909	−1.555

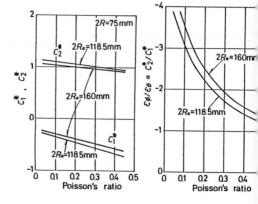

Fig.8 Strain coefficients for the axial loading test in Fig.7.

5. STRESS TENSOR DETERMINATION

From Fig.7, the elastic strains on a bottom surface can be estimated and the most probable values of original stress can be computed as demonstrated in Table 4, according to the mathematical procedure discussed in 2.2.

The theoretical distributions of the strains corresponding to the stress tensor determined are shown in Fig.9, with solid curves. As a matter of course, the curves must agree well with the measured strains plotted. The difference between the computed strain and the measured one is an useful information to approximate the error of the measurement.

6. LABORATORY BOREHOLE TEST

Preparing cubic rock samples of Kumamoto andesite with a borehole differently oriented for each test piece, the uniaxial compressive experiment named laboratory borehole test has been carried out to examine the practical accuracy in the stress determination by the present method and to calibrate the strain cell made from epoxy resin for the in situ strain measurement. The andesite is a homogeneous and isotropic rock, within the limit of macroscopic observation. The mean of Young's modulus is 18.0GPa, and that of Poisson's ratio is 0.27. These constants have been estimated from the linear rela-

Table 4 An example of stress tensor determination.

Test site: Imaichi underground power house (Japan),
Rock mass: Siliceous fine grained sandstone of E=54.8GPa and ν=0.20.

Observation matrix equation: $\{A\}\cdot\{\sigma\} = E\cdot\{\beta\}$,

$\{A\}$:

i \ j	1	2	3	4	5	6	$\{\beta\}$: (10^{-6})
1	0.355	−0.030	0.939	1.445	1.990	1.186	−384
2	−0.030	0.355	0.939	1.990	−1.445	−1.186	−168
3	0.355	−0.030	0.939	−1.445	−1.990	1.186	81
4	−0.030	0.355	0.939	−1.990	1.445	−1.186	70
5	2.153	−0.494	−0.333	−0.061	−0.010	−0.860	−198
6	−0.494	2.153	−0.333	−0.010	0.061	0.860	−318
7	2.153	−0.494	−0.333	0.061	0.010	−0.860	−148
8	−0.494	2.153	−0.333	0.010	−0.061	0.860	−310
9	−0.431	0.755	0.939	2.429	0.385	0.386	−305
10	0.755	−0.431	0.939	0.385	−2.429	−0.386	18
11	−0.431	0.755	0.939	−2.429	−0.385	0.386	122
12	0.755	−0.431	0.939	−0.385	2.429	−0.386	−120
13	0.399	1.260	−0.333	−0.036	−0.050	−2.647	−75
14	1.260	0.399	−0.333	−0.050	0.036	2.647	−362
15	0.399	1.260	−0.333	0.036	0.050	−2.647	−143
16	1.260	0.399	−0.333	0.050	−0.036	2.647	−358

Normalized matrix equation: $\{B\}\cdot\{\overline{\sigma}\} = E\cdot\{\overline{\beta}\}$,

$\{B\}$:

i \ j	1	2	3	4	5	6	$\{\overline{\beta}\}$: (10^{-6})
1	15.022	−3.586	−0.991	0.000	0.000	0.000	−1532.
2		15.022	−0.991	0.000	0.000	0.000	−1863.
3			7.948	0.000	0.000	0.000	−7.54
4				24.200	0.000	0.000	−2129.
5		Sym.			24.200	0.000	−1084.
6						37.216	−1846.

The most probable stress tensor: $\{\overline{\sigma}\} = E\cdot\{C\}\cdot\{\overline{\beta}\}$,

$\{C\}$:

i \ j	1	2	3	4	5	6	$\{\overline{\sigma}\}$: (MPa)
1	0.072	0.018	0.011	0.000	0.000	0.000	σ_x =−7.83
2		0.072	0.011	0.000	0.000	0.000	σ_y =−8.81
3			0.129	0.000	0.000	0.000	σ_z =−2.12
4				0.041	0.000	0.000	τ_{yz}=−4.82
5		Sym.			0.041	0.000	τ_{zx}=−2.46
6						0.027	τ_{xy}=−2.72

Principal stress components: σ_1 = +0.51MPa, σ_2= −5.72MPa, σ_3 = −13.55MPa.

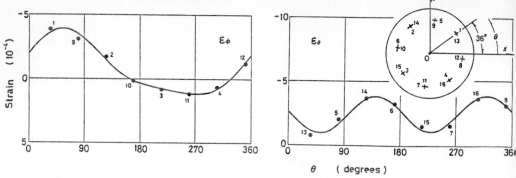

Fig.9 Comparisons between the measured strains and the elastic strain
distributions calculated theoretically from the most probable
stress tensor determined by the present method.

tionships between the recovering strains
and the compressive stress, measured by
the uniaxial compressive test with cylindrical specimens, where the limit of the
compressive stress has been conditioned
in consideration of the magnitude of compressive stress on the bottom surface induced by the laboratory borehole test.

Fig.10 shows cubic test pieces used,
the edge length of 38 cm. Each has a hemispherical bottom in its centre, the diameter of which is $2R=75$ mm. In Fig.10, the
Cartesian coordinates (X, Y, Z) used to
express the loading directions are given
as a fixed coordinates system located on
the cubic. In the test piece called "a",
the borehole is drilled perpendicular to
the X-Y plane and in the negative direction of Z-axis. Therefore, the Cartesian
coordinates x, y and z fixed to the borehole are parallel to X, Y and Z, respectively. In the test piece, "b", the axis
of borehole is inclined at $45°$ from the
X-Y plane, making the x-axis parallel to
the X-axis.

In the laboratory borehole test, the

uniaxial compressive loading to the tes
piece "a" has been carried out in the d
der of X, Y and Z-direction respectivel
and that to the test piece "b" in the d
der of Y and Z-direction.

After the uniaxial compression up t
the loading pressure of 6.3MPa, recover
ing strains in the successive un-loadir
process have been measured by means o
the strain cell bonded on the hemispher
cal bottom surface. The elastic strain
on the hemispherical surface under th
uniaxial loading condition have been de
termined respectively by reversing th
sign of measured strain.

Fig.11 illustrates the distribution
of elastic strains, expressed in demen
sionless forms, e.g. $E\varepsilon_\theta/\sigma_X$ where σ_X i
the loading pressure in the X-direction
The results obtained from the laborator
borehole test plotted are compared wit
the theoretical distributions with soli
curves. From the well agreement betwee
them, it can be confirmed that the infl
ence of the rigidity of the strain cel
is negligibly small.

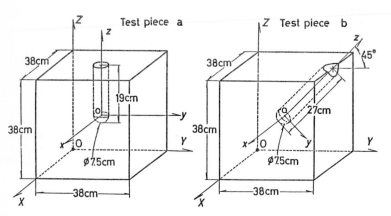

Fig.10
Andesite cubic
test pieces for
the laboratory
borehole test.

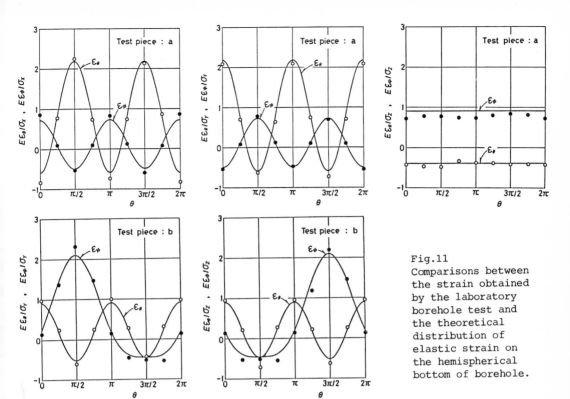

Fig.11
Comparisons between the strain obtained by the laboratory borehole test and the theoretical distribution of elastic strain on the hemispherical bottom of borehole.

For the examination of the practical accuracy in stress tensor determination, the stress state of loading has been computed from the measured strains, and compared with the actual load. The results computed are given in Table 5, in which each stress component is given by the dimensionless quantity : the ratio of the stress component to the loading pressure. In any case, the normal stress component in the loading direction should be equal to the actual pressure and the other components should be zero. But, the results of the test piece "a" have noticeable errors. Particularly, in the case of the loading in the Z-direction, σ_Z is clearly underestimated. This error can be considered to cause mainly by the miscount of the Young's modulus, and partially it may be due to the anisotropy of the material. By considering the fact that some correction of the Young's modulus of the test piece "a" leads to the more satisfactory estimation, the error due to the anisotropy and inhomogeneity of the material is presumed to be at most seven percent.

The strain coefficients can be evaluated by analyzing the results of the laboratory borehole test. Assuming E=18.0

Table 5 Stress state of loading computed from the measured strains on the hemispherical bottom surface of laboratory borehole.

Test piece	Loading direction.	Stress components referred to the co-ordinates (X, Y, Z), (p : loading pressure, -6.4MPa).					
		σ_X/p	σ_Y/p	σ_Z/p	τ_{YZ}/p	τ_{ZX}/p	τ_{XY}/p
a	X	1.007	-0.079	0.009	0.002	-0.001	0.007
a	Y	-0.061	0.944	0.006	0.010	-0.010	-0.010
a	Z	-0.059	-0.036	0.868	-0.013	0.003	0.010
b	Y	-0.020	1.054	-0.024	-0.037	-0.010	-0.007
b	Z	-0.063	-0.050	0.999	-0.045	0.015	0.012

GPa and the Poisson's ratio $\nu=0.27$, simultaneous equations for the strain coefficients are derived from the 80 observation equations and solved with the least squares method. The optimum solution is given in Table 1, with the strain coefficients evaluated by the FEM analysis. As a matter of course, the strain coefficients evaluated experimentally must involve the error due to the inhomogeneity and anisotropy of the material, to an extent presumed previously. Therefore, the numerical analysis is suitable for the evaluation of strain coefficients.

7. CONCLUSION

A hemispherical-ended borehole technique has been presented for the in situ stress measurement within the isotropic rock. The theory to determine the stress tensor from the strains on the hemispherical bottom surface in a single borehole has been presented, as well as the excellent system for in situ strain measurement with the over-coring operation.

The relationships between the stress tensor and the strains are expressed by the matrix equation and the coefficients of which are formulated with the strain coefficients evaluated by FEM analyses. The mathematical procedure for determing stress tensor has been demonstrated, including theoretical estimation of the error of stress tensor determined. Then it is clarified that the necessary accuracy in determining stress tensor is obtained by the gauge arrangement which minimizes the diagonal elements of the inverse matrix of normalized coefficients matrix. From this theoretical condition and the technical viewpoint to set the gauges on the hemispherical bottom surface, the axisymmetrical arrangement of eight strain cross-gauges along a circle of zenithal angle $\phi=130°$ on the hemispherical bottom surface has been suggested and the excellent sensitivity of this arrangement has been verified theoretically comparing to the conventional method for stress measurement.

As concerns the in situ strain measurement with the over-coring operation, some practical devices are presented to improve the reliability of strains measured. The spherical diamond bits to convert the bottom of borehole into a hemispherical shape, the strain cell to bond the necessary eight strain cross-gauges directly on the rock surface at the designated station in tight contact and the continuous strain measurement system for monitoring the changes in strain with in situ over-coring have been presented, as well as their successful application.

It is noted that the utility of the stress tensor determination is limited by the anisotropy and in-homogeneity of the rock. In order to overcome this difficulty, the load calibration procedure using the boring core obtained by the in situ over-coring has been presented with the necessary strain coefficients.

The practical accuracy of the stress tensor determination has been examined by the laboratory loading and un-loading tests to the cubic rock specimens with the appropriately oriented hemispherical ended borehole. From the comparison between the actual load to the cubic specimen and the stress state of loading computed from the bottom strains measured with the strain cell, the error due to the anisotropy and in-homogeneity of the rock has been presumed to be at most seven persent.

REFERENCES

Amadei, B. (1984). In situ stress measurement in anisotropic rock, Int. J. Rock Mech. Min. Sci. & Geomech. Abstr. 21, 327-338.

Duncan, Fama M.E. and M.J. Pender (1980) Analysis of the hollow inclusion technique for measuring in situ rock stress Int. J. Rock Mech. Min. Sci. & Geomech Abstr., 17, 137-146.

Erer, K.D. and A. Heidarieh-Zadeh (1985) A review of in situ stress measurement techniques with reference to Coal Measures rocks, Mining Science & Technology Vol.2, No.3, 191-206.

Hiramatsu, Y. and Y. Oka (1968). Determination of the stress in rock unaffected by boreholes or drifts, from measured strains or deformations, Int. J. Rock Mech. & Min. Sci., 5, 337-353.

Leeman, E. R. (1968). The determination of the complete state of stress in rock in a single borehole-laboratory and underground measurements, Int. J. Rock Mech. Min. Sci., 5, 31-56.

Sugawara, K., Y. Obara, H. Okamura and Wang (1985). The determination of the complete state of stress in rock by the measurement of strains on a hemispherical borehole bottom, J. of the Mining and Metallurgical Institute of Japan Vol.101, No.1167, 277-282.

Development of a new borehole stress-meter and installation tool

DUK-WON PARK
University of Alabama, Department of Mineral Engineering, University, Alabama, USA

ABSTRACT

For rock stress measurement, a borehole is commonly drilled and sensors, composed of photo-elastic borehole plugs, flat jacks, vibrating wire gauges or load cells, are inserted. Conventional sensors generally suffer the shortcoming of being expensive and difficult to install and use. A new gauge, PAL borehole stress-meter, and an installation tool have been developed. The major advanges of this system are: (1) low cost; (2) easy installation; (3) high resolution; and (4) both static and dynamic stresses can be continuously monitored. PAL stress-meters were installed at a longwall panel in an underground coal mine in Alabama and successfully monitored the stress change due to the longwall face advance.

RESUME

Pour mesurer les contraintes dans les roches, un trou de sonde est normalement foré, et des capteurs, composés de bouchons de trou de sonde photoelastiques, "flat jacks", jauges à filament vibreur, ou des cellules à charge (load cells), sont inserés. Les capteurs conventionnels sont generalement coûteux et difficiles à installer et à utiliser. Une nouvelle jauge de contrainte de trou de sonde, PAL, et un nouvel outil d'installation de cette jauge ont été developpés. Les principaux advan-tages du système sont: (1) coût reduit, (2) facilité d'installa-tion, (3) haute résolution, et (4) les contraintes statiques et dynamiques peuvent être control-lées sans interruption. Les jauges de contrainte PAL ont été installées dans un grand panneau dune mine souterraine de charbon à Alabama et ont mesuré avec succée les contraintes crée par le mouvement du grand panneau.

ZUSAMMENFASUNG

Um die Gesteinsbelastung zu messen, wird im allgemeinen eine Bohrung durchgefuehrt. Es werden Sensoren eingesetzt, die aus photoelastischen Bohrungs-stoepseln, Flachgestellen und vibrierenden Drahtmessern oder Ladezellen bestehen. Konvention-elle Sensoren leiden im allge-meinen unter dem Nachteil, teuer zu sein. Ausserdem sind sie schwer einzubauen und schwer zu handhaben. Eine neue Messvorrich-tung, der PAL Bohrlochbelastungs-messer, und eine Einbauvorrich-tung sind entwickelt worden. Das System hat folgende Vorteile:
1) geringe Kosten
2) leicht einzubauen
3) lange Lebensdauer und Bestaendigkeit sowie
4) die Moeglichkeit, sowohl statische als auch dynamische
Belastung ununterbrochen beobach-ten zu koennen. PAL Belastungs-messer wurden in einer Lang-frontbau-Beplankung in einer Untertage Kohlenmine in Alabama eingebaut.

INTRODUCTION

Stress measurement in rock is often necessary in fields such as mining, civil engineering and geology. Especially in rock mechanics, which is a part of the mining and the civil engineering fields adequate and accurate stress measurement is extremely important, because it plays an important role in the stability of a rock body. For most purposes, it is conventional to drill a borehole in the rock where stress is to be monitored, and to insert sensors into the borehole.

The sensors are photoelastic borehole plugs (Roberts, 1977), flat jacks (Lu, 1984), strain gauges (Cook and Ames, 1979), vibrating wire gauges (Hawkes and Hooker, 1974 and Fossum, et al, 1976), etc. The signals from the sensors are read by suitable conventional equipment and subsequently processed into numeric data indicative of the stress, by the use of calibration factors or equations developed from an analytical method.

Common difficulties encountered in using the conventional borehole stress-meters include:

1. Installation is difficult and time consuming.
2. In general the resolution is low.
3. Most of the meters are designed only for static stres measurement.
4. The stress-meters and installation tools are expensive.

The new borehole stress-meter, PAL gauge (Park and Ryan, 1985) and a setting device have been developed to eliminate the above mentioned deficiencies.

PAL GAUGE

PAL gauge utilizes a gauge plug upon which electrical resistance strain gauges are emplaced. The gauge plug is insertable within a hollow housing (shell) having a similar tapered configuration. In order to insert the shell within a borehole drilled in the rock, a setting device is provided.

As shown in Figure 1, the gauge plug has a tapered outer surface and is cut vertically on both sides in parallel. An electrical resistance strain gauge is attached vertically on the two opposite flat sides. From the strain gauges a four conductor wire is connected to a strain gauge readout box to make them either a half or a full bridge system. The shell is constructed with a cylindrical pipe having axial slots so that it can resiliently expand in the radial direction(Figure 1). At the inner wall of the shell there are two lugs connected to be used for engaging it with the installation tool during an installation process. The size of the gauge plug is determined in such a way that it can freely fit in one end of the shell but, at some point along its length contacts the tapered inner surface of the shell so that further movement of the gauge plug creates radial stresses in the shell and gauge plug.

The gauges and shells can be fabricated with any type of material, as long as it has elastic characteristics in the desired range of loading, such as aluminum, plastic, steel, stainless steel, etc., depending on the rock material and the required resolution of stress measurement.

INSTALLATION TOOL

In order to install a PAL gauge a borehole should be drilled with a slightly larger diameter than that of the gauge. The clearance between the gauge and borehole is governed by the length and tapering angle. The PAL gauge can be inserted into the borehole by an installation tool.

The installation tool is composed of a setting head and extension bars. The setting head

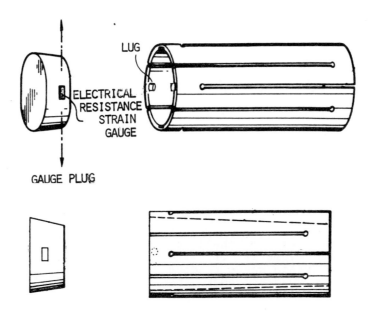

Figure 1.   PAL Gauge.

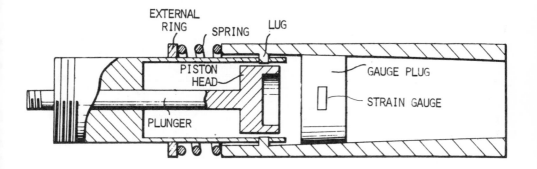

Figure 2.   Setting Head.

is provided with an external ring, and can be releasably connected to the shell of a PAL gauge by a twist lock during the installation process, as shown in Figure 2. A plunger in the form of a piston is slidable within the setting head which can engage the gauge plug.

The piston should be advanced until the gauge plug reaches approximately the center of the shell and some initial loading is applied in the gauge plug. In a situation in which the borehole diameter is oversized for the PAL gauge to be used, an adapter in the form of a plate can be attached to the outer surface of the shell to increase the diameter of the gauge. The strain gauge readout box should be read to check the amount of initial load applied in the gauge plug.

Extension bars are used for installing the stressmeters deeper than 5 feet (1.52 m) They are composed of a pipe and inner rod which can be connected to the piston in the setting head. For the manual setting system, a piece of solid bar is connected the inner rod to apply gentle impact for advancing the gauge plug. For the hydraulic system, a device composed of a hydraulic jack, piston and holder can be used as shown in Figure 3. This system is made in such a manner that the outside grip holds while the piston advances the inner rod which in turn pushes the gauge plug.

Another alternative is shown in Figure 4. A retractable miniature piston resides in the setting head and the hydraulic hose is connected between the piston and pump through the extension bar.

FIELD TESTING

To test the validity of the PAL gauges and installation tool, 4 gauges were fabricated and installed at a longwall panel in a coal mine in the Warrior Co. Basin in Alabama. The mi. employs several continuous mini sections and one longwa. section. The thickness of t coal seam is approximately 4.6. (1.4 m) and that of t overburden is about 500 ft (152 m). Due to a generally gent. topography, there are no sudde variation in the overburde thickness. The coal is dense ar high in compressive strengt Sandstone, shale, sandy shale ar mudstone are predominant ro units overlying the coal seam.

At the study area, there a 6 parallel longwall pane. planned (Figure 5). Each long wall panel is 600 ft (182.9 r wide and 5000 ft (1524 m) long The face is supported by 600 to Hemscheidt shields Between t panels there are four rows c chain pillars sized 90 ft (27. m) * 40 ft (12.2 m), and th width of the entries is 20 (6.1 m).

The gauges were instrumente in the first longwall panel whe there were frequent roof fal problems in the front abutmer area. The detailed diagram of th instrumentation station is show in Figure 6.

The PAL gauges, made c aluminum, were used fc monitoring stress increases i the coal seam as the longwal face advanced. The diameter c the PAL gauges was 1.45 inche (3.68 cm) and expandable to 1.5 inches (3.94 cm). Two conver tional vibrating wire gauges wer also used for comparison purpose The vibrating wire gauges ar quite commonly used for roc stress measurement. It consist of a hollow steel cylinder which in use, is preloaded diametrical ly to the sides of a borehole k means of a sliding wedge an changes in the diameter of th cylinder which are measured a changes in the natural frequenc of vibration of a highly tension ed steel wire stretched diametri cally across the cylinder wall (Hawkes and Hooker, 1974).

All the gauges were installed in the middle of the seam. As
shown in Figure 6, two types of
the gauges were installed at
about 5-ft (1.5 m) depth (Gauges
B and C) and 12-ft (3.66 m) depth
(gauges D and E). Figures 7 and 8
show the procedure of installation. At the the time the gauges
were installed, the distance between the face and the gauge location was 240 ft (73.2 m). The
gauges were read once every one
or two days until the face reached 30 ft (9.1 m) away from the
gauges and after that they were
read more frequently. Throughout
the stress monitoring period, the
PAL gauges behaved similarly to
the vibrating wire gauges, except
the PAL gauges responded to
stress changes more rapidly with
higher sensitivity.

The relationships between the
distance between the face and
gauge locations and stress
increases are shown in Figure 9.
Generally, stresses increased in
a slow rate until face is located
120 ft (36.6 m) away from the
gauge locations. The rate of
stress increase became more
obvious until face locations
around 30 ft (9.1 m) inby the
gauge locations, where all the
gauges registered rapid stress
increases. Generally, the maximum
abutment stress is distributed 5
to 10 ft (3.0 m to 4.6 m) ahead
of the face. The relatively
narrow yield zone seems to be
contributed by the unusually high
strength of the coal seam.

From the results, the
calibration factor for the PAL
gauges was about 1.0 psi/unit
(6896.6 pascals/unit). Considering that the normal resolution of
a vibrating wire gauge is about
5.0 psi (0.0345 pascals/unit),
the resolution of the PAL gauge
is five times greater.

CONCLUSION

The newly developed PAL
borehole stress-meters and
installation tools were proven to
be simple and practical from the
result of the field test. The
advantages are:
1. less expensive
2. easy to install
3. high resolution and
   sensitivity
4. data can be conti-
   nuously recorded and
   possibly dynamic
   stress can be
   recorded.
Calibration has not yet been
fully established. More laboratory testing will be conducted,
as well as the finite element
analysis, for different configuration and materials with various
material values such as modulus
of elasticity, Poisson's ratio,
etc.

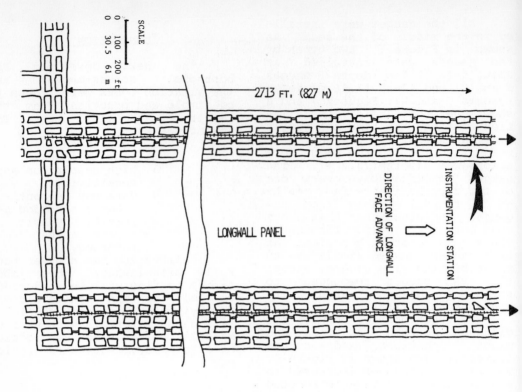

FIGURE 5. Instrumentation Station.

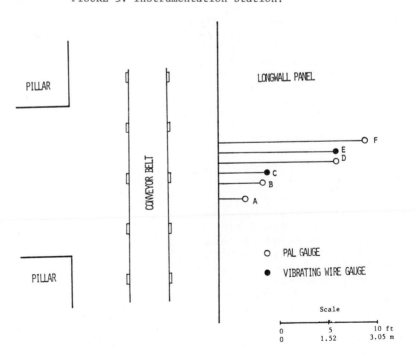

Figure 6. Detailed Instrumentation Plan.

A. ASSEMBLING PAL GAUGE
   ON INSTALLATION HEAD

B. INSERTING PAL GAUGE
   INTO BOREHOLE

C. ADVANCING INNER ROD

Figure 7.   Sequence of PAL Gauge Installation.

VIBRATING WIRE GAUGE READOUT BOX

PAL GAUGE READOUT BOX

Figure 8.   Readout Boxes.

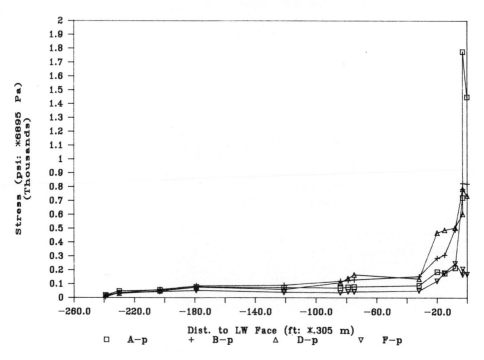

Figure 9.   Relationship Between Stress Increase and
Longwall Face Distance to PAL Gauges.

REFERENCES

Cook, C. W. and E. S. Ames, 1979, "Borehole-Inclusion Stressmeter Measurements in Bedded Salt.," Proceedings of the 20th U. S. Syposium on Rock Mechanics, Austin, TX, June 4-6, 1979

Fossum. A. F., et al, 1976, "Calibration Analysis for the In Situ Response of a Vibrating Wire Stress Gauge in Soft Rock," Society for Experimental Stress Analysis Spring Meeting, Silver Springs, MD, May 9-14, 1976

Hawkes, I. and V. E. Hooker, 1974, "The Vibrating Wire Stressmeter," Proceedings of the 3rd Congress, Int. Sciety of Rock Mechanics, 1974

Park, D., 1985, "Two Case Histories of Subsidence in the Warrior Coal Field," Proceedings of the 3rd Annual Workshop, Generic Mineral Technology Center, Mine Systems Design and Ground Control, Lexington, KY, November 25-26, 1985

Park, D. and T. W. Ryan, 1985, "Borehole Stress-Meter and Method and Apparatus for Installation Thereof," U. S. Patent No. 4542655, September 1935

Lu, P. H., 1984 "Mining- Induced Stress Measurement with Hydraulic Borehole Pressure Cells," Proceedings of the 25th U. S. Rock Mechanics Symposium on Rock Mechanics, Evanston, IL, June 25-27, 1984

Roberts, A., 1977, Geotechnology, Oxford: Pergamon, 1977

The type YG-73 piezomagnetic stress gauge for rock stress measurement

WANG LIANJIE
LIAO CHUNTING
DING YUANCHEN
OU MINGYI
Institute of Geomechanics, Beijing, China

ABSTRACT: In this paper, the principle, structure, performance and calibration of the Type YG-73 gauge are described. The verification of the reliability of the gauge in laboratory and in the field and some results of rock stress measurement in situ are given.

RESUME: L'article presente la jauge du type YG-73 en indiquant ses principes, structure, performance ainsi que la methode de la calibration et en fournissant les resultats de la rerification de sa fiabilite au laboratoire et sur le terrain et ceux des mesures sur les contraintes de roche in situ.

ZUSAMMENFASSUNG: In dieser Arbeit werden die Prinzip, die Struktur, die Eigenschaft und Einstellungs-methode des Spannungsmessers YG-73 Typ empfohlen. Es werden die Prüfung der Zuverlassigkeit des Spannungsmessers im labor und auf dem feld und die Messungsergebnisse in situ gegeben.

1. INTRODUCTION

The measurement of rock stress is of great significance in the design of mining, dam, power station, earthquake prediction and geotectonic analysis.

Since 1962, the YG-73 type piezomagnetic stress gauge (shortly called YG-73 cell) and its prestressing apparatus have been developed as a modification of Hast's cell (Hast 1958). Using the stress gauge, we have carried out a good many experiments which show that the YG-73 cell has a good linearity, repeatability, stability and sensitivity enough for measurement and gives a reliable result of measurement. At present, it has been widely used in China.

2. THE PRINCIPLE AND THE STRUCTURE OF THE YG-73 CELL

2.1 principle

The stress is recorded on the principle of magnetostriction. The cell consists of a nickle alloy core with windings and a screen (Fig.1)

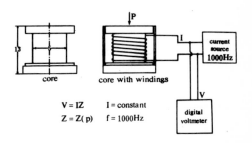

$$V = IZ \quad I = constant$$
$$Z = Z(p) \quad f = 1000Hz$$

Fig. 1 The nickel cell core and the core with windings and screen

If a load is applied to the cell parallel to its axis, the magnetic permeability of the nickle alloy is changed, and with it the impedance of the coil is changed too. If a stable alternating current is passing through the coil, there is a potential drop across it.

2.2 structure

The probe and its pre-stressing system are shown on the Fig.2.

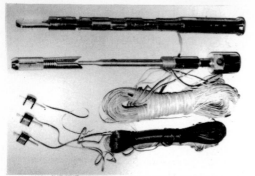

Fig. 2 The YG-73 piezomagnetic stress gauges and pre-stressing system

There are three cells in a probe at angle of 60° between directions of cells. The cell is mounted in a brass housing. The whole unit consists of core with coil, screen, housing, spacer, bearing, wedge, up-plate and down plate (Fig.3)

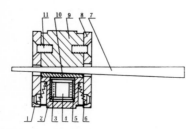

Fig. 3 The Type YG-73 cell

1—up plate; 2—housing; 3—coil;4—core
5—screen; 6—spring; 7—wedge;
8—down plate; 9—bearing; 10—spacer;
11—screw.

By moving the wedge through prestressing apparatus, the cell can be fixed in the bore hole and prestressed to a suitable value. The structure of the cell is designed in consideration of stability of contact state between the cell and borehole wall. During overcoring, even light relatively slip between the cell and the wall is not allowed. For this reason, the contact surface between the parts of the cell must be ground and fited well, especially the two sides of the cell contacted with the wall of borehole should be parallel strictly to each other. The angle between the two surfaces of the wedge should be smaller.

The sensitivity and stability of the

cell depends on the material of alloy, heat-treatment, cell structure and machining precision.

2.3 indicator

In the past, we used electric bridge for the measurement. At present, we have specially developed a digital piezomagnetic stress indicator that consists of a stable signal source and a digital voltage meter. The signal source supplies a stable alternating current of 1000Hz for the coil of the cell.

3.THE PROCEDURE OF MEASUREMENT

A rock hole of 36mm in diameter is drilled at the point where the stress is to be determined. A stress gauge is placed at the required position in the hole and pre-stressed to a suitable value, which is recorded, and the overcore is made. During overcoring, the readings are recorded. When the readings are no longer changed with overcore, the rock core is taken out of the hole and put into a calibrator for calibration (see section 4). The difference between the original readings and the last readings are used to calculate principle stresses. For two dimensional stress state, from three readings in different directions of diameter in single hole,the principle stresses can be calculated (Pan 1981). If at least six readings are obtained in three holes perpendiculor to each other,the three dimensional stress state can be determined.

In order to obtain more reliable results of measurements, it is neccessary that many measurements are carried out at a same measuring site and the least square method is used for data processing (Panek 1965, Wang 1977, Wang 1979).

4. CALIBRATION

For convertion of readings into recorded stress (or reduced displacement) so that the principle stresses can be calculated, it is neccessary for cell to be calibrated, and the calibration curve should be drown (Fig.4).
In the past we used a special rock prism for calibration (Fig.5).

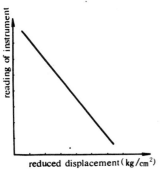

Fig. 4 Calibration curve

This method has two weaknesses:

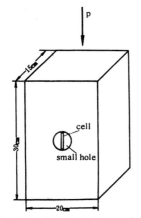

ℱig. 5 Calibration prism

1) Young's modulus of the calibration prism is not always the same as that of the rock mass in the measuring site, sometimes is quite different. Therefore, a correction of Young's modulus must be made; 2) the contact condition of the cell with the wall of borehole in the calibration prism is sometimes quite different from that in the measuring site. For the different contact condition there is different slope of calibration curve. Therefore, a big   error may be introduced in convertion. Especially in case of rough surface of the wall of borehole and low quality machine parts of the cell, the error may be even bigger.

At present, we have developed a new calibration method—the confining pressure calibration which can eliminate the two weaknesses mentioned above. A confining calibrator is used in this kind of calibration. The calibrator consists of a

pump and a confining pressure container (Fig.6). When calibrating, the rock core

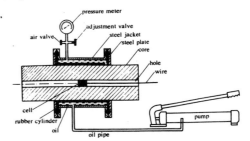

Fig. 6 The confining pressure cell-calibrator

with the cells in central small hole taken from the borehole after overcoring is put into the calibrator. Confining pressure is applied to the core to a expected value by pumping oil into the container. Then the pressure is reduced and the readings are recorded. A calibration curve can be drown according to the formula as following (Pan 1977):

$$S=\frac{EU}{3a}=\frac{2\sigma}{3(1-\frac{a^2}{b^2})} \quad \cdots \cdots (1)$$

where σ— the confining pressure applied (Fig.7);
a — the radius of the hole;
b — the external radius of the rock core;
E — Young's modulus of rock;
U — the displacement of the wall of the hole.

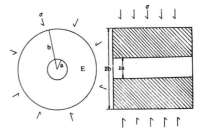

Fig. 7 The rock core under confining pressure
a— The radius of the hole
b— The external radius of the core

The calibration by using the calibrator is generally carried out immediatly after overcoring in situ. It is considered that the loss of moisture in the rock core is less, and the mechanical properties of rock is considered to be changed

229

very small. And the contact condition of the cell with the wall of hole does not change. Therefore, no error is introduced, if the confining pressure calibrator is used.

5. THE INFLUENCE OF THE PRE-STRESS OF THE CELL ON THE RESULT OF STRESS MEASUREMENT

As mentioned above, the cell has a pre-stress. Because the stiffness of the wall of the small borehole in rock mass is different from that in rock core taken from the borehole after overcoring, the pre-stress can cause an additional displacement of the wall of the small hole when overcoring. The corresponding reduced displacement ΔS can be given by the formula as follows (Wang 1986);

$$\Delta S = \frac{np^{\circ}}{2} \left(\frac{k_f - k^{\infty}}{k_f k^{\infty}} \right) \dots \dots (2)$$

where p° — the pre-stress of the cell;
$k_f = \frac{F}{2u}$ —— the stiffness of the wall of the small hole in rock core (Pan 1984);
F —— contact pressure between the cell and borehole wall;
K^{∞} —— the stiffness of the wall of the small hole in rock mass;
u —— displacement of the wall of borehole;

$\eta = \frac{E}{3a}$;
E —— Young's modulus of rock;
a —— the radius of the small hole.

The additional displacement ΔS may cause error unless it is deducted. The stiffness K_f and K^{∞} can be determined by using three dimensional finite element method.

In order to estimate the error, two dimensional FEM is used to calculate K_f and K^{∞}. The result of calculation shows that when pre-stress is 200kg and the external radius of rock core taken after overcoring is 6.5cm, the additional recorded stress is about 4kg/cm². The correction of error should be made if the pre-stress is higher and the radius of overcore is smaller.

6. THE CHARACTERISTICS OF THE TYPE YG-73 CELL

The study of the characteristic of the cell is of great significance to rock stress measurement. Therefore, experimental study of the cell characteristic is carried out in laboratory.

6.1 linearity, repeatability, stability and sensitivity of the cell

The characteristics of the cell are studied by calibrating the cells in rock prism (15×20×30cm, Young's modulus E= 8× 10⁵kg/cm²) in a press. It shows that when the uniform stress field in the direction parallel to the measuring diameter of the hole is changed by 1kg/cm², the change of reading is 30-100μH or 2-6 mv. The calibration curves obtained by independent setting cells many times show that the linearity and repeatablity are good (Fig.8)

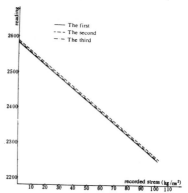

Fig. 8 The repeatability of the calibration curve for the Type YG-73 cell

Long term stability of the cell is also tested in rock prism. The cells are installed in the small hole in the prism and the calibration is performed once every certain time. Table 1 gives the results.

Table 1 The results of verification of stability of the cell

number of cell	number of prism	slope of calibration curve					average value	average error
		1974 Dec. 20.	1974 Dec. 30.	1975 Jan. 6.	1975 Jan. 18.	1975 Jan. 29.		
25	8	–	–	2.8	2.7	2.6	2.7	3.7%
4	5	5.5	5.6	5.5	5.5	5.75	5.57	3.2%

We can see from table 1 that the slope of the calibration curve is stable. The change of the slope is less than 3.7% about one and half months.

6.2 the relationship between the slope of the calibration curve and the pre-stressing value

The slope and linearity of the calibration curve is related to the pre-stressing value of the cell, which is determined by magnetization mechanism of magnetic material of the cell. Experiments show that when the pre-stressing value is about from 150 to 200kg, the calibration curve has a better linearity and the same slope.

6.3 the relationship between the slope and temperature

The temperature has no influence on the slope of the curve. Two curves at temperature of 17° and 20° have the same slope (Fig. 9).

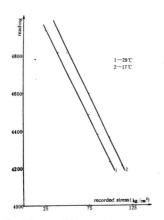

Fig. 9 The calibration curve of the Type YG-73 cell under different temperature

Because the course of rock stress measurement is short, it is considered that during overcoring, the temperature does not change and its influence does not exist.

7. VERIFICATION OF RELIABILITY OF THE CELL

7.1 verification by calibration prism

A load P is applied to the prism (Fig. 10). The cell is first set at the angle ψ_0 to the load P. The load on the prism is reduced in steps; and the cell readings are recorded. Then the cell is re-

moved. The prism is reloaded to the same value as before and the cell is replaced in the hole at an angle ψ_1, the same process as before being followed. The whole process is repeated for the angle ψ_2 $\psi_3 \dots \psi_{11}$. From the results (table 2) by this way, the magnitudes and directions of the principal stresses are calculated by using the least square method and compared with load (table 3). From table 3 it can be seen that the magnitude difference between the maximum

Table 2 The results of verification of reliability of the cell by prism

direction of cell	the cell 3. steel prism				the cell 7. limestone prism			
	1	2	3	4	1	2	3	4
0°	591 661	626	227	229	568 560 579	569	100	100
180°	639 621	630	223		512 603 595	570	100	
30°	411 109	410	149	150	396 446 467	436	76	69
210°	397 428	413	150		355 358 353	355	62	
60°	16 7	11	41	3	-24 17 22	5	1	0
240°	3 5	5	2		-15 -2 -3	-5	-1	
90°	-191 -166	-179	-65	-65	-184 -182 -187	-184	-32	-27
270°	-176 -181	-179	-65		-122 -126 -123	-124	-22	
120°	-51 -5	-23	-9	-4	-10 -38 -25	-18	-3	-2
300°	7 1	4	2		7 -18 -9	-7	-1	
150°	251 402	380	138	143	353 355 352	353	62	61
330°	317 491	404	147		350 325 329	336	59	

1. the readings of the cell;
2. the average readings
3. corresponding recorded stresses (kg/cm²)
4. the average recorded stresses (kg/cm²)

Table 3 The results of verification of accuracy of the cell by prism

number of cell	prism	load applied on the prism (kg/cm²)	major principal stress σ_1 (kg/cm²)	minor principal stress σ_2 (kg/cm²)	discrepancy in the direction of σ_1	discrepancy in magnitude of σ_1	confidence
71	limestone	100	98.4	1.9	1°21′	1.6%	95%
3	steel	227.3	223.8	3.6	47′	1.7%	95%

principal stresses measured and known load applied to the prism does not excess 1.7%; the discrepance in the direction of principal stress is less than 1° 20″. The magnitude of σ_2 should be zero. But in fact, there is a small value which is due to the finite width of the prism instead of the infinite width assumed in the formula.

231

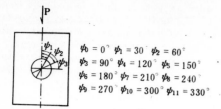

Fig. 10 The determination of
accuracy of the Type
YG-73 cell by cali-
bration prism

7.2 the verification of the reliability of the cell by overcoring in a big rock block

The procedure of test is as follows:

A load P is applied to the rock block
(Fig 11):

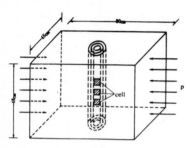

Fig. 11 The experiment of overcoring on big rock specimen

A small hole of 36mm in diameter is
drilled into the rock block of dimension
45 by 48 by 80 cm.

The cells are inserted and prestressed.
The overcore is made by drilling apparatus with bit of 150mm in diameter. The
magnitude and direction of the principal
stresses are calculated (table 4).

Table 4 The results of the exper-
ments of overcoring on big
rock specimens

load (kg/cm²)	value of stress σ_1 (kg/cm²)	deviation of value of σ_1	deviation of direction of σ_1
60	63	5%	1°
70	71	1.4%	-3°

The error for magnitude of maximum principal stresses in most cases is less than
5%. It is very rare for error to be bigger than 10%. The bigger error may be

related to residual stresses in rock.

The changes of readings curve with depth
of overcore is regular. At the begining
the curve goes up and then reaches a top
value nearby the cell. Then the curve
goes down and reaches a stable value beyond angle of 45° to the axis of the hole
(Fig. 12)

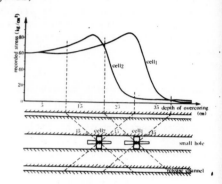

Fig. 12 The variation of the recorded stress with depth of
overcoring in rock specimen

The top value of the curve is induced
by the stress concentrition at the bottom of the stress release channel.

The shape of the readings curve is an
important basis for judging reliability
of the measurement. Therefore, during
overcoring it is neccessary to monitor
the change of reading.

In order to study the curve shape theoretically, the overcore is simulated by
axisymmetrical finite element method. A
theoretical curve of readings is obtained
(Fig. 13).

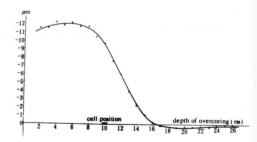

Fig. 13 The variation of the recorded stress with over-
coring (solution of finite
element method)

The comparison of Fig. 12 with Fig. 13 shows that they are much the same in shape.

8. THE VERIFICATION OF THE RELIABILITY OF THE CELL IN SITU

In order to determine the reliability of the cell in situ stress measurements were made at different structure positions and depth in different rocks. As an example, in situ measurement in Wu Xongsi, is presented as follows.

The measuring depth is 11-19m below the surface. Twelve readings are gained and treated statistically. The magnitudes and the directions of principal stresses and regression curve are given in table 5 and Fig. 14. It can be seen that the

Table 5 The results of measurements in **Wu Xiongsi**

major principal stress σ_1(kg /cm²)	minor principal stress σ_2(kg /cm²)	direction of σ_1	confidence
36 ± 2	4 ± 2	N73° ± 3° W	95%

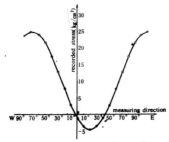

+ real measuring value
⊙ regressing value

Fig. 14 The regression curve of recorded stress obtained in **Wu Xiongsi**, Shun Yi County near Beijing

maximum principal stress is 2.6±0.2mpa, the relative error is about 8%; the minimum principal stress is 0.4±0.2mpa; the direction of the maximum principal stress is N73° W with the confidance of 95%; and the most of the measuring value fall near the regression curve, which indicates that the scatter of the values and the results of stress measurement are reliable.

9. THE RESULTS OF STRESS MEASUREMENT IN

NORTH CHINA AND IN JINCHUAN MINE

In order to research tectonic stress field and design reasonably mine project, in situ stress measurements were made by using type YG-73 piezomagnetic stress gauge in the North China and the Jinchun mine.

9.1 the stress measurement in North China

The stress measurement were made in depth of 30m below the surface. The results of measurement are shown in table 6.

Table 6 The results of stress measurments in North China

Measuring site	Time of measurment	Lithology and geological age	Max. principal stress (kg/cm²)	Min. principal stress (kg/cm²)	Direction of the max. principal stress
Longyao Maoshan	1966.10	Cambrian limestone	77	42	N54°W
Shunyi Wuxiongsi	1971.6	Ordovician limestone	31	18	N75°W
Shunyi Pangshan	1973.11	Ordovician limestone	1	1	N58°W
Shunyi Wuxiongsi	1973.11	Ordovician limestone	26	4	N73°W
Beijing Wenquan	1974.8	Ordovician limestone	36	22	N65°W
Beijing Changping	1974.10	Sinian limestone	12	8	N75°W
Beijing Dahuichang	1974.11	Ordovician limestone	21	9	N35°W
Liaoning Haicheng	1975.7	Presinian magnesite	93	59	N47°E
Liaoning Yingkou	1975.10	Presinian dolomite	166	104	N84°W
Longyao Yaoshan	1976.6	Cambrian limestone	32	21	N87°E
Luanxian NO.1	1976.8	Ordovician limestone	58	30	N61°E
Luanxian NO.2	1976.9	Ordovician limestone	66	52	N89°W
Shunyi Wuxiongsi	1976.9	Ordovician limestone	36	17	N83°W
Tangshan Fenghuangshan	1976.10	Ordovician limestone	25	17	N47°W
Sanhe Gushan	1976.10	Ordovician limestone	21	5	N69°W
Huainu Fentoushan	1976.11	Ordovician limestone	11	11	N83°W
Chicheng	1977.7	Precambrian ultrabasic rock	33	21	N82°E
Shunyi Wuxiongsi	1977.7	Ordovician limestone	27	21	N75°W

Based on the results of stress measurement some conclusions are drown as follows:

a). Keep the whole region in view, the direction of the stress field is predominantly NWW to near EW (Fig.15). The principal stresses measured at local site

Fig. 15 Directions of maximum principal stresses measured by overcoring and faulting plane solution of earthquake in North China

1— direction of maximum principal stress by overcoring
2— direction of the compression of faulting plane solution of earthquake

vary in direction. The principal stresses measured are compresive. The ratio of minimum to maximum principal stress is 0.19 to 0.78.

b). The results of stress measurements which are in good agreement with the geological structure and the results of photoelastic modelling reflect the characteristics of stress field of the Neocathaysian structure system.

9.2 the stress measurements in the Jinchun mine

The Jinchun mine is situated in western Gausu Province, in northwestern China. It is a large copper and nickel deposits, ranking second in reserves in the world. During construction and mining, the drifts were strongly deformed and severely damaged. To solve this problem we have made stress measurements in the mine district (Liao 1983). The results of stress measurement are shown in table 7.

Table 7 Results of ground stress measurements

Measuring point	Lithology	Depth below surface (m)	Max. principal stress Value MN/m²	Direction	Dip	Intermediate principal stress Value MN/m²	Direction	Dip	Min. principal stress Value MN/m²	Direction	Dip	Time of measuring	Remark
A	Marble	20	2.4						2.3			1977	
B	Marble	44	4.2	N20°E					3.5			1975	Hanging wall About 50m away from the Fis fault
C	Marble	375	19.8	N3°E					10.8			1975	
D	Granite	480	24.5	N25°W					15.4			1986	
E	Marble	460	50.0	N13°W	∠6°SE	33.4	N76°E	∠6°NE	28.2	S63°E	∠81°NW	1974	Foot wall about 80m away from
F	Very rich ore	480	32.0	N32°E	∠5°SW	21.4	S43°E	∠87°NW	20.6	N60°W	∠22°SE	1978	
G	Rich ore	240	34.4	N42°W	∠39°NW	21.1	N48°E	horizontal	2.6	S41°E	∠51°SE	1977	the Fi7 fault
H	Marble	120	16.8	N28°W	∠57°SE	12.1	S35°W	∠16°NE	5.8	S63°E	∠28°NW	1974	

It can be seen that the stresses operating in the mine district are predominantly horizontal and compressive. The maximum principal stress near the surface is about 3mpa, which is very close to the results obtained in North China. The value of stress increases with depth, and the maximum principal stress is generally 30mpa or so at 200-500m in depth. The veriation of horizontal principal stress with depth and the veriation with depth of the ratio between the mean horizontal stress and the vertical stress are shown in Fig.16a and Fig. 16b respectively.

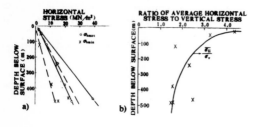

Fig. 16. a) Variation of horizontal principal stresses with depth
b) Variation with depth of the ratio between the mean horizontal stress and vertical stress

Drift stability is closely related to the state of stress. An upright-wall arch section was used for most of the drifts in the mine in the past. The drifts were strongly deformed and severely damaged. Based on the results of stress measurements and finite element analysis it is indicated that under the dominance of horizotal stresses, drifts with an upright-wall arch section are easy to be caused fracture on the side wall and floor swelling. Theoretically, a drift of flat elliptical cross-section is more reasonable, but it is difficult for construction. With the advantages of an elliptical cross-section as a basis, a quasi-elliptical cross-section of drift suited to the stress state of the mine has however been deviced and has been proved very successful in practice. In addition, optimum direction of drift, reasonable parameter of drift support and correct mining methods are selected based on the state of stress.

10. CONCLUSIONS

With the help of mumerous lab tests and in situ measurements it has been shown that the YG-73 piezomagnetic stress gauge is characterized by good linearity, repeatability, stability and enough sensitivity. Using this kind of gauge, one may get reliable results of measurement.

In lab, the discrepancy in measurement is usually less than 5% of the applied load for magnitude and less than 3° for direction. For in situ stress measurements the standard error is usually less than 10% for maximum principal stress magnitude and less than 3° for direction.

The results of measurement are found to be more accurate if rock core together with set-in gauges taken from the bore hole after overcoring is put into calibrato for calibration.

It is neccessary that in order to get reliable results, the overcoring procedure must be repeated, until a sufficient number of successful determinations are made. And then the magnitude and the directions of the principal stresses are calculated by least square method. The stress measurement indicate that the current state of stress closely related to geological structure and knowledge of stress state is important in mine reasonable desion.

ACKNOWLEDGMENTS:

We are grateful to prof. Sun Daigeng and prof. Chen Qingxuan and prof. Pan Lizhou for their guidance and help, and we are also grateful to Wang Wei for her help with the figures and tables.

REFERENCES

Hast, N. 1958.The Measurement of Rock Pressure in Mine. Stockholm.

Liao Chunting. 1983. In-Situ Stress Measurements and Their Application to Enginerring Design in the Jinchun Mine. International Congress on Rock Mechanics MELBOURNE (AUSTRALIA): D87-D89.

Panek, L.A. 1965. Calculation of the Average Ground Stress Components from Measurement of the Diametral Deformation of A Drill Hole. Testing Techniques for Rock Mechanics.

Pan Lizhou. 1977. In-Situ Determination of Elastic Coefficients by Using Borehole and Cells for Rock Stress Measurement. Collected Papers and Notes on Geomechanics (6): 33-35.

Pan Lizhou. 1981. Some Remarks on the Borehole Deformation Method in Measurement Ground Stress. Principies and Applications of Ground Stress Measurement. Publishing House of Geology. Beijing.

Pan Lizhou. 1984. On the Mechanics of the Whole Process of Measuring Ground Stress by the Borehole Deformation Method Using Pre-pressed Probes of Contact Type. ACTA GEOPHYSICA SINICA 27(6): 548-561.

Wang Lianjie. 1977. A least Square Method for Date Processing in Plane Stress Measurement in the Earth Crust.Collected Paper and Notes on Geomechanics (4): 19-32.

Wang Lianjie. 1979. A Calculation for the Three Dimensional In-Situ Stress Measurement. Collected Papers and Notes on Geomechanics(5): 106-124.

Wang Lianjie. 1986. The Inflence of Rock Stress Measurement. Bulletin of the Institute of Geomechanics. Chinese Academy of Geological Sciences(6)(in press).

A new method of rock stress measurement with hydraulic borehole pressure cells

P.H. LU
Denver Research Center, Bureau of Mines, Denver, Colorado, USA

ABSTRACT

This paper presents basic principles and required instrumentation for rock stress measurements with U.S. Department of the Interior, Bureau of Mines, hydraulic borehole pressure cells. Existing stresses and stress changes can be measured with the same instrumentation. Based on the elastic theories of plates and thick-walled cylinders, the magnitude of biaxial rock stresses existing in a rock mass can be determined by pressure convergence-divergence tests using a combination of one cylindrical and two encapsulated flat hydraulic borehole pressure cells installed in a single drill hole. Case studies are included to demonstrate the validity of the technique.

RESUME

Ce papier décrit les principes de base ainsi que l'instrumentation nécessarire pour mesurer les efforts dans les roches au moyen des cellules de pression du Bureau des Mines du ministère de l'Intérieur. Les efforts présents et les changements de ces efforts peuvent être mesurés par les mêmes instruments. La détermination des efforts est fondée sur la théorie de l'élasticité des plaques et des cylindres de paroi épaisse. La valeur des efforts biaxiaux qui existent dans une masse rocheuse est déterminée par des essais sous pression. On utilise a cette fin trois cellules de pression dont une est cylindrique, et les deux autres plates. Toutes les trois sont placées dans un seul trou perforé. Des études de cas particuliers sont traitées a fin de démontrer la validité de cette technique.

ZUSAMMENFASSUNG

Diese Arbeit beschreibt die Grundlagen und die notwendige Ausrustung fur die Messung von Spannungen in Gestein mittels der hydraulischen Bohrlochdruckzellen des U.S. Department of the Interior, Bureau of Mines. Bestehende Spannungen sowie Spannungsänderungen können mit denselben Instrumenten gemessen werden. Nach dem elastizitätstheoretischen Verhalten von Platten und dickwandigen Zylindern kann der Betrag von zweiachsigen Spannungen in einer Gesteinsmasse durch Druckkonvergenz und -divergenz Tests bestimmt werden. Dazu wird eine Kombination von einer zylindrischen und zwei eingekapselten, flachen, hydraulischen Bohrlochdruckzellen in ein einziges Bohrloch eingebaut. Zur Demonstration des Verfahrens werden Fallstudien angeführt.

1 INTRODUCTION

The U.S. Bureau of Mines' hydraulic borehole pressure cells, flat (BPC) and cylindrical (CPC), were initially developed in the early 1960's. Since then, the BPC has been used primarily for measuring uniaxial rock stress and relative changes in rock stress (Panek 1961), whereas the CPC has been used mainly for in situ determination of the modulus of rigidity of rocks (Panek et al 1964). The new technique of using a combination of BPC and CPC to measure biaxial and triaxial rock stresses, both static and dynamic, was developed during the last several years (Lu 1981, 1984).

In this paper, the basic principles and necessary instrumentation to measure static and dynamic rock stresses are described. The validity and practicality of the technique are demonstrated with three typical case studies.

2 BASIC PRINCIPLES

2.1 Determination of biaxial and triaxial rock stresses

Based on the elastic theories of plates and thick-walled cylinders, the magnitude of biaxial rock stresses existing in a rock mass can be determined by pressure convergence tests using a combination of one CPC and two pre-encapsulated BPC's, as shown in figure 1. With this instrumentation, the cylindrical cell provides the sum, whereas the two flat cells give the ratio of the biaxial stresses, provided the rock mass is homogeneous and isotropic and the stresses are uniform within that portion of the rock mass tested. Then, by drilling a pair of orthogonal holes for such instrumentation, the magnitude of the triaxial rock stresses can also be measured (Lu 1981).

The state of stress of an in situ intact rock mass, whether homogeneous or heterogeneous, isotropic or anisotropic, elastic or inelastic, is initially in equilibrium or inactive. However, once a hole is drilled into such a rock mass, the rock stress existing in the vicinity of the hole will become active owing to stress relief of the portion of that hole. Some types of rocks may be considered elastic, but most are

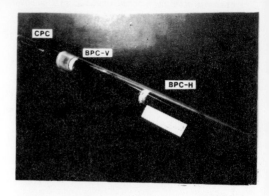

Fig.1 Combination of one CPC and two BPC's in one hole (Lu 1984).

viscoelastic and show time effects such as creep under an intermediate (compared to ultimate strength) constant stress. The general problem of stress-strain analysis, however, is the same for elastic and viscoelastic rocks. The only difference is that for viscoelastic rocks, Hooke's law is replaced by a viscoelastic stress-strain relationship derived from creep. Therefore, the viscoelastic solutions can be derived from those of the elastic analysis problem by replacing the elastic modulus with the viscoelastic modulus on the basis of the elastic-viscoelastic correspondence principle (Flügge 1967, Lu 1981).

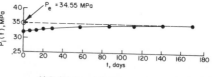

A) $P_i(t)$ versus t for long-term pressure convergence

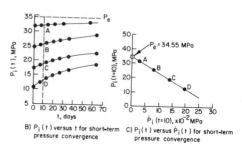

B) $P_i(t)$ versus t for short-term pressure convergence

C) $P_i(t)$ versus $\dot{P}_i(t)$ for short-term pressure convergence

Fig.2 Procedure of cell equilibrium pressure determination

238

Thus the problem of determining biaxial or triaxial rock stresses is reduced to finding the equilibrium pressures of the hydraulic borehole pressure cells. The cell equilibrium pressure can be determined from the long-term (1 to 6 months) pressure convergence of a single cell by taking the stabilized cell pressure as the equilibrium pressure, as shown in figure 2A. However, the cell equilibrium pressure can also be determined from the short-term (10 to 15 days) pressure convergence of several identical cells by using the rate of cell pressure change, as shown in figures 2B and 2C.

2.2 Sum of existing biaxial rock stresses

Based on the principle of superposition, the problem of the radial displacement of a long drill hole at depth in a uniform elastic rock formation, subjected to an internal pressure p_i, can be resolved into the problems of an infinite plate with a circular center hole subjected to a biaxial stress field, and of a thick-walled cylinder with an infinite outer radius and subjected to an internal pressure p_i as shown in figure 3.

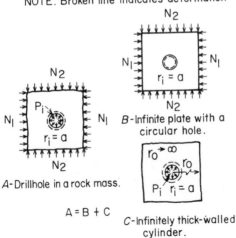

NOTE: Broken line indicates deformation

A-Drillhole in a rock mass.

B-Infinite plate with a circular hole.

C-Infinitely thick-walled cylinder.

A = B + C

Fig.3 Scheme of the problem of the radial displacement of a drill hole (Lu 1981).

Then the resulting radial displacements are converted to the volume change of the drill hole for the interval of the cell length. The resulting volume change relation listed below is used for the general cases, including elastic and viscoelastic rocks, by assuming the special plane strain condition in which the axial strain is zero and the hole is not deformed prior to cell insertion. The derivation of equations appears in Lu (1981).

$$V_d(t) = \pm\, 2\pi a^2 L(1 + \nu)[p_i(t) -$$

$$(1-\nu)(N_1 + N_2)]/E(t) \qquad (1)$$

where

$V_d(t)$ = volume change of the drill hole
a = radius of the hole
L = active length of CPC
ν = Poisson's ratio, assumed or determined from the same instrumentation
$p_i(t)$ = CPC pressure
N_1, N_2 = biaxial rock stresses
$E(t)$ = modulus of deformation
t = time,
and $t = 0$ is considered as the elastic case.

Whereas, empirically if a cylindrical pressure cell is pressurized and expanded in a drill hole and the outer shell of the cell is in full contact with the wall of the drill hole, the following relationship exists between the two volume-pressure ratios, V_d/p_d of the drill hole and V_c/p_c of the pressure cell (Panek et al 1964):

$$V_d/p_d = K_1 + K_2(V_c/p_c) \qquad \text{or}$$

$$P_d = V_d/C \qquad (2)$$

where $C = K_1 + K_2(V_c/p_c)$, V_d is the volume change and p_d is the pressure change in the drill hole, V_c is the fluid volume change and p_c is the fluid pressure change in the pressure cell, K_1 is a constant determined by the compressibility of the total fluid retained in the pressure cell, which has a negative value, and K_2 is a constant related to the response between drill hole and pressure cell, which is dependent on the bulk modulus of the pressure cell. These two constants, K_1 and K_2, can be calibrated by pressure cycling the CPC in two metal cylinders with known elastic constants (Panek et al 1964).

From equations (1) and (2) we obtain the relationship between the biaxial rock stresses N_1, N_2 and the pressure change in the drill hole:

$$P_d(t) = \pm\ 2\pi a^2 L(1+\nu)[P_i(t)-(1-\nu)$$
$$(N_1 + N_2)]/C\ E(t)\ . \qquad (3)$$

A drill hole subjected to external biaxial rock stresses and an internal dilating pressure tends to restore the strain equilibrium by means of stress compensation. Namely, when $p_d(t) = 0$, $V_d(t)$ becomes zero. Since all terms but $[p_i(t) - (1-\nu)(N_1 + N_2)]$ in equation (3) are nonzero, by equating $[\ p_i(t) - (1-\nu)(N_1 + N_2)] = 0$, we obtain

$$N_1 + N_2 = p_i(t)/(1-\nu) \qquad \text{or}$$
$$N_1 + N_2 = P_{e-CPC}/(1-\nu)\ , \qquad (4)$$

where P_{e-CPC} is the CPC equilibrium pressure.

2.3 Ratio of existing biaxial rock stresses

From field experiments, it became evident that when an encapsulated BPC is installed in a drill hole and pressurized, the directional displacement of the drill hole, U, will occur proportionally to the difference between the internal pressure of the cell. Therefore, we have the following empirical relationship (Lu 1981):

$$U = [\bar{P}_i - f\ N]/E_c\ , \qquad (5)$$

where E_c is the composite modulus of deformation of the rock mass and capsule material, $\bar{p}_i$ is the internal cell pressure, N is the resultant effective directional rock stress, and f is the response ratio between cell pressure and the effective directional rock stress. This response ratio, f is dependent on the composite modulus of deformation of the rock mass, capsule material, and cell material.

Also, there is a relation, $\bar{P}_d = m\ U$, existing between the directional displacement of the drill hole, U, and the pressure change at the inner wall of the drill hole $\bar{p}_d$, where m is the propor-

tionality constant. By substituting (5) into the above expression and generalizing the relationship to include both elastic and viscoelastic cases, we obtain

$$\bar{p}_d(t) = m[\bar{p}_i(t) - f\ N]/E_c(t)\ . \qquad (6)$$

From (6) it is evident $\bar{p}_i(t)-f\ N = 0$ is a sufficient condition for $\bar{p}_d(t) = 0$, namely for the cell pressure $\bar{p}_i(t)$ to reach the equilibrium pressure $\bar{p}_e$. By knowing the equilibrium cell pressures in the two orthogonal directions $\bar{p}_{e1}$ and $\bar{p}_{e2}$, the ratio $Q = \bar{p}_{e1}/\bar{p}_{e2}$ can be expressed in terms of N_1 and N_2 as $Q = (N_1 + S\ N_2)/(N_2 + S\ N_1)$, where S is the transverse sensitivity of the BPC body, which is equivalent to the ratio of effective cross-sectional areas in the two orthogonal directions. From this relationship, the ratio of the biaxial rock stresses can be derived as

$$N_1/N_2 = (Q-S)\ /\ (1-Q\ S)\ . \qquad (7)$$

The numerical value of S is 0.185 for the U.S. Bureau of Mines BPC currently in use. This S value was calculated from the geometry of the cell body.

2.4 Biaxial rock stress measurement with a two-BPC package

The induced biaxial rock stresses can also be measured by a combination of only two BPC's installed in a single drill hole, as shown in figure 4, if the

Fig.4 Combination of two BPCs in one hole (Lu 1984).

pressure response ratio, f, defined as the ratio of BPC pressure reading to the effective directional rock stress is known. This response ratio f can be determined by the following equation (Lu 1984):

$$f = \bar{p}_{e1}/(N_1 + S N_2) \qquad \text{or}$$

$$f = \bar{p}_{e2}/(N_2 + S N_1), \qquad (8)$$

where N_1 and N_2 are obtained from equations (4) and (7). Thus, with the known value of f, the biaxial rock stresses N_1^* and N_2^* can be derived from equation (8).

3 REQUIRED INSTRUMENTATION

3.1 Hydraulic borehole pressure cells

The U.S. Department of the Interior, Bureau of Mines hydraulic borehole pressure cells and auxiliary instruments are shown in figure 5. The CPC with a 37.5-mm diameter is installed in the 38.0-mm diameter portion of a drill hole. The complete system consists of

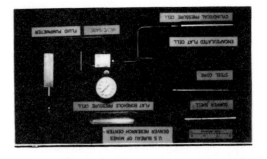

Fig.5 Hydraulic borehole pressure cells and auxiliary instruments.

CPC, tubing, valve-gage and/or valve-recorder unit, and fluid pumpmeter. The CPC is 20.3 cm long and has an effective length of 17.8 cm when installed in a drill hole. Glycerin or hydraulic oil is pumped through the steel tubing of 3.175 mm I.D. into the annulus between the steel core and the copper shell, which is forced against the wall of the drill hole.

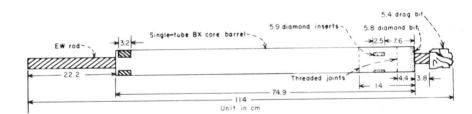

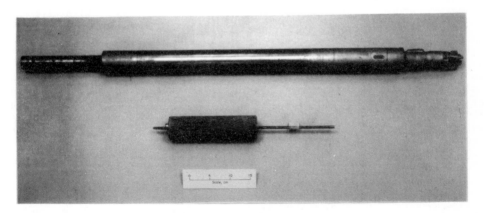

Fig.6 Combination precision bit

241

The BPC has a 59.3-mm-diam capsule
~~capsule~~ and is designed for a BX-size
(60-mm) installation hole. The other
parts of the system are those described
above for use with the CPC. The flat
cell body is made of 1.52-mm-thick
mild steel and is 20.3 cm long, 5.08 cm
wide, and 8.9 mm high. The same fluid
used in the CPC is pumped into the cell
to inflate it and press it against the
Portland cement capsule. Two
8.4-mm-diam tunnels are provided in
the capsule for a tubing passage.

3.2 Smooth and precise test holes

Smooth-walled drillholes with a precise
diameter are critical when employing
this instrumentation. The tolerance
should be within 1.0 mm. In hard rocks,
a diamond bit is used for drilling. For
softer rocks, the Bureau of Mines has
developed a combination bit to drill
smooth and precise instrumentation holes
by jointing a drag bit and a diamond bit
as shown in figure 6.

4 CASE STUDIES

4.1 Static rock stresses

A package of one CPC and two BPC's was
installed in a potash bed in a New
Mexico mine to measure the vertical and
horizontal stresses. The overburden
cover is 366 m thick. The potash bed is
nearly flat, dipping 4° to the northeast.
The package of pressure cells was
installed in a 30 m deep horizontal
borehole drilled into the potash bed at
midheight between the roof and floor.
The initial cell pressure was set at
slightly below 17 MPa for all three
cells. The cell pressure readings for
the initial 35-day period are plotted
in figure 7. All three cell pressures
converged to their equilibrium values in
25 to 30 days. By employing the
long-term pressure convergence method
described in section 2.1 and figure 2A,
the equilibrium pressures for the CPC,
the vertical BPC, and the horizontal
BPC, denoted by P_{e-CPC}, P_{e-BV}, and
P_{e-BH}, respectively, are obtained from
figure 7 as 11.0, 6.6, and 5.0 MPa.
Using equation (7), $N_H/N_V = 0.67$ is
obtained, where N_H and N_V are the
horizontal and vertical rock stresses
respectively. By assuming that no
tectonic stresses exist in the tested
area, Poisson's ratio ν is estimated

as 0.40 from the relation $N_H/N_V =$
$\nu/(1 - \nu) = 0.67$. Then from equation
(4), $N_H + N_V = P_{e-CPC}/(1-\nu) =$
$11.0/(1-0.4) = 18.2$ MPa. Thus, $N_V = 10.9$
MPa and $N_H = 7.3$ MPa.

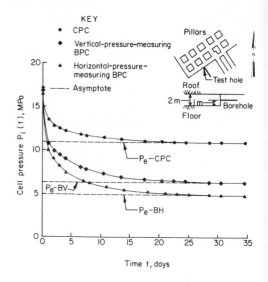

Fig.7 Long-term cell pressure
convergence plot.

After the biaxial rock stresses and
equilibrium cell pressures are obtained
by the above procedure, the BPC response
ratio f, defined as the ratio of the BPC
equilibrium pressure to the effective
directional rock stress, can be derived
from equation (8). Namely, $f = P_{e-BH}/(N_H$
$+ 0.185N_V) = 0.535$ or $f = P_{e-BV}/(N_V +$
$0.185N_H) = 0.535$. With this ratio
known, the biaxial rock stresses may be
determined from the measurement with a
two-BPC package.

Besides potash, this technique has
been applied to many other types of
relatively soft rock, such as salt,
coal, and metamorphic rocks. Results of
six case studies previously made by the
author are listed in table 1.

4.2 Rock stress changes

A package of one CPC and two BPC's was
installed in a coal pillar on a longwall
mining operation in West Virginia to
measure mining-induced stress changes in
the vertical and horizontal directions.
The test hole was drilled into the
center of an interpanel pillar from the
entry side (fig. 8A). The 25- by 30-m

Table 1. Measured existing rock stresses

Rock strata	Measuring site	Over-burden	Modulus of deformation	Poisson's ratio	Vertical pressure	Horizontal pressure	
						I	II
		m	10³ MPa		MPa	MPa	MPa
Potash bed, New Mexico	Unmined area, 20% excavated	366	20.16	0.40	10.9	7.3 NE-SW	
Potash bed, Utah	Development entry pillar, 18m x 42m, 20% excavated	1067	27.07	0.34	34.5	17.8 NW-SE	14.8 NE-SW
Salt bed, Ohio	Unmined area, 10% excavated	584	23.04	0.28	15.9	13.1 N-S	11.4 E-W
Coal seam, W. Virginia	Barrier pillar, 15% excavated	290	5.72	0.35	10.0	8.3 E-W	
Fractured monzonite porphyry, Arizona	Unmined block, 12% excavated	560	16.56	0.20	12.0	14.8 NE-SW	12.8 NW-SE
Gneiss, schist, and altered granite; Eisenhower tunnel, Colorado	3m by 3m pilot tunnel	396	42.76	0.20	15.9	13.8 E-W	6.9 N-S

pillar was under 230-m-thick overburden. The cell pressures, initially set at 14 MPa, converged to equilibrium pressures (P_e's) at -35-m face distance of Panel 1 (negative distance indicates the line of instrumentation is in the unmined area). Thereon the cell pressures diverged in accordance with mining progress until the cells were destroyed at zero face distance of Panel 2.

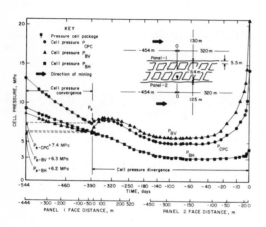

A) Cell Pressure versus time and face distance

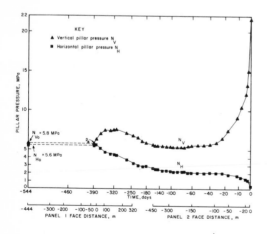

B) Vertical and horizontal pressures versus time and face distance.

Fig.8 Process of mining-induced pillar pressure determination (Lu 1984).

Thus from the cell pressure convergence curves and cell equilibrium pressures (fig. 8A, left of P_e), the premining vertical and horizontal pressures are calculated with equations (4) and (7) and plotted in figure 8B (left of P_e). In this case, the equilibrium pressures used for calculation may be slightly higher than the actual values, because the cell pressures could not converge to the asymptotes owing to the insufficiency of time before cell pressures start to diverge. Then from the cell pressure divergence curves (fig. 8A, right of P_e) the mining-induced vertical and horizontal pillar pressures are also calculated with equations (4) and (7) and plotted in figure 8B, right of P_e. The results revealed that the mining-induced pillar loading, in the vertical and horizontal directions, realistically matches mining progress.

4.3 Biaxial rock-stress changes measured with two-BPC packages

The two-BPC packages were installed in a series of boreholes drilled into a 12.8-by 30.5-m rectangular interpanel chain pillar across its section, as shown in figure 9A, to obtain progressive loading profiles across the pillar. The pillar was under 240-m-thick overburden.

The vertical and horizontal (in the direction of crosscut) pressures at each measuring point at different stages of longwall mining were calculated from the cell pressure readings by using equation (8). The response ratio, f, between BPC pressure and coal pillar pressure was predetermined as 0.93 by a separate instrumentation with the three-cell packages. The resulting vertical and horizontal pressure profiles across the pillar at four selected stages of longwall mining are plotted in figures 9B and 9C, respectively. The profiles reveal that the stress distributions across the pillar section at these particular stages of mining progress are realistic; they also clearly indicate the load transfer from the yielded zone adjacent to the pillar edge toward the pillar core in accordance with mining progress.

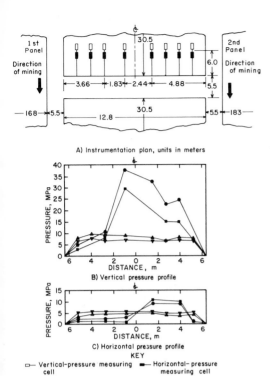

A) Instrumentation plan, units in meters

B) Vertical pressure profile

C) Horizontal pressure profile

KEY

□— Vertical-pressure measuring cell   ■— Horizontal-pressure measuring cell
▼ 1st Panel face at -130 m   ● 2nd Panel face at -7 m
▲ 1st Panel face at 0 m   ■ 2nd Panel face at 0 m

Fig.9 Progressive pillar loading profiles determined by the two-BPC packages (Lu 1984).

5 CONCLUSIONS

This technique is a direct method to determine rock stresses, both static and dynamic, without using the modulus of deformation of the rock for back-calculation. Therefore, it enables us to monitor continuous changes in rock stresses precisely. The method is applicable to all types of rock, but it is particularly suitable for softer and/or inelastic rocks. The method is proved to be practical with several case studies.

6 REFERENCES

Flügge, W. 1967. Viscoelasticity. Blaisdell/London.

Lu, P. H. 1981. Determination of Ground Pressure Existing in a Viscoelastic Rock Mass by Use of Hydraulic Borehole Pressure Cells. Proc., Int. Symp. on Weak Rock, Tokyo, Japan, A. A. Balkema/Rotterdam 1: 459-465.

Lu, P. H. 1984. Mining-Induced Stress Measurement With Hydraulic Borehole Pressure Cells. Proc., 25th U.S. Symp. on Rock Mechanics, Evanston, IL, SME/AIME Chap. 22: 204-211.

Panek, L. A. 1961. Measurement of Rock Pressure With a Hydraulic Cell. AIME Trans. 220: 287-290.

Panek, L. A., et al. 1964. Determination of the Modulus of Rigidity of Rock by Expanding a Cylindrical Pressure Cell in a Drillhole. Proc., 6th U.S. Symp. on Rock Mechanics, Rolla, MO, 427-449.

A soft inclusion instrument for in situ stress measurement in coal

K.W. MILLS
Consulting Engineer, Applied Rock Mechanics, Auckland, New Zealand

M.J. PENDER
University of Auckland, Auckland, New Zeeland

ABSTRACT A soft hollow inclusion strain measuring device that employs the over-coring technique of stress relief is described. The instrument has an inflatable rubber membrane with electrical resistance strain gauges mounted on the outer surface. These strain gauges are bonded with epoxy cement directly to the periphery of a 38 mm diameter pilot hole by inflating the rubber membrane. A pressuremeter test can be conducted in situ, prior to the overcoring operation, to verify correct strain gauge operation and to determine the modulus of the rock. The instrument has been used to measure in situ stresses in both a sub-bituminous coal and an aniso-tropic schist, and also to monitor stress changes in coal.

RESUME Un appareil de mesure de contraintes basé sur une inclusion souple et creuse est décrit. Cet instrument emploie la technique de relachement du stress par "overcoring". L'instrument est composé d'une membrane en caoutchouc gonflable sur la surface extérieure de laquelle sont installées des résistances électriques mesurant les stress. Ces jauges de mesures des contraintes sont fixées par résine epoxy directement sur la périphérie d'un trou pilote EX en gonflant la membrane. Un test de mesure de pression peut être effectué sur place avant l'opération d'"overcoring" pour vérifier que la jauge fonctionne correctement et pour déterminer le module de la roche. Cet instrument a été utilisé à la fois dans un charbon sub-bituminex et dans un schiste anisotropique pour mesurer les contraintes en place, et dans un charbon pour suivre les changements de tension.

ZUSAMMENFASSUNG Ein weiches, hohles Einschliessungs-Instrument zur Ausdehnungs-messung, das die Kernbohrungs-Technik der Spannungsbefreiung ausnutzt, ist beschrieben. Das Instrument besitzt eine aufblasbare Gummimembrane auf deren Oberflaeche eletrische Dehnmessstreifen exponiert sind. Durch Aufblasen der Gummimembrane werden diese Dehnmessstreifen mit Epoxyharz direkt auf die Peripherie eines Pilotloches von 38 mm Durchmesser geklebt. Ein Dilatometer Test kann vor der Kernbohrung vor Ort durchgefuehrt werden, um die korrekte Funktion der Dehnmess-streifen zu sichern und den Modul des Gesteines zu bestimmen. Das Instrument wurde sowohl in unter-bituminoeser Kohle als auch in anisotropischem Schiefer zur Messung von Spannungen vor Ort benuetzt sowie zur Beobachtung von Spannungsaenderungen in Kohle.

1 INTRODUCTION

This paper describes an instrument called the Auckland New Zealand Soft Inclusion (ANZSI) cell that was developed to measure in situ stress in coal. The instruments mode of operation is described together with the advantages that it offers for in situ stress measurements and stress change monitoring in coal as well as other rock types. Results of in situ stress measurements using the instrument are described elsewhere in these proceedings (Mills et al 1986).

Stress relief by overcoring of an installed instrument is a well established technique for measuring in situ stress in rock masses. Many instruments have been developed which use electrical resistance strain gauges either cemented directly to the rock (Leeman & Hayes 1966), or cast within an epoxy inclusion which is then cemented to the rock (Rocha & Silveira 1969), (Worotnicki & Walton 1976). These instruments have been used in a wide variety of rock types with best results achieved in hard competent rock. Practical advantages of waterproofing and general robustness of the instrument result from having strain gauges included within an epoxy annulus or cylinder which has a low elastic modulus relative to the rock.

For soft rocks, such as coal, the modulus of an epoxy inclusion is relatively high compared to the modulus of the rock. Consequently, large tensile stresses are induced in a radial direction at the instrument-rock interface during stress relief (Duncan-Fama & Pender 1980). Tensile stresses of the order of 800 kPa were generated when the CSIRO Hollow Inclusion cell was used in coal (Depledge et al 1980). These stresses were sufficient to cause tensile failure of the rock itself adjacent to the interface.

Stress measurement instruments of the type described above rely on a biaxial test to verify correct gauge function and to determine rock properties. In a competent rock, the chances of recovery of intact core are relatively high, so rock properties can be determined in a biaxial compression test. In a closely jointed rock, however, the chances of recovery of intact core are much less. Even if overcoring has been successful, as indicated by the stress relief curves, it may not be possible to determine the rock properties or verify correct gauge operation because the recovered core cannot be tested in biaxial compression.

Although the ANZSI cell was developed mainly to overcome the high tensile stresses generated during overcoring in coal with conventional instruments, its utilisation of the pressuremeter principle offers a number of other advantages. Among these is the ability to conduct a pressure test in situ and thereby to provide, before overcoring, information from which the rock properties can be determined and the correct operation of all strain gauges can be checked.

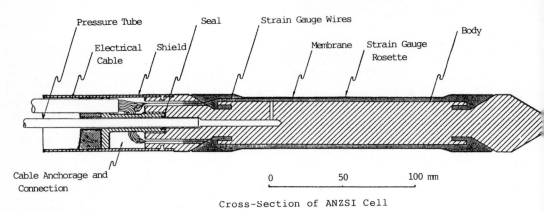

Pressure Tube   Seal   Strain Gauge Wires

Electrical   Shield   Membrane   Strain Gauge   Body
Cable   Rosette

Cable Anchorage and
Connection

0   50   100 mm

Cross-Section of ANZSI Cell

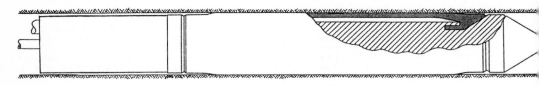

Inflated in Borehole

Figure 1 :   ANZSI Cell - Cross-Section and Inflated in a Borehole.

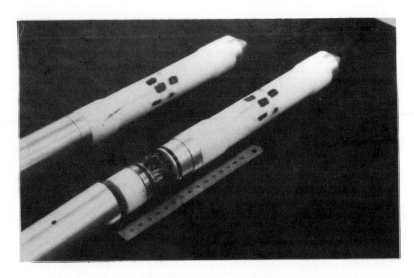

Figure 2 :   ANZSI Cell with and without the shield retracted.   The strain gauge rosettes can be seen beside the dark rectangular terminal pads.

2   INSTRUMENT DESCRIPTION

The instrument is illustrated in Figures 1 & 2. The main weight component of the instrument is the body. For ease of handling during installation, this is manufactured from lightweight material, such as aluminium, acrylic or PVC. A 2 mm thick rubber membrane is cast onto the body. Mounted flush with the outside surface of this membrane are nine, or more, strain gauges.

To inflate the membrane during installation and thereby press the strain gauges into contact with the periphery of the pilot hole, air is introduced through a remotely detachable air line. Inturned lips at either end of the membrane create a seal.

The central section of the membrane has a reduced diameter to protect the strain gauges from mechanical damage and provide a recess for epoxy cement during installation.

A shield at the back of the instrument protects and waterproofs the electrical connections and cable anchorage. Placing rods connect into this shield.

2.1   Membrane

The membrane is cast from a polyurethane elastomer. This material is flexible, robust and bonds well to the epoxy cement used during installation.

During manufacture, the membrane is formed between the body of the instrument and an external split mould. Strain gauge rosettes, with sense wires connected, are temporarily fixed to the external mould. When the elastomer has cured and the mould is broken, the strain gauge rosettes are left exposed on the surface of the membrane. The sense wires from the gauges run inside the membrane, out through holes in the rear of the body and are later connected to the cable leading from the instrument.

With careful manufacture, the electrical connections within the membrane could be completely waterproofed. So far, however, this has been difficult to ensure and best results with the instrument have been obtained in dry boreholes.

2.2   Strain Gauges

Three rosettes of three overlapping electrical resistance strain gauges are used. The orientation of the rosettes on the instrument can be varied according to the application. The strain gauges are of 5 mm gauge length. This is for three main reasons:

(i) There is no grain size effect in coal.

(ii) During manufacture, it is easier to mount and handle gauges of 5 mm gauge length.

(iii) A 5 mm gauge gives a more accurate representation of strain at a point than does a 10 mm gauge.

In laboratory calibration tests, the instrument was installed within a concrete test cube subjected to a uniaxial stress field. In such a stress field, large strain variations occur over relatively short distances around the periphery of the pilot hole. It was found that over a 10 mm gauge length the average strain indicated by the gauge can be significantly different to the strain at the middle of the gauge. This difference is smaller for a 5 mm gauge length.

The gauges are mounted on slightly raised humps on the surface of the membrane. These are necessary to attain a uniform pressure distribution on the gauge when it is inflated against the borehole wall. The gauge backing is stiffer than the polyurethane elastomer and so, without the humps, there is a tendency for the strain gauge to flatten as the membrane is inflated. This results in an air pocket under the gauge so precluding a good bond.

3   INSTALLATION PROCEDURE

With any strain gauge instrument, formation of a good bond between the strain gauges (or the inclusion in which the strain gauges are incorporated) and the rock is critical to the stress measurement operation. With the ANZSI cell, it has been found that best results are obtained when:

(i) The EX pilot hole is drilled at slow feed rates to avoid overbreak.

(ii) The hole is thoroughly cleaned with a cloth covered cleaning tool.

(iii) A solvent, such as methyl ethyl ketone, is used to degrease the periphery of the hole.

To install the instrument, epoxy cement is applied to the recessed section of the membrane. The instrument is inserted a distance of at least 300 mm into the pilot hole, oriented, and inflated to a pressure of 300 - 600 kPa. The strain gauges are pressed into contact with the rock and the epoxy cement is squeezed into a thin film. Excess cement fills any voids and joints in the periphery of the hole; this helps to hold the annulus together during overcoring. The epoxy cement selected takes approximately 24 hours to cure. It is designed to bond to wet surfaces and to cure in thin layers.

Successful results have been obtained using epoxy cement in coal. When, however, the instrument was used in rocks such as soft mudstones, the strain gauges did not bond because of a smear zone that formed on the periphery of the hole during drilling. Improvements in either the cement performance or the drilling technique are necessary to overcome this.

4 TEST PROCEDURE

4.1 Pressure Test

A pressure test is conducted after the epoxy cement has cured. All strain gauges are monitored as the pressure is incremented from zero to 1 MPa and back several times. This test establishes that the gauges are operating correctly and provides data from which the modulus of the rock is determined.

The instrument is sufficiently long (length/diameter > 4) that, at the strain gauge locations, the borehole can be considered to be in plane strain (Laier et al 1975). For a homogeneous, isotropic, elastic material:

$$\varepsilon_z = 0 \qquad (1)$$

$$\varepsilon_\theta = p\ (1+\nu)/E \qquad (2)$$

$$\varepsilon_{45} = (\varepsilon_z + \varepsilon_\theta)/2 \qquad (3)$$

where: ε_z, ε_θ, ε_{45} are strains on the borehole periphery,
E and ν are rock properties and
p is the inflation pressure.

When the gauges are operating correctly, the elastic modulus of the material can be estimated if Poisson's ratio is known or assumed. The determination of E is not particularly sensitive to variations in Poisson's ratio.

Following the pressure test, the air line and placing rods are withdrawn in preparation for overcoring.

4.2 Stress Relief by Overcoring

The electrical cable is threaded inside the drill string and out through an adapted water swivel so that all the gauges can be monitored as the instrument is overcored. In a closely jointed rock, there is a high probability of the gauges bonding across a joint. It is therefore very useful to have the complete stress relief curves which can then be diagnosed using the technique discussed by Blackwood (1978).

A double tube core barrel giving a 150 mm diameter core has been used successfully for overcoring in coal. Although the recovered core is sometimes closely jointed, the instrument acts to hold it together sufficiently for removal from the barrel.

4.3 Biaxial Test

When a suitably intact core is recovered, a standard biaxial test can be conducted to determine elastic modulus and Poisson's ratio. In coal however, intact core suitable for testing is seldom recovered, so that even if the overcoring test is successful, it is often not possible to verify correct operation of each strain gauge without the pressure test.

5 STRESS CHANGE MONITORING APPLICATION

A modification of the instrument can also be used for monitoring stress changes in rock under conditions where the assumption of linear elastic behaviour is valid. The strain changes measured by the instrument can be converted into stress changes. The ability to conduct a pressure test in situ is especially useful in this application because it provides confirmation of correct strain gauge operation and the only means of determining the local rock properties.

If the instrument body is manufactured from tube, rather than solid rod, several instruments can be installed in the same hole. Cables and permanently attached air lines from deep instruments pass through the inside of shallower instruments. A continuous positive pressure can be applied to keep the strain gauges in contact with the borehole surface.

6 APPLICATIONS

Successful measurements have been made in sub-bituminous coal. These are described elsewhere in the proceedings. The measured stress field was independently confirmed by a full scale tunnel monitoring program (Mills & Pender 1985).

Measurements have also been made in a strongly anisotropic schist. These tests were not quite as successful as those in coal, due mainly to difficulties with the recording equipment. However, a composite set of strain measurements from several tests allowed the stress field to be measured. The stress field determined in independent hydrofracturing tests showed good correlation (Mills & Gray 1985).

The instrument has also been successfully used to monitor stress changes during tunnel excavation (Mills & Pender 1985). The stress changes were in the elastic range and monitoring was conducted for a period of approximately 3 months during which time there appeared to be negligible creep. Figure 3 shows strain changes recorded by one instrument during tunnel excavation.

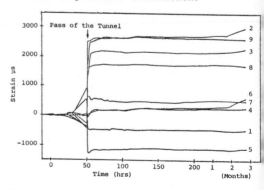

Figure 3 : Example of Stress Change Monitoring

7 CONCLUSIONS

The instrument described has several practical advantages over currently available instruments. These benefits are of particular importance for in situ stress measurements and stress change monitoring in soft and jointed rocks such as coal.

Some further development of the instrument is considered warranted to improve cement performance, strain gauge contact pressure, and reliability of waterproofing the strain gauge wires.

8 ACKNOWLEDGEMENTS

The authors wish to acknowledge the funding for the project provided by the New Zealand Energy Research and Development Committee, and the practical support given by New Zealand State Coal Mines.

9 REFERENCES

Blackwood, R.L. 1978. Diagnostic Stress- Relief Curves in Stress Measurement by Overcoring. International Journal of Rock Mechanics & Mining Science 15:205-209.

Depledge, D., Fama, M.E., Pender, M.J. and Mills, K.W. 1980. In Situ Stress Measurements - East Mine Huntly. New Zealand State Coal Mines Report.

Duncan-Fama, M.E. and Pender, M.J. 1980. Analysis of the Hollow Inclusion Technique for Measuring In Situ Rock Stress. International Journal of Rock Mechanics & Mining Science 17:137-146.

Laier, J.E., Schmertmann, J.H. and Schaub, J.H. 1975. Effect of Finite Pressuremeter Length in Dry Sand. Proceedings of the Conference on In Situ Measurement of Soil Properties, Raleigh, North Carolina.

Leeman, E.R. and Hayes, D.J. 1966. A Technique for Determining the Complete State of Stress in Rock using a Single Borehole. Proceedings of the First Congress of the International Society of Rock Mechanics 2:17-24.

Mills, K.W. and Gray, W.J. 1985. Kawarau Power Investigations - In Situ Stress Measurements and Laboratory Testing. Central Laboratories Report 2-85/3, Ministry of Works and Development, New Zealand.

Mills, K.W. and Pender, M.J. 1985. In Situ Behaviour of Coal Adjacent to an Underground Roadway at the Huntly West Mine. New Zealand Energy Research and Development Committee Report on Contract 3179.

Mills, K.W., Pender, M.J. and Depledge, D. 1986. Measurement of In Situ Stress in Coal. Proceedings of the International Symposium on Rock Stress and Rock Stress Measurements, Stockholm.

Rocha, M. and Silveira, A. 1969. A New Method for the Complete Determination of the State of Stress in Rock Masses. Geotechnique 19:116-132.

Worotnicki, G. and Walton, R.J. 1976. Triaxial Hollow Inclusion Gauges for the Determination of Rock Stress In Situ. Proceedings of International Society of Rock Mechanics Symposium on Investigations of Stresses in Rock - Advances in Stress Measurement. Institution of Engineers Australia, Conference Publication No. 76/4.

Rock stress determinations with the STT and SFJ techniques

J.L. PINTO
A.P. CUNHA
Laboratório National de Engenharia Civil, Lisboa, Portugal

ABSTRACT

Determination of the initial state of stress in rock masses remains one of the most important and complex problems in Rock Mechanics. The paper presents a brief review of the Stress Tensor Tube (STT) and the Small Flat Jack (SFJ) methods, deve loped at the LNEC, pointing out the most recent advances concerning apparatus, test ing and result interpretation. A synthesis of the data collected by the LNEC about the initial stress fields in rock masses is presented, as well as some significant applications of rock stress measurements in the design of structures.

RÉSUMÉ

La détermination de l'état de contrainte initiale dans les massifs rocheux est en core un des problèmes les plus importants et complexes de la Mécanique des Roches. On décrit deux méthodes — la cellule tridimensionelle (STT) et le vérin plat (SFJ) — dévelopées par LNEC pour la détermination de l'état de contrainte, en présentant les derniers perfectionnements sur les appareils, les éssais in situ et leur inter prétation. Une synthèse des donnés obtenues par le LNEC, pendant des années, sur l'état de contrainte est présentée, ainsi que quelques applications significatives de ces mesures à des ouvrages.

ZUSAMMENFASSUNG

Die Bestimmung des ursprünglichen Spannungszustandes in Gebirgen ist immer noch eines der wichtigsten und Komplexesten Probleme der Felsmechanik. Das Referat gibt einen kurzen Überblick über die im LNEC entwickelten STT – (Stress Tensor Tube — — Spannungstensorröhre) und SFJ – (Small Flat Jack — Kleines Druckkissen) - Verfahren, wobei die neuesten Fortschritte bezüglich der Apparate, der Versuchsausführung und der Interpretation der Ergebnisse herausgestellt werden. Eine Synthese der durch das LNEC zusammengetragenen Daten über die ursprünglichen Spannungsfelder in Gebirgen wird vorgestellt, sowie auch einige bedeutsame Anwendungen von Felsspannungsmessun gen.

1 – INTRODUCTION

It is well known that the initial sta te of stress in rock masses is a factor of the utmost importance for the behavi our of structures in rock, such as dams and underground structures. However, stress determinations in rock masses undoubtly remain one of the major problems in Rock Mechanics.

Since the virgin stresses depend on factors such as the weight of the overly

ing formations and forces associated with the geological history of the rock mass, such as genetic, orogenic and erosive actions, and they are conditioned by lithological, structural and topogra phic patterns, accurate forecasts of the stress state require in situ measurements.

The severe local meaning of the tests and the scattering of their results, con nected both with the available techniques and the complex morphology of rock masses, have, however, in most cases, so far prevented a satisfactory knowledge of the initial state of stress for design and construction purposes.

LNEC has developed two methods for in situ stress determinations, both of them based on the stress relief concept: the Stress Tensor Tube (STT), based on an overcoring process,which requires a knowledge of the deformability characteristics of the rock mass,and the Small Flat Jack Method (SFJ), using slot openings, which allows the direct measurement of the stresses in the rock mass.

The most recent developments concerning apparatus, testing methodologies and interpretation of results are referred to for both techniques, and a summary of LNEC experience on stress field measurements in rock masses, collected for several yars, is reported, as well as four significant case histories dealing with dams, mines, tunnels and caverns.

2 -- TECHNIQUES FOR MEASURING THE STATE OF STRESS

2.1 - SFJ method

The SFJ technique can be described briefly as follows:

a) Pairs of contact seats, between which the distances are measured, are placed on the wall surface, after it has been adequately evened.

b) Using a disk saw, a slot is cut open between those seats, thus releasing the normal stress in the plane of the slot. As a consequence, the distance between the contact seats varies, generally decreasing.

c) A suitably - shaped jack is introdu - ced into the slot and by means of oil pressure into the jack, the initial distance between the seats is restored.

d) The pressure required for obtaining a return to the initial position (can celling pressure), apart from minor correction factors, is the normal stress in the plane of the slot.

Execution of at least three tests of this type, with the slots forming a rosette, makes it possible to determine the state of stress at the point of the plane in question. Normally, three slots in

rosette at 45° are used, and by means an additional test a confirmation of t results is obtained.By carrying out th study on two further planes with diffe ent orientations it is possible to d termine the complete state of stress the point concerned (Fig. 1).

2.1.1 - Determination of the state of stress around a circular galle

The SFJ method makes it possible to termine the state of stress in a galle with circular cross-section, provid that the three rosettes are on differe planes (Fig. 1). By measuring the norm stresses at slots σ_1, σ_2 ... σ_{12}; t state of stress P_x, P_y ... P_{xy} is obt ned from the expressions:

$$P_x = \frac{a_1 b_1 - 6a_3 - 2b_2 a_4}{6b_4}$$

$$P_y = \frac{a_1 b_1 - 6a_2 - 2b_2 a_4}{6b_4}$$

$$P_z = \frac{2b_3 a_4 - 6\nu a_7 - a_1 b_2}{3b_4}$$

$$P_{yz} = \frac{3a_5 \mp a_6}{8} \quad ; \quad P_{zx} = \frac{3a_6 \mp a_5}{8}$$

$$P_{xy} = \frac{3a_7 - 4\nu a_4 - 2a_1}{2b_4} \quad , \text{ being}$$

$a_1 = 2(\sigma_1+\sigma_5+\sigma_9)+\sigma_2+ \sigma_4+\sigma_6+\sigma_8+\sigma_{10}+\sigma_{12}$

$a_2 = -\sigma_1+3\sigma_5+5\sigma_9-(0,5+\nu)(\sigma_2+\sigma_4)+(1,5+\nu)$
$(\sigma_6+\sigma_8)+(2,5+2\nu)(\sigma_{10}+\sigma_{12})+$
$+ 2\nu(2\sigma_{11}-\sigma_3+\sigma_7)$

$a_3 = 3\sigma_1-\sigma_5+5\sigma_9-(0,5+\nu)(\sigma_6+\sigma_8)+(1,5+\nu)$
$(\sigma_2+\sigma_4)+(2,5+2\nu)(\sigma_{10}+\sigma_{12})+$
$+2\nu(2\sigma_{11}+\sigma_3-\sigma_7)$

$a_4 = \sigma_3+\sigma_7+\sigma_{11}+0,5(\sigma_2+\sigma_4+\sigma_6+\sigma_8+\sigma_{10}+\sigma_{12}$

$a_5 = \sigma_2-\sigma_4 \mp \frac{\sqrt{2}}{2}(\sigma_{10}-\sigma_{12})$

$a_6 = \sigma_8-\sigma_6 \pm \frac{\sqrt{2}}{2}(\sigma_{10}-\sigma_{12})$

$a_7 = 4(\sigma_9+\nu\sigma_{11})+2(1+\nu)(\sigma_{10}+\sigma_{12})$

$b_1 = 16+6\nu+9\nu^2$; $b_2 = 3-2\nu+3\nu^2$

$b_3 = 9+6\nu+13\nu^2$; $b_4 = 8(3+2\nu+3\nu^2)$

In these expressions, the appearance i some cases of two signs corresponds,th upper, to the use of rosette C_1, th lower to the use of rosette C_2.

254

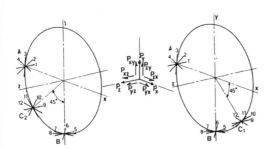

Figure 1 - Location of the rosettes for
a 3D state of stress determination

2.1.2 - Eliptical cross-section galleries

If the gallery is eliptical, the analysis becomes more complicated, but by
carrying out the measurements in roset -
tes whose position is identical to that
shown in Fig. 1, and taking into account
the expressions deduced by Greenspan (1944),
a system of equations is reached, which
can be solved using the least squares me
thod:

$$a_{11} \, P_x - a_{12} \, P_y + a_{13} \, P_z + a_{16} \, P_{xy} = b_1$$

$$-a_{12}P_x + a_{22} \, P_y + a_{23} \, P_z + a_{26} \, P_{xy} = b_2$$

$$a_{13} \, P_x + a_{23} \, P_y + 4,5 \, P_z + a_{36} \, P_{xy} = b_3$$

$$a_{44} \, P_{yz} + a_{45} \, P_{zx} = b_4$$

$$a_{45} \, P_{yz} + a_{55} \, P_{zx} = b_5$$

$$a_{16} \, P_x + a_{26} \, P_y + a_{36} \, P_z + a_{66} \, P_{xy} = b_6$$

in which:

$$b_1 = -\sigma_1 - (0,5+b\nu)(\sigma_2 + \sigma_4) - 2b\nu\sigma_3 + 2c\sigma_5 +$$

$$+(c+d\nu)(\sigma_6 + \sigma_8) + 2d\nu\sigma_7 + 2e\sigma_9 + (e-kh\nu)$$

$$(\sigma_{10} + \sigma_{12}) - kh\nu\sigma_{11}$$

$$b_2 = 2a\sigma_1 + (a+kb\nu)(\sigma_2 + \sigma_4) + 2kb \, \nu \, \sigma_3 - \sigma_5(0,5+$$

$$+kd\nu)(\sigma_6 + \sigma_8) - 2kd\nu\sigma_7 + 2f\sigma_9 + (f+h\nu)$$

$$(\sigma_{10} + \sigma_{12}) + 2h\nu\sigma_{11}$$

$$b_3 = 0,5(\sigma_2 + \sigma_4 + \sigma_6 + \sigma_8 + \sigma_{10} + \sigma_{12}) + \sigma_3 + \sigma_7 + \sigma_{11}$$

$$b_4 = \sigma_2 - \sigma_4 + i(\sigma_{10} - \sigma_{12})$$

$$b_5 = -\sigma_6 + \sigma_8 + k_i(\sigma_{10} - \sigma_{12})$$

$$b_6 = g \left[2\sigma_9 + 2 \, \nu\sigma_{11} + (1+\nu)(\sigma_{10} + \sigma_{12}) \right]$$

and: $a \approx 0,5+k$; $b = \dfrac{k(n-1)}{1-k}$; $c = \dfrac{2+k}{2k}$;

$$d = \frac{1-nk^2}{k(1-k)} \; ; \qquad e = \frac{k^4 + 2k^3 - 1}{2(1+k^4)};$$

$$f = \frac{1+2k-k^4}{2(1+k^4)} \; ; \; g = \frac{k(1+k^2)}{1+k^4} \; ; \; i = \frac{1}{\sqrt{1+k^2}}$$

$$h = \frac{n(1+k^4) - (1+k^2)}{(1-k)(1+k^4)} \; ; \; n = \frac{K(\varepsilon)}{E(\varepsilon)} \; ; \; k = \frac{p}{q}$$

p and q being the minor and major axes
of the ellipse, and $K(\varepsilon)$ and $E(\varepsilon)$ the
complete 1st and 2nd kind elliptical in
tegrals with the modulus angle ε.
The curves representative of the va-
riation of $a_{11}, a_{12}, a_{13}, a_{16}, a_{22}, a_{23}, a_{26},$
$a_{36}, a_{44}, a_{45}, a_{55}$ and a_{66} with k, for
$\nu = 0.2$, are those shown in Fig. 2.

2.2 - STT method

The stress tensor tube is a 'deformable inclusion' type strain gauge and
allows the determination of the state
of stress in rock masses, by means of
boreholes.
The STT technique (Charrua-Graça,1982)
consists essentially of the following:

a) Drilling a hole of large diameter
   (140 mm) to the neighbourhood of the
   point at which it is intended to determine the state of stress (about
   0.4 m above).

b) Drilling a hole of small diameter
   (37 mm),with a length of 0.6 m,from
   the bottom of the previous drilling.

c) Fixing to the wall of the small-dia-
   meter borehole of the STT, suitably
   oriented.

d) Initial reading of the electric
   strain gauges in the STT.

e) Overcoring of the test core containing the STT, down to a depth that en
   sures total relief of the stresses
   (0.4 m below the measuring point).

f) Final reading of the electric strain
   gauges in the STT.

g) Extraction of the overcoring contain
   ing the STT.

h) Introduction of this core, after it
   has been covered with a plastic sheet
   into a steel chamber,new readings of
   the strain gauges then being taken.

i) Application of a known lateral pressure to the core,followed by new read
   ings.

j) Determination,from this biaxial test
   of the elastic constants of the rock.

255

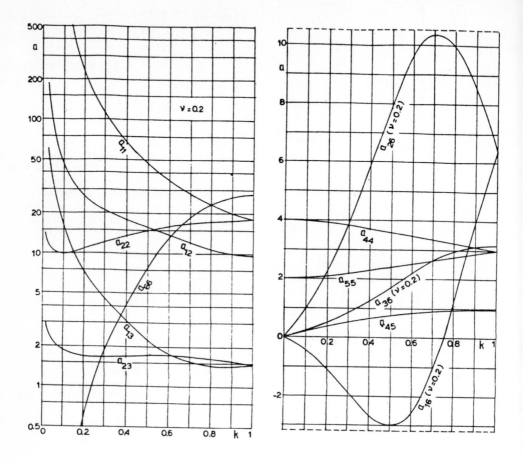

Figure 2 - Parameters defining the state of stress for an elliptic gallery

k) Calculation of the state of stress from the readings referred to in (f) and (d) and from the elastic constants determined in (j).

Although operations (h) to (j) are not always possible, owing to cracking of the core, their execution allows a far more realistic interpretation of the results, since the elastic constants are determined directly at the measuring points.

2.2.1 - Determination of the state of stress by means of the STT

The STT model now in use consists of an epoxy resin tube with a wall thickness of 2 mm and a length of 25 cm. On its middle surface 10 strain gauges are fixed, in positions corresponding to

those normal to the faces of an icosahedr centred at the origin. They are placed as shown in Fig. 3, which gives the plan ing of the central zone of the STT.

This arrangement of the strain gaug allows an equal sampling of the state o stress in all directions, with four add tional readings, thus greatly reducir the risk of a test failing as the resul of a breakdown of some gauges, since th functioning of only 60% of them is suff cient to obtain the complete state of stress at the point concerned.

At a given point of the rock mass, wh re the stresses are P_x, ... P_{xy}, th strain measured in any direction by th STT is:

$$\varepsilon = \varepsilon_z \, \text{sen}^2\alpha + \varepsilon_\theta \, \cos^2\alpha + \gamma_{\theta z} \, \text{sen}\,\alpha \, \cos\alpha$$

being:

256

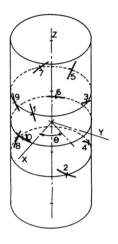 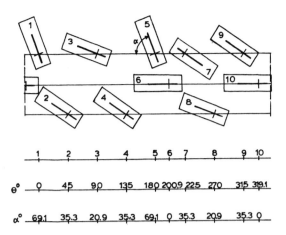

	1	2	3	4	5 6 7	8	9 10
$\theta°$	0	45	90	135	180 200.9 225 270	315 319.1
$\alpha°$	69.1	35.3	20.9	35.3	69.1 0 35.3 20.9	35.3 0

Figure 3 - Scheme of the position of the strain gauges in the new STT

$$\varepsilon_\theta = \frac{1}{E}\left[M_1(P_x+P_y)+N(P_x-P_y)\cos 2\theta-M_2P_z+ \right.$$
$$\left. + 2N\, P_{xy}\, sen\, 2\theta \right]$$

$$\varepsilon_z = \frac{1}{E}\left[-\nu\,(P_x+P_y)+P_z\right]$$

$$\gamma_{\theta z} = \frac{M_3}{E}\,(P_{yz}\,\cos\theta - P_{xy}\,sen\,\theta)$$

in which:

θ - angle between the normal to the strain gauge and the xx axis

α - angle between the direction of the strain gauge and the xy plane.

$M_1 = 1.204165 + 0.083507\nu$

$M_2 = 0.083507 + 1.204165\nu$

$M_3 = 4.424179\,(1+\nu)$

$N = -2.444020\,(1-\nu^2)$

From these expressions the strain according to any direction of the strain gauges is obtained. Once these values are known, by the least squares method it is possible to determine the initial state of stress. In order to determine the elastic constants, since $P_x = P_y = P$ and $P_z = P_{yz} = P_{zx} = P_{xy} = 0$, the expressions of ε_θ, ε_z, $\gamma_{\theta z}$ take the form:

$$\varepsilon_\theta = \frac{2P}{E}\,M_1 \quad;\quad \varepsilon_z = -\frac{2\nu P}{E} \quad;\quad \gamma_{\theta z} = 0$$

Once the biaxial test has been made and the strains have been read, in a maxi-

mum of 10 and a minimum of 2, from the least squares method the elastic constants E and ν are obtained.

All the preceding calculations have assumed an isotropic and linear-elastic behaviour of the test core. Should that behaviour not be linear, a correction of this effect is possible if the values of the elastic constants obtained in the biaxial test correspond to the secant values in the domain of variation of the stresses to which the test core has been subjected in its overcoring, i.e. if the pressure applied in the biaxial test is of the order of magnitude of the initial stresses to which the test core is subjected.

3 - SOME ROCK STRESS MEASUREMENTS

3.1 - State of stress in a coal mine in Spain

This mine is located along sedimentary formations, which consist of alternate sandstone, claystone and coal layers at the test site. Strata have a 20° dip towards the entry of the tunnel where tests with STT are performed. Given the depth at which the tunnel lies (about 325 m), joints are closed.

The four states of stress measured in the rock mass show that the direction of one of the principal stresses is roughly normal to the strata, whereas stresses parallel to the strata are not very different in any direction.

The stresses measured show that acting stresses are not only due to the dead weight, presenting concentrations between 2 and 10 in the plane of strata, whereas following the normal to the strata there is a relief that corresponds to about 0.65 and 1.75 of the expected stresses.

The scattering of results related to close points of the rock mass show the punctual meaning of stress measurements.

3.2 - Study of the foundation of a dam in Germany

In studying the dam foundations, SFJ tests were carried out in two galleries situated in the zones of the haunches of the dam and STT tests performed in three boreholes, two made from each of the galleries and one in the bottom of the valley. The rock mass is made up of a schistous formation of variable quality, crossed by veins of quartz and intensively jointed.

The results of the SFJ tests showed that the values of the main stresses were fairly similar and that the principal directions practically were the vertical, transversal and longitudinal directions. In the STT tests, higher stresses were found at the points nearer to the galleries, owing to the phenomenon of stress concentration, though this effect was not found in the borehole at the bottom of the valley. The horizontal stresses were very similar in each test, though there was a tendency towards a slight increase in the direction parallel to the valley in the gallery drillings and an opposite tendency in the valley bottom drilling. The vertical stresses were in the three boreholes slightly higher than the average for the horizontal stresses. The values of the stresses obtained with the SFJ and STT are perfectly in agreement, not only as regards their magnitude but also in the orientation of the principal directions.

3.3 - Alto Lindoso hydraulic circuit

The Alto Lindoso hydro-electric scheme, on the River Lima, corresponding to an installed capacity of 2 x 300 MW, is in the early construction stage. The hydraulic circuit consists of two penstocks followed by pressure shafts leading to an underground power plant downstream of the dam and about 200 metres below the river bed. After passing through the turbines

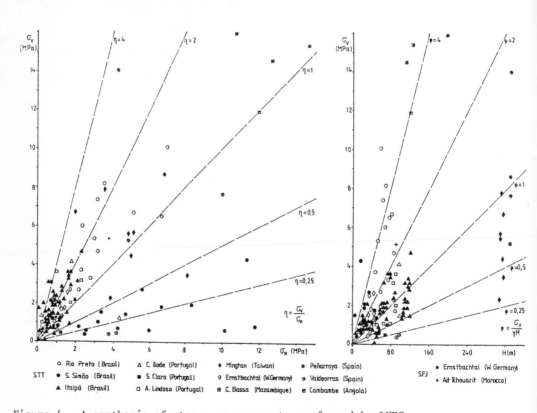

STT
○ Rio Preto (Brasil)   ● S. Simão (Brasil)   ▲ Itaipú (Brasil)   △ C. Bode (Portugal)   ■ S. Clara (Portugal)   □ A. Lindoso (Portugal)   ◆ Mingtan (Taiwan)   ◇ Ernstbachtal (W.Germany)   ▣ C. Bassa (Mozambique)   ● Peñarroya (Spain)   ◉ Valdeorras (Spain)   ◪ Cambambe (Angola)

SFJ   ● Ernstbachtal (W Germany)   + Ait Tkhouarit (Morocco)

Figure 4 - A synthesis of stress measurements performed by LNEC

ines, the tailrace conduits form a single tunnel with a length of about 5 km and a diameter of 8.30 m. The rock mass consists essentially of a granitic rock, though some parts of the hydraulic circuit probably pass through micaschistous formations (Neiva et al, 1983).

The power plant and most of the hydraulic circuit have an overburden of about 300 m, and for technical and economic reasons the in situ studies for the project took place at depths of little more than 100 m, their purpose being the investigation of the geological characteristics of the rock mass and their extrapolation to the depths concerning the work (Cunha et al, 1977).

Analysis of the results of stress measurement in boreholes using STT, are synthesised in Fig. 4 and showed the existence of variable stresses from one point to another, with the maximum principal stress being sub-vertical and two principal stresses being sub-horizontal (intermediate and minimum ones). The values determined for the vertical stress were not far from those that might be expected in the same direction owing to the dead load of the overlying formations, while the horizontal stresses showed values of the same order of magnitude, though always lower than the vertical stress (σ_V/σ_H varying between 1.2 and 3.6), being possible to consider the state of stress, in a good approximation, as axisymmetrical in relation to the vertical direction.

3.4 - Initial state of stress measurements for the Castelo do Bode Tunnel

The new water supply system to the Lisbon area, now nearing completion includes, after the water intake in the reservoir of the Castelo do Bode arch dam, a 3.0 m diameter pressure tunnel. In the preliminary design phase the tunnel was to be about 5 km long, excavated in a tectonized pre-cambrian metamorphic complex consisting of gneisses and migmatites. Among the geotechnical studies carried out for design purposes, STT tests were performed in order to assess the initial state of stress (Cunha et al, 1977). Though the final layout of the tunnel was changed to 1 km tunnel, since the final version crosses the same gneissic formations, results of the first site studies have been considered for the final short tunnel design,

since they allows a statistical appraised of the geotechnical conditions of the rock mass (Oliveira et al, 1983).

Analysis of the STT measurements during the preliminary design showed a complex state of stress in the gneissic rock mass, the vertical stress always being a principal stress, often the major stress. The dead load of the overlying formations seemed to be a good value for forecasting the vertical stress at every point. As regards horizontal stresses, they proved to be practically equal at every horizontal plane, e.g, an horizontally hydrostatic stress field was found, but the relationship between the vertical and the horizontal stress might change a great deal from point to point, assuming values greater and smaller than one. The measuring results are included in Fig. 4.

4 - SYNTHESIS OF THE RESULTS

Fig. 4 gives a synthesis of the results of the tests carried out by LNEC at various sites. This analysis is expressed in terms of the relationship between the vertical and horizontal stresses and of the correlation between σ_V and the overburden.

Taking into account the results given in previous chapters, and other tests carried out by LNEC, it may be concluded that:

— In depth, there is often a tendency for the state of stress to become hydrostatic ($\sigma_V/\sigma_H = 1$).

— Taking into account that the SFJ and STT tests can be regarded as punctual ones, it may be said that in depth the vertical stress tends to the value γh.

— As a rule the principal directions are close to the vertical and the horizontal, or are normal and parallel to the stratification or schistosity planes, unless a decisive influence of topographical factors occurs to modify those directions.

— Owing to the random nature of the tests for determining stresses, and the complex morphology of the rock masses, in order to have an approximate idea of the state of stress it is necessary to carry out a large number of tests.

REFERENCES

Charrua-Graça, J. 1982. Determination of
the State of Stress in Rock Masses by
the Stress-Tensor Tube Method (STT).
Proc. 14th Inter. Congr. ICOLD.

Cunha, A.P., Oliveira, R. and Rodrigues,
L.F. 1977. Geotechnical Studies for Hy
draulic Circuit of Alto Lindoso (in
Portuguese). LNEC Report, Lisbon.

Cunha, A.P., Barroso, M. and Oliveira,
R. 1977. Geotechnical Studies for the
Castelo do Bode Tunnel (in Portuguese).
LNEC Report, Lisbon.

Cunha, A.P. 1980. Mathematical Modell -
ing of Rock Tunnels (in Portuguese).
LNEC Research Officer Thesis, Lisbon.

Greenspan, M. 1944. Effect of a small
hole on the stresses in a uniformly
loaded plate. Quaterly Appl. Math.,
2, pp. 60-71.

Loureiro-Pinto, J. and Charrua-Graça,J.
1983. Determination of the state of
stress of Rock Masses by the Small
Flat Jack (SFJ) Method. Proc. 5th Int.
Congr. ISRM, pp. F79-F83, Melbourne.

Neiva, J.C., Guimarães, J.N. and Azeve-
do, M.M. 1983. Geology of the Hydraulic Circuit of the Hydro-Electric Development of Alto Lindoso. Proc. Int.
Symp. Engineering Geology and Underground Construction.(1): III-131-III-
-140.

Oliveira, R., Costa, C. and David, J.
1983. Engineering Geological Studies
and Design of Castelo do Bode Tunnel.
Proc. Inter. Symp. Engineering Geology and Underground Construction.(1):
II69-II85.

In-situ validation of the bore hole slotting stressmeter

H. BOCK
James Cook University, Department of Civil & Systems Engineering, Townsville, Queensland, Australia

ABSTRACT: A recently developed 2-D stressmeter, namely the "borehole slotter", satisfies important operational requirements. It is reuseable, does not rely on overcoring and allows for a large number of measurements at very reasonable costs.

Extensive in-situ tests at the Burdekin Falls damsite (Queensland/Australia) have been carried out in parallel with overcoring and hydraulic fracturing tests. Whilst providing results on the in-situ stress state with at least comparable accuracy, the borehole slotting technique was found to have major advantages over the established methods with regard to speed of operation, reliability and economy. Borehole slotting allows an internal check of the consistency of the stress measuring results with the degree of redundancy of the readings being adjustable to the particular situation. This proved particularly useful when interpreting the stress measurements.

RESUME: Le "Borehole Slotter", sonde-compteur récemment développée pour mesurer l'état de contrainte biaxial, répond pleinement à d'importantes exigences opérationnelles. Il est réutilisable, ne nécessite pas de surcarottage et permet d'enregistrer un grand nombre de mesures à des frais peu élevés.

On a effectué de nombreux tests sur le site de construction du barrage de Burdekin Falls (au Queensland, Australie), ainsi que des tests de surcarottage et de fracture hydraulique. A l'aide des tests effectués avec le "Borehole Slotter" on a mesuré l'état de contrainte avec tout au moins autant de précision qu'avec les autres méthodes. Mais quant à la vitesse, la sûreté de fonctionnement et le coût, le "Borehole Slotter" l'emporte. Le "Borehole Slotter" permet un contrôle interne dans l'obtention de résultats consistants. Le niveau de redondance des mesures peut être adapté à chaque situation; ce qui a été très utile, surtout quant à l'interprétation des mesures d'état de contrainte.

ZUSAMMENFASSUNG: Eine vor kurzem entwickelte 2-D Spannungsmessonde ("Bohrloch-Schlitzsonde") hat gegenüber bestehenden Sonden wesentliche versuchstechnische Vorzüge. Sie ist wiedergewinnbar, nicht auf ein Überbohren angewiesen und erlaubt die Durchführung einer großen Anzahl von Messungen bei vertretbaren Kosten.

Umfangreiche Bohrlochschlitzversuche wurden an der Burdekin Falls Dammbaustelle (Queensland/Australien) parallel mit Spannungsmessungen nach dem Überbohrverfahren und der Hydraulic Fracturing Methode durchgeführt. Sie ergaben, daß das Bohrloch-schlitzverfahren den in-situ Spannungszustand in Fels mit mindestens vergleichbarer Genauigkeit zu bestimmen gestattet wie bestehende Verfahren. Das neue Verfahren erwies sich den bestehenden gegenüber als eindeutig überlegen hinsichtlich Schnelligkeit, Zuverlässigkeit und Kosten. Es gestattet darüberhinaus eine interne Überprüfung der Meßdaten mit einem der jeweiligen Situation angepaßten Grad an Redundanz der Meßdaten. Dies erwies sich als besonders hilfreich bei der Auswertung der Spannungsmessungen.

1. INTRODUCTION

The borehole slotter is a recently developed 2-D stressmeter which satisfies important operational and scientific requirements. It is a stressmeter probe which is:
* reuseable;
* completely self-contained in both its stress release operations and its strain measuring capabilities; discontinuous operations such as those

associated with overcoring are no longer necessary;

*designed for both quick operations and a very high measurement density at reasonable costs.

Details of the borehole slotting technique and its instrumentation were first published in 1983 and 1984 by Bock and Foruria. In these publications a stage of the borehole slotter development was documented at which both laboratory and field tests suggested a great potential for quick and reliable 2-D stress measurements. At that time the number of field tests, however, was rather limited. A definite conclusion with regard to the suitability of the borehole slotting method was deferred until the results of additional in-situ tests, including comparisons with established stress measuring methods, became available.

This is now the case. Extensive in-situ borehole slotting tests have been carried out in 1984 and 1985 at a major dam construction site in parallel with overcoring and hydraulic fracturing techniques. An account of these investigations and the conclusions drawn with regard to the borehole slotting method are presented in this paper.

2. PRINCIPLE AND TESTING PROCEDURE OF BOREHOLE SLOTTING

The borehole slotting stress measuring method is based on the principle of local stress relief. A half-moon shaped radial slot is cut into the borehole wall by means of a small diamond-impregnated saw (Figs. 2 and 3). In the prototype borehole slotter (Fig. 1), which is designed

Fig. 2. Slotting the edge of a model borehole. Centre part of the borehole slotter with diamond blade (extended) and recoverable tangential strain sensor near-by.

Fig. 3. View into a model borehole after cutting a number of half-moon shaped slots.

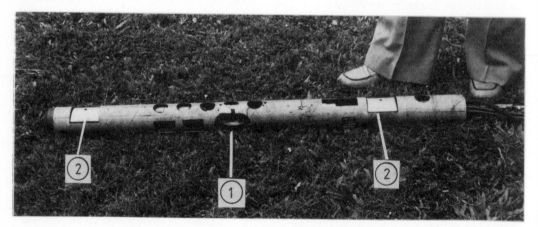

Fig. 1.   Prototype borehole slotter for HQ Boreholes. (1) = Centre part with diamond blade (retracted); (2) = clamping platens.

for HQ Boreholes of 96 mm diameter, the slot is 0.8 mm wide
and maximally 32 mm deep.
The saw is pneumatically driv-
en and is part of the stressmeter. Before, during and
after slotting, the change of
tangential strain is measured
at the borehole surface in the
immediate vicinity of the slot
where practically full stress
release occurs (Bock and Foruria, 1984; their Fig. 4).
The change is picked up by an
innovative strain sensor which
is recoverable and also is
part of the stressmeter probe.
Compared with the sensor documented in Bock and Foruria
(1984; their Fig. 9), the
currently-used type of sensor
has been improved with regard
to sensitivity and stability
(Azzam, 1985).

At a particular test location,
at least three slotting tests
with cuts in independent directions are made for a single
2-D measurement. The theory
of linear elasticity is employed to transfer the strain
readings into stresses. This
means that the Young's modulus
E of the tested rock must be
known for the stress measurement.

The testing procedure is described in the flow diagram of
Fig. 4. The timespan of a
single slotting test is approximately 5 minutes, that of a
complete 2-D measurement about
40 minutes.

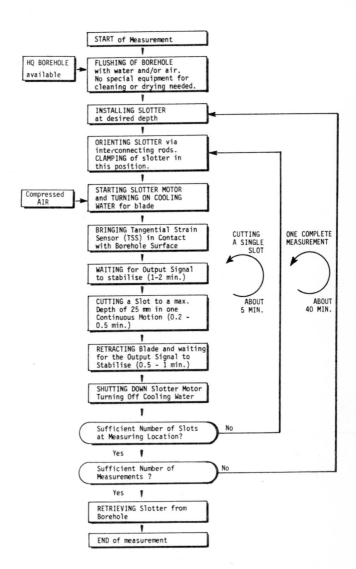

Fig. 4. Testing procedure of borehole slotting

3. SITE DESCRIPTION AND TESTING PROGRAM

The testing program was carried out at
the Burdekin Falls dam site which is
located approximately 210 km south of
Townsville/N.E. Australia. Figure 5
shows sections of the mass concrete
gravity dam which is currently under
construction. The dam has a total
length of 876 m, a spillway crest 504 m
long and a total concrete volume of
some 620 000 m³ (Russo et al., 1985).

The test site is characterised by an
andesitic lithic tuff of undifferentiat-
ed Devonian-Carboniferous age. All rock
tested is either fresh or fresh with

limonite-stained joints. The intact rock
is very strong with an average UCS of
260 MPa and an average Young's modulus E
of 80 GPa. The main structural feature
of the rock mass is sub-horizontal sheet
joints. They were intersected in drillholes to at least 70 m depth. Near the
surface, joint intensity is commonly in
the range of 3 to 1 per metre, but decreases quickly with depth. Open and
infilled joints have been recorded down
to 9 m depth although, more commonly,
joints are tight below 4 to 5 m depth
(Armstrong, 1985). Besides the sheet
joints there is also an orthogonal system of steeply-dipping joints. Some of

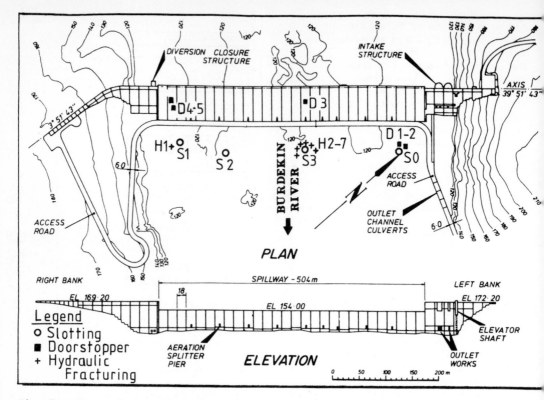

Fig. 5. Plan and elevation of Burdekin Falls dam with location of boreholes for in-
situ stress measurements (after Russo et al., 1985).

these are coated with zeolite or have de-
generated into zeolite veins of 0.5 to
2 mm thickness.

Indications of high horizontal stresses
in the widely exposed river bed rock were
obtained during the initial site investigations and during foundation work for
the dam. Armstrong (1985) reported numerous rock popping events after slabs
and surface layers of rock had been removed. While it is thought that the anticipated high horizontal stresses will
not directly adversely affect the stability of the dam, they may cause problems
in grouting and in scouring of the river
bed downstream of the dam. The latter
possibility requires particular attention after a precedent at another dam site
(Bowling and Woodward, 1979).

In two separate stress measuring campaigns the following methods were employed in parallel with borehole slotting:

Test Campaign 1 (November 1984): "Doorstopper" carried out by K.J. Armstrong
(Geological Survey of Queensland) (Armstrong, 1985)

Test Campaign 2 (August 1985): Hydraulic

fracturing carried out by J. Enever
(CSIRO, Division of Geomechanics)
(Enever, 1985).

The objective of this stress measuring
program was to determine the near-surface
stress state in the river bed rock with
regard to its magnitude and orientation
and also with regard to its degree of
variability in both horizontal and vertical directions.

4. RESULTS

4.1 In-situ stress state

In the first measuring phase the emphasis
of the client was on the established
"doorstopper" overcoring method, considering borehole slotting as a supplementary technique. Consequently the majority
of the drillholes were reserved for the
doorstopper tests (D1 to D5; Fig. 5) with
only a single HQ hole (S0) provided for
the slotter. The slotting tests were
concentrated in a particular section of
the vertically down-dipping borehole from
which fresh and completely intact rock
cores were recovered (3.95 to 6.75 m
depth).

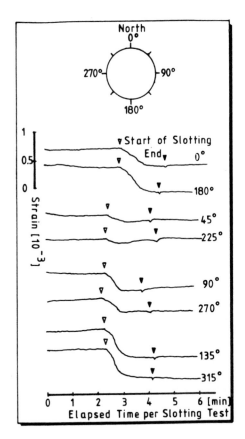

Fig. 6.   Tangential strain responses from
eight individual slotting tests.
The eight cuts were made in different directions at a particular borehole depth. They constitute one 2-D stress measurement.

At the beginning of the slotting tests,
a particularly high degree of redundancy
of the data was considered desirable.
For this a total of eight cuts were made
per borehole location, instead of the
minimum of three. Figure 6 shows tangential strain responses associated with
eight such cutting tests. The degree of
coincidence of the response from cuts in
opposite directions (e.g. 135° versus
315°) indicates the degree of homogeneity of the rock and of the testing conditions at the measuring location. In
the case of Fig. 6, this degree is relatively high. Objectively, it can be
expressed in terms of a correlation coefficient R^2 (Foruria, 1986; Otto, 1985).

In Fig. 7 the slotting stress measurement results are plotted over depth of
borehole and compared with results from

two "doorstopper" measurements. The
"doorstopper" drillhole was just 3.3 m
from the HQ hole. On inspection of Fig.7
it may be concluded that the slotting
test results are consistent and agree
very well with those from the "doorstopper" tests.

With this experience and furthermore considering the particular efficiency of
borehole slotting (ref. Section 4.2), the
client selected the slotting technique
as the main investigation technique for
the second phase of the stress measuring
program. In this phase, hydraulic fracturing was also carried out as part of a
joint research project between CSIRO,
Division of Geomechanics (J. Enever) and
James Cook University. Three vertical
boreholes were tested by borehole slotting down to a depth of 17.0 m.

Examples of the stress measuring results
from two boreholes are given in Figs. 8
and 9. The results from the third borehole are similar to those presented.

The result in Fig. 8 is remarkable for a
number of reasons. Firstly, the twelve
2-D stress measurements, each of them
based on 6 slotting tests, were carried
out within a single day. *This proves
the particular potential of the slotting
technique for quick measurements.* Secondly, the high measurement density of
12 measurements per 8.0 m borehole length allows the delineation of *structurally-controlled stress domains.* Three
such domains are identifiable; an unstressed or even negatively stressed
(= tensioned) surface layer of about 1 m
thickness; a 4 m thick zone between 1.0
and 5.0 m depth, which is fairly homogeneous with regard to stress magnitudes
but not so with respect to orientations
of principal stresses; and a higher
stressed zone beyond 5 m depth with fairly constant orientations of the principal
stresses. Each of the stress disconformities at 1.0 m and 5.0 m depth is associated with the occurence of sheet joints
(but not all sheet joints produce a
change in the stress regime). Finally,
the result of Fig. 8 presents a remarkable example of the *usefulness of an
internal consistency check of stress
measurement data.* Two measurements,
those at 4.5 m and 7.7 m depth, show un-
characteristic orientations of σ_1. The
measurement at 4.5 m depth has a very
high correlation coefficient, thus in-

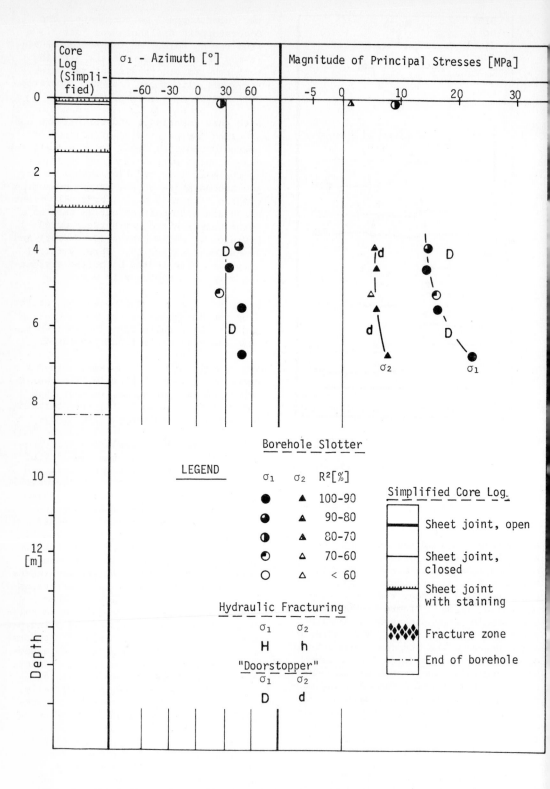

Fig. 7. Comparison of results from borehole slotting and "doorstopper" tests

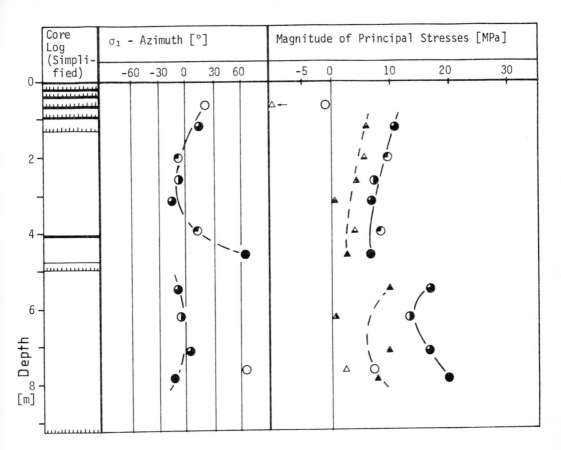

Fig. 8. Results of borehole slotting tests in Borehole S2. (Legend as in Fig. 7)

dicating that the change in orientation is real. The measurement at 7.7 m depth, however, has a very low degree of correlation and also unusually low principal stress magnitudes. On reassessment of the slotting records it was found that, during testing, the slotter was inundated by the quickly rising water table. The prototype slotter is not yet designed for submergence in water. The stress measurement at 7.7 m depth had therefore to be discarded.

Structurally-controlled stress patterns are also evident in the results presented in Fig. 9. Again, an unstressed 1.3 m thick top layer is underlain by a relatively homogeneously stressed zone down to a depth of about 5 m. A number of stress disconformities are identifiable at depths of about 1.3 m, 5.0 m, 9.0 m and (?)13.0 m. With the possible exception of the latter, all disconformities are matched by sheet joints or by fracture zones.

Also indicated in Fig. 9 are the results of hydraulic fracturing tests carried out by J. Enever (1985) in a vertically dipping BX Borehole just 4.1 m from the HQ slotter borehole. The agreement of the two methods is generally good particularly with regard to the principal stress orientations and to the magnitude of the minor principal stress σ_2. However, hydraulic fracturing tends to yield higher magnitudes of σ_1 than borehole slotting. This is particularly the case at very shallow depths.

4.2 Performance of borehole slotter

The performance of the borehole slotter with regard to reliability and efficiency is indicated in Fig. 10. The number of tests which were technically successful and which also yielded meaningful results by far exceeded the number of unsuccessful tests. The failure rate was as low as 9%. Unsuccessful tests were results of:

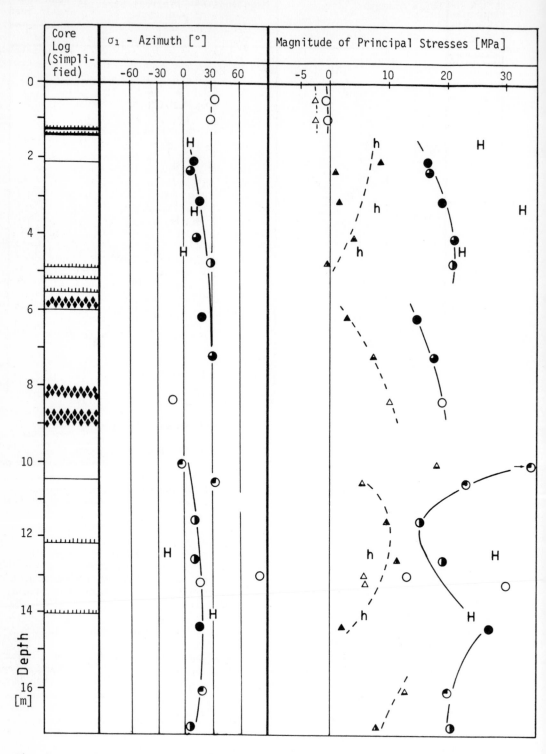

Fig. 9. Results from borehole slotting and hydraulic fracturing in Boreholes S3
         and H2, respectively. (Legend as in Fig. 7)

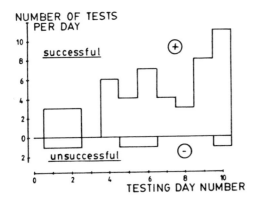

NUMBER OF TESTS PER DAY

Fig. 10. Successful versus unsuccessful
          slotting tests

*inundation of slotter by rising water
 table (2 tests);
*non-interpretable, erratic results,
 most probably due to cracks and joints
 (2 tests);
*unforeseen environmental conditions
 (local whirlwind dumping sand on recording instrument; 1 test).

Furthermore, a complete testing day was
lost due to malfunction of the electronic
components of the slotter. But in total,
the performance of the slotter was quite
satisfactory.

Figure 10 shows a trend of an increased
number of successful tests with increased experience. It is estimated that
under favourable geotechnical conditions
borehole slotting has the potential of
about 16 stress measurements per day.
The last day of testing almost realized
this potential.

5. CONCLUSION

Borehole slotting is a quick method for
the determination of the in-situ 2-D
stress state in rock. In field tests
this method has been compared with both
overcoring and hydraulic fracturing
methods. The high degree of agreement
in the results of these tests validates
borehole slotting as a sound stress measuring method.

Whilst borehole slotting provides results
on the in-situ stress state with at least
comparable accuracy, it has major advantages over established methods with regard to speed of operation, reliability
and economy. Most importantly, it allows
an internal check of the consistency of

the stress measuring results with the
degree of redundancy of the strain readings adjustable to the particular situation. The provision of a sufficiently
redundant data basis and of a consistency
check proved most valuable when interpreting the stress measuring results.

6. ACKNOWLEDGEMENT

The author is deeply indebted to numerous persons and institutions for most
valuable assistance, in particular to:
Mr. Ken Warner and Mr. Ken Armstrong
(Geological Survey of Queensland); Mr.
Ben Russo and Mr. Paul Johnson (Queensland Water Resources Commission); Mr.
Jim Enever (CSIRO, Division of Geomechanics); Mr. Victor Foruria, Mr. Bastian
Otto and Mr. Rod Matheson (James Cook
University); the Queensland Water Resources Commission (Contract Order No.
80103); and CSIRO - Division of Geomechanics, and James Cook University (joint
research project R CSIRO/JCU 14 85/86).

All this support is gratefully acknowledged.

7. REFERENCES

Armstrong, K.J. 1985. Burdekin Falls
 Dam. Report on rock stress measurements. Geol. Surv. of Queensland,
 Record 1985/16:31p.
Azzam, R. 1985. Wiedergewinnbare Sensoren zur Messung tangentialer Dehnungen an Bohrlochwandungen. Annual Rep.
 to Deutsche Forschungsgemeinschaft
 (unpubl.).
Bock, H. and Foruria, V. 1983. A new
 stressmeter for rocks. Australian
 Geomechanics, p.30-35, Canberra (Inst.
 of Eng., Australia).
Bock, H. and Foruria, V. 1984. A recoverable borehole slotting instrument
 for in-situ stress measurements in
 rocks, not requiring overcoring.
 Proceed. Int. Sympos. Field Measurements in Geomech., Zurich, Vol. 1:15-
 29, Rotterdam (Balkema).
Bowling, A.J. and Woodward, R.C. 1979.
 An investigation of near surface rock
 stresses at Copeton damsite in New
 South Wales. Australian Geomech. J.,
 1979:5-13.
Enever, J.R. 1985. Letter report, 4p.
 (unpubl.).
Foruria, V. 1986. A borehole slotting
 instrument for stress measurement in
 rock. MEngSc. Thesis (James Cook Uni).

Otto, B. 1985. Personal communication.
Russo, R., Richardson, J.K. and Allen,
  P.H. 1985. Design of Burdekin Falls
  Dam. Transact. Inst. of Eng. Austral-
  ia, CE27(4):362-370.

Borehole breakouts – a new tool for estimating in situ stress?

B.C. HAIMSON
C.G. HERRICK
University of Wisconsin, Madison, Wisconsin, USA

ABSTRACT: We have completed an initial experimental program studying the relationship between borehole breakout formation in Indiana limestone and the in-situ state of stress. We have confirmed that breakouts occur in two diametrically opposed borehole zones along the direction of σ_h. Recent thin section analysis suggests that the major breakout mechanism is tensile rupture along surfaces parallel to the borehole wall, aided by shear failure in the radial direction. Breakout depth and width appear to be directly proportional to the σ_h magnitude. The ratio of σ_H/σ_h when breakout is initiated, as well as when it is stabilized, is related to σ_h by well defined functions. The potential, thus, exists for utilizing breakout geometric parameters to estimate the two horizontal principal in-situ stresses.

RESUME: On a complété un programme initial expérimental étudiant la relation entre la formation des ruptures dans un trou de forage et l 'état des contraintes in-situ du calcaire d'Indiana. On a confirme que les ruptures des parois d'un trou de forage ont lieu dans deuse directions diami-tralement opposees, le long de la direction de σ_h. Des analyses recentes suggerent que le mecanisme de rupture est par traction le long de surfaces parallèles des parois, aidé par un cisiallement dans la direction radiale du trou. La profondeur et l'épaisseur des ruptures paraissent être fonction de l'intensité de σ_h. Le rapport σ_H/σ_h au depart de rupture ainsi qu'en etat de stabilite se relie a σ_h par des fonctions bien definiés. Il existe donc une possibilité d'utiliser la géométrie des ruptures dans l'estimation des contraintes horizontales principales in-situ.

ZUSAMMENFASSUNG: Ein vorläufiges experimentelles Programm wurde beendet, in dem die Beziehung zwischen der Bohrloch-Absplitterungsbildung in Indiana Kalkstein und des in-situ Spannungszustandes untersucht wurde. Wir haben festgestellt, daß Absplitterungen in zwei gegenüberliegenden Bohrlochzonen entlang der Richtung von σ_h auftreten. Neuere Dünnschichtanalysen geben Grund zu der Annahume, daß der Haupt-Absplitterungsmechanismus Dehnungsbruch ist entlang der Oberflachen parallel zur Bohrlochwand, begünstigt durch Abscherungsversagen in radialer Richtung. Absplitterungstiefe und-weite sind proportional zu σ_h. Das Verhältnis von σ_H/σ_h, wenn Absplitterung beginnt und stabilisiert wird, und σ_h wird durch wohldefinierte Funktionon beschrieben. Daher besteht die Moglichkeit, geometrische Absplitterungsparameter zu benutzen, um die beiden horizontalen Haupt-in-situ-Spannungen abzuschätzen.

1. INTRODUCTION

Currently the most common technique of measuring deep in situ stresses is hydraulic fracturing. However, the reliability of this method under hostile conditions (such as very high stresses, high temperature, or prefractured rock) encountered in geothermal, oil field, or ultra deep wells (used for crystal research or for oil and gas extraction) is still uncertain. A plausible alternative or backup method to hydraulic fracturing may be provided by the phenomenon of borehole breakout (borehole cross-sectional elongation resulting from spalling) where it occurs.

The phenomenen of borehole spalling has been recognized for many years. One of the earliest reported cases of breakouts was in the quartzites and conglomerates of the Witwatersrand deep gold mines in South Africa (Leeman, 1964), where spalling was observed to occur at diametrically opposed points on the borehole wall. These were also the points of maximum compressive stress concentration. Cox (1970) discovered breakouts while testing a new logging tool in oil wells drilled into the shales and carbonates of Alberta, Canada. The four-arm-high-resolution dipmeter, a modern version of the borehole caliper, showed numerous diametrical elongations (breakouts) in most of the 17 wells he used for his tests. In all cases the elongations occurred in the NW-SE direction which is also the direction of the least horizontal principal stress, σ_h, in much of North America. Babcock (1978), also using a four-arm dipmeter, extended Cox's results and showed that breakouts in Alberta wells appeared throughout the stratigraphic column. He suggested that breakouts were controlled by a pre-existing NW-SE joint set which was intersected by the boreholes. Bell and Gough (1979) independently supported Leeman's (1964) explanation that the existence and directional consistency of the breakouts were determined by stress concentrations around the borehole resulting from the in situ stress field. They showed that borehole elongation occurred in the known direction of σ_h in Alberta as well as in Colorado and Texas (Gough and Bell, 1981 and 1982).

Other investigators have reported evidence of breakouts using a variety of logging tools such as the sonic borehole televiewer (Zoback et. al., 1985), the down-hole fisheye movie camera (Springer et. al., 1984), and the six-arm caliper and downhole television (Carr, 1974). Breakouts have been found to occur in almost any rock type, from tuff to sandstone to granite. More importantly, in most cases it has been shown that borehole elongations are consistently aligned with the minimum horizontal principal stress (Hickman et. al., 1985; Teufel, 1985).

The advent of sophisticated downhole logging tools have made it possible not only to detect breakouts but also to determine their depth and span as well

as their orientation. Field evidence points to an unmistakable correlation between breakout orientation and principal stress directions. If a similar correlation could be determined to exist between breakout dimensions and principal stress mangitudes, a potentially powerful technique of estimating in situ stresses could evolve.

At the University of Wisconsin, we have embarked on a long-term research project to examine the mechanisms of breakout formation and to establish for different rock types and conditions the relationships between given in situ stresses and the size, shape, and orientations of breakouts. This paper summarizes the results obtained from our initial laboratory study in Indiana limestone. Our ultimate goal is to assess the potential of utilizing the phenomenon of borehole breakouts as a tool for the estimation of the in situ state of stress.

2. AN ANALYTICAL MODEL

The most complete analytical model available to date for predicting the occurrence as well as the location, size, and shape of borehole breakouts was proposed by Zoback et. al. (1985). In this plane strain model, the radial, tangential, and shear stresses in a horizontal cross-section are calculated at every point around the vertical borehole using the Kirsh elastic solution. They are then compared with the stresses required to cause shear failure of the rock based on the linear Mohr-Coulomb criterion. This criterion is characterized by the coefficient of internal friction μ and the cohesion S_0. Upon solving for S_0 at every given point around the borehole in terms of the radial (σ_r), tangential (σ_θ), and shear ($\tau_{r\theta}$) stresses the critical condition for shear failure becomes:

$$S_0 = (1+\mu^2)^{1/2} [(\frac{\sigma_\theta - \sigma_r}{2}) + \tau_{r\theta}^2]^{1/2}$$

$$- \mu (\frac{\sigma_\theta + \sigma_r}{2}) \qquad (1)$$

If the right-hand side of equation (1) is less than So, a stable condition prevails (point a in Figure 1); whereas, if the right-hand side is greater than S_0, failure may occur

272

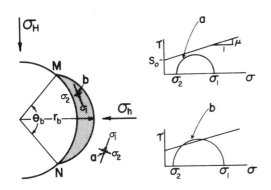

Figure 1. Borehole breakout (shaded area) given in terms of its depth (r_b) and angular span (θ_b) as suggested by Zoback et. al. (1985) model for a set of in-situ principal horizontal stresses (σ_H and σ_h). Explanation of stable and failed areas are given in the form of Mohr circles and Mohr-Coulomb criterion of failure (after Mastin, 1984).

(point b in Figure 1). A contour line can be drawn enclosing a zone within which the state of stress is sufficient to bring about shear failure. This contour line represents the size and shape of the borehole breakout and can be characterized by the maximum breakout depth, r_b, and by the breakout angle, θ_b. Since σ_r, σ_θ and $\tau_{r\theta}$ are functions of the maximum and minimum horizonal stresses, σ_H and σ_h, this model yields different breakout depths and angles in the same rock for different in situ stress conditions. More importantly, it suggests that one can estimate the two principal horizontal stresses, σ_H and σ_h, by accurately determining the breakout depth and angle.
The model has the advantage of mathematical simplicity. It is derived from a well-known elastic solution and a commonly accepted failure criterion. To utilize the model one only needs to ascertain two rock parameters, μ and S_0. However, the model does not anticipate the existence of discontinuities, the potential for material yielding, the time-dependent characteristics of some rocks, and the possibility that breakout is episodal. There is also the added difficulty that most observations to date are of breakouts created by rock splitting parallel to the borehole wall

and eventual spalling, rather than by pure shear as implied by the analytical model (e.g., Ortlepp, 1983; Mastin, 1984). Nevertheless, Zoback et. al. (1985) model is a very useful starting point toward a better understanding of the breakout phenomenon. Our experimental program was triggered in part by the potential for correlating breakout dimensions to in situ stresses as expressed in this analytical model, and our results are compared with its predictions.

3. EXPERIMENTAL PROGRAM

We are conducting a laboratory experimental program of inducing borehole breakouts under controlled conditions. In the initial set of experiments, dry and saturated rock blocks of Indiana limestone (about 13 cm on each side) having a central vertical borehole of 2.14 cm in diameter were subjected to a general traixial state of stress, $\sigma_H > \sigma_v > \sigma_h$. A polyaxial cell and a loading press were used to apply three independent and mutually perpendicular simulated in-situ principal stresses of up to 100 MPa. Each load was servo-controlled, ensuring that the constant "far-field" stresses (σ_h and σ_v) were prevented from drifting and that the slow increase in σ_H could be programmed to follow certain rates repeatable from test to test. For each specified value of σ_h and σ_v. we ran two tests. The range of σ_h tested was from 0.05 C_0 to 1.0 C_0, where C_0 is the unconfined compressive strength of the rock (C_0 = 27.7 MPa for the dry rock, C_0 = 25.0 MPa for the saturated rock). The central borehole was visually inspected after each 1-2 MPa increase in the magnitude of σ_H. The initiation and the apparent stabilization of borehole breakouts, as well as any intermediate stages of breakout formation were carefully recorded. At the end of each test, when the borehole breakout appeared to have stabilized, each specimen was removed from the loading cell, and was cut vertically in half along the σ_H direction. Each half specimen was then cut into approximately ten horizontal slices so that accurate measurements of the breakout geometry along the borehole could be carried out. In this manner forty measurements of the breakout depth and width could be obtained in each specimen.

Four separate specimens were used for a polished section and thin section analysis. All of these specimens were tested in the wet condition and at a σ_h of 0.875 Co. However, in each specimen the maximum horizontal stress, σ_H, was raised until a different stage of breakout formation was reached (see section 4 for a description of the various stages). The specimen was then removed from the testing apparatus and prepared for photographic examination. Polished sections were photographed using a Polaroid Land camera so that the entire breakout region was visible. Thin sections were photographed through a microscope with a similar camera at two different magnification factors - 10X and 40X.

4. TEST RESULTS

The laboratory tests in Indiana limestone yielded some important quantitative results with respect to the mechanism, direction, and dimensions of borehole breakouts.

We have observed on the borehole wall four stages leading to the formation of a stabilized breakout (Haimson and Herrick, 1985). The first evidence of failure is the appearance of short vertical hairline cracks along the general direction of the σ_h axis and spanning a horizontal segment of the borehole wall which increases with the magnitude of σ_h (Stage 1). The segment defined by these hairline cracks remains approximately constant through the test. As σ_H is increased, the hairline cracks tend to link up and form one or more long winding cracks (Stage 2). At higher values of σ_H spalling begins whereby thin slabs of rock are detached from the borehole wall. As the rock slabs spall off, others are detached from behind (Stage 3). Finally, a level of σ_H is reached at which spalling ceases and the breakout appears to stabilize (Stage 4). Further increase in σ_H produces no noticeable change in the size of the breakout.

Consistent results were obtained which established without a doubt that, when the only controlling factor is the state of in situ stress as in our tests, breakouts concentrate along two diametrically opposed arcs of the borehole cross-section. The centers of these arcs are aligned with the σ_h

direction. This, of course, confirms suggestions based on field evidence (e.g. Gough and Bell, 1981), and previous laboratory tests by Mastin (1984), which were conducted under a uniaxial external stress field.

Through our careful observation of the borehole condition during specimen σ_H loading (and constant σ_h and σ_v), we have recorded the state of stress sufficient to initiate failure at the borehole wall and that required to bring about a final stabilized breakout. A summary of these results is presented in Figure 2 in the form of the ratio of σ_H/σ_h as a function of σ_h/C_o. In this normalized fashion the resulting curve can be compared with other rocks that will be tested later. Figure 2 gives two stress values for each tested specimen, one for breakout initiation (Stage 1) and one for completion (Stage 4). The plot suggests that, regardless of whether the rock is wet or dry, the relationships between σ_H and σ_h upon breakout initiation and upon completion are well constrained. As σ_h is increased the required σ_H/σ_h ratio decreases, first rather sharply, and beyond $\sigma_h = 0.3 C_o$ at a much slower rate. As σ_h approaches the value of C_o the σ_H/σ_h ratio needed to initiate breakouts is about 1.5 and that sufficient to complete the breakout process is about 3.0. A corollary of Figure 2 is the relationship between the normalized σ_h and the calculated critical tangential stress (σ_θ) at the points on the borehole wall here breakouts initiated. It is expected that since the same rock was used throughout, the tangential stress at the point of failure would be the same regardless of the preset value of σ_h. As shown in Figure 3, σ_θ remained indeed approximately constant and independent of σ_h in the dry specimens. In saturated blocks, however, a similar behavior was observed only in tests in which σ_h/C_o was larger than 0.5. Using the results of Figure 3 indicating an average critical σ_θ of 90 MPa and 83 MPa for the dry and wet specimens, respectively, we estimated the points in Figure 2 where the breakout should initiate under uniform horizontal far-field stresses ($\sigma_H=\sigma_h$) at $\sigma_h/C_o \simeq 1.65$.

One of the more significant results of the experimental program to date has

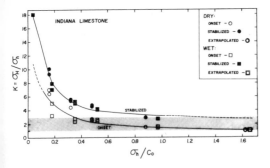

Figure 2. Relationships between the horizontal stress ratio and the normalized least horizontal in situ stress, σ_h, at the onset and at the point of apparent stabilization of borehole breakout. Extrapolated values for $\sigma_H = \sigma_h$ were calculated using the average tangential stress required to initiate borehole wall failure (see Figure 3). The shaded zone covers the horizontal stress ratio expected to prevail in situ.

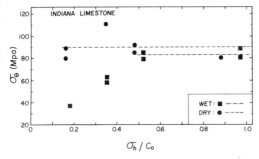

Figure 3. Relationship between the critical tangential stress σ_θ at the point of breakout initiation and the normalized least horizontal stress.

been the clear evidence that the breakout depth (r_b) and angle (θ_b) are directly proportional to the magnitude of the horizontal principal stresses. The measurements we made to determine breakout depth and breakout angle showed considerable consistency within each specimen and from specimen to specimen. The standard deviation under each stress condition averaged 5% for r_b and 18% for θ_b. Figure 4 presents photographs of vertical and horizontal cross-sections of stabilized breakouts from three specimens which were subjected to different constant values of σ_h and σ_v. The increase of r_b and θ_b with σ_v (and thus with the respective σ_H) can be clearly seen in the horizontal sections. The

consistency of the breakouts throughout the borehole lengths is demonstrated by the vertical sections.

In Figure 5 we plotted the experimental final breakout depth (r_b) as a function of σ_h/C_o. Generally, breakout depth increases with the magnitude of the horizontal stresses applied. The rate of increase is higher in the range of $0 < \sigma_h/C_o < 0.2$, but tapers off for $\sigma_h/C_o > 0.2$. In this latter range Indiana limestone appears to yield deeper breakouts when saturated. The two free-hand drawn curves representing the normalized behavior of r_b as a function of σ_h for dry and wet specimens are generally similar in nature to the theoretical curve based on Zoback et. al. (1985) model. Clearly, beyond $\sigma_h/C_o=0.5$ the sensitivity of r_b to increases in σ_h is rather poor both theoretically and experimentally, although more tests are clearly needed in the higher ranges of σ_h in order to establish this relationship unequivocally.

With respect to the horizontal span of the breakouts at the borehole wall (measured by the angle θ_b, see Figure 1) the experimental results are considerably more encouraging (Figure 6). The increase in θ_b with the horizontal stress is linear and is the same for both dry and wet specimens. The linearity is also predicted by Zoback et. al. (1985) model. This result implies that the sensitivity of θ_b to stress does not diminish throughout the range of in situ stresses expected to prevail in the field.

5. POLISHED AND THIN SECTIONS

In an effort to improve our understanding of the mechanism that brings about spalling, we conducted a polished section and thin section study of specimens subjected to different stages of the breakout process. As stated earlier, all the specimens were tested at $\sigma_h = 22$ MPa ($0.875\ C_o$) under saturated conditions. These parameters were chosen to contrast the previous work of Mastin (1984), who also studied breakout formation in sedimentary rock (Berea sandstone), but used dry specimens under a uniaxial state of stress ($\sigma_h = \sigma_v = 0$).

From the polished horizontal sections we learned that the failure process begins with grain splitting a short

275

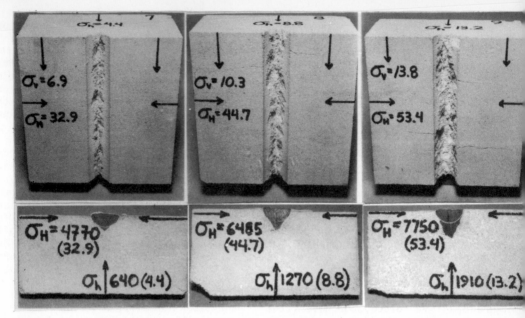

Figure 4. Photographs of vertical and horizontal cross-sections of three specimens subjected to different stress conditions (given in MPa for the vertical sections and in lbs/in^2 and MPa for the horizontal sections). Note the direct relationship between the horizontal stresses and the breakout orientation, depth, and width.

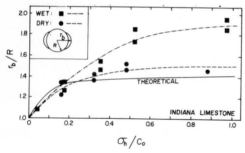

Figure 5. Normalized relationship between the breakout depth, r_b, and the least horizontal compressive stress, σ_h. The theoretical curve was derived using Zoback et. al. (1985) analytical model (S_0 = 8.0 MPa; μ = 0.56).

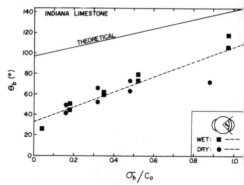

Figure 6. Relationship between the breakout angle θ_b and the normalized least horizontal compressive stress σ_h. The theoretical curve was derived using Zoback et. al. (1985) analytical model (S_0 = 8.0 MP$_\bullet$ μ = 0.56).

distance behind the borehole wall along the σ_h axis. With an increase in σ_H grain splitting intensifies, often forming chains of broken grains which may later become extensional fractures delineating thin slabs of rock approximately parallel to the borehole wall. This supports the explanation

given by Gallagher et. al. (1974) for the occurrence of rock slabbing aligned with the direction of the local maximum compressive stress. Once a slab has been detached by an extensional fracture, it may spall off by either buckling or more often by first shearing off at one of its ends and turning into the borehole. Spalling continues within the bounds of the initial spalled-out area by further shearing off of thin slabs detached through grain splitting.

Figure 7 is just a sample of the photographs and photomicrographs taken in this study. Figure 7a is a photograph of a polished half-section to illustrate the condition of a specimen that was removed in the penultimate stage of breakout formation. Extensive splitting has occurred just behind the borehole wall in the σ_h direction, with a thin slab in the process of being sheared off. Deeper into the rock the fracturing is less developed and consists mostly of chains of split grains. Well beyond the visible slabs and open cracks there is a triangular region where discoloration appears to indicate a zone of cement disintegration around the grains. The shape and size of this zone suggests that it may delineate the final breakout at the completion of the spalling-off process. Figure 7b is a photomicrograph (10X) of a thin section of 1 mm^2 area taken from the section in Figure 7a. It shows a portion of the major open fracture. Apart from the pure tensile opening of the fracture, no shear displacement can be detected.

6. DISCUSSION

The results of our borehole wall observations during the experimental program and the subsequent polished and thin section analysis create a relatively clear picture of the events that bring about breakouts. The state of stress in the horizontal plane along the σ_h axis and just behind the borehole wall is one in which the tangential stress attains its highest compressive value ($3\sigma_H - \sigma_h$ at the borehole wall), while the radial compressive stress is very low (it vanishes at the borehole wall). It may appear surprising at first that a compressive state of stress gives rise to splitting or extentional cracking parallel to the σ_H direction. However, a glance through the literature (e.g. Jaeger and Cook, 1979 p. 91-93) reveals that such observations have been made before in uniaxial compression tests (which are the closest to our stress condition). Careful uniaxial compression testing in a stiff machine using matched end pieces by Fairhurst and Cook (1966) resulted in failure by both longitudinal splitting and shear fracture, very similar to our observations. Gallagher et. al. (1974) provided an experimental explanation to the extensional cracking phenomenon by showing that uniaxial compression may· lead to individual grains being line-loaded as in a Brazilian test, resulting in array of grain splittings which then coalesce to form the observed tensile fracture. Freudenthal (1977) suggested that because of the

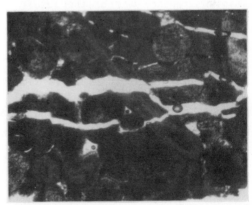

Figure 7. (a) Photograph of a polished section showing an advanced stage of breakout formation. Clearly discerned are a detached slab at the borehole wall, extensive fracturing further into the rock, and a discolored triangular zone (marked by a dashed line) believed to be the result of split grains and disintegrated cementing material. (b) A photomicrograph (10X) of a thin section (1 mm^2 in area) taken from the detached slab in (a), indicating that the major fracture crossing the slab is extensional with no visible shear displacement.

high compressibility and low shear modulus of rock, shear dilatancy may occur in a compressive stress field, which is comparable in magnitude to the volume compaction caused by non-deviatoric stresses. In the borehole case, shear dilatancy produces radial tensile stresses. Depending on rock properties, the latter can cause tensile fractures within the zone of high shear stresses unless shear failure occurs first. The zone of critical stress concentration is very similar in shape to that predicted by the Zoback et. al. (1985) model. The difference is that either or both shear and tensile failure can occur. The actual mode of failure does not imply that the Zoback et. al. (1985) model cannot be used since failure in uniaxial compression and in triaxial compression with low confining pressures generally follow the Mohr-Coulomb criterion.

The best proof that the analytical model is quite realistic is provided by our experimental results shown in Figures 5 and 6. Qualitatively, the theoretical curves relating the depth and the angle (or span) of breakouts to σ_h are in close agreement with the experimental results. Quantitatively, the expected and the observed results differ by a factor, which implies that some refinement of the model is still in order. Also, the breakout round shape predicted by the model (Figure 1) is not supported by the "V" shaped breakouts shown in Figure 4. However, this discrepancy may be the result of incomplete breakout, i.e. there is no guarantee that every failed element would be detached from the rock mass.

The most important result of the experimental work has been the clear correlation that appears to exist between breakout dimensions and the in situ stress. Figure 4 demonstrates this rather vividly. Figures 5 and 6 give quantitative relationships, which together with the results given in Figure 2 are rather promising with respect to the potential for using borehole breakouts to estimate the state of in situ stress. For example, assuming that the rock in the field is well simulated by our laboratory tests, one could use Figure 6 to determine σ_h/C_o from the average breakout angle $(\theta_b)^o$. The latter can be determined in the field from a borehole televiewer log or other measurements. Then Figure

2 could be used to determine σ_H/σ_h. Provided C_o can be determined, and this is a relatively easy task, both σ_H and σ_h can be estimated. The second choice, and one that can be used as a backup technique, is to use the plots of r_b versus σ_h/C_o (Figure 5). With r_b measured in the field σ_h could be estimated, and from it a projected σ_H could be obtained using Figure 2. Obviously, this technique is less desirable than the first one because of the low sensitivity of r_b to changes in σ_h in the range of stresses most expected to prevail in situ. A third method of estimating the stresses from breakout dimensions would be by using field data together with the relationships given by the analytical model. However, this can become operational only if experimental results closely follow predicted model values. As stated above, thus far only qualitative agreement between the two has been found to exist. Hence, the analytical model in its present form is not useful to quantitative estimation of in situ stress.

We would like to make it clear that in the above discussion of stress determination from breakout data we have made an idealistic assumption regarding the correlation of our test results to actual field behavior. Factors such as large borehole diameters, presence of joints, and field drilling under pre-existing in situ stress, can affect the results considerably and are now under study by us. However, as a first step in this investigation, we believe that the results presented are useful and encouraging.

7. CONCLUSIONS

We have conducted a series of experiments in Indiana limestone in which borehole breakouts were induced under simulated in situ stress conditions. All the breakouts occurred in two diametrically opposed zones along the borehole wall in the direction of the least horizontal stress.

Examination of polished sections and thin sections from the vicinity of boreholes at different stages of breakout formation reveals that the failure process begins with grain splitting parallel to the borehole wall. This is followed by the

detachment of an entire slab and its spalling off resulting from probable shear failure at its ends.
The total depth and the lateral extent of the completed breakout appear to be directly proportional to the state of horizontal in situ stress. This, together with the established relationship between the maximum and the minimum principal horizontal stresses upon breakout completion, have the potential of yielding estimates of the in situ stresses if breakout dimensions are known.

8. ACKNOWLEDGEMENTS

This work was supported by the National Science Foundation grant no. EAR-8511941. We would also like to thank the Los Alamos National Laboratory, and in particular D. Mann for preparing the polished and thin sections and T. Dey* for his useful suggestions.

9. REFERENCES

Babcock, E.A. 1978. Measurement of subsurface fractures from dipmeter logs. Amer. Assoc. Petrol. Geol. Bull. 62: 1111-1126.

Bell, J.S. and D.I. Gough 1979. Northeast-southwest compressive stress in Alberta: evidence from oil wells. Earth Planet. Sci. Let. 45: 475-482.

Carr, W.J. 1974. Summary of tectonic and structural evidence for stress orientation at Nevada Test Site. U.S.G.S. Open File Report 74-176.

Cox, J.W. 1970. The high resolution dipmeter reveals dip-related borehole and formation characteristics. Proceedings 11th Annual Logging Symp. Soc. Prof. Well Log Analysts. Los Angeles.

Fairhurst, C. and N.G.W. Cook 1966. The phenomenon of rock splitting parallel to the direction of maximum compression in the neighborhood of a surface. Proceeding 1st Cong. Inter. Soc. Rock Mechanics. Lisbon: 687-692.

Freudenthal, A.M. 1977. Stresses around spherical and cylindrical cavities in shear dilatant elastic media. Proceedings 18th U.S. Symp. on Rock Mechanics. Keystone.

Gallagher, J.J., Friedman, M., Handin, J., and G.M. Sowers 1974. Experimental studies relating microfracture in sandstone. Tectonophysics 21: 203-247.

Gough, D.I. and J.S. Bell 1981. Stress orientations from oil well fractures in Alberta and Texas. Canad. J. of Earth Sci. 18: 638-645.

Gough, D.I. and J.S. Bell 1982. Stress orientations from borehole wall fractures with examples from Colorado, east Texas and northern Canada. Canad. J. of Earth Sci. 19: 1358-1370.

Haimson, B.C. and C.G. Herrick 1985. In situ stress evaluation from borehole breakouts-experimental studies. Proceedings 26th U.S. Symp. on Rock Mechanics. Rapid City: 1207-1218.

Hickman, S.H., Healey, J.H., and M.D. Zoback 1985. In situ stress, natural fracture distribution, and borehole elongation in the Auburn geothermal well, Auburn, New York. J. Geophys. Res. 90(7): 5497-5512.

Jaeger, J.C. and N.G.W. Cook 1979. Fundamentals of rock mechanics, 3rd ed. Chapman and Hall. London: 593 p.

Leeman, E.R. 1964. The measurement of stress in rock - part 1. J. S. Afr. Inst. Min. and Met.: 76-77.

Mastin, L.G. 1984. Development of borehole breakouts in sandstone. M.S. Thesis. Stanford University. Palo Alto: 101 p.

Ortlepp, W.D. 1983. The design of mine tunnels and the selection of support in Rock Mechanics in Mining Practice, ed. S. Budavari. The South African Institute of Mining and Metallurgy Monograph Series No. 5. Johannesburg: 77-103.

Springer, J.E., Thorpe, R.K., and H.L. McKague 1984. Borehole elongation and its relation to tectonic stress at the Nevada Test Site. Lawrence Livermore National Laboratory. Paper UCRL-53528.

Teufel, L.W. 1985. Insights into the relationship between wellbore breakouts, natural fractures, and in situ stress. Proceedings 26th U.S. Symp. on Rock Mechanics. Rapid City: 1199-1206.

Zoback, M.D., Moos, D., Mastin, L., and R.N. Anderson 1985. Wellbore breakouts and in situ stress. J. Geophys. Res. 90(7): 5523-5530.

Stress conditions for initiation of secondary fractures from a fractured borehole

E. DETOURNAY
R.G. JEFFREY
Dowell Schlumberger, Tulsa, Oklahoma, USA

Abstract

A two-dimensional elastic analysis is made of conditions for initiating, by pressurizing a jacketed borehole, secondary fractures that extend perpendicular to the maximum in-situ stress, σ_1. The problem is uncoupled into two parts: first, the tangential stress is calculated at the points of initiation of the secondary fractures as a function of borehole pressure, far-field stress, and length of the primary fractures; and second, the stable length of the primary fractures is calculated using linear elastic fracture mechanics. This analysis leads to a simple method for determining σ_1 provided that σ_2 and the primary and secondary breakdown pressures are known, and does not require determination of the tensile strength of the rock.

Resumé

On étudie à partir d'un modèle élastique bi-dimensionnel les conditions d'initiation a la paroi d'un puits, mis en pression par un fluide maintenu dans le forage par une membrane imperméable, de fractures secondaires perpendiculaires à la plus grande contrainte in-situ horizontale. La méthode d'analyse consiste à décomposer le problème original: d'une part le calcul de la contrainte tangentielle au point d'initiation des fractures secondaires, en fonction des contraintes in-situ, de la pression du fluide dans le forage, et de la longueur des fractures primaires; et d'autre part le calcul de la longueur des fractures primaires, basé sur les principes de la mecanique de la Fracture. Cette analyse débouche sur une méthode relativement simple pour déterminer σ_1, pourvu que soient connues σ_2 et les pressions d'initiation des fractures primaires et secondaires, mais sans nécessiter toutefois la connaissance de la résistance à la traction de la roche

Zusammenfassung

Wir untersuchen jene Spannungsbedingungen die sekundäre Frakturen in Bohrlöchern mit bereits vorhandenen primären Frakturen verursachen und die eine Orientierung normal zur maximalen in-situ Spannung σ_1 haben. Wir führen unsere Studien in zwei Abschnitten durch. Zunächst berechnen wir die tangentiale Spannung am Ort des Ausbreitungsbeginnes der sekundären Frakturen als Funktion des Bohrlochdruckes, der Spannung im Unendlichen und der Länge der primären Frakturen. Dann berechnen wir die stabile Länge der primären Frakturen unter Anwendung der elastischen Festigkeitslehre. Unsere Analyse führt zu einer einfachen Methode mit der man σ_1 berechnen kann für den Fall, dass σ_2 und sowohl der primäre als auch der sekundäre Frakturationsdruck bekannt sind. Für diese Berechnungen ist die Kenntnis der Zugfestigkeit des Gesteines nicht erforderlich.

1. INTRODUCTION

Hydraulic fracturing is a widely used technique for determination of in-situ rock stresses. The most straightforward application of this technique to stress measurement entails injecting fluid at a low, constant rate into a packed-off section of an uncased borehole until a maximum value of the fluid pressure is reached. This maximum, called the breakdown pressure p_b, corresponds to an early unstable propagation of two radial fractures in the direction perpendicular to σ_2, see Figure 1. Kutter (1970) has indeed shown that, if both the borehole and the fractures are pressurized, propagation of two diametrically opposed fractures is favored over propagation of either a single fracture or more than two.

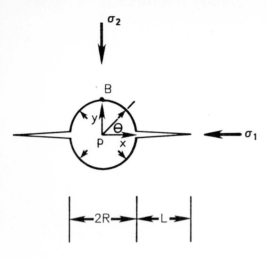

Figure 1: Problem definition

With continued pumping, the pressure drops to a level that corresponds to quasistatic propagation of the fractures. After fluid injection is stopped, the pressure in the sealed-off wellbore will gradually decrease. An inflection in the resulting pressure versus time curve defines the closure pressure, which is the point at which the hydraulic fracture closes on itself. The closure pressure is taken to be equal to the magnitude of the σ_2. Hydraulic fracturing can thus provide a direct measurement of the magnitude of the minimum horizontal principal stress σ_2. The strike of the fracture at the wellbore determines the principal stress directions.

However, the maximum horizontal principal stress is not determined directly by a hydraulic fracturing test, and various techniques have been proposed to evaluate σ_1 (see, e.g., Zoback and Pollard 1978, and Cornet and Valette 1984). The most common method of obtaining σ_1 is based on the assumption that the breakdown pressure p_b is indicative of stress conditions for which the tensile strength of the rock is reached at the borehole wall. For dry, impermeable rock the following relationship between p_b, the in-situ stress, and the tensile strength T of the rock is then used

$$\sigma_1 = 3\sigma_2 + T - p_b. \qquad (1)$$

If the tensile strength can be independently measured, then Equation 1 provides an additional relation for determining σ_1.

The major drawback in using Equation 1 lies in the fact that the tensile strength of rock is not a material property (Fairhurst 1976). Tensile failure at the borehole must instead be under-

stood as the unstable propagation of suitably oriented initial defects in the rock. The criterion for extension of these cracks is that the stress intensity factor K_I (a function of the load and the crack geometry) reaches a critical value K_{Ic}, the toughness, which is a material property. Moreover, different load conditions that result in the same value of K_I at the tip of the crack will generally not yield the same macroscopic tangential stress at the wellbore wall, except for initial flaws that are very small.

These points can be illustrated by considering the pressure required to extend two radial cracks from a circular hole in a plate, which is unstressed at infinity. The pressure in the hole, normalized by the factor $K_{Ic}/\sqrt{(\pi R)}$, is plotted versus the dimensionless crack length λ, for the two limiting conditions of either zero or uniform pressure in the cracks. λ is defined as the ratio of the length, L, of one wing of the primary fracture to the radius, R, of the borehole (Figure 2). Thus, by adopting the more fundamental viewpoint of fracture mechanics, it is recognized that the apparent tensile strength of the rock is strongly influenced by the size of the initial flaws and by the pressure distribution of the fracturing fluid into the pre-existing defects of the rock.

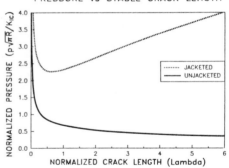

PRESSURE vs STABLE CRACK LENGTH

Figure 2: Pressure versus stable crack length.

Investigations into alternative ways of determining σ_1 led us to consider the conditions for initiating secondary fractures (in the direction perpendicular to σ_2) from a pressurized jacketed borehole. The advantage of a jacketed borehole test is that the influence of the fluid pressure distribution inside the crack is removed; the breakdown pressure then depends only upon the initial flaw size, the rock toughness, and the in-situ stress field. Moreover, as indicated in Figure 2, the propagation of two radial flaws, from a jacketed borehole, is at first unstable (as indicated by the negative slope of the curve), but very soon continued fracture growth is achieved only by continuously increasing the pressure in the borehole. Thus, after propagating a primary fracture, the pressure in a jacketed wellbore can be increased until a second set of fractures initiates at 90° off the primary direction.

By assuming that initial defects in the rock are small enough so that initiation of both primary and secondary fractures can be analyzed using the macroscopic tensile strength approach, and that the apparent tensile strength is isotropic, a measurement of the magnitude of the secondary breakdown pressure p_{b2}, together with the knowledge of the functional dependence of p_{b2} upon the far-field stress and the rock properties provides us with an additional relation with which to calculate σ_1.

This paper addresses the question of under what set of conditions of borehole pressure, p, far-field stresses, σ_1 and σ_2, and primary fracture half-length, L, will a secondary fracture initiate.

2. METHOD OF ANALYSIS

Calculation of the tangential stress concentration at point B (Figure 1) on the wall of a fractured borehole can be done by superposition of stress concentrations from each load component. In addition, the length of the primary fracture must be such that the fracture is in critical equilibrium with the stress conditions. These two calculations can be done separately, in an uncoupled manner.

First, the stress condition is broken into its fundamental components consisting of the pressure in the hole, p, and the horizontal far-field mean and deviatoric stresses P^o and S^o given by

$$P^o = (\sigma_1 + \sigma_2)/2$$

and (2)

$$S^o = (\sigma_1 - \sigma_2)/2.$$

Note that compressive stress is taken as positive. The tangential stress at a point on the borehole wall that lies along the radial line running parallel to the minimum horizontal principal stress σ_2 is then given by a linear superposition of contributions from each stress component:

$$\sigma_\theta = f_p(\lambda)p + f_d(\lambda)S^o + f_m(\lambda)P^o. \quad (3)$$

The stress concentration coefficients f_p, f_d, and f_m are functions of λ, which is defined as the ratio L/R.

The superposition used in Equation 3 is valid provided that the primary fracture is open over the length λ for the particular stress conditions p, S^o, and P^o. This requirement is always satisfied by $\lambda = \lambda_c$ where λ_c is the value of λ that is in critical equilibrium for the applied stress conditions and fracture toughness, K_{Ic}, of the rock.

By breaking the solution process into two steps, first the calculation of

stress concentration factors as functions of λ and then the calculation of a critical λ for a given stress condition, a complete yet simple solution to the problem was obtained.

3. STRESS CONCENTRATION FACTORS

To use Equation 3 for calculating the tangential stress, the elastic coefficients f_p, f_d, and f_m must be determined. The analytical solution for an unfractured hole (Timoshenko and Goodier, 1970) provides values for these coefficients at $\lambda=0$:

$$f_p(0) = -1, \ f_d(0) = 4, \ f_m(0) = 2.$$

Asymptotic values for some of the coefficients, corresponding to $\lambda = \infty$, also are available. The calculation of f_p, f_d, and f_m for intermediate values of λ was done numerically using a two-dimensional boundary element program. The numerically obtained values were then corrected by adjusting them by a small constant value ($\simeq 5\%$) determined by requiring that the theoretical and numerical values at $\lambda=0$ agree.

3.1 Internal Pressure Loading

The asymptotic value $f_p(\infty)$ corresponds to a pressurized semicircular notch in a half-plane and for this case $f_p \simeq -0.68$ (Detournay and Jeffrey, 1986). The function $f_p(\lambda)$ is plotted in Figure 3 for λ values that cover the range of interest.

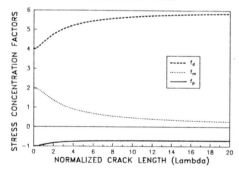

STRESS CONCENTRATION FOR FRACTURED HOLE

Figure 3: Stress concentration factors.

3.2 Deviatoric Far-Field Stress

To calculate the stress concentration factor $f_d(\lambda)$, associated with a far-field deviatoric stress, the deviatoric stress is decomposed into two far-field uniaxial stresses of same magnitude, one compressive and one tensile. The stress concentration coefficient f_d is then given by the difference of the two uniaxial coefficients:

$$f_d(\lambda) = f_x(\lambda) - f_y(\lambda). \quad (4)$$

The asymptotic value for $f_x(\infty)$ can be calculated semianalytically (Maunsell, 1937) and, as mentioned previously, $f_x(0)$ is also known:

$$f_x(0) = 3, \quad f_x(\infty) \simeq 3.065.$$

The coefficient $f_x(\lambda)$ appears to be not very sensitive to λ, with most of the change occurring over the range $0 \leq \lambda \leq 1$.

For the case of a uniaxial tensile stress, acting along the y-axis perpendicular to the fracture plane, the asymptotic value $f_y(\infty)$ of the corresponding stress concentration factor is at present not available. However, the following heuristic argument can be used to suggest that $f_y(\infty)$ must be about -3.

A stress concentration of -1 occurs at the midpoint of a line crack that is subject to a uniaxial tensile far-field stress acting perpendicular to the plane of the crack. If a small semicircular notch is made in the wall of the crack, at its midpoint, then it may be argued that as the size of the notch is decreased, the notch will be subject to an essentially uniaxial stress field and, therefore, $f_y(\infty)$ should be about equal in magnitude to the asymptotic value $f_x(\infty)$ (the two asymptotic values are however not expected to be identical, because the stress field is not uniform). The limits for $f_y(\lambda)$ are then:

$$f_y(0) = -1, \quad \text{and } f_y(\infty) \simeq -3.$$

Therefore, we can conclude that the stress concentration factor f_d will vary from a value of 4 for the unfractured borehole to an asymptotic value of about 6.

3.3 Mean Normal Far-Field Stress

The mean normal far-field stress can be generated by superposition of two equal uniaxial compressive stresses and, hence, the concentration factor, $f_m(\lambda)$, can be obtained from the factors $f_x(\lambda)$ and $f_y(\lambda)$ defined previously, i.e., $f_m(\lambda) = f_x(\lambda) + f_y(\lambda)$. The limiting values of $f_m(\lambda)$ are thus:

$$f_m(0) = 2, \quad \text{and } f_m(\infty) \simeq 0.$$

Figure 3 summarizes these results in the form of a graph of the various stress concentration factors, $f_p(\lambda)$, $f_d(\lambda)$, and $f_m(\lambda)$ for λ ranging from zero to 20.

4. LENGTH OF PRIMARY FRACTURE

The critical fracture length is the length of the fracture that is in critical equilibrium with the applied loads for the fracture toughness of the rock. In fracture mechanics terms, critical equilibrium occurs when the stress intensity factor just equals the fracture toughness of the rock,

$$K_I = K_{Ic}. \tag{5}$$

As the jacketed borehole is pressurized, the stress intensity factor for a initial flaw of size ω will increase until the fracture toughness of the rock is reached. Because of the stress distribution around the hole, the small flaw will extend in an unstable fashion (see Figure 2) until the stress intensity factor for the fracture again becomes equal to the critical value. Further pressurization of the borehole will result in slow, quasistatic propagation of the fracture requiring ever-increasing borehole pressure until secondary breakdown occurs at point B (Figure 1) on the borehole wall. This section describes how the length of the primary fracture, which is in critical equilibrium with the applied stress conditions, is found.

4.1 Calculation of the Stress Intensity Factor

The problem of calculating the stress intensity factor for a fractured hole a a function of stress conditions, fracture length, and size of the hole has been the subject of numerous investigations (Bowie, 1956; Ouchterlony, 1974; Bowie and Freeze, 1972; and Newmann, 1971). However, in the two limiting cases of very small ($\lambda \ll 1$) or very large ($\lambda \gg 1$) primary fractures, the corresponding stress intensity factors, K_I, can be computed from the well-known formulas for a small planar edge crack and for a line crack of length 2L. The formula for the planar edge crack is th key to the equivalence between the macroscopic tensile strength approach and the use of fracture mechanics principles, in predicting tensile failure a the borehole wall. Indeed, as the crac length approaches zero, the stress intensity factor and the tangential stress at the boundary obey the following relationship:

$$C_* \sigma_\theta = \lim_{L \to 0} \left[\frac{K_I}{\sqrt{(\pi L)}} \right] \tag{6}$$

where $C_* = 1.07$ (Rooke and Cartwright, 1974).

At the point of tensile failure, th macroscopic tensile strength concept requires that

$$\sigma_\theta = T \tag{7}$$

Therefore, if L is small enough ($L/R \leq 0.01$), the tensile strength is related to the fracture toughness of the rock and to the initial flaw size (ω) by

$$\frac{K_{Ic}}{\sqrt{(\pi\omega)}} = C_* T. \tag{8}$$

A computationally attractive procedure for calculating the stress intensity factor is the weight function methodology of Bueckner (1970) and Rice (1972). The stress intensity factor fo the fractured borehole is then represented by an integral of a product, consisting of the equivalent line-crack loading and the appropriate weight function:

$$K = \int_0^L m(x;R,L)\ \sigma(x)\ dx. \qquad (9)$$

The weight function, $m(x;R,L)$, depends only on the geometry of the problem and is independent of the loading. The equivalent line-crack loading is obtained from the elastic stress field existing in the crack-free problem subject to the same external loads. Thus, the effect of the stress concentration around the hole is taken into account.

The weight function for the fractured borehole problem is not known in closed form. Nelson and Proffer (1984) proposed the following form for $m(x;R,L)$:

$$m(x;R,L) = \frac{2}{\sqrt{\pi}}\ \frac{\sqrt{L}}{\sqrt{L^2-x^2}}\ \{g\} \qquad (10)$$

where

$$g = 1 + 0.3\left[1 - \frac{x}{L}\right]\left[1 + \frac{L}{R}\right]^{-4}.$$

Equation 10 has the correct form for small and large values of L/R: for very small values of L/R, m gives a good approximation of the weight function for a planar edge crack; for large values of L/R, m becomes equal to the exact expression for the weight function for a line crack of length 2L.

Knowing the form for m, and knowing $\sigma(x)$, the stress intensity factor can be found by integrating Equation 9 numerically.

4.1.1 Critical Fracture Length

By performing the change of variables, $x/L = 1-z$, and then dividing both sides of Equation 9 by $T\sqrt{(\pi L)}$, a normalized equation for the stress intensity factor is obtained:

$$\frac{K_I}{T\sqrt{\pi L}} = I(\lambda) \qquad (11)$$

where

$$I(\lambda) = \frac{2}{\pi}\int_0^1 \frac{h(z,\lambda)}{\sqrt{z}}\ dz \qquad (12)$$

and

$$h(z,\lambda) = \tilde{\sigma}(z,\lambda)\left[\frac{1 + 0.3z(1+\lambda)}{\sqrt{(2-z)}}\right]^{-4}$$

The function $\tilde{\sigma}(z,\lambda)$ is the equivalent line-crack loading expressed in terms of the variable z and normalized by the tensile strength of the rock. Thus, $I(\lambda)$ depends not only on λ, but also on the normalized stresses p/T, S^O/T, and P^O/T.

The normalized integral equation for the stress intensity factor (Equation 11) together with the relationship between the tensile strength and the stress intensity factor of a small initial flaw (Equation 8) is used to find the length of the fracture that is in critical equilibrium.

By solving Equation 8 for K_{Ic} and substituting this into Equation 11, a stability equation can be found:

$$\frac{1}{I(\lambda)} - \frac{1}{C_*}\sqrt{\frac{\lambda}{\lambda_*}} = 0 \qquad (13)$$

where λ_* is the ratio of the initial flaw size to the borehole radius (ω/R). Values of λ which make the left side of Equation 13 zero correspond to stable crack lengths. The two terms on the left side of Equation 13 are shown graphically in Figure 4 as is their difference.

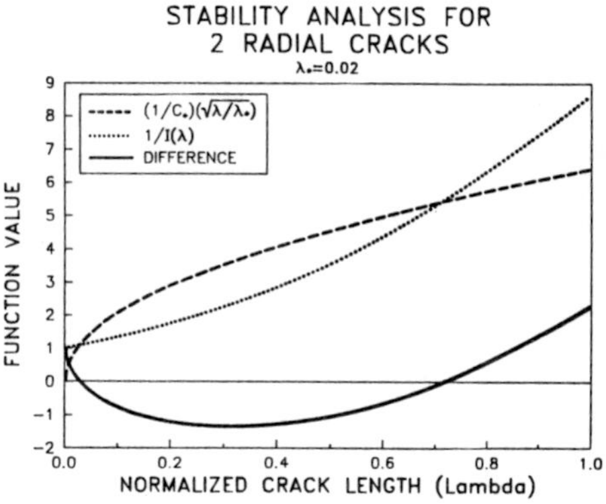

STABILITY ANALYSIS FOR
2 RADIAL CRACKS
$\lambda_*=0.02$

Figure 4: Stability analysis.

5. CALCULATION OF SECONDARY BREAKDOWN PRESSURE

The secondary breakdown pressure, P_{b2}, can now be determined by:

(1) Calculating the tangential stress at point B as a function of the primary fracture length λ, the borehole pressure p, and the far-field stress components P^O and S^O, through the use of the stress concentration functions $f_p(\lambda)$, $f_m(\lambda)$, and $f_d(\lambda)$;

(2) Calculating the stable crack length as a function of p, P^O, and S^O, using Bueckner's weight function methodology.

The secondary breakdown will occur when the tangential stress at B reaches the tensile strength, T, of the rock.

285

Using Equation 3, and after normalization of all stress quantities by T (the dimensionless stress is designated by $\tilde{P}$ over the symbol, e.g., $P^o = P^o/T$), the secondary breakdown pressure is given by

$$\tilde{P}_{b2} = \frac{[1 + f_m(\lambda_2)\tilde{P}^o + f_d(\lambda_2)\tilde{S}^o]}{f_p(\lambda_2)} \qquad (14)$$

where λ_2 is the stable primary crack length at secondary breakdown; λ_2 is the root ($> \lambda_*$) of an integral equation, formally written as

$$F(\lambda_2; \tilde{P}^o, \tilde{S}^o, \lambda_*) = 0 \qquad (15)$$

which is obtained by replacing p in Equation 13 by the right-hand side of Equation 14.

It is clear that for a given value of λ_*, the dimensionless breakdown pressure $\tilde{P}_{b2}$ is a unique function of the far-field component P^o and S^o. Therefore the results of a parametric analysis can be represented in the form of contour levels of $\tilde{P}_{b2}$ in the normalized stress diagram (P^o, S^o), for any given value of λ_*. Such a presentation of the results is illustrated in Figure 5 for the case $\lambda_* = 10^{-2}$. Contour levels of $\tilde{P}_{b1}$, which are

straight lines given by the equation

$$\tilde{P}_{b1} = 2\tilde{P}^o + 4\tilde{S}^o + 1, \qquad (16$$

and contours of $\tilde{P}_{b2}$ have been plotted (contours of $\tilde{P}_{b2}$ are dashed to avoid confusion between the two sets of lines).

Two limiting lines also have been plotted in Figure 5: one is the line o $S^o = P^o$ which corresponds to a uniaxia far-field stress; the other line is given by $S^o = P^o/2 + T/4$, which corresponds to a zero primary breakdown pressure. For stress fields above and to the left of this limiting line, a primary fracture will spontaneously be induced in an open hole.

Results given in Figure 5 clearly show that an increase of the in-situ stress deviatoric causes a decrease of the primary breakdown pressure $\tilde{P}_{b1}$ (a well-known result), but causes an increase of the secondary breakdown pressure $\tilde{P}_{b2}$.

A fundamental issue to explore at this stage is the sensitivity of $\tilde{P}_{b2}$ t the normalized initial flaw size λ_*. Parametric analysis indicates that within the constraints of small λ_*, $\tilde{P}_{b2}$ is relatively insensitive to the value of λ_*. There are two reasons for this property: (1) by normalizing by the

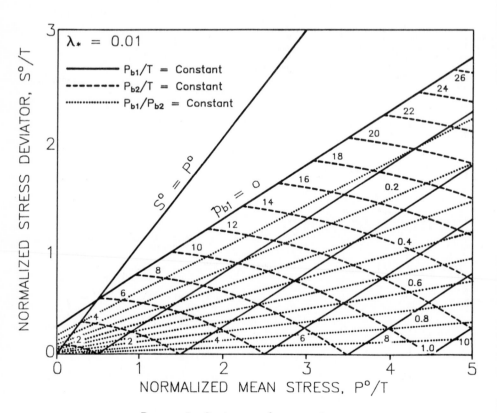

Figure 5: Contours of p_{b1} and p_{b2}

tensile strength, T, the influence of
the initial flaw size, ω, is indirectly
taken into account (recall Equation 8),
and (2) with increasing primary fracture
length, the role of the fracture
toughness progressively diminishes (even
more so under far-field compressive
stresses). Thus, within the constraints
and limitations of this analysis, the
diagram in Figure 5, giving $\tilde{p}_{b1}$ and $\tilde{p}_{b2}$
as a function of P^O and S^O, can be
considered, for all practical purposes,
independent of λ_*.

5. APPLICATION

A fracturing test, conducted using
an impermeable jacket in the borehole,
is a way of obtaining values for the two
breakdown pressures p_{b1} and p_{b2}. The
minimum horizontal principal stress, σ_2,
can be reliably found from a standard
hydraulic fracturing stress test where
fluid is allowed to enter and pressurize
the fracture.

5.1 Stress Field Determination from a Jacketed Test

The minimum horizontal principal
stress, σ_2, is related to the far-field
stress components by

$$\sigma_2 = P^O - S^O \qquad (17)$$

Using this equation with Equations 14
and 16, the three unknown parameters,
P^O, S^O, and T, can be calculated.
However, Equation 14 is not a linear
combination of the unknown parameters
and its use requires an iterative
solution method. Fortunately, a simpler
solution is possible by making use of
the fact that points representing
constant ratios of $\tilde{p}_{b1}/\tilde{p}_{b2}$ plot as a
straight line in the stress plot shown
in Figure 5. The equation of these
lines is

$$\tilde{S}^O = \alpha(\tilde{P}^O + \beta) \qquad (18)$$

where α is the slope of the line, and β
is its intercept with the P^O axis.
These coefficients are only a function
of p_{b1}/p_{b2}. The form of the functional
variation of α and β with this ratio is
shown in Figure 6.

SLOPE AS A FUNCTION OF P_{b1}/P_{b2}

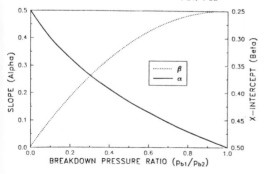

Figure 6 Coefficients α and β

The unknown parameters that must be
determined from the test are T, S^O, and
P^O. The known parameters are p_{b1}, p_{b2},
(from jacketed test), and σ_2 (from
unjacketed test). Equations 16 and 18,
written in dimensional form, with the
relationship between σ_2 and the field
stress components (Equation 17) provide
three equations with which the three
unknown parameters can be found.

The deviatoric field-stress component is
then given by

$$S^O = \frac{\alpha[\sigma_2 + \beta(p_{b1} - 2)]}{1 - \alpha(1 - 6\beta)}. \qquad (19)$$

The slope, α, and intercept, β, are
found using Figure 6 which, with Equations 17 and 16, makes it possible to
calculate P^O and T.

6. CONCLUSIONS

A quasistatic elastic analysis of
the conditions for initiation of
secondary fractures from a jacketed
borehole is presented in this paper.
The linear elastic analysis is based on
the assumptions that (1) the flaw size
in the rock is small enough, compared to
the borehole radius, that there is
consistency between the microscopic
fracture mechanics and the macroscopic
tensile strength concepts, and (2) the
tensile strength is isotropic and
uniform.

Calculation of the secondary breakdown pressure was performed by considering two auxiliary problems, on one
hand the determination of the stress
concentration factors as a function of
the primary crack length, and on the
other hand determination of the primary
crack length in critical equilibrium
with the applied stress conditions.

Under the constraints of the
analysis, it was found that the
secondary breakdown pressure depends
only on the far-field stress and on the
tensile strength of the rock. Although
the functional dependence of p_{b2} upon P^O
and S^O is not known explicitly, it was
found that for constant values of the
ratio of primary to secondary breakdown
pressure, a linear relationship exists
between P^O and S^O. The line
representing this linear relationship
has slope, α, and intercept, β, and
these coefficients depend only on the
ratio p_{b1}/p_{b2}. This linear equation
provides another relationship between S^O
and P^O that allows a direct determination of the maximum horizontal stress,
σ_1, provided that the primary and
secondary breakdown pressures are known
and provided that the minimum stress,
σ_2, has been measured in an independent
hydraulic fracturing shut-in test.

The practicality of this method will
depend on the ability to detect the two
breakdown pressures, either through
acoustic emissions or by the change of
compliance of the borehole. This
analysis may also prove useful in delin-

eating quasistatic mechanisms involved in the Tailored Pulse Loading technique (Cuderman, 1984; Swift and Kusubov, 1982), a propellant-based technology used to create multiple radial fractures around a borehole.

7. ACKNOWLEDGEMENTS

The authors wish to express their appreciation to the management of Dowell Schlumberger, Tulsa Technology Center, for allowing them to publish this paper and to J.-C. Roegiers for his support of this project.

8. REFERENCES

Bowie, O.L. 1956. Analysis of an Infinite Plate Containing Radial Cracks Originating from the Boundary of an Internal Circular Hole. J. Math. and Phys. 35:60-71.

Bowie, O.L., and C.E. Freese 1972. Elastic Analysis for a Radial Crack in a Circular Ring. Engineering Fracture Mechanics 4:315-321.

Bueckner, H.F. 1970. A Novel Principle for the Computation of Stress Intensity Factors. ZAMM 50:529-546.

Cornet, F.H., and B. Valette 1984. In Situ Stress Determination from Hydraulic Injection Test Data. J. Geophys. Res. 89(B13):11527-11537.

Cuderman, J.F. 1984. Rock Mechanics Effects Observed Subsequent to Multiple Fracturing of Wellbores. Proc. 25th U.S. Symp. on Rock Mechanics, Evanston, Ill.:127-134.

Detournay, E., and R.G. Jeffrey 1986. Manuscript in Preparation.

Fairhurst, C. 1976. The Application of Mechanics to Rock Engineering. Proc. Symp. on Exploration for Rock Engineering, Johannesburg:1-22

Kutter, H.K. 1970. Stress Analysis of a Pressurized Circular Hole with Radial Cracks in an Infinite Elastic Plate. Int. J. of Fracture Mech. 6(3):233-247.

Maunsell, F.G. 1936. Stresses in a Notched Plate Under Tension. Phil Magazine 21:765-773.

Newman, J.C. 1971. An Improved Method of Collocation for the Stress Analysis of Cracked Plates with Various Shaped Boundaries. NASA Tech. Note (D-6373).

Nelson, R.H., and W.J. Proffer 1984. Engineering Formulas for Fractures Emanating from Cylindrical and Spherical Holes. J. App. Mech. 51(12):929-933.

Ouchterlony, F. 1974. Fracture Mechanics Applied to Rock Blasting. Third Congress, Int. Soc. Rock Mechanics, Denver.

Rice, J.R. 1972. Some Remarks on Elastic Crack-tip Stress Fields. Int. J. Solids Structures 8:751-758.

Rooke, D.P., and D.J. Cartwright. 1976. Stress Intensity Factors. Her Majesty's Stationery Office, London.

Swift, R.P., and A.S. Kusubov 1982. Multiple Fracturing of Boreholes by Using Tailored-pulse Loading. SPE J.:923-932.

Timoshenko, S.P., and J.N. Goodier. 1970. Theory of Elasticity. McGraw Hill Book Co., New York.

Zoback, M.D., and D.D. Pollard 1978. Hydraulic Fracture Propagation and the Interpretation of Pressure Time Records for In-situ Stress Determination. Proc. 19th U.S. Symposium on Rock Mechanics.

In-situ stress measurements in deep boreholes using hydraulic fracturing, wellbore breakouts, and stonely wave polarization

M.D. ZOBACK
L. MASTIN
C. BARTON
Stanford University, Department of Geophysics, Stanford, California, USA

ABSTRACT

Direct measurement of in-situ stress magnitudes at mid-crustal depth is one of the primary motivations of deep scientific drilling programs. In this paper we discuss the potential for making such measurements using three methods. First, the usefulness of hydraulic fracturing in deep boreholes will be discussed. We demonstrate that extremely high breakdown and fracture extension pressures will be required at depth, especially in compressional tectonic environments. Second, as wellbore breakouts are likely to occur in deep boreholes and could make hydraulic fracturing extremely difficult, the potential for estimating stress magnitudes through analysis of the breakouts will be discussed. Breakouts reported in the Kola Penninsula hole in the Soviet Union will be analysed and the magnitudes of in-situ stresses estimated to depths of 11.6 km. Finally, a new stress measurement method will be briefly discussed based on utilization of stress-induced polarization of Stoneley wave particle motions. This method has been successfully used to determine stress orientation in several wells and has the potential for estimation of relative stress magnitudes.

RESUME

Determiner directement la valeur absolue des contraintes in situ a une profondeur environ egale a la moitie de l'ecorce terrestre, est l'un des objectifs principaux des programmes de forages profonds. Nous exposerons ici, trois methodes de mesures. Dans un premier temps, nous montrerons l'importance de la fracturation hydraulique dans les forages profonds, et nous demontrerons que les pressions de rupture et d'extension des fractures sont extremement fortes pour les environements tectoniques en compression. Dans un deuxieme temps, et puisque les breakouts sont tres communs dans les trous profonds et qu'ils pourraient compliquer l'operation de fracturarion hydraulique, nous exposerons une methode de determination de la valeur absolue des containtes par l'etude des breakouts. Nous analyserons des breakouts dans le puits Kola Peninsula situe en URSS, et nous calculerons la valeur de la containte horizontale principale jusqu'a une profondeur de 11 km. Enfin, nous exposerons brievement une nouvelle methode fondee sur la polarisation - induite par les contraintes in situ - de la trajectoire des particules dans les ondes de Stoneley. Cette methode a ete utilisee avec succes pour determiner l'orientation des contraintes dans plusieurs puits, et montre la possibilite d'estimer la valeur absolue relative des contraintes in situ.

ZUSAMMENFASSUNG

Die unmittelbare Bestimmung der in-situ Spannung in der mittlere Kruste ist eine der Hauptsachen der wissenschaftliche Projekte für Tiefbohrungen. Im Beitrag, werden drei Verfahren diskutiert. Erstens, wird die Nutzlichkeit der Hydraulic Fracturing in

Tiefbohrungen absegeschätzt and es werde gezeigt, daβ in tektonish komprimierte Zoner sehr höhe Versagen- und Bruchausweiterungsdrücke gebraucht sind. Zweitens, wird die Moglichkeit der Bestimmung der Spannung aus Tiefbohrversagen ausgewehrt. Bohrversagen von der Kola Halbinsel in der UdSSR werden analysiert und die mindeste horizontale Spannung wird bis zu Tiefen von 11km berechnet. Letztens, ein neues Verfahren wird kurz gemeldet. Sein Prinzip ist die Benutzung der Spannungspolarizatior der Stoneley Wellen. Die Ermittlung der Faltungsorientierung war mit diesem Verfahrer erfolgreich gemacht. Weiter ist dieses Verfahren auch für die Bestimmung der relative Größe der Spannung anwendbar.

1. INTRODUCTION

Led by the technological and scientific successes of the ultradeep scientific drilling program in the Soviet Union, a number of western countries are now undertaking continental scientific drilling programs to address fundamental geologic problems related to crustal composition, evolution, and active deformation. Scientific drilling, core recovery, and borehole experimentation to depths of 5 to 15 km has now been proposed for a number sites around the world in a wide-variety of tectonic settings. As many outstanding questions exist about the state of stress at mid-crustal depths, determination of in-situ stress at depth is often one of the most important goals of these deep-drilling progams. Nevertheless, determination of stress at such depths has not yet been done and we face many important technological and scientific challenges to make stress measurements in deep boreholes possible. In this paper, we review the potential for utilization of three different stress measurement methods in deep boreholes. In each case the stress measurement method is percieved to be relatively robust, and has the potential for working under the extreme environmental conditions likely to be encountered in deep holes.

2. HYDRAULIC FRACTURING IN DEEP WELLS

Over the past 15 years, the hydraulic fracturing stress measurement method has become widely used. The basic test procedures, limitations of applicability (e.g., one principal stress is required to be

parallel to the borehole and elastic ar isotropic behavior of the rock around th wellbore is required to determine th maximum principal stress), and potenti experimental difficulties are reasonab well-known. A summary of the manner which the technique has been implemente by a number of investigators around th world is described in a commendium papers edited by Zoback and Haims (1983). Zoback and Haimson (198 summarize the status of the method employed by a number of investigato around the world.

The most severe problems affectir the potential usefulness of hydrau fracturing in deep boreholes involve th high pressures required to initiate an extend the fracture, the high ambie temperatures at which the fractures mu work and the likelihood that stress-induce wellbore breakouts may result in a out-of-round hole and inelastic roc conditions around the wellbore. Th breakout issue is dealt with in the followir section.

While the problems of high pressur and temperature are clearly coupled fro the perspective of packer design ar performance, from a scientific perspectiv the temperature problem is quit straightforward. Nearly all commercial available inflatable straddle packers hav severe difficulty operating at temperature exceeding 200° C. Thus, except in lo heat-flow and stable cratonic areas (whei the thermal gradient is about 20° C/km bottom-hole temperatures could easil exceed the capabilities of current available equipment in many of the proposed drilling experiments. However, hydraulic fracturing has been done at temperatures as high as 260° C at relatively low pressures of 350 bars (Dreesen et al., 1986), and it seems that with considerable effort, the temperature problem could be solved as long as pressures were not excessive.

Unfortunately, very high pressures will be required at great depth in most cases. High pressures are difficult to deal with in boreholes because of the large forces exerted onto the packer systems in the relatively large diameter holes. For example, a pressure of 700 bars in a hole with a 24 cm diameter generates 317,000 kg of differential force on the packers. In fact, commercially available packer systems are limited to differential pressures of about 700 bars. Using this value, we can investigate the depth to which hydraulic fracturing can now be used as a function of depth and the tectonic setting.

To estimate the pressures necessary to initiate and extend hydraulic fractures at depth we make two different assumptions about the state of stress at midcrustal depths that bound likely conditions to be encountered. First, we can assume that the state of stress in the crust is controlled by the frictional strength of active faults, and compute the surface breakdown (P_b) and pumping (P_p) pressures as a function of depth in normal faulting, strike-slip, and reverse faulting tectonic environments. This approach seems well-justified by a number factors including stress measurements at depth in active faulting regions (Zoback and Healy, 1984) and the widespread occurrence of intraplate seismicity around the world (see Zoback and Zoback, 1981). In considering stress measurements made throughout the world, Brace and Kohlstadt (1980) show that for the appropriate vertical stress, S_v, computations based on the frictional strength of active faults bound essentially all of the reported measurements of S_{hmin}, the least horizontal compressive stress, and S_{Hmax}, the maximum horizontal compressive stress. For completeness, we

will also compute hydraulic fracturing pressures for the passive stress case in which shear stresses are quite low and the three principal stresses are approximately equal.

As shown by Zoback and Healy (1984), when the frictional strength of active faults is controlling the state of stress at depth, the following equation (after Jaeger and Cook, 1969) can be used to define the ratio of the maximum and minimum effective principal stresses:

$$(S_1 - P_0)/(S_3 - P_0) = (\sqrt{(\mu^2 + 1)} + \mu)^2$$

where P_0 is the pore pressure and μ is the coefficient of friction. The laboratory work of Byerlee (1978) suggests that the most reasonable value for μ at great depth is 0.6, which is basically consistent with the field measurements reported by Zoback and Healy (1984).

After Anderson (1951), we take $S_3 = S_{hmin}$ and $S_1 = S_v$ in a normal faulting environment; $S_3 = S_{hmin}$, $S_1 = S_{Hmax}$ and $(S_{hmin} + S_{Hmax})/2 = S_v$ in a strike-slip faulting environment; and $S_3 = S_v$ and $S_1 = S_{Hmax}$ in a reverse faulting environment. In order to compute the surface breakdown and pumping pressures (the latter is taken simply to be the magnitude of S_{hmin} corrected appropriately for the hydrostatic head), we will use the well-known equation after Haimson and Fairhurst (1970):

$$P_b = 3 S_{hmin} - S_{Hmax} + T - P_0$$

and assume a nominal tensile strength (T) of 200 bars and hydrostatic pore pressure (P_0).

Figures 1 and 2 show the expected principal stresses and the breakdown and pumping pressures necessary for hydraulic fracturing for the cases of reverse and strike-slip tectonic environments. These two cases are most important because these stress states characterize most continental regions. Areas of normal faulting, such as sedimentary basins and intraplate extension regions (like the Basin and Range province of western North America) are discussed seperately below.

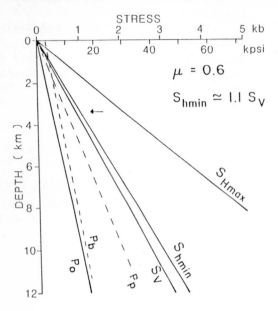

$\mu = 0.6$

$S_{hmin} \simeq 1.1\, S_v$

Figure 1- Estimated differential breakdown (P_b) and fracture extension (P_p) pressures in reverse faulting tectonic environment. S_{Hmax} is the maximum horizontal principal stress, S_{hmin} is the minimum horizontal principal stress, S_v is the vertical stress, and P_p is the pore pressure. The arrow at about 3 km indicates the depth at which the differential fracture extension pressure exceeds 700 bars, the limit of commercially available equipment.

As presented in Figs. 1-3, P_b and P_p are the differential pressures at any given depth. In other words, by subtracting the hydrostatic pressure, the pressure measured at the surface is shown in order to compare P_b and P_p with the 700 bar downhole differential pressure which defines the operational limit of commercially available equipment.

As shown in Figure 1 for the reverse faulting case, the required fracture extension, or pumping pressure, exceeds the 700 bar limit at a relatively shallow depth-only slightly greater than 3 km. This

is because of the rapid rate of increase S_{hmin} with depth. Importantly, we hav assumed only a minimal rate of stres

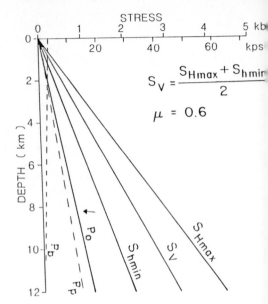

$$S_v = \frac{S_{Hmax} + S_{hmin}}{2}$$

$\mu = 0.6$

Figure 2- Same as Fig. 1 for a strike-slip faulting tectonic environment.

increase for a reverse faulting environment- a higher gradient could easily have been chosen which would have made the situation even worse. In the strike-slip faulting case (Fig. 2) the situation is somewhat better, but hydraulic fracturing is still not possible at depths much greater than 8 km. In this case too, a conservative value was chosen for the rate at which S_{hmin} increases with depth- a considerably greater value could have been chosen which would have limited the depth to which hydraulic fracturing was possible even more. Note that in both these cases the limiting pressure is not the breakdown pressure, but is instead the pumping pressure- simply reflecting the rapid increase of S_{hmin} with depth.

The passive tectonic case (Fig. 3), is clearly the worst case for hydraulic fracturing- a maximum depth of 2 km is seen due to the rapid increase of breakdown pressure with depth. This is because of the high rate of increase of S_{hmin} and the low

292

rate of increase of S_{Hmax}. In the normal faulting case, which is not shown, the breakdown pressure also limits the depth of hydraulic fracturing, but in this case at about 8 km (as in the strike-slip faulting case). In the normal faulting case the least principal stress increases at a very low rate (approximately 160 bars/km).

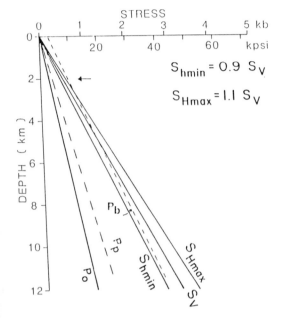

Figure 3- Same as Figs. 1 and 2 for the passive stress case in which the stress differences at depth are very small.

An attempt is now underway to develop a 1400 bar packer system for use to depths of 5 km in an upcoming set of stress measurements in a deep scientific drilling project at Cajon Pass, California, a site 4 km from the San Andreas fault (Zoback et al., 1986; Svitek et al., 1986). If this is successful it will be an important step forward. Nevertheless, all of the calculations presented above indicate that it is a certainty that very high pressures at relatively elevated temperatures will have to be dealt with in order to make in-situ stress measurements at great depth. This is an important technological problem that will require considerable attention in the coming years.

3. WELLBORE BREAKOUTS

Stress-induced wellbore breakouts have become increasingly important in the last few years because they seem to be such reliable indicators of the direction of the horizontal principal stresses (e.g., Bell and Gough, 1979; Plumb and Hickman, 1985; Hickman et al., 1985). The mechanism of their formation was first discussed by Gough and Bell (1981) and later expanded upon by Zoback et al. (1985). In the latter study it was shown that the detailed shape of wellbore breakouts could be roughly predicted using a relatively simple Mohr-Coulomb failure model. On the basis of laboratory studies, Mastin (1985) and Haimson and Herrick (1985) also discussed the applicability of Mohr-Coulomb analyses to the problem of breakout formation.

In this section, we first show why breakouts are likely to occur at depth in most holes. Although this will create obvious problems for hydraulic fracturing, the occurrence of the breakouts themselves will provide a means to estimate in-situ stresses. Thus, the second topic we will address are the inferences that can be made about the state of stress at depth in the Kola Penninsula ultradeep borehole based simply on where breakouts occur in the hole.

3.1 Mechanism of Formation and Expected Occurrence at Depth

Breakouts result from failure of the rock around the wellbore in response to the concentration of compressive hoop stress (Gough and Bell, 1981; Zoback et al., 1985). To evaluate this process, we start with the well-known equations derived by Kirsch (1898). For the case when the fluid pressure in the wellbore is equal to that in the formation, Figure 4 shows the variation of hoop stress as a function of azimuth around a well for nominal values of S_{Hmax} and S_{hmin}. If the uniaxial compressive strength of the rock is sufficiently high, as at C_1, the strength exceeds the concentrated stress and no breakouts occur. However, when the strength of the intact rock is exceeded by the concentrated stress , as at C_2, the rock will fail in a restricted section of the wellbore (at angles of 0 to e'). However, if the rock is sufficiently weak, as at C_3, failure would be expected to occur at all azimuths.

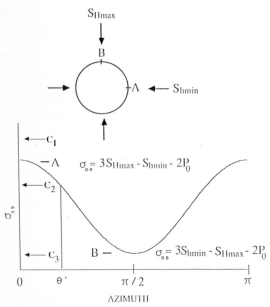

Figure 4- Variation of compressive hoop stress with azimuth. C_1, C_2, and C_3 are three nominal values of uniaxial compressive strength discussed in the text.

The basic problem in deep wells is quite simple- at the point of maximum stress concentration around the wellbore the compressive hoop stress is $3S_{Hmax}-S_{hmin}$ $-2P_0$, which can increase very rapidly with depth. For example, for the stresses presented in Fig. 2, the case of strike-slip faulting when pore pressure is hydrostatic, Fig. 5 shows that for a uniaxial compressive strength of 1,725 bars, breakouts would initiate at a depth of about 2.8 km. Utilization of denser drilling fluids helps to inhibit breakout formation, but even using fluids 60% denser the water only helps to prevent breakout formation until a depth of about 3.7 km. Of course, if the uniaxial

compressive strength was as high as 300●bars, breakouts could be inhibited to depth greater than 5 km. But in the general case we should not expect finding such strong rock at depth (see Kola example below) and it is easy to see why breakouts are so likely at great depth. The state of stress corresponding to reverse faulting leads to breakouts at considerably shallower depth than that shown in Fig. 5.

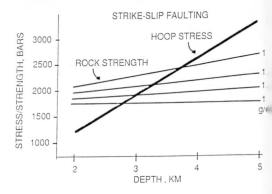

Figure 5- Maximum compressive hoop stress as a function of depth corresponding to the stress state shown in Fig. 2, and unixial compressive strength for different densities of drilling fluid. A nominal value of 1725 bars was chosen for the initial strength. The other values were determined from the presumed increase in strength as the wellbore fluid pressure increased.

The occurrence of breakouts does not necessarily preclude use of the hydraulic fracturing method. In several cases presented by Zoback et al. (1985) the breakouts are quite small and the borehole is not seriously out-of-round. Thus, inflatable packers would still work, the rock near the point of minimum stress concentration (where the hydraulic fracture is expected to initiate) would probably still be elastic, and the shape of the hole is still sufficiently close to circular that the stress concentration is close to that theoretically expected. As shown in the next section, however, this clearly is not the case in the Kola Penninsula well, and it would be simply impossible to use hydraulic fracturing in that well.

3.2 Estimating In-Situ Stresses From Wellbore Breakouts- Application to the Kola Ultradeep Well

As summarized in Table I (after Koslovsky, 1984), no significant borehole elongation is reported in the Kola well at 1 km. But at depths of 2.5, 5.0, 8.54, and 11.6 km breakouts apparently occured at the azimuth of maximum stress concentration as the small diameter of the hole was only slightly larger than the bit size (214 mm).

Table I
Observational Data for Kola

Depth	Small Diam.	Large Diam.	C_o
(km)	(mm)	(mm)	(bar)
1.0	214	214	1950
2.5	225	290	1620
5.0	250	390	1780
8.54	225	570	1920
11.6	240	370	1780

Note: The values for C_o at 5.0 and 11.6 km is the mean of measurements on a range samples.

To analyse the state of stress consistent with these observations we have used unpublished data on the uniaxial compressive strength, C_o, of core samples from the well. In the absence of other information, we have considered only whether the stress concentration exceeds the rock strength at point A, the region of maximum compressive stress concentration, but not at point B, the region of minimum compressive stress.

As shown in Fig. 6, we can straightforwardly define three fields where breakouts do not occur (as at 1 km), occur only at the point A (as at 2.5, 5.0, 8.54, and 11.6 km), or occur at A and B. We have assumed hydrostatic pore pressure conditions because it seems most consistent with drilling observations and compressional tectonics which is most characteristic of such stable cratons. We can

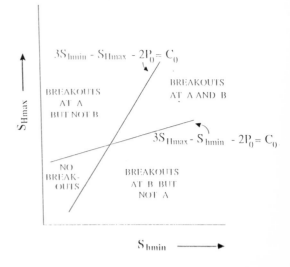

Figure 6- Possible fields of breakout formation in S_{Hmax}-S_{hmin} space. The field labeled breakouts at B but not at A is physically impossible as it requires the minimum principal stress to be greater than the maximum principal stress.

similarly place bounds on the in-situ stresses by limiting stress differences in accord with frictional faulting theory (Fig. 7) in a similar plot of S_{Hmax} versus S_{hmin} as Fig. 6. For this part of the analysis we have assumed that $\mu=0.6$. By analysing the areas of overlap between the two plots (as shown for a depth of 5 km in Fig. 8), the stress estimates presented in Table II were obtained.

Table II
Kola Stress Estimates

Depth	S_{Hmax}	S_{hmin}	S_v
(km)	(bars)	(bars)	(bars)
1.0	300 - 835	155 - 835	270
2.5	845 -2030	410-1385	675
5.0	1465-4050	760-2335	1350
8.5	2460-6800	1280-3470	2295
11.6	3249-9030	1738-4321	3132

Note: S_v is estimated from an assumed density of 2.7 g/cm^3

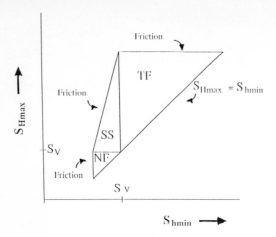

Figure 7- Possible stress states for different tectonic environments in S_{Hmax}-S_{hmin} space based on Anderson's theory of faulting and frictional constraints on the state of stress. NF- normal faulting, SS-strike-slip faulting, TF- reverse faulting.

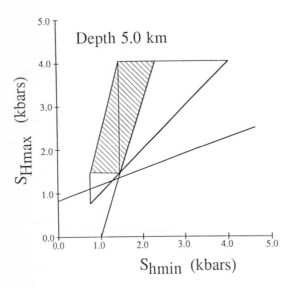

Figure 8- Superposition of plots shown in Figs. 6 and 7 for a depth of 5 km in the Kola Penninsula well shows possible range of stresses assuming that local tectonics are compressional (either field SS or TF in Fig. 7) and that breakouts occurred near point A but not B.

Unfortunately, the allowable range of values is quite large, especially at great depths. In part, this is due to the fact that no information is available on the tectonic stress state in the region. If, for example, we knew that strike-slip faulting were more characteristic of the region than reverse faulting (or vice versa), it would have been possible to considerably reduce the range of allowable stress values. Also, if any information was available on the exact shape of the breakouts it may have been possible to better-constrain the stress estimates (see Zoback et al., 1985).

4. STONELEY WAVE POLARIZATION

The propagation characteristics of Stoneley waves in boreholes is described by White (1962) and Cheng and Toksoz (1984). This type of borehole surface wave, often called tube waves, propagate along the borehole at phase velocities less than the shear velocity of the medium. These waves are very commonly observed during vertical seismic profiling (VSP) experiments. In a borehole drilled into a homogenous, isotropic, elastic solid, the tube wave particle motion is prograde elliptical, with the major axis along the borehole and the minor axis oriented in a radial direction. Based on the fact that seismic wave velocity near the borehole is very anisotropic due to the concentrated stress field, a new stress measurement technique is described by Barton and Zoback (1986) involving analysis of stress-induced polarization of tube wave particle motion. As this technique has potential for use in deep boreholes, a summary of recent results is briefly presented here.

If the rock around a wellbore has a uniform velocity distribution the horizontal component of tube wave particle motion is radial. However, we have found by studying three-component open-hole VSP data in two different wells that the particle motion direction is not radial, but is polarized into the direction of maximum horizontal compression. On the right sides of Figures 9 and 10, tube wave particle motion plots are presented for three depths for wells in

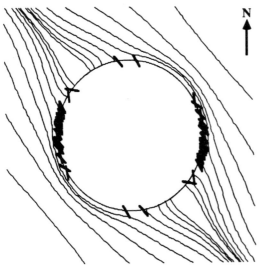

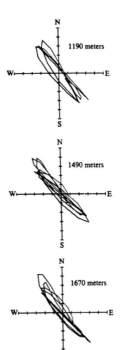

Figure 9- On the right side tube wave hodograms (particle motion) are shown with respect to north for three depths in a well in the Paris Basin. Note how polarized the particle motion is and the similarity of the aspect ratios at the three different depths. On the left side of the figure, the particle motion polarizations for tube waves recorded at all depths in the hole are projected onto a single cross-section and compared to the theoretical maximum horizontal stress trajectories.

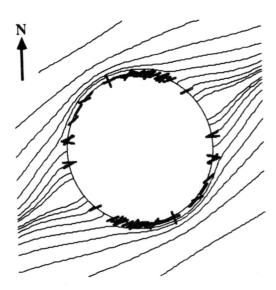

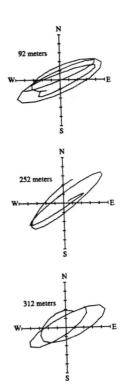

Figure 10- Same as Fig. 9 for a well drilled in Oklahoma.

the Paris Basin and Oklahoma. In each case it can be seen that particle motion is strongly polarized. In the case of the Paris Basin (Fig. 9), the polarization direction is about N35°W, consistent with the regional stress field for central Europe. The particle motion is polarized in the N70°E direction in the Oklahoma well (Fig. 10), again consistent with the regional stress field.

Perhaps one of the best ways to view the influence of the stress field on the tube wave particle motion is to project onto a single cross-section all of the particle motion polarization directions for the various depths and azimuths at which the seismometers were emplaced during the VSPs, and to show on the same plot the trajectories of maximum principal stress around the wellbore. This is shown on the left sides of figures 9 and 10. It is clear that the horizontal projection of particle motion is not radial, but instead follows the direction of the local stress maximum.

The differences between the particle motion ellipticities in Figs. 9 and 10 is clearly reflecting a difference in the local stress states and material properties. Our current research involves solving the theoretical problem to seperate these effects and make determination of stress magnitude possible. Because of the arguments presented above related to wellbore breakouts, it is clear that we will also have to solve this problem for non-circular boreholes.

4. CONCLUSIONS

The potential problems of making accurate measurements of in-situ stress at mid-crustal depths are appreciable. Considerable development efforts are necessary for active stress measurement programs to play an important role in deep scientific drilling projects. The hydraulic fracturing method still seems to be the most potentially useful stress measurement method. However, even after the technological problems with packer systems are solved, the strong likelihood that severe wellbore breakouts may develop makes utilization of the method in ultradeep holes

very questionable. Two other potenti methods for stress determination in dee holes were presented that clearly requi additional work to be of significant use fe in-situ stress measurements. Nevertheles because of the potential problems wi hydraulic fracturing, these and oth methods deserve very serious attention the coming years.

5. REFERENCES

Anderson, E.M. 1951. The Dynamics Faulting and Dyke Formation Wi Applications to Britain, 2nd ed. Oliver a Boyd. Edinburgh.

Barton, C.A. and M.D. Zoback 198 Determination of in-situ stress orientati from Stoneley wave polarization boreholes. Submitted to Jour. Geophy Res.

Bell, J.S. and D.I. Gough 197 Northeast-southwest compressive stress Alberta: Evidence from oil wells. Ea Planet. Sci. Lett. 45:475-482.

Brace, W.F. and D.L. Kohlstedt 1980. Lim on lithospheric stress imposed by laborato experiments. Jour. Geophys. Re 85:6248-6252.

Byerlee, J.D. 1978. Friction of rocks. Pur and Applied Geophysics. 116:615-626.

Cheng, C.H. and M.N. Toksoz 198 Generation, propagation and analysis tube waves in a borehole in Vertic Seismic Profiling, Part B, Advance Concepts. Geophysical Press.

Dreesen, D., J.R. Miller, F.A. Halbardier an R.W. Nicholson 1986. Openhole packer fo high-pressure service in a 500° Precambrian wellbore. IADC/SPE 14745 Soc. Petrol. Eng. Richardson, Texas.

Gough, D.I. and J.S. Bell 1981. Stres orientations from oil well fractures in Albert and Texas. Can. Jour. Earth Sci. 18:1981.

Haimson, B.C. and C. Fairhurst 1970. In sit

stress determination at great depth by means of hydraulic fracturing. Proc. 11th U.S. Symposium on Rock Mech. Soc. Mining Eng. of AIME. New York. 559-589.

Haimson, B.C. and C. Herrick 1985. In situ stress evaluation from borehole breakouts: Experimental Studies, Proc. 26th U.S. Symposium on Rock Mech. Soc. Mining Eng. of AIME. New York. 1207-1218.

Hickman, S.H., J.H. Healy, and M.D. Zoback 1985. In situ stress, natural fracture distribution, and borehole elongation in the Auburn geothermal well, Auburn, New York. Jour. Geophys. Res. 90:5497-5512.

Jaeger, J.C. and N.G.W. Cook 1969. Fundamentals of Rock Mechanics 2nd ed. Methuen and Co. London.

Kirsch, G. 1898. Die Theorie der Elastizitat und die Beaurforisse der Festigkeitslehre. V DI Z 1857 1968. 42:707.

Kozlovsky, Y. 1984. The world's deepest well. Scientific American. 251 (6):98-104.

Mastin, L. 1984. Development of borehole breakouts in sandstone. M.S. Thesis. Stanford University, Stanford, Ca.

Plumb, R.A. and S.H. Hickman 1985. Stress-induced borehole elongation: A comparison between the four-arm dipmeter and the borehole televiewer in the Auburn geothermal well. Jour. Geophys. Res. 90:5513-5522.

Svitek, J.F., J.H. Healy, and C.O. Stokely 1986. Testing packers for stress measurements in deep boreholes. EOS. 67:382.

White, J.E. 1962. Elastic waves along a cylindrical bore. Geophysics. 27:327-333.

Zoback, M.D. and B.C. Haimson 1982. Status of the hydraulic fracturing method for in-situ stress measurements. Proc. 23rd U.S. Symposium on Rock Mech. Soc. Mining Eng. of AIME. New York. 143-156.

Zoback, M.D. and B.C. Haimson, eds. 1983. Conference on Hydraulic Fracturing Stress Measurements. National Academy of Science. Wash., D.C.

Zoback, M.D. and J.H. Healy 1984. Friction, faulting, and in-situ stress. Annales Geophysicae. 2:689-698.

Zoback, M.D., D. Moos, L. Mastin, and R.N. Anderson 1985. Wellbore breakouts and in situ stress. Jour. Geophys. Res. 90:5523-5530.

Zoback, M.D., T. Henyey, L. Silver, and W. Thatcher 1986. Scientific drilling and experimentation at Cajon Pass, California. EOS. 67:379.

Stress determination from hydraulic tests on preexisting fractures – the H.T.P.F. method

F.H. CORNET
Laboratoire de Sismologie, Institut de Physique du Globe, Paris, France

Abstract.

A method for determining the complete regional stress field is presented. It is based on measurements of the normal stress supported by preexisting fracture planes (with various dip and strike) by means of hydraulic tests. The solution does not involve the stress field in the immediate vicinity of the well.

Two examples concerning granitic rocks are presented. The first one involves fourteen tests between 100m and 973m, the second one sixteen tests between 50m and 620m. For the second case, a stress discontinuity is observed around 300m Deep results are coherent with focal mechanisms of microseismic events.

Résumé.

Une méthode de mesure de contrainte, basée sur la détermination de la contrainte normale supportée par des fractures naturelles (de pendages et azimuts variés) est présentée. La solution ne fait pas intervenir le champ de contrainte au voisinage des forages utilisés.

Cette méthode est illustrée par les résultats de deux campagnes d'essai en massif granitique. La première concerne quatorze mesures entre 100m et 973m, la seconde seize essais entre 50m et 620m. Dans le deuxième cas, une discontinuité du champ de contrainte est mise en évidence autour de 300 m. Les résultats des essais profonds sont cohérents avec les mécanismes au foyer d'évènements microsismiques.

1. Introduction

The hydraulic fracturing stress determination technique is now well established (see e.g. Hubbert and Willis 1957 ; Scheidegger, 1962 , Fairhust, 1964 Haimson and Fairhurst, 1969 ; Haimson 1978 ; Haimson, 1983, Hickman and Zoback 1983). This method is based on analysis of pressure time records obtained in packed off zones of boreholes where the rock is homogeneous, linearly elastic and isotropic with respect to both its elastic characteristics and its "strength". When the borehole axis is parallel to one of the principal stress directions it provides ways to evaluate the magnitude and the direction of the two principal stresses which are perpendicular to the borehole axis.

In order to alleviate the constraining assumptions underlying the classical theory of hydraulic fracturing, Cornet (1980, 1982) and Cornet and Valette (1984) have proposed conducting hydraulic tests on preexisting fractures with various dip and strike for determining the complete regional stress tensor (H.T.P.F stress determination method). Bertrand et al. (1983) and Rummel and Baumgartner (1984) have reported successful stress measurements obtained with the H.T P.F. method. Their computational procedures are somewhat different from that proposed by Cornet and Valette (1984), but they also rest on the same hypothesis that the regional stress field is continuous and is a linear function of depth.

In the present paper the H.T.P.F. method described by Cornet and Valette is illustrated by field results obtained in two granite area of central

France, namely Auriat and Le Mayet de Montagne. In the first case a solution is presented for the stress field, which fits measurements taken between 150m and 980m. In the second (Le Mayet de Montagne), it is found that the stress field is not continuous in the depth range where measurements were conducted (50m, 620m). Results are compared to focal mechanisms obtained from microseismic events which occured in the very same depth interval.

2. The H.T.P.F. stress determination method.

The H.T.P.F. method is based on direct measurements of the normal stress supported by preexisting fracture planes with various dip and strike. The normal stress σ^i_n supported by the ith fracture plane is evaluated according to the technique used with the classical hydraulic fracturing method for the determination of the minimum principal stress.

A portion of a borehole, where a single preexisting fracture has been identified by a preliminary log (borehole televiewer, electrical log, etc..), is sealed off with a straddle packer and then pressurized at a large enough flow rate in order to reopen the fracture. The fracture may actually be completely healed by recristalization or still hydraulically conductive so that sometimes a pressure peak is observed, sometimes no peak occurs. If the fracture has been reopened, when injection stops a shut-in pressure P_s is observed when the well remains sealed. The instantaneous shut-in pressure (ISIP) (see e.g. Aamodt and Kuriyagawa 1982, Gronseth and Kry 1982, Hickman and Zoback 1983, McLenan and Roegiers 1982, Cornet and valette 1984, for various means of determining the I.S.I.P.) provides a first measurement of the normal stress supported by the fracture when the injected fluid has reached distances from the well larger than four or five well radii.

A second measurement of the normal stress is provided by the "constant pressure steps" test. The pressure is raised in a series of steps and the flow rate necessary to maintain constant the borehole pressure at each step (which lasts 4-5 min.) is measured. As soon as the fracture opens,

the flow rate necessary to maintain constant the borehole pressure increases drastically. Plots of pressure level versus corresponding flow rate yield an accurate determination of the pressure required to insure fracture opening.

Both the instantaneous shut-in pressure and the constant pressure steps test provide measurements of the total normal stress supported by the fracture, even for permeable rock matrices. Once the orientation of the fractures has been determined (by impression packer, borehole televiewer or electrical log) the problem is to determine the complete stress field $\sigma(x_i)$ at all points x_i where a test has been conducted so that :

$$\sigma(x^i)\underline{n}^{(i)} \cdot \underline{n}^{(i)} = \sigma^{(i)}_n \qquad (1)$$

where $\sigma^{(i)}_n$ is the normal stress supported by the ith fracture ; $\underline{n}^{(i)}$ is the normal to the ith fracture ($i=1,N$; $N \geqslant 6$ for N tests); $\sigma(x^i)$ is the stress tensor at point $X^{(i)}$. It involves six functions of the three components x_1, x_2, x_3, of points X.

When many boreholes can be drilled from an undergraound cavity, allowing measurements to be made on planes located roughly in the same volume, the stress $\sigma(x_i)$ can be assumed to be the same at all points x_i so that equation (1) provides a system of N linear equations with six unknowns. It can be inverted, for example, with a least squares procedure.

A more common situation is that in which $\sigma(x_i)$ is not constant from one point to the other.

When tests are conducted in sub-vertical boreholes, for example, the variations of $\sigma(x^i)$ depends only on depth so that equation (1) reduces to :

$$\sigma(x^i_3)\underline{n}^{(i)} \cdot \underline{n}^{(i)} = \sigma_n^{(i)} \qquad (2)$$

where x^i_3 is the depth of the ith test. The problem is now to determine six functions of the single variable x_3.

In homogeneous rock masses like granite formations, it may be assumed, as a first approximation, that the stress field, in a given depth range, is a linear function of depth so that $\sigma(x_3)$ can be represented by :

$$\sigma(x_3) = S + x_3 \, \alpha \qquad (3)$$

302

where S and α are two second order symmetrical tensors.

In the geographical frame of reference (x_1 oriented to the north, x_2 to the east, x_3 vertical positive downward), combining equations (3) and (2) yields :

$$(S_{kl} + \alpha_{kl} x_3^{(i)}) n_1^i n_k^i = \sigma_n^{(i)} \qquad (4)$$

$$k,l = 1,2,3$$

where

s_{kl} is the kl component of S in the geographical frame of reference ;

α_{kl} is the kl component of α in the same frame of reference ;

$n^{(i)}_1$ is the l component of the normal $\underline{n}^{(i)}$ to the ith fracture plane.

Equation (4) involves twelve unknowns so that a theoretical minimum of twelve tests, involving fractures with at least six different orientations (both in dip and strike), are required for the solution. In practice, because some errors are made on the determination of both the normal stress and the fracture planes orientation, a minimum of fifteen tests is probably necessary for the determination of the complete stress field.

When the ground surface is subhorizontal, the vertical direction is principal at the surface so that

$$S_{13} = S_{23} = S_{33} = 0 \qquad (5)$$

In such cases, when the depth range in which measurements are made involves superficial measurements, S represents the stress state at ground surface. In some instances, however, the linear variation approximation is not valid over the complete set of measurements so that, for the solution obtained from the deepest measurements, S has no physical meaning.

If the vertical direction is principal, in the depth range under consideration, then :

$$\alpha_{13} = \alpha_{23} = 0 \qquad (6)$$

so that equation (4) involves seven unknowns. This equation can be expressed in terms of eigen values of both S and α .

$$\alpha_3 x_3^i \cos^2 \theta_i - \frac{1}{2} \sin^2 \theta_i [S_1 + S_2 + (\alpha_1 + \alpha_2) x_3^i +$$

$$(S_1 - S_2) \cos 2(\phi_i - \lambda) + (\alpha_1 - \alpha_2) x_3^i .$$

$$\cos 2 [\phi_i - (\lambda + \eta)]] = \sigma_n^i \qquad (7)$$

where

θ_i is the angle between the normal $\underline{n}^{(i)}$ to the ith fracture plane and the vertical axis ;

ϕ_i is the orientation of the horizontal projection of $\underline{n}^{(i)}$ with respect to the north ;

S_i i=1,2 ; are the eigen values S

α_i i=1,2,3 are the eigen values of α

λ is the orientation of the S_1 direction with respect to the north (positive from north to east).

η is the orientation of the α_1 direction with respect to the S_1 direction.

The amount of unknowns can be reduced to 6 if the weight of overburden (α_3) can be evaluated by other means. Finally this six remaining unknowns can still be reduced to five if it is assumed that there is no rotation of principal stresses within the depth interval under consideration ($\eta = 0$). In such instances only six or seven tests can provide an estimation of the orientation of the horizontal principal stresses and of their magnitudes.

Solution of the inverse problem, as expressed either by equation (4) or (7) can be obtained by the generalized least squares procedure presented by Tarantola and Valette (1982) for solving non linear problems. This method assumes that measurements can be described by expected values, variances, and covariances with other measurements. It takes into account the uncertainty on both the normal stress measurements and the fracture plane orientation determinations. It yields an estimation of the standard deviation on the unknowns.

This method is not described here. The interested reader is referred either to the paper by Tarantola and Valette or to that of Cornet and Valette (1984) where its application to the H.T.P.F. method is presented.

3. Results from Auriat

Hydraulic tests were conducted in two boreholes with a wireline operated straddle packer from the University of Bochum (Rummel et al., 1982). The first well is 1000 m deep whilst the second one, about 20 m apart from the first one, is 500 m deep. The site is located

303

n°	z	φ	Δφ	θ	Δθ	P_rq	P_fi min	P_fim max	P_f	σ_n	Δσ_n	σ_v
1	115	333	4	35	3	24	22	36	29	26	4	30
9	153	27*	5	90	2.5		25	32	28	28	3	40
		190	3	67	5							
7	235	88	10	79	5	46	52	60	57	51	5	62
6	277	339*	3	90	2.5	51	53	67	59	56	4	73
		91	4	34	4.							
5	288	65	6	89	2.5	42	39	42	40	41	2	76
4	331	182	12	67	7	56	63	103	63	59	4	87
3	361	36	10	39	4	79	78	108	82	80	2	95
		199*	8	33	5							
2	379	122	3	80	3		64	104,5	98	98	5	100
17	413	3	5	90	2.5	78	68	82	70	74	5	109
18	491	199	5	90	2.5	84	75	95	75	80	5	129
19	525	14	7	90	2.5	119	84	122	106	112	12	138
		2*	6	81	3							
21	562					103	94	95	95	99	5	148
10	585	180*	5	90	2.5	125	133	157	133	129	5	154
		257	5	76	4							
11	808	183	8	81	3	186	185	199	187	187	2	212
12	922					172	161	167	167	169	5	242
13	928					202	202	208	205	203	2	244
14	968				3	177	160	166	164	170	10	255
15	973	21*	2	70	2.5	183	192	204	198	190	12	256
		158	10	83	7							
		56	3	76								

Table 1. Results from hydraulic tests at Auriat. z = depth of the tests (in meters) ; ϕ, θ = azimuth and dip of the normal to the fracture plane ; $\Delta\phi$, $\Delta\theta$ standard deviation on ϕ and θ ; P_{rq} quasistatic reopening pressure ; $P_{fi\ min}$, $P_{fi\ max}$, minimum and maximum values of the instantaneous shut in pressure ; P_f, mean value of ISIP for an injected volum of 1 to 2 $10^{-3}m^3$; σ_n = normal stress ; $\Delta\sigma_n$ = standard deviation on σ_n ; σ_v = vertical stress component . The * refers to the planes which have been selected for the inversion with the fourteen tests.

depth (m)	σ_H (MPa)	ε_H (MPa)	$\dfrac{\varepsilon_H}{\sigma_H}$	σ_h (MPa)	ε_h (MPa)	$\dfrac{\varepsilon_h}{\sigma_H}$	orientation of σ_H	ε
250	6.8	0.8	0.11	1.8	1.1	0.61	121	5
500	13.0	1.0	0.08	7.2	1.2	0.17	136	8
750	19.8	2.2	0.11	12.0	3.0	0.25	145	11
1000	26.8	3.1	0.12	16.7	4.7	0.28	150	14

Table 2. Results obtained for Auriat with the eight single fracture tests. σ_H is the maxium horizontal stress and ε_H the corresponding standard deviation ; σ_h is the minimum horizontal principal stress and ε_h the associated standard deviation. ε is the standard deviation on the orientation of σ_H.

depth (m)	σ_H (MPa)	ε_H (MPa)	$\dfrac{\varepsilon_H}{\sigma_H}$	σ_H (MPa)	ε_h (MPa)	$\dfrac{\varepsilon_h}{\sigma_h}$	orientation of σ_H	ε
250	6.0	0.6	0.1	3.2	1.1	0.34	130	13
500	14.7	0.8	0.05	6.8	1.65	0.24	137	10
750	21.4	1.7	0.08	10.4	2.7	0.26	139	11
1000	29.1	2.6	0.09	13.9	4.0	0.29	140	12

Table 3. Determination of the stress field from 14 tests. The variable are the same as in table 2.

depth (m)	σ_H (MPa)	ε_H (MPa)	$\dfrac{\varepsilon_H}{\sigma_H}$	σ_H (MPa)	ε_h (MPa)	$\dfrac{\varepsilon_h}{\sigma_h}$	orientation of σ_H	ε
250	6.5	0.8	0.12	2.2	0.6	0.27	120	5
500	13.6	1.0	0.07	6.3	1.1	0.17	139	6
750	21.3	2.2	0.10	9.7	2.5	0.26	145	8
1000	29.2	3.3	0.11	13.1	4.1	0.31	148	9.5

Table 4. Determination of the stress field from 12 tests ; the two most superficial tests have not been considered. The variables are as in table 3.

near the village of Auriat, about 30 km to the east of Limoges in central France (N 51°58', 00°42'·w). The granite in which these boreholes have been drilled is outcroping on site. Twenty one hydraulic tests were conducted between the depths 115 m and 972 m, eighteen of which yielded satisfactory ISIP and quasistatic reopening pressure measurements. Orientation of the fractures was determined with an impression packer. Only fourteen successful impressions were taken so that only fourteen complete tests wereavailable. Results are presented in Table 1. It can be observed that for six tests, two,and even three,fractures are observed so that only eight tests lend themselves to a straight forward interpretation.

The local area is fairly flat so that the hypothesis of the vertical direction being principal seems reasonable. Further, density measurements of samples taken at various depth yielded a value of α_3 equal to 0.0263 MPa/m. Thus inversion has been conducted with equation (7). It yields :

Solution 1 :
S_1 = -4.35 MPa ; S_2= 1.32 MPa ;
   λ = 15.4 MPa
α_1 = 0.0290 , α_2 = 0.0174

α_3 = 0.0265 ; η = - 30.6

where the values for α'_3 are in MPa/m and those for the angles in degrees. The resulting stress field, as computed at four different depth is indicated in Table 2.

The average difference between observed and computed normal stress for the planes considered in this inversion is 0.03 MPa whilst the largest difference is 0.08 MPa.

Table 2 indicates that, although σ_H and its orientation are fairly well determined, the value for σ_h is not constrained as well, especially near the surface.

The inversion has been undertaken then for the complete set of fourteen tests with various combinations of fracture planes (for those tests which present two or three fracture planes).

The best solution has been obtained with the set indicated by stars in table 1. The average difference between

observed and computed values for the normal stress is 0.25 MPa whilst the largest difference is 1 MPa. Results are as follow :

Solution 2.
S_1 =-0.05 MPa; S_2 =-2.05 MPa; λ = 69.7

α_1 = 0.0142 MPa/m; α_2= 0.0309MPa/m
     α_3= 0.0260MPa/m

η = - 17.8

The resulting stress field as computed at various depths is indicated in Table 3.

Because the differences between observed and computed normal stresses were larger for tests near the surface than for the others, a new inversion has been run in which the two most superficial tests have not been considered. Results are as follows :
Solution 3 :
,S_1 = -3.95MPa ; S_2 = 1.33MPa, λ= 0.6

α_1 = 0.0319 MPa/m ; α_2 = 0.0129 MPa/m
     α_3 = 0.0264 MPa/m

η = -25°

This yields the stress field indicated in table 4.

For this solution the average difference between observed and computed normal stress is equal to 0.06MPawhilst the largest difference is 0.21 MPa.

For all these solutions it can be observed that the value of σ_H is better contrained than that of σ_h. For the last solution, the standard deviation on the orientation of σ_H remains smaller than 10° whatever the depth. This solution clearly indicates a rotation of the principal horizontal stress directions with depth, a feature which was already indicated by solution 1.

Further the determination is best constrained between 300m and 400m where the amount of tests is the largest. The determination at 1000m is only an extrapolation : this is why the standard deviations are fairly large for these results. For σ_H it is of the order of 10 %, it is about 30 % for σ_h and around 12° for the determination of the σ_H direction. At this depth the maximum principal stress is σ_H for all solutions (σ_v around 26.0 MPa).

4. Results from Le Mayet de Montagne
4.1. Results from the H.T.P.F. method

The site of Le Mayet de Montagne is located in central France, 25 km to the South East of Vichy about 80 km to the North-East of Clermont Ferrand. This site has been developed for investigating a method for extracting heat from impervious rocks.

Three, 200m deep boreholes, 30m apart from each other, have been drilled in the local granite which is covered by a thin soil layer (between 0 and 10 m deep).

The site is on a horst, about 550 m above sea level. Ground level in the neighboring grabben (Limagne d'Allier where Vichy is located) is about 250m above sea level.

A set of seven hydraulic tests were run in these wells, at depth ranging between 56m and 186m, so that they were all located above the grabben.

In 1984, a 780m deep hole was drilled within 10m of one of the above mentioned wells. Nine hydraulic tests on preexisting fractures were run in this well at depth ranging between 345m and 621m.

The complete set of results is shown in table 5. No unique solution could be found for the complete set of data. However before drilling the 780m deep well, the data from the superficial tests had been successfully inverted (Cornet and valette, 1984).

Results were as follow
$S_1 = 6.9$ MPa $S_2 = -0.08$ MPa, $\lambda = 16^O$
$\alpha_1 = 0.0024$ MPa/m ; $\alpha_2 = 0.024$ MPa/m ;
     $\alpha_3 = 0.0265$ MPa/m ;
$\eta = 1$

The corresponding stress field, as computed at three different depth, is shown on table 6.

Inversion of the nine tests run in the 780m deep well could not be achieved because the iterative process used in the generalized least squares method did not converge. A new inversion was undertaken for the tests conducted between 380m and 621m on the assumption that there was no rotation of the principal stress directions with depth (only five unknowns for seven tests). Results are as follow :

$S_1 = -1.0$ MPa ; $S_2 = 8.8$ MPa ; $\lambda = -104^O$

$\alpha_1 = 0.0179$ MPa/m ; $\alpha_2 = 0.007$ MPa/m ,
     $\alpha_3 = 0.0262$ MPa/m
($\eta = 0$ imposed in the version process)

The corresponding stress field computed at various depth is shown on table 7.

Comparison between table 6 and 7 leads to a few conclusions.

The direction of σ_H has rotated by about 30° between 200m and 380m. The fact that the tests at 345m and 349m are not coherent with the deeper ones suggests that at least one discontinuity in the stress field occurs within the 350m and 380m depth interval. Since these tests are not coherent either with the superficial measurements, it is expected that another stress discontinuity occurs between 200m and 340m.

The value of σ_h as extrapolated to 300m from the results of the deeper tests, is smaller than that computed at 200m with the superficial tests. This supports the proposition that stress discontinuities exist between 200m and 380m and outline the lack of physical meaning for S when it is determined from deep tests.

Between 400m and 500m the vertical stress becomes larger than σ_H. This is coherent with the normal faulting tectonics of the area (horst and grabben structure). This is confirmed by the focal mechanisms of microsismic events observed between 550m and 800m during large fluid injections: For all the deep events a normal faulting mechanism is observed.

The direction of σ_H at depth is precisely that of the horst structure. It is not very different from that measured at Auriat which is located about 200 km to the west of Le Mayet de Montagne.

4.2 Comparison with results from the micro seismic activity

During a hydraulic stimulation test, conducted with a straddle packer set at 443m in the 780m deep well, 110 m^3 of water were injected at a flow rate of the order of 1 m^3/min. The microseismic activity induced by this injection was monitored with a fourteen stations network, so that focal mechanisms could be identified for the strongest events (Talebi and Cornet, 1985).

Five events (numbered 2 to 6) were observed on most of the stations leading to five well defined focal mechanism. These mechanisms are characteristic of shear events so that two nodal planes are associated with each event, one of which is the slip plane.

307

depth (m)	ϕ	ε_ϕ	θ	ε_θ	σ_n (MPa)	ε_{σ_n} (MPa)
56	52	5	85	3	4.0	0.2
90	65	5	83	3	4.4	0.3
113	−65	10	75	3	2.7	0.1
143	−61	5	84	3	3.5	0.1
163	65	5	84	3	5.3	0.2
174	−21	5	84	3	5.7	0.1
186	−35	5	85	3	5.5	0.1
345	7	2	77	2	6.4	0.4
349	5	2	68	2	6.7	0.2
385.5	315	7	82	3	10.2	0.2
390	283	4	80	3	7.2	0.3
396.5	225	2	84	3	7.7	0.3
400	315	3	86	1	10.2	0.3
460	58.5	5	49	1	9.3	0.3
528	190	5	73	3	11.9	0.3
621	58	5	73	3	11.0	0.4

Table 5. Results from hydraulic tests at Le Mayet de Montagne ; ϕ and θ are the azimuth and the normal to the fracture plane ; ε_ϕ and ε_θ are the standard deviations on ϕ and θ ; σ_n is the normal stress , ε_{σ_n} is the standard deviation on the normal stress.

For events 5 and 6 the same focal mechanism is observed as well as for events 2 and 3. Further, for these two last events, the second nodal plane is not well constrained so that only two reliable independent focal mechanisms have been obtained. They correspond to events at depth 439m and 456m (figure 1).

The uncertainty on dip and azimuth on the nodal planes for event 5 is estimated to be about 10° whilst that for event 4 is about 15°. For each nodal plane, a slip vector can be defined the orientation of which can be compared to that of the resolved shear stress as computed from the above stress determination for the corresponding nodal plane.

It is considered that the fracture plane, for each focal mechanism, is the plane with the slip vector the closest to the computed resolved shear stress. For event 5 the angle between the resolved shear stress and the slip vector is 19° whilst for event 4 it is 22°.

Given the uncertainty on both the stress determination and the nodal planes orientation these results are considered to be in reasonably good agreement.

It may be of interest to note that the principal stress directions, as determined from the hydraulic tests, do not coincide with those of the P and T axis of the focal mechanisms although their azimuths are within 20° from each other.

5. Discussion and conclusion

Although the H.T.P.F. method does not depend on as many hypotheses as the classical hydraulic fracturing technique does, it suffers some drawbacks :
- A relatively large amount of tests on fractures with various dip and strike is required ;
- The rock mass must not be too much fractured so that single fractures can be efficiently tested.
- An a priori guess must be made with respect to the stress variation within the volume where measurements are conducted.

As far as the first point is concerned the wireline operated straddle packer developed by Rummel and coworkers has revealed very efficient in slim boreholes (diametre smaller than 100mm). it is now possible to obtain four to five normal stress measurements per day, below 500m. The time consuming operation is now to take impressions of the fractures. Thus with available equipment, it is not uncommon to obtain between fifteen and twenty measurements at a given site. The main difficulty is to test fractures with enough different orientations . it is therefore necessary to conduct propper logging of the wells before undertaking the stress measurements. With this respect the electrical log developed by Mosnier (1984) provides a very efficient way for determining, in real time, both the dip and azimuth of preexisting fractures. This log is also taken to advantage to locate isolated single fractures so that interpretation of hydraulic tests remains simple.

The most constraining aspect of the method is certainly the necessity of obtaining a sufficiently large amount of results in zones where the stress field is continuous. Yet stress field discontinuities are identified only after inverting the data. Thus it is desirable to undertake the inversion process right on site in order to optimize the selection of preexisting fracture planes and make sure that enough tests are conducted in zones where the stress field is continuous.

Because the inversion process is based on a least squares procedure, it is not always easy to determine those depth where stress discontinuities occur. An example of such a case is given by results of Le Mayet de Montagne for tests conducted at 345 m and 349 m. For these tests an excellent agreement has been observed between ISIP measurements and quasistatic reopening pressure measurements so that the results for the normal stress measurement cannot be considered as being erroneous. Yet when these normal stress measurements are included with the results of the deep tests (between 380m and 620m) no solution can be found. When they are included with the set of superficial data (between 50 and 200m) a solution can be found which involves a strong rotation of the principal stress directions with depth. This rotation is not in agreement with results from deeper tests. Furthermore the solution

depth (m)	σ_H (MPa)	ε_H (MPa)	$\dfrac{\varepsilon_H}{\sigma_H}$	σ_H (MPa)	ε_h (MPa)	$\dfrac{\varepsilon_h}{\sigma_h}$	orientation of σ_H	ε
50	6.9	1.1	0.16	1.2	0.8	0.67	16°	5
100	7.0	1.2	0.17	2.3	0.6	0.26	17°	3
200	7.2	2.6	0.36	4.6	0.9	0.18	19°	8

Table 6. Results for Le Mayet de Montagne for the seven tests conducted between 50m and 186m. Variables are the same as in table 2.

depth (m)	σ_h (MPa)	ε_H (MPa)	$\dfrac{\varepsilon_H}{\sigma_H}$	σ_H (MPa)	ε_h (MPa)	$\dfrac{\varepsilon_h}{\sigma_h}$	orientation of σ_H	ε	σ_ν
300	10.9	2.7	0.25	4.3	0.9	0.21	166	4	7.9
400	11.6	2.2	0.19	6.1	0.7	0.11	166	4	10.5
500	12.3	2.1	0.17	7.9	0.8	0.10	166	4	13.1
600	13.0	2.3	0.18	9.7	1.1	0.11	166	4	15.7
700	13.7	2.8	0.20	11.5	1.5	0.13	166	4	18.3

Table 7. Results for Le Mayet de Montagne for the seven deepest tests. Variables are the same as in table 2, except for σ_v which is the vertical stress component.

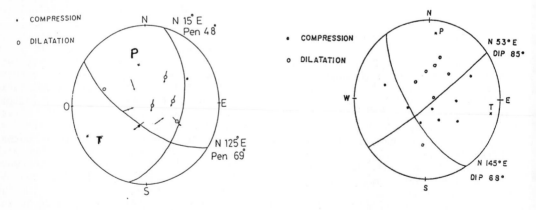

Figure 1. Focal mechanisms a) for event 4 (focal depth is 456m) and b) for event 5 (focal depth is 439m). P and T axes refer respectively to compression and tension axes. Arrows for the focal mechanism of event 4 correspond to the direction of first motion for S waves.

obtained in this case involves a much larger average difference between observed and computed normal stress than when these tests are not included. A similar observations was made for the two superficial tests at Auriat. This illustrates the necessity to test the robustness of the solution with respect to doubtfull data.

As a conclusion, it should be emphasized that the H.T.P.F. method is very complementary to the classical hydraulic fracturing stress determination method. When possible, both methods should be applied so that a more occurate stress determination is obtained. When only a few preexisting fractures are available for testing, they should always be taken to advantage to validate a stress determination obtained with the classical hydraulic fracturing technique.

References

Aamodt R.L. and M. Kuriyagawa ; 1982 ; Measurement of instantaneous shut-in pressure in crystalline rock ; Proceed workshop on hydraulic fracturing stress measurement ; U.S. Geol. Sur. open file rep. 82-1075, pp.394-403.

Bertrand L., M. Bouilleau and E.Durand; 1983 ; Méthode d¡évaluation du tenseur des contraintes dans un massif à partir de tests de fracturation hydraulique ; B.R.G.M. report nb. 83SGN 914 GEG ; Orléans, France.

Cornet F.H. ; 1980 ; Analysis of hydraulic fracture propagation. A field experimentation ; Proc. 2nd Int Sem. on results of EC Geothermal Energy Research ; pp.1032-1043 ; Reidel publ.

Cornet F.H. ; 1982 ; Analysis of injection tests for in-situ stress determination ; Proc. workshop on hydraulic fracturing stress measurements ; U.S. Geol. Surv. open file rep. 82-1075, pp.414-443.

Cornet F.H. and B. Valette ; 1984 ; In situ stress determination from hydraulic injection test data ; Jou. Geophys. Res., vol.89, nb.B 13, pp.11527-11537.

Fairhurst C. ; 1964 ; Measurement of in-situ rock stresses with particular reference to hydraulic fracturing ; Rock Mech. and Eng. Geol., nb.2, pp 129-147.

Gronseth J.M. and P.R. Kry ; 1982 ; Instantaneous shut-in pressure and its relationship to the minimum in situ stress ; Proc. worshop on hydraulic fracturing stress measurements ; U.S. Geol. Surv. open file pp.82-1075.

Haïmson B.C. ; 1978 ; The hydro-fracturing stress measuring method and recent results ; Int. J. Rock Mech. Min. Sc., vol. 15, pp.167-178.

Haimson B.C. ; 1980 Near surface and deep hydrofracturing stress measure-ments in Waterloo quartzite ; Int. J. Rock Mech. Min. Sc., vol. 17, pp.81-88.

Haimson B.C. and C. Fairhurst ; 1969 ; In situ stress determination at great depth by means of hydraulic fracturing;Proc. 11th U.S. Symp. Rock Mech., pp.559-584.

Hickman· S.H. and M.O. Zoback ; 1983 ; The interpretation of hydraulic fracturing pressure-time data for in-situ stress determination ; Hydraulic fracturing stress measure-ments ; pp.44-54 ; National Academy Press.

Hubbert M.K. and D.G. Gillis ; 1957 ; Mechanics of hydraulic fracturing ; J. Petroleum Tech., nb.9, pp 153-168.

McLennan J.D. and J.C. Roegiers ; 1983; Do instantaneous shut-in pressure accurately represent the minimum principal stress ? Hydraulic fracturing stress measurements, pp.79-85. National Academy Press.

Mosnier J. ; 1985 ;Detection electrique des fractures dans les forages. Bilan et prespectives de la recherche française en geothermie ; workshop organized by BRGM and CNRS ; Orléans.

Rummel F., J. Baumgartner, H.J. Alheid; 1983 ; Hydraulic fracturing stress measurements along the eastern boundary of the SW-German block. Hydraulic fracturing stress measure-ments, pp.3-17. National Academy Press.

Scheidegger A.E. ; 1962 ; Stress in earth¡s crust as determined from hydraulic fracturing data ; Geol. Bauwes.; nb 27, p.45.

Talebi S. and F.H. Cornet ; 1985 ; Seismo-acoustic activity generated by fluid injections in a granitic rock mass ; 4th conf. on Acoustic emission and microseismicity activity ; the Pennsylvania State Univ. Hardy Editor.

Tarantola A. and B. Valette ; 1982 ; Generalized non linear inverse problem solved using the least squares criterion ; Rev. Geophys. Space Phys., vol. 20, pp.219-232.

A new way to determine the state of stress and the elastic characteristics of rock massive

Ph. CHARLEZ
K. SALEH
D. DESPAX
Ph. JULIEN
Total CFP, St Remy les Chevreuse, France

ABSTRACT : The rockmeter is an inflatable packer fitted with radial displacement transducers. This apparatus is traditionnally used in geotechnics to measure the shear modulus of rocks. If the test, (known as pressiometric test) is run until yielding occurs, it can be shown that the displacement field during drilling (isotropic when there is no fracture) will become anisotropic. The multiplication of the number of equations relating the radial displacement of a borehole (depending this time on the azimuth) and the pressure, makes it possible, by applying any inverse method (probabitist, least squares) to determine, with a single test, the two horizontal geostatic stresses, the elastic constants, and the azimuth of the fracture.

RESUME : Le rockmètre est un packer gonflable équipé de capteurs de déplacement radiaux. Cet appareil est traditionnellement employé en géotechnique pour mesurer le module de cisaillement des roches. Si l'essai (appelé essai pressiométrique) est conduit jusqu'à la rupture, on peut montrer que le champ de déplacement au contour du forage (isotrope si ce dernier n'est pas fracturé) devient anisotrope. La multiplication du nombre d'équations reliant le déplacement radial du forage (dépendant cette fois de l'azimuth) à la pression, permet par une méthode inverse quelconque (probabiliste, moindres carrés) de déterminer en un seul essai les 2 contraintes géostatiques horizontales, les constantes élastiques et l'azimuth de la fracture.

ZUSAMMENFASSUNG : Der "rockmeter" ist ein aufblasbarer "packer", der mit einem "Radiann- Bewegungsempfaenger ausgeruestet ist. Dieses Geraet wird ueblicherweise in der Geotechnik benutz, um das Modul der Gesteinsabscherung zu messen. Wenn der Versuch (tressiometrischer Versuch genannt) bis zur Fraktur gefuehrt wird, kann gezeigt werden, dass das Bewegungsfeld im Bereich der Bohrung (isotrop, wenn es nicht gebrochen ist) anisotrop wird. Die Multiplikation der Anzahl der Gleichungen, die die radiale Bewegung der Bohrung (die diesmal von dem Azimut abhaengig ist) mit dem Druck verbindet, erlaubt mit einem beliebigen umgekehrter Method (Wahrscheinlichkeit, kleinstes Quadrat) mit einem einzigen Versuch die beiden geostatischen, horizontalen Spannungen, die elastischen Konstanten und den Azimut der Fraktur zu bestimmen.

INTRODUCTION

The in situ methods used today in geo-technics make it possible to determine either certain components of the geostatic state of stress [overcoring (BUYLE--BODIN F., 1980), restablishment method (TINCELIN E., 1951), hydraulic fracturing (HAIMSON and FAIRHURST, 1969 - ROEGIERS J.C., 1975)], or to measure the elastic properties of the rock [radial or sectional pressiometric test (JEAGER J.C. and COOK NWG, 1969 - CHARLEZ Ph., 1983)]. Taken separately, therefore, these tests only provide part of the parameters required. If several are combined in the same borehole soon makes the overall cost prohibitive, especially if the measurements are taken at great depths. The purpose of the rockmeter is to combine <u>two essential elements</u> on the same device : the uniform radial pressurization of the borehole above the yielding point using an inflatable packer, and the measurement of the deformation of the same borehole for different azimuths. As we will see, this method makes it possible, with a single test, to determine all the parameters required.

Theoretical approach

We will consider an infinite medium, which is elastic, homogenous and isotropic (elastic modulus E, and Poisson's ratio ν) subjected to a geostatic state of stress with a major principle component direction assumed vertical.

The borehole is vertical with a radius R. Using an inflatable packer, fitted with radial (or diametral) transducers, we will apply an increasing pressure, P. As long as rupture does not occur, the displacement field at the wall of the borehole is uniform. The displacement measurement allows one to assess the shear modulus, G, of the material using the relation (JEAGER J.C. and COOK NWG, 1969).

$$(1) \quad G = \frac{PR}{U_D}$$

U_D is the diametral displacement of the borehole. If the test is continued until rupture, the data will be much more complete.

1. INITIATION OF A PRESSIOMETRIC FRACTURE

For a specific value P_R, of the pressure, a symmetrical fracture will initiate at the edge of the borehole when the minimum tangential stress (the compressions are considered as positive) reaches a critical value P called "traction resistance of the rock". As the loading of the borehole is axysymmetric the problem can be considered in plane strain.

In this case , the tangential stress at the borehole results from the superposition of the horizontal geostatic state of stress, disturbed by the presence of the borehole over a distance of about four times the radius and the one due to the rockmeter pressure.

This superposition gives the relation (Fig. 1) :

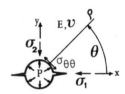

Fig. 1 – Position of the problem

$$(2) \quad \sigma_{\theta\theta}{}^\rho =$$

$$(\sigma_1 + \sigma_2) - 2 (\sigma_1 - \sigma_2) \cdot \cos 2\theta - P$$

where σ_1 and σ_2 are the major and minor principle horizontal components of the geostatic tensor.

θ is counted from σ_1. According to the proposed criterion, rupture will occur for a value P_R of the pressure such as :

$$(3) \quad MIN (\sigma_{\theta\theta}) = - R^T (R^T > 0)$$

i.e. for $\theta = 0°$ so that

$$(4) \quad P_R = 3 \sigma_2 - \sigma_1 + R^T$$

314

2. PROPAGATION OF A PRESSIOMETRIC FRACTURE

Once a fracture has been initiated, it will propagate in the direction of the major principle component σ_1. According to the Griffith criterion (GRIFFITH A.A., 1921), the fracture will continue to propagate as long as the stress intensity factor K_I at the tip of the fracture remains above the critical stress intensity factor K_{IC}.

The problem was calculated numerically by Clifton (CLIFTON R.J. and al., 1976) (Fig. 2), for a cylindrical ring provided with a radial fracture of a length L. For values of W over 7, it can be noted that at the start, the propagation of the fracture is unstable $(\partial K_I / \partial L) > 0$ but the effect of the pressure soon decreases and the propagation becomes stable $(\partial K_I / \partial L) < 0$.

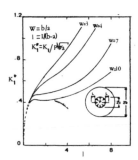

Fig. 2
Propagation conditions (rockmeter)

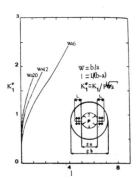

Fig. 3
Propagation conditions
(hydraulic facturing)

In other words, in order to continue fracture propagation, the pressure has to increase. The case of hydraulic fracturing (Fig. 3) is obviously very different, as fracturing pressure drops with the lenght of the fracture $(\partial K_I / \partial L) > 0$ whatever W.

3. REOPENING TEST

Once the fracture has propagated, the rockmeter is deflated, which may cause the fracture to close completely.

Repressurization will reopen the fracture, first of all, at the borehole. The pressure value corresponding is known as the "reopening pressure", P_0. Requiring absolutely no more resistance from the rock, this value will be :

$$(5) \quad P_0 = 3\,\sigma_2 - \sigma_1$$

From the relations (4) and (5), it is then possible to evaluate the rock's resistance :

$$(6) \quad R^T = P_R - P_0$$

This reopening test is only valid if the horizontal stress field is not excessively isotropic (if, $\sigma_1 > 3\,\sigma_2$, the fracture is already reopened at zero pressure). If the pressure is now increased further, but remains below the maximum pressure reached during the rupture test, the fracture whose propagation conditions are not required, will not propagate. The problem can then be considered as a linear elastic problem. Once the fracture has been reopened, in fact, the displacement field around the borehole can be expressed as follows :

$$(7) \quad U_R(\theta) = F(\sigma_1, \sigma_2, P, R, L, E, \nu, \theta)$$

Knowledge of relation (7), for a certain number of different azimuth will therefore allow one, by any inverse method, to determine, in a single test σ_1, σ_2, E, ν, plus, as will be discussed further fracture azimuth.

However the complexity of the boundaries (singularities at the fracture - borehole contacts), prevents this problem from being solved analytically.

We have therefore decided to use a numerical model, based on the "displacement discontinuities method" (CROUCH S.L., 1976). This consists in meshing the limits of the zone within which the stresses distribution is being studied, into a certain number of segments, on which the mechanical boundary conditions are constant. Thus a system of linear equations is established where the unknowns (the discontinuities within the displacement field between each segment) are calculated in such a way as to satisfy the boundary conditions. The symmetry of the problem posed, allows numerical treatment using a single borehole quarter modelled by 18 segments. The fracture itself is represented by segments, of similar lenghts, placed on the axis of the maximum principle stress σ_1. The calculations gave the following results :

- Deformation of the fractured borehole

    The deformation should not take into account the borehole deformation due to geostatic stresses. This deformation is anterior to the pressurization, and cannot be monitored during the test. The displacements recorded during the test are the result of the operation shown in Fig. 4, where the initial state is that of stressed but not pressurized borehole. A comparison is established on Fig. 5 between the case with (dashed line) and without fracture.

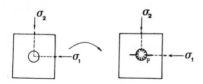

Fig. 4 - Initial and final state

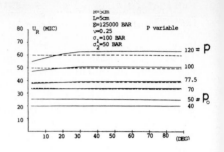

Fig. 5
Displacement field
for different values of P

Below the reopening pressure, the fracture has no effect on the displacement field but as soon as the pressure value exceeds P_0, it becomes anisotropic and its maximum value is observed, theoretically in a direction perpendicular t that of the fracture. However, fo the anisotropy of the displacemen field to be high, the pressure ha to considerably exceed P_0. Eve for high values (120 bar o Fig. 5) the anisotropy remains lo calised around the borehole. Th method does not, therefore give very accurate idea of the fractur azimuth during reopening, and i is only within the vicinity of th fracture that relations suc as (7) are independant. sufficient number of transducer are therefore necessary for th inverse method to be applicable.

- Influence of the parameters

A parametric study gave the fol lowing results :

- the radial displacement Ur (θ) is in inverse propor tion to the Young's modulus whatever azimuth θ , is consi dered

- the radial displacement depend only slightly on Poisson's ra tio

- the fracture must be segmente over a distance greater tha that over which the fractur opens. Otherwise it will be artificially blocked, and the direct problem could no longer be treated as elasticity.

- In principle σ_1 tends to open the fracture, and σ_2 tends to close it. In other words the effect of the fracture on the displacement field increases with the deviator.

4. BEHAVIOUR FOR HIGH PRESSURE VALUES

If the pressure continues to increase, the propagation will also continue, but becomes more and more difficult, due to the stress intensity factor, whose value drops fast as the length of the fracture grows.

Two phenomena can be seen to occur here : first of all, the stress intensity factor at the borehole (initially lower, in a direction other than that parallel to the major principle component of the stress tensor) may become preponderant in an other azimuth θ (Fig. 6). A second fracture is created which disturbs the displacement field. At this point, the curves become extremely difficult to interpret.

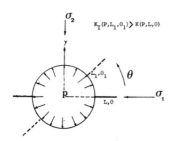

Fig. 6 - Multiple rupture

Secondly, when the overall fracturing process ceases, the geometry of the medium having been thoroughly disturbed, there is often a considerable stiffening in certain directions. This phenomenon is however, less general than the preceding one.

At the beginning, the problem had five unknowns (σ_1, σ_2, E, ν and the fracture azimuth). The direct problem

makes it possible to reduce considerably the number of unknowns :

- the linear part, prior to fracturation which gives G (**eq 1**).
- the fracture reopening pressure gives a relation between σ_1, and σ_2 (**eq 5**).
- the anisotropy of the displacement field makes it possible to evaluate the fracture azimuth.

Only two unknowns remain for the problem (σ_1 or σ_2, E or ν) which can be solved only at an inverse calculation.

The inverse problem

Given a physical system determined by a vector $\vec{m}$, a vector $\vec{d}$ and a non-linear operation g to that :

$$(8) \quad \vec{d} = g \ (\vec{m})$$

Finally we will consider the vector $\vec{d}_o$ known as the "data vector". In the specific problem of pressiometric fracturing $\vec{m}$ is the unknown vector (E or ν, σ_1, or σ_2) and $\vec{d}_o$ is the displacement vector measured at different points of the borehole. The operator g represents the displacement discontinuities method. The direct problem, thoroughly developed in the preceding paragraph consisted in calculating $\vec{d}$, knowing $\vec{m}$. The inverse problem has the objective of calculating $\vec{m}$ so that :

$$(9) \quad \vec{d}_o = g \ (\vec{m})$$

The problem must be treated in two parts : the probabilistic approach, and the optimization.

a) The probabilistic approach
   (JULIEN Ph., 1984)

It is not possible to proceed directly with an optimization by least squares, as there is only a very vague idea of the parameters, E and σ_1. The first step consists in determining a reasonable margin for these two parameters.

The approximate estimation $\vec{m}$ is choosen within a grid (Fig. 7) on which the two parameters vary considerably (obviously defined with a certain physical coherence).

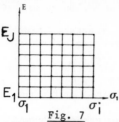

Fig. 7
Probabilist approach : meshing

At each node of the grid, where a pair of values E, σ_1, is given, g ($\vec{m}$) is calculated using the direct problem. A density of probability is then allocated to each node, ij, (in fact, this is more of a measurement density) so that (assuming a Gauss law).

$$f_{ij} = Exp - \left\{ \sum_{k=1}^{n} \frac{(d_i - d_{oi})^2}{\sigma_i^2} \right\}$$

Where σ_i represents the error on the displacement measurements , d_i and d_{oi}, the calculated $[\vec{d} = g(\vec{m})]$ and measured displacement respectively. This density of measurement (which can be normalized) is applied by plotting marginal density curves for each of the two parameters.

The final estimation will be calculated by central estimators.

Generally, the probabilistic approach is carried out in several steps : first of all a "zone" is identified using a large grid, then this zone is meshed in a much finer grid. The exact solution can thus be found within approximately 15 %. The result (recorded $\vec{m}_o$) is known as "preliminary estimation" and will be used as a starting value in the optimization phase. It should be noted that the calculation time required for the probabilist approach may be very long.

b) Optimization (TARANTOLA A. and VALETTE B., 1982)

Optimization consists in tooking for the final estimation $\vec{m}$ * of $\vec{m}$, giving a vector $\vec{d}$ very close to d_o so that :

$$|| \vec{d} - \vec{d}_o || = || g(\vec{m}) - \vec{d}_o$$
is a minimum.

However, through the probabilist approach, we know that $\vec{m}_o$, which represents the initial model injected into the inversion i fairly close to the final result Also, it is necessary for the fi nal estimation $\vec{m}$ * to be suc that :

$$|| \vec{m}^* - \vec{m}_o || \text{ is a minimum.}$$

The solution to the inverse problem is the model m * which minimizes the expression :

$$S = 1/2 ||g(\vec{m}) - \vec{d}_o||^2 + ||\vec{m} - \vec{m}_o||$$

This equation is solved by iteration.

c) Example

We have calculated by a direct computation the displacement field with the following parameters :
$\sigma_1 = 100$ bar, $\sigma_2 = 50$ bar, $P = 150$ bar, $E = 125.000$ bar, $\nu = 0.30$
The results were :

θ (degree)	U_R (microns)
9	77.5
18	79.7
27	81.8
36	83.3
45	84.3
54	85
63	85.4
72	85.7
81	85.9
90	85.9

The probabilist computation was realised in two steps with only one parameter σ_2 (E is supposed to be known). In the first step the values proposed were 25 bar to 85 bar with an interval of 10 bars. The marginal

density is maximum between 45 and 55 bar. The average state of stress gives the values $\sigma_1 = 102.3$ bar and $\sigma_2 = 51.5$ bar, values already very closer to the exact solution. The marginal density curve for the second calculation (Fig. 8) for which the meshing varies from 44 to 56 bar with steps each two bar shows that the average solution is :
$\sigma_1 = 100.03$ bar
and
$\sigma_2 = 50.05$ bar.

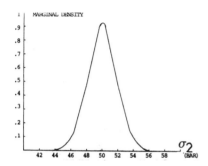

Fig. 8 - <u>Example of marginal density</u>

In a last calculation with least squares, the initial estimator m_o was chosen as :
E = 120.000 bar
and
$\sigma_2 = 45$ bar

The final solution is very closer to the exact one :
E = 125.000 bar
and
$\sigma_2 = 50$ bar

We can see that when the data $\vec{d}_o$ are very precise (here it is computed and not measured), the solution is easily obtained. The sensibility of the method when experimental or theoretical errors exist (for instance the material is not perfectly elastic) has to be tested in the future.

Experimental results

Two series of tests were run on limestone and cement blocks, in order to verify the theoretical approach experimentally. The cell consists of a packer 9.5 cm in diameter fitted with three 120° diametral

displacement gauges. It is designed to work in 10 cm diameter boreholes. The maximum operating pressure is 250 bar, and the useful length is 90 cm.

a) <u>Tests on non-stressed blocks</u>

Three tests were first run on non-stressed limestone and cement blocks, in order to check the anisotropy of the displacement field when fracture initiates.

For test 1 (limestone) there are four clearly distinct phases : firstly the inflation of the packer, secondly the linear elastic zone (very low anisotropy of the material, with a shear modulus between 51.000 and 60.000 bar) ; at 220 bar, the rupture appears perpendicular to the probe n° 3. A stage can be seen for the three probes, but that of probe n° 3 is twice that of the two others. An extra increase in pressure shows that the material becomes linear elastic again, with a considerable increasing of stiffness in direction 3, where the material has been strongly compacted.

Two more tests were run on metric blocks of concrete with a geometric anisotropy.

The initial rupture can be seen perfectly, especially in test 3 (Fig. 9), where it is single, and perpendicular to probe 1. For test 2 (Fig 10), the rupture is multiple, and hence, the post-rupture stiffening is not observed in the direction of the probe, but in that of probe 3, perpendicular to the second fracture.

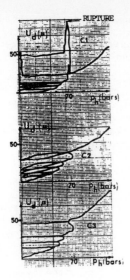

Fig. 9 - Unstressed concret block
(third test)

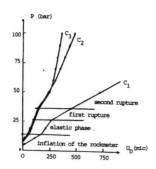

Fig. 10
Unstressed concrete block (second test)

b) Tests on blocks stressed

A second serie of pressiometric tests was run using the same cell on blocks of cement, 30 cm x 30 cm x 30 cm, with a 10 cm diameter hole in the centre. These blocks were loaded biaxially by a "100 ton" hydraulic press.

The inflation of the probe was realised using a pressure servo-controlled system. The ratio between the borehole diameter and the length of the cube is only 3, so formula (1) and (5) were modified (see attachement).

The results of the three tests (test 2 is represented on Fig. 11) give fairly similar results to the preceding ones, i.e. :

- the fracture appears perpendicular to σ_2 (except in the third test, where it appeared inclined and then turned perpendicular to σ_2).

- the displacement field around the borehole becomes anisotropic as soon as the fracture appears, and reaches a maximum value perpendicular to the latter.

- the reopening pressure is lower than the rupture pressure, but the change in slope is not always easy to determine, except perpendiculary to the fracture.

- the cement is not completely elastic, which obviously leaves some doubt regarding the starting hypotheses.

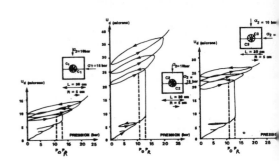

Fig. 11
Stressed cement block (test 2)

However, we have attempted to inverse the data of the three diametral probes (which, in our opinion is not enough) for tests 2 and 3. The results are given in the table below (this is an inversion for a single parameter, E having been tested on cylindrical samples.

Test N°	ν	G (bar)	P_0 (bar)	$\sigma_1$calc	$\sigma_2$calc	σ_1	σ_2
2	0.25	105800	11	18.5	12.1	15	10
3	0.25	79700	17	23.6	16.35	20	15

Table 1 : Determination of the geostatic stresses by inversion of pressiometric data.

The overall error is 20 %, which is high, considering the method used. This is mainly due to the experimental conditions, i.e. :

- insufficient number of probes

- the selected material

- the inadequate dimensions of the cubes compared with these of the pressiometer and the friction effect of the press's plates.

- the weight of the pressiometer on the lower part of the borehole.

CONCLUSIONS

The main advantage of this method is to allow, with a single test the determination of several parameters, whereas with traditional hydraulic fracturing only one can be determined, i.e. σ_2.

The stability of the propagation, due to the fact that the fracture is not loaded, makes it possible to solve the problem through elasticity, and apply very sophisticated inversion methods. However, the anisotropy is only marked in the vicinity of the fracture. Therefore many probes are necessary for the inversion to converge. Moreover, if for any reason, the elastic zone is exceeded, the fracturing may become multiple, which makes interpretation almost impossible.

Although the method is attractive, more experimental results are needed to prove it definitively.

Acknowledgments : We thank Professor Cornet for his help and advice regarding the solution of the direct problem.

APPENDIX : Laboratory simulation of a rocky block with a central cylindrical hole, is obviously carried out on a finite medium. An approximate analytical calculation in plane elasticity (SALEH K., 1985) shows that corrections are necessary. If L is the length of half one edge of the cube, and R is the borehole radius, the stress $\sigma_{\theta\theta}$ resulting from the geostatic stresses is :

$$\sigma_{\theta\theta} = \frac{M(\sigma_1 + \sigma_2)}{2(M - R^2)}\left(1 + \frac{R^2}{\rho^2}\right) - \frac{M(\sigma_1 - \sigma_2)}{2(M - R^2)^3}$$
$$\left[(M^2 + MR^2 + 4R^4) - 12R^2\rho^2 + \frac{3M(M + R^2)R^4}{\rho^4}\right]\cos 2\theta$$

with $M = 0.37 L^2 (3.64 - \cos 4\theta)$.

and that resulting from the uniform pressure P is :

$$\sigma_{\theta\theta} = -\frac{PR^2}{(M - R^2)}\left[1 + \frac{M}{\rho^2}\right]$$

ρ and θ being the polar co-ordinates of any point on the cube.

References

BUYLE-BODIN F. (1980)
"Mesure des contraintes in situ dans les massifs rocheux".
Thèse de docteur ingénieur - Institut de physique du Globe Paris
Published by BRGM - Rapport 81SGN 254-GEG.

TINCELIN E. (1951)
"Les études de pression de terrain entreprises dans les mines de fer de Lorraine".
Conférence sur les pressions de terrains 24-28 avril 1951.

HAIMSON et FAIRHURST (1969)
"In situ stress determination at great depth by means of hydraulic fracturing".
11th Symposium on rock mechanics June Berkeley pp. 559-584.

ROEGIERS J.C. (1975)
"The development and evaluation of a field method for in situ stress determination using hydraulic fracturing".
Final report Department of Army Contract N° DACW 45-74 - C - 0066.

JEAGER J.C. et COOK NWG (1969)
"Fundamentals of Rock mechanics" Methuen and Co Ltd.

CHARLEZ Ph. (1983)
"Determination de l'état de contrainte dans les massifs rocheux élastiques et peu perméables".
Thèse de docteur ingénieur IPG Paris.

GRIFFITH A.A. (1921)
"The phenomenon of rupture and flow in solids".
Phil. Trans. Roy. Soc. London A 221.

CLIFTON R.J. and al. (1976)
"Determination of critical stress intensity factor for internally pressurized thick walled vessel".
Exp. Mech. 16 pp. 223-238.

CROUCH S.L. (1976)
"Solutions of plane elasticity problems by the displacement discontinuity method".
Int. J. for Numerical methods.
Vol. 10, pp. 301-343.
JULIEN Ph. (1984)
Rapport d'étude sur l'inversion de données pressiométriques.
IPG Paris - Not published.

TARANTOLA A. et VALETTE B (1982)
"Generalised nonlinear inverse problems solve using the least squares criterion".
Rev. Geogh., Space, physi. Vol. 20 n° 2, p. 219-232.

SALEH K. (1985)
"Determination de l'état de contrainte et des propriétés élastiques d'un massif rocheux par inversion des données récoltées lors d'un essai de fracturation pressiométrique".
Thèse de docteur ingénieur ECP.

Sleeve fracturing – A borehole technique for in-situ determination of rock deformability and rock stresses

C. LJUNGGREN
O. STEPHANSSON
Division of Rock Mechanics, Luleå University of Technology, Luleå, Sweden

ABSTRACT: This paper presents a new, deep-hole dilatometer technique, intended for determination of rock deformability and in-situ stresses. The borehole instrument consists of four parts; a sleeve, a pressure intensifier, a linear displacement transducer and a pressure transducer. As the membrane is inflated against the rock wall, a pressure-volume curve is recorded. From the linear part of this curve the deformability of the rock is calculated. Further pressurization will lead to the initiation of axial fractures in the borehole wall. This is recorded as an abrupt change in slope of the pressure-volume curve. To date, the work has comprised development of the instrument and laboratory testing in blocks of granite and diabase. Test results are in good agreement with results obtained by uniaxial compression tests.

RÉSUMÉ: Cette communication présente une nouvelle technique de pressiométrie à grande profondeur, conçue pour déterminer la déformabilité des roches et leur état de contraintes in-situ. L'instrument pour trous de forage se compose de quatre éléments: une membrane gonflable en caoutchouc, un amplificateur de pression, un lecteur de pression, et un lecteur de déplacements linéaires. Au fur et à mesure que l'on gonfle la membrane contre la roche encaissante, une courbe pression-volume est enregistrée. La partie linéaire de cette courbe permet de calculer la déformabilité de la roche. Une augmentation de la pression provoque l'initiation de fractures axiales dans la roche, ce qui se traduit sur la courbe par une brusque rupture de pente. Jusqu'à présent, les travaux ont porté sur la mise au point de l'équipement et sur des tests de laboratoire sur blocs de granite et de diabase. Les resultats obtenus sont cohérents avec ceux obtenus par tests de compression uniaxiale.

ZUSAMMENFASSUNG: Dieses Referat stellt eine neue Tiefloch-Dehnungsmesstechnik für die Bestimmung von Gesteinsdeformierbarkeit und Spannungen vor Ort ver. Das Bohrlochinstrument besteht aus vier Teilen, der Hülse, dem Druckverstärker und den Messwertumformern für Linearverdrängung und Druck. Beim Aufblasen der Membrane an der Gesteinswand wird eine Druck-Volumenskurve festgehalten. Aus dem linearen Teil dieser Kurve wird die Deformierbarkeit des Gesteins berechnet. Weitere Beaufschlagung der Membrane mit Druck führt zu anfänglichen Axialfrakturen in der Bohrlochwand. Diese sind als plötzliche Änderung der Neigung der Druck-Volumenskurve merkbar. Bis heute hat die Arbeit die Entwicklung der Instrumente und Laborversuche mit Granit und Diabas umfasst. Die Versuchsergebnisse stehen in guter Übereinstimmung mit den Ergebnissen einachsiger Verdichtungstests.

1 INTRODUCTION

The concept of using an inflatable membrane in boreholes for measuring deformation properties was introduced by Kögler in 1933. The development continued with Lois Ménard, who invented the pressuremeter. In 1957 the first pressuremeter for soil engineering was taken into use. Panek et al. (1964) developed a borehole cell called the Cylindrical Pressure Cell (CPC) for determining the modulus of rigidity of rock. The CPC system had, however, some problems. One of these was that the copper membrane that was pressurized inside the borehole underwent permanent deformation during each test. Hustrulid and Hustrulid (1975) improved the system, the calibration and data reduction procedure, and called the new system the Colorado School of Mines (CSM) cell. Ozdemir and Wang (1981) further improved the CSM cell. Our sleeve is a further development of the CSM cell.

Sleeve fracturing is, in many aspects, very similar to hydraulic fracturing. For both methods the classical equation for stress determinations is used. From Hubbert and Willis (1957):

$$P_b = 3\sigma_2 - \sigma_1 + T - P_p \qquad (1)$$

where P_b is the breakdown pressure, σ_1 and σ_2 the maximum and minimum principal stresses in a plane perpendicular to the borehole axis, T is the tensile strength of the rock, and P_p is the pore pressure in the rock mass. However, sleeve fracturing is a technique whereby axial fractures are induced at any depth without introducing fluid into the rock during the fracturing process. That is, no pore pressure is built up in the vicinity of the borehole during pressurization.

The sleeve fracturing system offers the possibility of determining two rock parameters in-situ in one and the same test. The system is first pressurized to a level where no axial fractures are initiated. From the linear part of the pressure-volume curve the modulus of rigidity of the rock mass is determined. If the Poisson's ratio of the rock is known or can be estimated, the elastic modulus (E) can be calculated. By increasing the pressure further, two axial fractures are induced and a sleeve breakdown pressure (P_b) is recorded. The direction of the fractures indicates the direction of maximum stress in a plane perpendicular to the axis of the borehole. By conducting a second pressurization and recording the pressure for reopening the fracture and knowing the tensile strength (T) of the rock mass the magnitude of principal stresses can be determined by using equation (1).

In this paper we present the design of the sleeve fracturing system and the methods for determination of rock mass modulus and rock stresses. Results from testing blocks of granite and diabase are presented and future development are described.

2   DESIGN OF THE SLEEVE FRACTURING SYSTEM

The pressuremeter is widely used for investigating static and cyclic strength and deformation properties of soils. The use of the pressuremeter in rock is, however, very limited. There are two main reasons for this; (i) difficulties with constructing rubber membranes which can withstand such high pressures, and (ii) low system stiffness. In some cases, in order to create sleeve fractures the membrane must withstand pressures as high as 100 MPa. The membrane should have a low stiffness but yet a stiffness high enough to avoid shear failure at the endcups. So far the limitations with the CSM-cell has been the low stiffness of the system. When testing in hard rock (E > 60 GPa) the stiffness of the system becomes so dominant that it is impossible to observe any difference in stiffness for various rock types. This problem has also limited the maximum tube/pipe length with the CSM-cell. This is because the longer the pipe between the pump and the cell, the lower the stiffness of the system. We have solved this problem by constructing a pressure intensifier which is placed next to the sleeve, Figure 1. The pressure intensification is 4.22:1. The stiffness of the CSM-cell system and the LUT sleeve fracturing system is shown in Table 1.

Table 1.   System stiffness.

System	$\Delta V_{sys}/\Delta V_{cyl}$
LUT	4.5
CSM	11.1*

*Calculated from Stripa Data (Hustrulid, personel communication).

The sleeve fracturing system, developed at the Luleå University of Technology, consists of the following components (Figure 1).

1. High pressure generator with a maximum pressure capacity of 35 MPa and a fluid capacity of 60 cm³.

2. Pneumatic water pump with a maximum pressure capacity of 49 MPa at P_{air} = 0.7 MPa.

3. A control panel.

4. Pressure gauge rated at 0-45 MPa.

5. Linear displacement transducer, with a measuring length of 0-50 mm.

6. Pressure intensifier with an intensification of 4.22:1.

7. Borehole cell.

8. Pressure gauge rated at 0-75 MPa.

9. X-Y-Y recorder.

10. 4 channel, time based strip-chart recorder.

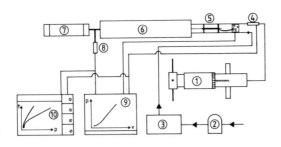

Figure 1. System for sleeve fracturing in the laboratory.

The borehole cell that has been used in our studies has a diameter that fits into boreholes with a diameter of 38 mm. It will later be enlarged for 56 mm boreholes. The cell consists of three parts:

(i) A membrane made of a single component polyester based polyurethane elastomer, Monothane Shore A 95.

(ii) A central steel mandrel with an end cup.

(iii) A removable steel end cup.

The membrane has a self-sealing construction so that when the pressurizing fluid (water) enters the cavity between the mandrel and the inner membrane wall, the pressure seals the flange of the membrane against the mandrel and the ends against the steel end cups. The membrane is moulded directly on the mandrel to pre-

vent leakage. Before the membrane is cast on the mandrel a release agent is applied to the surfaces where the fluid will enter. After the membrane is moulded it is connected to the pressure intensifier in water to prevent air from entering the system.

The main difference between, and advantage, with this system compared to the CSM-cell is the pressure intensifier. As seen from Table 1 the stiffness of the LUT system is almost 2.5 times higher than the CSM cell system.

The pressure intensifier consists of two plungers with different areas, resulting in a 4.22:1 pressure intensification. An LVDT-gauge records the position of the plungers, and thereby the fluid volume injected into the membrane.

The geometry of the membrane is shown in Figure 2. The sleeve is cylindrical with an effective length of approximately 4 times the diameter. If the load length is too short, the volume of rock subjected to pressure might be too small to accurately reflect the properties of the rock mass. It has been shown by Misterek (1970) that the magnitude of the surface deflection increases rapidly as the loaded length is increased to a value about equal to the diameter of the hole but that additional increases in pressurization length produce only small increases in radial displacement.

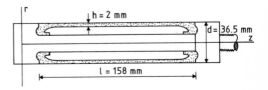

Figure 2. Geometry of the membrane for sleeve fracturing.

3   DETERMINATION OF ROCK MASS MODULUS AND ROCK STRESSES BY MEANS OF SLEEVE FRACTURING

The sleeve fracturing system offers the possibility of determining two parameters in-situ in one and the same test; the modulus of elasticity (E) and rock

325

stresses in a plane perpendicular to the borehole axis. It should, however, be pointed out that to this day no attempts have been made to calculate in-situ rock stresses with the LUT sleeve fracturing system. The system is, at present, under development. At this point we have only determined rock mass modulus in the laboratory.

3.1 Determination of rock mass modulus

The complete derivations of equations required for the calculation of the deformation modulus of rock by means of a borehole dilatometer is presented by Hustrulid and Hustrulid (1975). The basic equations for rock modulus determination are presented here. The only difference is that instead of calculations of pressure/turn we now express it as pressure/volt, where voltage is a direct measure of the volume.

Prior to testing, the stiffness (pressure-volume relationship) of the LUT sleeve fracturing system (M_s) must be determined. This is done by inserting the cell in a calibration cylinder with known properties and dimensions and then pressurizing it. During the pressurization a pressure-volume curve is recorded. The slope of the calibration curve (M_m) specifies the stiffness of the system and the calibration cylinder together. Such a calibration curve is shown in Figure 3.

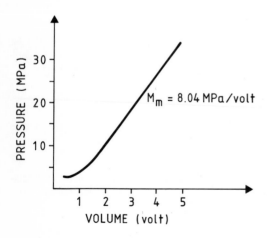

Figure 3. Typical calibration curve when pressurizing the LUT sleeve in an aluminium cylinder.

It is observed that the curve is not perfectly linear over the entire testing range having a slope that increases with pressure. This indicates a small amount of air in the system. Therefore, it is necessary to select a pressure range over which the slope will be calculated. This range should be the same for both the calibration cylinder and borehole tests. In this study the analysis was made for the range 15–30 MPa. The first two pressurizations should be neglected due to settling of the membrane against the borehole wall.

The stiffness of the calibration cylinder (M_C) alone can be calculated using equation (2).

$$M_C = \frac{\gamma \cdot G_C}{\pi \cdot L \cdot r_{ic}^2 \left[\dfrac{1 + \beta_C - 2\nu_C \beta_C}{1 - \beta_C} \right]}$$

$$[\text{MPa/volt}] \qquad (2)$$

where:

γ = volume of fluid injected to the membrane/volt (502.65 mm^3/volt).

L = effective length of membrane (158 mm).

r_{ic} = radius of the hole in the calibration cylinder (mm).

r_{oc} = outer radius of the calibration cylinder (mm).

$\beta_C = \left(\dfrac{r_{ic}}{r_{oc}}\right)^2$

G_C = modulus of rigidity of the calibration cylinder (MPa).

ν_C = Poisson's ratio for the calibration cylinder.

M_C = stiffness of the calibration cylinder (MPa/volt).

When M_m and M_C are known the system stiffness (M_s) can be calculated using equation (3).

$$M_s = \frac{M_C \cdot M_m}{M_C - M_m} \qquad [\text{MPa/volt}] \qquad (3)$$

where:

M_s = stiffness of the LUT-sleeve system (MPa/volt).

M_m = measured stiffness of the LUT-system and calibration cylinder (MPa/volt).

After calibration is finished the cell is inserted into a borehole in a rock mass with unknown elastic properties. The cell is pressurized and a pressure-volume curve is recorded. The slope (M_T) of the linear portion of the curve is then determined using the same pressure range (15-30 MPa) as for the calibration curve. The stiffness of the rock mass (M_R) is then computed as,

$$M_R = \frac{M_s \cdot M_T}{M_s - M_T} \quad [MPa/volt] \quad (4)$$

If a cylinder of rock is tested, then the modulus of rigidity (G_R) is calculated using equation (5).

$$G_R = \frac{M_R \cdot \pi \cdot L \cdot r_{ir}^2}{\gamma} \left[\frac{1 + \beta_r - 2\nu_r\beta_r}{1 - \beta_r} \right]$$

$$[GPa] \quad (5)$$

where:

G_R = modulus of rigidity of the rock.

r_{ir} = inner radius of the rock cylinder.

r_{or} = outer radius of the rock cylinder.

$\beta_r = \left(\frac{r_{ir}}{r_{or}} \right)^2$

ν_r = Poisson's ratio of the rock.

If the cell is instead inserted in a borehole in an infinite rock mass, the modulus of rigidity (G_R) is computed as

$$G_R = \frac{M_R \cdot \pi \cdot L \cdot r_i^2}{\gamma} \quad [GPa] \quad (6)$$

For this case the Poisson's ratio of the rock mass need not be known to calculate the modulus of rigidity.

The modulus of elasticity (E_R) is calculated for a known Poisson's ratio as

$$E_R = G_R (1 + \nu_r) \cdot 2 \quad [GPa] \quad (7)$$

As is evident from the above equations Poisson's ratio is required for calculating the modulus of elasticity (E_R).

It has been shown by Misterek (1970) that the maximum error in the calculated modulus will be approximately 10 % if the value of Poisson's ratio is known to an accuracy of ± 0.1. Normally, Poisson's ratio will be known to an accuracy better than ± 0.1.

3.2 Determination of rock stresses

The principle for rock mass stress determinations by means of sleeve fracturing and hydraulic fracturing is identical. However, the hydraulic fracturing technique is more sensitive to pre-existing fractures and flaws in the pressurized interval resulting in a lower breakdown pressure.

Prior to sleeve fracturing the circumferential stress at a given direction, θ, of the borehole wall is

$$\sigma_{\theta\theta}(\theta) = -P_o + \sigma_1 + \sigma_2 - 2(\sigma_1 - \sigma_2) \cos2\theta$$

$$(8)$$

As the sleeve pressure increases the tangential stress at the borehole wall will decrease until it becomes equal to the tensile strength (T) of the rock. At breakdown pressure (P_b) an axial fracture will form at an angle $\theta = 0°$ and equation (8) results in

$$P_b = 3\sigma_2 - \sigma_1 + T \quad (9)$$

The equation is valid under the assumption that the breakdown pressure (P_b) is equal to the contact stress between the borehole wall and the sleeve. This is, however, not true since there is a reduction in contact stress caused by the membrane. The reduction in contact stress needs to be calculated for the particular material properties of the sleeve.

The least principal stress (σ_2) is determined as the pressure when the fracture reopens in the second pressurization. That is, from the inflection point of the pressure-volume curve. This is based on the assumption that the rate of volume change for the pressurized sleeve is different prior to, and after, opening of the fracture.

Knowing the breakdown pressure (P_b), the least principal stress (σ_2) and the tensile strength (T) of the rock, determined

327

by sleeve fracturing on core samples,
one can calculate the maximum principal
stress (σ_1) by using equation (9).
Ljunggren (1984) has shown the importance
of using sleeve fracturing of core samples in determining the tensile strength
(T).

Fracture orientation is determined by
impression on the sleeve and a compass.
As the sleeve is pressurized in the borehole, a print of the fractures is marked
on the surface. By knowing the orientation of the sleeve in the borehole the
maximum principal stress is determined
as the direction of the fractures marked
on the sleeve.

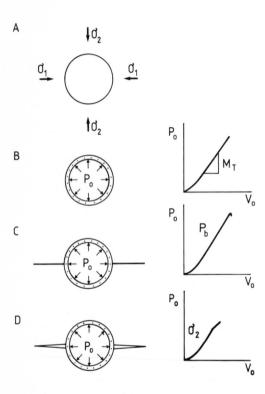

A

B

C

D

Figure 4. Principles for sleeve fracturing of boreholes. A, virgin state of
stress. B, pressurization and determination of stiffness M_T for the system and
rock mass. C, sleeve fracturing and
determination of breakdown pressure (P_b).
D, repressurization and determination of
least principal stress in a plane perpendicular to the borehole axis.

4   LABORATORY RESULTS

Prior to testing in blocks the sleeve was
calibrated in an aluminium cylinder with
known properties and dimensions. Six cycles were run in the calibration cylinder
after which the sleeve was installed in
the boreholes. Once more six cycles were
run. Upon completion of testing in the
borehole, the sleeve was calibrated once
again to verify the original calibration.
In every test the two first cycles were
neglected due to low stiffness. An average value of the four remaining cycles
were calculated and used as the stiffness
value. The pressure range for every calculation was 15-30 MPa, and linear regression was used for calculating the
slope of the curves.

4.1 Modulus determinations

Blocks of granite and diabase with the
dimensions 300 • 300 • 300 mm were tested
in the laboratory. A 38 mm hole was
drilled in the central portion straight
through the block. The blocks were homogeneous and free of visible fractures.

The modulus of elasticity for an aluminium cylinder was also determined. A steel
cylinder was then used as calibration
cylinder.

As seen from Table 2 the calculations
for the two different assumptions are in
good agreement with the results obtained
by uniaxial compression tests (Mathis
et al. (1986).

Table 2. Modulus of elasticity for
granite, diabase and aluminium.

Test method	Modulus of Elasticity (GPa)		
	granite	diabase	aluminium
Borehole sleeve	43.7[1] 44.4[2]	80.1[1] 92.5[2]	75.1[1] 69.5[2]
Uniaxial compression	58.3	86.2	

[1] Calculated for contact stress equal to fluid pressure in the membrane.

[2] Calculated for membrane thickness of 2 mm.

4.2 Sleeve fracturing

So far no attempts have been made to fracture rock with the sleeve in a bore-hole in a rock mass. One sleeve fracturing attempt has been conducted in a granite block without loading. The result of the fracturing is shown in Figure 5.

Figure 5. Sleeve fracturing of a cubic block of granite.

The pressure-volume curve began to deviate from its linear shape at approximately 40 MPa. The final breakdown pressure, when the block split into two pieces, was 50 MPa.

5   FUTURE DEVELOPMENT

A 500 m long multi-hose is used for hydraulic fracturing at the Division of Rock Mechanics in Luleå. The sleeve is intended to be a new tool easily attached to the multi-hose. The new system will allow for in-situ determination of rock deformability and rock stresses to a depth of 500 m. A combination of sleeve fracturing and conventional hydraulic fracturing for stress determination will also be investigated. A field computer is under construction for handling the calculations and regression analyses necessary for sleeve testing in the field.

6   CONCLUSIONS

At this stage of development of the LUT-sleeve fracturing technique the following conclusions can be drawn:

1. The pressure intensifier works well resulting in a system stiffness 2.5 times higher than that of the CSM-cell.

2. The reproducability of test results is good.

3. More effort is required to develop a reliable method for construction of membranes capable of 100 MPa pressure.

4. Deformability measurements on granite and diabase blocks are in good agreement with results obtained by other methods.

7   ACKNOWLEDGEMENTS

The authors are most grateful to Mr B. Leijon for valuable support and stimulating discussions. Mr B. Selberg and Mr A. Torikka are greatly appreciated for their valuable suggestions during the construction work. This work was supported by the National Swedish Board for Technical Development under contract 83-3356 and the Swedish Geological Company.

8   REFERENCES

Baquelin, F., Jezequel, J.F. and Shields, D.H. 1978. The pressuremeter and foundation engineering. Trans. Tech. Publ., Clausthal. 617 p.

Hubbert, M.K. and Willis, D.G. 1957. Mechanics of hydraulic fracturing. Trans. A.I.M.E., 210:153-168.

Hustrulid, W. and Hustrulid, A. 1975. The CSM cell - a borehole device for determining the modulus of rigidity of rock. In: E.R. Hoskins Jr. (Ed). Applications of Rock Mechanics. Proc. 15th U.S. Symposium on Rock Mechanics, Sept. 17-19, 1973. American Society of Civil Engineers, New York, 181-225.

Hustrulid, W. Personel communication.

Koopmans, R. and Hughes, R.W. 1985. Determination of near-field excavation disturbance in crystalline rock. In: L.O. Werme (Ed). Proc. 9th Int. Symp. on the Scientific Basis for Nuclear Waste Management, Sept. 9-11, 1985.

Materials Research Society, Pittsburgh, 567-576.

Ljunggren, C. 1984. Laboratory determination of rock tensile strength by hydraulic and sleeve fracturing. Master thesis 1984:078 E. Luleå University of Technology, Luleå. 54 p.

Mathis, J., Stephansson, O., Bjarnason, B., Hakami, H., Herdocia, A., Mattila, U., Singh, U. and Eriksson, L. 1986. Heat induced fracturing of rock in an existing uniaxial stress field. Research Report TULEA 1986:02. Luleå University of Technology, Luleå. 69 p.

Misterek, D.L. 1970. Analysis of data from Radial Jacking Tests. Determination of the In-Situ Modulus of Deformation of Rock. ASTM STP, 477. American Society for Testing and Materials, 27-38.

Ozdemir, L. and Wang, F.D. 1981. Development of an inclusiongaged sleeve for use on a cylindrical pressure cell. Excavation Engineering and Earth Mechanics Institute of CSM. U.S. Bureau of Mines. 66 p.

Panek, L.A., Hornsey, E.E. and Lappi, R.L. 1964. Determination of the modulus of rigidity of rock by expanding a cylindrical pressure cell in a dril hole. 6th U.S. Symposium on Rock Mechanics, Rolla, Missouri, 427-449.

Stephansson, O. 1983. Sleeve fracturing for rock stress measurements in boreholes. Proc. Int. Symposium on Soil and Rock Investigations by In-Situ Testing, Paris, May 18-20, 1983, 2: 571-578.

Proceedings of the International Symposium on Rock Stress and Rock Stress Measurements/Stockholm/1-3 September 1986

Hydraulic fracturing testing method for rock stress measurements in Italy

G. BARLA
Polytechnic of Turin, Italy

P. BERTACCHI
A. ZANINETTI
ENEL – Hydraulic and Structural Research of Milan, Italy

P.P. ROSSI
ISMES of Bergamo, Italy

I. VIELMO
CONSONDA of Milan, Italy

ABSTRACT   The in situ stress measurements in Italy performed up to the present by means of the CSIR "doorstopper", have evidenced complex geological features of the single earth's regions, changing from one place to another. More recently, consideration has also been given to hydraulic fracturing, with the interest to use this technique in rock engineering for the design of large cavities and tunnels. The results obtained so far by laboratory tests on rock specimens and modeling materials are illustrated in the present paper. Also mentioned are the first in situ applications related to fields other than stress measurements, and future developments of the research work being carried out.

RESUME   La détermination de l'état de contrainte dans le massif rocheux   éffectuée jusqu'à présent en Italie au moyen de la technique de décompression du CSIR "doorstopper", a mis en évidence une situation géologique très complexe changeant de lieu en lieu. Plus récemment on a envisagé d'utiliser la technique de la fracturation hydraulique pour projeter de grandes excavations souterraines et de tunnels. Dans ce rapport on présente les résultats obtenus au laboratoire sur des échantillons de roche et de matériel artificiel. On mentionne aussi les premières applications de cette technique non reliées à la mesure de l'état de contrainte et les développements prévus pour le futur.

ZUSAMMENFASSUNG   Die Bestimmung des Spannungszustandes im Fels, die bisher in Italien mit   der   CSIR   "doorstopper"   Überbohrtechnik   ausgeübt   wurde,   hat   ein   stark veränderliches   Verhältnis   der   Geologie   bewiesen.   Kürzlich   ist   die   hydraulische Felsfrakturierung   für   die   Untertagehohlraumen-   und   Tunnelsentwürfe   in   Betracht genommen worden. In diesem Bericht werden Ergebnisse von Laboratorium-Experimente auf Fels-   und   Modellproben   vorgelegt;   die   ersten   Anwendungen,   die   nicht   mit Spannungszustand verbunden sind, und die vorgesehenen Entwiklungen werden ebenfalls erwähnt.

1. INTRODUCTION

In the past twenty years, rock stress characterization   for   design   and construction of underground cavities and tunnels acquired increasing importance, because of more complexity of problems and   applications   being   considered, increased depth of new tunnels being excavated,   modern technologies of rock excavation   and   reinforcement   systems being used (Barla and Mahtab, 1983).

Also,   the   past   experience   does   not translate into practical judgement and the function of some of the underground openings (such as storage cavities) may involve questions of long–term stability under   coupled,   thermal,   mechanical,   and hydrological   environments.   Finally, numerical   methods   of   analysis   of structures in rock are well advanced and require quantification of the rock mass characteristics to an unprecedented degree of sophistication and confidence.

In Italy, where the territory is highly characterized by the presence of hills and mountains in a most irregular pattern, the same problem of identification and quantification of significant properties of rock mass, expecially for rock stress determination, has become relevant and stringent in a number of design projects dealing with underground construction (Barla,1985). On the contrary, rock stress measurements were carried out mostly in underground structures near to the surface by means of CSIR "doorstopper" and flat-jack methods, often resulting in irregular and uncertain stress distributions with depth. With this in mind, an effort has been made recently to approach the HYDRAULIC FRACTURING technique as a tool to be used in rock engineering practice for the purpose of rock stress determination.

2. ROCK STRESS MEASUREMENTS IN ITALY

In order to give a perspective of the main geological features of the single earth's regions of Italy, reference is made to the large scale division of the lithosphere into major tectonic units (AGI, 1985). In fact, depending on the distinctive features of these major tectonic units, geological investigations and rock mechanics studies, including rock stress measurements, will be characterized by substantial methodological differences and results. At the same time, the extrapolation of rock stress data from one site to another is to be considered with great caution and in most cases it becomes even impossible.

Given the effects of a long tectonic evolution, the present geological features allow one to subdivide the exposed portion of the earth's crust

into two large structural units: (i) Tectonically active alpine-type fold belts (mountain chains, forming 10÷15 percent overall); (ii) Platforms (forming 80÷90 percent of the land). Secondary suprastructures such as rifts, molasse troughs, intramontane basins, etc. complete the group of major tectonic units.

i) The alpine-type fold belts formed during repeated orogenic cycles from Upper Cretaceous to Pliocene, and are still in an uplifting phase (Neotectonics). Lithostratigraphic sequences of considerable thickness including typical rock types (turbidites, cherts and siliceous shales, etc.) from the chain frame. Such sequences have been deformed by general intense tectonics. A low grade metamorphism and volcanism developed on the inner side of these chains. Seismic activity is a peculiar feature of the alpine-type fold belts.

ii) Platforms consist of two distinct planes: a basement of folded old rocks, and an upper part (or cover) formed by flat-lying, slightly deformed or undeformed sedimentary formations. Ancient and young platforms can be distinguished. The basement of ancient platforms consists of intrusive and metamorphic rocks of Prepaleozoic times, whereas the basement of young platforms consists of Paleozoic intrusive, metamorphic and sedimentary rocks of fold mountain chains which formed during the Caledonian (430÷340 MA) and Hercynian (280÷225 MA) orogenic cycles. The sedimentary formations have the same characteristics as those typical of alpine-type fold belts such as elongated basins, lithostratigraphic sequences, intense tectonic deformations, etc. The covers of ancient and young platforms consist of almost flat-lying slightly deformed Paleozoic and Mesocenozoic (ancient platforms) and Mesocenozoic (young platforms) continental or neritic formations. Mild folds some hundred to some thousand kilometres in radius are peculiar structural forms.

This summary of the distinctive features of major tectonic units would show that geological characteristics of two sites may either differ greatly, or have much in common, depending on whether the sites, independently of their mutual distance, belong to the same or to different structural units.

These different geological characteristics seem to be well emphasized in terms of rock stresses by the results of in situ measurements performed in Italy over the last fifteen years (Martinetti and Ribacchi, 1980). By using the CSIR "doorstopper" method, measurements were carried out in underground power-plants and some important mines (Fig. 1), thus covering different geological conditions, structural setting and morphological features.

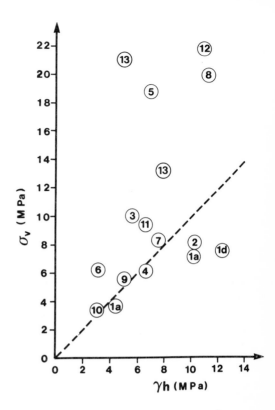

Fig. 2 - Vertical stress in the test sites versus overburden pressure.

Fig. 1 - Location of sites in Italy where in situ stress measurements have been carried out.

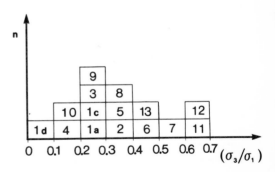

Fig. 3 - Histogram of the ratio between minimum and maximum principal stresses.

According to the illustrations reported in Figures 2 to 4, the following observations are made (Martinetti and Ribacchi, 1980):

- In mountain slopes or buttresses, the inclination of the maximum stress in the vertical section falls between that of the slope and the vertical. This is in agreement with the theoretical evaluation of the stresses that are generated within the rock mass following the excavation of the valley.

- The vertical stresses σ_v are mostly equal or greater than the γh values that can be calculated on the basis of the overburden thickness h . Theoretical

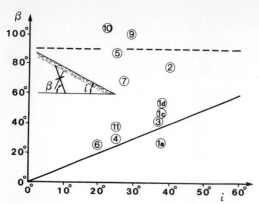

Fig. 4 – Inclination β of the greater secondary stress versus slope inclination i.

analyses carried out by assuming either elastic or elastoplastic behavior of the rocks show that in correspondence to a slope, σv should be somewhat higher than γh.

- In the Raibl, S.Giovanni and Masua mines, the vertical stresses are by far greater than those corresponding to the overburden. For the first case, this is certainly due to the measuring site being located on the floor of a valley which is surrounded by high mountains; for the second site, it is more difficult to supply an explanation. At the Masua mine the results are affected by the vicinity of the testing site to the mine openings.

- The principal secondary stresses, on the horizontal plane are often oriented according to the axis of the valley. In some istances (Roncovalgrande, S.Fiorano, Edolo) the longitudinal component is considerably high; on the other hand, in the Timpagrande site, the deep incision of the two valleys that isolate the buttress which includes the measuring zones, justifies the low values of this component. Finally, the high values of the horizontal stresses, in the Raibl mine must be pointed out; they are probably one of the factors that account for the rock bursts occurring in the mine.

- The values of the ratio between minimum and maximum principal stresses

vary within a very wide range; however for most cases they fall within the 0.15÷0.40 range. The lower limit of this ratio is determined by the limit strength of the rock mass, corresponding to the long-term strength of its weaker elements (more highly fractured zones, faults).

3. THE APPROACH TO HYDRAULIC FRACTURING

As stated above, the information presently available in Italy on the state of stress in the earth's crust, given the complex geological features of its territory, does not allow to draw satisfactory conclusions on possible general trends, as related to different regions or tectonic units. At the same time, the need to obtain reliable data on the in situ stresses in rock masses, where important underground structures (i.e. hydroelectric projects, deep tunnels in the Alpine and Appennines regions) need be constructed, is becoming very clear.

In most cases, the assumption of geostatic conditions, as introduced in the initial design, are misleading with respect to shape, size and orientation of underground openings, so as to render any change during the actual excavation very expensive. This fact, related to the disadvantages common to the indirect methods for rock stress measurements (i.e. CSIR doorstopper) such as:

- the difficulty and expenses associated with driving pilot or access tunnels in the area of a planned underground cavity;

- the depth of the tunnel to be designed, which can be reached only by means of boreholes drilled from the surface;

- the point measurements which involve very small areas;

- the need to measure the elastic parameters to convert measured strain to stress;

- the effect of highly differential stresses where overcoring could

produce discing of rock;
made it imperative to look for a
possible application of HYDRAULIC
FRACTURING to rock engineering, in the
design stage of underground cavities and
tunnels.

The hydraulic fracturing technique
(Haimson and Fairhurst,1970) is not
affected by the disadvantages mentioned
above. The same equipment to be used
down the hole may be simple and not very
sophisticated, mainly in the depth range
of interest in civil engineering
projects.

The method consists of sealing-off a
section of a borehole at the required
depth by two rubber packers, and
hydraulically pressurizing the
packed-off segment. When the breakdown
pressure is reached, the rock
surrounding the borehole fails in
tension and develops a fracture. This
fracture can be extended away from the
hole by continuous pumping. When pumps
are shut off with the hydraulic circuit
kept closed, a shut-in pressure is
recorded. This is the pressure necessary
to keep the fracture open. The breakdown
and shut-in pressures can be related to
the prevailing stresses on site. A
commercial impression packer is finally
used to determine the exact direction
and inclination of the hydrofracture. In
this manner, both the magnitudes and the
directions of the principal stresses can
be evaluated. The hydrofracturing
technique can be used in deep holes or
in short holes around tunnels.

For example, taking a site of a planned
underground hydro project, the
hydrofracturing technique can be used
directly in exploration holes drilled
into the general area of the planned
caverns (Haimson,1984). Thus, no
additional expenses are needed for
drilling special holes for stress
measurements. Moreover, the stresses are
estimated as part of the preliminary
investigation before the actual design,
causing no delays, and requiring no
design changes. If necessary, overcoring
tests can also be carried out later on,

when the pilot or access tunnels are
excavated. They can provide a check on
the hydrofracturing results and increase
confidence in the stress boundary
conditions used in design. Also, it is
to remark that traditionally the shape
of the tunnels and caverns and their
orientations are decided early in the
design process, while overcoring
measurements are conducted considerably
later.

The different factors mentioned above
prompted us to start a research program
on HYDRAULIC FRACTURING, oriented to
stress measurements for rock engineering
purposes. At present, consideration is
given mostly to laboratory testing on
rock specimens (cylindrical shape) and
on modeling material (cubic shape);
equipment has being set up and is due to
be tested in the field.

The purpose is to gain confidence with
the hydraulic fracturing concepts, by
verifying the theoretical relationships
holding true between rock stress and
pressures recorded during testing. Also,
in view of applying the technique in a
thermal environment (Geothermal Fields),
testing was extended to thermal
conditions.

4. LABORATORY TESTING

A number of factors are known to
influence the results of theoretical
interpretation of field data. The
following are considered to be of
interest:
- hole diameter;
- rock tensile strength;
- fluid viscosity and rock permeability;
- stiffness of the packers;
- flow and/or pressurization rate;
- thermal conditions (for deeper holes);
- interaction between induced fractures
  and rock with preexisting joints
  (Zoback et Al.1977), which are often
  met during excavation in Italy;
and are being investigated throghout
laboratory testing.

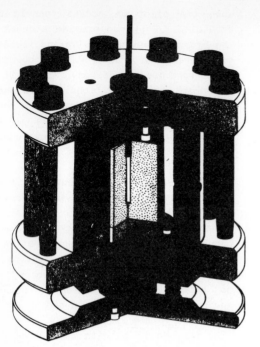

Fig. 5 – A partly sectioned, isometric view of the triaxial cell used for testing rock specimens.

4.1 Testing on rock specimens.

A triaxial cell to be used under a hydrostatic confining pressure up to 75 MPa and a vertical stress (applied by a 5 MN loading machine), in a temperature range from 18° to 200°C, has been designed and developed at the ENEL-CRIS Rock Mechanics Laboratory (Figg. 5,6). Rock specimens, 80 mm in diameter and 100 mm in height, can be tested; each specimen contains a hole 8 mm in diameter, to be used for injecting the fluid for the hydrofracturing process. The inlet tube is sealed with a special resine, at the top of the specimen; in a similar way, the plug at the bottom is also sealed, in order to obtain the same stiffness at both ends of the hole. The chamber surrounding the rock specimen (encapsulated by a sylicone membrane) is obtained by a steel hollow cylinder, closed at its ends by means of two flanges. These are locked by ten vertical tie-rods, which allow for tests to be performed in conditions where .the

Fig. 6 – The cell between the plates of the 5 MN loading machine.

lateral stress is greater than the vertical stress. An hydraulic system is used to apply the lateral and hydrofracturing pressures (up to 140 MPa) to the rock specimen.

In all cases, the pressure gradients are controlled very carefully, with a number of transducers being mounted so as to measure the pressure in the cell and near to the fluid injecting tube.

The rock specimen can be gradually heated, according to the desired heating cycle, chosen before testing. Two different systems have been set up for this purpose. Either heating elements near the specimen, like a furnace inside the cell (ten group-connected thermo-resistances for gradually heating in order to avoid shocking the rock), or a heating exchanger, external to the cell, can be used. A number of controllers and thermosensors are applied for monitoring. Also, vertical loading and different pressure conditions (lateral and hydrofracturing pressures) are controlled and continuously plotted during testing.

The results of a typical test, carried out to reproduce the hydrofracturing phenomenon under high temperature and pressure conditions, is shown in Fig.7 (test performed with the pressurization

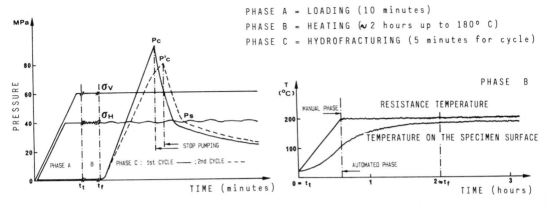

PHASE A = LOADING (10 minutes)
PHASE B = HEATING (∿ 2 hours up to 180° C)
PHASE C = HYDROFRACTURING (5 minutes for cycle)

Fig. 7 - The results of a typical hydrofracturing test.

rate control). With a given state of stress (σv=vertical stress; σh = σh max = σh min = horizontal stress) applied to the specimen, the heating cycle is started, so as to obtain gradually (5÷7°C/min) the desired temperature. With steady state conditions being reached, water is injected in the specimen center hole; the pressure conditions are continuously monitored in order to know the stress-path which is applied during testing.

Particular attention has been devoted to the method for immediately stopping pumping, when the peak pressurization value is reached. The inlet pressure is electronic filtered and stored for a comparison with a very small prefixed step of pressure in real-time. At the peak value, when a sudden decrease of pressure is reached, a relay releases a pneumatic actuator, which is positioned on the delivery side, to stop fluid pumping. Consequently, the equilibrium conditions ps = σh can be attained. The test is then repeated with a new pressure cycle, to obtain the lower limit pressure p'c. It is known that the two peak values pc and p'c allow one to measure the rock tensile strength σt = pc - p'c, for the conditions being reproduced during testing. A tonalite specimen after hydrofracturing is shown in Fig.8.

4.2 Testing on modeling materials.

True triaxial stress conditions are being investigated at the Rock Mechanics Laboratory of ISMES, Bergamo, by using cubic specimens 180 mm in side. The hydraulic fracturing tests are performed on a modeling material (i.e. obtained by means of mixtures of chalk-celite and water), giving a uniaxial compressive strength σc = 1.32 MPa. This material is shown to exhibit a linear elastic behaviour up to brittle failure. A very viscous fluid is being used as hydrofracturing fluid, given that the modelling material is pervious.

Fig. 8 - A Tonalite specimen after hydrofracturing.

337

Fig. 9 – A view of the triaxial device used for testing modeling materials.

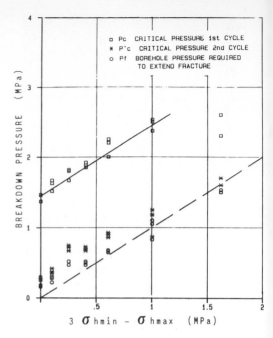

Fig.10 – Relationship between breakdown pressure and horizontal stresses.

This is the opposite of what is assumed for in situ testing (impervious rock with water as hydrofracturing fluid), however the results are comparable satisfactorily.

A stiff metallic frame and six flat jacks allow for the application of a triaxial state of stress on the cubic specimen being tested (Fig. 9). An interfaced gas-oil lung is used to keep the stresses constant during testing. Pressures transducers are being applied for measurement and control. A soft plate, provided with prismatic neoprene elements and no-friction teflon papers, is inserted between the flat jacks and the specimen, thus giving a uniform pressure distribution on each plane surface. After loading the specimen, the hydrofracturing fluid is injected into a vertical hole in the specimen. The inlet pressure is measured and monitored by means of a computer, which is programmed to stop immediately the pumping phase, when the breakdown pressure is reached. This provision in testing is extremely important in order to avoid fracture propagation.

A number of tests have been performed to verifying the following influencing factors and test conditions, under different stress states (Fig.10).

- Lining of the internal hole with rubber or sylicone membrane, or epoxy-resine, has been studied in order to obtain an impermeable hole up to the fracture initiation, without sudden elastic energy release due to stiffness inadequacy of the lining itself.
- Fluid viscosity has been investigated in a large range (from 27 to 10000 centistokes at 20°C), to simulate different permeability conditions (Figg.11,12); satisfactory results have been obtained by using glycerine.

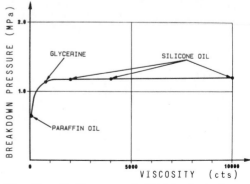

Fig.11 - Influence of fluid viscosity.

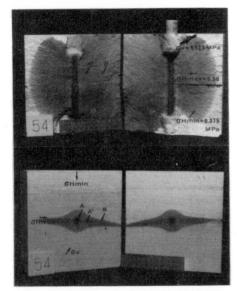

Fig.12 - *Vertical and horizontal cross-sections of two model-specimens.*

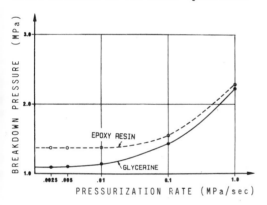

Fig.13 - *Influence of pressurization rate on breakdown pressure.*

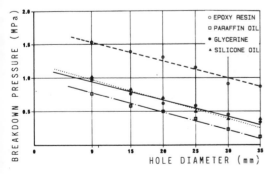

Fig.14 - *Influence of hole diameter on breakdown pressure for different fracturing fluids.*

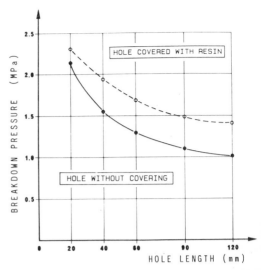

Fig.15 - *Influence of pressurized hole length on breakdown pressure.*

- Different pressurization rates ($2.5 \times 10^{-3} \div 1$ MPa/sec) have been analysed with respect to the breakdown pressure (Fig.13). Similarly, the flow rate effect has been investigated, by finding it to be negligible so as to carry out all tests under constant flow rate (3.3 cc/sec).
- Hole diameters and pressurized range extensions (Figg. 14,15 respectively) have been correlated with the specimen sizes: the results are in very good agreement with the experiences performed by other Authors.
- Particular attention has been devoted to the tensile strength of rock, obtained as difference between the first and the second peak pressure values, for different stress conditions, or by the hydraulic fracturing test itself without confining pressures being applied ($\sigma_t = 1.48 \pm 0.13$ MPa against 1.45 ± 0.15 MPa respectively).

5. IN SITU TESTING

The applications of hydraulic fracturing in Italy has been mostly oriented to the need of petroleum

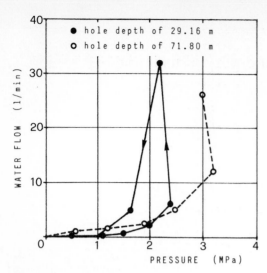

Fig. 16 - Water flow versus pressure as obtained at the Ridracoli Dam site.

industry and geothermal energy. However, a number of tests have been carried out involving the same technique in rock engineering, mostly with reference to the design of dam curtain grouting (Fig. 16) and prestressing of rock around tunnels. The experience gained in this manner is of help in the actual setting up of the equipment needed for in situ stress measurements.

The hydraulic fracturing tests performed by Consonda (Milan) at the Ridracoli Dam site, in holes 72 m deep, are of interest. As shown in Figure 16, these tests were directed towards measuring the maximum water flow absorption through the existing fractures in the rock mass, under different pressure levels. The purpose was to evaluate correctly the influence of wedging, squeezing fluid-fracturing, and compaction grouting in given field conditions.

6. CONCLUDING REMARKS

With the main purpose to increase the present knowledge of the in situ state of stress in Italy, as related to rock engineering (i.e. underground large cavities and tunnels), a testing equipment for hydraulic fracturing in situ is being set up. Possible applications are envisaged in the near future, in a site where previous measurements of the in situ state of stress were carried out by overcoring.

At the same time, the laboratory experimental work on hydraulic fracturing is being continued, with emphasis placed on the influence of factors such as preexisting joints and discontinuities, anisotropy. The hydrofracturing attitude at the hole contour and in the surrounding rock, in such unusual conditions, is to be investigated so as to help the interpretation of tests carried out in Italian rock complexes.

REFERENCES

A.G.I.1985. Geotechnical Engineering in Italy, Associazione Geotecnica Italiana on the occasion of the ISSMFE Golden Jubilee.

Barla G.and Mahtab A. 1983. Characterizing and Modeling Rock Mass for Design and Construction of Underground Cavities. Final Report on the Joint U.S. - Italy Workshop, Polytechnic of Turin.

Barla G. 1985. Rock Mass Characterization for Design and Construction of Underground Cavities and Tunnels. Geotechnical Engineering in Italy.

Haimson B.C.and Fairhurst C. 1970. In situ Stress Determination at Great Depth by Means of Hydraulic Fracturing. Proc.11th U.S.Symp.on Rock Mechanics. W.H.Somerton,ed.,AIME,559-584.

Haimson B.C. 1984. Pre-excavation In situ Stress Measurements in the Design of Large Underground Openings. ISRM Symp. on Design and Performance of Underground Excavation.Cambridge,U.K.

Martinetti S.and Ribacchi R. 1980. In situ Stress Measurements in Italy. Rock Mechanics, 31-47.

Zoback M.D., Rummel F., Jung R. and Raleigh C.B. 1977. Laboratory Hydraulic Fracturing Experiments in Intact and Pre-fractured Rock. Int.J.Rock Mech. Min. Sci. Vol. 14.

Is the microcracking of a rock a memory of its initial state of stress?

Ph. CHARLEZ
C. HAMAMDJIAN
D. DESPAX
Total CFP, St Remy les Chevreuse, France

ABSTRACT : After a short review of the "Differential strain Analysis" method, several models based on elastic brittle fracture are given : it has been proved that only a hypothesis based on initial relaxed state of stress at the crack tip will respect both the propagation criterion and the stability condition. Several examples have made it possible to assess the influence of various parameters (Young's modulus, surface energy and porosity) on the intensity of the microcraking.
Finally, experimental results make it possible to confirm the model and establish a regional state of stress in the Middle East.

RESUME : Après un bref rappel de la méthode "Differential Strain Analysis", plusieurs modèles, basés sur la mécanique des roches élastiques et fragiles, sont présentés. Il est prouvé que seule une hypothèse sur un état de contrainte initial relâché, en tête de fissure, permet de respecter à la fois le critère de propagation et le critère de stabilité dans le phénomène de microfissuration dû à la décompression d'un échantillon de roche. Plusieurs exemples permettent de chiffrer l'influence des différents paramètres intrinsèques (module'd'Young, énergie de surface, porosité) sur l'intensité de la microfissuration.
Enfin, des résultats expérimentaux permettent de valider le modèle et de tirer un état de contrainte régional au Moyen Orient.

ZUSAMMENFASSUNG : Nach einem kurzen Hirweis auf der "Differential Strain Analysis" -Methode, werden meherere Modelle vorgestellt, die auf der Mechanik von elastischen und zebrechlichen Gesteinen basiert sind. Es wurde festgestellt, daß nur eine Hypothese, die einen initialen entspannten Spannungszustand am Rißkopf zugrunde liegt, die Ausbreitungs- und Stabilitätstkriterien erfüllen kann, im Microrißbildungsphänomen infolge der Dekompression eines Gesteinprüfstücks.
Durch Mehrere Beispiele wurde der Einfluß von verschiedenen Parametern (Youngs Modul, Fläche-energie, Porosität) auf die Microrißbildungsintensität bestimmt.
Zum Schluß, durch experimentelle Ergebnisse wurde das Modell für gültig erklärt, und ein regionaler Sparrungszustand im Nahenosten aufgestellt.

1 INTRODUCTION

Considering recent problems which have arisen geothermal recovery projects in hot dry rocks, and the economic exploitation of hydrocarbon fields with low permeability, the knowledge of the state of stress in deep rocks has gained increasing importance regarding rock mechanics. The method used the most commonly for the last twenty years (i.e. hydraulic fracturing) although still the most reliable, is extremely expensive (especially offshore) and an operator will often hesitate to make such an outlay. This is why, for the last five years certain authors have been wondering whether a rock sample, taken from its original block would retain in. its matrix a "memory" of its present state of stress.
This idea gave birth to the DSA (Differential Strain Analysis) method, developed by SIMMONS and al (1974). The method is based on the following assumption :
"When a rock sample is taken (by coring for instance) within a stressed deep layer, the material will microcrack in proportion to the pre-existing effective state of stress".
This principle involves certain complementary hypotheses :
- before relaxation the material contains no open microcracks,
- the relaxation of the state of stress is the only source of microcracks. Any other phenomena of a thermal (cooling of

the core) mechanical (actual coring procedure) or other (knocks, transport, preparing the samples) nature, will not cause any extra microcracking.
A cubic-shaped sample is then cut from the microcracked core, and strain gages are sticked in 9 directions (Six of which are independant) (Fig. 1).

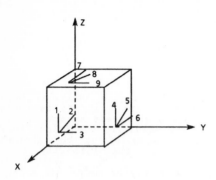

Fig. 1 - Gages arrangement on the sample

It is then moulded in a rubber envelope and replaced under increasing hydro-static pressure.
Nine pressure-strain curves are recorded, similar to these given in Fig. 2.

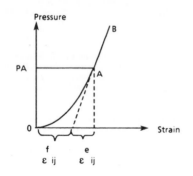

Fig. 2 - Pressure versus strain, theorical curve

First a non-linear portion can be seen, which corresponds to the gradual closing of the microcracks (OA) in the corresponding direction. Then comes a linear-section, characteristic of the elastic behaviour of the porous material.
At any point on the curve, the deformation can be divided into a part $\overset{f}{\varepsilon}_{ij}$, due exclusively to the closure of the microcracks, and a part $\overset{e}{\varepsilon}_{ij}$ including the purely elastic deformation. The particular value of the pressure P_A, corresponds to the total

closure of the microcracks in th considered direction.

The associated deformation $\overset{f}{\varepsilon}_{ij}$ for th value P_A, will assess the memory of th state of stress in this direction.
The overall memory will be represented by the tensor $\underset{\sim}{\varepsilon}$ and thus :

(1)
$$\underset{\sim}{\overset{f}{\varepsilon}} = \begin{bmatrix} \overset{f}{\varepsilon}_{xx} & \overset{f}{\varepsilon}_{xy} & \overset{f}{\varepsilon}_{xz} \\ \overset{f}{\varepsilon}_{yx} & \overset{f}{\varepsilon}_{yy} & \overset{f}{\varepsilon}_{yz} \\ \overset{f}{\varepsilon}_{zx} & \overset{f}{\varepsilon}_{zy} & \overset{f}{\varepsilon}_{zz} \end{bmatrix}$$

the reference system beeing that o Fig. 1.

According to the hypothesis of propor tionality

(2)
$$\underset{\sim}{\overset{*}{\sigma}} = \lambda \underset{\sim}{\overset{f}{\varepsilon}}$$

where $\overset{*}{\sigma}$ is the effective state of stress. $\sim$

For the evaluation of the propor tionality constant, λ, it is necessar to make an extra hypothesis : the tota vertical stress σ_{zz} is purely litho static (no vertical tectonic component and equal to the weight of th overburden layers i.e. :

(3)
$$\lambda = \frac{\rho_m g z}{\overset{f}{\varepsilon}_{zz}}$$

where z and ρ_m are respectively th depth and the average density of th overburden layers.

Apart from secondary hypotheses (whic certainly have their importance) thi theory is mainly based on the empirica nature of the linear relation (2).

This relation only has any theoretica value if the original state of stres was isotropic.

If, indeed, this is so, and assumin perfect homogeneity of the material, th probability of this material micro cracking would be identical in al directions. In the case of a anisotropic state of stress, there is n reason why this hypothesis should b valid.

342

In the following pages of this work we therefore propose a mechanism which could partially answer the question and then check some of the results obtained experimentally.

2 RELAXATION AS A MICROCRACKING MECHANISM

We will consider the rock at time t_0 (i.e. just prior to coring) as a brittle elastic medium, with the intrinsic characteristics E (elasticity modulus), γ (Poisson's coefficient) and δ (surface energy). This medium contains a certain number of elliptical defects, infinitely flat (but free of stress).

The sample, initially stressed is gradually relaxed ; the defects will open and propagate. The defects become microcracks.

As we have defined, defects will therefore appear as potential microcracks. For simplicity, we will assume that there is only one defect with an initial lenght $2a_0$ perpendicular at time t_0 to a uniaxial stress σ (Fig. 3).

σ

$2a_0$

Fig. 3 - Defect perpendicular to a uniaxial stress

In order to be valid the model must respect two conditions :

- The propagation criterion (GRIFFITH 1921) :
"The work of the stresses which relaxes along the crack during decompression is dissipated in various forms, in particular, in elastic strain energy (opening of the microcrack) and energy of cohesion (propagation of the initial defect)".

If the propagation is assumed to be quasistatic and adiabatic, during a decompression increment, $d\sigma$, it can be written :

(4) $\qquad dW_R = dW_{el} + dW_S$

where dW_R is the work of relaxation, dW_{el} the elastic strain energy and $d W_S$ the energy of cohesion. The latter term can be written in the form :

(5) $\qquad dW_S = 4 \delta\, dS$

where δ is the specific surface energy of the material.

By inserting (5) into (4) and assuming :

$$ g = \frac{\partial}{\partial S}(W_R - W_{el}) $$

the criterion can be written :

(6) $\qquad g = 4\delta$

where g is the "energy release rate". The equation (6) represents the condition of quasistatic propagation of the crack. It can also be expressed from stress intensity factors. To do so, one has simply to calculate g using the field of stress at the tip of the crack (IRWIN 1957) ; the condition of propagation will be written :

(7) $\qquad K_I = K_{IC}$

where K_{IC} is the tenacity of the material.

- The stability condition (BUI 1978) : the energy required to propagate the defect increases with the length of the crack.

In other words to obtain stability, g (or K_I) must decrease when the length of the crack increases, which is written :

(8) $\qquad \dfrac{\partial g}{\partial a} < 0 \;\; or \;\; \dfrac{\partial K_I}{\partial a} < 0$

3 VARIOUS TYPES OF MODEL

Below we give three types of relaxation models. As will be seen, only one satisfies both the propagation criterion and the stability condition.

3.1 Equivalent Traction Model (ETM) (Fig. 4)

In this model it is considered that the transition from the state of stress σ, to the state 0 is equivalent to the passage from the state 0 to the state σ in traction.

For an incremental relaxation $\Delta\sigma$, the energy release rate would be (SIH and LIEBOWIETZ 1968) :

(9) $\qquad g = \dfrac{2\Pi a_o\, \Delta\sigma^2\,(1 - \gamma^2)}{E}$

343

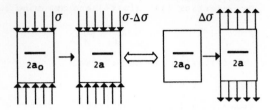

Fig. 4 - Equivalent traction model

Propagation would initiate as soon as $g = 4\bar{\sigma}$ i.e. for $\Delta\sigma_{cr}$ so that :

(10)
$$\Delta\sigma_{cr} = \sqrt{\frac{2\bar{\sigma}E}{\Pi a_o(1 - \gamma^2)}}$$

This type of load does not lead to a stable process because g is increasing monotonous with a.
This model is only acceptable if $\Delta\sigma < \Delta\sigma_{cr}$ which provides an opening of the crack without propagation.

3.2 Relaxation Elastic Model (REM) (Fig. 5 and 6)

The relaxation in this type of model consists in superposing an increasing traction $\Delta\sigma$ ($\Delta\sigma < \bar{\sigma}$) on an invariable compressive state of stress.

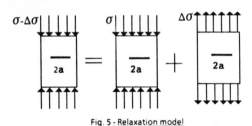

Fig. 5 - Relaxation model

σ : initial stress
$\Delta\sigma$: decompression increment

The stress field at the crack tip would have the form shown on figure 6. It's clear that the stress field at the crack tip is compressive whatever the level of relaxation is.

So, the condition of propagation is never reached. Indeed, the stress intensity factor resulting from the superposition of the two states is :

$K_I = K_I$ traction $- K_I$ compression

or, replacing then by their values :

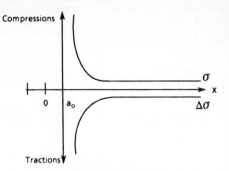

Fig. 6 - Stress state at the crack tip for the relaxation elastic model

(11) $K_I = (\Delta\sigma - \sigma) \sqrt{\Pi a_o}$

which is always negative, as $\Delta\sigma < \sigma$. The process will therefore not produce any cracking of the material.

3.3 Relaxation Rheological Model (RRM) (Fig. 5 and 7)

The difference between this and the former model resides in the initial state.
It is assumed that the stress σ is sufficiently anterior to the time of coring, for the state of stress at the defects tip to be relaxed to a finite value $\varrho\sigma$ ($\varrho \geq 0$) at the time t_c (Fig. 7).

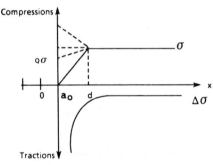

Fig. 7 - Stress state at the crack tip for the relaxation rheological model

The instantaneous decompression $\Delta\sigma$ (which is the driving force of the microcracking) is superposed on this intial relaxed state. The defect, when the propagation conditions are ensured will progress within a compressed zone providing the stability of the process. A simple analogy can be used to illustrate this mechanism : take a flexible sheet of metal placed on an infinitely rigid table (Fig. 8).

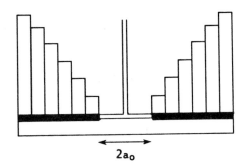

Fig. 8 - Analogy for the relaxation rheological model

Over a distance a_0 on either side of the centre of the table, the metal sheet is free, whereas for $|x| > a_0$ it is sticked to the table. For $|x| > a_0$, loads are placed on the table. Their weight varies continuously over a distance d, from $Q\sigma$ to σ.

This constitues the state at time t_0. From a mechanical point of view, the action of a traction at infinity is equivalent to that of a pressure $\Delta\sigma$ on the faces of the crack.The decompression can therefore be represented by the injection of a fluid (via a hollow tube welded to the table). This pressure will be the driving force of the microfissuration. Two phenomena will be working against this process : the glue, whose action is irreversible and which simulate the cohesion of the material (σ, K_{IC}) ; the loads whose action is reversible, but their absolute values do not vary during propagation as it is an initial state.

Propagation will therefore occur as soon as :

(12) $$K_I^T = K_I^C + K_{IC}$$

where K_I^T is the stress intensity factor due to the pressure (i.e. due to the incremental decompression) and K_I^C that of the action of the initial compression on the part of the crack concerned.

Initially the defect is only loaded in traction. The critical decompression $\Delta\sigma_{cr}$ above which propagation starts, will be :

(13) $$\Delta\sigma_{cr} = \frac{K_{IC}}{\sqrt{\Pi a_0}}$$

One propagation has been initiated the crack will penetrate the compressed zone. The stress intensity factor under compression is given by the relation (BUI 1977) :

(14) $$K_I^C = \frac{1}{\sqrt{\Pi a}} \int_{-a}^{+a} \sigma(x) \sqrt{\frac{a+x}{a-x}}\, dx$$

where 2a represents the lenght of the microcrack propagated and $\sigma(x)$ the compression load in the part of the crack concerned (i.e. between $|a_0|$ and $|a|$ in this case). Equation (12) therefore makes it possible to calculate the length of the crack corresponding to a value of the decompression $\Delta\sigma > \Delta\sigma_{cr}$. To simplify the calculations we have integrated the relation (14) in the case of a compression distribution varying linearly from $Q\sigma$ to σ over a length $d - a_0$ (d is called zone of perturbation), then constant and equal to σ. The integration gives the following result :

for a < d

(16) $$K_I^C = \frac{1}{\sqrt{\Pi a}} [Q\sigma(\Pi a - 2a\,arc\,sin\,\frac{a_0}{a})$$

$$+ (\frac{\sigma - Q\sigma}{d - a_0})(2a\sqrt{a^2 - a_0^2} + 2a_0\,a\,arcsin\,\frac{a_0}{a} - a_0 a\Pi)]$$

for a > d

$$K_I^C = \frac{1}{\sqrt{\Pi a}}[\sigma(\Pi a - 2a\,arc\,sin\,\frac{d}{a})$$

$$+ Q\sigma(2a\,arc\,sin\,\frac{d}{a} - 2a\,arc\,sin\,\frac{a_0}{a})$$

$$+ (\frac{\sigma - Q\sigma}{d - a_0})(2a\sqrt{a^2 - a_0^2} - 2a\sqrt{a^2 - d^2}$$

$$+ 2a_0\,a\,arc\,sin\,\frac{a_0}{a} - 2a_0\,a\,arc\,sin\,\frac{d}{a})]$$

On Fig. 9, $K_I^T 1, K_I^T 2, K_I^T 3$ are the stress intensity factors corresponding to increasing values of decompression.

In the case (1) and (2) for which $\Delta\sigma < \Delta\sigma_{cr}$, propagation is not initiated.

However, in case (3) for which $\Delta\sigma > \Delta\sigma_{cr}$, the defects propagates as long as $K_I^T > K_I^C + K_{IC}$.

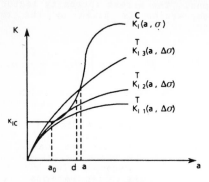

Fig. 9 - Propagated length for several decompression increments

Propagation, at first unstable, becomes stable when :

$$\frac{\partial K_I^T}{\partial a} \leq \frac{\partial K_I^C}{\partial a}$$

Propagation stops when $K_I^T = K_I^C + K_{IC}$.
The value for which this relation has been checked, is the length of the crack propagated.
The deformed shape of the crack can be calculated by integrating the England and Green's formula (1963) :

$$v(x) = \pm \frac{4(1-\gamma^2)}{\Pi E} \int_{|x|}^{a} w\,(w^2 - x^2)^{-1/2}dw \int_{0}^{w}$$

$$\sigma(t)\,(w^2 - t^2)^{-1/2}\,dt \qquad |x| \leq a$$

The sign of the displacement $v(x)$ will be positive for the upper side of the crack in the case of traction load (decompression), negative in the case of compression load. $\sigma(t)$ corresponds to the superposition of the decompressed state $\Delta\sigma$ and the compressed state on the part of the crack concerned.

For the compressed state, it is defined as follows :

$$\sigma(t) = 0 \qquad |t| < a_0$$

$$\sigma(t) = Q\sigma + \frac{\sigma - Q\sigma}{d - a_0}(x - a_0) \qquad a_0 < |t| < d$$

$$\sigma(t) = \sigma \qquad |t| > d$$

The total displacement of the sides of the crack is obtained by adding together the displacements $v_1(x)$ and $v_2(x)$, due to the compression and decompression loads respectively.

Once programmed this calculation will allow the deformed shape to be vizualised according to the propagation

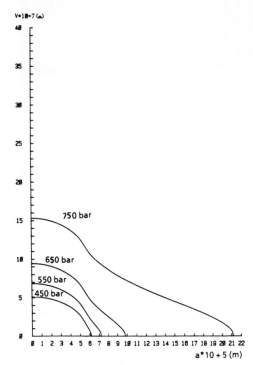

Fig. 10 - Crack shape for several values of decompression

For a level of decompression $\Delta\sigma_1$ ($< \Delta\sigma_{cr}$) the crack opens but does not propagate (initial lenth of the defect is ao).

For decompression $\Delta\sigma_2$ and $\Delta\sigma_3$, the crack propagates.

A slight "pinching" of the crack can be seen as it enters the compressed zone ($|x| > a_0$).

4 RESULTS AND DISCUSSIONS

It has been decided to characterize the intensity of microcracking by the parameter A : volume of the crack per unit of length when decompression is total.
The influence on A of the various parameters was then quantified : in situ compression stress, elastic modulus E, surface energy γ, and initial length of the crack a_0 (Fig. 11 to 14).

346

Crack's area x 10^{12} (m²)

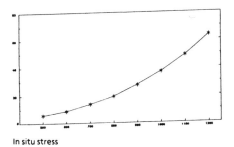

In situ stress

Fig. 11 - Crack's area versus in situ stress

Crack's area x 10^{11} (m²)

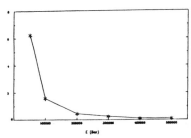

Fig. 12 - Crack's area versus Young's modulus

Crack's area x 10^{11} (m²)

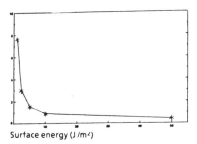

Surface energy (J/m²)

Fig. 13 - Crack's area versus surface energy

The most important conclusions are :

1) The relation between microcracking intensity and the in situ stress is only sublinear for small values of σ (Fig. 11). For high values of σ , the relation is exponential.

2) The intensity of the microcracking drops considerably as ˙ soon as

Crack's area x 10^{11} (m²)

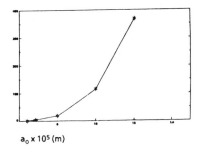

a_0 x 10^5 (m)

Fig. 14 - Crack's area versus crack's initial length

E > 200.000 bar or σ > 10 J/m2 (Fig. 12 and 13).
3) The intensity of the microcracking rises considerably when the initial length of the crack is over 5.10^{-5} m (Fig. 14).

5 EXPERIMENTAL RESULTS

Experimental tests were performed on 2 wells in the Arabian Gulf A and B. The levels treated lie at about 2500 m. They are made up of alternatives dolomitic reservoirs with low permeabilities (between 1 and 20 mD) and much stiffer anhydritic interbeds. For both of the wells, the cubic samples (16 for A, 20 for B) were cut along a vertical direction, making allowances for the slope of the wells (25 for A, 10 for B). Due to a stratification which was not perpendicular to the core axis, it was possible to orientate the samples in relation to a fixed geographical reference system. Orientations were different for the two wells.

First, it should be noted that on average, the total closure pressure P_c of the microcracks is about 300 bar, which is a <u>much lower</u> value than the in situ stresses (the principal minimal stress is above 430 bar). According to the classic Sneddon formula, the pressure required to close an elliptical crack with a and b axes, will be:

$$(16) \qquad P_c = \frac{b\,E}{2\,(1 - \gamma^2)a} = \frac{\alpha\,E}{2\,(1 - \gamma^2)}$$

where $\alpha = (b/a)$ is the shape coefficient of the crack. As the pressure P_c is below σ in situ, $\alpha < \alpha_0$, α_0, being the shape coefficient of the initial defects. This is a tangible proof that cracking occurs during relaxation.

The results of orientations have been recorded on frequency diagrams (Fig. 15 and 16).

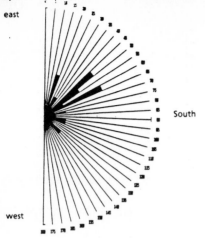

east

South

west

Fig. 15 - Projection of the minor principle deformation on a horizontal plane

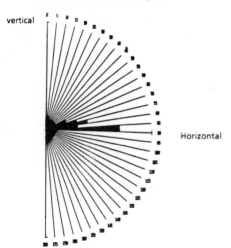

vertical

Horizontal

Fig. 16 - Angle made by the deformation with the vertical

deformations $\varepsilon^f{}_{ij}$ (corresponding to the same direction) were cumulated over all the samples taken in each well. The results of the matrix diagonalisation are given in the table below :

	$\bar{z}$ (m)	θ (°)	φ(°)
A	2320	E 69°S	82
B	2343	E 59°S	89
A + B	2331	E 61°S	88

Dispersion regarding direction appears to be fairly small between the two wells, both regarding azimuth θ and inclination φ. The latter is very close to the horizontal.

The azimuth has been placed, on the figure 17, in a geographical reference system.

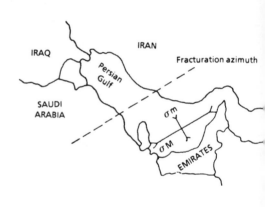

IRAQ

IRAN

Fracturation azimuth

Persian Gulf

SAUDI ARABIA

σ m

σ M

EMIRATES

Fig. 17 - Closure of the Arabian Gulf

Fig. 15 represents the projection of the minor principle deformation on a horizontal plane. Whereas Fig. 16 represents the angle made by this deformation with the vertical. Although the results are fairly dispersed, a clear NW-SE tendency can be noted. In many cases, the vertical is found to be the principle major direction. It is clear that the anhydritic levels, for which the microcracking is about ten times less intense than for dolomite, have a major role regarding dispersal. Certain anhydritic levels may, in fact, show no apparent microcracking.
Rather than giving an arithmetical average of no theoretical value, the

It shows a perfect agreement with regional tectonics (i.e. the closure of the Arabian Gulf following the opening of the Red Sea).
The stress field was calculated using the functional relation (2) and the average overburden pressure (average density taken equal to 25 Kg/m3).

Results are given in the table below :

	$\sigma 1$ (bar)	$\sigma 2$ (bar)	$\sigma 3$ (bar)
A	448	482	572
B	425	549	608
A + B	456	510	573

The <u>maximum</u> dispersion, is in the order of 13 %, which appears perfectly acceptable.

All these values are therefore in good agreement with each other. These tests also provided the opportunity to check the influence of the different parameters on the intensity of the microcracking. As predicted by the model, microcracking is all the more intense as the elastic modulus and surface energy are low, and porosity high (fig. 18 to 20).

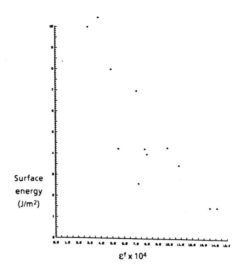

Surface energy (J/m²)

$\varepsilon^f \times 10^4$

<u>Fig. 19</u> - Surface energy versus principle major strain

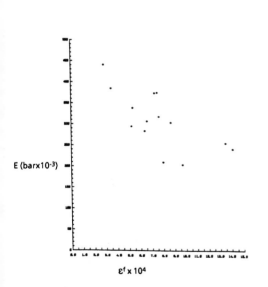

E (barx10⁻³)

$\varepsilon^f \times 10^4$

<u>Fig. 18</u> - Young's modulus versus principle major strain

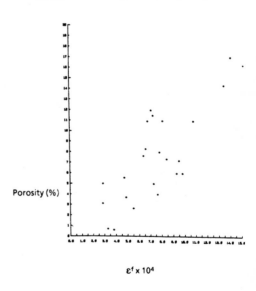

Porosity (%)

$\varepsilon^f \times 10^4$

<u>Fig. 20</u> - Porosity versus principle major strain

6 CONCLUSIONS AND PROPOSED LINES OF RESEARCH

As a whole, the experimental observations (intense microcracking in rocks with low elastic modulus, low surface energy and high porosity) indicated a brittle elasticity model.However a purely elastic model (REM or ETM type) will not respect either the propagation criterion on one hand, or the stability condition, on the other. Only the hypothesis of a relaxed finite initial state at the defect tip will allow (by superposing a purely elastic decompression) the construction of a model which respects both criteria simultaneously. The model shows thay microcracking drops considerably as soon as E and δ increase and the porosity decrease.

At an experimental level, the model is, above all, a statistical model, and only provides reliable results if the quantity of data gathered is sufficient. With this in mind, the method referred to as "cumulative" allowed a comparison of the average state of stress of two neighbouring wells. The low dispersion obtained and the coherence of the results with the regional tectonics of the Arabian Gulf (as well as with a hydraulic fracturation test carried out at the same place) is most encouraging. We consider that research work should be developed both theoretically (cracks not perpendicular to the stress, biaxial states of stress, case of several cracks, etc.) which obviously will demand powerful numerical models, and experimentally where the use of deformation gages presents many drawbacks (theoretical, technological and economic).

These progress should, in the near future, make the DSA competitive with hydraulic fracturing.

ACKNOWLEDGEMENTS

We wish to gratefully acknowledge the help and advice of Mrs BUI (EDF), CORNET (IPG).

BIBLIOGRAPHIE

SIMMONS, G. SIEGFRIED, R.W. and M. FEVES. 1974
Differential Strain Analysis : A new method for examining cracks in rocks. Journal of Geophysical Research 79 (29) : 4383 - 4385.

GRIFFITH, A.A. 1920. The phenomena of rupture and flow in solids. Metallurgical classics.

IRWIN, G.R. 1957. Analysis of stress and strain near the end of a crack traversing a plane. Journal of Applied Mechanics. 24 (3) : 361 - 364.

BUI, H.D. 1978. Mecanique de la rupture fragile. Masson. Paris.

SIH, G.C. and H. LIEBOWIETZ. 1968 Mathematical theories of brittle fracture. Fracture. Academic Press. New York

ENGLAND, and GREEN 1963. Proceedin Cambridge Phil. Society 59 (2) : 489 500.

Stress measurements in a deep granitic rock mass using hydraulic fracturing and differential strain curve analysis

T.N. DEY
D.W. BROWN
Los Alamos National Laboratory, Los Alamos, New Mexico, USA

ABSTRACT: We measured in situ stresses in a Hot Dry Rock geothermal reservoir using hydraulic fracturing of the rock mass as well as the novel technique of differential strain curve analysis (DSCA). We found that the DSCA method gave reliable stress estimates for deep rock masses, as well as provided complete stress tensor information from single core samples. Our results also showed the existence of unexpected and substantial changes of stress state: the stress state rotates from a normal faulting to a strike-slip faulting system within 1 km depth change.

Nous avons mesuré des contraintes in situ dans un réservoir souterrain de roche chaude et sèche en employant le procédé par fracturation hydraulique du massif rocheux ainsi que la nouvelle méthode d'analyse differentielle de la courbe de déformation. Nous trouvons que cette méthode donne des évaluations fiables pour les matériaux rocheux profonds et qu'elle fournit les informations entières du tenseur contrainte d'un échantillon unique de carotte. Nos résultats montrent aussi l'existence de changement imprévus et importants de l'état de contraintes: l'etát de contraintes se tourne de la formation normale de failles à un systeme de faille à rejet horizontal dans le changement de profondeur dans les limits de 1 km.

Wir haben in-situ Spannungen in einem Erdreservoir von heissem trockenem Tiefengestein gemessen und wir haben die neue Methode der Differentialanalyse von Dehnungskurven benutzt. Wir finden, dass diese Methode zuverlässige Spannungsabschätzungen für Tiefgebirgsmassen gibt und vollstandige Angaben über den Spannungstensor von einer einzigen Kernprobe liefert. Unsere Ergebnisse zeigen auch die Existenz von unvorhergesehenen und beträchtlichen Veränderungen des Spannungszustandes: Der Spannungszustand dreht sich von einer normalen Sprungbildung bis zu einem Seitenverschiebeungssystem in einer Tiefenveränderung innerhalb 1 km.

1. INTRODUCTION

As part of the development of a Hot Dry Rock geothermal reservoir, we estimated in situ stresses using hydraulic fracturing methods and the novel technique of differential strain curve analysis (DSCA). This geothermal project is being conducted by Los Alamos National Laboratory with funding from the United States Department of Energy, Japan's New Energy Development Organization and West Germany's Ministry for Science and Technology.

The experimental site is located on the western flank of the Valles Caldera at Fenton Hill, New Mexico, USA. The age of caldera formation is about 1.1 m.y. with volcanism occurring between about 10 m.y. and 0.1 m.y. ago. Two wells, one of which is sidetracked and redrilled into a different geometry, penetrate the geothermal reservoir region which extends from about 3 km depth to about 4.5 km depth. The geology (Laughlin et al. 1983) consists of Precambrian metamorphic and igneous intrusive rocks with temperatures ranging from 200-320°C.

The great depth of the reservoir, coupled with the presence of numerous pre-existing fractures, makes conventional hydraulic fracturing stress measurement difficult to carry out. The depth, coupled with the high temperatures, produces conditions too severe to use the borehole tools necessary for finding and isolating unfractured intervals as is conventionally done (e.g. Bredehoeft et al. 1976). Consequently, an additional method for estimating stresses at these severe conditions was sought, and the method of differential strain curve analysis (DSCA) of core samples was chosen to provide additional information on the state of stress. Ren and Roegiers (1983) used this technique successfully to estimate the state of stress in deep boreholes drilled for petroleum exploration and production.

2. DIFFERENTIAL STRAIN CURVE ANALYSIS

Based on the theoretical work of Walsh (1965), Simmons et al. (1974) developed an experimental method for measuring total microcrack volumes and orientations in rock samples in the laboratory. Samples are prepared with foil strain gages attached in appropriate orientations. After being jacketed, the sample is loaded hydrostatically to a pressure sufficient to close essentially all the crack porosity: 200 MPa or so. Projecting the asymptotic slope of the strain-pressure curves back to zero pressure, as Walsh described, gives the contribution of crack closure to the strain recorded by each gage. With a minimum of six appropriately oriented gages, this crack strain contribution can be resolved into a strain tensor with both the three principal crack strains and their directions determined (e.g. Solkolnikoff 1956).

Under suitable conditions, this crack strain tensor can be interpreted to give the in situ stress state. A necessary condition is that the great majority of microcracks present in the sample are due to the relief of the in situ stress during and following cutting of the core sample. The number of microcracks present in situ must give only a negligible contribution to the measured crack strains. A further assumption necessary is that microcrack porosity oriented in any given direction is produced in proportion to the magnitude of the effective compressive stress that was relieved in that direction. In other words, if the in situ stresses in the x and y directions are in the ratio of 1:2, then the crack strains measured in these directions must also be in the ratio of 1:2. At this time, there is no proof of this assumption; however, the success of number of workers (Strickland and Ren 1980; Ren and Roegiers 1983) in using this method for estimating in situ stress indicates that this assumption is at least approximately valid. Given this assumption, the in situ effective stress tensor (total stress minus pore water pressure) has the same orientation as the crack strain tensor and the principal effective stress values are proportional to the principal crack strain values. Requiring the resolved component in the vertical direction to equal the calculated effective overburden stress gives the proportionality constant so that the stress values themselves can be found. Ren and Roegiers (1983) observed a good correspondence for stress values and orientations between DSCA results and hydraulic fracturing results in fine grained sandstones at 1150-1800 m depth in Texas and at 1500-2440 m depth in Colorado.

The core samples used in the study of our Hot Dry Rock reservoir came from four depths: 2.880 km, 3.315 km, 3.536 km and 3.791 km. Cubical samples approximately 3 cm on a side were cut from these cores and three-gage rosettes were glued to each of three mutually perpendicular faces (see Figure 1). The three-gage rosettes have the gages aligned at 45 degrees to each other. Only six gages are required to measure the complete strain tensor, so this configuration gives redundancy in three of the directions and helps to reduce the error. Samples were encapsulated in silicone rubber and pressurized in a hydrostatic pressure vessel using an oil as the pressure medium.

Estimation of the errors in the principal strain magnitudes and their directions due to variations and errors in the measured strain is a difficult problem because of the non-linear

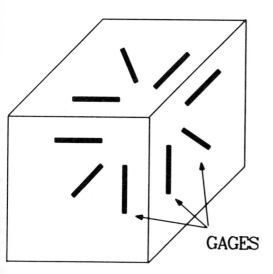

GAGES

Figure 1. Strain gage configuration used on cubic sample cut from Hot Dry Rock core.

nature of tensor analysis and the co-variance terms created by constraints for the principal directions to be mutually perpendicular. Instead of trying to carry out error analysis analytically, a different approach was taken--one which uses a Monte Carlo statistical method. The scatter in the strain measurements was measured by arranging four parallel gages on each of a number of samples and in each of a number of directions and carrying out a DSCA experiment. The standard deviation of the strain measurements themselves varied by 3-7% of the mean value; but the standard deviation of the crack strains was uniformly 15% of the mean crack strain throughout the various cores, except for the 3.3 km depth core which had a standard deviation of 30-50%. Starting with the actual DSCA crack strain measurements, a random number generator was used to generate sets of data which were distributed about the actual measurement according to a normal distribution with a 15% standard deviation. Each of these artificial data sets was then resolved into its principal strain magnitudes and orientations. The resulting scatter of points about the true DSCA data then gives an estimate of the errors in this method.

3. HYDRAULIC FRACTURING STRESS MEASUREMENTS

Stress measurements at the Hot Dry Rock site using hydraulic fracturing data are described by Kelkar, et al. (1986). Typically no evidence of rock breakdown is observed, indicating that water injection is occurring into previously existing joints.

One method used for measuring the fracture extension pressure is to plot the pumping pressure versus square root of the flow rate and extrapolate to zero flow rate. A difficulty with this method is estimation of the pressure losses of the flow through the fracturing string and associated hardware. A second method uses the instantaneous shut-in pressure (ISIP) as an estimate of the earth stress. Often, however, the ISIP is not distinct and estimates of it must be made by applying methods such as those of Muskat (Aamodt and Kuriyagawa 1981) to the shut-in pressure versus time curve from the following hours. An additional problem with hydraulic fracturing stress measurement in this deep pre-fractured crystalline rock mass is that hydraulic stimulation does not necessarily open fractures perpendicular to the least compressive stress. Seismic monitoring of microseismic events caused by the hydraulic stimulation shows that the events recorded are predominantly shear and not tensile events (Murphy and Fehler 1986). Shear on pre-existing joints can occur at lower pressures than direct opening, so the hydraulic fracture results may be slightly low.

4. STATE OF STRESS AT THE FENTON HILL HOT DRY ROCK SITE

Hydraulic fracturing results for stress are shown in Figure 2. Also indicated are the calculated overburden stress as well as the water pressure. Results are consistent with a 19 MPa/km gradient, except for a low fracturing pressure region at 3 km depth. For comparison, results of DSCA are shown in Figure 3. The horizontal bars show the standard error of this method calculated by the procedure described earlier. The comparison of hydraulic fracturing results with the least com-

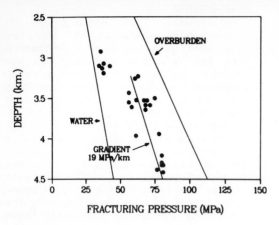

Figure 2. Hydraulic fracturing stress results in the Hot Dry Rock reservoir. Each solid circle represents one determination of fracture opening pressure.

pressive stress is generally good. In addition, the DSCA results show a substantial increase in the maximum and intermediate stresses below about 3.2 km depth. Figure 4 shows the orientations of the principal stress directions. At the shallowest depth, 2.88 km, the maximum compression is vertical and the minimum is aligned along the E-W direction--a stress state consistent with normal faulting. With increasing depth, the stress tensor rotates so that by the deepest core the maximum compression is nearly horizontal and aligned near NNW and the minimum compression is once again horizontal and close to E-W--a stress state consistent with strike-slip faulting.

The error bars on the DSCA stress estimates get substantially larger with increasing depth. The reason for this is not any particular degradation in the strain measurements or the rock itself; rather, it is due to the rotation of the maximum compression away from the vertical. As the maximum compression nears horizontal, its contribution to the resolved vertical stress changes rapidly with errors in its orientation angle. Consequently, the analysis step where the stresses are scaled to match the calculated overburden stress is particularly sensitive to orientation errors when the maximum

compression is nearly horizontal. The sensitivity increases as the maximum compression becomes much greater than the other two stress components. If all three stress components were very close in magnitude, there would be little sensitivity to angular error and the error bars would be much smaller. Repeating DSCA measurements on additional samples cut from a given core will also reduce the size of the error bars for the mean estimate.

Additional information on the state of stress is provided by seismic fault plane solutions from microseismic events occurring during hydraulic stimulation of the reservoir. The two predominant fault plane solutions occurring in the region between about 3.3 km and 4 km depth are shown in Figure 5. The first solution corresponds to normal faulting with the minimum compression along a line dipping roughly 45 degrees to the west. The second solution is a strike-slip solution with the minimum compression roughly horizontal along the E-W direction. These two solutions correspond reasonably well with the direction of the least compressive stress estimate from the DSCA method.

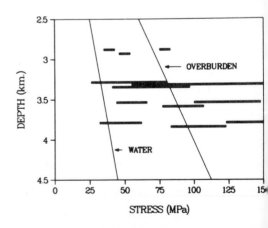

Figure 3. DSCA estimates of principal stresses. Horizontal bars represent one-standard-deviation-error bars on the estimates. The three bars at any given depth are slightly offset vertically for clarity and represent from left to right the minimum, intermediate, and maximum principal stress values.

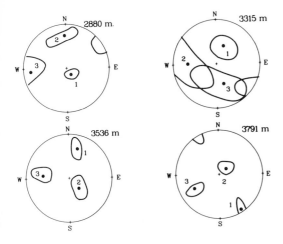

Figure 4. DSCA estimates of principal stress directions. Contours show the range of uncertainty of the direction estimates. Plots are done on a lower hemisphere conformal stereonet.

5. DISCUSSION

The results of our investigations show two important conclusions: 1) DSCA appears to be a useful and reasonably accurate method of obtaining the complete stress tensor in crystalline rock masses of sufficient depth, and 2) substantial stress inhomogeneities can exist in large crystalline rock masses and can be apparently unrelated to their structure.

The DSCA results show reasonably good agreement with the fracture opening pressures obtained from hydraulic fracturing data. The DSCA results show the least ambiguity due to scatter in the strain measurements when the maximum compression is oriented near vertical. The DSCA stress estimates become much less precise as the maximum compression rotates away from vertical, especially when there are substantial differences between the three principal stress values. According to the seismic results, orientation information from the DSCA is reasonably accurate with the uncertainties of orientation being only ± 10-15 degrees or so for our site. As two principal stress values become close in magnitude this orientational error will become greater in the plane containing the two principal directions. For two equal

principal values, the stress tensor is degenerate and the error contours on the stereonet will encircle the unit sphere.

The major criterion required for the use of DSCA as a stress measurement method is the validity of the assumption that most of the microcrack strain is due to the release of the present day in situ stress when the core sample is cut. Conditions in the Fenton Hill Hot Dry Rock site are especially favorable for satisfying this requirement. The depth to the reservoir region means that ambient stress levels will be high; this, coupled with the high temperatures, is favorable to various creep processes healing pre-existing microcracks. Consequently, most of the microcrack strain observed is indeed most likely due to the relief of the in situ stress. The success of Ren and Roegiers (1983) at depths of only 1.1 km and much lower temperatures, as well as the results of Dey and Kranz (1986) at 0.87 km depth, indicates that the DSCA technique may be useful at depths as shallow as about 3/4 km. At these shallower depths, caution is obviously required and the validity of this criterion must be evaluated for each application of DSCA on a case by case basis.

These results show a substantial heterogeneity of the state of stress in the rock mass. At about 3.2 km depth, the fracture opening pressure shows a jump of about 20 MPa within about 200 m depth change. The maximum compressive stress values also increase dramatically at this level, and the orientation of the maximum compression

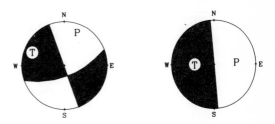

Figure 5. Predominant microseismic fault plane solutions from reservoir region. The T axes represent the seismic estimate of the minimum principal stress direction. Plots are on a lower hemisphere conformal stereonet.

rotates away from vertical eventually becoming horizontal.

This change in stress state was unexpected. Between the depths of 2 and 2.75 km at this site, a smaller scale Hot Dry Rock system had been developed and extensively tested before work was begun on this deep system. In addition, extensive surface mapping of fault slickensides and volcanic dikes had been done in the area (Aldrich and Laughlin 1982, Laughlin et al. 1983). This experience indicated a state of stress consistent with that observed in the core from 2.88 km depth--namely, a vertical maximum compression and a horizontal E-W minimum compression. The substantial and unexpected change in conditions observed here shows the need for a much more detailed site exploration before designing a deep geoengineering project where stress state is as critical as in a Hot Dry Rock geothermal system.

6. CONCLUSIONS

Differential Strain Curve Analysis appears to be a reliable and accurate method of measuring the in situ state of stress in crystalline rocks. A major advantage is that the complete stress tensor can be determined from core samples extracted from a single borehole. Unlike more conventional methods, such as overcoring, there are no practical limits on how deep in a borehole this method can be used other than the ability to extract oriented core. The major limitation is the requirement that most of the microcrack volume present be related to the present day in situ stress; this requires substantial depth of at least 3/4 km and probably deeper at some sites.

At least at our Hot Dry Rock site, substantial unexpected changes in state of stress can exist at depth in crystalline rock. This indicates that considerable caution must be exercised in extrapolating stress measurement results even over distances as small as a few hundred meters.

REFERENCES

Aamodt, R.L. and M. Kuriyagawa 1983. Measurements of instantaneous shut-in pressure in crystalline rock. Proceedings of the Workshop on Hydraulic Fracturing Stress Measurements, National Academy Press, Washington, D.C.

Aldrich, M.J. and A.W. Laughlin 1982. Orientation of least principal horizontal stress: Arizona, New Mexico, and the trans-Pecos area of West Texas. Los Alamos National Laboratory Report LA-9158-MAP, Los Alamos, NM.

Bredehoeft, J.D., R.G. Wolff, W.S. Keys and E. Shuter 1976. Hydraulic fracturing to determine the regional in situ stress field, Piceance Basin, Colorado. Geological Society of America Bulletin 87: 250-258.

Dey, T.N. and R.L. Kranz 1986. State of stress and relationship of mechanical properties to hydrothermal alteration at Valles Caldera Corehole #1, New Mexico. Submitted to the Journal of Geophysical Research.

Kelkar, S., H. Murphy and Z. Dash 1986. Earth stress measurements in deep granitic rock. 27th U.S. Symposium on Rock Mechanics, University of Alabama.

Laughlin, A.W., A.C. Eddy, R. Laney and M.J. Aldrich, Jr. 1983. Geology of the Fenton Hill, New Mexico Hot Dry Rock Site. Journal of Volcanology and Geothermal Research 15: 21-41.

Murphy, H.D. and M.C. Fehler 1986. Hydraulic fracturing of jointed formations. Society of Petroleum Engineers, International Meeting on Petroleum Engineering, Beijing, China.

Ren, N.K. and J.C. Roegiers 1983. Differential strain curve analysis - A new method for determining the pre-existing in situ stress state from rock core measurements. Proceedings, 5th International Conference of the International Society of Rock Mechanics, Melbourne, Australia: F117-F128.

Simmons, G., R.W. Siegfried and M. Feves 1974. Differential strain analysis: A new method for examining cracks in rocks. Journal of Geophysical Research 79: 4383-4385.

Sokolnikoff, I.S. 1956. Mathematical Theory of Elasticity. McGraw-Hill Book Company, New York: 476 p.

Strickland, F.G. and N.K. Ren 1980. Predicting the in situ stress for deep wells using differential strain curve analysis. Proceedings of the 1980 SPE/DOE Symposium on Unconventional Gas Recovery SPE/DOE 8954: 251-258.

Walsh, J.B. 1965. The effect of cracks on the compressibility of rock. Journal of Geophysical Research 70: 381-389.

Proceedings of the International Symposium on Rock Stress and Rock Stress Measurements/Stockholm/1-3 September 1986

Kaiser effect gauging:
A new method for determining the pre-existing in-situ stress
from an extracted core by acoustic emissions

D.R. HUGHSON
A.M. CRAWFORD
University of Toronto, Department of Civil Engineering, Toronto, Ontario, Canada

ABSTRACT

Extensive laboratory investigations have resulted in the development of Kaiser Effect Gauging as a practical system to determine the pre-existing in-situ stress by Acoustic Emission (AE) analysis of an extracted core. The principle is based on the phenomenon of Kaiser Effect which is a characteristic AE rate increase as an increasing stress exceeds the previous maximum stress. It is further based on a newly identified AE characteristic which notes that if stress is maintained at a new historic maximum, continuing AE decays exponentially at a rate related to the material's remaining stable strength.

RESUME

Des recherches approfondies en laboratoire ont mené au développement de la méthode Kaiser Effect Gauging. Il s'agit d'un système pratique pour déterminer la contrainte in-situ préexistante provenant d'une carotte extraite par l'intermédiaire de l'analyse d'Emission Acoustique (AE). La théorie repose sur le changement de Kaiser Effect de la vitesse AE lorsqu'une contrainte croissante dépasse la contrainte maximum précédente. La théorie est aussi basée sur un caractéristique AE, nouvellement identifié, selon lequel si la contrainte est maintenue au nouveau niveau maximum, le AE restant ralentit de façon exponentielle à une vitesse relative à la capacité restante de la matière.

ZUSAMMENFASSUNG

Ausführliche Laboruntersuchungen haben zu der Entwicklung von Kaiser Effect Gauging geführt, einem praktischen System zur Bestimmung der vorhergegangenen örtlichen Spannung mit Hilfe der Acoustic Emission (AE) Berechnung an einem Bohrkern. Das Prinzip beruht auf dem Phänomen des Kaiser Effects, dem Anstieg der charakteristischen AE-Rate sobald eine anwachsende Spannung die vorausgegangene Maximalspannung überschreitet. Es basiert zudem auf einer kürzlich identifizierten AE-Charakteristik die besagt, daß anhaltende AE mit einer Geschwindigkeit, die mit der verbleibenden stabilen Materialfestigkeit zusammenhängt, exponential abklingt, wenn die Spannung auf einem neuen Maximalspannungsniveau gehalten wird.

1. INTRODUCTION

The design of an adequate support structure requires two basic data components: the magnitude of the stress to be carried; and the strength of the selected structural material. In a structure such as a mine, the reliability of both of these data components may be in doubt. In order to allow for the resulting reduced confidence in the adequacy of such a structure, it is normal practice to generously size its components. The effect of this conservative practice may be a low extraction ratio and elevated production costs.

More readily obtained and reliable data on the stresses to be carried by a structure and a better indication of its capability for carrying more, could result in improved confidence in its structural adequacy. This could lead to improved extraction ratios without sacrificing safety margins. It could also lead to awareness of hazardous situations which had not been otherwise identifiable.

A number of techniques are currently available for determining the in-situ stress (14). Among these are: overcoring, hydraulic fracturing, flatjack, stressmeter, and sound propagation velocity. There are also recognized procedures for assessing the load-bearing capacities of materials.

A fundamentally new method has been developed for both the determination of in-situ stress, and the assessment of remaining additional load capacity of the material. This method is titled Kaiser Effect Gauging and is based on the natural phenomenon of Acoustic Emissions (AE).

This paper will describe the development of Kaiser Effect Gauging and its application as a routinely workable and practical technology.

2. PRINCIPLES

The phenomenon of Acoustic Emissions was first identified in the late 1930's (13,7). AE consists of minute ultrasonic pulses that can be detected in substantially inelastic materials when subjected to compressive stress. The wave form is similar to that of a seismic event but the pulse frequency in the context of this paper is in the approximate range of 50 KHz to 500 KHz with pulse duration in the order of 2 miliseconds (4). The occurrence rate, depending on many variables, can be in terms of thousands per second. They can thus be individually indistinct and might be looked upon as a measurable but non-uniform continuum of events.

Although the mechanics at the AE source is not fully understood, (4,12) it is observed that the behaviour is consistent with their being acoustic manifestations of micro-sized inelastic strain occurrences within the material.

An early researcher in Acoustic Emission, Dr. Eng. Joseph Kaiser of Munich drew attention to a specific relationship of stress and the resulting pattern of AE (8). He observed that when the stress on a polycrystallized metal is relaxed from a level of historic high, and then restressed, there is a significant increase in the rate of acoustic emission as the stress exceeds the previous maximum. This characteristic increase of AE at the transition from past experience stress into the new experience level has become known as the Kaiser Effect. Various researchers have tested a variety of materials (Table 1) and all have exhibited Kaiser Effect characteristic in their AE response.

TABLE 1
Materials Proven to Display Kaiser Effect

By These Authors

Amphibolite	Limestone (Owen Sound)
Andesite (Red Lake)	Matchewan Diabase
Concrete	Metavolcanics
Felsic Gneiss (Sudbury)	Quartz
Gabbro	Quartzite (Elliot Lake)
Gneiss	Rhyolite (Timmins)
Granite (Lac du Bonnet)	Sandstone (Berea)
Granite (Sudbury)	

By Other (Reference)

Aluminum (8)	Mica Gneiss (2)
Andesite (16)	Mica Schist (2)
Cement Motor (9,10)	Mudstone (6,5,6)
Conglomerate (9,6)	Potash (15)
Copper (8)	Sandstone (8,2)
Dolomite Marble (2)	Shale (2)
Dolomite (9,2,6,11)	Siltstone (1)
Lead (8)	Steel (8)
Limestone (2,16)	Tuff (5,10)
Marble (2)	Zinc (8)

2.1 First Principle

It has been noted (9) that:

if a sample of material is extracted from its stressed environment, it carries a Kaiser Effect recollection of the maximum stress that had existed prior to extraction. The testing of a specimen made from that sample will retrieve that recollection.

One of the objectives of Kaiser Effect Gauging is to provide a practical means for the preparation and restressing of a specimen extracted from its native environment and, through observing the stress level at which the Kaiser Effect takes place, determine the magnitude of the Recalled Maximum Stress (RMS) that existed at the specimens site.

2.2 Second Principle

It has been noted by a previous researcher (15) that if loading is held constant at a new high, the AE peak would progressively "fall off to a level at or near background".

Investigation by these authors has revealed another basic characteristic of Acoustic Emission behaviour:

If the stress is raised to a new-experience level and held there, the AE output decays exponentially. The rate of decay is inversely related to the magnitude of stress relative to the sample's strength.

Thus, if the stress is held at a new high level being relatively low to the sample's strength, the exponential rate of AE decay is rapid. Whereas, if the stress is held at a relatively high level, the decay rate will be much slower. At some point the decay rate will become zero and AE output will continue undiminished. This however is only a transient state and soon changes to one of accelerating AE. At this point, unless the stress is reduced, gross failure is imminent. Fig. 3 depicts this AE decay during dwell at various stress levels.

Since the decay rate appears to be exponential, theoretically even at a low stress the AE will continue although at a very low rate. It might be that AE is a manifestation of creep (3).

The second objective of Kaiser Effect Gauging is to provide a new determination, and a practical means for establishing it, of the Stability Limited Stress (SLS) of a specimen. This is the highest stress level at which the rate of AE decay is unlikely to reach zero within the practical future.

3. OPERATING PROCEDURE

In order to effect the Kaiser Effect Gauging procedure, the following steps are used:

3.1 Prepare the specimens from a sample of material extracted from the site to be investigated. This includes: coring the sample in the testing direction and to the standard specimen dimensions; grinding ends smooth and true; and applying the end caps to the specimen.

3.2 Gradually raise the uniaxial stress on the specimen until the Recalled Maximum Stress can be identified.

3.3 Hold the stress constant at incremental levels long enough to establish that the AE rate continues to decay at a rapid rate. Then raise the stress to the next incremental level while monitoring the rate of AE decay. When it becomes evident that the AE output might continue at a significant rate, it could be interpreted that the Stability Limit Stress has been exceeded.

4. FUNCTIONAL EQUIPMENT

During the course of verifying the functional reality of the Kaiser Effect Gauging procedure, the equipment employed might be characterized as being standard, commercially available, general purpose laboratory equipment with broad capabilities beyond the specific needs of the programme. Certain special adaptations were made but these took the form of accessories and not modifications. The principal characteristics of all items used were that they were adequate and available:

- drill press with compound cross-feed vice and adapted for diamond core drilling.
- diamond wheel masonry saw.
- Harig surface grinder with vertical V block clamps.
- Wykeham Farrance 5T compression testing machine with variable speed power operations.
- Acoustic Emission Technology Corp model 204A AE system including pre-amplifier and transducer with 100 to 250 KHz bandwith. This instrument provides an output signal representing amounts from 0 to 2000. At full scale it automatically resets to zero. Since the actual count can be vastly higher than 2000 the instrument is provided with a Scale control by which

the detected count will be a multiple
of the indicated output. The available multiples are: 1, 10, 100, 1000,
10000.
- Honeywell model 540 X-Y Plotter.
- Load cell of 330 kN capacity with
  Vishay/Ellis digital strain indicator.
- Various higher capacity compression
  testing machines were used to apply
  prestress to larger samples prior to
  extracting specimens from them.

5. DEVELOPMENT OF TESTING TECHNIQUE

5.1 Specimen Geometry

Consistent with the objective of
developing a practical system it was
determined that the shape of the specimen should be simple and easily generated with uniform cross sectional area
over the full length of its stress axis.
A right-circular cylinder is the obvious
result.

An extensive series of tests indicated that the length/diameter ratio
is a non-critical factor and successful
results were obtained with lengths
ranging from 2 to 3 times the diameter.

5.2 Specimen Preparation

A particularly critical aspect in
the detection of AE is the minimizing of
extraneous noises (10,17). The AE
detecting system is unable to distinguish between platen interface noise and
acoustic emissions caused by stress
within the specimen. A specimen end
which is either rough or not precisely
perpendicular to the stress axis will
result in noise which either overwhelms
or grossly distorts the actual AE pattern of the specimen. Particular care
must be exercised that the specimen ends
are smooth, parallel and perpendicular
to the axis. This however, is not
enough.

It had been previously recognized
that erroneous AE signals were caused by
"corner effect" (9,10) and a resin
"haunch" is successful in reducing this.

Once again, consistent with the
objective of developing a practical
system, it was determined experimentally
that a very thin film of epoxy could be
cast onto the ends of the specimen. The
thickness of this film can be merely
sufficient to fill the microscopic pores
remaining from the end-grinding process,
and presents a glass-smooth surface for
platen interface. This procedure was
found to be notably successful in
reducing End Effect noise. It is also
sufficiently simple that the technique
can be readily learned and end caps
applied on a routine basis with insignificant unit cost. More than 900 of
such specimens have been prepared and
tested by these authors.

5.3 Wave Guide

The detecting face of the AE signal
transducer is normally disk shaped and
could be larger in diameter than the
height of the specimen. It was found
that the AE detection could be improved
by the use of a steel wave guide. This
is mounted to the surface of the transducer and presents a concave face
matching the radius of the specimen with
a height less than the minimum specimen
length.

5.4 Couplant

It is well known in ultrasonics
that air pockets reduce or insulate the
transmission of signals to the transducer (1). It was found that almost any
viscous fluid applied to the contact
surface of the wave guide in a manner
to expel air from the interface, gives
adequate results.

5.5 Mounting Specimen in Tester

Despite the precautions already
described, extraneous AE signals were
still detected.

The application of a very thin film
of high pressure grease made a significant reduction in the extraneous noise.
Hardened platen faces made a further
reduction.

5.6 Compression Testing

The rate of stress increase was
found to be a non-critical factor in
recognizing the Kaiser Effect change in
AE rate. The reason for this is evident
from the Dwell Profile which is later
described. It is valuable however to
maintain a reasonably uniform loading
rate.

5.7 Data Acquisition

Various authors have used different parameters in the measuring of AE output (1) and comparing it to an associated stress. For the purpose of readily recognizing the magnitude of stress at the RMS and SLS, it was determined that the following measures would be used. Acoustic Emission: cumulative total ringdown count (1) above an automatically floating threshold and at a gain of 100 dB. The count scale factor is manually set in accordance with the material under test, the specimen size and the type of plot being generated. Stress: the loadcell detects force which is converted into stress in MPa at the recording instrument.

5.8 Plotting

Some minor advantages were seen in establishing the plotting format with stress indicated on the ordinate (x axis) and the Cumulative AE Count on the abcissa (y axis). The stress scale is adjusted to accommodate the anticipated ultimate strength of the material under test within the bounds of the graph page on the plotter. A single line continuous plot of stress versus AE count, independent of time, could thus be produced. Multiple plots of a series of comparable specimens could be produced in the same graph page by employing a y zeroing off-set adjustment at the plotter.

6. VERIFICATION TESTING

Although the first principle enunciated previously of the Kaiser Effect Gauging system has been reported or suggested by previous researchers (2, 4,5,6,9,10,12) a test programme was undertaken to specifically verify the functional validity of both principles.

6.1 Integrity of Kaiser Effect

Many materials have been previously shown to conform with Kaiser Effect expectations. This research programme has specifically applied the Kaiser Effect Gauging procedures to many more material types (Table 1). All materials tested verify that the Kaiser Effect can be readily identified when the past

maximum stress was within a range of up to the approximate SLS.

It should be noted however that the Kaiser Effect:

6.1.1 does not occur abruptly at a precisely definable point but within a transitional zone; and

6.1.2 the position and abruptness of this zone varies between types of materials (2,9,12) and the magnitude of previous stress relative to the material's SLS; and

6.1.3 the transitional zone becomes large and indistinct if the time period of the previous stress was too brief.

6.2 Recollection of the Environment Stress

This characteristic was extensively verified. In the cyclic restressing of a particular specimen there is virtually no AE output in the "past experience" range and the transition zone tends to be abrupt. However, the single stressing of an extracted specimen from its stressed environment, displays some AE output in the "past experience" range although this is typically at a uniform rate; and the Kaiser Effect transition zone is larger.

6.3 Confining Stress

Some previous research (17) has been directed towards the effect of a confining stress accompanying the axial prestress. These authors have also done considerable work in this area but have not yet been able to establish conclusive evidence in the matter. It would appear at this juncture however, that there is no significant variation in the fidelity of the Kaiser Effect resulting from confining stress.

6.4 Material Individuality

It has been previously noted that different types of materials produce individually characteristic patterns of AE responses. Since this could effect the interpretation of RMS, it is evident that each material should be considered in terms of its own individual AE

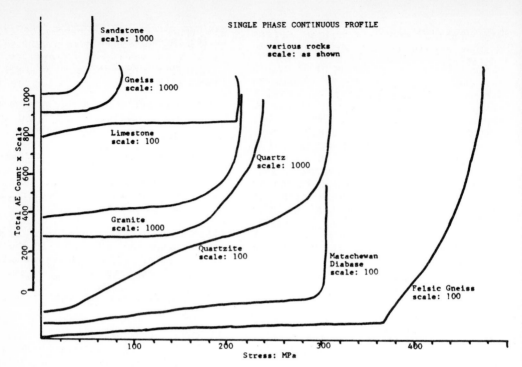

Fig. 1. Single Phase Continuous Profile (1φCP)

characterization. A specific series of basic AE patterns was developed, referred to as AE Signature Profiles, to assist in the interpretation of a material's AE responses.

6.4.1   Single Phase Continuous Profile (1φCP) (Fig. 1)

This consists of a single continuous plot from zero stress up to gross failure using the same AE scale throughout. Primarily, it provides an indication of the appropriate stress and AE scales to best depict the overall behavior of the material. Certain individual characteristics appear in the shape of this Profile in such aspects as: the rate of AE increase in various regions; the curvature or abruptness of the plot as the specimen enters the impending failure region; the total AE at failure; the abruptness of the failure event. Fig. 1 compares the Single Phase Continuous Profile of several materials so that their individuality can be readily seen.

The AE scale for each was selected in order to give the plot as much Y axis significance as possible, yet remain

within the chart confines at gross failure without a zero re-set. The use of a different scale would alter the appearance of the plot without altering the depicted facts.

6.4.2   Two Phase Continuous Profile (2φCP) (Fig. 2)

It is evident from the Single Phase Continuous Profile that employing an AE scale sufficient to include the failure process, does not provide much detail of AE output data in the low stress range. The use of a larger scale in this region would be more indicative. To capture the data relative to the higher stress levels, the AE scale is switched (point d) when the plot becomes very steep, to the scale used in the 1φCP. Although it would be difficult to recognize overall individual characteristics from a 2φCP, the scale magnification makes more evident any change in the rate of AE output relative to stress.

Thus it can be seen in Fig. 2 that there appears to be an exponential increase in AE even at low stress levels which is not as evident in the 1φCp as seen in Fig. 1. The 100 scale however might still make any Kaiser Effect change within the 20 MPa range too indistinct.

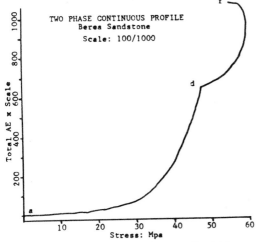

Fig. 2. Two Phase Continuous Profile (2φCP)

6.4.3 Dwell Profile (DP) (Fig. 3).

As is reported in section 2.2, if the stress is held at a new high level, the AE output decays exponentially and at a decay rate inversely related to the stress level relative to the sample strength. It has been found that this relationship is one of the factors of a material's AE response individuality. The Dwell Profile graphically depicts this factor. It provides an estimate of the SLS of that material. It also gives

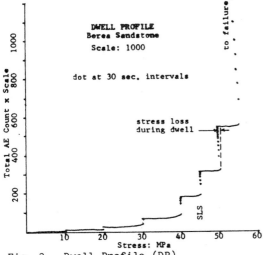

Fig. 3. Dwell Profile (DP)

an indication of the degree of change that could be expected in a 1φCP if the rate were varied. Except in the relatively high stress levels, the difference in the plot would be very small.

Another individual characteristic of a material can also be noted from its DP. During the dwell periods, if the load of the Compression Testing machine is not maintained constant, different materials show varying rates of stress loss. This is graphically represented on the DP plot by a gradual decline of stress while the AE count continues to increase.

Fig. 3 shows that residual AE at up to about 20 MPa is very small and fully expended within the first 30 seconds. At 30 and 40 MPa it takes longer for the residual AE to be dissipated but it does settle down to virtually a zero rate. At 50 MPa, although the residual AE at the end of 15 minutes is very small, it might continue that way for a long time. Thus the stability may be in question. At 55 MPa the rate started to decay but then continued uniformly for about one minute. This condition then evolved into an accelerating output which signals impending gross failure. On this basis the SLS was estimated to be about 45 MPa.

6.4.4 Intermittent Profile (IP) (Fig. 4)

As is reported in section 6.1.2, the Kaiser Effect transition zone varies with different materials and stress levels relative to a material's strength. The Intermittent Profile graphically depicts how the transition zone for a particular material changes with the magnitude of previous stress. It assist in interpreting the portion of the transition zone which is best indicative of the RMS. It should be noted however, that the IP depicts a repetitive stress cycling. A single restressing of an extracted specimen will show a slightly different transition zone. This difference should be taken into account in the interpretation of the RMS.

Fig. 4 shows the cyclic restressing of a sandstone specimen to progressively higher increments. The Kaiser Effect change is clearly evident at each subsequent cycle.

It may be seen as generally typical of Intermittent Profiles that at low previous stress levels, the transition zone does not start until the new stress has exceeded the previous maximum. Whereas, at the high stress levels, the transition zone starts prior to the stress reaching the level of previous maximum.

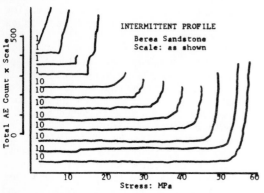

Fig. 4. Intermittent Profile (IP)

7. EXAMPLE TEST PROCEDURE

As an example of the testing procedure, the results obtained from a Berea Sandstone are shown. This is the same rock whose AE Signature Profiles are shown in Figs. 1, 2, 3 and 4.

A 54 mm diam core of this rock was stressed at 40 MPa for sufficient time to establish reasonable stability. It was then sub-cored parallel to the axis and 7 specimens tested. A resulting Two Phase Continuous Profile, typical of the group consensus, is shown in Fig. 5.

It shows the low and substantially uniform AE increase associated with the "past experience" region (a-b). It shows the start of the Kaiser Effect transition zone (b) and the accelerating rate of AE through it. The transition zone ends (c) with an almost straight and very steep plot typical of the "new experience" region. At that point (d) the AE scale was switched from 10 to 1000 and the remaining portion of the plot is consistent with the Single Phase Continuous Profile shown in Fig. 1 in

which the Ultimate Strength is in the order of 55 MPa.

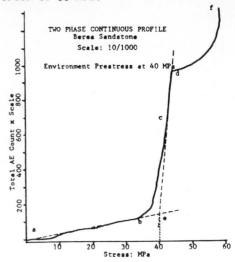

Fig. 5 Example Test for RMS

The RMS for this order of stress magnitude on sandstone may be best identified as the intersect (e) of the two tangents of the transition zone (a, b, e and c, d, e).

8. PRACTICAL APPLICATION OF KAISER EFFECT GAUGING

It is anticipated that with the above described techniques it will be readily feasible and practical to assess the stress field at a specific site by the laboratory testing of a sample extracted from that site. In order to facilitate this, a basic specimen size of 13 mm diameter has been selected and proven satisfactory. Thus, specimens may be prepared from subcores extracted in any direction from a standard rock core of size AQ (27 mm diam) or larger. Seven specimens can be extracted axially from a core size NX (54 mm diam).

Although the small size of specimen may cause reduced precision for some rocks due to large grain size, the small size makes multiple testing feasible resulting in improved statistical confidence in the derived results.

It is recognized that the equipment used to conduct the research relative to this investigation (see section 4) might not possess some of the desired features for practical application of this process. Some of these less desirable features are: high capital cost, low efficiency, bulky, and requiring considerable operator skill. Specialized equipment is currently under development which will overcome these conditions and provide a completely integrated "package" making the system available, on a practical and efficient basis to those who could benefit from it.

Some specific application opportunities for the system might be:

- the assessment of the maximum historic in-situ stress for a specific location and direction.

- the estimation of the additional amount of stress that can be withstood at a location without endangering its stability.

- by taking a series of tests from a location subject to increasing stress, determine the rate of stress increase and thus, the rate at which probable instability is approaching.

- estimation of the maximum stress and its distribution, experienced by a structural member.

- a new avenue of research relative to the strength and behaviour of materials under stress.

- a means for calibrating any instrument intended for in-situ monitoring.

9. CONSIDERATIONS FOR FUTURE INVESTIGATION

9.1 Kaiser Effect Retention Span (KERS)

Some previous authors (2,11,16) have raised questions relative to the capability of materials retaining a Kaiser Effect recollection over the passage of time, or under conditions of changing temperature and moisture. No firm conclusions have been reached. Preliminary studies by these authors suggest that different materials might have differing retention time spans. (A limestone apparently lost its recollection in about 20 days, whereas a granite specimen shows no loss of recollection after 65 days).

The KERS-Time could suggest from what depth into the past, the indicated RMS is being recalled (11).

KERS-Temperature and KERS-Moisture might reveal factors over which special care should be exercised.

9.2 AE Response versus Strain

It is felt likely that there is a relationship between AE output and dimensional strain of the specimen. If such a relationship could be established it might contribute to the science of testing materials.

9.3 Effect of Angular Deviation

Additional research should reveal the relationship between the AE response and the angle of deviation between principal stress axes within a stress field and the testing direction. If such a relationship cab be established, it will enable the determining of principal stress directions from a number of tests at various angles.

9.4 Rate of Stability Decay

The Dwell Profile provides an indication of the rate of AE decay at a particular stress level. It is likely that this data could be converted into a practical interpretation of the available time period before a structure under constant stress might become unreliable.

10. SUMMARY

It has been experimentally demonstrated that a sample of rock or concrete can be extracted from a stressed environment and through Acoustic Emission testing, it will reveal not only the magnitude of the maximum stress but how much more it might carry before becoming unstable. The techniques for performing this Kaiser Effect Gauging process are described showing it to be a functionally workable technology. Equipment is currently under development which will make it a practical system for determining the in-situ stresses in rock and concrete structures.

11. ACKNOWLEDGEMENT

These authors are grateful to Dr. H. Reginald Hardy, Jr. for his encouragement and assistance in the developing of this concept. They are also grateful to several Canadian mines and CANMET for providing samples of various rocks for testing. The work of A.M. Crawford was supported by the Natural Sciences and Engineering Research Council of Canada.

12. REFERENCES

1. Beattie, A.G., 1983, Acoustic Emission Principles and Instrumentation, Journal of Acoustic Emission, Vol. 2, No. 1/2, pp. 95-128.

2. Boyce, G.M., 1981. A Study of the Acoustic Emission Response of Various Rock Types, Master of Science Thesis, Drexel University.

3. Hardy, H.R., Jr., 1977. Proc. First Conf. on Acoustic Emission/Microseismic Activity in Geologic Structures and Materials, Hardy & Leighton, Trans Tech Publications.

4. Hardy, H.R., Jr., 1981. Applications of Acoustic Emission Techniques to Rock and Rock Structures: A State-of-the-Art Review, Acoustic Emissions in Geotechnical Engineering Practice. STP 750 American Society for Testing and Materials, pp. 4-92.

5. Hayashi, M., Kanagawa, T., Hibino, S., Motozima, M. and Y. Kitahara, 1979. Detection of Anisotropic Geo-Stresses Trying by Acoustic Emission and Non-linear Rock Mechanics on Large Excavating Caverns, Proc. 4th Int. Congress on Rock Mechanics, Montreux, Vol. 2, pp. 211-218.

6. Hayashi, M., 1979. Acoustic Emission to Detect the Geostress. Proc. 4th Int. Congress for Rock Mechanics, Montreux, Vol. 3, pp 230-231.

7. Hodgson, E.A., 1943. Trans. of the Canadian Inst. of Mining and Metallurgy, Toronto, Canada, Vol. 46, pp. 313.

8. Kaiser, J., 1953. Erkenntnisse und Folgerungen aus der Messung von Gerauschen bie Zugbeansprunchung von metallischen Werkstoffen, Archiv fur das Eisenhuttenwesen, Vol. 24, pp. 43-45.

9. Kanagawa, T., Hayashi, M., and Y. Kitahara, 1981. Acoustic Emission and Over Coring Methods for Measuring Tectonic Stresses. Proc. International Symposium on Weak Rock, Tokyo, Sept. 1981, pp. 1205-1210.

10. Kanagawa, T., Hayashi, M., and H. Nakasa, 1976. Estimation of Spatial Geo-Stress Components in Rock Samples using the Kaiser Effect of Acoustic Emission, Third Acoustic Emission Symposium, Tokyo, pp. 229--248.

11. Kurita, K., and N. Fujii, 1979. Stress Memory of Crystalline Rocks in Acoustic Emission, Geophysical Research Letters, Vol. 6, No. 1, pp. 9-12.

12. Lord, A.E., Jr., and R.M. Koerner, 1983. Journal of Acoustic Emission, Vol. 2, No. 3, pp. 195-219.

13. Obert, L., and W.I. Duvall, 1949. R.I. 3797 and 3803, U.S. Department of the Interior, Bureau of Mines.

14. Ren, N.K., and J.-C., Roegiers, 1983. Differential strain curve analysis - a New Method for Determining the Pre-Existing In-Situ stress state from Rock Core Measurements. 5th Int. Congress on Rock Mechanics, Melbourne, pp. F117-F127.

15. Vance, J.B. 1983. Application of Microseismic Techniques in Potash Mines, Potash Technology, R.M. McKercher ed. Pergaman Press, pp. 179-184.

16. Yoshikawa, S., and K. Mogi, 1978. Kaiser Effect of Acoustic Emission in Rocks. Influence of Water and Temperature Disturbances, The 4th Acoustic Emission Symposium, Tokyo, 1978, pp. 7/21-7/39.

17. Zhang, D.L., 1982, Use of the Kaiser Effect for the Estimation of the Previous State of Stress in Rock, Internal Report RML-IR/82-4, Dept. of Mineral Engineering, Pennsylvania State Universitgy.

A remotely operated borehole deformation gauge
for monitoring stress change in rock

R.L. BLACKWOOD
Consultant, Sydney, Australia

C. BUCKINGHAM
Department of Mining.Engineering, The University of New South Wales, Kensington, Australia

ABSTRACT: The initial prototype development of a new, high-technology, re-usable and relatively low cost instrument is described. The instrument uses an optical technique to measure borehole deformation, and microprocessor control to transmit the data in digital form via an infra-red signal to the operator.

RESUME: On décrit le développement du prototype d'un nouvel appareil à technologie avancée, réutilisable et relativement peu cher. L'appareil utilise une technique optique pour mesurer les variations de diamètre de trous de sonde, et se sert de contrôle par microprocesseur pour communiquer à l'opérateur les données en forme numérique au moyen d'un signal infra-rouge.

ZUSAMMENFASSUNG: Die erste Entwicklung eines Prototyps eines neuen, mit fortgeschrittener Technologie arbeitenden, mehrfach verwendbaren und relativ kostengünstigen Gerätes wird beschrieben. Das Gerät verwendet ein optisches Verfahren, um Verformungen des Bohrloches zu messen, und Kontrollen vermittels Mikroprozessoren um die Daten in digitaler Form über ein Infrarotsignal an den Maschinenführer weiterzuleiten.

1. INTRODUCTION

The principle of borehole deformation measurement as a rock stress measurement technique is well known. The best documented of the devices using this method is the U.S. Bureau of Mines borehole deformation gauge (BDG), described originally by Merrill (1967). If at least three diametral length changes due to stress relief by overcoring are measured in a plane normal to the borehole axis, the principal strains (and hence stresses) may be calculated for that plane. For determination of the complete stress tensor, at least three non-parallel overcored installations are required in isotropic rock; more, if the rock is anisotropic.

Present methods, including the BDG, measure changes in hole diameter by means of the deflection of strain gauged cantilevers pressing rigid probes against the wall of the hole. They present no resistance to borehole deformation, and hence the inference of planar stress is relatively straightforward (using the formulae contained in Obert and Duvall,

1967, pp 413-417, for instance). The cantilever/strain gauge response to diametral displacement must be calibrated before use. This system has a resolution of measurement, after calibration, of about $\pm 1 \times 10^{-6}$ m, equivalent to ± 26 microstrain in a 38 mm diameter (EX) hole. This is relatively insensitive when compared with electrical resistance strain gauges which nominally have a resoluton of ± 1 to 2 microstrain under favourable conditions (e.g. no creep or amplifier drift). Such a system, like most instrumentation, has both advantages and disadvantages when it comes to practical stress measurement in the field.

The advantages are: the instrument is re-usable, and is capable of multiple measurements in a single installation hole without great difficulty; it is stable compared to epoxy devices, because it is more or less unaffected by temperature changes in the rock or the drilling water.

Problems mainly arise from the obvious practical and economical constraints caused by the need to overcore three holes to obtain a single three-dimensional stress value. Other disadvantages arise from the need to calibrate the device before and after installation and, in common with all strain gauge techniques, the data is obtained in the form of a very small analogue signal which must be transmitted by cable and is thus subject to electrical interference in a typical mining or construction environment. In practice, this has mainly nuisance value, however, and can be overcome in most instances by the use of shielded cable, short lengths, careful choice of measuring site and so on. (The very need for an electrical cable, until now regarded as essential, causes practical problems at every stage of handling, installation and overcoring. It virtually prevents instruments like the BDG from being used as stress monitoring devices).

The natural and obvious tendency has been to develop instruments which measure the complete strain tensor during a single overcoring operation to reduce both the time and cost factors associated with stress measurement. Most of these employ strain gauge arrays in some form, either cemented directly to the wall of the borehole (Leeman/CSIR triaxial cell) or else in a hollow inclusion or solid inclusion configuration. These are commercially available for the most part and are so well known that it is not felt necessary to describe them further here.

It is interesting to note the results of comparative overcoring field tests in closely jointed rock (Gregory et al., 1983). The BDG was found to give the best performance, along with the CSIR doorstopper device, on the basis of consistency of results. Also, due to its simpler setting-up and installation procedures, the BDG technique enables a greater number of measurements to be carried out in a given time period, providing a larger sample of stress data and hence better confidence in the results than the other techniques tested. The BDG was also considerably more stable than the others, being relatively unaffected by temperature-induced creep. (The other instruments were: the CSIRO hollow inclusion device; the Swedish LuH triaxial cell (similar in concept to the Leeman cell); and the less well-known solid photoelastic cell developed at the University of California at Berkeley). Current Australian work on controlled overcoring trials tends to support these findings (Blackwood and Cai, in preparation).

2. BACKGROUND TO PRESENT DEVELOPMENT

The proven principle of the USBM/BDG has been adapted to updated technology to give:

a. Remote operation (no strain gauge cable or other connection).

b. Simplified installation.

c. Simplified data collection by the operator.

d. Immediate conversion of data into digital form before transmission to eliminate problems associated with serial transmission of very small analogue signals (e.g. microvoltage changes) over medium to long distances.

e. Comparable or better measurement precision.

f. A high degree of stability: no strain gauge drift, no epoxy creep, no installation cement creep, unaffected by moisture, temperature change etc.

In principle the USBM/BDG in its present form could be used for stress monitoring except perhaps for the questions of the cable (inviting accidental or malicious damage to the installation) and possibly strain gauge drift. Presumably for these and related reasons the BDG does not seem to have been seriously considered for this purpose. Other considerations include the relatively high initial cost of re-usable devices, each of which would be left on site for perhaps lengthy periods. Another important objection to the use of strain gauge based instruments for stress monitoring, apart from their technical performance as a whole, has to do with problems of re-connecting strain gauge leads to the read-out device, meaning that a strain amplifier and/or data logger may also be required to be left on site connected to the stress instrument on a semi-permanent basis. This is clearly undesirable close to a working excavation face where the risk of damage is high.

Nevertheless the principle of the BDG seems ideal for stress change monitoring if the above practical objections were overcome. In comparison with existing monitoring instruments, notably the vibrating-wire (Irad-type) gauge, the BDG has the decided advantage of acting as a "soft inclusion" that does not resist borehole deformation. Instruments that act as "rigid inclusions" which have an elastic modulus at least four times greater than the host rock may cause crushing of the rock in direct contact with the instrument and thus yield a truncated set of readings, since the crushed (yielded) rock no longer behaves elastically. This is particularly the case in weak rocks such as coal, for example.

3. PRINCIPLE OF OPERATION

The sensor of the present instrument uses a combination of old and new technologies. A re-usable borehole device contains radial probes which are pressed into contact with the rock wall of the hole; the probes are connected to superimposed, angularly misaligned glass plates having a grating of regular, closely spaced lines photographically inscribed on them. Displacement of the probes with rock deformation causes interference bands (moiré fringes) to move across the field of view. The movement of the fringes is an amplified measure of the movement of the probes. In the sensor, a small light source produces enough light to create a moiré fringe pattern. Movement of the fringes caused by borehole deformation is detected electronically and converted into a digital signal by a microprocessor built into the body of the instrument.

3.1 Moiré fringe method

In conventional use of moiré fringes for strain measurement on a surface, a grating is bonded to the surface and another grating is superimposed onto it, either in contact with it or as part of an optical projection system. Angular misalignment and/or spacing pitch difference between the two gratings creates an interference fringe pattern (the "moiré effect"). Straining of the surface causes relative movement between the gratings which is observed as movement of the fringes. With commercially available gratings having a spacing of, say, 40 lines/mm (1000 lines/in) and using various interpolation techniques a direct strain measurement sensitivity of ±100 microstrain, at best, can be achieved in this way (Luxmoore, 1978).

In the present case, however, the gratings are used to measure displacement rather than strain and the sensitivity is correspondingly improved; this is set out in more detail below. A typical moiré fringe pattern of the type used here is shown in Figure 1.

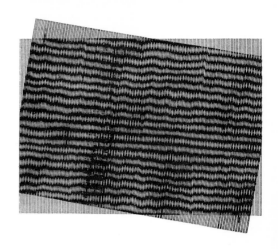

Figure 1. Moiré fringes on similar gratings having a small angular misalignment.

In this instance we are faced with the problem that the gratings are located in a borehole in rock and cannot be directly observed by an operator. Thus as well as the inbuilt light source, a means of remotely observing fringe movement is required. This has been resolved in the following way.

3.2 Electro-optic sensor

Movement of the moiré fringes is detected by an infra-red light emitting diode shining a beam through the gratings such that the moiré fringes are directly imaged onto a charged coupled device (CCD) which behaves as a simple line camera of 128 pixels resolution. The number of moiré fringes directed onto the CCD and the grating line density together govern the precision of measurement of the system. In the prototype, 1.5 to 3 fringes and 40 lines/mm were adopted. The distance corresponding to one fringe movement is then approximately 25×10^{-6} m which gives a precision of better than $\pm 1 \times 10^{-8}$ m when divided by the pixel resolution, which is comparable to the USBM/BDG. Minor modification of the sensor can improve this displacement resolution by a factor of at least 10, i.e. down to 0.1×10^{-6} m, which corresponds to a strain resolution of ±2 microstrain in a 50 mm diameter borehole, for instance. This is approximately the same as the best attainable with

371

electrical resistance strain gauges even under laboratory conditions. It appears highly probable that this level of resolution will be significantly improved with further development in hand.

Timing signals for the CCD (for transport of the charge to the output, charge reset, and timing between scans) are supplied through drivers from a single chip microprocessor, which also handles all processing and control of the data transmission.

The sensor is entirely controlled by a microcomputer operated by the observer, so that operating parameters can be modified by software changes only.

4. PROTOTYPE DEVELOPMENT

The first prototype consisted of an aluminium body containing the sensor, moiré gratings, probes and control hardware wired by a single serial line to the receiver (initially an Apple microcomputer); see Figure 2.

The output display shown in Figure represents 128 successive samples of location of the fringe as seen by CCD. These are dislayed in the form o: sine wave. The apparent movement of wave is from right to left. probability of occurrence of a point any one pixel is computed by an iterat. Gaussian smoothing technique written machine code into the microprocess Crossover points across the average determined and this information finally tabulated in micrometres displacement of the moiré gratings.

In a further development the ser line was replaced by a remote infra-transmission system which eliminates need for any wire link between sensor receiver. This theoretically allows instrument to be located in relativ long holes.

The transmitted data is read by observer as diametral deformation on portable display unit.

Eventually, field versions of instrument will be cast in epoxy protect components.

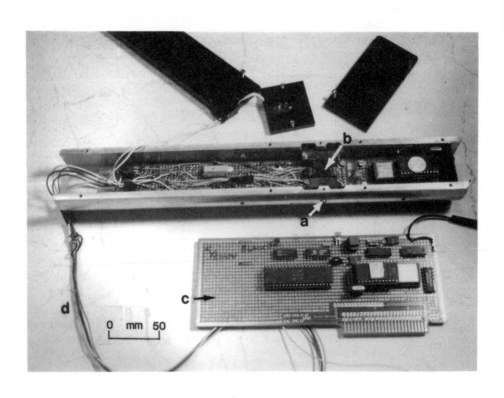

Figure 2. Prototype instrument showing (a) probes; (b) moiré gratings on glass plat (c) receiver circuit board used with Apple p.c.; (d) serial transmission line (la replaced by remote infra-red system).

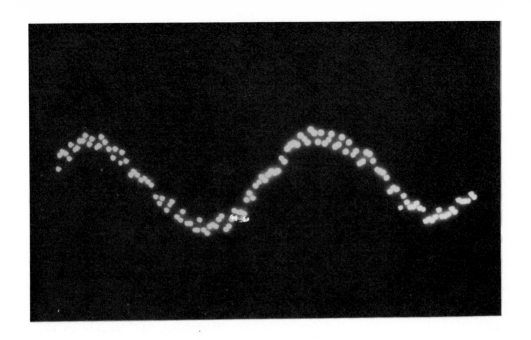

Figure 3. Visual display of location of moiré fringe relative to initial position, shown as a sine wave made up of individual pixels, during Gaussian smoothing process.

5. APPLICATION OF THE INSTRUMENT

The instrument is seen primarily as a stress monitoring device, since it does not require any cable connection to the data receiver. It can be left in the borehole during the critical phase of the stress change being studied and data may be collected by the observer whenever required from a position somewhere near the collar of the hole. This will give a visual display of the diametral change in the borehole which is directly correlated with the previous readings, whether an hour, day or several weeks previously, because the sensor/probe system is inherently stable. Suitable programming can then be used on site to compute the stress change represented by the diameter change. Since the data is in digital form, an alternative system might use a data logger, remote acoustic (telephone line) transmission to a central site, or a combination of these.

The prototype contained only a single pair of sensors across one diameter. It is a simple matter to multiplex and transmit data from three or more identical sensors within one instrument, oriented in delta or 90 degree rosette configuration, to enable principal strains to be computed in the diametral plane without further instrument re-orientation. This modification is in hand at the time of writing.

In the above description, the emphasis has been on the use of the instrument as a monitoring device, since this is where there is a perceived need in rock mechanics field instrumentation. The instrument could also be used to measure absolute stresses in the same way as the present USBM/BDG, however, in conjunction with overcoring. More important perhaps is the significance of the possibility of very fine resolution measurement down to $\pm 0.01 \times 10^{-6}$ m or better. This implies that methods of partial stress relief (e.g. parallel boreholes close to the installation hole, Habib et al., 1969, or the in-hole slotting technique of Bock and Foruria, 1984) could become viable with precision equal to that of overcoring but using a simpler, quicker and cheaper method. The ability to transmit deformation data continuously will greatly simplify the important ancillary task of monitoring changes in borehole diameter during complete or partial stress relief to validate field readings (Blackwood, 1978).

6. CONCLUSION

The instrument described enables a greatly enhanced use of the BDG principle, especially as a sensitive, stable and easily used stress-change monitoring instrument. The ability to transmit digital data without cables is an important advance in the technique.

7. ACKNOWLEDGEMENT

The authors would like to record their gratitude to Unisearch Limited, a research and development subsidiary company of The University of New South Wales, in Sydney, Australia, for financial assistance in the initial prototype development and for encouragement and assistance in the processing of patents application. The invention has been assigned to Unisearch who are currently seeking to establish its commercial development.

8. REFERENCES

Blackwood, R.L. 1978. Diagnostic Stress-relief Curves in Stress Measurement by Overcoring. Internat. J. Rock Mechanics & Geomechanics Abstracts 15:205-209.

Blackwood, R.L. and M. Cai 1986. A Comparison of Stress Measurement Devices in Different Rock Conditions. Univ. New South Wales School of Mines. In preparation.

Bock, H. and V. Foruria 1984. A Recoverable Borehole Slotting Instrument for In Situ Stress Measurement in Rocks, Not Requiring Overcoring. Proc. Internat. Symp. on Field Measurements in Geomechanics, Zürich, publ. Balkema, Rotterdam, 1:15-29.

Gregory, E.G., T.A. Rundle, W.M. McCa and K. Kim 1983. In Situ Stre Measurement in a Jointed Basalt. Pro Rapid Excavation and Tunnelli Conference, Chicago 1:42-61.

Habib, P., L.M. Phong and K. Pakdam 1969. Mesures des Contraint Naturelles par une Méthode Relâchements Successifs. Pro Symposium on Determination of Stress in Rock Masses, Internat. Soc. Ro Mechanics, Lisbon, 135-144.

Luxmoore, A.R. 1978. Developments Moiré and Laser Methods of Stre Analysis. In "Developments in Stre Analysis - 1" (G.S. Holister, ed. Applied Science Publishers, Londo 161-191.

Merrill, R.H. 1967. Three-compone Borehole Deformation Gage f Determining the Stresses in Rock. U. Bureau of Mines Report of Investigati No. RI 7015.

Obert, L. and W.I. Duvall 1967. Ro Mechanics and the Design of Structur in Rock. Wiley, New York.

About the rock stress measurement using the LFJ (large flat jack) technique

N.F. GROSSMAN
R.J.C. CÂMARA
Laboratório Nacional de Engenharia Civil, (LNEC), Lisboa, Portugal

ABSTRACT

The LFJ test is often also employed for the determination of the mean normal stress existing at the test location in the direction perpendicular to the cutted slot(s). As is shown with the help of a three-dimensional Finite Element study, many of the measuring point patterns used so far for that determination, together with the rather great frequency of the readings performed, lead to a huge amount of data, the major part of which has no practical interest. Recommendations are made about the measuring point patterns to be used, and the frequency of the readings to be made.

RÉSUMÉ

L'essai LFJ est souvent aussi employé pour la détermination de la contrainte normale moyenne existante à l'endroit de l'essai dans la direction perpendiculaire à la(aux) saignée(s) coupée(s). Comme il est montré à l'aide d'une étude tridimensionelle par éléments finis, beaucoup des dispositions de points de mesure utilisées jusqu'ici pour cette détermination, conjointement avec l'assez grande fréquence des lectures effectuée, conduisent à un nombre très élevé de données, dont la plupart n'a aucun intérêt pratique. On fait des recommandations concernant les dispositions de points de mesure à utiliser, et la fréquence des lectures à faire.

ZUSAMMENFASSUNG

Der LFJ Versuch wird oft auch zur Bestimmung der am Versuchsort in der Richtung senkrecht zu dem (den) gesaegten Schlitz(en) herrschenden mittleren Normalspannung angewandt. Wie mit Hilfe einer dreidimensionalen Finite-Element-Untersuchung gezeigt wird, fuehren viele der bisher fuer jene Bestimmung benutzten Messpunktanordnungen, zusammen mit der recht grossen Haeufigkeit der durchgefuehrten Ablesungen, zu einer sehr hohen Anzahl von Daten, deren Grossteil keinen praktischen Wert hat. Es werden Empfehlungen bezueglich der zu benutzenden Messpunktanordnungen, und der Haeufigkeit der durchzufuehrenden Lesungen nahegelegt.

1 - INTRODUCTION

The LFJ (large flat jack) test, developed by the Laboratório Nacional de Engenharia Civil (LNEC), has been announced during the 1st ISRM Congress (Rocha 1966), was officially presented with its first applications during the 1st ISRM-sponsored International Symposium (Rocha 1968), and had its baptism of fire at the location of an international project still in 1968 (LNEC 1969). Since then, it has already been employed by the LNEC in 11 countries of 4 continents.

The LFJ test is basically a slot opening test for the determination of the deformability of a large volume of rock mass in undisturbed conditions. Its main advantage in relation to other slot opening tests lies in the fact that the slot(s) is(are) opened by means of a diamond-disk saw with 1 m diameter, and, therefore, the slot walls are usually smooth, making it possible to have the special jacks with the form of the slots (LFJs) (Fig.1) ap-

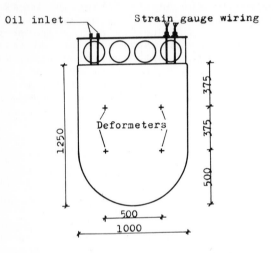

Oil inlet ____ Strain gauge wiring

Deformeters

1250

375

375

500

500

1000

Fig.1 Large flat jack (LFJ)

ply their pressure directly onto the rock mass surface. Descriptions of the LFJ technique and equipment are given both in (Rocha 1968) and (Loureiro-Pinto 1981), the latter paper presenting also a full account of the theory of the test, and of the interpretation of the results in terms of the determination of the deformability modulus of the concerned rock mass.

Already for the first applica - tions, the possibility of using the LFJ test for the determination of the mean normal stress existing at the test location in the direction perpendicular to the cutted slot(s), was also considered, and the fact that the existence of an unloaded strip near the test chamber surface introduced a certain error in this determination, duly acknow-

ledged (Rocha 1968).

This paper, which is based on the experience gained during the almost 20 years of application of the LFJ technique, wishes to give a contribution towards an easier, but equally efficient performance of the part of the LFJ test aiming at the determination of the cancelling pressure.

2 - TEST TECHNIQUE

2.1 Contact seat pattern

If a LFJ test is also to be used for the determination of the mean normal stress existing at the test location in the direction perpendicular to the cutted slot(s), contact seats have to be set on the rock mass surface, or on bolts embedded in the rock mass, already prior to the opening of the auxiliary hole (for the diamond disk support column) of the first slot. The number and emplacement of the contact seats (and bolts) has no fixed rules. It is, however, usual to have the contact seat pattern around each future slot correspond to the vertices of a rectangular grid with slot-perpendicular columns and slot-parallel rows, the whole pattern being symmetric in relation to the saw column borehole.

The initial spacing between the 2 contact seats of each pair whose distance is to be monitored during the test, has, of course, to fall into the measuring range of the mechanical deformeter used ((20, 30, or 40)±0,25 cm in the case of the instrument developed by the LNEC (Fig. 2), which is fitted with

Fig.2 Mechanical deformeter with a measurement base of 40 c

a 0,001 mm dial gauge).On the other hand, the location of the slot-perpendicular contact seat columns has also some limitations imposed by the presence of the base of the frame which supports the disk saw (Fig. 3), during the drilling and

Fig.3 LFJ cutting machine with support frame

cutting operations, and by the prominent parts (oil inlets and electric connections) of the LFJ (Fig. 1), after the introduction of the jack into the slot.
When using a LNEC-made mechanical deformeter, the base of the support frame will prevent readings to be made on contact seats belonging to slot-perpendicular lines at a distance between 19 and 31 cm from the saw column borehole axis. If, however, the contact seats are placed in recesses of the test chamber surface, this limitation is not absolute, as the monitoring will only be impossible during the drilling and cutting operations.
The prominent parts of the LFJ prevent, for the same deformeter, readings to be made on contact seats belonging to slot-perpendicular lines at a distance between 27 and 43 cm from the saw column borehole axis, with the exception of the lines at the distance of 35 cm, for which the instrument fits exactly between the 2 oil inlets, or the 2 cable outlets. This limitation is, on the contrary, imperative, as it affects not only intermediate, but also the final readings.
As to the localization of the contact seats in relation to the test

chamber surface, the best, although, from a practical point of view,more difficult choice is to have them placed in recesses of the surface. This solution prevents the colli - sions with the contact seats of the usually wet and/or greasy heavy equipment pieces, like the support frame, the filled up core barrel, the disk-saw, etc., which have often to be handled by the crew in quite awkward positions, under the habitual bad illumination of the test chambers.
The question of whether to place the contact seats directly on the rock mass surface, or on bolts embedded in the rock mass, should be preferably decided in favour of the first solution, on the grounds that it is the easier procedure,and that it does not cause any disturbance to the rock mass.
A major reason to be eventually in favour of the second solution,would be the presence of approximately test chamber surface-parallel open discontinuites (rock mass joints, or the contact surface between the test chamber surface mortar and the rock mass), preventing the external rock and/or mortar block with the contact seat(s) from moving together with the more interior zones of the rock mass during the application of the pressure by the LFJ. It should, however, be kept in mind that the presence of bolts will always constitute a kind of rock mass reinforcement, and that,therefore, some changes will probably occur in the deformability characteristics of the rock mass tested. Unfortunately, these changes usually cause the results of the test to lie on the unsafe side.

2.2 Test execution

Once the contact seats have been placed, the initial reading of the different distances to be monitored should be performed a couple of times, in order to reduce errors to a minimum.
The monitoring during the opening of the saw-column borehole will usually have no practical interest, and should, therefore, be reduced to only a few control readings of

the contact seat pairs in the imme
diate vicinity of the borehole.
The monitoring during the slot opening,
on the contrary, should include,if possible, readings of all contact seat pairs,
in order to detect eventual anomalies
of the rock mass behaviour. These readings are especially important during the
first part of the slot opening.
Immediately after the insertion of the
LFJ in the slot, and the removal of the
disk-saw support frame, the final slot-
-opening reading should be performed,and,
as it is again an important reading, a
couple of times, in order to reduce
errors to a minimum.
One of the main handicaps of the LFJ test,
when used for the determination of the in
-situ stresses, lies in the large period
of time (some days) which usually elap-
ses between the insertion of the LFJ(s)
in the slot(s), and the start of the pres
sure application. This disadvantage is
especially important when the test is
performed in a creepy rock mass subjected to a high state of stress.
In order to minimize the influence of'
the creep phenomena, the pressure application should always take place as soon
as possible after the completion of the
slot(s).
The new initial reading of all pairs of
contact seats just before the start of
the pressure application, should again
be performed a couple of times, in order
to reduce errors to a minimum.
The monitoring during the pressure application has the main purpose of determining the cancellation
pressure, this being the pressure
for which the movements induced
with the pressure application between the contact seats of the
different pairs, are just the
opposite of the movements caused
by the borehole and slot opening.
It follows, therefore, that the
monitoring of the different distances has basically to be perfor
med during the first loading of
the rock mass, especially for the
pressure levels in the immediate
vicinity of the cancellation pressure, for which it would again be
convenient to carry out the readings a couple of times, in order
to reduce errors to a minimum.
The monitoring of the different
contact seat pair movements once
the cancellation pressure has been
determined, will usually have no

practical interest, and should, th
refore, be reduced to only a few
control readings, in order to detect
eventual anomalies of the rock mas
behaviour.

3. TEST ANALYSIS

3.1 Description of the model

In order to assess the evolution
of the displacements of the differen
points on the test chamber surfac
during the borehole and slot open
ing procedure, as well as with th
pressure application, a three-dime
sional finite element model was
studied.
The used mesh (Fig.4) had 940 noda
points and a total of 693 elements
and the assumed isotropic elastic
material characteristics were:

E=10.000 MPa
V=0,2

A three-orthogonal coordinate sys
tem (x,y,z) was chosen, in which
axis z was normal to the test cha
ber surface, axis y normal to th
slot plane, and axis x, therefore
parallel to the test chamber surf
ce, and lying in the slot plane.
Two cases were considered, in bot
of which the initial state of stres
was reduced to only one normal stres
of 1MPa. In case A, the normal stres
occurred in the direction of axi
x, and, in case B, it occurred i
the direction of axis y.
The borehole and slot opening pro
cedure was simulated in 4 stages:
1) Opening of the borehole;
2) Opening of a slot with a dept
    of 0,63 m (Zone 1) (Fig.4);
3) Opening of further 0,37 m of th
    slot (Zone 2);
and
4) Full opening of the slot (Zone 3
For the calculation correspondin
to the loading of the slot surfac
by the LFJ, a pressure of agai
1 MPa was considered.

3.2 Analysis of the results

The analysis of the movements obtaine
for the different nodal points o

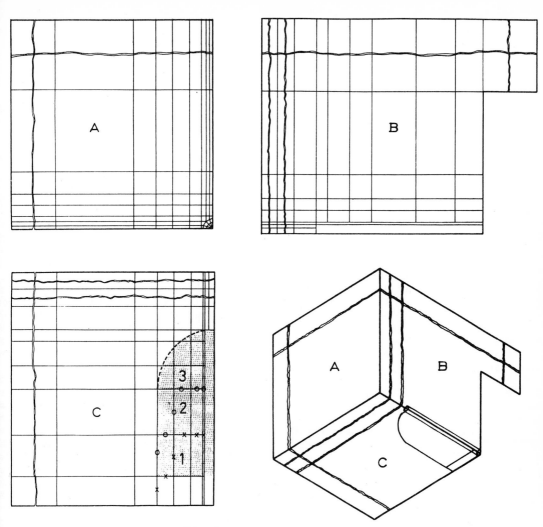

Fig.4 Finite element model

the test chamber surface, during the borehole and slot opening, shows that the maximum slot-perpendicular displacements will be measured on the central slot-perpendicular contact seat pair(over the borehole). With a 20 cm measurement base deformeter, for case A (slot-parallel normal stress only), an increase of the contact seat distance of about 12 μm, after the borehole drilling, and of about another 4 μm (giving a total of 16 μm), after the slot cutting, would be determined, while, for case B (slot--perpendicular normal stress only), a decrease of about 29 μm, after the borehole drilling, of about another 107 μm, after the first

part of the slot cutting (Zone 1), and of about another 35 μm (giving a total of 171 μm), after the full slot cutting, would be measured. For a 40 cm measurement base deformeter, the corresponding values would be, respectively, 8 μm, 4 μm, (12 μm), 15 μm, 99 μm, 35 μm, and (149 μm).

The conclusions to be drawn from these results are:

a) The use of a deformeter with a smaller measurement base will permit the reading of larger slot-perpendicular displacements, and, therefore, increase the accuracy of the cancellation pressure determination;

b) Due to the large difference in

the order of magnitude of the slot-perpendicular displacements induced in cases B and A (a relation of more than 10 to 1), a primary analysis, considering only the existence of a slot-perpendicular normal stress, is usually justifiable; and

c) As has already been hinted above, the major part of the slot-perpendicular displacements induced by the slot cutting, occur during the first part of that operation (about 75% of the displacement, for less than 50% of the slot depth).

Considering the movements of the nodal points corresponding to the slot-perpendicular contact seat pairs over the slot, at a distance of, at least, 10 cm from the saw column borehole axis, the total slot-perpendicular displacements to be measured during the borehole and slot opening, are, for case A, always less than 8 μm, and practically inexistent for those contact seat pairs whose distance from the borehole axis is more than about 25 cm.

For case B, however, although the borehole drilling also only induces slot-perpendicular displacements of less than 11 μm, which again become practically inexistent for the contact seat pairs whose distance from the borehole axis is more than about 25 cm, the total slot-perpendicular displacements, after the slot cutting, are, for the contact seat pairs, at a distance of, 10, 20 and 35 cm from the borehole axis, respectively, about 95, 85, and 58% of the corresponding displacement for the central slot-perpendicular contact seat pair (over the borehole).

From these results, the following conclusions may be drawn:

d) Although the accuracy of the cancellation pressure determination diminishes continuously with the increasing distance from the saw column borehole axis of the considered contact seat pair, even at a distance of 45 cm, readings are still useful, as a slot-perpendicular displacement of more than 25% of the correspond

ing displacement of the central contact seat pair will b observed;

e) As the relation between th slot-perpendicular displacemen induced in cases B and A, in creases continuously with th increasing distance from th saw column borehole axis of th considered contact seat pair the influence of the slot-para lel normal stress decrease rapidly with the increase o that distance; for distance of more than about 25 cm, th slot-perpendicular displace ments are independent of th slot-parallel normal stress and

f) As has already been hinte above, no slot-perpendicula displacement will be observe during the saw column borehol drilling, for contact sea pairs, at a distance of, a least, about 25 cm from th borehole axis.

Considering now the movements o the nodal points corresponding t the slot-perpendicular contact sea pair row lying next to the ro formed by the pairs having on contact seat on each side of th slot, the total slot-perpendicula displacements to be measured du ing the borehole and slot openin are, for case A, always less tha 5 μm, and pratically inexisten for all contact seat pairs excep the central one (the one for whic the two contact seats lye on line cutting the saw column bo rehole axis).

For case B, however, although th borehole drilling also only ind ces slot-perpendicular displace ments of less than 10 μm, whic again are pratically inexisten for all contact seat pairs excep the central one, the total slot -perpendicular displacements after the slot cutting, are, fo the contact seat pairs to be rea with a 20, 30, or 40 cm measure ment base deformeter, respectively about -12, -16, or -22% of th corresponding displacement fc the neighbour slot-perpendicula contact seat pair over the slo to be read with the same defor meter. These last results hold fo those contact seat pairs, for which the two contact seats lye on a line at a distance of not more than about 25 cm from the saw column borehole axis. Curiously, for those contact seat pairs, for which the two contact seats lye on a line at a distance of more than 30 cm from the borehole axis, the slot-perpendicular displacements are independent of the measurement base length of the used deformeter, and vary between an increase of the contact seat distance of about 12 μm (for the contact seat pair, for which the two contact seats lye on a line at a distance of 35 cm from the borehole axis) and a decrease of the contact seat distance of about 8 μm (for the contact seat pair, for which the two contact seats lye on a line at a distance of 50 cm from the borehole axis).

From these results, the following conclusions may be drawn:

g) On the contrary of what had been concluded for the slot-perpendicular contact seat pairs over the slot (conclusion a)), for the slot-perpendicular contact seat pairs of the neighbour rows, it is the use of a deformeter with a larger measurement base that will permit the reading of larger displacements, and, therefore, increase the accuracy of the cancellation pressure determination;

h) Anyhow, as the absolute values of the slot-perpendicular displacements for the slot-perpendicular contact seat pairs of the neighbour rows are always less than 25% of the maximum corresponding displacement observable for the slot-perpendicular contact seat pairs over the slot, the use of slot-perpendicular contact seat pairs other than those over the slot, is always questionable; and

i) Conclusions e) and f) are also valid for the slot-perpendicular contact seat pairs of the neighbour rows, if the distance considered is the one from the point half-way between the contact seats, to the saw column borehole axis.

The analysis of the movements of the nodal points corresponding to the slot-parallel contact seat pairs, shows that the maximum slot-parallel displacements to be measured during the borehole and slot opening, are of the same order of magnitude as the maximum slot-perpendicular displacements to be measured on the off the slot slot-perpendicular contact seat pair rows.

It further shows that, for those contact seat pairs, for which the maximum slot-parallel displacements are to be expected, the movements induced in cases A and B, are of opposed signs and of the same order of magnitude.

The following conclusions may be drawn from the results:

j) Due to the small values of the slot-parallel displacements induced, the use of slot-parallel contact seat pairs is always questionable;

k) The maximum slot-parallel displacements are measured on those slot-parallel contact seat pairs, for which both contact seats are at the same distance from the saw column borehole axis, and these maximum displacements increase with the decrease of the distance between the contact seats and the slot; and

l) As the slot-parallel displacements induced after the borehole drilling, are bigger in case A than in case B, these values may, eventually, allow a guess on an existing slot-parallel normal stress.

Finally, the movements of the nodal points during the loading of the slot surface by the LFJ, shall be considered.

Using the movements of the nodal points in the vicinity of the LFJ deformeter locations, a back-analysis of the elastic modulus of the rock mass was performed, giving the following results:

$$E_e = 10.200 \text{ MPa}$$

$$E_i = 11.200 \text{ MPa}$$

E_e denoting the value obtained

using the displacements in the vi
cinity of the LFJ deformeters situated nearer to the test chamber
surface, and E_i the value obtained
using the displacements in the vi
cinity of the LFJ deformeters situated deeper in the rock mass.
While the agreement between the mo
del value and the first value indicated is remarkable, the slight
difference for the second value
may be explained by the geometry
of the used loading area (Fig.4).
As concerns the slot-perpendicular
displacements to be measured on
the slot-perpendicular contact seat
pairs over the slot, at a distance
of less than 25 cm from the saw
column borehole axis, with a 20,
30, or 40 cm measurement base deformeter, they are, respectively,
about 31, 35, or 38% of the corresponding displacements during
the borehole and slot opening. For
the slot-perpendicular contact seat
pairs over the slot, at a distance of 35 cm from the borehole axis,
the displacements to be measured
are, even, respectively, 28, 31,
or 38%.
A part of this reduction is, of
course, due to the difference betwe
en the area of the cutted slot
$(1,39 \text{ m}^2)$ and the area loaded by
the LFJ $(1,14 \text{ m}^2)$. But the major
part of the reduction is a consequence of the fact that a strip
of the rock mass in the vicinity
of the test chamber surface remains unloaded.
It must, however, be noticed that,
in the practice, the unloaded strip
is usually much smaller, as the
rock mass stresses only act fully
behind a surface defined by the
rock mass recesses which existed
prior to the application of the
mortar onto the test chamber surface.
In order to give an idea of the
relation between the displacements
induced during the different stages of the borehole and slot open
ing, and those caused by the load
ing with the LFJ, Fig.5 presents
the slot-perpendicular displacements
along the 2 slot-parallel lines,
at a distance of 10 cm from the slot,
shown in that figure. The numbers
1 to 3 correspond to the different
slot opening stages defined in

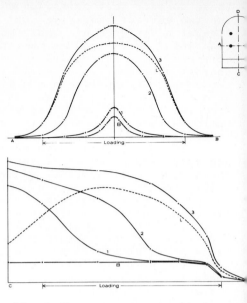

Fig.5 Slot-perpendicular displacemen

Fig.4, while B denotes the curve f
the borehole opening, and L t
one for the loading with the LF

4 - CONCLUSION

In order to minimize some of the
curring errors, and taking into c
sideration that usually a LFJ te
will be performed with, at least,
jacks, it is proposed to use for the
termination of the in-situ state
stress the following procedure:
1) To open, at the location of t
1st slot, before the opening
of the saw column borehole,
slot with only 45 cm depth, a
to introduce therein immedia
ly a half-moon shaped flat j
without unloaded strip.
The measuring point pattern shou
consist of 4 or 5 slot-perpe
dicular contact seat pairs o
the slot, preferably to be re
with a 20 cm measurement base
formeter.
2) Should a significant displac
ment have been recorded duri
that slot opening, a measuri
point pattern consisting of
contact seat pairs over the
rehole, at angles of $45°$, shou
be installed at the location
the 2nd slot, and readings

382

ken for the first about 50 cm saw
column borehole drilling.
The 1st slot would give the cancellation pressure, and with the
readings of the 2nd borehole, and
the elastic modulus obtaïned with
the LFJ test, a certain information on the stresses existing in
the not-slot-perpendicular directions could be obtained.

5 - REFERENCES

LNEC (Laboratório Nacional de En-
    genharia Civil). 1969. In Situ
    Tests at the Reza Shah Kabir Dam
    Site (Karun River), a report.
    LNEC, Lisboa PORTUGAL.
Loureiro-Pinto J. 1981. Determina-
    tion of the Deformability Modu-
    lus of Weak Rock Masses by Means
    of Large Flat Jacks (LFJ), a pa
    per. In Weak Rock — Soft, Fractur
    ed and Weathered Rock (Akai K.,
    Hayashi M., and Nishimatsu Y.,
    Ed.) (Proceedings of the Inter
    national Symposium on Weak Rock,
    Tokyo JAPAN, 1981 September 21-
    -24). A.A.Balkema, Rotterdam NE
    THERLANDS. 1:447-452.
Rocha M. 1966. Rock Mechanics in
    Portugal — La Mécanique des Ro-
    ches au Portugal — Felsmechanik
    in Portugal, an address. In Pro
    ceedings of the First Congress
    of the International Society of
    Rock Mechanics — Comptes-Rendus
    du Premier Congrès de la Société
    Internationale de Mécanique des
    Roches — Sitzungsberichte des
    Ersten Kongresses der Internatio-
    nalen Gesellschaft fuer Felsme-
    chanik (Lisboa PORTUGAL, 1966
    September 25 - October 01). Labo
    ratório Nacional de Engenharia
    Civil,Lisboa PORTUGAL. 3:121-141.
Rocha M. 1968. New Techniques for
    the Determination of the Defor-
    mability and State of Stress in
    Rock Masses, a paper. In Procee
    dings of the International Sym
    posium on Rock Mechanics — Comp
    tes-Rendus du Symposium Interna
    tional de Mécanique des Roches —
    — Berichte des Internationalen
    Symposiums fuer Felsmechanik
    (Madrid SPAIN, 1968 October 22-
    -24). Editorial Blume, Madrid
    and Barcelona SPAIN. 289-302.

3. Interpretation of rock stresses

A critical examination of basic concepts associated with the existence and measurement of in situ stress

A.J. HYETT
C.G. DYKE
J.A. HUDSON
Department of Mineral Resources Engineering, Imperial College of Science and Technology, London, United Kingdom

Abstract

The stress state in a rock mass is a function of both the present tectonic regime and the stress history. Mechanical and geometrical factors must also be considered. Residual stresses are discussed and a glossary of terms is presented. The effect of measurement scale and the consequence of stress field superimposition are highlighted. The ramifications for interpreting measured stress fields and establishing the appropriate boundary conditions for design are included.

Resumé

L'etat des contraintes dans un massif rocheux dépend du regime tectonique, à la fois présent et passé, ainsi que de différents facteurs mécaniques et géometriques. Une discussion des contraintes résiduelles et un glossaire sont présentés. L'importance de l'éffet d'échelle et les résultats de la superposition des champs de contraintes sont mis en évidence. Les conséquences sur l'interprétation des mesures des contraintes en place et sur l'établissement de conditions aux limites adéquates lors du design d'ouvrages sont établies.

Zusammenfassung

Die Spannungsverteilung in einer Gebirgmasse ist eine Funktion der gegenwärtigen tektonischen Regime und auch der historischen Spannungsverteilung der Masse. Mechanische und geometrische Faktoren müssen auch in Acht genommen werden. Restspannungen werden besprochen und es gibt auch ein Glossar der Fachausdrücke. Effekt des Gesteinvolumens und Auswirkung der Spannungsfelduberlagerung werden hervorgehoben. Die Verzweigungen fur die Interpretation der abgemessenen Spannungsfelder und die Herstellung der entsprechenden Grenzzustände fur die Entwurf werden auch dargestellt.

1. INTRODUCTION

Since problems in rock engineering were first approached on a fundamental mechanics basis (requiring a knowledge of the rock properties and the boundary conditions), it has been recognized that the natural in situ rock stress is an important component for analysis and design. This recognition has been heightened in recent years by projects in which the in situ stress can be crucial (eg geothermal energy) and the increasing computing capability available for analyzing the stresses in complex rock engineering projects. Also, increasing current awareness of the subject is evidenced by this Symposium initiative, the recent compilation of the ISRM Suggested Methods for measuring in situ stress, and enhanced research activities throughout the world.

Many difficulties have arisen over the years during the consideration and measurement of in situ stress. These difficulties have been caused by the nature of in situ stress itself. The stress field in a rock mass cannot be measured directly; stress is a tensor quantity with six independent components; the stress field is affected by the anisotropic, inhomogeneous and discontinuous nature of rock masses; there is often confusion about the many terms used to describe in situ stress, etc.

At this stage in the development of rock mechanics, we have reached a watershed in the subject of in situ stress. A great deal of work has been completed, measurement techniques are steadily being enhanced, and the importance of knowing the stress field for engineering design is now recognized. In this paper, therefore, we report the results of a re-examination of the basic concepts associated with the existence and measurement of in situ stress. What are the geological factors governing the development of in situ stress? What types of stresses could exist in a rock mass? Are the many terms describing in situ stress well defined? What, for example, is a residual stress? These aspects are discussed in the next section of the paper.

In Section 3, we consider the stress field produced by the super-imposition of two or more component stress fields - both via fundamental theory and the Mohr circle representation. In Section 4, there is discussion of the conflict between stress as a point property and the need to obtain average values over a representative elemental volume to account for the presence of

discontinuities. This leads naturally to the concept of a 'macro-stress measurement' which would probably be achieved in practice by tunnel undercoring. Finally, the ramifications of the ideas are presented in the contexts of in situ stress measurement programmes, data reduction, and research activities.

2. EXISTENCE OF ROCK STRESS AND GLOSSARY OF TERMS

2.1 Existence of In Situ Stresses

Natural in situ stresses are a complex interaction between four fundamental driving mechanisms:
gravitational loading,
tectonic forces,
thermal energy variations, and
physico-chemical processes
(see Glossary in Section 2.3).

In situ stress measurements and earthquake focal mechanisms indicate that tectonic forces are the dominant driving mechanism for regional scale in situ stresses. How are these stresses generated and how are they transmitted over sub-continental distance? In relatively homogeneous oceanic crust, the distribution of in situ stress is primarily a reflection of present tectonic activity (Richardson, 1978). However, the situation is more complex in continental crust because existing geological stuctures complicate the regional mechanical behaviour at both crustal and sub-crustal depths.

Meissner and Strelau (1982) recognized a relation between the depth-frequency distribution of shallow earthquakes and the predicted limits of shear stress in a quartzo-feldspathic crust. Their result (illustrated in Fig. 1) predicts that high levels of stress are generated in the middle crust, probably by displacement of the middle and upper crust above pervasive shear zones within the weak lower crust - an intra-continental response to inter-continental displacements (cf. Gillcrist et al., in press).

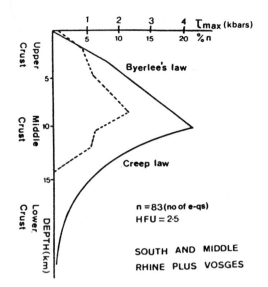

Figure 1. Maximum shear stress-brittle behaviour for the upper crust combined with ductile behaviour (quartz rheology) for the lower crust (solid line), compared with the depth-frequency distribution of hypocentres for earthquakes in the Rhinegraben and Vosges (dashed line), after Meissner and Strehlau (1982).

The stresses thus generated will be most effectively transmitted through the strong middle crust and can be subsequently released to the upper crust by displacement along pre-existing middle and upper crustal faults. Indeed, it is widely recognized that most intra-continental deformations within the seismogenic regime (<10 km) defined by Sibson (1983) are accomodated by reactivation of pre-existing discontinuities, rather than by the generation of new faults (McKenzie, 1972; Sykes, 1979; Sibson, 1985).

The displacement direction on these faults is controlled primarily by the tectonically induced middle crustal stress but also by lateral variation in the morphology of the fault surfaces generated by previous movement. This will constrain the fault to move in a direction similar to that of previous displacements,

hence influencing the orientation of upper crustal in situ stresses.

Hence, we might expect that in situ stresses within continental crust should reflect the present tectonic activity but will be modified by the geometry of pre-existing, possibly ancient, fault systems. Preliminary studies by the authors of data from the eastern United States and central Europe support this conjecture.

2.2 Residual Stress

Residual stress is defined as "that component of stress existing in a material in the absence of applied loads or changes in temperature" (McClintock and Argon, 1966). Although a residual stress state is associated with stored elastic strain energy, it is capable of causing strain and is, therefore, a fundamentally active stress. An attempt will be made to emphasize the scale dependence of residual stress and its relation to the equilibrium volume concept (cf. the self equilibriating unit of Russel and Hoskins, 1972). The scale dependence has significant ramifications for the measurement and interpretation of in situ stress states.

The three fundamental requirements for the generation of residual stresses are
(1) a change in the energy level, e.g., a stress or temperature change,
(2) a heterogeneity caused by different constituent parts of the material, and
(3) compatability (at least partial) of these constituent parts.
These requirements are highlighted in the discussion of polygranular and multi-layer induced residual stress presented below.

Consider a granite block formed under elevated temperature and pressure. All the constituent grains perfectly interlock at the time of crystallization. On

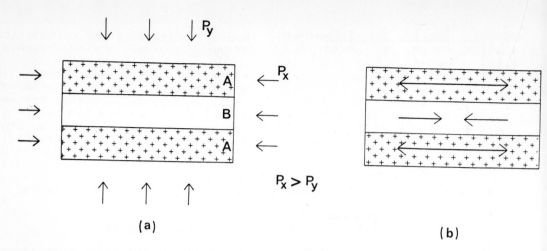

Figure 2. Elastic multilayer comprised of stiff (A) and soft (B) layers. Initially, (a), contacts between layers are frictionless but are bonded while under the applied boundary tractions. On removal of external stresses, residual stresses are set up - tensile in the stiff layers and compressive in the soft layers (b).

cooling, the grains will change shape, each by a somewhat different amount due to the varying elastic moduli, non-preferred orientation of anisotropic grains and different coefficients of thermal expansion. If each grain were free to strain unhindered and contained no smaller scale heterogeneities, each would assume a stress free state; however, the compatability of the contacts and hence the integrity of the block would not be maintained. Stresses are induced by the confining effect of neighbouring mineral grains and these are the residual stresses.

On a larger scale, residual stresses can be induced by larger scale heterogeneities within the rock mass. One example is a multi-layered system comprised of a sequence of stiff and soft layers (Fig. 2) as might occur in sedimentary layering.

Because the forces associated with the residual stresses are in equilibrium at a certain volume, the concept of an equilibrium volume has been developed. The equilibrium volume is defined as the smallest volume of rock for which all components of the average residual stress tensor are effectively zero. Thus, a rock mass may be considered as being composed of equilibrium volumes at different scales, depending on the suite of heterogeneities that is present.

An equilibrium volume does not have a specific location. By definition, it can be superimposed on any region within a statistically homogeneous rock mass. The internal stresses within that region will not be associated with any external tractions - they will 'balance out'.

However, apparent orientations may be manifested on the small scale, depending on the size and other geometrical aspects of the measuring technique. For example, a large circular overcore within a body containing small elongate equilibrium volumes will measure larger strains parallel to the long dimension (Fig. 3). In this direction, the magnitudes of both the relieved tension and compression components will be greater on the average, allowing any moduli contrast between loading and unloading to produce anisotropic strain relaxation.

The energy changes and heterogeneities that enable generation of residual stress encompass the complete range of geological scales. However, the scales at which residual stresses are important are not continuous but reflect the generally discrete scales at which energy changes and heterogeneities (e.g., grain scale, layer scale, and pluton scale) occur within rocks. The generation of residual stresses at various scales is affected by brittle deformation - a process which releases residual stress. The brittle structures observed in rocks are also discrete with respect to scale (e.g., microcracks, joints and faults). Thus, the elastic strain energy released by brittle deformation at any particular scale may be transferred to another scale within the system or transformed into another form of energy, particularly surface energy during crack growth.

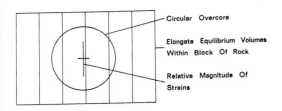

Circular Overcore

Elongate Equilibrium Volumes Within Block Of Rock

Relative Magnitude Of Strains

Figure 3. A possible mechanism for the formation of apparent residual stress orientations.

2.3 Ramifications for Engineering Design

Size differences between the various equilibrium volumes and the dimensions of an engineered structure have marked ramifications on the stress boundary conditions required for design. Consider an overcore stress measurement located at the scale position shown in Fig. 4. This will measure strains from from all stresses balanced at scales larger than the overcore, from which a stress tensor A can be calculated. Field stress magnitudes at the engineering scale, stress tensor C, are required for the design of a proposed tunnel - essentially to

predict the induced stress concentration magnitudes at the appropriate scale. This tensor C should only comprise those stresses which can be concentrated by the excavation; i.e., those existing at equilibrium volume scales greater than that of the proposed tunnel cross-section. Hence, the energy associated with C will always be less than or equal to that associated with A because residual stress below a certain scale is not included in C.

Similarly, considering a proposed borehole, the required field stresses B will comprise those stresses balanced at a scale greater than the borehole cross-section. The energy associated with B will be of intermediate magnitude to that of A and C. Consider the stresses balanced at scales less than the scale of the proposed engineering structure. Those balanced at scales lower than that of the sample size used for material property determination will be taken into account indirectly through the rock strength values (Barker, 1981). However, treatment of intermediate scales of equilibrium volumes is more troublesome. The related residual stresses will decrease the strength of the rock mass around the opening and be capable of increasing the stress concentration around any parts of the cross-section with severe curvature.

2.4 Glossary of in situ stress terms

A wide variety of terms has been used to describe in situ stress. This is not surprising given the factors that have been described in the previous three subsections. At this stage, therefore, it was thought useful to summarize the terms in common usage. The following explanations of in situ stress terms are not intended to be definitions but to provide some clarification of the terms and to introduce some consistency into their use.

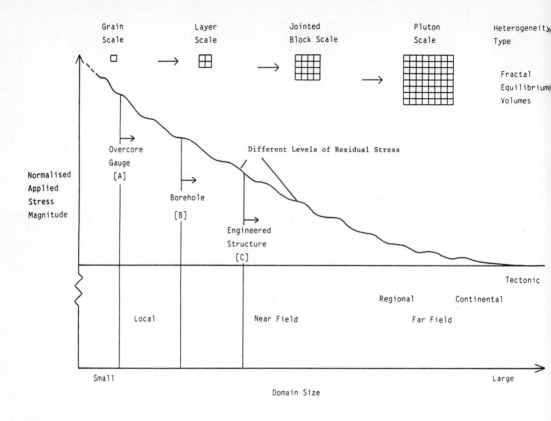

Figure 4. Stress state - scale relations.

Natural stress: The stress state which exists in the rock prior to any artificial disturbance. The stress state is the result of various events in the geological history of the rock mass. Therefore, the natural stresses present could be the product of many earlier states of stress. Synonyms include 'virgin', 'primitive', 'field' and 'active'.

Induced stress: The natural stress state as perturbed by engineering.

Residual stress: The stress state remaining in the rock mass, even after the originating mechanism(s) has ceased to operate. The stresses can be considered as within an isolated body that is free from external tractions; neither are they caused by the action of body forces or thermal gradients, etc. Sometimes the word 'remanent' is used as a synonym for 'residual'.

Tectonic stress: The stress stat[e] due to the relative displacemen[t] of lithospheric plates.

Gravitational stress: The stres[s] state due to the weight of th[e] superincumbent rock mass.

Thermal stress: The stress stat[e] set up as a result of temperatu[re] variation.

Physico-chemical stress: Th[e] stress state set up as a result o[f] chemical and/or physical change[s] in the rock, eg, recrystalliza[-] tion, absorption of water and flu[c]tuation of groundwater levels.

Paleostress: A previously activ[e] in situ stress state no longer i[n] existence. It can be considere[d] as old and no longer present whereas, a residual stress is ol[d] and remains. Paleostress can b[e] inferred from geologica[l] structures but cannot be measure[d]

Near field stress: The stress
state perturbed by a heterogeneity
(usually caused by engineering
activities, eg, a tunnel as a low
modulus inclusion).

Far field stress: A stress state
which is not perturbed by a
heterogeneity.

Regional stress: The stress state
in a relatively large geological
domain.

Local stress: The stress state in
a small geological domain –
usually of the dimensions of an
engineering structure.

Active stress: A stress state with
an associated strain state.

Passive stress: This term should
not be used.

3. SUPERIMPOSITION OF STRESS FIELDS

From the discussion in Section 2,
it is clearly of interest to be
able to superimpose two separate
stress fields and consider the
resultant stress field. There is
no difficulty in adding two scalar
values, but how should two tensors
be added? Also, if say ten stress
measurements are made and ten
stress tensors are obtained, how
should a mean stress tensor be
obtained?

3.1 Summing Stress Tensors in 2-D

To add N stress tensors, the
individual components of each
tensor must be determined so that
the values are with reference to
the same global axis. The individual components can then be added
to provide the total components
for the total stress tensor. If it

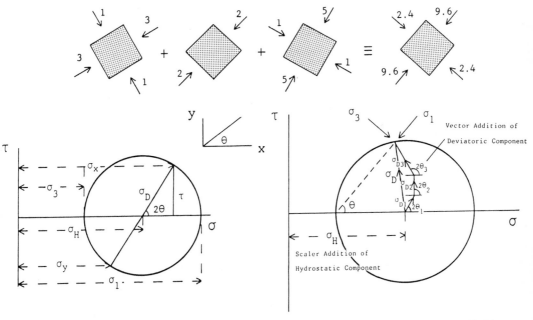

Mohr's Circle Representation

(a)

Graphical Summation of Stress Fields

(b)

Figure 5. Illustration of the superimposition of three stress states.
The general 2-D Mohr circle representation (a) is used to indicate the
separate scalar and vector addition of the hydrostatic and deviatoric
components in σ – τ space in order to generate the total stress field
shown in (b).

is the mean stress tensor which is required, these total components should be divided by N. Finally, the principal stress magnitudes and directions can be calculated from the components of the total or mean stress tensor.

The summation of stress tensors is well illustrated by the Mohr's circle method of graphical presentation (Fig. 5a). For principal stresses, σ_1 and σ_3, the hydrostatic and deviatoric stress components can be defined as

$$\sigma_H = (\sigma_1 + \sigma_3)/2$$

$$\sigma_D = (\sigma_1 - \sigma_3)/2$$

The normal and shear stress components can then be expressed as

$$\sigma_x = \sigma_H + \sigma_D \cos 2\Theta$$

$$\sigma_y = \sigma_H - \sigma_D \cos 2\Theta$$

$$\tau_{xy} = \sigma_D \sin 2\Theta$$

The addition of these components for N superimposed stress fields is expressed as

$$\text{global } \sigma_x = \sum_{i=1}^{N} \sigma_{H_i} + \sum_{i=1}^{N} \sigma_{D_i} \cos 2\Theta_i$$

$$\text{global } \sigma_y = \sum_{i=1}^{N} \sigma_{H_i} - \sum_{i=1}^{N} \sigma_{D_i} \cos 2\Theta_i$$

$$\text{global } \tau_{xy} = \sum_{i=1}^{N} \sigma_{D_i} \sin 2\Theta$$

It can be seen that the global hydrostatic component is the scalar summation of the individual hydrostatic components; whereas, the global deviatoric component is obtained as the vectorial resultant of the individual deviatoric components. This is shown by the example in Fig. 5b in which the summation of three stress fields is graphically presented.

The three component stress fields are

$$(\sigma_1,\sigma_3)_1 = (3,1); \quad \Theta_1 = 30°$$

$$(\sigma_1,\sigma_3)_2 = (2,0); \quad \Theta_2 = 45°$$

$$(\sigma_1,\sigma_3)_3 = (5,1); \quad \Theta_3 = 60°$$

with total hydrostatic component of 6 and total deviatoric component of 3.6327. The global principal stresses are

$$\sigma_1 = 9.6327$$

$$\sigma_3 = 2.3673$$

with σ_1 being inclined at an angle of 48.96° to the x-axis as illustrated in Fig. 5b.

3.2 Summing Stress Tensors in 3-D

The same principle is used for summing separate stress tensors in three dimensions. An example is shown in Fig. 6 where two stress fields have been added to produce a total stress field. The cube faces are perpendicular to the three principal stresses in each case.

Note that the first stress invariant (the sum of the principal stress values) for the total stress field is the sum of the six principal stresses of the two component fields.

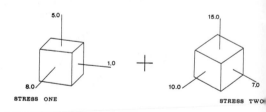

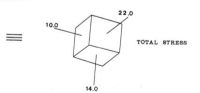

Figure 6. The addition of two stress tensors. Each cube represents the stress state at a point, with the orientation of the principal stress directions given by the face normals. Magnitudes of the compressive principal stresses are as indicated.

4. THE REPRESENTATIVE ELEMENTARY VOLUME FOR IN SITU STRESS

In the discussion so far we have concentrated on the nature of in situ stress, the effects of rock inhomogeneity and superimposition of stress fields. Another vital factor is the discontinuous character of rock masses.

Adjacent to a discontinuity, the stress field can be significantly affected by the presence of the discontinuity. Under these circumstances, localized measurements of the in situ stress tensor can give a very misleading impression of the overall regional stress field.

In fact, there is a conflict between the concept of stress as a point property (and hence a very variable quantity) and the idea of making measurements in rock over a representative elemental volume (REV) - which could be very large. The REV idea has been traditionally invoked for considering the permeability of fractured rock. With the discontinuities dominating the water flow, measurements of rock mass permeability can only be accurate and precise if the sampled volume is large enough to contain a representative sample of discontinuities. Below this volume, measured values can be highly scattered as different discontinuity configurations are sampled.

This is also true for rock mass deformability measurements where again the particular sample of discontinuities will individually affect the results until the representative elemental volume is being loaded. The same concept applies for any rock property which is significantly affected by the presence of discontinuities.

It follows, therefore, that if the stress field is locally affected by discontinuities then either many measurements are required or tests have to be made on a sample at the size of the representative elemental volume or larger. In either case there are problems.

For the former with the use of many tests, the usual arithmetic mean of the tensor components related to the same set of axes is inappropriate because the stress component variation is most unlikely to be linear along a line through a discontinuity. For the latter, the idea of an in situ stress test at the scale of the REV, say many tens or hundreds of cubic metres, has never been used, ie, a 'macro-stress test'. Perhaps the only practical method of achieving such a test configuration would be to drill boreholes at various angles ahead of the face of an advancing excavation to generate an undercoring test on a large scale in a similar manner to Maconochie et al. (1979) and Kaiser and Mackay (1983).

When making stress measurements on the usual scale, a very wide scatter in results is to be expected and a set of values should not be regarded as suspect simply because of a wide scatter. Conversely, however, there is a major problem in interpretation. Not only is the arithmetic averaging wrong but the stress measurements themselves will be biased because conventionally one tries to avoid making measurements near discontinuities and hence perhaps the relatively destressed regions within blocks are inappropriately emphasized.

5. CONCLUSIONS

The geological history of a rock mass has an important influence on the existence and character of in situ stress. This is firstly because geological structures affect the mechanical properties of rock from grain scale to subcrustal scale; and, secondly, because of the presence of residual stress.

Emphasis has been placed on residual stress which is most easily understood in terms of the equilibrium volume concept - whereby several orders of residual stress exist possessing a fundamentally fractal geometry. The relative scales of in situ stress measurement, engineering structure and equilibrium volumes are especially important in assessing whether in situ stress tests will provide results relevant to the boundary conditions needed for engineering design.

Residual stresses are responsible for a significant component of the scatter in results experienced during most in situ stress measurement programmes and they therefore deserve greater attention. Methods of stress field superimposition could assist in appreciating the contribution that the various stress components make to measured values and hence enhance the quality of interpretation.

The representative elemental volume concept normally invoked for permeability and deformability is equally applicable to in situ stress and naturally suggests the idea of a 'macro-stress' test which is large enough to eliminate the effect of local discontinuity stress field perturbations. Perhaps this could be achieved by tunnel under-coring.

The complexity of in situ stress is highlighted by the Figure in this paper showing stress versus scale. Scatter in test results is bound to occur during in situ stress measurements, unless they are conducted at the large REV scale. Such scatter should not be rejected as an unfortunate experimental inconvenience but accepted as a useful indicator assisting in the interpretative methods.

6. ACKNOWLEDGEMENTS

The work described in this paper forms part of an in situ stress research programme funded by BP International and the UK Science and Engineering Research Council. The authors are extremely grateful to Dr M V Barr of BP International for providing them with the opportunity to conduct the research.

The authors also appreciate Dr J W Bray's elegant contribution to the methods for superimposing stress fields illustrated in Figure 5(b) and stimulating discussions with Mr C R Windsor on the possibility of 'macro-stress' measurement methods.

7. REFERENCES

Barker, L.M. 1981. Residual Stress Effects on Fracture Toughness Measurements. Presented at the 5th Int. Conf. on Fracture, ICF 5, Cannes, France.

Gillcrist, J.R., Coward, M.P and J.L. Mungier 1986. Structural Inversion: Examples from the Alpine Foreland and Western Alpine Collisional Belt. In preparation.

Kaiser, P.K. and C. Mackay 1983. Development of Rock Mass and Liner Stresses During Sinking of a Shaft in Clay Shale. 1st Int. Conf. on Stability in Underground Mining held in August 1982, Ed. C.O. Brawner A.I.M.E., New York.

Maconochie, D.J., Potts, E.L.J. and A.G. Reid 1979. Proc. of the 4th I.S.R.M. Congress, Montreux, Vol.2, 379-388.

McClintock, F.A. and A.S. Argon 1966. Mechanical Behaviour of Materials, Addison-Wesley, Reading, PA.

Mckenzie, D.P. 1972. Active Tectonics of the Mediterranean Region. Geophys. J. Royal Ast. Soc., 30, 109-118.

Richardson, R.M. 1978. Finite Element Modeling of Stress in the Nazca Plate: Driving Forces and Plate Boundary Earthquakes. Tectonophysics, 50, 223-248.

Russell, J.E. and E.R. Hoskins 1973. Residual Stresses in Rock. In New Horizons in Rock Mechanics. H.R. Hardy and R. Stefanko (Eds.) Proc. 14th Symposium on Rock Mechanics, American Society of Civil Engineers New York, 1-24.

Sibson, R.H. 1983. Continental Fault Structure and the Shallow Earthquake Source. J. Geol. Soc. London, 140, 741-767.

Sibson, R.H. 1985. Short Notes on Fault Reactivation. J. Struct. Geol., 7, 6, 751-754.

Sykes, L.R. 1978. Intraplate Seismicity, Reactivation of Pre-Existing Zones of Weakness, Alkaline Magmatism ad Other Tectonism Post-Dating Continental Fragmentation. Rev. Geophys. Space Phys., 16, 621-687.

Statistic analysis applied to rock stress measurements

C. CHAMBON
Laboratoire de Mecanique des Terrains, Ecole des Mines, Nancy, France

R. REVALOR
Departement Techniques Miniéres, CERCHAR, France

SUMMARY : Over the last ten years, CERCHAR (CENTRE D'ETUDES ET RECHERCHES DE CHARBONNAGES DE FRANCE) has developed various methods for measuring natural stresses in very varied areas. Furthermore, an important study has been carried out concerning the treatment of these measurements in order to guarantee the validity of the measured stresses. The paper presents the developed methods, their application to the same site and the statistical approach applied to the measurement processing.

RESUME : Dans la derniére decennie, le CERCHAR (CENTRE D'ETUDES ET DE RECHERCHE DE CHARBONNAGES DE FRANCE) s'est constitue une panoplie permettant la mesure des contraintes naturelles dans des sites trés varies. En outre, une importante reflexion a ete conduite dans le domaine du depouillement de ces mesures afin de garantir la validite des contraintes mesurees. L'article presente les methodes developpees, leur application sur un même site et l'approche statistique appliquee au traitement des mesures.

ZUSAMMENFASSUNG : Warhend des letzten Jahrzehntes hat CERCHAR (CENTRE D'ETUDES ET RECHERCHES DE CHARBONNAGES DE FRANCE) eine Erfahrungs – Sammlung fur die Messung der naturlichen Beauspruchung in sehr verschiedenen Landschaften hergestellt. Daneben, wurde eine bedeutsame Uberlegung in Gebiet der Auswertung dieser Messungen geleitet, um die Gultigkeit der gemesserren Beaus pruchungen zugewahrleisten. Der Aufsatz stellt die entwickelten Methoden, ihre Verwendung auf einer selben Landschaft und die statistische Annaherung fur die Verarbeitung der Messungen dar.

For several years, CERCHAR (CENTRE D'ETUDES ET RECHERCHES DE CHARBONNAGES DE FRANCE) has been led to develop its techniques for measuring rock stresses. The flat jack, overcoring and hydrofracturing methods have been adapted and applied in areas with very varied conditions : deep underground mines, development roadways, underground quarries at low depth...

The développment of these methods has been effected for each of them following two axes :
* choice of equipment permitting precise measurements but also sufficiently robust for faultless functioning in reputedly difficult workings

* research into a methodology permitting the correct carrying out of a measuring campaign and the disposal, at the end, of a sufficient quantity of data of required quality.

Parallel to this, an important study was effected concerning the interpretation of these measurements in order to give means of judging the validity of the obtained results. In fact, the high cost of these measurements and their importance justify that particular attention should be given to the problem of the robustness of these results.

After having described the choices made for each method, the paper presents the statistical approaches developed to appreciate the quality of the measurements and to estimate the representativity of the final result obtained.

The effectiveness of these approaches is tested on the results of a measuring campaign carried out in a deep coal mine.

1 - THE MEASURING METHODS

1.1 - Flat jack

The flat jack method is a relatively old technique (MAYER, 1951 ; ROCHA, 1966) and simple to put into effect. Its principle is not recalled here and reference can be made to numerous publications dealing with it (BORSETTO, 1983 ; FAIELLA, 1983 ; BERTRAND, 1983).

However, the quality of the final measurement obtained depends in the main part on the equipment used and on the respect given to a rigorous operational procedure.

In the first place, the choice of measuring zone must be effected with great care and great importance must be given to detecting too fractured areas by a surface or deep survey (endoscopy). The surface where the future cut is to be implanted is set up, which facilitates its implementation thereafter (photo 1). The measuring pins are then implanted according to the layout given in figure 1. They consist of a base embedded in the rock mass and a bolt whose head is equipped with an off-centered steel ball. This system allows an easy regulating, as well as a precise measuring, of the distance between pins. This measurement is carried out using an extensometer which allows obtaining precision to a micron and which is frequently checked during the operation using a standard.

The cut is executed by a diamond cutting circular saw which allows reaching a depth of 250 mm (photo 2). A correct and adapted setting of the saw diamonds is capital. In very

resistant rocks, it allows significantly decreasing the time taken to make the cuts. The saw is driven by a 13 KW hydraulic motor capable of turning at 2000 tr/min, supplied by a pump ensuring a nominal flow of 60 l/min at 170 bar, coupled with a 22 KW hydraulic motor. This available power is necessary for sawing the very hard rocks met with in certain workings. The blade guides and the rigid cradle supporting the saw have been built in such a way as to facilitate its positioning and orientation and to avoid any vibration during sawing.

PHOTO 1

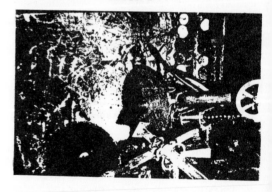

PHOTO 2

Because of their incidence on the quality of the measurements, flat jacks are very carefully constructed in the precision workshops at Cerchar.

Using a threedimensional calculation by finite elements, BONVALLET (1978) has finely studied the influence of a certain number of elements of the preceding procedure on the obtained result. As far as the measurement interpretation is concerned, software with a calculation by finite elements allows going back to the natural stresses which gives the best account of the measurements taken on the side of the roadway (TINCHON, 1982).

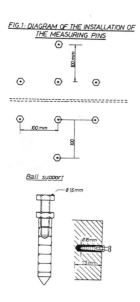

FIG.1: DIAGRAM OF THE INSTALLATION OF THE MEASURING PINS

Ball support

1.2 - Overcoring

The principle of the method and the different variations developed are relatively well described (BONNECHERE, 1971 ; HELAL, 1982 ; BERTRAND, 1983).

Its application ncessitates using equipment generally more sophisticated than that used for the flat jack method.

The material developed for CERCHAR's needs distinguishes itself mainly by an original overcoring cell, of the dilatometer type, and by a data recording material which continuously assures data collecting during testing (HELAL, 1983).

The cell (L = 500 mm, ⌀ = 95 mm) is planned to be used in a 97 mm diameter hole whilst the overcoring is carried out at 210 mm. 6 induction displacement transducers, in 3 pairs positioned out of line at 120° in relation to each other, are placed in the central inflatable part (L = 200 mm) of the cell (figure 2). For obstruction reasons, these 3 pairs are placed in 3 planes, 40 mm away from

each other. The head of each transducer is fixed to the inflatable sleeve which allows, with an inside inflatable pressure in the region of 0.2 MPa, applying each transducer against the bore wall. This pressure is maintained constant during the test by a servo-controlled system. Furthermore, a 7th blocked transducer is installed in the cell body to serve as a reference.

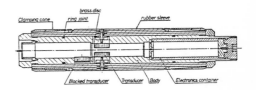

FIG. 2 : SCHEMATIC DIAGRAM OF THE CERCHAR CELL

The possibility of determining the rock deformation modulus by a pressiometric test prior to every overcoring test is the originality of this unit. The cell and accessory assembly is shown in photo 3.

During each test (pressiometric or overcoring), the data are collected continuously by a microcomputer HP 9825 with a scanner, a frequency meter and a printer (photo 4). The collected data are stored on small magnetic tapes for later processing.

Furthermore, for the checking of operations, the data can be sent back by cable to the measuring site where they are displayed on a television screen (photo 4).

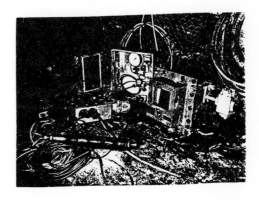

PHOTO 3

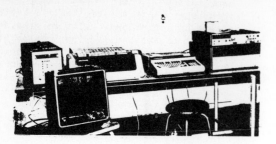

PHOTO 4

This continuous monitoring permits the analysis of the evolution of the displacement graphs of each transducer, which appears to be indispensable for judging the quality of the measurements. Figure 3 gives a diagram of the whole of the equipment used.

The procedure for applying the overcoring method using this material, as well as the influence of a certain number of factors on the obtained results, have been thoroughly studied par HELAL (1982).

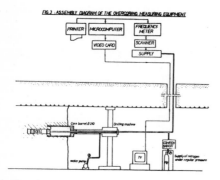

1.3 - Hydrofracturing

Because of its adaptability, this method has been rapidly developed over recent years. Its principle and the procedure have been defined by different authors (HAIMSON, 1978 ; CORNET, 1981 and 1984).

The equipment assembly consists of (REVALOR, 1984) :
* a dual obturator system (TAM INTERNATIONAL) capable of functioning in boreholes of a diameter between 76 and 100 mm. These packers can work at relatively high pressures (45 MPa). The length of the fracturing chamber is adaptable to the natural cracks

space of the strata. In fact it can vary from 60 to 150 cm (photo 5).
* classic pressure apparatus (PETROMETALLIC) functioning on the compressed air network, equipped with adequate recording systems (photo 6).

PHOTO 5

The orientation of the crack is obtained using an impression packer (MAZIER) which can be seen in photo 6.

The whole of the equipment is shown in diagram form in figure 4.

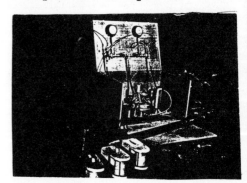

PHOTO 6

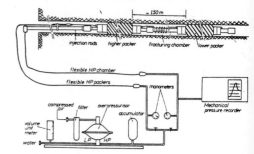

400

The choice of this equipment was guided by a certain number of necessities (REVALOR, 1984) :
. strength for its adaptation to often difficult mine workings
. simplicity for avoiding too large and therefore too costly campaigns
. no electrical apparatus to allow functioning without any problem in methane atmospheres
. power for measuring stresses at great depth.

1.4 - Adaptation of different methods

Putting these different methods into operation on varied sites currently allows us to fix their limits and to delimit the sites for which these methods appear best adapted.

Thus, if an attempt is not at all made to go back to the natural stresses prevailing over the strata, the flat jack is the only method which allows measuring superficial stresses. It is thus particularly adapted to measuring the stresses in ribsides (pillars, roadways), for application to the sizing of supports. In this very strict context, the fact that the measurement is direct (pressure) gives it an undeniable advantage.

Because of the precision of the measurements taken, the overcoring is the only method permitting the measurement of low stresses (or small variations in stresses). The method is therefore above all advised for shallow depth sites. In very deep sites (> 1000 m), it can be applied if the rock mass has a high strength. In the opposite case, breaking of the cores being drilled by discing (photo 7) can render the metho d completely inoperative. In all cases, application of the method necessitates a practically perfect elasticity of the rock masses. It is therefore not advised (more than the 2 others) in the case of fractured strata or those with a very marked viscous behaviour.

Its known qualities, recorded by different authors (in particular, the scale of the effected measurements), give hydrofracturing powerful to measure the state of natural stresses in rock masses away from all work disturbance.

PHOTO 7

In this context, it efficiently takes over from overcoring for mine working at great depth or highly fractured. However, the method cannot be implemented everywhere : it can be inoperative, for example, in rock masses with a high anisotropy where the planes of the rock weakness systematically guide the created cracks (1 measuring direction only).

2 - STRESS MEASUREMENT PROCESSING

2.1 - Problem of the validity of the results

Generally, except concerning the hydrofracturing method applied on natural existing cracks in the hole (CORNET, 1981), the processing of the stress measurements is based on the hypothesis of the homogeneity, elasticity and isotropy of the rock mass. In this context, the model of the circular hole in an infinite medium (HIRAMATSU, 1968) brings the stress calculation down to the resolution of a linear system with 6 unknown values.

The goodness of the obtained results depends on :
* the validity of the beginning hypothesis which is the basis for the physical model used for formulating equations
* the resolution method adopted (statistical fit criterion).

Furthermore, the calculation should be carried out on a batch of apparently "good" data, thus after elimination of erroneous, or at least suspect, measurements.

401

Although there is a relatively large amount of litterature giving descriptions of sites and measuring methods, there is very little concerning methods for processing the stress measurements and in particular for estimating the validity of the obtained results.

As far as the overcoring method is concerned, taking medium's anisotropy into consideration has been envisaged (HIRASHIMA, 1977 ; RIBACCHI, 1977). AMADEI (1982) underlines, moreover, that in a highly anisotropic medium, the ground isotropic hypothesis can lead to a 50 % error in the stress estimation. This error is all the higher when the boreholes are paralle l to the axis of maximum anisotropy of the rock mass.

As far as the fit criterion is concerned, DUVALL (1979) considers that least squares method is the best adapted because the most powerful for resolving such systems. However, GRAY (1973) reports that in heterogeneous media where the rock mechanical characteristics can vary from one measuring point to another, the precision of the results can be highly over-estimated by the classical least squares method.

As far as the appreciation of suspect measurements is concerned, HELAL (1982) and CORNET (1981) propose, for the overcoring method, several indications which allow judging the quality of the effected measurements ie the evolution of the displacements during overcoring, the stability of measurements, the relative orientation of the main axes of the hole's deformation, ...

2.2 - Statistical approach

Whatever the measuring method used, the stress calculation comes down to the resolution of a matrix equation

$$Y = Xa$$

Y is a vector column constituted by the n measurements of campaign (displacements in the case of overcoring, pressures in the case of flat jack or hydrofracturing).

X is the matrix nx6 which expresses the stress-measurements relations in the geographical trihedron. This matrix, which is different according to the measuring method, gives an account of the physical model adopted to represent the phenomenon (circular hole, elasticity, isotropy).

a is a vector constituted by the 6 unknowns, which are the 6 components of the stresses, expressed in the geographical trihedron (OX = East ; OY = North ; OZ = vertical).

If the measurements are redundant (n>6) and if their directions are such that X is not singular, then the resolution of this system comes down to a problem of linear regression without constant term which can be solved with the help a suitable fit criterion.

The quality of the representation can then be estimated :
. by applying different fit criteria and, by analysing the sensitivity of the results, to the chosen fit criterion : least squares, minimum of the sum of absolute values of residuals, minimum of maximum of absolute values, HUBER estimation,...
. by looking for statistical indexes permitting locating influential or suspect observations : residual, reduced residual, weight of the observation, D of COOK,...
This approach is formalized in Appendix.

3 - APPLICATION TO A MEASURING SITE (VOUTERS SHAFT - LORRAINE COLLIERIES - FRANCE)

3.1 - The measuring site

The collieries of the Lorraine coalfield are mining a coal deposit in the North East of France whose production represents 2/3 of the total French production.

This deposit, dating from the Carboniferous age, presents very varied working conditions, ranging from flat seams (horizontal) to steep seams (sub-vertical). It is affected by 2 folds one of which is the MERLEBACH anticline which is represented in figure 5. The working area of the VOUTERS mine is situated on the East face of this anticline. From a geological point of view, the zone is characterized by (DONSIMONI, 1981) :

. workable seams spread out in 2 parts called the "Flambants Supérieurs" in the East and the "Flambants Inférieurs" in the West. These two areas are separated by the MERLEBACH conglomerate.

. by a dividing into 3 compartments of the area by two faults, the DORA and REUMAUX faults (figure 6). The central compartment thus delimited appears in abutment on the heart of the anticline (THOMAS, 1983).

. relatively steep strata in the area (65°) but which present 2 inflexion axes: one is well-known between 600 and 800 m deep, and the other is supposed further than 1250 m deep.

During the preparation of a working level at 1250 m deep, a roadway being driven in the sandstone of "Flambants Inférieurs" was the seat of intense and brutal failure of the rock mass, accompanied by considerable firedamp emissions (JOSIEN, 1983 ; CHEMAOU, 1984).

In order to evaluate the incidence of the state of natural stresses on the observed phenomena, a campaign for in situ stress measurements was carried out.

The chosen site was a 20 m2 section roadway, situated in the MERLEBACH conglomerate, at about 500 m away from the affected works (figure 6). This roadway was approximately parallel to the anticline axis. The sector's rock mass (sandstone type) has a 65° dip. It is relatively resistant and straight : the resistance in simple compression and the Young modulus respectively equals 150 and 20000 MPa.

3.2 - Measuring campaigns

The three measuring methods (flat jack, overcoring, hydrofracturing) were used on the site. Figure 7 localizes the different measuring points.

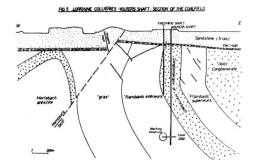

FIG.5 LORRAINE COLLIERIES ·VOUTERS SHAFT· SECTION OF THE COALFIELD

FIG.6 : STRUCTURAL DIAGRAM AT VOUTERS COAL MINE

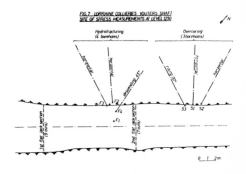

FIG.7 LORRAINE COLLIERIES ·VOUTERS SHAFT SITE OF STRESS MEASUREMENTS AT LEVEL 1250

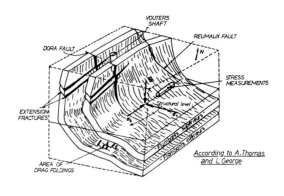

VOUTERS SHAFT
REUMAUX FAULT
DORA FAULT
STRESS MEASUREMENTS
Structural level
EXTENSION FRACTURES
AREA OF DRAG FOLDINGS

According to A.Thomas and L.George

σ_1 = 38 MPa
σ_2 = 28 MPa
σ_3 = 18 MPa

Flat jack : 16 cuts divided into 2 measuring sections were effected (PIGUET, 1979). 11 cuts were perpendicular to the tangential stress $\sigma\theta$ at the level of the measuring points, 5 cuts were perpendicular to the axial stress σz.

The different cuts are shown in figure 8 in association with the balance pressure measured in the jack on each one of them.

FIG.8 : LORRAINE COLLIERIES-VOUTERS SHAFT-LEVEL 1250
RESULTS OF THE STRESS MEASUREMENTS
WITH THE FLAT JACK METHOD

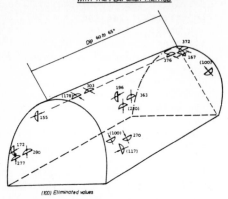

(100) Eliminated values

TABLE 1 : LORRAINE COLLIERIES - VOUTERS SHAFT - LEVEL 1250

RESULTS OF PRESSIOMETRIC AND OVERCORING TESTS

			PRESSIOMETRIC TEST					OVERCORING TEST		
			Modulus in MPa					Displacements in Microns		
HOLE	TEST	∅ in y	Trans-ducer 1/2	Trans-ducer 3/4	Trans-ducer 5/6	Avera-ge	Root mean squa-res	Trans-ducer 1/2	Trans-ducer 3/4	Trans-ducer 5/6
S1	103	98457	10850	10330	9440	10210	710	276	252	201
	105	98457	9190	11550	9600	10110	1260	553	261	465
S2	108	96926	14240	13200	7260	11570	3770	411	302	473
	110	98590	17540	17830	16990	17450	430	363	375	215
S3	113	98724	20150	23170	28650	23990	4310	316	247	325
	115	98724	17020	12100	6190	11770	5420	237	181	417
	117	98350	28030	10950	22340	20710	9050	198	263	192
	AVERAGE ON SITE					15120	8550			

Overcoring : 7 tests were carried out in 3 holes with different orientations referenced S1, S2 and S3 in figure 7 (REVALOR, 1985). 3 tests were situated in hole S1 at 6.8, 8 and 10 m deep, 2 in the S2 hole at 7.9 and 9.8 m deep and 2 in the S3 hole at 5 and 7.2 m deep. The CERCHAR cell supplying three diametral measurements, there were consequently 21 displacements measurements available at the end of the campaign. Each overcoring test was preceded by a pressiometric test consisting of 3 cycles of charge-discharge of 0 to 6 MPa and destined to estimate the rock elasticity modulus at the measuring point.

Figure 9 represents an example of the graphs obtained. Table 1 assembles the different results.

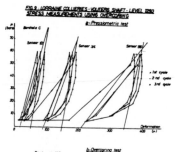

FIG.9 : LORRAINE COLLIERIES- VOUTERS SHAFT- LEVEL 1250
STRESS MEASUREMENTS USING OVERCORING

a-Pressiometric test

b-Overcoring test

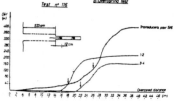

Test n° 116

Hydrofracturing : the tests were carried out in 4 holes called F1, F2 F3 and F4 in figure 7 (THOMAS, 1983) 14 tests were carried out.

However, a certain number of technical problems were met with during the campaign, linked in particular to the low quality of the obtained imprints. In the last analysis, 5 pressure measurements can be interpreted.

3.3 - Statistical interpretation : Application to overcoring measurements

The overcoring campaign was chosen as reference because of the high number of measurements carried out. Thus, the 21 measurements give the system represented in table 2.

TABLE 2 : OVERCORING - VOUTERS 1250 - Y = Xa SYSTEM

Y	X_1	X_2	X_3	X_4	X_5	X_6
275.92	-0.5146	-0.5067	2.61	-0.5673	0	0
251.53	0.8191	0.79	0.0596	2.086	2.1743	2.2049
200.63	0.8963	0.8645	0.0652	2.2823	-2.3793	-2.4128
553.46	-0.6031	-0.5938	3.0596	-0.6649	0	0
260.63	0.7272	0.7013	0.0529	1.8515	-1.9303	1.9574
464.56	0.8749	0.8438	0.0637	2.2276	-2.3224	-2.355
411.06	-0.3867	-0.3808	1.9614	-0.4263	0	0
392.15	0.6322	0.6097	0.046	1.6098	1.6782	1.7018
473.49	1.1495	1.1086	0.0836	2.9269	-3.0513	-3.0942
362.72	-0.4634	-0.1691	1.6184	-0.1955	-0.0882	0.0266
374.96	0.9855	-0.0502	0.0345	0.6316	0.5113	1.725
214.73	1.0069	-0.0253	0.0362	0.7452	-0.5548	1.8048
316.01	-0.4042	-0.1475	1.4115	-0.1795	-0.0769	0.0232
246.73	0.7598	-0.0387	0.0266	0.4869	0.3942	1.3299
325.18	0.5982	-0.015	0.0215	0.4427	-0.3296	-1.0723
236.57	0.0364	-0.4795	1.4642	-0.2606	-0.2716	1.1402
180.76	0.1251	1.2899	0.0213	1.6097	2.3983	0.7408
416.71	-0.5588	3.3249	0.0416	-0.0347	-4.8375	-0.8212
197.68	0.0215	-0.2834	0.8653	-0.154	-0.1695	0.6738
263.48	0.1384	1.4268	0.9236	1.7806	2.653	0.8195
192.39	-0.155	0.7222	0.0115	-9.6E-3	-1.3418	-0.2278

3.3.1 - Robustness of results

The different fit criteria previously presented were applied to the resolution for this system. The different state of stress obtained are assembled in table 3.

TABLE 3 : OVERCORING - VOUTERS 1250

INFLUENCE OF FIT CRITERIA

FIT CRITERION	σ_x (MPa)	σ_y (MPa)	σ_z (MPa)	τ_{xy} (MPa)	τ_{yz} (MPa)	τ_{zx} (MPa)
1) LEAST SQUARES	33.8	19	26.3	-5.8	0.4	-0.3
2) HUBER (k = 1)	30	17.4	26.9	-3.4	-0.5	0.3
3) MINIMUM SUM ABSOLUTE VALUES	39.7	19.4	27.9	-8.2	0.7	-1.3
4) HUBER (k = 0.05)	39.6	19.5	27.9	-8.3	0.7	-1.3
5) MINIMUM OF MAXIMUM OF ABSOLUTE VALUES	33.4	25	25.5	-7.8	4.1	-3.3

On the whole, the results tally with each other. It may be noted :
. that vertical stress is very stable whatever the criterion. It oscillates between 26 and 28 MPa which represents, to the nearest 10 %, the weight of overlying strata
. that the 2 other normal horizontal stresses are more variable (10 to 30% variation according to the stress and the criterion in regard to the least squares solution).

However, systematically, all the criteria translate a high anisotropic stress ratio in the horizontal plane with a stress σ_x which varies between 30 and 40 MPa. The anisotropic ratio is near 2.

Criterion n° 5 gives an estimate relatively different to the others. This is specially the case for the 2 shearing stresses τ_{yz} and τ_{zx} which appear relatively high. These results seem linked to the criterion itself which, by definition, gives great importance to isolated values and thus appears unadapted to this type of measurement.

On the other hand, these two stresses are analogous concerning the other estimates. They are very low and indicate that one of the principal axes of the stresses in close to vertical.

These 3 tendancies (very stable vertical stress, anisotropy of the horizontal stresses, vertical

principal axis) therefore appear strongly confirmed by the different criteria which in this case confirm the classical estimating by the least squares method.

3.3.2 - Influential or suspect values

Based on the least squares method applied to the 21 campaign measurements, statistical indexes were calculated allowing the evaluation of the influence of each measurement on the obtained result.

The results are set out in table 4. They allow questioning the 6 measurements 1, 3, 6, 12, 15, and 18 which simultaneously present indexes significantly higher than the others.

TABLE 4

INDEXES FOR THE DETECTION OF SUSPECT VALUE

(Least squares method - 21 measurements)

N° Measurement	Y Obs. in micron	Y Est. in micron	Residual in micron	Reduced Residual	D de COOK	Hi
1	275.920	448.560	-172.640	-1.964	.223	.257
2	251.530	322.439	-70.909	-.817	.042	.275
3	200.630	350.557	-149.927	-1.721	.183	.270
4	553.460	525.644	27.816	.339	.010	.353
5	260.630	286.274	-25.644	-.284	.004	.217
6	464.560	342.203	122.357	1.393	.112	.258
7	411.060	337.092	73.968	.705	.017	.145
8	302.150	248.871	53.279	.571	.011	.164
9	473.490	449.569	23.921	.315	.013	.445
10	362.720	247.366	115.354	1.205	.033	.119
11	374.960	292.663	82.297	1.002	.091	.351
12	214.730	305.639	-90.909	-1.420	.516	.606
13	316.010	215.724	100.286	1.031	.018	.091
14	246.730	225.641	21.089	.232	.002	.209
15	325.180	181.586	143.594	1.588	.114	.214
16	236.570	316.589	-80.019	-.879	.033	.203
17	180.760	205.794	-25.034	-.303	.009	.342
18	416.710	441.111	-24.401	-.845	1.363	.920
19	197.620	187.085	10.595	.105	.000	.071
20	263.480	227.651	35.829	.461	.025	.419
21	193.390	122.332	70.058	.713	.006	.071

Careful examination effectively permits noting, for certain of these 6 measurements, abnormal evolutions of the corresponding tests (in particular, the relatively discontinuous evolution of the transducers during overcoring). However, it must be kept in mind that for the others nothing abnormal can be detected during the tests : these last tests (measurements 12, 15, 18) could not therefore be eliminated a priori.

Figure 10 shows the influence of the 21 measurements. It represents the obtained result by suppressing each of

405

measurements in turn and by calculating the stresses with the remaining 20.

It is surprising to note the influence of a single measurement on the result obtained. In fact, the simple fact of withdrawing measurement 12 has the consequence of practically doubling the principal major stress σ1.

It is the same for measurement 15, the withdrawal of which provokes a rotation of the principal axes in the region of 30° in relation to the basic solution (figure 11).

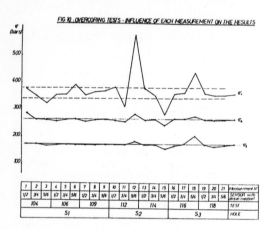

FIG 10. OVERCORING TESTS - INFLUENCE OF EACH MEASUREMENT ON THE RESULTS

1	2	3	4	5	6	7	8	9	10	11	12	13	14	15	16	17	18	19	20	21	Measurement N°
1/2	3/4	5/6	1/2	3/4	5/6	1/2	3/4	5/6	1/2	3/4	5/6	1/2	3/4	5/6	1/2	3/4	5/6	1/2	3/4	5/6	SENSOR with strain measint
104			106			109			112			114			116			118			TEST
S1								S2							S3						HOLE

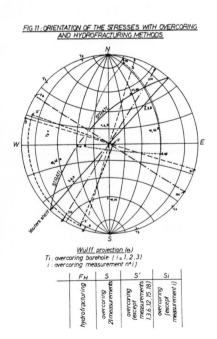

FIG. 11: ORIENTATION OF THE STRESSES WITH OVERCORING AND HYDROFRACTURING METHODS

Wulff projection (a.)
Ti: overcoring borehole (i = 1, 2, 3)
i : overcoring measurement n°i)

	FH	S	S'	Si
	hydrofracturing	overcoring 21 measurements	overcoring (except measurements 1,3,6,12,15,18)	overcoring (except measurement i)

The two other stresses appear more stable with this procedure (variation in the region of 10% around the average value). This observation which was also made elsewhere (REVALOR, 1984), seems linked to the fact that, taking into account the orientation of the overcoring holes and that of the cell in each hole, the 21 measurements systematically make a high angle (50° to 60°) with the major principal stress. This stress would therefore be badly "apprehended" during tests. On the other hand, for the two other stresses, directions of measurements exist sub parallel (to the nearest 15°) to each of them (figure 11).

Despite these important variations when 6 measurements are simultaneously taken away, the determination is notably improved (multiple correlation coefficient in the region of 0.8 instead of 0.5) but without the result in terms of stress modulus (table 5) and orientation (figure 11) being fundamentally modified.

The result obtained using the remaining 15 measurements appears very stable regarding this procedure, each of the 15 measurements intervenes equitably in the calculation : the robustness and the quality of this evaluation are thus confirmed.

3.4 - Comparison with other measuring methods

The processing of flat jack measurements, based on the results of a calculation with finite elements (PIGUET, 1979 ; TINCHON, 1982), led to a state of stress practically hydrostatic whose level appeared very low in view of the overcoring result (table 5). This evaluation was based on the hypothesis (imposed by the modelization by finite elements) that one of the principal stresses was parallel to the roadway axis.

In order to be free of this hypothesis, the campaign results were again processed by treating the roadway as a circular roadway and by applying the same statistical approach as previously developed to the overcoring measurements. Although the detection indexes of suspect measurements effectively permit recuperating most of the measurements whose quality had been doubted during the campaign (cracks in the zone surrounding the cut), the results are not in fact better, whatever the fit criterion chosen. They express the major inconvenience of the flat jack method, reported by different authors (one of which is BERTRAND, 1983), of being situated on the ribside of the roadway and thus in a zone likely to be deconsolidated and destressed.

On the other hand, despite the low number of measurements capable of being interpreted, hydrofracturing is in excellent accordance with overcoring, both methods giving, to the nearest 10 %, the same result (table 5).

be more or less perpendicular to the axis of the MERLEBACH anticline structure.

This résult is worth being connected to :
. the structural study which leads to suppose that the high horizontal stresses perpendicular to the structure axis could dominate the sector (THOMAS, 1983).
. the phenomena of brutal failure observed in the excavations in this area. In fact, a simple calculation of the stress distribution at the face of the roadway has shown that the anisotropy of observed natural stresses could contribute to the triggering of these phenomena (REVALOR, 1985).

TABLE 5

COMPARISON OF THE RESULTS OF THE DIFFERENTS STRESS MEASUREMENT METHODS   (•) CI : Confidence Interval (90 %)

		σ_x (Mpa)	σ_y (MPa)	σ_z (Mpa)	τ_{xy} (Mpa)	τ_{yz} (Mpa)	τ_{zx} (Mpa)	CORRELATION COEFFICIENT	σ1 CI (•) (MPa)	σ1 ORIENTATION	σ2 CI(•) (MPa)	σ2 ORIENTATION	σ3 CI(•) (MPa)	σ3 ORIENTATION
OVERCORING	LEAST SQUARES (21 MEASUREMENTS)	33.8	19	26.3	-5.8	-0.4	-0.3	0.54	35.9 ± 22	N108E Horiz.	26.3 ± 8	Vertical	17 ± 12	N18E Horiz.
	LEAST SQUARES (15 MEASUREMENTS)	35.1	20.1	27.5	-6.7	0.6	-0.7	0.83	37.7 ± 20	N110E SE	27.5 ± 8	85 N	17.5 ± 10	N20E 2N
FLAT JACK									HYDROSTATIC STATE OF STRESS (= 16 à 18 MPa)					
HYDROFRACTURING									37.3	N120E Horiz.	29	Vertical	17.7	N30E Horiz

This convergence between the two methods and between the different statistical approaches put into operation confirms the evaluation. In the measurement area, numerous elements seem in fact to confirm :
. that the mean principal stress is subvertical and probably close to the weight of the over-lying strata
. that the two other principal stresses are horizontal and very different (anisotropic ratio close to 2).

Taking into account the precision given to its orientation, the major principal stress can be considered to

4 - CONCLUSION

For a number of years, the stress measuring methods in rock formations have made obvious progress, which shows the growing interest taken in these measurements.

However, although the procedures and methodologies for measuring have been improved, the problem of evaluating the validity of the obtained estimations has rarely been dealt with.

Now, these measurements are only justified when they lead to estimations which are representative of the state of stress in a relatively important volume of rock mass (on the scale of workings, for example). Because of this, these estimations would not be able to integrate values which are too singular, frequently occuring in the domaines concerning the surveying of natural media.

The pin-pointing of these values is not simple. Certainly, criteria, which are a priori well founded, exist but they remain very qualitative. In the end, such a set of data gives rise to a great state of perplexity !

The statistical approach presented attempts to formalize this problem. Its application to a measuring campaign has permitted testing its effectiveness. By evaluating the sentitivity of the estimations regarding the chosen fit criterion and regarding each measurement it has helped to confirm the final estimation.

On account of the cost of these measurements and, in this particular case, their incidence regarding worksite safety, this procedure seems promising. It is worth pursuing in order to be tested and perfected using other sets of data.

ACKNOWLEDGEMENTS : The authors would like to thank the COLLIERIES OF THE LORRAINE COALFIELD for the means given over to the taking of these measurements.

APPENDIX

1) Fit criteria

With the notation used in the paper, the system is written $Y = Xa$

. Least squares method

e = résidual vector = $Y - Xa$
$e'e$ minimum => $a = (X'X)^{-1} X'Y$
(': transposed matrix operation)

Apart from the problem of its very restrictive hypotheses (and which are not always verified !), the method accords much importance to the observations which differ from the sample of measurements.

. Pondered least squares method

Calling P the diagonal matrix of the weights affected at each residual
$e'Pe$ minimum => $a = (X'PX)^{-1} X'PY$

. HUBER estimation

If s is the root mean squares of residuals, P is such that

$pi = 1$ for $|ei| < ks$
$pi = 1/ei$ for $|ei| > ks$
$i = 1$ to n, n = number of measurements

. Minimum of the sum of the absolute values of residuals

a is such that $\Sigma |ei|$ is minimal.
This criterion can be considered as a particular case of the HUBER estimation with k very low.

. Minimum of the maximum of the absolute values of residuals

a is such that $max |ei|$ is minimum.

These two last criteria can be treated with the algorithms of the linear programming.

2) Influential or suspect observations

Using the preceding notations and in the context of the least squares method

$Y = Xa = X (X'X)^{-1} X'Y = HY$

. Reduced residual

Calling Hii the diagonal term of H

$ri = ei/s \sqrt{1 - Hii}$

. Diagonal terms of H

. D of COOK

Calling a_i the estimation effected by removing the observation i

$D = (a_i -a)' X'X (a_i -a)/ps$
p = number of unknowns (in general case, 6)

High values for these 3 indexes express a very strong influence of the measurement under consideration on the estimation.

REFERENCES

AMADEI B., GOODMAN R.E. (1982) : The influence of rock anisotropy on stress measurements by overcoring techniques - Rock Mechanics, 15 : 167-180

BERTRAND L., DURAND E. (1983) : In situ stress measurements : comparison of different methods - Proc. Int. Symp. "Soil and Rock Investigations by in situ Testing", Paris, 2 : 449-470

BONNECHERE F. (1971) : Contribution à la détermination de l'état de contraintes des massifs rocheux - Thèse de doctorat - Faculté des Sciences Appliquées, Liège

BONVALLET J. (1978) : Critères de stabilité des exploitations souterraines à faible profondeur. Application au cas des carrières du Nord - Thèse Docteur Ingénieur. Institut National Polytechnique de Lorraine. Ecole des Mines, Nancy

BORSETTO M., FRASSONI A., GIUSEPPETTI G., ZANINETTI A. (1983) : Flat jack measurements and interpretation : recent advances. Proc. Int. Symp. "Soil and Rock Investigations by In Situ Testing", Paris, 2 : 517-522

CHEMAOU O. (1984) : Etude des phénomènes dynamiques dans les creusements au rocher et recherche de méthodes de prévision. Application au cas des sur-tirs de Merlebach (Houillères de Lorraine) - Thèse Docteur Ingénieur. Institut National Polytechnique de Lorraine. Ecole des Mines, Nancy

CORNET F.H. (1981) : La mesure des contraintes dans un massif rocheux. Tunnels et Ouvrages Souterrains, 48 : 262-273

CORNET F.H., VALETTE B. (1984) : In Situ Stress Determination from Hydraulic Injection Test Data - J. of Geophys. Res., 89 (B13) : 11527-11537

DONSIMONI M. (1981) : Le bassin houiller lorrain : Synthèse géologique - Mémoire BRGM, 117 : 1-102

DUVALL W.I., AGGSON J.R. (1979) : Least square calculation of horizontal stress from more than three diametral deformations in vertical boreholes - US Bureau of Mines Inv. Rep., 8414

FAIELLA D., MANFREDINI G., ROSSI P.P. (1983) : In situ flat jack test : Analysis of results and critical assessment - Proc. Int. Symp. "Soil and Rock Investigations by In Situ Testing", Paris, 2 : 507-512

GRAY W.M., TOEWS N.A. (1973) : Analysis of variance applied to data obtained by means of a six element borehole deformation gauge for stress determination - Proc. 15th U.S. Symp. Rock Mech., Custer

HAIMSON B.C. (1978) : The hydrofracturing stress measuring method and recent field results - Int. J. Rock Mech. Min. Sci., 15 : 167-178

HELAL H. (1982) : Etude et développement d'une méthode de mesure des contraintes par surcarottage. Applications à l'étude de la stabilité d'ouvrages souterrains - Thèse Docteur Ingénieur - Institut National Polytechnique de Lorraine - Ecole des Mines, Nancy

HELAL H.M., SCHWARTZMANN R. (1983) : In situ stress measurements with the CERCHAR dilatometric cell - Proc. Symp. "Field measurements in geomechanics" Zurich

HIRAMATSU Y., OKA Y. (1968) : Determination of the stress in rock unaffected by boreholes or drifts, from measured strain or deformation - Int. J. Rock Mech. Min. Sci., 5 : 337-353

HIRASHIMA K.I., KOGA A. (1977) : Determination of stresses in anisotropic elastic medium unaffected by boreholes from measured strains or deformations - Proc. Int. Symp. "Fiels Measurements in Rock Mechanics", Zurich : 173-182

JOSIEN JP., REVALOR R. (1983) : Prévision et maitrise des phénomènes dynamiques (coups de terrains) - Communauté Européenne du Charbon et de l'Acier. Convention d'étude n° 7220 AC 1309 - Rapport final

MAYER A., HABIB P., MARCHAND R. (1951) : Mesure en place des pressions de terrains - Conf. Int. Pressions Terrains, Liège

PIGUET JP., GEORGE L. (1979) : 6ème campagne de mesures de contraintes naturelles à l'étage 1250 (Houillères de Lorraine, siège de Merlebach) par la méthode du vérin plat - CERCHAR - Laboratoire de Mécanique des Terrains - Rapport interne 79-76-1580 - 18

REVALOR R. (1985) : Maitrise des phénomènes dynamiques - Communauté Européenne du Charbon et de l'Acier - Convention d'étude n° 7220 AC 312 - Rapport final

REVALOR R. (1984) : Mesures des contraintes naturelles par surcarottage et fracturation hydraulique. Houillères de Lorraine. Siège Simon. Champ Ouest F1 4ème TB extraction 850 - CERCHAR - Laboratoire de Mécanique des Terrains - Rapport interne 84(1)22-72-1132 - 15

REVALOR R., ARCAMONE J., JOSIEN JP., PIGUET JP. (1985) : In situ rock stress measurements in French coal mines : relation between virgin stresses and rock bursts. Proc. 26th US. Symp. Rock Mech., Rapid City, 2 : 1103-1112

RIBACCHI R. (1977) : Rock stress measurements in anisotropic rock masses - Proc. Int. Symp "Field Measurements in Rock Mechanics", Zurich : 183-196

ROCHA M., LOPES JB., DA SILVA J.N. (1966) : A new technique for applying the method of the flat jack in the determination of stresses inside rock masses - Proc. 1st Int. Cong. Rock Mech.. Lisbonne

TINCHON L., DAUMALIN C., GEORGE L., PIGUET JP. (1982) : Evolution des contraintes en fonction de la profondeur et des facteurs naturels - Proc. 7th Conf. Int. Pressions Terrains, Liège : 587-606

THOMAS A. (1983) : Mesures de contraintes au rocher par fracturation hydraulique dans la mine de Merlebach - Puits Vouters - Etage 1250 - Ecole Nationale Supérieure de Géologie - Laboratoire de tectonophysique fondamentale et appliquée - Rapport interne

THOMAS A., GEORGE L., PIGUET JP. (1983) : Interprétation des mesures de contraintes en site minier à partir d'un modèle tectonique - Rev. Industrie Minérale, 51 : 169-178

Experience with hydraulic fracture stress measurements in granite

J.R. ENEVER
CSIRO, Division of Geomechanics, Mount Waverley, Victoria, Australia
P.N. CHOPRA
Bureau of Mineral Resources, Geology and Geophysics, Canberra, Australia

ABSTRACT. Hydraulic fracture stress measurements have been made in granite at 3 sites in Australia. Independent estimates of the *in situ* stress at each site obtained with the overcoring technique are in substantial agreement with the hydraulic fracture results. In the hydraulic fracture test results reported, two types of induced fracture geometries have been observed, fractures in the test section and fractures under the sealing packers. Each fracture geometry results in a distinctive pressure record. In both cases appropriate analysis of the results can provide reliable estimates of the *in situ* stress.

RESUME. Des mesurages de la fracture hydrolique de granite sur 3 locations en Australie correspondent substantiellement à des estimations indépendentes de la tension obtenues par des épreuves de carottage à cettes locations. Les rapports des épreuves de fractures hydroliques ont révélé deux types de fracturation générée: des fractures de la section d'épreuve, et des fractures aux points des fermetures hermétiques. Chaque fracturation produit un enregistrement de pression typique, et l'analyse propre des deux resultats peut fournir des estimations reliables sur la tension locale.

ZUSAMMENFASSUNG. Hydraulische Bruchstellen Druck Messungen wurden an drei Granitaufschlüssen in Australien gemacht. Unäbbangige Ergenbnisse von diesen Stellen wurden von Bohrlochversuchen erlangt und sind in starker Übereinstimmung mit den hydraulischen Bruch Ergenbnissen. In den berichteten hydraulischen Bruch Ergenbnissen werden zwei Typen von induzierten Bruch Ebenen beobachtet, namlich Bruche im Versuchsteil und Bruche unter den verschlossenen Packer. Jede Bruch Ebene hat ein deutliches Druck Bild. In beiden Fällen Können die angemessenen Darlegungen der Ergebnisse einenzuverlässigen Überschlag vom ortlichen Druck geben.

1. INTRODUCTION

CSIRO (Commonwealth Scientific and Industrial Research Organisation, Division of Geomechanics, Australia) and the BMR (Bureau of Mineral Resources, Geology and Geophysics, Australia) have been co-operating for a number of years in a programme of regional stress measurements in granite outcrops through-out Australia (Denham et al, 1979; Denham et al. 1980; Denham and Alexander, 1981). The aims of this programme have been to investigate the magnitude, orientation and distribution of tectonic stress within the continent, to study the relationship between this stress field and large scale geological structure, and to obtain data for the assessment of earthquake risk.

Initial efforts made use of overcoring techniques (United States Bureau of Mines (USBM) borehole deformation gauge and the CSIRO hollow inclusion cell) near to the surface (generally less than 5 metres depth) at a number of locations throughout Australia. Where the results obtained were considered to be reliable, they generally indicated a NE-SW or E-W orientation of the maximum horizontal principal stress.

These results, while they have served to delineate some broad features of the stress field, have pointed to the need to carry out measurements at greater depth to overcome the influence of the relatively deep weathering profiles that characterise the near surface rocks throughout much of Australia and to avoid problems associated with near surface measurements, such as diurnal temperature effects and the effect of topography.

In view of these factors it was decided to substitute a stress measurement programme based on hydraulic fracturing, offering the opportunity of making *in situ* stress determinations at much greater depths in fresh, "tectonically-coupled" rock. The application of hydraulic fracturing to the stress measurement programme has drawn heavily on extensive experience with hydrofracture obtained by CSIRO in sedimentary basin rocks (Enever and Wooltorton, 1983). The design philosophy of the downhole tools and the instrumentation that is reported here is broadly similar to that used previously by CSIRO.

2.   EQUIPMENT

A hydrofracture system, comprising a fracture tool and an impression packer,

has been designed and constructed specifically for the programme. Figure shows the essential components of the fracture tool, together with the handli system and the up-hole hydraulic and electronic equipment. The tool is connected to the surface control system means of two flexible high pressure hos and a seven conductor armoured co-axial cable. The former allow independent connection of the packers and the isola test interval to separate hydraulic pum housed in the control vehicle, while th latter provides the necessary electrica and mechanical connections. This syste allows for independent pressurisation o the packers and the test interval, to facilitate control of the (packer-test interval) pressure margin during testin Important components of the fracture to include two transducers for the measure ment of pressure in the packers and the test interval, a flow meter for the measurement of fluid movement into or o of the test interval, and a solenoid operated dump valve to permit deflation the packers at the end of a test. The length of the test interval can be varied to suit rock conditions by using different length spacers (currently 0.5 and 1 metre spacers are used). The

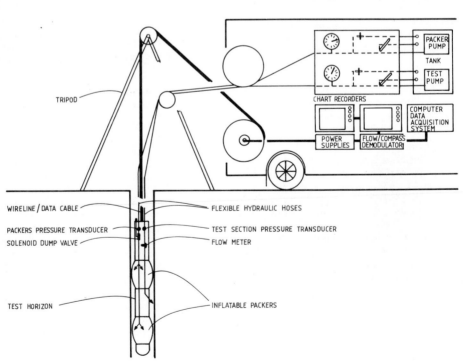

Fig. 1.   Schematic representation of hydraulic fracture test facility.

impression packer also incorporates a
solenoid dump valve and includes a
digital compass which provides an up-
hole display of the tool's orientation
in the hole. This arrangement provides
a reliable means of determining the
orientation of the induced fractures at
the borehole wall. Figure 2 shows the
system in operation.

3. EXPERIMENTAL PROCEDURES

Field tests have been carried out at
each site in a similar fashion. In each
case water has been used as the fracture
fluid and the rates of pressurisation
have been relatively slow (approximately
5 MPa per minute). The field test
procedure followed has involved an
initial fracturing phase followed by a
number of cycles of repressurisation and
subsequent venting of the test interval.

Initial fracturing is accomplished by
concurrently but independently increasing
the pressure in the packers and the test
interval, maintaining the minimum excess
of packer pressure commensurate with
containment of fluid in the test interval.
This ensures that when crack initiation
occurs the level of uncertainty as
regards the initiation pressure (packer

pressure-test section pressure) is
minimised. Pumping is stopped as soon as
a crack is formed (sudden drop in test
section pressure) in order to preserve
the initial geometry (approximately as
recorded by the impression packer) and to
allow a first shut-in pressure to be
recorded. The test interval is then
vented to atmosphere to allow the induced
crack to close. A build-up of pressure
in the test interval upon temporarily
sealing the system during venting
(pressure "rebound") is taken as evidence
of continued flow of fluid out of a
closing crack. Venting is continued
until this phenomenon ceases.

Further cycles of pressurisation and
venting are used to determine the crack
re-opening pressure and to gauge whether
the orientation of the crack changes as it
is propagated. Such a change of crack
orientation may be reflected in systematic
changes in shut-in pressure from cycle to
cycle. Crack re-opening pressure is
determined with the aid of the downhole
flow meter.

All field testing to date has been
restricted to cored holes. This facilitates optimum selection of test horizons
(free of joints, cracks etc) and provides
a supply of material for laboratory
testing. As a matter of course,
laboratory tests are conducted on samples
prepared from core corresponding to the
test horizons (including packer locations)
to determine fracture strength and poro-
elastic constants. Samples are prepared
by cutting them to length (length to
diameter ratio 2-3:1) and grinding the
ends flat. A small central hole is
drilled along the axis of the sample and
a hydraulic probe glued into one end.
The other end is sealed with a metal
plug. The central hole is pressurised
with water, at pressurisation rates
compatible with the corresponding field
pressurisation rate, until fracture
initiation (usually a crack in an axial
plane) occurs. Some tests are conducted
without any external load being applied
to the sample, to measure fracture
strength directly. Others are conducted
under various combinations of axial
compression (applied in a loading frame)
and external radial pressure (applied by
means of a triaxial cell) specifically
to examine the influence of circumferential compressive stress around the test
hole on fracture initiation. Some

Fig. 2.   Hydraulic fracture test
          facility in operation.

samples have been loaded in diametric
compression (line loading) to examine the
influence of circumferential tensile
stress around the test hole on fracture
initiation.

4. TEST SITES

In this paper discussion will be limited
to three of the sites where hydrofracture stress measurements have been
made in granitic rocks. These sites
characterise two different styles of
results obtained in the programme, both
in terms of the form of the pressure-time
data recorded and the nature of the
fractures produced. These sites are also
of particular interest because independent
estimates of the stress state are
available from overcoring measurements
made nearby (less than 10 m laterally)
using the U.S.B.M. borehole deformation
gauge. These sites are:

Berrigan, New South Wales (Fig. 3). The
measurements at this site were made in a
vertical borehole drilled in a granite
of Upper Silurian age, at depths between
4 metres and 169 metres. The borehole
is located in a small disused quarry in
flat lying country in southern New South
Wales, on the western flank of a major
fold belt trending approximately North-
South (Lachlan Fold Belt). The rock
has an average grainsize of 1670 microns
and in thin-section is seen to be
essentially free of deformation induced
micro-structures other than a few non-
pervasive microcracks which are located
principally along grain boundaries.
Ample evidence in the form of "pop-ups"
and stress controlled jointing exists in
the area to suggest that the ground is
currently being subjected to a strong
horizontal compressive stress field. The
area has a history of frequent seismicity,
with a magnitude 5.5 earthquake recorded
in the vicinity in 1938.

Lancefield, Victoria (Fig. 3). This site
is located in a broad valley in gently
rolling country near the town of
Lancefield approximately 75 kilometres
north of Melbourne. The vertical borehole used for the tests penetrates an
undeformed graniodorite outcrop of Upper
Devonian age, with an average grainsize of
1440 microns. This site is located within
the Lachlan Fold Belt. The hydrofracture
measurements are made at this site at a
depth of approximately 10 metres.

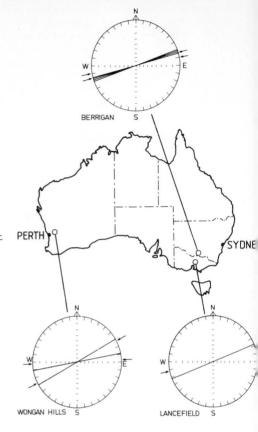

ORIENTATION OF THE MAXIMUM PRINCIPAL STRESS
——— INFERRED FROM HYDRAULIC FRACTURE MEASUREMENTS
→ ←— INFERRED FROM OVERCORING MEASUREMENTS

Fig. 3.   Location map showing
test sites and orientations
of fractures induced at
the respective sites.

Wongan Hills, Western Australia (Fig. 3
This site is approximately 150 kilometr
north-east of Perth and within an area
bounded by the towns of Meckering,
Calingiri and Cadoux, the sites in
recent years of earthquakes of magnitud
6.9, 5.9 and 6.5 respectively. This
area is part of the Yilgarn Block, a
multiply deformed Archaean craton. The
rock penetrated by the vertical borehol
used for the tests is a deformed granic
diorite outcrop which has probably
undergone recrystallisation during its
deformation history and is now relative
fine grained. The average grainsize
determined from thin-section is 980
microns. Tests were conducted at depth
between 60 and 70 metres.

5. RESULTS OF FIELD TESTS

Vertical hydraulic fractures were initiated during testing at each site. At Berrigan, the fractures were found generally to correspond with the test interval, extending at each end into the regions occupied during testing by the packers. In contrast, at the Lancefield and Wongan Hills sites the fractures were found to be restricted to the zone occupied during testing by one or other of the inflatable packers. The orientations of the fractures induced at the three sites are shown on Fig. 3.

Also shown on Fig. 3 are the corresponding orientations of the major horizontal stress component determined by overcoring at each site. For each site, irrespective of the relative location of the induced crack, the orientational correspondence between overcoring and hydraulic fracturing can be considered good, if the orientation of the hydraulic fracture is taken to represent the orientation of the major horizontal stress component.

The difference in the locations of the fractures induced at Berrigan compared to Lancefield and Wongan Hills was reflected in the form of the pressure records obtained from the respective sites. Figure 4a is typical of the pressure records obtained for the majority of tests conducted at Berrigan, exhibiting a distinct (sharp) crack initiation, well defined shut-in pressure for successive cycles of pressurisation, noticeable pressure "rebound" during venting of the test section between pressurisation cycles, clear crack re-opening pressures (defined by the onset of flow as measured by the down hole flow meter) for each repressurisation and relatively constant pressure during crack propagation. In most respects, Fig. 4a can be considered consistent with expectations based on the classic understanding of hydraulic fracturing.

Figure 4b, obtained from the Lancefield site, is generally representative of the pressure records obtained for tests at Lancefield and Wongan Hills, and for one test at Berrigan (approx. 4 m depth). The notably different features of Fig. 4b compared to Fig. 4a are the relatively more rounded crack initiation, more diffuse shut-in phases, lack of significant pressure "rebound" during venting of the test section, indistinct crack re-opening and, most noticeably, a distinct hump in the pressure curve during the first repressurisation cycle. All of these features can be attributed to the initiation of fractures by the packer pressure in preference to the pressure in the isolated test interval.

The relatively less distinct crack initiation and more diffuse shut-in phases result from the fluid in the isolated test interval having to leak past the inflated packer to enter the induced fracture, producing a dampening of the test interval pressure response. The lack of significant pressure "rebound" and a distinct re-opening pressure can be related to the propping effect of the packer on a crack initiated under it. The distinct hump in the pressure record presumably represents the excess pressure required to extend the originally initiated crack along the length of the hole to a position where fluid from the test interval has direct access to the crack. For the test represented by Fig. 4b (Table 2), it was noticeable that for pressurisation cycles from the second repressurisation onward, the pressure response was approximately the same for each crack propagation phase, and the shut-in pressures were identical. This is indicative of the diminishing influence of the original location of the fracture as crack propagation proceeds. During the last repressurisation cycle shown in Fig. 4b the packer pressure was increased, relative to previous cycles, leading to a relatively elevated crack propagation pressure but without influencing shut-in pressure.

Analysis of the Berrigan field data was based on the conventionally accepted use of shut-in pressure (to estimate the minor horizontal stress component magnitude (σ_2) and crack re-opening pressure (to estimate the magnitude of the major horizontal stress component (σ_1)), based on the assumption that these were principal stress components and that the third principal stress component (σ_3) was vertical and therefore co-axial with the test hole. The methods used to select the salient data from the test records are shown on Fig. 4a. A summary of the data is given in Table 1, along with a summary of the analysis of the data based on the relationship (Haimson, 1978):

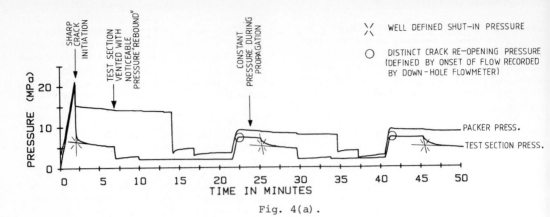

Fig. 4(a).

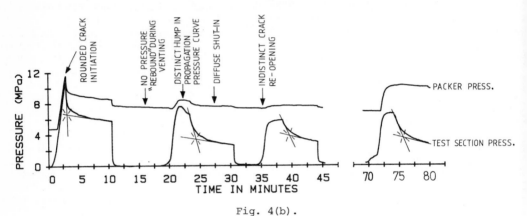

Fig. 4(b).

Fig. 4. Abridged test records showing methods used to select salient data.

$$\sigma_1 = 3\sigma_2 - Pr - Po \qquad (1)$$

where: σ_2 is estimated directly by
shut-in pressure

Pr is the crack re-opening pressure

and Po is the ambient pore pressure
at the location of the test
horizon (based on the assump
tion of the water table being
at the surface)

Included in Table 1 is a summary of the
results of the overcoring tests conducted
at the Berrigan site.

The data in Table 1 show a high degree
of consistency, both in terms of the
relatively small ranges observed for
shut-in pressure and re-opening pressure
for any given test, and in terms of the
general agreement between results for
the six hydrofracture tests. There is
also reasonable agreement between the
hydrofracture tests and the overcoring
results.

The absence of distinct re-opening
pressures for the data obtained from the
Lancefield and Wongan Hills sites
necessitated the use of a different
approach to analysis in these cases.
As with the Berrigan data, shut-in
pressure was used to estimate the
magnitude of σ_2. The magnitude of σ_1
was determined from the relationship
(Haimson, 1978):

$$\sigma_1 = 3\sigma_2 + S - KPi - (2-K)Po \qquad (2)$$

where: S is the fracture strength

Pi is the crack initiation
pressure, and

K is a poro-elastic constant

Core recovered from the test holes at
the Lancefield and Wongan Hills sites
was tested in the laboratory to determi
appropriate values of S and K for each
site. The outcome of this laboratory
testing is discussed in detail in secti
6. Table 2 gives a summary of the

TABLE 1. SUMMARY OF DATA FOR BERRIGAN SITE

Depth of Test Horizon (m)	Estimated Pore Pressure (Po) MPa	Crack Initiation Pressure (Pi) MPa (Corresponding packer press.)	Range of Shut-in Pressures (1st cycle-nth cycle) MPa	Range of Re-opening Pressures (Pr) MPa	Estimate of σ_2 MPa	Estimate of σ_1 MPa	Orientation of σ_1
4-5	0	11.6 (14.2)	5.6-5.8-6.0	5.7-6.0	5.6-6.0	11.1-12.0	
69-70	0.7	15.5 (16.2)	5.6-5.5-5.3	5.6-5.5	5.3-5.6	9.7-10.5	70° East of True Nth
100-101	1.0	17.4 (18.9)	6.0-5.5-4.9	6.3-5.6	4.9-6.0	8.1-10.7	75° East of True Nth
125-126	1.3	18.5 (19.7)	6.3-6.2-6.1	6.7-6.7	6.1-6.3	10.3-10.9	70° East of True Nth
154-155	1.5	20.7 (21.5)	6.3-6.1-5.7	7.0-7.0	5.7-6.3	8.6-10.4	72° East of True Nth
168-169	1.7	18.6 (19.0)	7.7-8.0	8.4	7.7-8.0	13.0-13.9	73° East of True Nth
Results from Overcoring in Adjacent Hole							
3.5					5.6	11.4	74° East of True Nth
3.8					9.5	12.1	80° East of True Nth

TABLE 2. SUMMARY OF DATA FROM LANCEFIELD AND WONGAN HILLS SITES

Depth of Test Horizon (m)	Estimated Pore Pressure (Po) MPa	Crack Initiation Pressure (Pi) MPa (Corresponding packer press.)*	Range of Shut-in Pressures (1st cycle-nth cycle) MPa	Range of Re-opening Pressures (Pr) MPa	Laboratory Strength Range, MPa (Average)	Estimate of σ_2 MPa	Estimate of σ_1** MPa (Average)	Orientation of σ_1
Lancefield								
approx. 10m	0	10.9 (11.6)	7.0-3.9-3.9- 3.9-3.9-3.9	4.6-4.2- 4.2-4.2-4.6	10.0-12.0 (11.0)	3.9	10.1-12.1 (11.1)	68° East of True Nth
Results from Overcoring in Adjacent Hole								
Average of two tests at approx. 10m						3.4	11.0	78° East of True Nth
Wongan Hills								
66-67	0.7	9.5 (9.5)	6.3-5.1-4.3- 4.3	4.2-3.9- 3.9	13.2-15.0 (14.1)	4.3	15.9-17.7 (16.8)	79° East of True Nth
69-70	0.7	11.4 (11.4)	5.5-6.1-6.6- 6.6	3.9-3.9- 4.2	13.2-15.0 (14.1)	6.6	20.9-22.7 (21.8)	60° East of True Nth
Results from Overcoring in Adjacent Hole								
6.5						3.4	18.2	62° East of True Nth
10.5						6.8	20.4	87° East of True Nth

* Pressure in packers at crack initiation used in analysis
** K = 1.0 used in analysis

salient field and laboratory data for the Lancefield and Wongan Hills sites, along with a summary of the analysis of the data. Also included in Table 2 is a summary of the results of the overcoring tests conducted at both sites.

In general terms, the data in Table 2 reflect reasonable agreement between the hydraulic fracture and overcoring results, particularly when the average laboratory measured strength is employed for analysis of the hydraulic fracture data. This agreement is evidence of the ability of hydraulic fracturing to reliably estimate the *in situ* stress field even when fractures are initiated under packers, provided that the crack initiation pressure and laboratory measured strength are used in the analysis rather than the re-opening pressure. Scrutiny of the data contained in Table 2 readily suggests that use of re-opening pressures in all instances would have led to a serious underestimation of the value of σ_1.

It would appear from the data contained in Table 2 that when crack re-opening occurs it does so at a pressure approximating the value of σ_2 rather than the value of $3\sigma_2 - \sigma_1$ as generally assumed for analysis employing crack re-opening pressure. This discrepancy may be due in part to the tendency for the packers to hold cracks open. In the case of both the Lancefield and Wongan Hills sites, however, the net horizontal stress fields tended toward a situation $(\sigma_1 \geqslant 3\sigma_2)$ where it might be expected that cracks, once initiated, would not reclose even if they occurred in the isolated test interval rather than under a packer.

The other notable feature of the data contained in Table 2 compared to Table 1 is the relatively greater range in the recorded shut-in pressures in the former case. This can probably be attributed to variations in the influence of the inflated packer on the access of fluid from the isolated test interval into the crack throughout the progress of a test. Use of the long term shut-in pressure to estimate σ_2 appears to give best correspondence between hydraulic fracturing and overcoring.

6.   RESULTS OF LABORATORY TESTS

Figure 5 summarises the results of laboratory tests conducted on core recovered from the Lancefield site. The samples were all tested without external load. This testing strategy was choosen in recognition of an *in situ* stress field that would produce approximately zero circumferential stress in the borehole wall at the location of crack initiation (i.e. $\sigma_1 \doteq 3\sigma_2$ in equation (2)). In Fig. 5 crack initiation pressure is shown plotted against rate of pressurisation. These results do not suggest a systematic variation in crack initiation pressure with change in the rate of pressurisation. The limits of strength used in the analysis of the Lancefield field data are

indicated by the horizontal lines on Fig. 5. In the absence of specific laboratory data, a value of K = 1.0 was assumed for the analysis, based on general experience (Haimson, 1978).

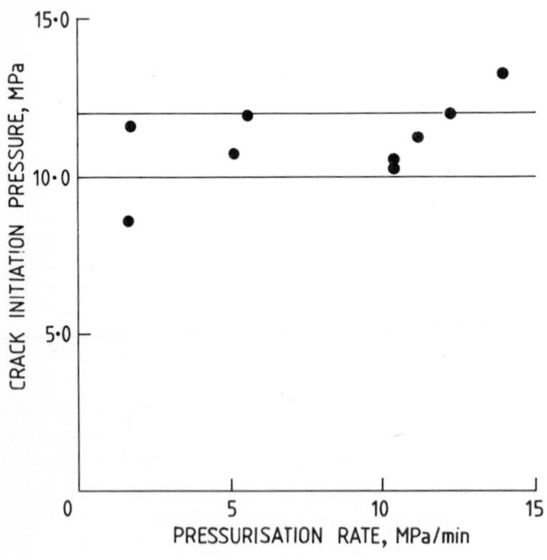

In the case of the material from the Wongan Hills site, samples were tested under external diametric loading to produce a net tensile stress at the point of crack initiation in the samples. This procedure was used to simulate the effect of an *in situ* stress field that would produce a circumferential tension in the borehole wall at the location of crack initiation (i.e. $\sigma_1 > 3\sigma_2$).

Figure 6 presents the results of this series of laboratory tests, with crack initiation pressure plotted against the uniform transverse tensile stress produced a short distance away from the borehole wall by external diametric loading (Jaeger and Hoskins, 1966). The data in Fig. 6 are not inconsistent with an approximately linear relationship between initiation pressure and applied stress, within a reasonably well defined band. The trend of this relationship suggests a value of K = 1 (from equation 2 if $3\sigma_2 - \sigma_1$ is taken equal to the tensile stress and $P_o = 0$). This value was used in the analysis of the Wongan Hills field data, together with the strength measured from the samples test without external loading (Fig. 6).

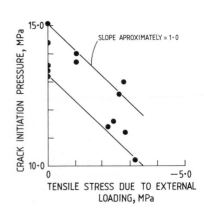

Fig. 5.   Summary of laboratory results for Lancefield rock. Internal pressurisation rate versus crack initiation pressure.

Fig. 6.   Summary of laboratory results Wongan Hills rock. Tensile stress due to external loading versus crack initiation pressure.

7. DISCUSSION

The two most obvious aspects of the field results evident from the data contained in Fig. 3 and Tables 1 and 2 are the apparent orientational consistency of the horizontal stress field over vast distances (probably coincidental) and the suggestion (based on the Berrigan and Wongan Hills data) of a lack of a systematic gradient in the horizontal stress component magnitudes with depth. The latter observation may simply reflect a lack of sufficient data to a depth at which such a gradient might be expected to become obvious. However, if this observation is substantiated by further testing, it will have significant implications for assessing regional stress patterns.

From the viewpoint of the hydraulic fracturing technique, an interesting feature of the experience gained at the three sites has been the relative location (under packer versus within the test interval) of induced fractures, and the commensurate implications on analysis of field data. The practical implications of crack location have been treated above. The factors influencing crack location warrant some further discussion.

For the field tests conducted at Lancefield and Wongan Hills, the packer pressure during initial pressurisation was kept only marginally above the test interval pressure, such that at crack initiation there was only a very small (if any) excess pressure in the packers. For the fractures to be initiated under the packer (as they were) it is a necessary condition that the value of K must have been very close to 1.0. If the value of K had been significantly greater than 1, cracks would have been expected to have formed preferentially in the test section, where the rock was exposed to the influence of test fluid penetration. For a value of K = 1.0, fracture initiation by the packers could be expected even if the packer pressure were only very slightly in excess of the test interval pressure. A value of K approximately equal to 1 for the Wongan Hills rock is consistent with the results of laboratory tests conducted in the tension regime on this material.

In contrast, even though the packer pressure during initial pressurisation was greater than that in the test interval for the Berrigan tests, the cracks still apparently initiated in the test interval rather than under the packers (except for one test). The most obvious explanation for this is that in this instance the value of K must have been somewhat greater than 1, in order to compensate for the excess packer pressure and lead to crack initiation in the test section according to equation (2). A value of K only slightly greater than 1.0 is suggested by the field test conducted at 4 metres at the Berrigan site. During this test the packer pressure was allowed to exceed the test interval pressure by 2.6 MPa, compared with an average of 0.9 MPa for the other tests. In this particular case, fracture initiation occurred under a packer rather than within the test interval.

The different fracture initiation location between Berrigan and the other sites might simply reflect small differences in the value of K for the materials involved. On the other hand, it is possible that the answer lies in the fact that for the Berrigan site the prevailing stress field was such as to produce a net circumferential compression in the test hole wall, while at the other sites the stress fields produced a net circumferential tension or approximately zero stress condition at the point of fracture initiation. This, in turn, might imply a somewhat different failure criterion for crack initiation in stress fields with very large stress ratios ($\sigma_1 > 3\sigma_2$) compared with more balanced stress fields ($\sigma_1 < 3\sigma_2$).

8. CONCLUSIONS

The tests conducted to date in the regional stress programme have revealed the ability of hydraulic fracturing to produce estimates of the *in situ* horizontal stress field, in granite bodies, in close agreement with the results of overcoring measurements. Preliminary results suggest, at least to 170 metres, no evidence of any systematic trend of the horizontal stress magnitude with depth, rather an approximately constant horizontal stress field regardless of depth.

Two distinct forms of fracture initiation have been identified:

(a) fracture initiation occurring in the isolated test interval

(b) fracture initiation occurring under one or other of the inflatable packers.

Distinctly different styles of pressure records are associated with these two cases. In both instances it has been shown that it is possible to undertake satisfactory analysis of the data. When fractures initiate in the test interval and the net circumferential stress is compressive ($\sigma_1 < 3\sigma_2$), crack re-opening pressure provides a reliable means of estimating the major stress component magnitude. When fractures initiate under packers and/or the net circumferential stress at the location of crack initiation is tensile ($\sigma_1 > 3\sigma_2$), crack initiation pressure and the laboratory measured strength can be used to estimate the major stress component magnitude. In both cases, shut-in pressure (particularly the long term shut-in pressure when a crack initiates under a packer) provides a reliable means of estimating the minor stress magnitude.

9. ACKNOWLEDGEMENTS

The equipment used for the field work was designed and developed by Mr. J. Edgoose of the CSIRO Division of Geomechanics. His considerable contribution to the programme is gratefully acknowledged. The Engineering Services Unit of the BMR was responsible for the construction of the down-hole tools and associated handling system.

This paper is published with the permission of the Chief, CSIRO Division of Geomechanics, and the Director, Bureau of Mineral Resources, Geology and Geophysics.

10. REFERENCES

Denham, D., Alexander, L.G. and Worotnicki, G. 1979. Rock stress measurements in the Lachlan Fold Belt, N.S.W. CSIRO Aust. Division of Geomechanics, Technical Report No. 84.

Denham, D., Alexander, L.G. and Worotnicki, G. 1980. The stress field near the sites of the Meckering (1968) and Calingiri (1970) Earthquakes, Western Australia, Tectonophysics 67:283-317.

Denham, D. and Alexander, L.G. 1981. Rock stress measurements, Cadoux to Wagin W.A. CSIRO Aust. Division of Geomechanics, Technical Report No. 125.

Enever, J.R. and Wooltorton, B. 1983. Experience with hydraulic fracturing as a means of estimating in situ stress in Australian Coal Basin sediments, In: Hydraulic Fracturing Stress Measurement, National Academy Press, Washington.

Haimson, B.C. 1978. Borehole hydrofracturing for the dual purpose of in situ stress measurement and core orientation, Proceedings of the third International Congress of the International Association of Engineering Geology, Madrid.

Jaeger, J.C. and Hoskins, E.R. 1966. Stress and failure in rings of rock loaded in diametral tension or compression, British Journal of Applied Physics, Vol. 17.

Four years of hydrofracturing rock stress measurements in Sweden

B. BJARNASON
O. STEPHANSSON
A. TORIKKA
K. BERGSTRÖM
Division of Rock Mechanics, Luleå University of Technology, Luleå, Sweden

ABSTRACT: Hydraulic fracturing rock stress measurements at the Luleå University of Technology in Sweden started in 1982. A new, truck mounted system of field equipment has been developed, based on a compact multihose containing pressure lines and signal cables. The system enables fast and inexpensive measurements down to 500 m depth. Rock stress measurements have been conducted at five sites in crystalline rock formations in Sweden and Finland. The paper reviews the status of the hydrofracturing method in Sweden and the general experience gained from the field measurements. Results from the test site of Gideå are briefly presented.

RÉSUMÉ: Les travaux de mesures de contraintes des roches par fracturation hydraulique ont débuté, à l'Université de Luleå (Suède), en 1982. Une nouvelle unité autonome d'équipement de terrain a été développée sur le principe d'un cable hydrau-électrique qui regroupe un multiconducteur et les conduites d'eau sous pression. Cet équipement permet d'effectuer des mesures rapides et peu coûteuses jusqu'à une profondeur de 500 mètres. Des mesures de contraintes de roches ont été conduites sur cinq sites cristallins, en Suède et en Finlande. Cette communication fait le point sur la méthode de fracturation hydraulique en Suède ainsi que sur l'enseignement des campagnes de terrain. Les résultats obtenus sont rapidement présentés pour l'un des sites testés.

ZUSAMMENFASSUNG: Seit 1982 werden an der technischen Hochschule von Luleå hydrofrakturierende Gesteinsspannungsmessungen durchgeführt. Eine neue, auf LKW montierte Feldausrüstung mit einem kompakten Vielzweckschlauch, der Druckleitungen und Signalkabel aufnimmt, ist entwickelt worden. Dieses Gerät ermöglicht schnelle und kostengünstige Messungen bis zu 500 m Tiefe. Gesteinsspannungsmessungen wurden an fünf Stellen in Schwedischen und Finnischen kristallinen Gesteinsformationen durchgeführt. Das Referat gibt einen Überblick über den Zustand der hydrofrakturierenden messmethode in Schweden und die allgemeinen Erfahrungen aus dem Aussendienst. Ergebnisse von der Versuchmesstelle in Gideå werden kurz dargelegt.

1 INTRODUCTION

The first hydrofracturing stress measurements in the Nordic countries were conducted in Iceland 1976 (Haimson and Voight, 1977). These were followed by measurements at three powerhouse sites and finally by a detailed study of rock stresses in the Iceland Research Drill Hole Project (Haimson and Rummel, 1982). The first measurements in Sweden were conducted by Tom Doe at the Stripa mine in Sweden (Doe et al., 1983). In 1982 the Division of Rock Mechanics at the Luleå University of Technology obtained its first version of instruments for hydraulic fracturing rock stress measurements. Since then, hydrofracturing stress measurements have been conducted by the research group at the Luleå University of Technology at five sites in Sweden and Finland (Stephansson and Ångman, 1986, Bjarnason, 1986, and Johansson et al., this volume).

2.1 Multihose field testing unit

The basic idea behind the hydrofracturing instrumentation was to build a versatile borehole testing unit for field use. The unit should be independent, excluding the high costs and complications of a drill rig operated system. A system of a multihose wound on a hydraulically driven drum was chosen, Figure 1. The multihose is 500 m long, consisting of three high pressure hoses, a signal cable and a steel wire, all contained in a strong synthetic rubber cover. The multihose is run up and down the hole by the drum and a hose feeder, placed directly above the hole. All the instruments are mounted on a truck bed which is enclosed in a cabin. All testing is conducted from the cabin. A detailed description of the hydrofracturing instrumentation is given in Bjarnason (1986).

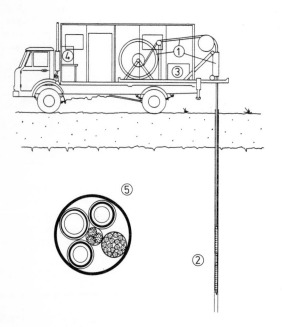

Figure 1. Hydrofracturing field unit.
1) multihose, drum and feeder, 2) packers, 3) pump and water control system, 4) data recording system, 5) cross section of the multihose.

High pressure water is supplied by a hydraulically driven, 3 cylinder piston pump. Maximum pressure is 100 MPa and maximum flow rate is 15 1/min. The pressure in the system is set to a predetermined constant value for each test by two bypass valves. Packer pressure and test section pressure are controlled independently. The water system is schematically shown in Figure 2.

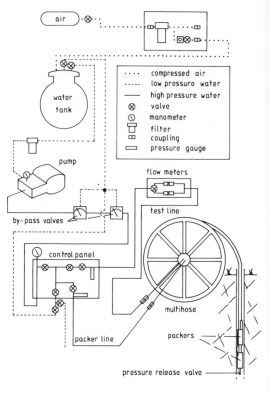

Figure 2. Pump and water control system.

Two packer systems are used during the measurements:

- Straddle packer during fracturing and shut-in registration

- Impression packer for fracture orientation

All packer elements are made of inexpensive nylon reinforced rubber hoses, with pressed-on steel bindings. The maximum differential packer pressure is 35-40 MPa. Active sealing length of the packers is 1 m. The straddle packer is equipped with an internal piston, activated by the water pressure in the packer, to counteract packer elongation during pressurization. This has increased the maximum packer pressure and the packer life time. The packer systems presently used are designed for 56 and 76 mm hole diameters, which are the most common sizes of core holes for investigation purposes in Sweden. Packer orientation during impression is determined either by a conventional single-shot camera or an electrical-magnetic borehole surveying instrument, type BOREMAC, giving direct readings to the surface via the signal cable. A borehole TV-camera belongs to the field instrumentation, for inspection of the borehole walls prior to testing, if access to drill core is not possible.

The following parameters are recorded as a function of time during testing:

- Downhole pressure in the test section, measured immediately above the straddle packer

- Test section pressure measured at the surface

- Packer pressure

- Water flow rate to the test section and the backflow volume

The entire field instrumentation is powered by the truck engine via the hydraulic system. The field unit is totally independent of external energy sources which makes it fast and flexible in operation. All field work is conducted by two persons.

2.2 Laboratory equipment

Small scale laboratory equipment has been developed to test the hydrofracturing tensile strength of rock cores from the test borehole, Figure 3. A core specimen with planar and parallel ends is drilled through by a central axial hole. The specimen is subjected to confining pressure in a bi-axial cell and loaded axially in a small loading frame. The central hole is pressurized by oil or water until fracturing occurs. Seals in the hole ("packers") confine the internal pressure to the central portion of the rock core. This simulates actual field conditions, although on a much smaller scale. Internal pressure, confining pressure and the axial stress are continuously recorded during the test together with the acoustic emission from the specimen. A typical test record is shown in Figure 4.

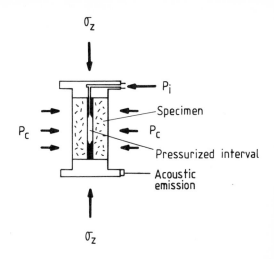

Figure 3. Laboratory simulation of hydraulic fracturing for determination of the tensile strength of rock core specimens.

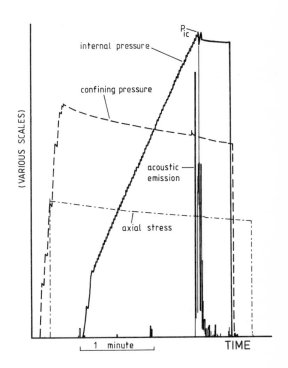

Figure 4. Typical results from laboratory testing of hydrofracturing tensile strength.

423

3   PRESENT APPLICATION OF THE METHOD

Application of the hydrofracturing method
is based on the classical theory of
stresses around a circular opening in a
linearly elastic and isotropic rock material, established by Hubbert and Willis
(1957), and further developed and discussed in numerous papers within the
field of hydrofracturing rock stress measurements. Measurements by the hydrofracturing group in Luleå have mostly been
conducted in vertical holes in a flat
topography where one of the principal
stresses is assumed to be nearly vertical, parallel to the axis of the borehole
and equal to the overburden pressure at
the test depth.

The vertical stress is defined as follows:

$$\sigma_v = \gamma z \qquad (1)$$

where: σ_v = assumed vertical stress,
γ = unit weight of the rock, z = depth.
The least horizontal stress, σ_h is

$$\sigma_h = P_s \qquad (2)$$

where: P_s = instantaneous shut-in pressure, usually determined from the 3rd
pressurization cycle or from slow pumping
reopening tests.

The maximum horizontal stress, σ_H, has
been calculated according to the first
and second breakdown method (Doe et al.,
1983):

First breakdown method:

$$\sigma_{HI} = 3\sigma_h + T - P_{c1} \qquad (3)$$

where: I denotes the first breakdown
method, T = hydrofracturing tensile
strength derived from laboratory tests
on rock cores according to section 2.2,
P_{c1} = first breakdown pressure.

Second breakdown method:

$$\sigma_{HII} = 3\sigma_h - P_{c2} \qquad (4)$$

where: II denotes the second breakdown
method, P_{c2} = second breakdown pressure.

The method of second breakdown pressure
assumes that the tensile strength of the
rock is the difference between the first
and second breakdown pressures,
$P_{c1} - P_{c2}$. The second breakdown pressure
is defined as the pressure at which the

initial borehole pressurization rate in
the later cycles deviates from that established in the first pressurization
cycle, prior to fracturing the rock
(Hickman and Zoback, 1983).

The natural pore pressure at the test
depth is a matter of controversy within
hydraulic fracturing studies. Some authors, e.g. Haimson (1978), and Doe et
al. (1983) include the pore pressure
when testing in crystalline rocks. Other
e.g. Rummel et al. (1983) neglect the
pore pressure, and state that the sub-
traction of the water column from the
maximum horizontal stress in impermeabl
crystalline rocks will give misleading
and meaningless results. In this study
the pore pressure at depth is neglected
in the evaluation of the virgin rock
stresses.

4   RESULTS FROM THE GIDEÅ STUDY SITE, SWEDEN

The rock stress measurements at Gideå i
Northern Sweden (Figure 5), were conducted within the Swedish program of
site selection for nuclear waste dispos
in crystalline rock. Measurements were
done down to 500 m depth in a vertical
borehole, centrally located within one
of the possible repository blocks in th
area. A detailed report of the measurements is given in Bjarnason and Stephan
son (1986).

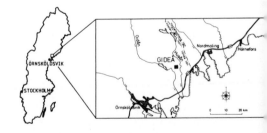

Figure 5. Location of the Gideå study
site, Sweden.

The main rock type is migmatized gneiss
A study of the intrinsic mechanical pro
erties of the rocks from Gideå is presented in Ljunggren et al. (1985). Rock
stresses were measured at 31 points fro
14.5 m depth down to 501 m. Fracture

impressions were attempted at all 31 points. Six of the impressions showed single, horizontal or subhorizontal fractures in the test section. Results from these points were rejected in the evaluation of the horizontal stress field in the area. Results from the remaining 25 test points are plotted in Figure 6.

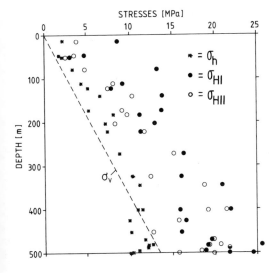

Figure 6. Rock stresses as a function of depth in borehole Gi-1 at Gideå.

A typical pressure-time record from the measurements at Gideå is shown in Figure 7. The test curves are generally of good quality, showing distinct instantaneous shut-in pressures and slow pressure bleed-off after shut-down. The tensile strength of the rock ($P_{c1} - P_{c2}$) is generally high, with an average of 9.2 MPa for all test points.

The hydrofracturing tensile strength of core samples from borehole Gi-1 was tested in the laboratory. The tensile strength from the 10 mm holes in the laboratory was extrapolated to the 56 mm borehole in the field according to a deterministic fracture mechanics approach, based on Paris and Sih (1965) and applied by Doe et al. (1983) for hydrofracturing stress measurements at Stripa in Sweden. The hydrofracturing tensile strength measured in the laboratory was found to vary from 12.6 MPa to 22.3 MPa between series of samples at different depth levels in the borehole. An average extrapolated tensile strength of 11.4 MPa was applied to calculate σ_{HI}.

To summarize the results: The horizontal stress field at Gideå is moderate in magnitude, no extreme values are recorded.

The minimum horizontal stress, σ_h, increases continuously with depth, from 2 MPa close to the surface to roughly 11 MPa at 500 m depth. The scatter in the measured values is low. At approximately 300 m depth there is a change in the gradient of the minimum horizontal stress. Below 300 m the gradient is lower. The change in the gradient of σ_h coincides with reduced fracture frequency and hydraulic conductivity from 300 m depth in the rock mass at Gideå and especially in the stress measurement borehole, Gi-1. The gradient of the minimum horizontal stress is interpreted according to Figure 8b.

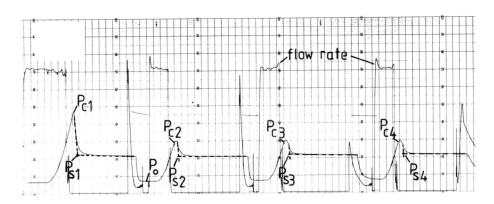

Figure 7. A typical pressure-time record from the hydrofracturing measurements at Gideå, Borehole Gi-1, 345 m depth.

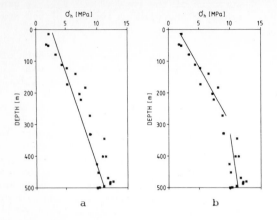

Figure 8. Linear regression analysis of the minimum horizontal stress as a function of depth for borehole Gi-1, Gideå. a) linear increase of σ_h throughout the measuring range, b) discontinuity in the stress gradient around 300 m depth.

The maximum horizontal stress is interpreted according to the second breakdown method. The ratio between the maximum and minimum horizontal stress, σ_H/σ_h, has a nearly constant value of 1.6 at all depths. The average strike of the maximum horizontal stress is N67°E, which does not tend to rotate with depth within the uppermost 500 m for the rock mass at Gideå.

5   GENERAL CONCLUSIONS

- The overall experience of the new, hydrofracturing field instrumentation is good. The system of a multihose containing pressure lines and a signal cable has proven to be flexible and easily operated, offering fast measurements at relatively low cost. Improvements in the packer system have resulted in increased packer life time (up to 80 test points with the same packer elements) and higher maximum packer pressure. The truck-mounted unit has cut down transport and operational costs and highly improved the working environment at the test site.

- The small scale laboratory test equipment for simulating hydrofracturing field tests provides a realistic method of determining the laboratory hydrofracturing tensile strength of rock samples.

- A considerable scatter is observed in the hydrofracturing tensile strength in field measurements and laboratory tests on rock cores. The extrapolatio of the small scale laboratory data to the borehole in the field is an uncer tain operation. The good quality of intact crystalline rocks results in a reliable field tensile strength deter mination from pressure-time records. Therefore, the first breakdown method for calculating the maximum horizonta stress should generally not be applie when testing in crystalline rocks.

REFERENCES

Bjarnason, B. 1986. Hydrofracturing Roc Stress Measurements in the Baltic Shield. Licentiate Thesis 1986:12 L, Luleå University of Technology, Luleå Sweden.

Bjarnason, B. and Stephansson, O. 1986. Hydraulic Fracturing Rock Stress Measurements in Borehole Gi-1, Gideå Tes Site, Sweden. Technical Report, Swedi Nuclear Fuel and Waste Management Co. Stockholm. (in press)

Doe, T.W., Ingevald, K., Strindell, L. Leijon, B., Hustrulid, W., Majer, E. and Carlsson, H. 1983. In Situ Stress Measurements at the Stripa Mine, Sweden. Report LBL-15009, SAC-44. Swedish-American Cooperative Program on Radioactive Waste Storage in Mined Caverns in Crystalline Rock.

Haimson, B.C. 1978. The Hydrofracturing Stress Measuring Method and Recent Field Results. Int. J. Rock Mech. Min Sci. & Geomech. Abstr., 15:167-178.

Haimson, B.C. and Rummel, F. 1982. Hydr fracturing Stress Measurements in the Iceland Research Drilling Project, Drill Hole at Reydarfjördur, Iceland. J. Geoph. Res., 87(B8):6631-6649.

Haimson, B.C. and Voight, B. 1977. Crustal Stresses in Iceland. Pure and Appl. Geoph., 115(1/2):153-190.

Hickman, S.H. and Zoback, M.D. 1983. Th Interpretation of Hydraulic Fracturir Pressure-Time Data for In-Situ Stress Determination. Proc. Workshop on

Hydraulic Fracturing Stress Measurements, Dec. 2-5, 1981. National Academic Press, Washington D.C:44-54.

Hubbert, M.K. and Willis, D.G. 1957. Mechanics of Hydraulic Fracturing. Trans. A.I.M.E., 210:153-168.

Ljunggren, C., Stephansson, O., Alm, O., Hakami, H. and Mattila, U. 1985. Mechanical Properties of Granitic Rocks from Gideå, Sweden. Technical Report No. 85-06. Swedish Nuclear Fuel and Waste Management Company, Stockholm.

Paris, P. and Sih, G. 1965. Stress Analysis of a Crack. In: Fracture Toughness and its Testing. American Society of Testing and Materials Special Publications:30-83.

Rummel, F., Baumgärtner, J., and Alheid, H.J. 1983. Hydraulic Fracturing Stress Measurements Along the Eastern Boundary of the SW-German Block. Proc. Workshop on Hydraulic Fracturing Stress Measurements, Dec. 2-5, 1981. National Academic Press, Washington D.C:3-17.

Stephansson, O. and Ångman, P. 1986. Hydraulic Fracturing Stress Measurements at Forsmark and Stidsvig, Sweden. Bull. Geol. Soc., Finland, 58:307-333.

Zoback, M.D. and Haimson, B.C. 1982. Status of the Hydraulic Fracturing Method for In-Situ Stress Measurements. Issues in Rock Mechanics. Proc. 23rd U.S. Symp. Rock Mech., Univ. of California, Berkeley, California, August 25-27, 1982:143-156.

Stress distribution within an artificially loaded, jointed block

S.M. BROWN
Golder Associates, Seattle, Washington, USA

B.A. LEIJON
Division of Rock Mechanics, Luleå University of Technology, Luleå, Sweden

W.A. HUSTRULID
Department of Mining, Colorado School of Mines, Golden, Colorado, USA

ABSTRACT: The in-situ response of an 8 m^3 block of jointed biotitic gneiss to uniaxial and biaxial boundary loading was monitored using two types of borehole gauges; the USBM Borehole Deformation Gauge and the LUT Triaxial Strain Cell. From the displacements and strains recorded by the gauges as loads were applied, pointwise stresses were calculated assuming both isotropic and anisotropic rock behaviour. Independent of instrument type, the results obtained are characterized by large variations between the stress magnitudes measured in different parts of the block. The measured stress directions are however in close agreement with the directions of the applied boundary loads.

RÉSUMÉ: Le comportement d'un bloc de gneiss à biotite soumis, in-situ, à une charge limite uniaxial et biaxial a été observé en utilisant deux types de jauges pour trous de mines: la jauge USBM de déformation de trous de mines et la cellule LUT de mesure de contrainte triaxiale. A partir des déplacements et déformations enregistrés par les jauges au cours de l'application des charges, on a calculé ponctuellement les contraintes internes subies, en se basant sur la double hypothèse d'un comportement isotropique et anisotropique de la roche. Indépendamment du type d'instrument utilisé, les résultats obtenus se caractérisent par des variations considérables entre les intensités de contrainte mesurées en différents points du bloc. Les directions des contraintes mesurées sont en corrélation étroite avec l'importance des charges limite appliquées.

ZUSAMMENFASSUNG: Das Verhalten eines 8 m^3 zerklüfteten Biotitgneis-Blockes vor Ort bei uniaxialer und biaxialer Grenzzonenbelastung wurde mit zwei Arten von Bohrloch-Messgeräten – dem USBM Bohrloch-Deformationsmesser und der LUT-Messzelle für triaxiale Dehnung – gemessen. Aus den Verschiebungen und Dehnungen, die bei Angringung von Lasten von den Messgeräter ermittelt wurden, berechnete man punktweise Spannungen unter der Annahme von sowohl isotropischem als auch anisotropischem Gesteinsverhalten. Unabhängig von dem jeweiligen Messgerättyp zeichnen sich die erhaltenen Ergebnisse durch grosse Unterschiede zwischen den in verschiedenen Teilen des Blockes festgestellten Spannungsgrössen aus. Die gemessenen Stressrichtungen stimmen gut mit den Richtungen der angebrachten Grenzzonenbelastungen überein.

1 INTRODUCTION

Block tests have recently become an important method for determining the mechanical characteristics of rock masses for modeling of planned nuclear waste storage repositories. An important advantage that block tests have over laboratory and borehole tests is that a relatively large, in-situ volume of rock is placed under known boundary conditions.

This allows comparisons to be made between a known perturbance at the rock mass scale with a measured disturbance at a localized scale. This testing strategy well applies to study the complex problem of stress distributions in discontinuous rock masses.

A series of tests of this category have recently been completed in a load controlled two meter cube of precambrian gneiss. The primary objective of the tests was to study the distribution of stress in the jointed rock mass constituting the block, when subjecting it to known boundary loadings. Two types of instrument, both based on point deformation measurements in boreholes, were used to monitor the response of the block to loading. One was the USBM Borehole Deformation Gauge (BDG), and the other was the triaxial strain cell used by the Luleå University of Technology (LUT-Gauge). An additional test objective was to compare the results produced by these two instruments.

2 TEST BLOCK DESCRIPTION

The testing took place at the Colorado School of Mines' Experimental Mine in Idaho Springs, Colorado, USA. The block itself is located in the floor of the mine in an underground research laboratory developed for the Office of Crystalline Repository Development (OCRD). The surface of the block is at floor grade while the bottom is continuous with the surrounding rock mass. To minimize the effect of these conditions it was decided that all measurements be made at the block midplane. 2.5 meter deep vertical slots on the four sides define the block perimeter. In each vertical slot, grouted flatjacks existed providing a means of applying normal stresses of magnitudes up to about 5 MPa to the block boundaries.

The rock comprising the block contains fractures on several scales. Three major fractures were evident on the block's surface as shown in Figure 1. A number of vertical boreholes were drilled in the block as part of an earlier study (Hardin et al., 1983). Both EX (38 mm) and NX (76 mm) boreholes were drilled that provide access to the block interior. Their locations and designations are shown in Figure 1. Additional fracture data was available from TV-logs of these boreholes (Sour, 1985) indicating that the major fractures dip vertically and are continuous throughout the test block. Also evident from these logs were randomly dispersed smaller fractures.

3 DETERMINATION OF MECHANICAL PROPERTIES

For each gauge location, detailed definition of the rock deformability was necessary. Unfortunately the cores from the block drill holes were unavailable for those tests. Instead, dilatometer tests using the CSM-cell were conducted at the block midplane in each borehole to determine the Young's modulus, E, of the rock and the relative stiffness of different zones in the block. The results of these tests are given in Table 1. Note the wide variation in modulus indicating a high degree of heterogeneity within the rock block.

In addition, the rock was suspected of being anisotropic because of its pronounced foliation. Laboratory tests utilizing NX cores from diamond drilling in the near vicinity were run to quantify the anisotropy assuming transverse isotropic characteristics in the foliation plane. A best fit of these test results is summarized below:

E_1 = Modulus along the foliation direction = 78.7 GPa
E_2 = Modulus normal to the foliation = 53.4 GPa
G = $E/[2(1 + \nu)]$ = 31.5 GPa
G' = Independent rigidity modulus = 26.7 GPa
ν = Poisson's Ratio in foliation plane = 0.246
ν' = Independent Poisson's Ratio = 0.134

Application of these results to the block required scaling by the dilatometer results to include the heterogeneity of the rock mass. Surface mapping and television borehole logs indicated the foliation was throughout the block, trending N75°W with respect to block north. Since the plane of elastic symmetry is vertical the dilatometer results are an average of E_1 and E_2 or:

$$E = \frac{E_1 + E_2}{2}$$

From the tests on the Nx core, we obtain:

$$E_1 = 1.47 \ E_2$$

and hence:

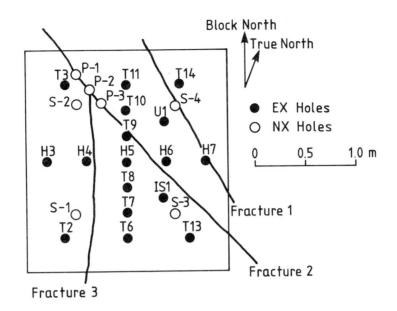

Figure 1. Surface expression of test block showing major discontinuities and vertical borehole locations.

Table 1. Dilatometer results from block midplane measurements. All values GPa.

Borehole	E	E_1	E_2
H3	16.6	19.7	13.5
H4	12.4	14.7	10.1
H5	15.2	18.0	12.4
H6	16.6	19.7	13.5
H7	7.6	9.0	6.2
T2	25.5	30.3	20.7
T3	22.1	26.2	18.0
T6	16.6	19.7	13.5
T7	21.4	25.4	17.4
T8	10.3	12.2	8.4
T9	28.3	33.6	23.0
T10	37.9	45.0	30.8
T11	67.6	80.3	54.9
T13	32.4	38.5	26.3
T14	30.3	36.0	24.6
U1	20.0	23.7	16.3
IS1	8.3	9.9	6.7

Mean = 22.9
St. dev. = 14.4

$$E = \frac{E_1 + E_2}{2} = \frac{2.47\ E_2}{2} = 1.235\ E_2$$

$$E_2 = \frac{1}{1.235}\ E = 0.81\ E$$

$$E_1 = \frac{1.47}{1.235}\ E = 1.19\ E$$

allowing anisotropic elastic constants to be calculated for each hole.

The results of this operation are given in Table 1. Note that G' was not scaled.

4   BOREHOLE DEFORMATION GAUGE TESTS

4.1 Test procedures

Standard, well established methods were used for the calibration and installation of each gauge in the test block. Care was taken to orient a measurement axis of each gauge perpendicular to the foliation plane for uniformity in the subsequent anisotropic analysis. Once all of the gauges were installed, the boundary pressure was increased in about 0.34 MPa increments by pumping oil into the flat-jacks. A scan of the entire gauge array with an automatic data aquisition system followed each increment. Tests of different compressional loading directions were performed including:

- North-South Uniaxial
- East-West Uniaxial
- Equal Biaxial

beginning at no load and continuing up
to a 5.3 MPa peak load. The block was
then stress relieved by releasing oil
from the flatjacks in about 0.34 MPa
decrements. The response of the gauge
array was then monitored at each of
these levels.

4.2 BDG test results

The overall performace of the BDG's was
excellent. Useful results were obtained
from all of the seventeen instrumented
EX-holes. The evaluation of stresses
from the measured diametral deformations
was made assuming both isotropic and
anisotropic rock characteristics. The
isotropic reduction followed the procedure given in detail by Merrill and
Petersen (1962). Plane stress conditions were assumed. The modulus values
required for the evaluation were taken
to be those obtained from the dilatometer tests, as given in the left column
of Table 1. The displacement values entered into the calculations were defined
as the differences between readings taken
at zero load prior to load application,
and the readings taken at the load level
for which the stress evaluation was done
(loading-up curve). The anisotropic reduction was simplified by the favourable
orientation of the anisotropy relative
to the measurement plane, which allowed
the method of Becker and Hooker (1967)
to be used. This method ignores G' and
ν'. ν is not ignored and was taken to be
0.25 in accordance with the results from
the laboratory tests.

Typical results of BDG response as a
function of applied load are shown in
Figure 2. The parameters plotted are the
calculated, secondary horizontal principal stresses, denoted P and Q. A relatively slow response during initial loading was observed in some of these curves
(borehole T10 in Figure 2). This was attributed to the closure of fractures in
close proximity to the monitored location
at low applied stress levels. Other holes
exhibited sharp initial response to
applied load (borehole T13), indicating
either that the gauge was located in a
fractured zone where nonelastic deformations were sensed or in a stress concen-

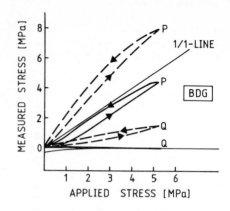

Figure 2. Load-response curves for bore
hole T10 (solid curves) and borehole T13
(dashed curves). BDG measurements, East-
West Loading.

tration zone. In fact it is suspected
that both of these situations had occurred due to the fractured and heterogeneous nature of the rock.

Common to all of the curves was that
after about 2 MPa of applied load the
calculated stress change approached a
constant ratio with the applied stress
change. This indicates that as the bound
ary loads are increased the major fractures close and lock up, which in turn
allows a uniform distribution of further
boundary stress changes throughout the
block.

Figure 3 shows calculated principal
stresses and their orientations at 1.0,
1.6, 2.4 and 3.8 MPa nominal applied
loads. With the exception of some of
the results from the equal biaxial loading, the stress rotations as the applied
load increases are small.

Peak load principal stress plots are
given in Figures 4 and 5, representing
anisotropic and isotropic reduction procedures respectively. The side-by-side
plotting allow direct comparison of the
two methods of analysis. It can be seen
that the inclusion of anisotropy generally has a very limited effect on the
stress results, despite the rather high
E_1/E_2 ratio given above.

432

5   LUT-GAUGE TESTS

5.1   Test procedures

The LUT-Gauge is an adaption of the CSIR-cell developed in South Africa. It was developed and is used by the Luleå University of Technology. The device has been described in detail by Leijon (1983) and more briefly by Leijon (1986). The gauge essentially serves to glue an array of twelve strain gauges to the wall of a borehole. The use of strain gauges bonded directly to the rock surface, and the possibility to obtain three dimensional stress results from one measurement constitute the major, principal differences in relation to the Borehole Deformation Gauge. The LUT-Gauge is intended for overcoring measurements, and some modifications were made for the present project. This included cable arrangements to allow continuous monitoring of the gauges installed in the block.

As for the tests using the BDG, the intention was to locate the LUT-Gauges at or close to the block midplane, and hence at locations corresponding to the dilatometer tests. This was achieved in most cases but not all. The sequence of block loading and the scanning routines were identical to that applied for the BDG-tests. A number of duplicate tests were also made to ensure repeatability and to check instrument performance. The approximately 5000 individual strain readings resulting from a load cycle called for an automatic data acquisition system. A multichannel strain recorder was therefore constructed and linked to a microcomputer system.

5.2   LUT-Gauge test results

With a few exceptions, the performance of the LUT-gauges was good. The duplicated loadings indicated very good repeatability of the gauge responses to loading. Results were obtained from 16 locations distributed in 13 boreholes in the block. This implies two data points in three of the holes. These points were spaced 5 cm apart in the hole. "Empty" holes indicate tests that were considered as being experimentally invalid and therefore rejected.

The evaluation of stresses from the measured strains was made assuming isotropic material characteristics only. The procedures adopted with regard to both choice of the modulus of deformation, and to definition of gauge responses to loading, were exactly identical to those applied for the BDG data reduction. Once these input data were available, the calculation of stresses essentially followed the procedure applied when evaluating overcoring measurements. This includes a multiple regression treatment of the redundant number of strain readings obtained from each test point, to derive the best-fitting stress tensor.

As mentioned, the LUT-Gauge provides three dimensional results. It is, of course, of interest to see whether a complete, three dimensional representation of the stress results is required for the subsequent data interpretation, or, if a two dimensional treatment considering only the horizontal plane is adequate. A complete three dimensional analysis of the LUT-Gauge data was therefore performed. The result can be summarized as follows:
- In the case of biaxial boundary loading, the two measured, major principal stresses, σ_1 and σ_2, were directed close to horizontal. The least principal stress, σ_3, was thus nearly vertical. This is true for all measuring points (average deviation from horizontal was $5°$). The magnitudes of σ_3 were much lower than for σ_1 and σ_2. Furthermore, the sign of σ_3 altered nonsystematically between compression and tension.
- In the case of uniaxial boundary loading, σ_1 was nearly horizontally directed. The directions of σ_2 and σ_3 were not well defined within the near-vertical plane perpendicular to σ_1. The magnitude of σ_1 was much larger than the magnitudes of σ_2 and σ_3. These results are true for all measuring points.

From these findings it was concluded that the verical dimension can be neglected without losing any significant information. The remainder of the result presentation is therefore restricted to the horizontal plane. In the biaxial case, this means that σ_1 and σ_2 are replaced with P and Q respectively. In the uniaxial load case, σ_1 is replaced by P, whilst $\sigma_2 \geq Q \geq \sigma_3$. A further interpretation of the three dimensional analysis results is that the assumption of plane stress conditions, which was made when evaluating the BDG-results, appears to

BDG – RESULTS,
STRESS VS. LOAD

BDG – RESULTS,
PEAK LOAD STRESSES,
ANISOTROPIC REDUCTION

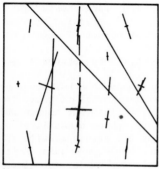

North – South Loading

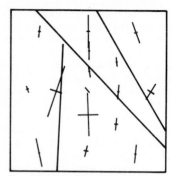

North – South Loading

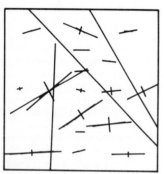

East – West Loading

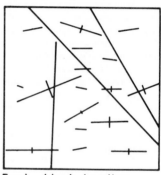

East – West Loading

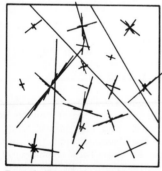

Equal Biaxial Loading

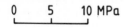

0   5   10 MPa

Figure 3.

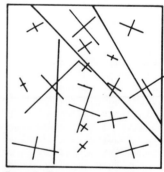

Equal Biaxial Loading

0   10   20 MPa

Figure 4.

BDG – RESULTS,
PEAK LOAD STRESSES,
ISOTROPIC REDUCTION

LUT – GAUGE RESULTS,
ISOTROPIC REDUCTION

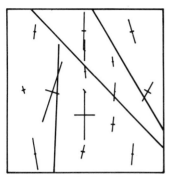

North – South Loading

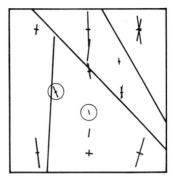

North – South Loading

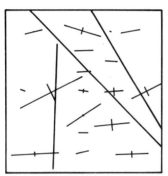

East – West Loading

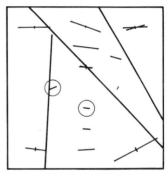

East – West Loading

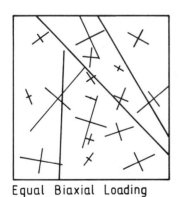

Equal Biaxial Loading

0   10   20 MPa

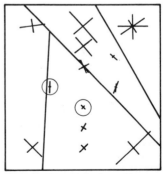

Equal Biaxial Loading

0   10   20 MPa

Figure 5.

Figure 6.

435

be justified.

Adopting the same order of presentation as for the BDG-results, the results from the LUT-measurements are presented in Figures 6 and 7. Thus, Figure 7 displays the values of P and Q plotted versus applied load for the tests in holes T10 and T13. These results are to be compared with the BDG-results in Figure 2. In general, the LUT-results verified the findings from the BDG-tests as regards the nature of the gauge responses with applied load. Figure 6 presents the secondary horizontal principal stresses at peak load as obtained from the LUT-Gauge tests and for the three cases of block loading. The comparable BDG-results are given in Figure 5.

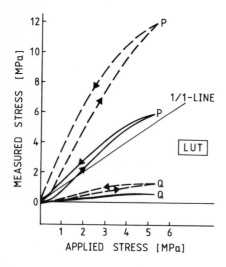

Figure 7. Load-response curves for borehole T10 (solid curves) and borehole T13 (dashed curves). LUT-Gauge measurements, East-West loading.

6   INTERPRETATION AND DISCUSSION

Some comments relating to the results obtained with each technique have been given earlier. Before the results are discussed from the point of view of block stress distribution, the two sets of data should be compared by method of testing for the sake of mutual verification of results. Figures 5 and 6 are relevant for this purpose. The similarities between these two figures become obvious if two test points are excluded. These are the

tests in holes H4 and T8 (indicated wi circles in Figure 6). It is interestin to note that in these very holes, the LUT-Gauges were, due to practical con- straints, not located at the same dept as the BDG's and the dilatometer tests The difference in vertical distance wa about 10 cm in both cases. Since the evaluations were based on the same mo- dulus values (refers to the case of is tropic BDG-data reduction), the degree of agreement in stress magnitudes can quantified by calculating the pointwis ratios between the BDG-results and the LUT-results. Averaging these ratios wi reveal systematic differences. The re- sult of this calculation, performed fo the largest principal stress, P, at 5. MPa applied load is given in the table below. The tests in H4 and T8 are ex- cluded:

Loading	P_{BDG}/P_{LUT} ± std. de~
Equal biaxial	1.22 ± 0.6
Uniaxial N-S	1.21 ± 0.4
Uniaxial E-W	(1.56 ± 1.5)
Mean	1.22 (1.33)

The higher value obtained for the E-W case is due to one deviating observatio (H6). The table indicates that the BDG- tests produced stress results that are at least 20 % higher than those obtaine with the LUT-Gauge. No explanation to this systematic difference has been found.

Considering now the results irrespectiv of measuring technique but with emphasi on the interpretation of the stress dis tribution within the block, the overall impression is that the directions are quite consistent with the direction of the applied load (refers, of course, to uniaxial loading only), whilst the stre magnitudes are highly variable. Some po sible sources of this nonuniform patter of stress magnitudes may be identified, viz:
1) Shear forces developing at the block boundaries due to friction between the flatjack arrangement and the block.
2) Disturbance from discontinuities on different scales in the block.
3) Variations in the modulus of deforma tion between different parts of the blo (zones of varying stiffness).

Referring to 1), confining shear components from the flatjacks could occur in
the case of uniaxial loading. The effects
in the block would be concentrated to
the loaded sides of the block, and would
furthermore affect the stress directions
to a higher degree than the magnitudes.
This does not seem to be the case, and
consequently it is concluded that 1) is
not a factor of major concern.

The large scale jointing of the block
has been proven to have a major influence on its overall deformation characteristics (Richardson et al., 1985). It
was also mentioned as a likely reason
for the observed, sometimes irregular
initial response to loading, cf. Figure
2. These effects tend to diminish as
higher loads are attained. This would
suggest a locking-up effect as joint
closure takes place. To study effects of
the three major joints that intersects
the block, a series of two dimensional
FE-analyses were conducted. The joints
were assigned nonlinear deformation
characteristics based on the measurements by Hardin et al. (1981) and the
empirical procedures for derivation of
joint properties suggested by Bandis et
al. (1983). This divided the block into
four subblocks. These subblocks were
treated as elastic bodies with constant
material properties. Figure 8a shows the

stresses in the subblocks, calculated
when simulating equal biaxial loading of
the FE-model. It can be seen in the figure that the calculated stress magnitudes are, as a whole, more even than those
measured in the field. The figure also
indicates a considerable disturbance of
the stress field close to the joints.
This was again not observed in the field,
cf. Figures 5 and 6. We must thus conclude that the FE-model fails to explain
the observed magnitude variations, and
seems to overestimate the local effects
ot the major joints.

Considering then the effects of local
variations in stiffness, the dilatometer
tests indicate a rather wide variation of
the in-situ modulus. A crude check of the
experimental validity of the modulus results can be made by studying the internal force balance in the block. Figure 9
illustrates, for the case of East-West
uniaxial loading, one procedure that can
be applied for a two dimensional analysis; A section is taken perpendicular to
the loading direction, and so as to intersect a row of boreholes. The stress
components measured normal to the section
in these boreholes are assumed to act
over attributable intervals of the section. The contribution to the total force
from each interval is then calculated by
multiplying the length of the interval

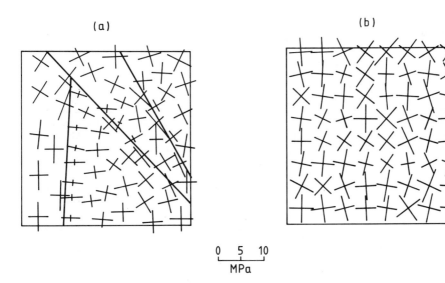

(a)   (b)

0   5   10
      MPa

Figure 8.   Secondary horizontal principal stresses from FE-analysis, biaxial loading,
5.3 MPa. a) Discontinuous model, considering the three major joints intersecting the
block. b) Continuous model, but with domainwise varying value of Young's modulus.

437

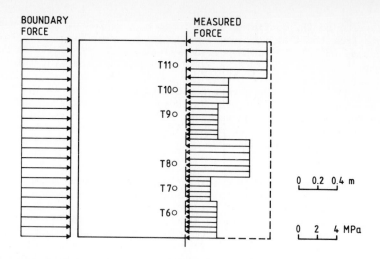

Figure 9. Basis for calculation of force balance in the block during East-West loading.

with the measured stress. The total "measured force", calculated by adding up the contributions, can then be compared to the applied boundary force. Performing this calculation yields a ratio of measured force to applied force of about 1.0. This indicates that no serious experimental errors are attached to the dilatometer test results.

The effects of the documented modulus variation in terms of stresses were studied by means of a second set of FE-analyses. This time, the whole block was treated as a continuous, elastic body (major joints neglected) but was subdivided into 25 domains to which different modulus values were assigned. The values used were those locally obtained with the dilatometer, slightly modified to account for the local fracture density. The results of these analyses is exemplified in Figure 8b, which shows the principal stresses for the case of biaxial loading of the model. Again, we note a much more uniform stress field than the one observed in the field. Consequently, we can not attribute the measured stress variations to the measured, local stiffness variations.

Thus, so far, the attempts to explain the measured data on the basis of the previously listed factors likely to influence them have not been very sucessful. However, the picture changes if:
- Discontinuities others than those considered in the analysis above cause sig-

nificant decoupling between different portions of the block.
- The modulus results, though experimentally valid, are not applicable for calculation of stresses from the present type of pointwise deformation/strain measurements.

In view of the low boundary stresses applied and the nature of rock, decoupling effects are likely to occur. This will cause a very complex pattern of force transmittance through the block. The modulus results, in turn, can be "wrong" in the sense that they are not localised enough to provide a modulus value that is applicable to the very localised displacement/strain sampling provided by the BDG and the LUT-Gauge. The CSM-cell "integrates" the deformability over a borehole section being about 16 cm long. This may well be too crude in the present type of locally heterogeneous rock.

Regardless of the relative dignity of the two factors indicated above, it must be concluded that the results of the present study do not indicate that pointwise borehole deformation measurements can be applied with satisfactory result for the purpose of stress monitoring in jointed rock masses subjected to low stresses.

7   CONCLUSIONS

- The work has been experimentally successful and the instruments used have

performed satisfactorily.
- The BDG and the LUT-Gauge produced very similar stress results.
- Under the present test conditions, the inclusion of the anisotropy, caused by the foliation of the rock, in the calculation of stresses from measured borehole deformations, does not significantly affect the results.
- The stresses that developed in the block as a consequence of the flatjack boundary loading were essentially horizontal. The directions in the horizontal plane were in good agreement with the applied boundary loadings.
- The stress magnitudes measured were highly variable. The causes of this variation can not be satisfactorily understood, although it is believed that decoupling effects caused by discontinuities and local variations of the deformation modulus are the most important contributing factors.
- When applied for the purpose of stress monitoring in jointed rock masses subjected to low stresses, pointwise measurements of the present type may not provide useful results..

8   ACKNOWLEDGEMENTS

The financial support for this work was through contract E512-11800 with the Project Management Division of the Batelle Memorial Institute. The helpful attitude of Mr W. Ubbes and Mr E. Lindner at Batelle is gratefully acknowledged. The Swedish contribution to the work was supported by the Swedish Natural Science Research Council.

9   REFERENCES

Bandis, S.C., Lumsden, A.C. and Barton, N.R. 1983. Fundamentals of Rock Joint Deformation. Int. J. Rock Mech. Min. Sci. & Geomech. Abstr., 20 (6):249-268.

Becker, R.M. and Hooker, V.E. 1967. Some Anisotropic Considerations in Rock Stress Determinations. U.S. Bureau of Mines, RI 6965.

Hardin, E., Lingle, R., Board, M. and Voegle, M. 1981. A Heated Flatjack Test Series to Measure the Thermomechanical and Transport Properties of In Situ Rock Masses. ONWI Report (ONWI 260), Columbus, Ohio.

Leijon, B. 1983. Rock Stress Measurements with the LUH-Gauge at the Near-Surface Test Facility, Hanford Test Site. Research Report TULEA 1983:19. Luleå University of Technology, Luleå.

Leijon, B. 1986. Application of the LUT Triaxial Overcoring Technique in Swedish Mines. This volume.

Merrill, R. and Peterson, J. 1962. Deformation of a Borehole in Rock. USBM Report, Investigation No. 5881. Denver, Colorado.

Richardson, A.M., Hustrulid, W.A., Shi, G. and Lindner, E. 1985. A Mechanical Study of the Influence of Joints on Block Test Results. Proc. Int. Symp. on Fundamentals of Rock Joints. Centek Publ., Luleå, 143-152.

Sour, L. 1985. Fracture Characterization of the CSM/OCRD Test Block. Technical Report BMI/OCRD-4 (6), Columbus, Ohio.

An interpretation of highly scattered stress measurements in foliated gneiss

A.M. RICHARDSON
Colorado School of Mines, Department of Mining, Golden, Colorado, USA

S.M. BROWN
Golder Associates, Seattle, Washington, USA

W.A. HUSTRULID
D.L. RICHARDSON
Colorado School of Mines, Department of Mining, Golden, Colorado, USA

ABSTRACT

Stress measurements in jointed rock are frequently scattered, reflecting non-homogeneity of the stress field and other factors. Integrating a scattered set of stress measurements to obtain a solution for the in situ stress tensor is difficult. In this paper, two alternative approaches are applied to a set of overcoring data taken from the CSM/OCRD underground test facility. One approach involves averaging the data after observations on magnitude and orientation variance compared to the results of a nearby in situ block test, supporting the quality of the data set. The second approach involved selective culling of the data set to include only the best data, then weighting the average to eliminate bias caused by the selection process. Both methods gave results which were in satisfactory comparison with equilibrium overburden weight.

1. Introduction

Techniques for local determination of the stress tensor have been the focus of much interest in the past 30 years, and the bulk of research in stress measurements has been concentrated in this area. The fact remains that in jointed-crystalline rock, wide scatter in local stress measurements is to be expected, even when the best of these techniques are carefully applied. The probable explanation is that some of this scatter reflects spatial variation in the stress field, not experimental error. As aptly stated by Brady and Brown (1985); "The requirements for successful definition of the in situ state of stress are a technique for a local determination of the stress tensor, and a strategy for integration of a set of observations to derive a representative solution for the field stress tensor throughout the sampled volume (p. 40)." The bulk of the published literature concerning stresses deals with the first of these requirements, the technology of stress determinations. This paper is concerned with the second requirement, the strategy for integrating a widely scattered data set.

When presented with a typical, highly variable set of local stress measurements, the "classical" approach is to use an averaging technique to obtain a single set of values representing the average stress tensor. Most interpretations then resort to the concept of equilibrium as a check on the vertical stress component. Brown and

Hoek (1978) and others have shown that the vertical stresses in any region fall close to the level required for equilibrium of the overburden stress, whereas the horizontal stresses only rarely comply with elastic solutions based on no lateral strain. If the mean of the vertical component of the stress tensor closely matches the calculated overburden stress, then the condition of equilibrium is assumed to be satified. If the mean deviates from that calculated, the commonly accepted implication is that there is either a problem with measurement technique, or there are an insufficient number of measurements for a representative average. The existance of either or both of these problems in the vertical stress determination does not lend credibility to the other components of the stress tensor.

A number of in situ stress determinations have been made in the vicinity of the Colorado School of Mines/Office of Crystalline Repository Development (CSM/OCRD) underground test facility. The purpose of the present investigation is to explore alternate strategies for interpreting these measurements and thereby determine the in situ state of stress, taking advantage of the special knowledge of the behavior of local rock in response to stress developed in a recent in situ block test nearby. The block test provided a unique opportunity to analyze a high density of in situ stress measurements under controlled stress boundary conditions.

2. Description of the CSM/OCRD Test Facility

Figure 1 is a plan view of the CSM experimental mine, superimposed on a topographic map of the immediate region. The mine portal is located in a hillside, and overburden thickness is seen to increase rapidly with distance into the mine. The CSM/OCRD experimental room was carefully excavated using smooth blasting techniques to minimize blast damage, and is located approximately 250 meters from the portal, under approximately 80 meters of overburden. The room dimensions are 3.7 x 4.6 meters, and 24 meters long.

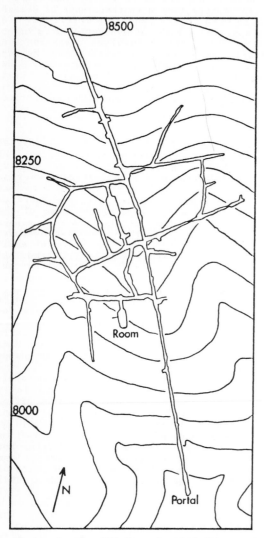

Figure 1. The CSM Experimental Mine and the Topography over the Mine. Contour intervals are in 50 ft. increments.

The mine is located in the Idaho Springs Formation, a Precambrian migmatized biotite gneiss (Hutchinson, 1983). The gneiss is structurally very complex, with ptygmatic folding, and local areas of pegmatite. A foliation trends roughly perpendicular to the long axis of the room. Several joint sets are encountered in the room, and numerous small joints are also encountered which do not fit major joint sets. Despite the complex geologic structure, the rock is largely competent. However, one would expect a complex stress field in such a heterogeneous and discontinuous rock mass.

3. Borehole stress determinations

A pilot hole was drilled horizontally into the rib of the CSM/OCRD test room in a direction perpendicular to its length (see Figure 1). Stress determinations were made, applying standard overcoring techniques, at 22 locations using both USBM Borehole Deformation gages (BDG) (Tadolini and Dolinar, 1981) and CSIRO gages (El Rabaa, 1981). Fractures along the borehole were then mapped using television borehole equipment to aid in interpretation of stress measurements. Figure 2 shows the locations of the stress measurements and discontinuities along the borehole. In some areas, the measurements were taken in highly fractured areas.

At most of the measurement points, overcores were obtained and biaxial tests conducted to determine modulus values for use in stress reductions. Secondary principal stresses were calculated for each measurement point using an anisotropic solution, and resolved into vertical and horizontal components. Where modulus values were not available, values from adjacent tests were utilized and an isotropic analysis conducted. Although the configuration of the CSIRO gage enables three-dimensional stress calculations, the data was reduced to the secondary principal stresses to be comparable to the BDG data, in keeping with the objectives of the present study. Stress values calculated in this fashion are highly scattered, as shown in Figure 2.

4. Expected Vertical Stress

The best available criteria for assessment of the overcoring results is by comparison with the vertical stress expected for equilibrium of the overburden weight. Since the mine is located in a mountainous region, the expected vertical stress calculation included topographic effects on stress magnitudes and directions, following the lead of

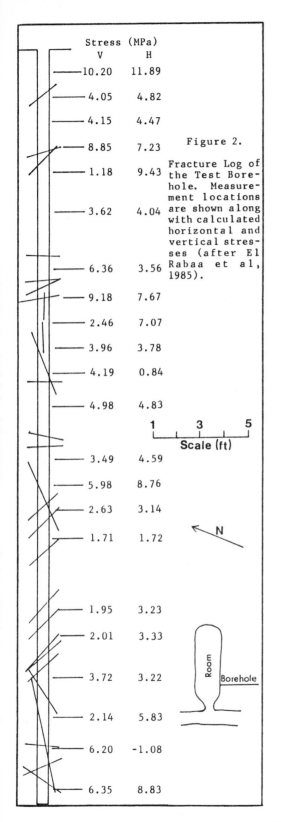

Stress (MPa)
V   H

—10.20   11.89

— 4.05   4.82

— 4.15   4.47

— 8.85   7.23   **Figure 2.**

— 1.18   9.43   Fracture Log of
                  the Test Bore-
                  hole. Measure-
                  ment locations
— 3.62   4.04   are shown along
                  with calculated
                  horizontal and
                  vertical stres-
                  ses (after El
— 6.36   3.56   Rabaa et al,
                  1985).

— 9.18   7.67

— 2.46   7.07

— 3.96   3.78

— 4.19   0.84

— 4.98   4.83

— 3.49   4.59

— 5.98   8.76

— 2.63   3.14

— 1.71   1.72

— 1.95   3.23

— 2.01   3.33

— 3.72   3.22

— 2.14   5.83

— 6.20   -1.08

— 6.35   8.83

Tadolini and Dolinar (1981). Figure 3 shows a cross section parallel to the room, perpendicular to the horizontal measurement boreholes. Vertical stress in the vicinity of the room was determined to be 2.55 MPa from equilibrium considerations

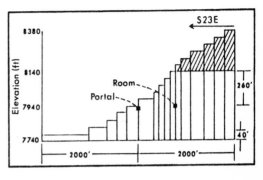

Figure 3. Cross Section used to Calculate the Effects of Topography on the Expected Vertical Stress in the Test Room (after Tadolini and Dolinar, 1981).

5. Classical Approach to Stress Measurements

Due to the extreme scatter of the data obtained from overcoring, it is not readily evident how to interpret the data with respect to the in situ stress field. The stress determinations vary by several MPa over distances of tens of centimeters along the borehole. One approach to interpretation of the in situ stress field, which will be called the "classical" approach, was supported by several observations of scatter in stress magnitude and orientation of principal stresses in tests conducted in the test block.

The in situ block test, which was conducted nearby (Brown et al, 1985 and 1986, and Brown, 1986), provided a useful model of the overcoring situation. The two-meter cube of rock isolated on all four sides by grouted flatjacks represents perhaps the best achievable controlled stress situation in a large in situ volume of rock, although questions exist about true boundary conditions on the block. Although stresses were measured at 17 locations in the block, only a row of 7 measurements that bisect the block orthogonal to the applied stress direction will be presented here, as shown in Figure 4. This row is considered a physical model of the overcoring borehole.

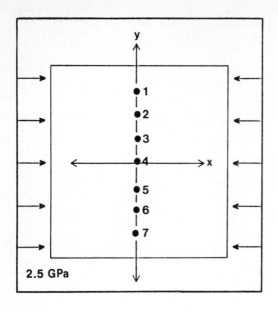

Figure 4. Configuration of the Test Block used to Compare Stress Measurement Results with the Borehole Test.

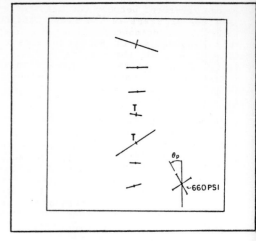

Figure 5. Stress Vectors Determined from Uniaxially Loading the Test Block. Load = 5.2 MPa.

It was observed that in cases where the block was primarily stressed using one opposing pair of flatjacks ("uniaxial loading"), the measured principal stress direction was aligned very closely to the applied stress axis at nearly every location. Although there was considerable scatter in the magnitudes of the stresses determined at the 7 individual locations in the block, there was a strong clustering of stress vector orientations in uniaxial tests. This is evident in Figure 5, which shows the results of x-direction uniaxial loading to 5.2 MPa.

The scatter in the magnitudes of the individual stress determinations in the block bears further discussion. For purposes of comparison with the overcoring tests, the block test was treated as a series of overcoring measurements. The row of 7 instrument stations along the y axis of the block was "overcored" by unloading from an x-direction uniaxial stress level of 2.55 MPa, simulating overcoring experiments from an in situ stress level of approximately 2.5 MPa. For equilibrium, the mean stress level along the measurement plane must equal the applied flatjack pressure. Since the stress measurements in this case represent point measurements along a cross-sectional slice perpendicular to the applied stress direction, the mean of these measurements is an estimator of

the applied stress level. How closely this mean is expected to approach the applied stress level depends upon the sample size (number of measurements) and the variance, assuming no measurement bias.

Table 1 shows the results of the block test. Stresses have been resolved into x and y components parallel and perpendicular to the applied stress axis. An anisotropic reduction was used with dilatometer moduli taken at the point of measurement being adjusted to reflect expected block anisotropy.

Table 1. Stresses Measured in Block Test in Response to x-direction Loading.

Measurement	Stress (MPa)	
	x	y
1	5.53	1.27
2	2.61	0.21
3	2.13	0.25
4	1.54	0.35
5	6.23	-0.19
6	1.34	0.15
7	1.57	0.42
mean	2.99	
standard dev.	2.03	

A statistician might argue that the close agreement between the measured and applied stresses in the block test results is coincidental, given the large variance and small number of measurements. However, the results support the notion that scatter in magnitudes reflects spatial variation in the stress field and modulus used for stress calculations. Systematic bias appears to be absent.

Figure 6 is a histogram of the orientations of the maximum principal stresses obtained by overcoring. Figure 2 showes the vertical and horizontal stresses obtained at each measurement point.

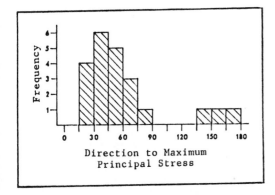

Figure 6. Histgram showing the Frequency of Occurence of the Orientation of Maximum Principal Stress within 15 Degree Intervals.

Although the magnitude shows considerable variance, a strong preferred orientation is evident. The orientation is in the direction of the topographic high above the test room, and shows less scatter than the magnitudes. The in situ stress field is not likely to be predominately uniaxial, as was the case for the block test. The remarkable degree of clustering of stress orientation shown in Figure 6 adds to the impression that the data set is good and does not need to be culled, although no conclusive proof exists.

The line of reasoning for the "classical" approach can now be summarized as follows: 1) Although the block test stress magnitudes showed considerable scatter, the mean approached the mean applied stress; 2) The overcoring stress data showed similar magnitude and orientation scatter characteristics as the block test data, and was obtained nearby in the same rock type; therefore, 3) the overcoring data is likely of good quality and can be averaged to calculate the in situ state of stress.

Figure 7 is a plot of the vertical stress data from the overcoring hole. Observations near the room are high but tend to taper off with distance. Stress concentrations due to the excavation are one possible explanation. A curve showing the general trend is superimposed on the measurement data. A straight arithmetic mean of all data cannot be used because of the stress concentrations. Stress concentration factors could be obtained by modeling, but the horizontal to vertical stress ratio must be known for such modeling. The procedure used here was to simply observe the general trend of the data, which levels off at about 2.5 MPa.

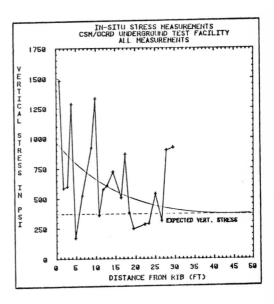

Figure 7. Plot of the Vertical Stress versus Distance Down the Borehole.

Although this method is not rigorous, it can be seen from Figure 7 that any method of averaging this data that avoids the presumed sharp stress concentration factors near the opening will yield a value not far from the expected vertical stress. More measurements taken farther from the rib would improve the average.

6. Alternate Method for Stress Reductions

An alternate method of integrating the overcoring stress data was employed which is based on a completely different philosophy than the classical method. Instead of assuming that all data points are good, the alternate method involved selecting only the very best data points, then weighting the mean to remove bias from the culling process.

In this approach, all data points taken within 2.5 meters of the room were eliminated. This minimizes the influence of a suspected blast damage zone where inelastic material behavior could negate stress measurement techniques based on elasticity. The remaining 16 data points are summarized in Table 2. Eight of these were located in areas where intact overcores were retrieved for biaxial testing, and were sufficiently far from mapped fractures to alleviate concerns about inelastic effects. These eight were considered to be the "good" data points, and yielded a mean vertical stress of 4.06 MPa, and a mean horizontal stress of 3.79 MPa.

Table 2. Overcoring Hole Data used in Calculations for Alternate Method.

Meas- ment	Frac/.3m	Modulus (GPa)	Stress (MPa) v	h
7	1	42.97*	6.36	3.56
8	4	15.72	--	--
9	2	32.21	--	--
10	2	32.21	--	--
11	1	35.93*	4.19	0.84
12	0	61.38*	4.98	4.83
13	0	49.31*	3.49	4.17
14	1	55.66*	5.98	8.77
15	3	21.86	--	--
16	0	64.83*	1.71	1.62
17	2	21.86	--	--
18	1	62.41*	2.01	3.33
19	2	64.83*	3.72	3.22
20	1	32.21	--	--
21	2	32.21	--	--
22	1	32.21	--	--
Mean		41.11	4.06	3.79

* Biaxial test data available

The second part of the procedure consists of weighting the data for modulus variations. The rationale for such an adjustment is as follows. Assume that the vicinity of the measurement borehole can be idealized as a 2-dimensional horizontal strip, loaded vertically, with constant displacement boundaries. The strip is not uniformly stiff, but has modulus variations along its length caused by varying amounts of fracturing. If the strip is loaded vertically by an increment of displacement, high stresses would be generated in the strip in stiff regions as soft regions yielded and transferred the stresses. The concept is identical to the pressure arch concept in coal mine rock mechanics, where soft yield pillars cause stress transfer to stiff barrier pillars. Point stress measurements taken at random along this strip, if averaged, should yield a mean stress that is an unbiased estimator of the true mean stress in the strip.

The problem occurs when the measurements are not taken at random, but are concentrated in the stiff regions of the strip. This is generally the case, since the stress measurements which are considered "reliable" are the ones taken in competent rock where good overcores can be taken for biaxial testing. In situ stress determinations in fractured rock may tend to be biased because they are based on measurements which are predominately located in stiffer zones which are bearing more load. This concept has been discussed by Brown (1986).

This bias can be eliminated by calculating the average rock stiffness at the measurement locations, and comparing this with the average stiffness of the entire borehole. The optimal approach would employ dilatometer modulus values taken continuously down the borehole. The ratio of the mean measurement location stiffness to the overall mean borehole stiffness is an adjustment factor that can be used to account for modulus variations.

In the present study, modulus values at the eight "good" measurement points were obtained by biaxial testing of overcores, with a mean value of 54.69 MPa. The mean value for the entire borehole could not be precisely determined because measurements were not available along its entire length. However, a correlation was found between mapped fracture frequency and modulus in the areas where modulus was measured. This relationship was used to estimate the modulus in zones where it was not measured. The mean overall modulus for the borehole was 41.11 MPa, calculated in this fashion, yielding a modulus reduction factor of 0.75 for the mean vertical stress. When this factor is applied, a mean vertical stress of 3.05 MPa is obtained from overcoring, which compares very favorably to the expected value of 2.5 MPa. Hence we have:

446

σ_{vm} = Mean measured vertical stress

= 4.06 MPa

$\bar{E}^*$ = Mean modulus at measurement locations = 54.69 GPa

$\bar{E}$ = Mean modulus along borehole length

= 41.11 GPa

Assuming stresses induced by constant displacement loading:

$\bar{\sigma}_v$ = mean in situ vertical stress

$$= \bar{\sigma}_{vm} \frac{\bar{E}}{\bar{E}^*} = 3.05$$

where $\dfrac{\bar{E}}{\bar{E}^*}$ = reduction factor = 0.75

A similar calculation gives a horizontal stress of 2.71 MPa.

7. Conclusions

Two methods have been presented for reducing a set of stress measurements to obtain estimates of the vertical and horizontal components of the in situ stress. The first involved a classical averaging procedure using all the data, and was justified by consistant orientations and similarity of the data with nearby block test results in a known stress environment. The second approach employed selecting only the best quality stress data points, then weighting the arithmetic mean of these values for modulus variations down the borehole. Both methods yielded estimates near the expected vertical stress calculated from equilibrium considerations.

If the procedures employed in this paper seem rather crude, it is the experience of the authors that determination of stress in jointed rock is far from an exact science. With numerous point measurements and application of considerable engineering judgement, ballpark estimates of the in-situ stress can be made. Such estimates are of considerable use for engineering design, if an appreciation exists for the level of inherent uncertainty.

8. Acknowledgements and Disclaimer

The financial assistance provided by R. Robinson and W. Ubbes of OCRD/-Battelle under Contract No. E 512-11800 made this work possible. The ideas presented herein are those of the authors and do not necessarily reflect the views of Battelle or the U.S. Department of Energy.

9. References

Brady, B.H.G. and E.T. Brown. 1985. Rock Mechanics for Underground Mining, Allen and Unwin, 527 pp.

Brown, E.T. and E. Hoek. 1978. Trends in Relationships between Measured Rock, In situ Stresses and Depth, International Journal of Rock Mechanics and Mining Science, Vol. 15, pp. 211-215.

Brown, S., A.M. Richardson, and W.A. Hustrulid. 1985. A Study of the Validity of Stress Measurements in Jointed Rock, Proceedings, 26th U. S. Symposium on Rock Mechanics, Rapid City, June, pp. 1247-1254.

Brown, S.M. 1986. Stress Fields in Jointed Rock, Colorado School of Mines, M.S. Thesis, T3152, 251 pp.

Brown, S.M., B.A. Leijon, and W.A. Hustrulid. 1986. Stress Distribution within an Artificially Loaded Jointed Block, Proc. of the International Symposium on Rock Stress, Stockholm, in Press.

El Rabaa, A.W. 1981. Measurements and Modeling of Rock Mass Response to Underground Excavation, Colorado School of Mines, M.S., Thesis, T2470, 274 pp.

El Rabaa, A.W., W.A. Hustrulid, B. Leijon, L. Sour. 1985. Stress Field in the Vicinity of the CSM/OCRD Room, BMI/OCRD - 4(10), Draft.

Hutchinson, R.M. 1983. Geological and Structural Setting of the CSM/OCRD Test Site: CSM Experimental Mine, Idaho Springs, Colorado, BMI/OCRD - 4(2)

Tadolini, S.C. and D.R. Dolinar. 1981. In Situ Stress Determination ONWI Test Facility, Degar Mine, Idaho Springs, Colorado, Progress Report 10027, Submitted to the Colorado School of Mines by the U.S. Bureau of Mines, July 15.

Horizontal in situ stresses versus depth in the Canadian Shield at the underground research laboratory

P.A. LANG
R.A. EVERITT
L.K.W. NG
P.M. THOMPSON
Atomic Energy of Canada Limited, Pinawa, Manitoba, Canada

ABSTRACT

A comprehensive overcore testing program is underway at the Canadian Underground Research Laboratory (URL). In the initial phase, 42 USBM overcore tests were conducted in vertical and near vertical drill holes from the shaft bottom at four depths during shaft sinking, and from the two shaft stations after shaft sinking. The results of this initial phase are presented: the horizontal in situ stresses are plotted against depth, related to the shaft geology, and compared with other stress measurements on the Canadian Shield.

RÉSUMÉ

Un programme complet d'essais de surcarottage est en cours au Laboratoire de Recherches Souterrain (LRS) canadien. Dans la première phase, on a mené 42 essais USBM de surcarottage dans des sondages verticaux et presque verticaux à partir du fond du puits, à quatre profondeurs, lors du fonçage du puits et à partir de deux postes de puits après le fonçage du puits. On présente les résultats de la première phase: on porte les mesures de tensions horizontales in situ en fonction de la profondeur, on établi leur relation avec la géologie du puits et on les compare avec d'autres mesures de tensions dans le bouclier canadien.

ZUSAMMENFASSUNG

Ein umfassendes in situ Messprogramm wird gegenwäertig im Kanadischen Untergrund Forschungslabor (URL) durchgeführt. In der ersten Phase wurden in vier Tiefen während und nach dem Schachtteufen insgesamt 42 USBM konzentrische Doppelkernbohrungen durchgeführt. Zu diesem Zwecke wurden senkrechte und nahezu senkrechte Borhrlöcher in den Boden des Stollenschachts eingebracht. Die Ergebnisse dieser ersten Phase werden hier zusammengefasst: Die horizontalen in situ Spannungen werden als Funktion der Tiefe graphisch dargestellt und im Zusammenhang mit der Bohrlochgeologie diskutiert. Ausserdem werden Vergleiche mit anderen Spannungsmessungen im Kanadischen Schild vorgenommen.

INTRODUCTION

Atomic Energy of Canada Limited (AECL) has the responsibility for developing a method for the safe permanent disposal of Canada's nuclear fuel wastes. Efforts are being concentrated on evaluating the concept that disposal deep in stable plutonic rock of the Canadian Shield will be viable and acceptably safe.

Geotechnical studies are underway to assess the conditions that exist in plutonic rock bodies within the Canadian Shield, and to determine the changes in these conditions that may be caused by excavation, operation and closure of a nuclear fuel waste disposal vault. These studies are focussing on those characteristics of plutons that may contribute to the potential for radionuclide transport between a disposal vault and the surface environment.

An important area of geotechnical research is aimed at understanding the in situ stress conditions in plutonic rock bodies, and the stresses induced around excavations in these bodies. This understanding is needed because the stresses affect
· the stability of underground excavations over both the short and the long term;
· the permeability of fractures in the rock mass, and, hence, the potential for movement of radionuclides in groundwater to the biosphere, and
· the development of damaged zones around excavations; damaged zones are potential pathways for radionuclide leakage from a vault.

As an aid to geotechnical research, AECL is constructing an Underground Research Laboratory (URL) in the Lac du Bonnet Batholith, 100 km northeast of Winnipeg, Manitoba. The URL will provide researchers with representative geological environments in which to carry out a variety of in situ geotechnical experiments (Simmons and Soonawala 1982).

A comprehensive in situ stress measurement program is underway at the URL and will continue throughout the operating life of the laboratory. The objectives of this overall program are outlined in the next section. A limited initial program was conducted in conjunction with shaft sinking. This paper describes the results and early conclusions from this initial program.

OBJECTIVES OF THE OVERALL STRESS MEASUREMENT PROGRAM AT THE URL

The objectives of the overall in situ stress measurement program at the URL are
· to assess, and further develop, the technology for measuring in situ stresses;
· to determine how stresses in a typical rock mass in the Canadian Shield vary throughout the rock mass, and how they are affected by inhomogeneities and discontinuities in the rock mass. This information is needed so that we can determine how far we can predict stresses away from a measuring point, and hence determine what spacing of measuring points is required to enable us to interpolate with acceptable confidence between measuring points;
· to provide the in situ stress information necessary for designing the optimum shape and orientation of the URL excavations; and
· to provide the in situ stress information for understanding the origin of the fractures and main fracture zones in the rock mass at the URL. An understanding of their origin is an important step in developing an ability to predict their presence and extent in other plutons in the Canadian Shield.

INITIAL STRESS MEASUREMENT PROGRAM

At the time of writing (1986 April) the URL consists of a 2.8 m x 4.9 m x 255 m deep shaft, with shaft stations at the 130 m and 240 m depths. Instrument rings were installed at depths of 15 m, 62 m, 185 m and 218 m during shaft sinking (Lang and Thompson 1985). The overcore testing discussed in this paper was conducted from the shaft bottom at each instrument ring as they were installed and from the shaft stations after completion of shaft sinking. The program consisted of overcore testing with the U.S. Bureau of Mines (USBM) gauge (Hooker and Bickel 1974) in vertical and near-vertical drill holes.

Only a minimum amount of overcore testing was done in the shaft during sinking because of the high cost of standby charges for the shaft sinking contractor. A more comprehensive stress measurement program was delayed until sinking was complete. The results will be presented in a future paper.

Overcore testing in conjunction with shaft sinking, although costly, was required

- to provide USBM results in a vertical hole for combining with results from two horizontal holes to be drilled at each instrument ring in the next phase of the program. (Three approximately orthogonal holes are required to determine the triaxial state of stress from USBM tests);
- to provide preliminary horizontal stress field information for interpreting the instrument ring results (Lang and Thompson 1985);
- to provide elastic modulus values of overcore samples for preliminary analysis of the triaxial strain cells installed for stress change monitoring at each instrument ring; and
- to provide preliminary horizontal stress field information for designing the orientation layout and the cross-section shape for the excavations at the lower shaft station (Lang, Humphries and Ayotte 1986).

GEOLOGY

The URL site is situated within the boundaries of the Lac du Bonnet granite Batholith, which is considered to be representative of many of the granitic intrusion in the Precambrian Shield of Canada. Airborne, surface and borehole geological, geophysical, and hydrogeological site-characterization studies were carried out from 1979 to 1983 by researchers from AECL and Energy, Mines and Resources Canada to determine the general geology of the site (Brown et al 1983). Recent mapping of the URL excavation has provided further detailed geologic information (Brown et al 1986).

The batholith consists of several granitic phases. At the shaft, a moderately fractured, pink granite with porphyritic, biotite-rich, biotite-poor, gneissic-foliated and xenolith-rich zones grades downward below a depth of approximately 220 m into a grey quartz monzonite. Diamond drilling and fracture mapping indicate that the grey granite is much less fractured than the pink granite.

At the URL site, there are three, major, extensive, shallow-dipping, hydraulically conductive fracture zones in the upper 500 m of the batholith

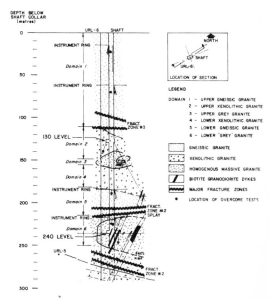

FIG. 1 Geology of the URL Shaft showing overcore test locations.

(Davison 1984). These dip about 25° southeast. The upper two are shown with the shaft geology on Fig. 1.

Apart from these main fracture zones, the rock mass is of very good quality. Near-vertical fractures are most common and of these a set striking about 030° is predominant. Fig. 2, a plot of depth (concentric circles) versus strike of the fractures, shows:

- trend of the fractures varies progressively with depth through the various lithologic-domains, and changes suddenly at domain boundaries; and
- the fracture-domain boundaries coincide with the main lithologic-domain boundaries.

Surface and underground mapping indicate that the spacing of these fractures is zonal. The spacing of the zones and the spacing of the joints within the zones vary with location. Some of these fractures are water bearing and they are responsible for the vertical hydraulic conductivity at the site.

The 030° trending vertical fractures are interpreted as extensional in origin. These fractures, together with lineation analysis, photo-elastic strain relief measurements at surface and other geological evidence from the site, indicate that the stress field, at the time of their formation, was oriented

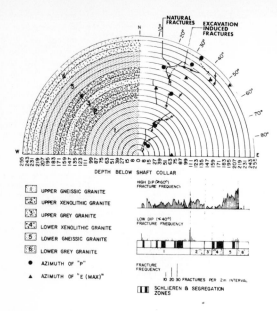

FIG. 2 Strike of natural and excavation
induced fractures, and direction
of maximum horizontal stress and
maximum horizontal Young's
modulus, versus depth below
ground surface.

with σ_3 horizontal and perpendicular to
the fracture planes, and σ_1 and σ_2 in the
fracture plane (with σ_2 near vertical and
σ_1 oriented 030°).

TESTING, ANALYSIS AND QUALITY CONTROL

Some significant features of the
testing and quality control procedures
used (see also Snider, Lang and Thompson
1986 and Thompson, Lang and Snider 1986)
are:
· At least five successful tests was the
  objective at each location. Five was
  considered the minimum number of tests
  necessary to have statistical
  significance. However, only one and
  two successful tests were achieved at
  the instrument rings at 15 m and 62 m
  depth for reasons noted in Table 1.
  Four consistent tests were accepted at
  the 185 m instrument ring because of a
  particular time constraint. For the
  remainder of the program eight to ten
  successful tests were achieved at each
  location (see Table 1).
· The outside diameter of the overcore is
  86 mm instead of the more commonly used

146 mm. A testing program, conducted to
determine the effect of the smaller
diameter, indicated that the diameter had
a negligible effect on the measured in
situ stresses. It was concluded that
better results could be obtained using
the 86 mm size because more tests could
be conducted for a given cost.
· The USBM gauges were calibrated after
  approximately every five tests using
  the standard USBM field calibration
  device.
· Drill water pressure was controlled at
  a constant 200 kPa to minimize the
  effects of pressure fluctuations on the
  USBM cantilevers, and to prevent water
  pressure from depressing the gauge
  buttons.
· Drill water temperature entering and
  leaving the drill hole was monitored
  throughout the tests. For the testing
  in the shaft stations the drill water
  temperature was controlled to maintain
  temperatures at the inner surface of
  the core cylinder to within 2°C of the
  in situ rock temperature.
· For the tests in the shaft stations
  data loggers were used. This enabled
  improved accuracy, with fewer data
  translation errors, and more continuous
  data (advantageous for identifying
  problems with a test).
· Biaxial testing was conducted in a
  temperature and humidity controlled
  chamber as soon as possible after completion of the overcore test (generally
  15 to 30 minutes).
· A biaxial chamber with 3.8:1 length to
  diameter ratio instead of the standard
  1.4:1 ratio was used to minimize end
  effects.
· The biaxial tests were repeated with
  the USBM gauge rotated at 15° increments from 0° to 60°. Plots of modulus
  for each cantilever pair versus rotation angle gives a measure of the rock
  anisotropy in the plane normal to core
  axis. The modulus values quoted are
  the secant Young's modulus over the
  stress range from zero to the in situ
  stress at the sampling location.
· All biaxial tests were data logged.

Anisotropic analysis methods
(Hooker and Johnson 1969; Becker and
Hooker 1976) were used. The axial stress
was assumed to be equal to the lithostatic stress (0.0265 MPa x depth in metres)
in these analyses, except at the shaft
stations where the vertical stress was
known from other testing.

DRILL HOLE NUMBER	DEPTH BELOW SURFACE (m)	DRILL HOLE DEPTH (m)	MODULI			ASSUMED			STRESSES			NOTES
			Emax (GPa)	Emin (GPa)	AZ Emax	Ez (GPa)	σ_2 (MPa)	ν	P (MPa)	Q (MPa)	P(az) (utm)	
275-SM-S83	21.85	7.83	44.00	36.50	38	45.0	0.50	0.25	6.27	2.50	39	I
	22.72	8.70	36.50	32.00	38	45.0	0.50	0.25	9.22	4.01	25	E 1
MEAN			40.25	34.25	38				6.27	2.50	39	
n			2	2	2				1	1	1	
228-SM-E83	69.23	7.33	47.80	45.60	38	45.0	1.65	0.25	-	-	-	E 4
	69.60	7.70	48.60	46.50	38	45.0	1.65	0.25	4.13	2.35	3	E 2
	70.30	8.40	54.50	50.50	128	45.0	1.65	0.25	-	-	-	E 4
	70.76	8.86	52.00	47.50	83	45.0	1.65	0.25	6.94	3.92	40	E 2
228-OC-N1	67.93	5.52	48.50	43.00	163	45.0	1.65	0.25	9.88	4.85	25	I
	68.31	5.90	51.75	46.50	103	45.0	1.65	0.25	11.16	8.81	5	E 1
	68.90	6.49	58.00	52.00	78	45.0	1.65	0.25	15.00	7.75	-27	E 1
	69.49	7.08	61.50	49.50	88	45.0	1.65	0.25	9.82	5.13	36	I
MEAN			53.55	47.93	90				9.85	4.99	31	
95% C.L.			±3.1	±1.92	±27				-	-	-	
n			8	8	8				2	2	2	
101-S09-OC1	141.28	11.36	60.00	48.50	17	60.0	7.00	0.22	9.46	4.45	30	I
	142.15	12.23	57.00	47.50	2	60.0	7.00	0.22	12.64	5.25	29	I
	143.32	13.40	56.00	46.00	32	60.0	7.00	0.22	16.58	6.87	34	I
	143.85	13.93	55.00	45.50	2	60.0	7.00	0.22	17.17	7.16	49	I
	145.46	15.54	55.00	49.00	2	60.0	7.00	0.22	16.65	6.55	28	I
	146.01	16.09	47.00	63.50	167	60.0	7.00	0.22	19.09	5.68	17	I
	146.52	16.60	60.00	48.00	17	60.0	7.00	0.22	14.38	3.10	17	I
	147.05	17.13	57.75	49.00	47	60.0	7.00	0.22	13.62	4.26	7	I
MEAN			58.03	47.56	14				14.95	5.41	27	
95% C.L.			±1.92	±0.86	±12				±1.98	±0.92	±8	
n			8	8	8				8	8	8	
105-OC-F	190.38	5.27	53.50	46.50	68	45.0	5.00	0.25	16.73	3.16	2	I
	190.82	5.71	53.00	44.50	68	45.0	5.00	0.25	16.31	4.31	18	I
	191.30	6.19	47.50	41.50	8	45.0	5.00	0.25	15.22	5.50	19	I
	191.74	6.63	42.00	50.00	158	45.0	5.00	0.25	14.09	4.45	21	I
MEAN			51.00	43.63	31				15.59	4.35	15	
95% C.L.			±2.37	±1.98	±37				±1.0	±0.8	±8	
n			4	4	4				4	4	4	
72-SM-N83	221.97	5.08	51.00	36.00	47	45.0	5.80	0.25	25.56	16.07	36	I
	222.37	5.48	45.00	34.50	52	45.0	5.80	0.25	23.36	12.81	32	I
	222.84	5.95	53.50	39.00	17	45.0	5.80	0.25	23.23	15.78	33	I
	223.24	6.35	59.50	46.00	7	45.0	5.80	0.25	23.70	10.39	41	I
	223.70	6.81	64.00	41.50	47	45.0	5.80	0.25	31.05	19.37	40	I
72-SM-S83	222.40	5.41	36.00	47.50	157	45.0	5.80	0.25	22.38	17.15	36	I
	222.79	5.80	54.00	41.00	37	45.0	5.80	0.25	28.31	27.36	28	E 3
	223.20	6.21	47.50	34.00	22	45.0	5.80	0.25	23.93	17.08	29	I
	223.66	6.67	46.50	37.00	7	45.0	5.80	0.25	23.82	15.04	25	I
	224.10	7.11	51.00	38.00	37	45.0	5.80	0.25	24.01	16.08	17	I
MEAN			51.95	38.30	43				24.56	15.53	32	
95% C.L.			±3.55	±2.18	±26				±1.59	±1.61	±4	
n			10	10	10				9	9	9	
206-014-OC1	243.35	5.53	48.50	38.00	43	55.0	13.00	0.25	29.98	24.03	22	I
	243.87	6.05	49.50	38.50	43	55.0	13.00	0.25	26.75	20.63	32	I
	244.41	6.59	54.00	41.00	53	55.0	13.00	0.25	25.08	23.33	-16	I
	248.03	10.21	41.00	33.50	43	55.0	13.00	0.25	26.40	21.79	39	I
	248.55	10.73	45.00	35.75	65	55.0	13.00	0.25	29.64	25.78	24	I
	249.06	11.24	46.00	36.00	88	55.0	13.00	0.25	27.34	24.91	62	I
	249.57	11.75	39.50	30.50	48	55.0	13.00	0.25	26.84	22.90	26	I
	250.11	12.29	44.00	34.00	53	55.0	13.00	0.25	32.33	23.48	48	I
	250.62	12.80	45.00	36.50	43	55.0	13.00	0.25	27.71	24.98	58	I
	251.13	13.31	48.00	36.50	48	55.0	13.00	0.25	28.37	23.57	36	I
MEAN			46.05	36.50	53				28.04	23.54	33	
95% C.L.			±2.47	±1.71	±8				±1.23	±0.90	±14	
n			10	10	10				10	10	10	

NOTES:

I = results included in mean and 95% Confidence Limit
E = results excluded for reasons as follows:
1. Gauge response appears abnormal. Results not reliable.
2. Subsequent drilling revealed a fracture beside, and parallel to this drill hole.
3. Channel 1 performed abnormally during test.
4. Channel 3 performed abnormally during test.

TABLE 1 - Summary of stress and moduli

RESULTS AND DISCUSSION

The locations of the overcore tests are plotted, with the shaft geology, in Fig. 1. The test results are listed in Table 1. P and Q are the maximum and minimum secondary principal stresses in the plane normal to the drill hole axis. Since the drill holes are vertical to near vertical, P and Q are effectively the maximum and minimum horizontal stresses (also called σ_H and σ_h in this paper).

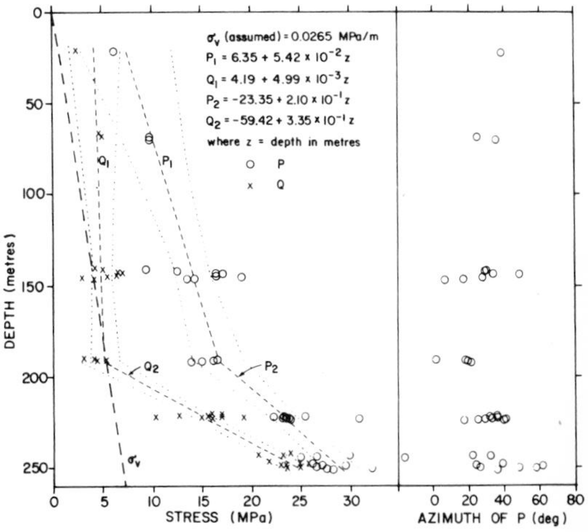

FIG. 3 Horizontal in situ stress versus depth below ground surface.

Fig. 3 is a plot of P and Q, and direction of P, versus depth below ground surface. The linear regression lines and 95% confidence intervals (Mandel 1964) for the 34 successful tests are shown. Note the bilinear curves and the sharp slope changes at the 185 m depth. These lines are described as follows:

· from 0 to 185 m depth

$$P = 6.35 + 5.42 \times 10^{-2} z$$
$$Q = 4.19 + 4.99 \times 10^{-3} z$$

· from 185 m to 250 m

$$P = -23.35 + 2.10 \times 10^{-1} z$$
$$Q = -59.42 + 3.35 \times 10^{-1} z$$

where z = depth below ground surface in metres and units of stress are MPa.

The higher stress gradient below the 185 m depth indicates a stress anomaly associated with fracture zone 2. The stress measurements at the 223 m and 250 m depths (where the higher stresses were measured) were made in unfractured grey granite between fracture zone 2 splay and the main fracture zone 2. A better understanding of this variability and the geology will be possible when the triaxial stresses are available from the comprehensive overcoring program now being conducted in the shaft and shaft stations.

Fig. 4 shows the mean and the 95% confidence limits of the maximum and minimum elastic modulus and the orientation of the maximum elastic modulus in the horizontal plane versus depth below ground surface.

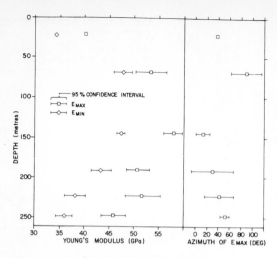

FIG. 4   Maximum and minimum Young's
moduli in the horizontal plane
versus depth below ground
surface. Moduli were obtained
from biaxial tests on overcored
rock cylinders.

Fig. 2 is a plot of direction of
certain features versus shaft depth. The
directional features plotted are the
strike of natural and excavation induced
fractures, and the direction of P, and
the direction of the maximum modulus.
Note that the direction of P agrees within ±10° with the direction of the natural
and induced fractures. The maximum modulus agrees with this overall trend within
±20° (except at the 63 m depth where
there were only two samples tested).

Comparison of the present stress
field with the paleo stress field indicates that σ_1 is still oriented 030°
(parallel to the vertical fractures) but
σ_2 and σ_3 are reversed so that σ_3 is now
vertical. Having σ_1 parallel to the
fractures, especially if there is a high
ratio between σ_1 and σ_2 favours open
(water bearing) fractures. This is
indeed the case at the URL. Coupled
hydrogeology and rock mechanics experiments in the shaft (Lang and Thompson
1985) indicate that the 030° trending
fractures are sometimes open and water
bearing. They are the main vertical
conduits at the site. In selecting a
site for a nuclear waste disposal vault,
a condition that should be considered
unfavourable is one where the stress
normal to the fractures is low in relation to the maximum stress in the plane
of the fracture.

Fig. 5 shows the URL overcore data
plotted onto Herget's (1980) results for
the Canadian Shield. This figure is a
plot of k (ratio of average horizontal
stress to vertical stress) versus depth.
The assumed lithostatic stress (0.0265
MPa x depth in metres) was used for
calculating the k values for the URL
results. The URL data confirms Herget's
expression. The URL data is particularly
useful in that it provides six data
points in the top 250 m where Herget had
no previous Canadian Shield data.

Fig. 5 indicates that, in a very
broad sense, the ratio of average horizontal to vertical stress, as a function
of depth, is fairly consistent in the
Canadian Shield (at least at the locations measured so far). Therefore, the
average horizontal stress can be
predicted, within these wide bounds, at
other sites on the Canadian Shield where
no measurements have been made. However,
the ratio of the horizontal stresses
varies widely even over short distances;
e.g., from 1.5:1 at the 245 m depth to
4:1 at the 185 m depth. This (and the
stress anomaly near fracture zone 2)
supports the widely held view (e.g.,
Herget 1980) that in situ stresses cannot
be predicted from surface measurements or
known geology; they must be measured. It
is the ratio of the stresses that is

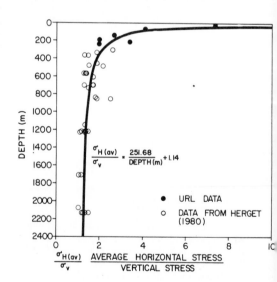

FIG. 5   Variation of ratio of average
horizontal stress to vertical
stress as a function of depth in
the Canadian Shield (after Herget
1980).

often of prime importance in designing underground structures, and in creating damaged zones around unsuitably shaped excavations.

CONCLUSIONS

The program achieved the objective of providing preliminary horizontal in situ stress information, for analyzing the instrument ring results and for use in designing the lower test level. Preliminary modulus values were obtained for analyzing the triaxial strain cell results from the instrument rings, and the third hole of USBM tests is available for combining with USBM tests from horizontal holes that will be drilled during geotechnical characterization.

In addition, the program of USBM testing discussed here provided interesting preliminary information on the horizontal stress field at the URL site. Of particular interest, these initial results
· provide data points in the top 250 m that support Herget's curve for k versus depth in the Canadian Shield;
· demonstrate that the direction of the maximum horizontal stress coincides with the strike of the prominent vertical fracture set at the site. This would be an unfavourable condition for a nuclear waste disposal site because it tends to enhance the permeability of fractures;
· indicate that the ratio of the stresses varies widely over short distances supporting the widely held view that in situ stresses cannot be predicted from surface; they must be measured; and
· indicate that horizontal stress versus depth at the URL can be described by the following:
from 0 m to 185 m depth
$\sigma_H = 6.35 + 5.42 \times 10^{-2}z$
$\sigma_h = 4.19 + 4.99 \times 10^{-3}z$
from 185 m to 250 m depth
$\sigma_H = -23.35 + 2.10 \times 10^{-1}z$
$\sigma_h = -59.42 + 3.35 \times 10^{-1}z$
where σ = stress in MPa and
z = depth in metres.

REFERENCES

Becker, M. and V.E. Hooker 1976. Some Anisotropic Considerations in Rock Stress Determinations. USBM, RI 6965. 23p.

Brown, A., C.C. Davison, P. Kurfurst, D. Peters, G.R. Simmons 1983. The Influence of Geotechnical Data on the Design of the Underground Research Laboratory at Lac du Bonnet, Canada. Proceedings of the International Conference on Underground Mining, Lisbon, Portugal, 1983 September 3:141-154.

Brown, A., R.A. Everitt, A. Holloway, N. Soonawala and D.C. Kamineni 1986. Geology and Geophysics of URL Shaft and Site, Manitoba. Proceedings of Geological Association of Canada - Mineralogical Association of Canada Annual Meeting, Ottawa, Ontario.

Davison, C.C. 1984. Hydrogeological Characterization at the Site of Canada's Underground Research Laboratory. Proceedings of the International Groundwater Symposium on Groundwater Resources Utilization and Contaminant Hydrogeology. Montreal, 1984 May:310-335.

Herget, G. 1980. Regional Stresses in the Canadian Shield. 13th Canadian Rock Mechanics Symposium, CIM Special Volume 22, Toronto, Ontario.

Hooker, V.E. and D. L. Bickel 1974. Overcoring Equipment and Techniques Used in Rock Stress Determination, USBM, REPT. BUMINES-IC-8618. 38p.

Hooker, V.E. and C.F. Johnson 1969. Near-Surface Horizontal Stresses Including the Effects of Rock Anisotropy, USBM, RI-7224. 29p.

Lang, P.A. and P.M. Thompson. 1985. Geomechanics Experiments During Excavation of the URL Shaft. 20th Nuclear Fuel Waste Management Information Meeting, Winnipeg, Manitoba. Atomic Energy of Canada Limited Technical Record, TR-375*.

Lang, P.A., R. W. Humphries and J. G. Ayotte 1986. Blasting in the Lower Shaft Station of Atomic Energy of Canada Limited's Underground Research Laboratory. In Proceedings of the 12th Annual Conference on Explosives and Blasting Techniques, Society of Explosives Engineers, Atlanta, GA., February 1986.

Mandel, J. 1964. The Statistical Analysis of Experimental Data. John Wiley & Sons, Inc., New York. 410p.

Simmons, G.R. and N. Soonawala. 1982.
Underground Research Laboratory
Experimental Program. Atomic Energy of
Canada Limited Technical Record, TR-
153*.

Snider, G.R., P. A. Lang and P. M.
Thompson 1986. Procedures used for
overcore testing during sinking of URL
shaft. Atomic Energy of Canada Limited
Technical Record (in preparation).

Thompson, P.M., P. A. Lang, and G. R.
Snider 1986. Recent improvements to in
situ stress measurements using the
overcoring method. For presentation at
the 39th Canadian Geotechnical
Conference, Ottawa, August, 1986.

---

* Unrestricted, unpublished report,
available from the SDDO, Atomic Energy
of Canada Limited Research Company,
Chalk River, Ontario K0J 1J0.

Rock stresses and geological structures in the Forsmark area

A. CARLSSON
Swedish State Power Board, Stockholm, Sweden

R. CHRISTIANSSON
VIAK AB, Falun, Sweden

ABSTRACT

The paper describes in-situ rock stress measurements carried out in eleven boreholes in the Forsmark area of Sweden. The influence of different rock types and the influence of structures on the rock stresses are discussed, as is the stress distribution down to a depth of 500 m below the rock surface.

RESUME

L'article décrit les mesures d'intensité de contraintes dans la roche réalisées in-situ dans onze trous de sonde dans la zone de Forsmark de Suède. L'influence des différents types de roches et l'influence des structures sur les contraintes dans la roche sont discutées, de même que la répartition des contraintes jusqu'à une profondeur de 500 m au dessous de la surface de la roche.

ZUSAMMENFASSUNG

Dieser Artikel beschreibt Messungen von Bergspannungen in-situ die in elf Bohrlöchern in Forsmark, Schweden, ausgeführt sind. Die Einwirkung von verschiedenen Bergarten und Bergstrukturen auf die Bergspannungen wir behandelt, ebenbo die Spannungsverteilung in dem Bergmassen bis 500 m unter die Bergfläche.

1. INTRODUCTION

The stress situation in the Earth's crust is determined largely by of the present conditions, but it also reflects tectonic history. Knowledge of the stress field is therefore crucial in understanding processes such as faulting and fracturing. Local variations in the principal stress field are related in one way or another to geological discontinuities in the rock mass. It is therefore important that any geological discontinuities be examined and included as an integral part of the interpretation of rock stress measurement results.

This paper discusses in-situ rock stresses and their relation to geological structures. The study is based on site investigations carried out within the construction areas of the Forsmark nuclear power station and the final repository for low and intermediate reactor waste (SFR), both of which are located in northern Uppland, about 130 km north of Stockholm.

2. FORSMARK POWER STATION AND THE SFR

The Forsmark power station is a nuclear power plant with three boiling water reactors of light-water design. All three units are founded on rock. The cooling water from the units is discharged through two submarine rock tunnels (cf. Figure 1)

The repository (SFR) is to be located adjacent to the power station and the rock caverns are being built under the sea about 1000 m from the Forsmark harbour. The rock cover is about 60 m from the top of the caverns to the sea

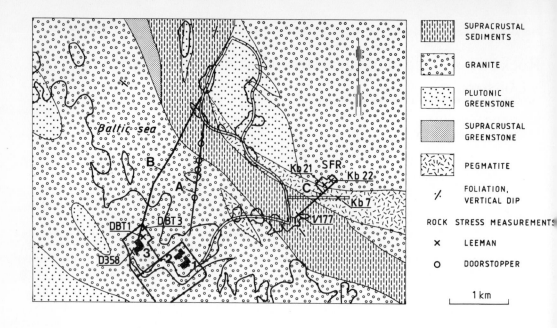

Figure 1. General map of the geology in the Forsmark area. (Hansen, 1985) The locations of the boreholes used for rock stress measurement are indicated in the figure. A; B: submarine discharge tunnels. C: submarine access tunnels, 1, 2, 3: Forsmark units.

bed. Two access tunnels have been excavated from the harbour to the site chosen for the rock caverns. In all, about 9 km of submarine tunnels have been driven at Forsmark.

3. SITE INVESTIGATIONS

Site investigations within the Forsmark area were started in 1971 and have been in progress ever since. The continuation of investigations is a consequence of the size of the plants and the special requirements imposed for nuclear power and reactor waste disposal.

In all, about 120 km of seismic profiling and 15 km of diamond drilling have been carried out. In addition to standard core logging routines a great variety of hydraulic tests and geophysical logging have been performed in the boreholes.

The rock excavation for the foundation of the units and the tunnelling work were followed-up continuously by engineeringgeological surveying. In-situ tests to determine deformation characteristics and the state of stress

of the rock mass were carried out primarily during construction. Furthermore, a number of laboratory tests were performed to determine rock mass properties.

4. ROCK STRESS MEASUREMENTS

The Swedish State Power Board has carried out rock stress measurements for more that 20 years at different construction sites in Sweden and overseas. During this period, the demand for such measurements has increased and accordingly resulted in the development of a new measuring technique (Hiltscher et al, 1979). A special effort was made to perform rock stress measurements in deep, water-filled boreholes, which was hampered mainly by the problems of cementing strain gauges into position. This cementing problem has now been solved in a reliable way.

The well-known method of Leeman and Hayes (1966) was chosen for measurements since the late 70s. Some earlier measurements, using Doorstopper, have also been performed (Hiltscher and

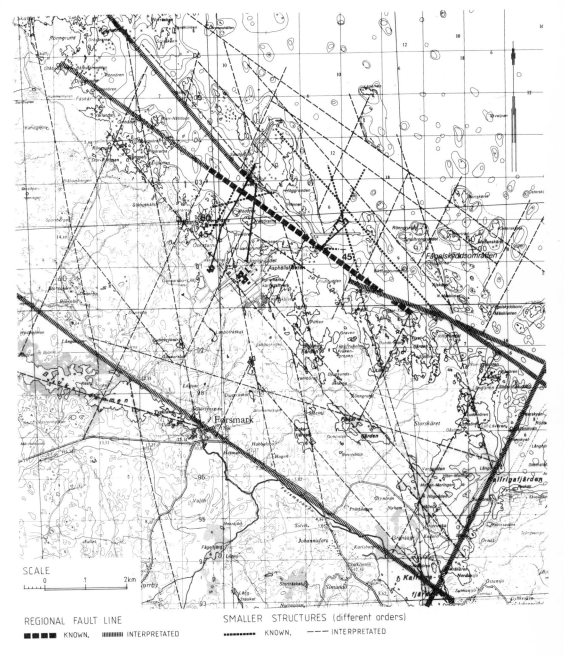

REGIONAL FAULT LINE　　　　SMALLER STRUCTURES (different orders)

▬▬▬▬ KNOWN, ⅢⅢⅢⅢⅢ INTERPRETATED　　　▬▬▬▬▬ KNOWN, ——— INTERPRETATED

Figure 2. Tectonic map of the Forsmark area.

Strindell 1976).

The in-situ rock stress measurements were made in 11 boreholes as shown in Figure 1. In borehole DBT1, measurements were made down to a depth of 500 m below the rock surface, while in boreholes DBT3 and D358, they were performed down to a depth of 250 and 30 m respectively below the rock surface (Carlsson and Olsson, 1982). In-situ rock stress measurements using Doorstopper were also made in the discharge tunnel for Units 1 and 2. Tests in Kb7 were performed from the rock surface down to a depth of 140 m, and in boreholes 1/177, Kb21 and Kb22 from underground parts of the SFR. Youngs's modulus and Poisson's ratio were determined by calibration against cores from each measurement level.

5. GEOLOGY AND TECTONICS

The rock in the Forsmark area belongs to three main groups (cf. Figure 1)

1. Supracrustal rocks form a layer, with a strike from southeast to northwest, about 1 km off the coastline. Several smaller lenses of supracrustal rock accur in the granitic rocks.

   The supracrustal rocks are more than 2000 million years old and consist of leptite - a more or less mica-bearing quartzofeldspathic rock of volcanic origin, metasediments, mainly with layers of garnetbearing biotite schist, and meta-arenite and greenstone (basaltic lava).

2. Primorogen intrusions are predominant in the Forsmark area. These rocks are mostly of Sveccofennian age (1900-1700 million years old) and may be divided into five main types: 1) Plutonic greenstone, 2) Granodiorite to tonalite, 3) Granite to granodiorite, 4) Acid granite, and 5) Pegmatite.

3. Dykes and veins of the rocks mentioned earlier are common. Amphibolite and aplite occur also. Folding and faulting are common.

According to tests of cores the uniaxial strength of the granite-granodiorite is 220-320 MPa, of the pegmatite 120-200 MPa and of the greenstone 120-200 MPa. The Youngs's moduli are 70-80 GPa, 40-80 GPa and 70-90 GPa respectively.

The tectonic pattern (mostly vertical structures) is shown in Figure 2. The Singö zone, about 1 km off the coast is a regional fault zone, which is in its central part about 200 m wide and complex, with smaller crushed zones running in different directions, partly altered schistosed rock and veins of clay.

Smaller zones of weakness and structures form a blocky pattern. The steeply dipping structures run in the directions about NW-SE, NE-SW and N-S. Structures running in the direction of E-W/45°S and subhorizontal have also been encountered.

The rock mass shows also a blocky joint pattern in the same directions as the structures (cf. Figure 3).

The tectonic history of the Forsmark area is partly known. Subhorizontal fold axes and schistosity in the primorogen intrusions indicate that the direction of the first rock stress situation was mainly horizontal and run E-W at the time when the intruded rock was still elastic. It is possible that the Singö zone and structures parallel to it were activated as shear zones in the supracrustal rock.

Younger fold axes show that next main stress direction was NNE-SSW, when the rock mass was at least partly elastic. The joints running NE-SW may have been propagated by shear forces.

The time between the above-mentioned elastic deformation phases could have been some 100 million years. The main stress direction of the next deformation phase was NNW-SSE and reactivated joints running NW-SE and NE-SW by shear forces. Tensile forces may have progated joints running N-S to NNW-SSE. The intrusions of dykes and veins probably occurred mainly during this phase.

It is known, primarily by investigation of cores from weak zones in the Forsmark area, that some structures are brecciated with 3-4 different minerals, which are partly crusched. It may therefore be said that the rock mass has been subjected to tectonic forces of a magnitude sufficient to move large blocks in relation to one another at at least four occasions.

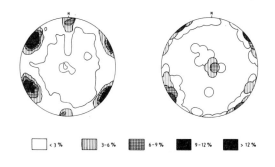

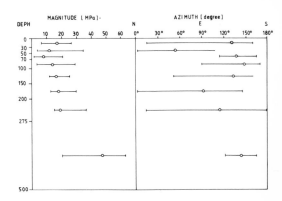

Figure 3. Polar fracture plots from unit 3 (above) and from the SFR. The data is based on mapping in orthogonal directions.

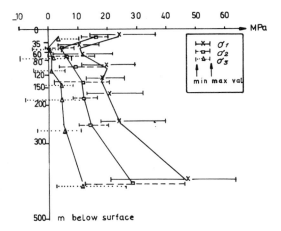

Figure 4. Principal stresses in six boreholes. The lines connect average stresses at each measurement level.

6. RESULTS OF ROCK STRESS MEASUREMENTS

The results of the rock stress measurements at unit 3 (D358), the discharge tunnel from units 1 and 2 and the deep holes, DBT 1 and 3, have been reported earlier (Carlsson and Olsson, 1982). Those, as well as later measurements for the SFR, show that the largest principal stresses are horizontal with the main direction running NW-SE. However, large local scatter of the directions was found. The magnitude of the principal stresses increases with increasing depth below the rock surface, but local scatter of the magnitude was found as well.

Figure 5. Statistical plot of rock stress measurements. The class limits were chosen to obtain 10-15 values in each class. Line: scatter, circle: median. Values are a projection of σ_1 in the horizontal plane.

The results from all 74 measurement points using the Leeman and Hayes method and the Swedish State Power Board equipment in six boreholes are shown in Figure 4.

A statistical plot of the median magnitude and direction of the main principal stress is shown in Figure 5. The scatter of median values is greatest down to a class limit of 70 m, but the scatter within each class is also great.

7. GEOLOGY IN RELATION TO ROCK STRESSES

Rock stresses in relation to rock types have been studied on both a regional and local scale. It is not possible to distinguish any significant difference in the stress field as regards the regional scale (Cf. Figures 1 and 7). On the local scale, the borehole Kb21 was studied. The core penetrates some lenses of metasediments in the granite. Rock stress measurements in the two rock types show no special differences as regards direction or magnitude.

It seems reasonable to assume that different crystalline rock types of about the same age gave similar rock stress distribution.

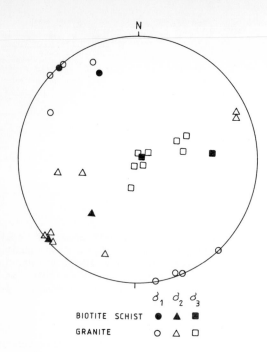

BIOTITE SCHIST   ●   ▲   ◼

GRANITE   ○   △   ▢

$\sigma_1 \quad \sigma_2 \quad \sigma_3$

Figure 6. Rock stress measurements in Kb21, polar plot.

Rock stresses in relation to vertical structures for different levels are shown in Figure 7. There is a tendency for the direction of the stresses at several levels in the boreholes to be parallel to the direction of a nearby structure. However, in one borehole - 1/177, drilled close to the central part of the Singö zone - the measured stresses are almost perpendicular to the zone and the magnitude of the stresses is low. One reason could be that there are large disturbances of the rock stress in the Singö zone. Another reason could be that the measurements have been made in a block and because of early movements the block has been isolated from later tectonic activities and is only subjected to residual stresses (cf. the discription of the tectonic history).

A subhorizontal, highly fractured and crushed zone was penetrated at a depth of about 320 m below the rock surface in borehole DBT1. The magnitude of the stresses was very high below the zone. For almost 50 m below the zone it was not possible to carry out any measurements because of discing of the core. Between 375 and 500 m below the rock surface, 8 stress measurements showed a magnitude for σ_1 of 42-65 MPa (cf. Figure 4 (Carlsson and Olsson, 1982)

In many cases, local structures, such as minor folds and an increase in the joint frequency, caused local variations in stress orientation and magnitude. Out of 74 measurements, 15 measurements down to 250 m have shown tensile vertical stresses (σ_3) and two have shown negative σ_2. Suprisingly high stresses have been obtained at other measurement points. One example of local extreme stress values is shown in figure 8. One reason for the divergency in stresses may be the existence of a fold penetrated by the borehole.

8. INTERPRETATION OF MEASUREMENTS

From a statistical point of view, it is possible to compare measurements down to 250 m below the rock surface because results down to this depth are available from at least two boreholes. Below that level, measurements are only available from DBT1. However, down to 300 m the stress distribution is basically similar to that above 250 m. The stress situation below the subhorizontal zone at a depth of 320 m is possibly a consequence of local conditions.

Down to 50-60 m below the rock surface, there are large variations in stress magnitudes (cf. Figures 4, 9, and 10). This applies to individual measurement as well as mean values. Down to 15 m below the rock surface the magnitudes are low but increase to about the double between 15 and 30 m below the rock surface, to decrease again deeper down. There are also large variations in the directions of stresses.

Even if the superficial rock mass down to about 5 m is very broken (cf. Carlsson, 1979), it seems that the stress field indicates similar disturbances to another scale (larger blocks, smaller displacements) down to 50-60 m below the rock surface. A reasonable explanation seems to be the influence of earlier glaciations. They included not only the pressure from a 2-3 km thick ice-cap, but also shear forces caused by glacier movements and frost activity.

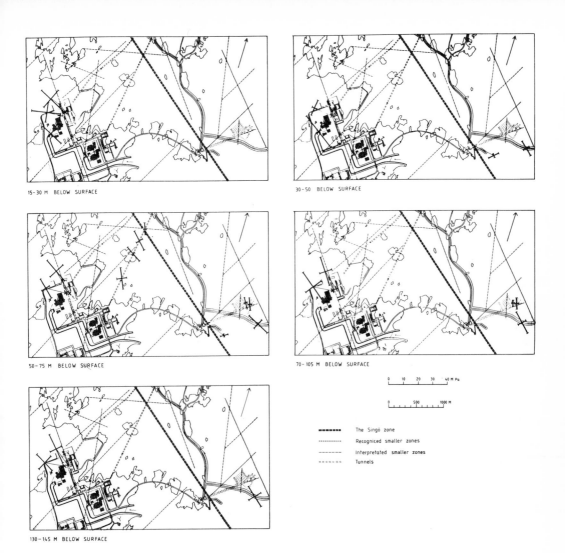

15-30 M BELOW SURFACE

30-50 BELOW SURFACE

50-75 M BELOW SURFACE

70-105 M BELOW SURFACE

0   10   20   30   40 M Pa

0   500   1000 M

▬▬▬▬▬▬   The Singö zone

-----------   Recogniced smaller zones

-------   Interpretated smaller zones

= = = = = =   Tunnels

130-145 M BELOW SURFACE

Figure 7. Horizontal stresses for different measurement levels. The figure represents all measurements carried out at Forsmark.

Below the 60 m level the stresses increase relatively constantly (cf. Figure 4). The average stress, σm also increases with increasing depth (cf. Figure 9).

The magnitude of the deviator stress, $\sigma 1 - \sigma m$, is relatively constant between 60 and 300 m below the rock surface (cf. Figure 10). The deviator stress, as defined above, may reflect earlier displacements in a rock mass - lower magnitude or large variations indicate larger displacements (cf. Carlsson and Christiansson, 1986 b).

The ratio of the horizontal to the vertical stress is shown in Figure 11. It is statistically relatively constant at a 2.9.

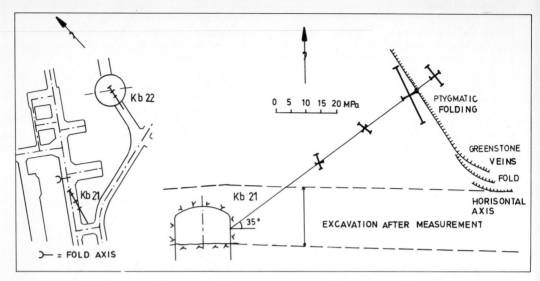

Figure 8. Section for Kb21 including horizontal projection of $\partial 1$ and $\partial 2$ (mean values). The folded vein caused locally higher stresses at the third measurement level. At the second level, two of three measurements gave negative $\partial 3$.

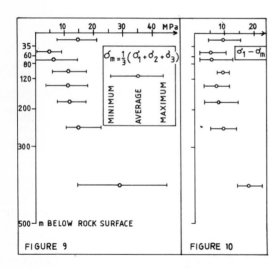

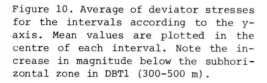

FIGURE 9

FIGURE 10

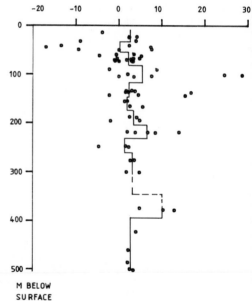

M BELOW
SURFACE

Figure 9. Average stresses for the intervals shown on the Y-axis of the graph. Mean values are plotted in the centre of each interval.

Figure 10. Average of deviator stresses for the intervals according to the y-axis. Mean values are plotted in the centre of each interval. Note the increase in magnitude below the subhorizontal zone in DBT1 (300-500 m).

Figure 11. Average of ∂_H / ∂_V for the intervals shown on the y-axis. Mean values are plotted in the centre of each interval. Note the higher value just below the subhorizontal zone in DBT1.

9. CONCLUSIONS

The rock stress measurements at Forsmark indicate that there is no significant difference in stress field between different rock types (local scale) or between larger intrusions.

Larger structures, such as the Singö fault, seem to influence the direction of the principal stresses. There is a tendency for stress directions to be parallel to an adjacent structure. Minor structures, such as folds and geological irregularities (for example increased joint frequency), influence the magnitude as well as the direction of the rock stresses.

There seems to be a significant relationship between rock stresses and depth below the rock surface. The superficial rock mass down to a depth of 50-60 m below the rock surface shows a stress situation with large deviation in stress magnitude and direction. This may be an effect of the latest glaciations.

The relationship between the average horizontal and vertical stresses seems to be almost constant (2.9) from the rock surface down to a depth of 500 m.

REFERENCES

Carlsson, A, 1979: Characteristic features of a superficial rock mass in southern, central Sweden. Horizontal and sub-horizontal fractures and filling material. Striae 11. Uppsala.

Carlsson, A. and Olsson, T. 1982: Characterization of deep-seated rock masses by means of borehole investigations. Swedish State Power Board, Tech. report 5 (1). Stockholm.

Carlsson, A. and Christiansson, R. 1986: Geological and tectonic conditions at Forsmark, Swedish. State Power Board, R & D-report. In preparation.

Christiansson, R. 1985: Byggnadsgeologisk uppföljning, delrapport 1-6 SFR 85-04 (Engineering Geology Followup. Sub-report 1-6 SFR 85-04). Swedish Nuclear Fuel and Waste Management Company.

Hansen, L. 1985: Lithology of the Forsmark Area. Statens Vattenfallsverk, Tek.rapp.

Hiltscher, R. and Strindell, L. 1976: Forsmark kraftstation. Mätning av bergets initialspänningar (Forsmark Power Station. Measurement of Initial Rock Stresses). Statens Vattenfallsverk, Tek.rapp. L-522. Stockholm.

Hiltscher, R., Martna, J. and Strindell, L. 1979: The measurement of triaxial rock stresses in deep boreholes and the use of rock stress measurements in the design and construction of rock openings. 4th Int. Congr. in Rock Mech., 2: 227-234.

Leeman, E.R. and Hayes, D.I. 1966: A technique for determining the complete state of stress in rock using a single borehole. Proc. 1st Congr. Int. Soc. Rock Mech. 2: 17-24.

The results of in situ stress determinations by seven methods to depths of 2500 m in the Carnmenellis granite

A.S. BATCHELOR
Geoscience Limited, London, United Kingdom

R.J. PINE
Camborne School of Mines, Redruth, United Kingdom

ABSTRACT

An extensive programme of stress measurements has been undertaken in Cornwall, England as part of a major geotechnical investigation. The results cover a depth range of 0-2800 m and have been obtained by three direct methods and four indirect methods. The least principal stress and its variation with depth has been determined reliably. The maximum principal stresses are subject to some uncertainty but the results do show that there is a severe and persistent anisotropy between the horizontal stresses. The orientation of the stress field is in good agreement with results from Western Europe and is consistent with compression from the Alpine orogenic event.

RESUME

Un programme approfondi de mesures des contraintes a été entrepris dans la région de la Cornouailles en Angleterre, dans le cadre d'une étude géotechnique majeure. Les resultats courvent une gamme de profondeur de 0-2800 m et ont été obtenus par trois méthodes directes et quatre méthodes indirectes. La moindre contrainte principale et ses variations en fonction de la profondeur ont pu être déterminées de façon fiable. Les contraintes principales maximum sont sujètes à un certain niveau d'incertitude mais les résultats montrent bien qu'il existe une anisotropie sévère et persistante entre les contraintes horizontales. L'orientation du champ de contraintes concorde bien avec les résultats obtenus en Europe de l'Quest et elle est en accord avec la compression issue de l'événement orogénique alpin.

AUSZUG

Im Rhmen einer wichtigen geotechnischen Untersuchung in Cornwall, England, wurde ein umfangreiches Programm mit Spannungsmessungen durchgeführt. Die Ergebnisse umfassen einen Tiefenbereich von 0-2800 m und wurden durch drei direkte und vier indirekte Mthoden erzielt. Die geringste Hauptspannung wurde in Abhängigkeit von der Tiefe zuverlässig bestimmt. Die Hauptbelastungsmaxima weisen gewisse Ungenauigkeiten auf, die Ergeb nisse zeigen jedoch, daB es zwischen den Horizontalspannungen zu einer starken und dauernden Anisotropie kommt. Die Lage des Spannungsfeldes stimmt mit den Ergebnissen aus Westeuropa uberein und ist mit der Kompression der Alpengebirgs-bildung vereinbar.

1 INTRODUCTION

A major geotechnical research programme is being undertaken in Cornwall, England, to study the feasibility of extracting geothermal energy by the Hot Dry Rock (HDR) process; summaries of the procedures and progress to date are given by Batchelor (1982, 1986) and Pine (1983).

The success of the process depends on stimulating pre-existing joints by hydraulic injections to form low resistance flow paths between injection and production wells. These flow paths must be coupled to a large heat exchange area if the system is to be viable. The process is critically dependent upon the magnitude and orientation of the in situ stresses and the properties of the joints within the interwell region.

This paper presents summaries of the results from seven direct and indirect methods that have been used to derive the current understanding of the stress field. Other evaluations are still in progress and these are mentioned towards the end of the paper. A consistent interpretation of the prevailing stress field has been derived and the future activities at the research project have been based on the values obtained during this work.

1.1 Local Geology and Tectonic Setting

Figure 1 shows a geological sketch map of the test area. Geophysical investigations have shown that the exposed granites are part of a single granite batholith extending for 200 km along the axis of South West England. The granite is the source of the regional geothermal anomaly because of the concentration of radiogenic elements within the rock. The granite was intruded incrementally during the late

Carboniferous and early Permian times. The stress measurements have been made at the test site, Rosemanowes Quarry and South Crofty Mine. Both of these locations are within the Carnmenellis granite. Age dating of this particular pluton shows that it was intruded 280 million years ago. The country rock adjacent to the granite margin near South Crofty consists of contact metamorphosed shales (with minor sandstones) and basic intrusive and volcanic rocks of Devonian age. The area is extensively mineralised around the margins of the granite and mining activity has continued since Roman times.

The joint directions have been mapped extensively across the pluton, Figure 2, and similar directions have been observed to depths of 2600 m during the drilling associated with the research programme. There are two major sub-vertical joint sets striking approximately 160-340° and 75-255°. Two other joint sets are present at various locations.

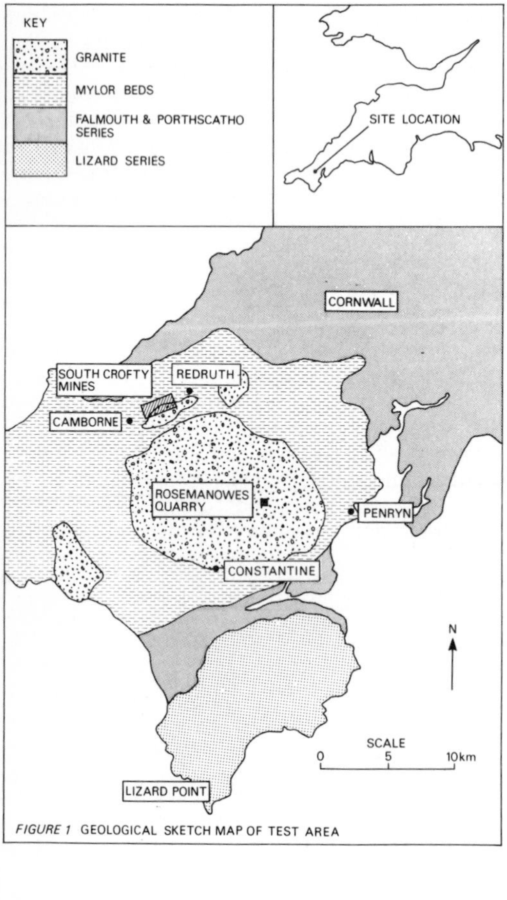

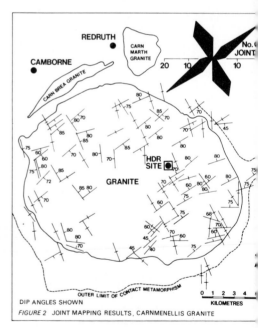

FIGURE 1 GEOLOGICAL SKETCH MAP OF TEST AREA

FIGURE 2 JOINT MAPPING RESULTS. CARNMENELLIS GRANITE

In the deep, active mines at the edge of the Carnmenellis granite there are thermal springs which issue predominantly from the north north west south south east trending joint systems. This is indicative of the major principal stress acting parallel to those joints. This could correspond to the direction of "Alpine" compression in the area.

The permeability of the rock fabric has been shown to be extremely low with values of the order of $10^{-3} \mu D$ determined by water diffusion (Pearson 1980). The overall permeability of the rock mass at low injection pressure is typically in the range 10-100 μD. This equates to flowing joint apertures of the order of 10 microns for typical joint spacings assuming laminar flow (Pine and Ledingham 1983).

The effective tensile strength of the granite was measured by drilling 100 mm diameter holes into 2-3 m diameter boulders and conducting hydraulic fracturing tests with a straddle packer. The results gave an average hydrofracture tensile strength of approximately 15 MPa.

2 HYDRAULIC FRACTURE STRESS MEASUREMENTS TO DEPTHS OF 2550 METRES

The first tests to be undertaken were hydraulic fracture stress measurements. Four series of tests have been conducted during the research programme at progressively greater depths to a maximum of 2550 m; the last set were conducted in 1985.

The tests have been successful in establishing reliable magnitudes for the minimum horizontal stress and its variation with depth. Interpretation of the maximum horizontal stresses has been less reliable, but consistent trends have emerged.

Attempts to orientate the induced fractures using television, borehole televiewer and impression packers were not generally successful.

Stress anisotropy was very significant throughout the tested interval with maximum and minimum horizontal stresses of approximately 70 and 30 MPa respectively at a vertical depth of 2000 m. The overburden stress at this depth was estimated as 52 MPa.

The full details of these tests are given by Pine et al (1983a) and Camborne School of Mines (1986). The latter reference includes the only test where the orientation of the induced fracture

was determined reliably using the borehole televiewer.

Sixteen tests have been completed successfully and the results are shown in Figure 3. The interpretation of the results has been based on the use of total rather than effective stresses because of the extremely low porosity and permeability of the granite fabric.

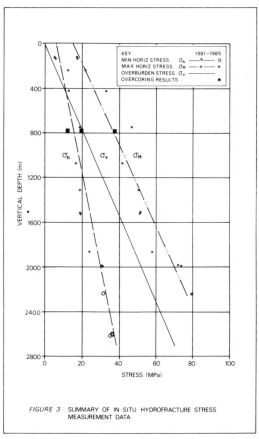

FIGURE 3 SUMMARY OF IN SITU HYDROFRACTURE STRESS MEASUREMENT DATA

A comparison of the stress field at depth with the Mohr's envelope for the intact granite shows that no compressive failure of the borehole wall should occur. However, if effective stress conditions apply (borehole pressure matched by the pore fluid pressure in the surrounding rock fabric) then shear failure of the rock fabric is predicted. An extensive examination of the geophysical logs with caliper information (dip-meter, four-arm caliper and borehole televiewer) did not show any breakouts before the wells were exposed to high hydraulic pressures. It seems likely that the wells were stable and that total stresses did apply, although this area is open for debate (see Pine et al, 1983a).

The results of the measurements gave the following trends with depth:

$$\sigma_H = 15 + 27.5 \ d$$
$$\sigma_h = 6 + 11.8 \ d$$
$$\sigma_v = 26 \ d$$

where

σ_H = maximum horizontal stress (MPa)

σ_h = minimum horizontal stress (MPa)

σ_v = vertical stress (MPa)

d = depth (km)

It can be seen that the maximum shear stress is increasing rapidly with depth. An analysis based on similar data (Pine and Batchelor 1984) has shown that this stress condition is critical for strike slip shearing during hydraulic stimulation at the site.

3   OVERCORING MEASUREMENTS

At the time when the bulk of the hydrofacture measurements were made, the orientation of the stress field was not obtained. It was considered essential to undertake overcoring stress measurements as deep as possible to obtain the necessary data. The results should also provide a check on the stress magnitudes at one depth.

A programme of overcoring stress measurements at a depth of 790 m in the Carnmenellis granite was undertaken in a local mine, South Crofty, who granted access to some of their deepest workings. Before the tests were undertaken, the geological and tectonic setting of the two sites were reviewed and it was concluded that the stress regimes should be similar. A finite element model of the pluton and its surrounding metamorphic cover was used to confirm that the variation in stress direction was within experimental tolerance. Two types of overcoring system were used, the Commonwealth Scientific and Industrial Research Organization of Australia (CSIRO) and the United States Bureau of Mines (USBM).

A total of six CSIRO and seven USBM

tests were completed successfully in two near horizontal boreholes with a 100 azimuth difference. Agreement between the two sets of tests was excellent Full details are given by Pine et al (1983b). The interpretation of the CSIRO results was based on the method of Duncan et al (1980); the results are given below:

Stress	Magnitude (MPa)	Azimuth (°)	Dip (°)
σ_H	37.7	130	5
σ_h	11.3	41	-3
σ_v	18.5	347	85

It can be seen that the direction of maximum principal stress was 130-320° and that the stress magnitudes agree well with those determined from the hydrofracture method, see Figure 3. The significant anisotropy is present in these measurements and the direction of the maximum stress is in good agreement with the "Alpine" tectonic forces that are thought to be dominating the current stress conditions.

4   DIFFERENTIAL STRAIN ANALYSIS

Differential strain analysis (DSA) is based on the assumption that a rock specimen will expand due to the generation of microcracks when it is removed from the confinement due to the in situ stresses. The frequency and direction of the microcracks should be related to the magnitudes and orientation of the relieved stresses. Several authors have predicted that the crack spectrum could be used to evaluate the past history of a particular formation (Simmons and Richter 1974). The complete theory is described by Ren and Roegiers (1983) and Strickland and Ren (1980).

During the deep drilling programme, several attempts were made to obtain oriented core. None of these attempts were successful so the DSA technique cannot be used to derive true orientation data with the available core. However, an estimate of the principal strain directions for the cores can be obtained if it is assumed that one of the principal strains is vertical. The cores were taken from inclined sections

of the wells and the relevant transformations were made using the borehole
survey data for azimuth and inclination.

Granite cubes were cut from the
cores taken from depths of 1500 m to
2400 m. The cubes were cut with the
sides parallel to the core axes longer
than the other sides to preserve the
orientation. Each cube was strain
gauged, sealed and loaded in a hydraulic
cell.

The microcrack reclosure strain
tensor for each cube was assumed to be
proportional to the in situ strain
relief tensor and the overburden stress
was used to nomalise the stress
magnitudes.

Figure 4 shows the stresses derived
from the DSA measurement superimposed on
a simplified version of Figure 3
including the hydrofracturing and overcoring measurements. The results from
the cubes at approximately 1500 m are in
reasonable agreement with those from

hydraulic stress measurements. However,
the results from the cubes taken at
depths greater than 1500 m did not agree
with the overall pattern.

Some of the deeper cores in the
drilling programme were found to be
heavily disked and it is thought that
incipient disking maybe the reason for
the overestimate of the magnitude of the
maximum stress along the axis of the
core (Milburn 1986). As the core is
being cut, it will experience stress
relief and generate a high stress
concentration at the junction of the
core to the rock mass. This mechanism
produces microcracks and fractures
across the junction that is perpendicular to the core axes. The results
obtained from a cube containing disking
microcracks would give excessive strain
values parallel to the core axes with a
consequent underestimate of the
horizontal stresses. This appears to
have been observed at depths below
1700 m. It can be seen that the least
principal stress seems to have been
determined with a reasonable accuracy,
but neither the ratio, orientation or
the stresses at depth matched the
previous results.

5 HYDRAULIC INJECTION DATA

The last three sections have
presented the results from attempts at
direct stress measurement. However,
several other activities at the site led
to information relating to the magnitude
of the minimum principal stress. One of
the more repeatable measurements, is the
relationship of injection flow rate to
injection pressure. Figure 5 shows a
plot of flow rate against wellhead
pressure for a short packed off interval
during repeated pressurization of a
single feature. The very marked
increase in flow rate above 8 MPa can be
seen.

Similar behaviour has been observed
throughout the experimental programme
despite the range of injection flow
rates from less than 1 kg/s to 264 kg/s.

The open hole lengths of the three
wells are 357 m, 722 m and 575 m
respectively. The flowmeter and
temperature logging over these intervals
has shown that the water leaves or
enters the well on joints that are
aligned within 30° of the direction of

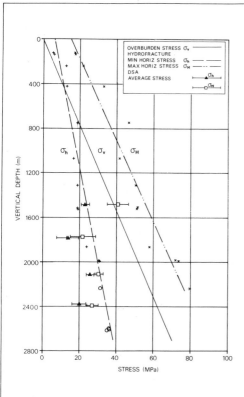

FIGURE 4   DEPTH Vs STRESS PLOT FOR THE THREE PRINCIPAL
STRESSES

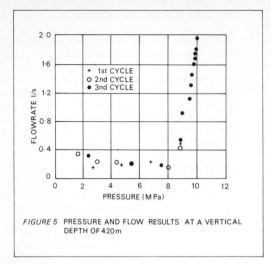

FIGURE 5 PRESSURE AND FLOW RESULTS AT A VERTICAL
DEPTH OF 420m

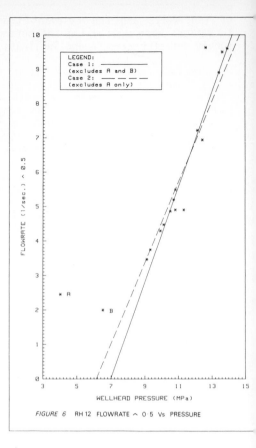

FIGURE 6 RH 12 FLOWRATE $\wedge$ 0 5 Vs PRESSURE

the maximum principal stress. However, not all of the joints in this set form entries or exits from the wells.

At the higher flow rates, the pressure dependent response of each well did not show such a sharp change of slope as that shown in Figure 5. This has been attributed to the averaging effect of several flow zones within the well. The threshold pressure of the opening can be determined by plotting pressure change as a function of the square root of the flow rate; this approach is due to Aamodt (Haimson 1978). Figure 6 shows an example from Well RH12 giving a minimum effective stress of 7.0 MPa at 1800 m. This should be compared to a value of 9.0 MPa interpolated from Figure 3.

It is considered that this technique may give an estimate of the minimum principal stress that is slightly lower than the true value because of the complex mechanisms that govern the flow characteristics of individual joints. As the effective stress within the joint approaches zero, both normal dilation and shear motion will increase the permeability of the joint and, hence, its ability to accept increasing flow rates. However, the results do indicate that the threshold pressure for the accelerating joint dilation is close to the confining stress on the joint.

6 ANALYSIS OF "SHUT IN" DATA

Nolte (1979) and Lee (1985) describe techniques to determine a range of parameters for a hydraulic fracture from an analysis of the pressure decay curve at the end of a fracturing operation. One of the values is the "fracture closure pressure" which corresponds to the normal confining stress on the fracture. This is generally assumed to be the minimum horizontal stress.

In July 1985 a massive hydraulic stimulation operation was undertaken in one of the wells to generate a fracture at a depth of 2370 m. 5500 m³ of viscous fluid were pumped into the well over a period of 8 hours. At the end of the injection the well was shut in and the pressure decay observed. Figure shows the downhole pressure for 24 hour covering the 8 hours of injection and the first 16 hours of shut in. It ca be seen that there is no sharp break o gradient during the decay so a plot o pressure gradient was used to determin the closure point. This was found to b 30.25 MPa, approximately 5 hours afte shut-in.

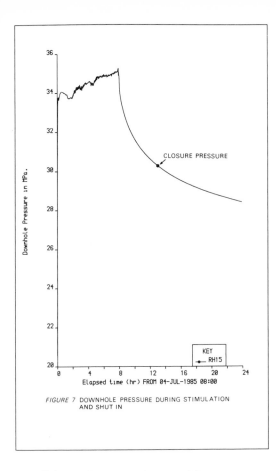

FIGURE 7 DOWNHOLE PRESSURE DURING STIMULATION
AND SHUT IN

This value was in excellent agreement with the results of a "mini frac" test but is 10% less than the value interpolated from the hydraulic fracturing stress measurement results. The subsequent analysis confirmed a fracture closure time of 5 hours, in good agreement with the time determined from the change of slope and it tends to confirm the measurement of closure pressure. The hydrostatic pressure at 2370 m was measured at 20.55 MPa. This means that closure occurred at a wellhead pressure of 9.7 MPa. This is in reasonable agreement with the value of 8 MPa shown in the previous section for the break of slope during water injection. The reason for the slight discrepancy between "closure stress" values and hydraulic fracture stress measurements is partly due to the non-ideal nature of the closure between the faces of the fracture. There was a significant increase in the residual permeability after the stimulation which must mean that the fracture is "self-propped " by its own asperities.

7   STRESS ORIENTATION FROM MICROSEISMIC FAULT PLANE SOLUTIONS

Each of the various injections at the test site was monitored by a comprehensive microseismic network. The data from this system was used to locate the seismic activity and to determine the source mechanisms of the various events. The use of first motion data from seismic networks to determine fault plane solutions is a standard seismological technique (Honda 1962). The method involves recording the sense of the P-wave first motion at each station, eg a compression or dilation. This approach can also be is used to determine the far field radiation pattern for a microseismic event (Lee and Stewart 1981). There are a number of fault mechanisms that can generate different far field radiation patterns. The most commonly recognised mechanism corresponds to an infinitesimal shear dislocation that is expressed as a double-couple source without moment or a system of dislocation forces acting at 45° to the dislocation plane (Bullen and Bolt 1985).

The P-wave first motions with the double couple mechanism will define two orthogonal nodal planes. Only one of these planes will define the fault plane, the other defines the auxiliary plane. Further information is required to define the true direction of the fault plane. This information may come from an interpretation of the S-wave behaviour or from a knowledge of the local geology.

Whichever of the two planes is chosen as the fault plane, it is common to quote the centres of the dilatational and compressional quadrants, P and T axes, as the directions of the maximum and minimum principal stresses. This assumption assumes classical shear behaviour of an initially homogeneous and fault free material but it does not apply directly to most shallow earthquakes (MacKenzie 1969). When earthquakes produce surface displacements they usually occur along pre-existing lines of weakness, faults, or major joint directions. In addition, the shear stresses involved are usually too small to produce fracturing of intact material. This suggests that it is more realistic to evaluate the stress directions that could produce the observed slip on a given fault plane. In this case the only constraint is that the maximum principal stress must lie in the dilatational quadrant.

At the test site in Cornwall the joint directions have been mapped extensively and the majority of the induced seismic events were at depths ranging from 1000-3000 m. The data was scanned manually to determine the stress axes.

With a large seismic network it is possible to determine fault plane solutions for individual events. The network at the geothermal energy project has insufficient sensors to define a fault plane for a single event; however, if the entire data set is used for all the events, it is possible to generate a composite solution. To generate such a solution, all the first motion data from a particular experiment are plotted together. This assumes that all the events occurring closely in space and time are likely to have the same solutions. This is an over-simplification but nevertheless it does indicate the nature of the predominant fault mechanism.

The data shown in Figure 8 is from the large viscous fracturing injection described in Section 6. The seismicity generated by this experiment has been presented in Baria et al (1985). The data is presented on an equal area of projection of the upper hemisphere. First motion data from all of the 202 located events has been used. The solution suggests that either left or right lateral strike slip motion on near vertical fault planes has occurred. The two directions are 353° or 263° respectively. The plane with a strike of 353° has a similar orientation to one of the major joint sets at 2000 m as determined from the borehole televiewer data. This is thought to represent the orientation of the majority of the mobile joints. Fault plane solutions from previous injections have been analysed by similar techniques and the results are consistent with those presented in Figure 8.

These fault plane solutions indicate that the maximum principal stress direction must lie to the west of 353° in the dilatational quadrant. Over 80% of the events indicate sinistral strike

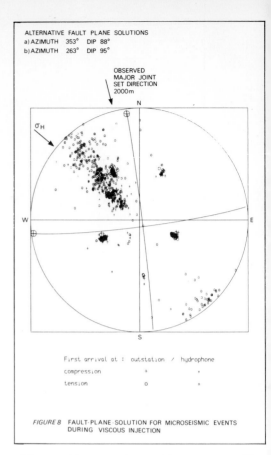

ALTERNATIVE FAULT PLANE SOLUTIONS
a) AZIMUTH 353° DIP 88°
b) AZIMUTH 263° DIP 95°

OBSERVED MAJOR JOINT SET DIRECTION 2000 m

σ_H

First arrival at : outstation / hydrophone
compression + +
tension o o

FIGURE 8   FAULT-PLANE-SOLUTION FOR MICROSEISMIC EVENTS DURING VISCOUS INJECTION

slip motion and, making reasonable assumptions of the friction between the joint surfaces (ϕ = 35-45°) this gives a stress direction of 320-330°. This is in agreement with the directions measured during the overcoring experiments at South Crofty, described in Section 3 of this Paper. Those events that do not agree with the composite solution may be a result of ill defined first motion directions, varying joint orientations and different mechanisms caused by the three dimensional nature of the intersecting sub parallel joints. More stations would be necessary in the seismic network to ensure that individual events can be examined and the reason for the anomalous behaviour identified.

8   LOCATION OF MICROSEISMIC EVENTS

Figure 9 shows two orthogonal views of the locations of microseismic events that were detected during the various stages of the project. A full description of this work is given by Batchelor et al (1983) and Baria et al

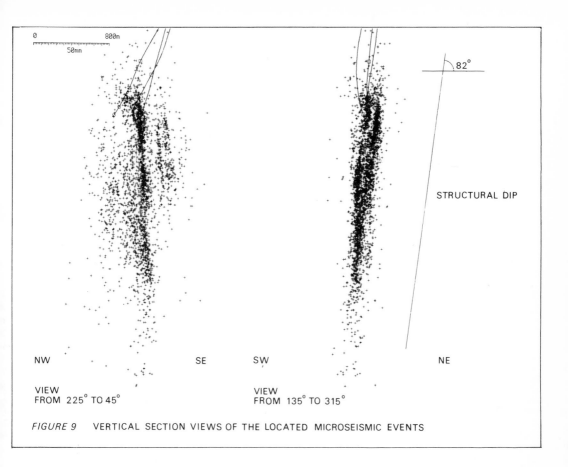

FIGURE 9   VERTICAL SECTION VIEWS OF THE LOCATED MICROSEISMIC EVENTS

(1985). It is apparent that the events form a 'cloud' with an overall strike of approximately 135-315°.

Figure 10 shows the strike directions of the major joint sets and the 'cloud' with the directly measured horizontal in situ stress directions superimposed. This combination of joints and stresses has constrained the growth of the hydraulically stimulated reservoir to a predominant direction between the maximum principal stress direction and the set 1 joints. However, detailed examination of its internal structure shows families of planes striking at about 350° but forming an overall composite pattern much closer to the stress direction. The shape and orientation of this overall structure is excellent supporting evidence for the measured in situ stress directions and strengthens the case that the fault plane solutions provide further confirmation of the orientation of the stress fields.

The locations of the microseismicity reached depths of over 4 km and there was no significant change in the

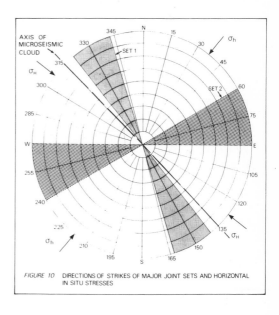

FIGURE 10   DIRECTIONS OF STRIKES OF MAJOR JOINT SETS AND HORIZONTAL IN SITU STRESSES

directions determined by either the locations or the fault planes. Natural seismicity occurs in the depth range 4-7 km and these events have fault plane solutions that are consistent with those from the microseismicity, (Walker 1986). These results can be taken to show that no significant rotation of the stress field occurs at depth, major joint structures persist to those depths and the stress field is critically aniso-tropic with fluids present in near vertical joints.

9 OTHER TECHNIQUES

Several other techniques have been investigated to determine further information on the stress fields. These include wellbore breakouts (Gough and Bell 1982; Zoback et al 1985) and the anisotropy of tube wave motions (Barton and Zoback 1986).

An analysis of wellbore breakouts showed that the borehole deformation only occurred as a result of high pressure fluid injections. No breakout evidence was visible in the unstimulated wells.

Features were visible on the bore-hole televiewer that were consistent with an azimuth of the maximum principal stress of 135-315° after the wells had been pressurized. However, it must be said that knowledge of the stress directions from the overcoring and other measurements was helpful in seeking patterns in the well that were due to stress induced damage. During the various logging activities, several pieces of granite have been caught in the centralisers of the various sondes. One of these pieces, approximately 300 mm long, showed clear evidence of tangential failures in a section of the borehole wall as would be expected in a breakout failure mode. However, the results from this technique are not convincing at the moment.

The tube wave anisotropy inves-tigation has not been conclusive but this should not be taken as criticism of the technique. An inadequate data set was acquired for other purposes and is in a difficult form to use effectively.

10 CONCLUSIONS

1   The least principal stress has bee measured reliably and its variation wit depth can be described by the followin equation:

$$\sigma_h = 6 + 11.8 \ d$$

It is considered that the estimat of in situ stress given from thi equation is probably better than ±10% t a depth of 3000 m.

2   The maximum horizontal stress can b described by the following equation:

$$\sigma_H = 15 + 27.5 \ d$$

Confidence in these values is muc less than for the least horizonta stress. Deviation could be more tha 20% at any one depth. However, analyse have shown that the anisotropy betwee the two horizontal stresses is jus sub-critical for strike slip shearing o a favourably aligned joint set unde hydrostatic pore pressure conditions Shallow, naturally occurring seismicit has been detected in the area and it i believed that the degree of anisotrop between the stresses is genuine an persists to at least 7 km.

3   The orientation of the maximu horizontal stress is 140-320 ± 10° an this is in agreement with other measure ments in Western Europe and seems t correspond to stresses induced durin the Alpine orogeny.

4   The measurement of vertical stres confirms that it can be calculated a follows:

$$\sigma_v = 26 \ d$$

This stress is the intermediat stress in Cornwall below a depth o 1000 m.

The stress evaluations presented i this paper produce a consistent mode for the stress field in South Wes England. The severe anisotropy wa unexpected and caused several majo difficulties during the execution of th research project before its influenc was fully recognised. These result confirm that no one technique should b used on its own without independen corroborative support. However, by using all the available information, the degree of confidence in the results can be improved substantially. The authors would advocate the use of multiple techniques to obtain stress information, particularly if the results are of critical importance.

The authors are currently facing the problem of extrapolating the results to much greater depth to determine the possibility of operating commercial geothermal systems in Cornwall. Even with this substantial and comprehensive data set there can be no great confidence in the extrapolation of all aspects of the stress tensor. However, the persistence of the severe anisotropy and the directions of the stresses can be predicted and the minimum horizontal stress trend may well persist in the 3000-7000 m depth range. The inter-action of the joint behaviour with the stress field appears to be the factor limiting the stress anisotropy as suggested by McGarr (1980).

ACKNOWLEDGEMENTS

The field work referred to in this Paper was undertaken when the first author was the Project Director for the Camborne School of Mines Geothermal Energy Research Project. The results were achieved by a team of 60 dedicated staff and the authors gratefully acknowledge the support and commitment from each member of the group.

The work was supported in its latter stages by contract E/5A/CON/125/160 from the UK Department of Energy and contract EN3 G/E1/019/GB of the EEC and their support is gratefully acknowledged.

REFERENCES

Barton, C.A. and Zoback, M.D. 1986. Determination of in situ stress orientation from Stoneley wave polarization in boreholes. Submitted to Journal of Geophysical Research.

Batchelor, A.S. 1982. Stimulation of a hot dry rock geothermal reservoir in the Cornubian granite, England. In 8th workshop on geothermal reservoir engineering, Stanford University, California, Dec 1982.

Batchelor, A.S. 1986. Reservoir behaviour in a stimulated hot dry system. In 11th workshop on geothermal reservoir engineering, Stanford University, California, Jan 1986.

Batchelor, A.S. Baria, R. and Hearn, K. 1983. Monitoring the effects of hydraulic stimulation by microseismic event location: a case study. In SPE-AIME 58th annual technical conference, San Francisco, California, Oct 1983. (SPE 12109)

Bullen, K.E. and Bolt, B.A. 1985. An introduction to the theory of seismology. Cambridge University Press, Cambridge.

Camborne School of Mines Geothermal Energy Project. 1985. Microseismic results. Phase 2 report, Group II, Part 8, Vol 1, 228 pp.

Camborne School of Mines Geothermal Energy Project. 1986. Hydrofracture stress measurement in well RH15. Phase 2B report, 93 pp.

Duncan Fama, M.E. and Pender, M.J. 1980. Analysis of the hollow inclusion technique for measuring in situ rock stress. International Journal of Rock Mechanics Mining Sciences & Geomechanical Abstracts 17:137-146.

Gough, D.I. and Bell, J.S. 1982. The use of borehole breakouts in the study of crustal stress. Canadian Journal of Earth Sciences, 19:1358-1370.

Haimson, B. 1978. The hydrofracturing stress measuring method and recent field tests. International Journal of Rock Mechanics Mining Sciences & Geomechanical Abstracts 15:167-178.

Honda, H. 1962. Earthquake mechanism and seismic waves. Journal of the Physics of the Earth 10:1-97.

Lee, W.S. 1985. Pressure decline analysis with the Khristianovich and Zheltov and penny-shaped geometry method of fracturing. In SPE/DOE joint low permeability gas reservoirs symposium, Denver, Colorado, May 1985. (SPE/DOE 13872)

Lee, W.H.K. and Stewart, S.W. 1981. Principles and applications of microearthquake networks. In Advances in Geophysics: supplement 2, Academic Press, New York.

McGarr, A. 1980. Some constraints on levels of shear stress in the crust from observations and theory. Journal of Geophysical Research 85(B11):6231-6238.

McKenzie, D.P. 1969. The relation between fault plane solutions for earthquakes and the directions of the principal stresses. Bulletin of the Seismological Society of America 59(2):591-601.

Milburn, N.F. 1986. The use of differential strain curve analysis in predicting the in situ stress conditions for deep boreholes. Camborne School of Mines Geothermal Energy Project, Phase 2B report.

Nolte, K.G. 1979. Determination of fracture parameters from fracturing pressure decline. In SPE-AIME 54th annual technical conference, Las Vegas, Nevada, Sep 1979. (SPE 8341)

Pearson, C.M. 1980. Permeability enhancement by explosive initiation in the South West granites, with particular reference to hot dry rock energy systems. PhD thesis, Camborne School of Mines.

Pine, R.J. 1983. Pressure transient analysis for large scale hydraulic injections in the Carnmenellis granite, England, In 9th workshop on geothermal reservoir engineering, Stanford University, California, Dec 1983.

Pine, R.J. and Batchelor, A.S. 1984. Downward migration of shearing in jointed rock during hydraulic injections. International Journal of Rock Mechanics Mining Sciences & Geomechanical Abstracts 21(5).

Pine, R.J. and Ledingham, P. 1983. In situ hydraulic parameters for the Carnmenellis granite hot dry rock geothermal energy reservoir. In SPE-AIME 58th annual technical conference, San Francisco, California, Oct 1983 (SPE 12020)

Pine, R.J., Ledingham, P. and Merrifield, C.M. 1983a. In situ stress measurement in the Carnmenellis granite: 2 - Hydrofracture tests at Rosemanowes Quarry to depths of 2000 m. International Journal of Rock Mechanics Mining Sciences & Geomechanical Abstracts 20(2):63-72.

Pine, R.J., Tunbridge, L.W. and Kwakwa, K.A. 1983b. In situ stress measurements in the Carnmenellis granite: 1 - Overcoring tests at South Crofty mine at a depth of 790 m. International Journal of Rock Mechanics Mining Sciences & Geomechanical Abstracts (20(2):52-62.

Ren, N.K. and Roegiers, J.C. 1983. Differential strain curve analysis - a new method for determining the pre-existing in situ stress state from rock core measurements. In International Society for Rock Mechanics 5th congress, Melbourne, Australia, 1983.

Simmons, G. and Richter, D.A. 1974. Microcracks in rocks: a new tool (abstract). Eos - Transactions of the American Geophysical Union 44:478.

Strickland, F.G. and Ren, N.K. 1980. Use of differential strain curve analysis in predicting in situ stress state for deep wells. In 21st symposium on rock mechanics, University of Missouri, Rolla, Missouri.

Walker, A. 1986. Personal communication. British Geological Survey Global Seismology Unit, Edinburgh.

Zoback, M.D., Moos, D., Mastin, L. and Anderson, R.N. 1985. Wellbore breakouts and in situ stress. Journal of Geophysical Research 90(B7):5523-5530.

A comparison of three borehole instruments for monitoring the change of rock stress with time

R.J. WALTON
G. WOROTNICKI
CSIRO, Division of Geomechanics, Mount Waverley, Victoria, Australia

ABSTRACT

Three borehole instruments have been investigated for their suitability for monitoring rock stress changes; the yoke gauge, a purpose designed, non-reusable, three component borehole deformeter, and the conventional and thin-wall versions of the CSIRO triaxial hollow inclusion stress measurement cell. Laboratory experiments and field trials were carried out to investigate the effect on instrument stability and sensitivity of such factors as moisture absorption, temperature variation, polymer shrinkage and time since installation.

RESUME

On a étudié l'aptitude pour le contrôle des variations des tensions des roches de trois appareils de carottage: l'indicateur à étrier, un déformomètre à trois éléments concu dans ce but et incapable d'être remployé, et les modèles conventionnel et à paroi mince de la cellule de mesure triaxiale développée par la CSIRO. On a fait des essais au laboratoire ainsi que sur place pour étudier l'influence sur la stabilité et la sensibilité des instruments exercée par des facteurs telles que l'absorption d'humidité, la variation de la température, la contraction du polymère et le délai suivant l'installation.

ZUSAMMENFASSUNG

Drei Bohrlochgeräte sind nach ihrer Eignung zur Kontrolle von Änderungen der Gesteinsbeanspruchung untersucht worden: das Rahmenmessgerät, ein zielskonzipiertes, nicht wiederverwendbares Drei-Komponenten-Bohrlochverformungsmessgerät, sowie die beiden herkömmlichen und dünnwändigen Typen der von CSIRO entwickelten Spannungs-messzelle. Versuche wurden im Labor sowie im Feld durchgeführt, um die Auswirkung auf die Apparatsbeständigkeit und -Empfindlichkeit von Faktoren wie Feuchtigkeitsaufnahme, Temperaturschwankungen, Polymerschwindung und Zeitdauer nach dem Einsetzen zu untersuchen.

1. INTRODUCTION

The requirement to measure changes in the stress field in rock is generally twofold. Rock stresses surrounding excavations are monitored to assess the onset of unstable behaviour; this is particularly true for excavations for underground mining. Monitoring is also carried out to assess the performance of a particular design. The current frequent use of design tools such as finite and boundary element modeling techniques has greatly increased the importance of monitoring stress change in rock. The primary output from these design aids are estimates of rock deformation and stress, and the effectiveness of an adopted design can only be confirmed by monitoring either, or both of these variables in-situ.

Currently, the most viable method used to determine the change in rock stress is to employ an instrument fixed into a borehole drilled into the rock mass. These instruments fall into two non-rigorous categories; rigid and soft inclusions. Both types have certain advantages and disadvantages in use.

A soft inclusion instrument or strainmeter has a low modulus of elasticity relative to that of the host rock. In order to calculate the change of stress in the host rock it is necessary to know or assume the constitutive law between stress and strain for the rock. In practice, a linear elastic law is usually assumed. A soft inclusion may only be employed to measure compressive stress magnitudes up to the point when the rock yields at some position around the borehole. However, a soft inclusion does not usually suffer from instrument-to-rock contact problems (as may occur with rigid inclusion instruments), and is thus well suited to be configured in biaxial or triaxial form, and for measuring stress reductions. A triaxial instrument is required to measure any rotation of the principal stresses and to monitor stress changes in a situation where a borehole cannot be drilled perpendicular to the stress direction or plane of interest.

This paper discusses the performance of three soft inclusion borehole instruments for monitoring stress change in rock. Two are capable of triaxial measurement; one of biaxial measurement. The investigation is part of an ongoing program of research being conducted by the CSIRO in collaboration with the Australian Minerals Industry Research Association (AMIRA) and its sponsor companies.

2. INSTRUMENTS

2.1 Yoke Gauge.

This instrument is similar to the USBM three component borehole deformation gauge (Hooker and Bickel 1974), but is designed specifically for stress change monitoring purposes. Three changes in diameter of a borehole are measured which enables the change in the secondary principal stresses in the plane perpendicular to the axis of the borehole to be calculated.

The instrument transducers are one-piece, 1mm thick, beryllium-copper cantilevers shaped into the form of a "C" or a "yoke". The centre of the cantilever is strain gauged on both sides to enable the deflection of the cantilever, tip-to-tip to be measured. Three such cantilevers, which have a

length that exceeds the diameter of the borehole by appoximately 1mm, are encased in the annulus formed between two, thin-walled PVC tubes and are located so that the cantilever tips protrude from the outer tube at intervals of 60° around the circumference (Fig. 1). For each cantilever, the electrical resistance strain gauges are wired into a full, active, Wheatstone bridge configuration and are powered by an individual voltage regulator. All electrical components are encapsulated in epoxy resin and the space surrounding the cantilevers filled with silicone moisture proofing compound to prevent moisture ingress. When installed into a borehole, the cantilevers are compressed and pre-mixed epoxy cement is extruded into the annular space between the outer PVC tube and the wall of the borehole. The purpose of this cement is to hold the instrument firmly in position during periods of high vibration (e.g. due to blasting) and to act as a primary moisture barrier. It is not used to transmit borehole deformations to the cantilevers. The cement is held in an annular cavity in the nose of the instrument, and is forced out when a spacer rod contacts the end of the borehole, a pre-placed grout column, or a pre-placed instrument. The hollow inner tube provides a passage to the borehole collar for signal cables from instruments installed deeper in the borehole. Each cantilever gives a voltage output, which can be measured by a portable microvoltmeter or recorded by a data acquisition system having microvolt resolution. The sensitivity of the cantilever transducers lie in the range 5.5×10^{-5} to 5.0×10^{-5} mm/microvolt. The instrument also contains a temperature sensor accurate to 0.1°C.

2.2 CSIRO Hollow Inclusion Stress Measurement Cell.

The CSIRO HI cell (Worotnicki and Walton 1976) was designed and developed to improve the accuracy and reliability of absolute stress measurement using the overcoring technique. In the late 1970's, two major Australian mining companies commenced using HI cells as triaxial stress change monitoring devices due to the unavailability of any other comparable instrument. Since that time, many other rock mechanics investigators have followed suit. Not many of these experiences have been

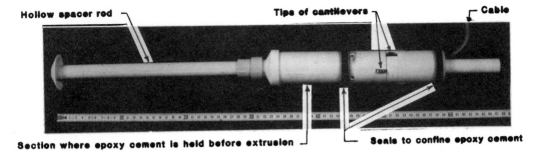

Hollow spacer rod — Tips of cantilevers — Cable

Section where epoxy cement is held before extrusion — Seals to confine epoxy cement

Fig.1 CSIRO yoke borehole deformation gauge.

documented, but it appears that some have been successful (Matthews et al 1983, Wold and Pala 1986), others less so.

A recent development of the conventional HI cell has been to provide an additional three strain gauges (the standard is nine) to make the cell more suitable for measurement in anisotropic rock or to provide additional strain measurement redundancy.

2.3 Thin-Wall Hollow Inclusion Stress Measurement Cell.

A variant of the HI cell with reduced thickness of the wall of the strain gauge carrying epoxy tube has been developed to improve the performance of the cell when used for overcoring in weak rock. This modification considerably reduces the stiffness of the HI cell in its response to the rock stress relief deformations during overcoring. Thus, the possibility of tensile failure of the rock around the borehole periphery is reduced.

The thin-wall HI cell is in prototype form only. A relatively simple modification to the manufacturing procedure of the conventional HI cell was developed to test the concept. The thickness of the epoxy body was effectively reduced to one third of that of a conventional cell by allowing the outer section (to which the strain gauges were bonded) to separate or decouple from the inner section. A small separation is usually induced when the epoxy cement used to bond the cell into a borehole cures, see Section 5.2. It is possible that a future design may incorporate a significant air-gap under the strain gauged area similar to the prototype conventional HI cell shown in Fig.1 of Worotnicki and Walton 1976.

3. YOKE GAUGE: TESTS AND APPLICATIONS.

3.1 Laboratory Test

The aim of this test was to establish long term performance characteristics of the yoke gauge.

A yoke gauge was inserted into the central section of a 56.1mm diameter radial hole, drilled at mid-length through a 300 mm diameter, 550 mm long aluminium cylinder. The cylinder was subjected to a constant axial load, or zero load, for extended periods. A constant, evenly distributed axial load could be applied to the cylinder via two circular flat jacks located at each end of the cylinder, which in turn were constrained by a passive reaction frame. One of the flat jacks was filled with a constant volume of oil and used as a "passive pillow". The oil pressure in the other could be varied to change the axial load.

The yoke gauge was installed when the test cylinder was subjected to zero applied load. Epoxy cement of the type used for HI cell installation (see Section 4.2.1) was used. On installation of the gauge into the hole, each of the yoke cantilevers were compressed approximately 0.8mm tip-to-tip. Three days following installation, the output from each cantilever was measured and recorded as a zero datum.

The test cylinder was left unloaded for 125 days after which a constant load of either 5 MPa, 8.5 MPa or 0 MPa was applied to the cylinder for various periods over the following 125 days. Deformation changes for each transducer, along with the Young's modulus and Poisson's ratio of the aluminium cylinder (see Section 4.2.1) were used to compute the stress changes in the cylinder relative to the original datum.

481

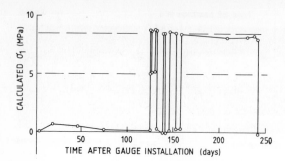

Fig.2 Axial stress in aluminium cylinder calculated from yoke gauge output; positive change is compressive.

Fig.2 depicts the performance of the gauge over this period in terms of the calculated major secondary principal stress versus time. The calculated direction of σ_1 was within $+2.5°$ and $-0.6°$ of the direction of the applied load for each load change.

3.2 In-situ Experiences

Small numbers of prototype instruments, designed for use in 56mm diameter boreholes, have been trialled as stress change monitors in a coal mine (Walton and Fuller 1980), and in metalliferous mines. Figure 3 is an example of the output from a yoke gauge which was installed into a vertical up-hole with the purpose of monitoring stress changes in a horizontal plane adjacent to a developing open stope of a

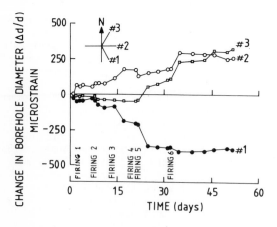

Fig.3 Output from a yoke gauge installed in-situ showing response to stope firings; positive change is tensile.

metalliferous mine. The gauge was installed three days prior to the initial stope firing so little information was obtained regarding gau stability immediately following installation. Stope firings ceased 35 days after gauge installation, but the gauge was monitored for a total of 305 days. The rock temperature was approximately 16°C.

This example shows the value of an instrument which is suitable for measuring stress reductions as well as stress increases. At some stage during the period of stope firings, two of the cantilever transducers have indicated tensile changes. If the changes due to Firing 5 are taken as an example and using a value of 70 GPa (measured from core tests) for the elastic modulus of the rock, the stress changes due to thi firing are: $\sigma_1 = 3.7$ MPa, $8°$ south of east $\sigma_2 = -3.3$ MPa (positive change equals compression). This corresponds to an increase in stress perpendicular to the strike of the stope and a decrease in stress parallel to it as was expected.

For the 250 days following the cessation of stope firings, the three cantilevers showed a compressive drift of $\Delta d/d$ of approximately $1\mu\varepsilon$/day . Yoke gauges installed in other locations and at different temperatures (up to 40°C) have shown similar compressive drift rates when monitored for periods in excess of one year.

4. HI CELLS; TESTS AND APPLICATIONS FOR STRESS MONITORING.

4.1 General Considerations

Instrument related problems when HI cells are left installed for long periods may include break-down of electrical insulation between the strain gauges (and connections) and the rock, volume changes in the epoxy body and in the epoxy cement due to continuing polymerization (which would cause shrinkage), absorption of moisture which would cause swelling, and deterioration of the epoxy cement bond due to the effect of moisture. Temperature changes in normal mining operations are usually small, but for applications in some civil engineering projects they can be significant and this can affect cell output.

In overcoring tests the borehole nearly always expands as a result of relaxation of compressive stresses. Thus, the epoxy body of the cell is pulled away from the hollow plunger and behaves independently to it. However, rock stress changes in mining are often compressive which would cause, at least at some stage, the epoxy body to press against the plunger over all or most of its surface. In this case it would be more appropriate to assume that the body and plunger behave as one thicker shell. This behavior affects the values of the K-Factors (Worotnicki and Walton 1976) used to relate the observed strains to various components of the stress tensor. Formulae to calculate K-Factors can be found in Duncan-Fama and Pender 1980. Typical values are given in Table 1. It can be seen that an effective reduction of the inner radius of the body of the cell on the K-Factor values is much higher when the elastic modulus of the rock approaches that of the cell (3 GPa).

4.2 Laboratory Tests.

4.2.1 Study of drift and change of sensitivity.

The aim of these tests was to establish, for both types of HI cell, long term performance characteristics such as zero drift and change in sensitivity with time. To determine instrument performance under ideal conditions, the two instruments were subjected to the following laboratory test programme.

One of each instrument type was installed into the centre of two radial holes drilled through a 300 mm diameter, 550 mm long aluminium cylinder which was subjected to a constant axial load, or zero load, for extended periods. The test set-up was very similar to that used for the yoke gauge laboratory test. The two radial boreholes were 38.1mm in diameter and located in the central region of the cylinder, longitudinally 175 mm apart, centre-to-centre.

Prior to installation, both HI cells were heat treated at 50°C for 7 days. This was carried out to ensure that the epoxy resin of the body of the cell was properly polymerized at temperatures below 50°C. The cells were glued into the boreholes using the recommended cement formulation (as at January, 1985) for the temperature range 15-30°C.; Shell Epikote 828/ Shell Epikure 153/ Silica flour in the ratio 100:60:100. The cells were monitored using a portable strain indicator and two, manually switched, 10 channel switch and balance boxes.

Both HI cells were installed when the cylinder was subjected to a uniaxial load of 10 MPa. The thin-wall HI cell was installed 27 days after the installation of the conventional HI cell due to a malfunction during the installation of the initial thin-wall cell. For both cells, the load was held constant at 10 MPa for 9 days following installation, before it was reduced to zero. The uniaxial load applied to the cylinder was varied 11 times between 10 MPa and 0 MPa over a period of 376 days.

The performance of the cells was analysed in three ways:-

(i) the strains as sensed by the nine strain gauges of a cell immediately before the initial load change were recorded as a zero datum. These datum strains were subtracted from the strains measured at each subsequent load change and the resultant values were plotted

TABLE 1. HI cell: K-Factors when thickness of hollow plunger is included.

	Thin-wall HI cell (no plunger)		Conventional HI cell					
			No plunger		2mm wall plunger		3mm wall plunger	
E rock(GPa)	7	70	7	70	7	70	7	70
K1	1.064	1.122	1.014	1.113	0.924	1.094	0.876	1.083
K2	1.079	1.218	0.911	1.117	0.704	0.980	0.635	0.932
K3	1.041	1.076	1.009	1.067	0.955	1.051	0.928	1.043
K4	0.957	0.918	0.991	0.925	1.051	0.937	1.082	0.945

against time. As the curves were close to linear, a linear regression analysis was carried out to compute an average rate of drift at each applied load value. These values are presented in Table 2.

(ii) the computed strains from (i) above, along with the physical properties of the aluminium cylinder, were used to compute the stress changes in the cylinder. A Young's modulus of 72 GPa and a Poisson's ratio of 0.33 was used for the analysis. The standard analysis program and K Factors were used (Worotnicki and Walton 1976). Figures 4 and 5 are plots for each cell type of the calculated change in the normal stress components versus time. The "vertical" component is parallel to the direction of the applied load, the "east-west" component is perpendicular to both the load and the borehole axis and the "north-south" component is parallel to the borehole axis. Compressive stress change is negative.

(iii) the strain changes as sensed by the nine strain gauges of the cell at each load change, along with the physical properties of the aluminium

cylinder, were used to compute the stress changes in the cylinder. For the conventional cell and for six tensile and five compressive changes of applied load, the calculated magnitude of σ_1 remained within 6% of that calculated for the first load change. For the thin-wall cell and for five tensile and four compressive changes of applied load, the calculated magnitude of σ_1 remained within 2% of that calculated for the first load change. For both cells, the calculated direction of σ_1 was within $2°$ of the theoretical for each load change.

4.2.2 Effect of Change in Temperature.

A HI cell has two forms of response to change in temperature depending on whether the cell is "free" or bonded into a borehole. When a cell is not bonded into a borehole, the hollow body of the cell expands and contracts at approximately 80 $\mu\varepsilon/°C$ which is the coefficient of thermal expansion of the epoxy material from which the body is manufactured. As the strain gauges used

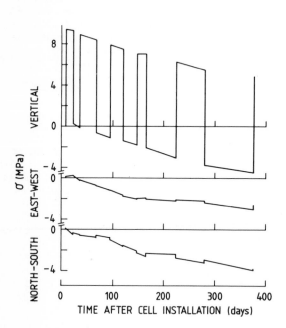

Fig.4 Stresses in the aluminium cylinder calculated from strain changes recorded by a conventional HI cell. Strain changes calculated from a datum determined immediately before the first load change.

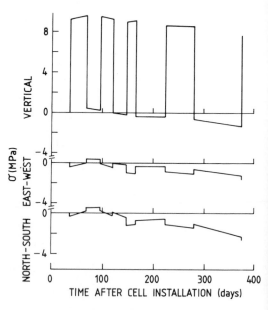

Fig.5 Stresses in the aluminium cylinder calculated from strain changes recorded by a thin-wall HI cell. Strain changes calculated from a datum determined immediately before the first load change.

484

TABLE 2. Laboratory test of CSIRO HI cells. Average rate of strain drift at two
levels of applied load.

HI cell Type	Load (MPa)	Strain drift (με/day)								
		A0	C0	A90	B90	C90	A45	B45	B135	C45
Conventional	10	-.07	0	-.34	-.12	-.41	-.18	-.15	-.13	-.19
	0	-.07	0	-.26	-.09	-.43	-.15	-.15	-.14	-.21
Thin-wall	10	-.06	-.07	-.10	-.09	-.11	-.08	-.06	-.09	-.09
	0	-.06	-.06	-.11	-.08	-.13	-.09	-.07	-.07	-.09

N.B. A0, A90, A45: respectively; axial, circumferential and diagonal strain gauges
of rosette A.

have a self temperature compensation
value of 11 με/°C the measured
coefficient of thermal expansion of the
unrestrained cell body is approximately
70 με/°C. However, when the cell is
properly bonded into a borehole with an
epoxy cement which has similar
properties to that of the cell body, the
response is modified significantly.
Tests have been carried out on cores of
rock and a "core" of mild steel which
contained installed HI cells to quantify
this response.

The average response of the strain
gauges of like orientation of the cell
installed into the steel core which was
subjected to three cycles of temperature
changes in the range of 11-43°C is shown
in Fig.6. With increase in temperature,
the circumferentially orientated strain
gauges show an average compressive
output of 16.8 με/°C . The 45°/135°
orientated strain gauges show a
compressive output of approximately half
the magnitude of the circumferentially
orientated strain gauges. The axially
orientated strain gauges show a
compressive output of low magnitude.

An expression has been derived to
describe this behaviour (for core
stiffness >> cell stiffness):

$$\varepsilon_\theta = T \left\{ \alpha - (\beta - \alpha)(1+\nu) \frac{R_1^2 (R_2^2 - r^2)}{r^2 [R_2^2 (1-2\nu) + R_1^2]} - C \right\}$$

$$\varepsilon_{ax} = T \{\alpha - C\}$$

where: ε_θ = observed circumferential
strain at position r
ε_{ax} = observed axial strain
T = temperature change
α = coefficient of thermal
expansion of the rock
β = coefficient of thermal
expansion of the epoxy
R1 = inner radius of cell
r = radial position of strain
gauges
R2 = radius of pilot borehole
ν = Poisson's ratio of the
epoxy
C = self temperature
compensation value of the
strain gauges

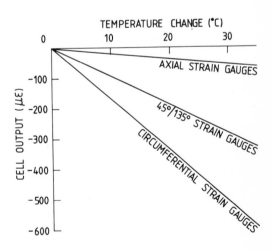

Fig.6 Average output from a
conventional HI cell installed into a
"core" of mild steel which was subjected
to three cycles of temperature change.
Negative change is compression.

485

For the example shown in Fig. 6 and for T=1°C, α=11μϵ/°C , β=80 μϵ/°C , R1=16mm, r=17.3mm, R2=19.1mm, ν=0.4, C=11 μϵ/°C:

$$\epsilon_\theta = -16.4 \ \mu\epsilon/°C; \quad \epsilon_{ax} = 0$$

The dimensional response of a borehole drilled into a rock mass to a change in temperature depends on the boundary conditions that apply. When heat is applied or withdrawn through a borehole drilled into a rock mass of large volume, the effective coefficient of thermal expansion of the rock is zero. This is theoretically the case, as a local temperature change in a hole drilled into an elastic material produces no change in diameter or length of the hole. The temperature response of a HI cell used in this situation can be calculated from Equations 1 & 2 when α=0.

4.2.3 Moisture absorption tests.

Epoxies are known to absorb up to 1% moisture and thus show a small volume expansion. For an HI cell installed into a borehole, the resultant behaviour can be expressed mathematically similarly to the thermal expansion discussed above.

The rate of moisture absorption by the epoxy body of an HI cell was measured by comparing the output from two cells over a two week period. At a constant temperature of 30°C, one cell was immersed in water (with the open end sealed so that only the outer surface was in contact with the water) and the other cell was kept in dry air. Relative to the "dry" cell, the "wet" cell showed a circumferential expansion of 1000 μϵ.

The rate and effect of moisture absorption of an HI cell when glued into a borehole was measured by carrying out another comparative test. A 135mm diameter core of sandstone was cut into equal lengths. One half of the core was immersed in water for a two week period; the other half kept in dry air. Following this period, an HI cell was installed into each core using the recommended epoxy cement formulation. The cells were installed within one hour of each other. The surface of the wet borehole was wiped clean of free water before the cell was installed. This core was then kept in a humid environment before it was re-immersed in water 20 hours after cell installation. The cells were monitored with the aid of a datalogger. The outputs from identical strain gauges of each cell were compared. Twenty four hours after installation of the cells, the circumferentially orientated strain gauges of the cell installed into the "wet" core showed a linear compressive drift of approximately 6μϵ/day relative to the "dry" core.

4.3 Field Tests.

HI cells have been used to monitor three dimensional stress changes in coal pillars (Wold and Pala 1986) and in pillars at metalliferous mine sites (Matthews et al 1983, Worotnicki et al 1983). The measured stress changes were generally consistent with the expected and the observed behaviour of the pillars.

As part of this present investigation, HI cells have been installed to monitor stress changes in hard rock pillars over a temperature range of 20°C to 40°C. All cells were heat cured at approximately 50°C (to ensure full polymerization of the epoxy body of the cell) before installation. The output of all cells which were properly installed showed a similar trend with time to that shown in Fig.7. This cell was installed into an area which, due to a revised mining schedule, remained free from stress change for a period in excess of 1.3 years. The cell was installed into a borehole which was drilled into an area of rock at a temperature of 22°C. The borehole dipped at 17° and was "making" a small amount of water at the time that the cell was installed.

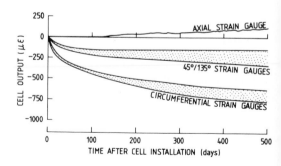

Fig.7 Example of the output from a conventional HI cell installed in-situ.

5 DISCUSSION.

5.1 Yoke Gauges.

The laboratory test of the yoke gauge showed that this instrument is capable of measuring stress changes with an accuracy of approximately ±½MPa (in material of elastic modulus 70 GPa) over a period of 250 days. The observed average rate of zero drift was small at approximately .004 MPa/day .

When installed in-situ, yoke gauges showed compressive drift, although the magnitude of the drift was considerably less than for the initial response of HI cells; a linear response equivalent to 1-2µε/day was often observed. This response may be due to moisture absorption of the epoxy cement used to surround the cantilever section of the gauge (see Section 2.1). Moisture absorption by the epoxy cement would cause it to expand, thus forcing the outer PVC body of the yoke gauge to move inwards towards the centre of the hole. Even though the tips of the cantilevers are isolated from the cement by a small pad of silastic rubber, the cantilevers may still reflect some of this movement. To test this hypothesis, future yoke gauge installations will be tried with gauges that will not have epoxy cement surrounding the cantilever section of the gauge .

5.2 HI Cells.

There is an obvious difference in the long-term behaviour of HI cells used as stress change monitors under ideal conditions to those installed in the field.

For the HI cells installed into the aluminium test cylinder:
- as the epoxy cement cured, the body of the cell was drawn towards the wall of the borehole and a tensile circumferential strain of approximately 200 µε was measured. These strains were measured by both cell types and are thought to be caused by the epoxy cement shrinking as it cures.
- for the conventional cell, after the cement had cured, the axial strain gauges showed low drift rates, whilst the circumferential gauges showed a mean compressive drift of .35µε/day ; see Table 1. The combined effect of the drift of all strain gauges on the computation of stress changes is shown in Figure 4 as an effective compressive

zero shift of approximately .013 MPa/day (when the host material has an elastic modulus of 70 GPa.).
- for the thin-wall cell the circumferential compressive drift was much less at approximately .10µε/day . The resultant effective compressive zero shift shown in Fig. 5 is .005 MPa/day .

The difference in observed behavior between the conventional and thin-wall HI cells is probably due to partial recovery (with time) of the tensile strains induced during curing of the epoxy cement. The thicker wall of the conventional cell would cause strain recovery of larger magnitude than for the thin-wall cell.

For HI cells installed in-situ:
- tensile circumferential strains induced by the curing of the epoxy cement are often observed.
- following the installation of a cell and after the epoxy cement has cured, there is a high rate of compressive drift shown by the circumferential and 45°/135° strain gauges. Strain gauges of like orientation generally behave similarly (as shown in Fig.7). The rate of drift for the circumferential strain gauges can be of the order of 15µε/day during the initial 10 days following cell installation; for the 45°/135° strain gauges 7µε/day ; for the axial strain gauges, 0µε/day. The rate of circumferential strain drift decreased to approximately 1µε/day , 50-100 days after installation of the cell.

A number of possible causes of the observed initial compressive drift of HI cells installed in-situ have been considered. These have included shrinkage of the epoxy body and of the epoxy cement with continuing polymerization, breakdown of the bond between the rock and the cell, deterioration of electrical insulation, pore water effects at the cell/borehole interface, creep of the rock into the borehole and swelling of the epoxy cement and the cell body due to moisture absorption. All have been discarded except for the last three, with moisture absorption being considered the most likely. However, as this initial compressive response occurs in HI cells installed into apparently dry boreholes, commences very rapidly after the epoxy cement has cured and the magnitude of the response is not matched by the magnitude observed in laboratory tests (see Section 4.2.3), this has not yet been proven as the only cause.

487

6. CONCLUSIONS

In laboratory tests, the yoke gauge and both types of HI cell showed high sensitivity to load changes and no change in sensitivity with time. The HI cell of conventional design exhibited a slow, linear, compressive zero shift. The thin-wall cell exhibited less compressive zero shift than the conventional cell. The accuracy of determination of rapid stress changes was not affected.

The yoke gauges which were installed in-situ were generally more stable than HI cells in the first 100 day period that follows instrument installation, although in some, a linear compressive drift equivalent to 1-2 $\mu\varepsilon$/day was observed during this time.

HI cells tested under field conditions exhibited a larger biaxial compressive drift than was observed in laboratory tests. (Axial drift was low for both test situations). This drift commenced immediately after the epoxy cement used to fix the cell into the borehole cured and is probably of different origin to' the slow drift observed in the laboratory tests. As the drift decreases significantly with time, it is suggested that HI cells should be installed at least one to three months prior to the expected occurrence of the stress changes to be monitored. If HI cells are installed correctly (and thus a good cell-to-rock bond is assured) and after the drift rate drops to 1-2$\mu\varepsilon$/day , an accuracy of approximately 1 MPa can be achieved in rocks with an elastic modulus of 70 GPa over monitoring periods of 1-1½ months. They are best suited for monitoring large, sudden, compressive or tensile stress changes rather than gradual changes. The response of the instrument to temperature change is known and corrections can be calculated.

Thin-walled HI cells should continue to be developed as they require a lower rock-to-cell bond strength than conventional cells and exhibited superior long-term performance than conventional HI cells in laboratory tests.

7. ACKNOWLEDGEMENTS

The authors gratefully acknowledge the contributions of the staff of the AMIRA sponsor companies at which field exercises were performed. They also wish to thank their colleagues; Mr. L. Alexander for many valuable discussions regarding the temperature response and the possible causes of drift of HI cells and Mr. R. Thompson, Mr. N. Litterbach and Mr. G. Cadby for laboratory testing and instrument manufacture.

8. REFERENCES

Duncan Fama, M.E. and M.J. Pender, 1980. Analysis of the Hollow Inclusion Technique for Measuring the In-Situ Rock Stress. Int.Jour. of Rock Mech. & Min. Sci. & Geomech. Abstr., Vol.17, No.3, pp. 137-146.

Hooker, V.E. and D.L. Bickel, 1974. Overcoring Equipment and Techniques Used in Rock Stress Determination. United States Bureau of Mines Information Circular 8618.

Matthews, S.M., V.H. Tillman, and G. Worotnicki, 1983. A modified cable bolt system for the support of underground openings. Proc. Aus.I.M.M. Conf., Broken Hill, N.S.W., Aust., 243-255.

Walton, R.J. and P.G. Fuller, 1980. An Investigation of a Bolted Coal Mine Roof During Mining at Nattai North Colliery. CSIRO Div. App. Geomech., Geomech. of Coal Mining Report No.24.

Wold, M.B. and J. Pala, 1986. Three-dimensional Stress Changes in Pillars During Longwall Mining at Ellalong Colliery. CSIRO, Aust., Div. Geomech. Coal Mining Report No.65.

Worotnicki, G. and R.J. Walton, 1976. Triaxial Hollow Inclusion Gauges for Determination of Rock Stresses In-Situ. Proc. Symp. on Investigation of Stresses in Rock - Advances in Stress Measurement, Inst. Eng., Aust. Nat. Conf., Pub. No.76/4, PP. 1-8.

Worotnicki, G., M.W. Fabjanczyk, K.E. McNabb and R.J. Thompson, 1983. Rock Stress Monitoring Trial at Cleveland Tin Mine, Luina, Tasmania. CSIRO, Aust., Division of Geomechanics, Monitoring of Rock Stresses In-Situ in Ore Bodies, Project Report No.2 (Restricted circulation).

Proceedings of the International Symposium on Rock Stress and Rock Stress Measurements/Stockholm/1-3 September 1986

On the accuracy and evaluation of rock stress measurements in the Kanto-Tokai region, Japan

Y. NISHIMATSU
H. KOIDE
S. KOIZUMI
University of Tokyo, Department of Mineral Development, Tokyo, Japan

ABSTRACT

The rock stress is measured by means of borehole deformation gauge in several test sites in the western region of Tokyo. The accuracy of rock stress measurement with this gauge is discussed from the technical point of view.

The state of rock stress determined by this gauge is compared with those determined by other principles of rock stress measurements, and discussed from the view point of plate tectonics.

It is indicated that results of the present measurement agree with those of several other measurements in a reasonable range of deviation from the view points of measurement engineering and plate tectonics.

ZUSAMMENFASSUNG

In unterschiedlichen Orte im Westen von Tokyo, wird die Gebirgsspannung mittels eines Verformungsmessgeräte des Bohrloch gemessen. Es behandelt die Messgenauigkeit des Gebirgsspannungen aus dem messtechnischen Gesichtpunkt.

Der Zustand der Gebirgsspannungen in dieser Region die ist bestimmt mittels der Verformungsmessgeräte wird mit die bestimmt mittels anderes Messprinzip verglicht und aus dem Gesichtpunkt der Plattentektonik bewertet.

Es wird gezeigt dass die Abweichung zwischen die Ergebnisse dieser Messungen und die einiger anderen Messungen ist vernachlässigt in Hinsicht auf den Messtechnik wie auch Plattentektonik.

RESUME

Les contraintes dans les roches s'ont mesurés à une cellule extensométrique dans les trous de forage à l'ouest de Tokio. La précision au mesure des contraintes par la cellule extensométrique sont en discussion au point de vue technique.

L'etat de contrainte dans les roches mesuré par la cellule extensométrique se compare aux résultats dérivés par les principes différentes au mesure. Nous mettons le champ de contrainte en discussion en vue de la tectonique de plaque.

Il s'indique que les résultants aux présentes mesures sont en accord avec les résultats aux méthodes différentes à la portée acceptable de déviation aux points de vue de l'art de la mesure et de la tectonique de plaque.

1. INTRODUCTION.

One of the most reliable and popular principles of rock stress measurement would be the stress relief principle by overcoring among several principles proposed for rock stress measurement. Several techniques or gauges have been developed and used in practice as applications of the stress refief principle.

For examples, it is reported that the complete state of stress has been determined in a single borehole by means of CSIR triaxial strain cell (Leeman 1968) as well as the doorstopper type strain cell (Hiramatsu, et al 1979). However, they have an inherent difficulty to be applied in the borehole in which the wall is wet and/or some water inflows occur, because the strain cell must be glued to the rock wall of boerhole.

As another technique of the stress relief principle, the borehole deformation gauge (Obert 1962, Suzuki et al 1970) can be applied in the wet or submerged borehole, although this technique needs three boreholes at least, for determination of the complete state of stress in the rock mass.

The accuracy of rock stress measurement has been discussed by several authors for each technique, and the coefficient of variance more than 20% has been sometimes reported (Gray et al 1975, Van Heerden 1976). A few authors have measured the rock stress at the same test site by two different techniques, and reported the deviation of about 20% of the major principal stress measured by doorstopper strain cell from that measured by borehole deformation gauge (Van Heerden et al 1967, De La Cruz et al 1972).

As well known, all of techniques of rock stress measurement by overcoring becomes more difficult to be conducted as deeper becomes the borehole. This is a reason that the hydrofracturing technique is frequently used for rock stress measurement in the deep borehole (Haimson 1978). However, it is very difficult to determine exactly the direction or azimuth of generated crack. In order to reaveal the accuracy of hydrofracturing technique, the rock stress is measured by means of hydrofracturing in the test site where the rock stress has been determined by the borehole deformation gauge in short boreholes drilled from an underground roadway (Haimson et al 1974). The discrepancies between the results by these two techniques have been given as 9% and 30% for the major and minor principal stresses in the horizontal plane, respectively.

Since 1978, the authors have conducted the rock stress measurement in several test sites in Kanto-Tokai region, Japan. In this series of rock stress measurements which have been conducted as a part of the nationa project for prediction of large scale earthquake, the substantial interest concerns to the state of stress in the horizontal plane in the rock mass. As more data of rock stress measuremen have been accumulated and compared with each other, as more necessities for evaluating the accuracy of measure- ment have been revealed.

In this paper, the authors describ the procedure and result of rock stress measurements conducted by means of borehole deformation gauge. The accura cy and error sources of rock stress measurement are evaluated, and the revealed state of stress in Kanto-Tokai region is discussed from the viewpoint of plate tectonics.

2. ROCK STRESS MEASUREMENTS NEAR SURFAC

2.1. Measuring instruments, divices and procedure.

There are neither tunnel nor mine in the vicinity of selected test site, because the test site has been selected from viewpoint of plate tecto- nics which is concerned with predictior of earthquake.

The borehole must be drilled vertically from ground surface, and a three components borehole deformatior gauge must be set in the submerged borehole at the depth more than 10m. The gauge has been developed by K.Suzuk

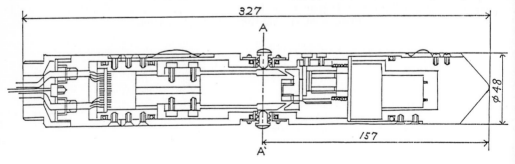

Fig.1. The Three Components Borehole Deformation Gauge.

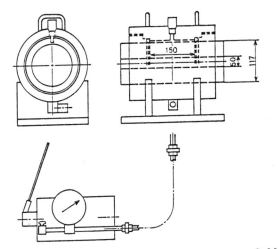

Fig.2. The External Hydraulic Pressure Cell

(Suzuki et al 1970), and modified by authors to be water-tight. It is provided with six elements to detect the change of diameter in three directions at every 60° around its periphery as shown in Fig.1. The stud or piston of each six element is glued into the bellows and isolated from the water-tight main part. The connecter of electric cable at the end of main part is molded by rubber. The electric cable is drawn out through a packer, lower and upper ends of which are flexiblely connected to the upper end of the gauge and lower end of pipe for inserting the gauge, respectively. The packer is expanded by Nitrogen gas and fixes the gauge together with spring plates mounted on the periphery of gauge. An electric motor is provided for driving the contracting disc which is drawn back and releases six studs, when the gauge has been set in the borehole. Considering the possible irregularity of rock stress caused from various topographical and geological irregularities near ground surface as well as the technical restriction of measuring procedure, the rock stress measurement has been conducted at the depth between 10 and 20m from ground surface.

The recovered hollow cylindrical rock core is covered by the hot-shrinkable polyolefin seat and loaded radially in the external hydraulic pressure cell (see Fig.2). The change in diameter of centre hole is measured again by the borehole deformation gauge to determine Young's modulus of the rock cylinder.

2.2. Results of rock stress measurements

The rock stress measurements are conducted at several test sites where the outcrop of intrusive rock mass has been found, in the vicinity

Table 1   The Result of Rock Stress Measurements in Kanto-Tokai Region

Test Site	Latitude	Longitude	Altitude (m. S.L.)	Depth from Surface (m)	Maximum Horizontal Compression (MPa)	Minimum Horizontal Compression (MPa)	Azimuth of Maximum Horizontal Compression	Rock Type	Time of Measurement
Tanzawa A	35°28' N	139°4' E	500	5.73	11.7	3.2	N 7° E	Quartz Diorite	1978.11
Tanzawa D	35°28' N	139°4' E	500	14.89	7.5	2.6	N 9° E	"	1979.12*
Tanzawa E	35°28.5'N	139°5.5' E	900	11.25	12.3	4.5	N 27° E	"	1979.11
Shimoda	34°40.5'E	138°56.5'E	12	19.0	4.0	2.0	N 20° W	Porphyrite	1981. 3
Tsukuba	36°11' N	140°5.5' E	40	16.26	1.0	0.0	N 66.5°W	Granite	1982. 3
Tanzawa F	35°28' N	139°4' E	500	12.78	6.9	1.8	N 30° E	Quartz Diorite	1983. 2
Toi	34°54' N	139°50' E	12.50	350	4.7	2.1	N 8° W	Diorite	1983.12
	"	"	"	350	7.6	5.1	N 8° W	"	**
Kanbara	35°07' N	138°36' E	20	14.25	1.1	0.0	N 65° W	Andesite	1984. 3
Shibakawa	35°17' N	138°33' E	299	10.93	2.3	0.0	N 21° W	"	1985. 3

*   measured by a soft inclusion type gauge
** measured by hydrofracturing technique

of boundary zone between Phillippine Sea, Eurasian, and North American plates. The state of stress in the horizontal plane is determined for each test site on the assumption of the plane state of strain.

The extension U of borehole diameter due to stress relief is given by (Panek 1966)

$$U = f_1 \sigma_u + f_2 \sigma_v + f_3 \tau_{uv} \quad ---(1)$$

where

$$\left. \begin{array}{l} f_1 = \dfrac{d}{E}(1 - \nu^2)(1 + 2\cos 2\theta) \\[2mm] f_2 = \dfrac{d}{E}(1 - \nu^2)(1 - 2\cos 2\theta) \\[2mm] f_3 = 4\dfrac{d}{E}(1 - \nu^2)\sin 2\theta \end{array} \right\} \quad ---(2)$$

d is the diameter of borehole, E and ν are Young's modulus and Poisson's ratio of rock cylinder, respectively, θ is the angle of the diameter measured with respect to u axis of the u-v coordinate system in the plane perpendicular to the axis of borehole.

The observed changes of borehole diameter in three directions at every 60° are substituted into Eq.(1) to dtermine three components of rock stress.

The results of rock stress measurements conducted by the present authors are summarized in Table 1. They are compared with the results of several other measurements which have been conducted by means of hydrofracturing (Tsukahara et al 1984) and other measuring methods (Koide et al 1986). On the basis of all of those results of measurements, the azimuth of major principal stress in the horizontal plane(horizontal maximum compression) is plotted in Fig.3.

It has been revealed that the azimuth as well as magnitude of the principal stress show an evident discrepancy each other. Although a part of those discrepancies or fluctuations would reflect the real fluctuation of the state of stress in this region, it is desired to verify the accuracy of rock stress measurement. Furthermore the knowledge on the complete state of stress in the rock mass has been necessary to evaluate the accuracy of rock stress measurement.

3. ROCK STRESS MEASUREMENT IN UNDERGROUND MINE.

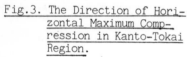

Fig.3. The Direction of Horizontal Maximum Compression in Kanto-Tokai Region.

Short bars indicate the measured directions of the maximum horizontal compression. Large stars are results of stress relief method in this study with the value of the maximum horizontal compression(in MPa) and the measured years.
Open circles are other results of stress relief method(Koide et al 1986).Closed circles are results of hydrofracturing technique by N.R.C.D.P.(Tsukahara et al 1983). Tu: Tsukuba,Ta: Tanzawa,To: Toi, Sm: Shimoda,Sb: Shibakawa,Ka: Kanbara.

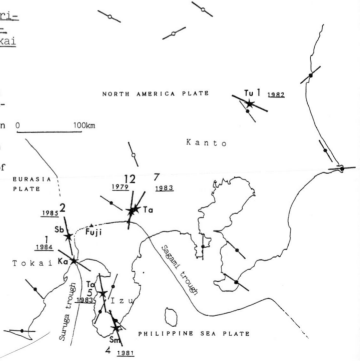

3.1. Location and geology of the test site.

As well known, at least 3 boreholes in 3 different directions are necessary for determining the complete state of stress by means of borehole deformation gauge (Hiramatsu et al 1968). They would be easily drilled from the roadway of underground mine.

Considering geographical and geological conditions, it is decided to locate the test site in Seigoshi gold mine (34°54'N, 138°50'E) near Toi at the North-West coast of Izu peninsula. Ore deposits are shallow hydrothermal fissure filling type quartz veins including gold and silver. The veins occur in the country rocks which consist of basaltic andesite, tuff and pyroclastic rocks, and belong to Yugashima formation group deposited in Miocene of the Tertiary. The ore deposit consists of main veins of N30°-45°E in strike and 70°-75°SE in dip, and branch veins of N-S in strike.

The test site is located at the acess roadway of mine water processing plant and distant about 150m North-West from the main shaft at 0m level (+12,5m S.L.) i.e. the depth of 350m from surface (see Fig.4).

The horizontal boreholes for measurement are drilled to East and North, respectively. Another borehole for measurement is drilled down vertically. All of three boreholes are drilled in the large intrusive rock mass consisted of andesite and diorite, which include few fractures and show low permeability.

The mechanical properties of

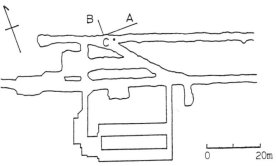

Fig.4. The Location of Test Site in 0m Level in Seigoshi Gold Mine.

rock sample which are obtained by core boring of 50mm in diameter (the diameter of core is 32mm) and tested in uniaxial compression are shown in Table 2. On the other hand, the deformation of hollow cylindrical rock core (external and internal diameters are 117 and 50mm, respectively) recovered by overcoring are measured by means of the external hydraulic pressure cell, and Young's modulus is determined as secant value of stress-strain diagram up to 20 MPa. The results are shown in Table 3, and used for determining the rock stress. However, they are remarkablly different from those determined from uniaxial compression test of centre core and shown in Table 2.

3.2. Measurement by borehole deformation gauge.

The gauge and procedure are same as those used for the measurement

Table 2 Mechanical Properties of Boring Core

Borehole	Compressive strength (MPa)	Tensile strength (MPa)	Young's modulus (50% secant) ($\times 10^3$ MPa)	Poisson's ratio (50% secant)
A	225 (38.9)*	19.1 (1.52)	71.1 (0.45)	0.280 (0.019)
B	281 (57.1)	18.3 (4.08)	77.2 (1.82)	0.280 (0.005)
C	259 (31.7)	19.9 (1.59)	67.9 (5.07)	0.313 (0.016)

* Standard deviation is given in ( )

Table 3 Young's Modulus of Rocks Measured by the Radial Pressure Test

Position of measurement	Mean ($\times 10^3$ MPa)	Standard deviation ($\times 10^3$ MPa)
A-1	63.8	1.08
A-2	63.4	1.71
B-1	79.8	13.78
B-2	62.2	0.10
C-1	60.6	2.82
C-2	65.1	2.24

near surface which is described in § 2. The instrumental error is verified as ± 2 μm for measuring the extension of borehole diameter.

In this case, the borehole of 50mm in diameter is firstly drilled up to about 10m deep, then the overcoring is conducted step by step. However, the rock stress measurement is not conducted up to 3m deep. For every 3 boreholes, the rock stress measurements are conducted at two different depths, and the test results are shown in Table 4.

Assuming the plane state of strain, the state of stress in the plane perpendicular to each borehole axis is determined by substituting the test result shown in Table 4 into Eq.(1), and illustrated in Fig.5, which indicates a remarkable difference between the states of stress at different depth in the same borehole.

However, it is difficult to evaluate the accuracy of rock stress measurement, because the differnce might be caused from some stress disturbance around the roadway. Furthermore, the effect of the axial stress σ_w in each borehole would not be ignored in this test site, because the overburden pressure is estimated as about 9MPa. Thus, considering to minimize the effect of stress disturbance around the roadway, three data sets obtained at the deeper measuring points in each three boreholes are used for determining the complete state of stress.

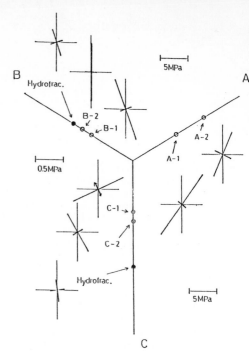

Fig.5. The State of Stress in the plane Normal to the Axis of Each Borehole

In this case, the observation equation is given by (Panek 1966)

$$U = f_1\,\sigma_u + f_2\,\sigma_v + f_3\,\tau_{uv} + f_4\,\sigma_w \qquad ---(3)$$

where

$$\left. \begin{aligned} f_1 &= \frac{d}{E}(1-\nu^2)(1+2\cos2\theta) + \frac{d}{E}\nu^2 \\[4pt] f_2 &= \frac{d}{E}(1-\nu^2)(1-2\cos2\theta) + \frac{d}{E}\nu^2 \\[4pt] f_3 &= 4\,\frac{d}{E}(1-\nu^2)\sin2\theta \\[4pt] f_4 &= -\frac{d}{E}\nu \end{aligned} \right\} \quad (4)$$

the w axis of local coordinate system of u,v and w coincides with the axis of each borehole.

Let assume the same state of stress at these three measuring points and the common coordinate system of x,y and z, directions of which are selected as East, North and upwards vertically, respectively. Then, every axis of local coodinates of three boreholes coincides with any appropriate one of the common coordinate. Substituting three data sets of three boreholes into Eq.(3), we have 9 observation

Table 4   Diametrical Deformation in the Borehole U(i)

Position	Distance from the mouth of borehole (m)	Extension of diameter		
		U (1)* (μm)	U (2) (μm)	U (3) (μm)
A-1	3.59	30.0	5.0	42.7
A-2	6.00	26.4	1.7	20.9
B-1	3.46	30.5	19.4	-4.8
B-2	4.21	40.5	2.4	3.5
C-1	3.62	-1.7	0.3	8.9
C-2	4.31	1.8	1.7	0

* U(1) is measured in the direction from top to bottom, or North to South. U(2) and U(3) are measured in the direction of 60° and 120° counterclockwise from the direction of U(1), respectively.

equations to determine 6 components of rock stress in three dimensions.

The most probable values of rock stresses and their estimated standard deviations are determined by means of the least square method. As shown in Table 5, the result shows a remarkable standard deviation for each stress component.

3.3. Measurement by Hydrofracturing.

In order to verify the accuracy of measurement by hydrofracturing, the rock stress is measured by hydrofracturing in the same three boreholes used for measurement by borehole deformation gauge. The measuring point in each boreholes are shown in Fig.5 and Table 6.

After finishing the measurement by borehole deformation gauge, the borehole of 66mm in diameter is drilled more than 1m in depth from the bottom of overcored borehole of 167mm in diameter, because the double packer system of 66mm in diameter are used for pressurinzing the borehole. The plunger pump of 0.5 l/min in capacity and 50MPa in maximum pressure is used to supply the hyraulic pressure. The flow rate of water for hydrofracturing is kept constant in 0.3 l/min, and shut down to zero, after keeping constant pressure for about 15min.

The procedure described above is repeated several times to determine the break-down pressure Pb, the crack reopening pressure Pb' and the shut-in pressure Ps from each record of test result.

Avoiding many technical difficulties concerned with the impression packer for fracture delineation, the

overcoring in the same diameter of 167mm as it for stress relief overcoring is conducted to recover the hollow cylindrical rock core including the fractures generated by hydrofracturing.

In order to observe the orientaion of recovered rock core as well as generated fracture cracks, the plunge line is marked on the drill pipe immediately after finishing the overcoreing and the core is recovered without any rotation of core barrel for two horizontal borehole, and a borehole compass provided with time-set clamp is fixed in the centre hole after recovering the packer system for a vertical borehole.

The test results including the orientation of generated fracture cracks are shown in Table 6.

The major and minor principal stresses in tha plane normal to the axis of each borehole can be determined from the following equations (Haimson 1978):

for the break-down pressure Pb

$$P_b - P_0 = \frac{T + 3\sigma_{Hmin} - \sigma_{Hmax} - 2P_0}{K}$$

$$---(5)$$

for the shut-in pressure Ps

$$P_s - P_0 = \sigma_{Hmin} \quad ---(6)$$

and for the crack reopening pressure Pb'

$$P_b' - P_0 = \frac{3\sigma_{Hmin} - \sigma_{Hmax} - 2P_0}{K}$$

$$---(5')$$

where T is the hydrofracturing tensile strength, P_0 is the pore pressure, and K is the constant concerned with effect of permeability. In the present measurement, K and P_0 are assumed as zero, because the rock mass at the test site is intact and shows little water inflow. Considering that the hydrofracturing tensile strength does not coincide with the tensile strength of the core sample (Haimson 1973), Eq(5') for the crack reopening pressure is used to determine the rock stress together with Eq.(6).

It has to be indicated that Eq.(5') and Eq.(6) are valid when the deviation of direction of a principal stress from the axis of borehole is not evident and the plane of generated fracture

Table 5   The state of stress in three dimensions determined by means of the least square method

Stress	Borehole deformation method (MPa)		Hydrofracturing method (MPa)	
σ_x	2.17	(4.55)*	5.30	(4.05)
σ_y	4.67	(3.74)	7.70	(6.52)
σ_z	16.17	(3.35)	8.86	
τ_{xy}	-0.36	(1.94)	-1.81	(6.96)
τ_{yz}	-3.82	(1.89)	-3.92	
τ_{zx}	0.22	(1.89)	-1.31	

* Standard deviation is given in ( )

Table 6   Observed Critical Pressures in Hydrofracturing

Position of measurement	Break-down pressure Pb(MPa)	Crack reopening pressure Pb'(MPa)	shut-in pressure Ps(MPa)	Orientation of crack
9.88-10.20m deep in borehole A	12.65		4.06 (0.12)*	see Fig.5
4.84-5.16m deep in borehole B	8.46	5.19 (0.04)	4.82 (0.13)	16-20°from plumb line to west
7.22-7.54m deep in borehole C		7.14 (0.12)	4.90 (0.0)	5-10°from North to west

* Standard deviation is given in parentheses

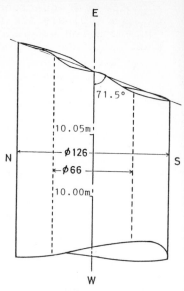

Fig. 6. Schmatic View of Oblique Crack in the Borehole A.

crack includes the axis of borehole.

Substituting data shown in Table 6 into Eq.(5') and (6), we can determine the major and minor principal stresses in the plane mormal to the axis of borehole B and C respectively, because the generated cracks are nearly parallel to the axis of hollow cylindrical rock core for both of borehole B and C. The results are shown in Fig.5.

However, the generated fracture crack of borehole A is nearly vertical, but intersects obbiquely the axis as illustrated in Fig.6. In this case, Eq.(5') would not be valid, but we can apply Eq.(6) to determine the minor principal stress, under the assumption that the generated crack is normal to the minor principal stress.

Let coincide x' axis of local coordinate system to the direction normal to the generated crack, then we have

$$\tau_{x'y'} = \tau_{z'x'} = 0 \qquad ---(7)$$

regardless of the direction of y' and z' axis. When z' axis coincides with z axis of the common coordinate system, applying Eqs.(6),(7), and the formula for transformation of coordinates, we have

$$
\begin{aligned}
\sigma_{x'} &= \sigma_x \cos^2\theta + \sigma_y \sin^2\theta \\
&\quad - 2\tau_{xy}\sin\theta\cdot\cos\theta = P_s \\
\tau_{x'y'} &= (\sigma_x - \sigma_y)\sin\theta\cdot\cos\theta \\
&\quad + \tau_{xy}(\cos^2\theta - \sin^2\theta) = 0 \\
\tau_{z'x'} &= -\tau_{yz}\sin\theta + \tau_{zx}\cos\theta \\
&= 0
\end{aligned}
\right\}
$$

$$---(8)$$

where θ is the angle between x and x' axes.

On the basis of the major and minor principal stresses determined for borehole B and C, we can determine 3 components of the rock stress as

$$
\begin{aligned}
2\tau_{zx} &= (\sigma_{Hmin} - \sigma_{Hmax})\cdot\sin2\theta \\
2\sigma_{xx} &= (\sigma_{Hmin} + \sigma_{Hmax}) \\
&\quad + (\sigma_{Hmin} - \sigma_{Hmax})\cos2\theta \\
2\sigma_{zz} &= (\sigma_{Hmin} + \sigma_{Hmax}) \\
&\quad - (\sigma_{Hmin} - \sigma_{Hmax})\cos2\theta
\end{aligned}
\right\}
$$

$$---(9)$$

for the borehole B, and

$$
\begin{aligned}
2\tau_{xy} &= (\sigma_{Hmin} - \sigma_{Hmax})\sin2\theta \\
2\sigma_{xx} &= (\sigma_{Hmin} + \sigma_{Hmax}) \\
&\quad + (\sigma_{Hmin} - \sigma_{Hmax})\cos2\theta \\
2\sigma_{yy} &= (\sigma_{Hmin} + \sigma_{Hmax}) \\
&\quad - (\sigma_{Hmin} - \sigma_{Hmax})\cos2\theta
\end{aligned}
\right\}
$$

$$---(10)$$

for the boregole C, respectively, where θ is the angle between x axis and the normal to the generated crack i.e. the direction of minor principal stress σ_{Hmin}.

These 9 equations in Eqs.(8) (9) and (10) are the observation equations for determining the complete state of stress. σ_{zz}, τ_{zx} and τ_{yz} can be definitively determined, because 6 among 9 equations don't include these 3 components. However, σ_{xx}, σ_{yy}, τ_{xy} should be determined by means of the least square method. The results are shown in Table 5.

4. DISCUSSION ON VARIOUS SOURCES OF THE ERROR OF MEASUREMENT.

Most of differences between each component of rock stress determined by borehole deformation gauge and hydrofracturing are smaller than their standard deviations. It means that the test results shown in Table 5 are not satisfactory but reasonable.

Such a low accuracy of rock stress measurement as suggested by the standard deviation of several MPa would be caused from the following reasons:
(1) The distance between the gauge position and rock wall of the roadway is about 2.5m fore borehole A. Considering the cross-section of the roadway of 2.5m x 2.5m, the gauge position would be affected by the stress concentration around the underground opening.
(2) Although the accuracy of borehole deformation gauge is 2μm, the borehole deformations induced by the stress relief are sometimes smaller than 2μm, as shown in Table 4. This would be the most imortant reason of the low accuracy of the present measurement.
(3) Boreholes A, B and C have been drilled from the same position of the roadway in three different directions perpendicular to each other by some technical reasons. The gauge position in three different boreholes is distant more than 10m each other. It means that the mechanical properties of rock mass as well as the state of stress might be different from a gauge position to other gauge positions. The remarkable difference between each mean value and the standard deviation of Young's moduli shown in Table 3 suggest the fluctuation and/or anisotropy of mechanical properties of rock mass.

5. STATE OF STRESS IN KANTO-TOKAI REGION

The stress field derived from rock stress measurements in Kanto-Tokai region (Fig.3) is generally consistent with the plate tectonics model in spite of all possible measurement errors and topographic disturbances. The horizontal maximum compressions in the generally east-west direction in the northern part of Kanto area are likely to be the effect of pinching between the Pacific plate and the Eurasia continent. The horizontal maximum compressions in the northwest-southeast direction and in the nearly north-south directions are distinguished in the southern Kanto and Tokai areas.

The nearly north-south compressions are observed in some measurement points relatevely close to the plate boundaries. The measured state of stress is rather abnormal in many sites under the nearly north-south compression. The abnormally high horizontal compression in the nearly north-south direction which was measured in the shallow borehole in the Tanzawa area coincides with geologic features such as the east-west trending anticlines and thrust faults. The rapidly uprising Tanzawa mountain is the area of stress concentration due to the thrust of the Philippine Sea plate.

On the other hand, the extremely low horizontal maximum compression in the east-west direction indicates the horizontal extensional state of stress at the Toi area in the northwestern Izu peninsula. The east-west horizontal extension in the northwestern Izu peninsula, which is also indicated by north-south trending normal faults and tension fractures in young gold-bearing vein systems, is the effect of bending of the Philippine Sea plate which is subducting under the Eurasea plate along the Suruga trough (Nakamura, 1981).

The stress is rather low at the Shibakawa site, west of Mt. Fuji., which locates on the northeast-southwest trending thrust fault with left-slip component, which is one of northern extensions of the Suruga trough.

The results of rock stress measurements suggest that the general orientation of horizontal maximum compression is northwest-southeast in the southern

Kanto and Tokai areas, but that the stress field is disturbed to form areas of stress concentration or stress release, where the horizontal maximum compression tends nearly north-south.

Disastrous major earthquakes occur along the plate boundaries in the southern Kanto and Tokai areas such as the Great Kanto earthquake along the Sagami trough and the forthcoming Tokai earthquake along the Suruga trough. The areas of stress disturbance, where the direction of horizontal maximum compression is nearly north-south, are directly affected by the plate interaction and possibly make the most sensitive and critical areas for prediction of major earthquakes in Kanto-Tokai region.

REFERENCES

De la Cruz,R.V. and C.B.Raleigh. 1972. Absolute stress measurements at the Rangely Anticline, Northwestern Corolado. Int.J.Rock Mech.Min.Sci. 9(5):625-634.

Gray,W.M. and N.A.Toews. 1975. Analysis of variance applied to data obtained by means of a six-elements borehole deformation gauge for stress determination. Applications of Rock Machanics (ed. by E.R.Hoskins). ASCE. New York:323-356.

Haimson,B.C. 1973. Earthquake related stresses at Rangely, Colorado. New Horizons in Rock Mecanics (ed. by H.R.Hardy and R.Stefanko). ASCE. New York:689-708.

Haimson,B.C., J.Lacomb,A.H.Jones and S.J.Green. 1974. Deep stress measurements in tuff at the Nevada test site. Proc.3rd Int.Congress on Rock Mech.ISRM. Vol.2A:557-562.

Haimson,B.C. 1978. The hydrofracturing stress measuring method and recent field results. Int.J.Rock Mech.Min. Sci.15(4):167-178.

Hiramatsu,Y & Y.Oka. 1968. Determination of the stress in rock unaffected by boreholes or drifts, from measured strains or deformations, Int.J.Rock Mech.Min.Sci.5 (4):337-353 .

Hiramatsu,Y.,Y.Oka and Y.Kameoka. 1979. Pillar-robbing supported by field measurements in Yanahara mine, Proc.4th Int.Congress on Rock Mech. ISRM.Vol.2:235-241.

Koide,H. et al. 1986. Comparison among several methods for stress measurement

in Kanto-Tokai district,Japan. Proc. 18th Symp.Rock Mech. J.S.C.E.,Tokyo: 261-265.

Leeman,E.R. 1968. The dermination of the complete state of stress in rock in a single borehole — Laboratory and underground measurements. Int.J.Rock Mech.Min.Sci. 5(1):31-56.

Nakamura,K.1981. An interpretation of current crustal deformations around the Suruga bay,Japan. Zishin (J.Seis.Soc.Japan) 34 (2):272-274.

Obert,L. 1962. In-situ determination of stress in rock, Min.Engg. 14(8): 51-58.

Panek,L.A. 1966. Calculation of the average groundstress components from measurements of the diametral deformation of a drill hole. Testing Techniques for Rock Mechanics. ASTM. STP 402, Philadelphia:106-132.

Suzuki,K. and Y.Ishijima. 1970. Rock stress measurements at rockburst danger area. Proc.2nd Int.Congress on Rock Mech.ISRM.Vol.2 Privredni Pregled.Belgrade:577-581.

Tsukahara,H. and R.Ikeda. 1984. In-situ stress measurement by hydraulic fracturing method — Stresses measured in the boreholes 100m to 800m deep —, Proc. 6th Japan Symp.Rock Mech. Japanese Committee for ISRM,Tokyo: 367-372.

Van Heerden,W.L. and F.Grant. 1967. A comparison of two methods for measureing stress in rock. Int.J.Rock Mech.Min.Sci.4(4):367-382.

Van Heerden,W.L. 1976. Practical application of the CSIR triaxial strain cell for rock stress measurements. Exploration for Rock Engineering (ed. by Z.T.Bieniawski) Balkema, Rotterdam. Vol.1:189-194.

A new approach for calibration and interpretation
of IRAD GAGE vibrating-wire stressmeters

NAI-HSIEN MAO
Lawrence Livermore National Laboratory, Livermore, California, USA

ABSTRACT

IRAD GAGE vibrating-wire stressmeters were installed in the Spent Fuel Facility
at the Nevada Test Site to measure the change in in-situ stress during the Spent
Fuel Test-Climax (SFT-C). This paper discusses the results of removing a
cylindrical section of rock and gages as a unit through overcoring, and the
subsequent post-test calibrations of the stressmeters in the laboratory. The
estimated in-situ stresses based on post test calibration data are quite consistent
with those directly measured in nearby holes. The magnitude of stress change
calculated from pre-test calibration data is generally much smaller than that
estimated from post test calibration data.

RESUME

Des jauges de contrainte à corde vibrante, IRAD, ont été installées au
Spent-Fuel Test, Nevada Test Site, pour mesurer les changements de contraintes
in-situ, pendant le test. On décrit les mesures obtenues par hypercarottage des
jauges, suivies de calibration des carottes contenant les jauges, au laboratoire.
Les valeurs des contraintes in-situ estimées sur la base de calibration apres-test
sont proches de celles mesurées directement en place, dans des forages
avoisinants. Par contre, le changement de contraintes calculé à partir de
calibration avant-test est, en général, beaucoup plus faible que celui estime à
partir de calibration apres-test.

ZUSAMMENFASSUNG

IRAD-GAGE-Meßgeräte mit schwingendem Draht zur Messung der
Spannungsbeanspruchung wurden in der Anlage für abgebrannten Brennstoff auf dem
Testgelände von Nevada eingelagert, um die Veränderungen der in-situ-Spannungen
während der Spent Fuel Test-Climax (SFT-C) zu messen. Die vorliegende Arbeit
referiert über die Ergebnisse nach Entfernung eines zylindrischen Felsabschnittes
samt Meßinstrumenten mittels Overcoring und über die anschließenden, nach dem
Testablauf durchgeführten Eichungen der Spannungsmesser im Labor. Die Schätzwerte
der auf nach dem Test erhaltenen Eichwerten basierenden in-situ-Spannungen stimmen
mit in benachbarten Löchern direkt gemessenen Daten durchaus überein. Die
Größenordnung der auf der Grundlage von vor der Einlagerung der Spannungsmesser
erhaltenen Veränderungen der Spannungswerte liegt allgemein bedeutend unter der auf
Grund der Eichdaten nach dem Test geschätzten Größenordnung.

1. INTRODUCTION

The Spent Fuel Test - Climax
(SFT-C) is part of the Department of
Energy's (DOE) Nevada Nuclear Waste
Storage Investigations Project. The
overall objective of the SFT-C is to
evaluate the feasibility of safe and
reliable short-term storage of spent
reactor fuel assemblies at a plausible
repository depth in a typical granitic
rock, and to retrieve the fuel
afterwards (Ramspott et al. 1979).

In this generic test, located 420 m below the surface in the Climax granite stock at the Nevada Test Site, 11 canisters containing spent fuel assemblies were emplaced in the floor of a storage drift along with six electrical simulator canisters. Over 900 data channels were installed to monitor the response of the rock to the heat and radiation produced by the fuel assemblies. A number of laboratory and field studies for site characterization and instrument calibration were carried out and reported (Carlson et al. 1980; Heuze et al. 1982; Patrick et al. 1981, 1982, 1983; and Brough and Patrick 1982). Among these studies, IRAD GAGE vibrating-wire stressmeters were installed in the facility to measure the change in in-situ stress during the SFT-C. This paper discusses the results of post test stressmeter calibrations which were conducted in the laboratory following removal of a section of the rock and gages as a unit through overcoring.

2. PREVIOUS WORK

2.1 Laboratory Calibration:

IRAD GAGE, Inc. was contracted to perform laboratory calibration studies of the vibrating-wire stressmeter in Climax granite (Dutta et al. 1981). A comprehensive test program was developed to study nine important factors which influence stressmeter response: test sample size, stressmeter stiffness, gage reproducibility and hysteresis, gage preload, initial stress field, platen geometry, platen orientation, elevated temperature, and rock anisotropy.

The IRAD GAGE vibrating-wire stressmeter uses a tensioned wire across a hollow steel cylinder which is preloaded diametrically across the sides of a 1.5 in. (3.8 cm) borehole by means of a sliding wedge platen assembly. The operation of the vibrating-wire stressmeter is based on the fact that the fundamental frequency of a stressed wire is proportional to the applied stress in the wire. Any deformation of the borehole will change the compression in the gage body and, through deformation of the body, change the

stress in the wire. The output of the stressmeter is the vibration frequency of the wire as:

$$f = \frac{1}{2\ell_w} \sqrt{\frac{\overline{\sigma_w g}}{\rho}} \qquad (1)$$

where f is the natural frequency of wire (sec^{-1}), ℓ_w is the length of vibrating-wire (in.), σ_w is the stress in the wire (psi), ρ is the density of the wire ($lb/in.^3$), and g is the acceleration due to gravity ($in./sec^2$).

For the IRAD GAGE stressmeter, ℓ_w = 0.780 in. and ρ = 0.283 $lb/in.^3$. Defining T as the 4 digit display of the IRAD GAGE vibrating-wire readout unit, where T is given by $10^7/f$, then

$$\sigma_w = 1.78422 \times 10^{11} \times \frac{1}{T^2} \text{ (psi)} \qquad (2)$$

The ratio of the wire stress change ($\Delta \sigma_w$) to the change in rock stress ($\Delta \sigma_r$) is defined as the "stress sensitivity factor" (α) which provides a simple factor to characterize the stressmeter response in various rocks.

The stressmeter sensitivity factor is nonlinear with Young's modulus and is also a complex function of the platen contact area and, hence, the preload. Therefore, the change in sensitivity α with modulus and load should be precisely determined through laboratory calibration for the host materials of interest.

Gage reproducibility was investigated under two conditions, single setting with multiple-load cycles and multiple settings with a single-load cycle. In all tests, a zero shift was observed between the initial and the second load cycles. The shift, as a percentage of the maximum applied wire stress, was 18% in Climax granite. This is probably a result of the stressmeter "bedding in" on the first cycle since, for later cycles, the effect is almost non-existent.

Test results indicate that above a minimum preload value, sensitivity α is essentially constant with load. For Climax granite, the threshold is + 175 units in T.

The influence of temperature on a stressmeter was a primary concern in pre-installation temperature calibration studies because of the temperature changes expected on the

SFT-C. As it turned out, changes in stressmeter sensitivity with increasing temperature were negligible. Changes in temperature merely cause an offset in the initial gage reading (T_1) by an amount

$$T_1' - T_1 = 1.55 \, \Delta t \qquad (3)$$

Based on Eqs. 2 and 3, it was postulated that rock stress changes ($\Delta \sigma_r$) can be estimated according to following relation (Patrick et al. 1982)

$$\Delta \sigma_r = (1.7842 \times 10^{14}) A \frac{1}{T_1'^2} - \frac{1}{T_2^2} , \qquad (4)$$

where $\Delta \sigma_r$ is the stress change in pascals, T_2 is the gage reading, $T_1' = T_1 + 1.55 \, \Delta t$ is the initial set reading, offset by the temperature change Δt (°C), and A is 1.6, 1.8, or 2.0 depending on whether the initial set preload remained stable, dropped slightly (5% to 10%), or dropped by more than 10%.

2.2 Stressmeter Installation:

Eighteen IRAD GAGE vibrating-wire stressmeters were installed in the SFT-C facility during the week of March 17, 1980 (Abey and Washington 1980). Six stressmeters "rosettes" were used, each rosette consisting of three stressmeters. One was aligned at 0° (0° is vertical for the horizontal holes and perpendicular to the drift axis for the vertical holes), one was rotated 60° ccw, and the third was rotated 60° cw, as viewed from the end of the hole through which the gage was inserted. Figure 1 shows the location of the vibrating-wire stressmeters and other instruments. CSG01 and CSG02 are vertical holes in the canister drift floor. NSG03 and NSG04 are horizontal boreholes, and are located approximately 2 m above the floor in the pillar between the canister and north heater drifts. Each horizontal hole has two rosettes: one installed from the Canister Drift and one from the North Heater Drift.

Prior to placing the stressmeters at the facility, laboratory tests in a setup designed to simulate field conditions were carried out (Abey and Washington 1980). Two distinct

calibration curves were found: a "normal" curve associated with little or no drop in preload when the installation tool was removed and a "subnormal" curve associated with a substantial drop (> 10%) in stressmeter preload. The "subnormal" curve is approximately 30% less sensitive than the "normal" curve.

2.3 Stressmeter Failure:

Four of the six gages in vertical holes near the canister emplacement holes failed within 4 months after installation. By June, 1981, 13 of the 18 gages failed. The cause was identified as internal rusting, especially of the wire itself, due to moisture. IRAD GAGE, Inc. redesigned the gage, providing a welded hermetic seal in place of the O-ring seal previously used. All gages were sealed under vacuum. Nine gages of the new design were installed in place of failed units June 16-17, 1981 (Brough and Patrick 1982, Patrick et al. 1981).

By October, 1982, the remaining 5 originally installed gages also failed. Nine additional stressmeters of the modified version were installed on October 25-27, 1982.

2.4 Field Data:

Field data of 9 replaced gages are available from June 17, 1981 to September 30, 1983 and of others from October 27, 1982 to September 30, 1983. The spent fuel was retrieved and the electrical heaters were turned off between March 3 and April 6, 1983. Figure 2 shows the raw data of NSG245 during the last year of operation. The y-axis is labeled count which is the gage readout (T), and the x-axis is the spent fuel age expressed as the number of years out of core. As a reference, the date October 25, 1982, when the last batch of gages was replaced corresponds to 4.93 years out of core. The sharp drop of count near 5.3 years out of core is due to the retrieval of spent fuel and the turning off the power to the heaters.

Figure 3 shows the temperature changes at the gage NSG244 next to NSG245 for the same period.

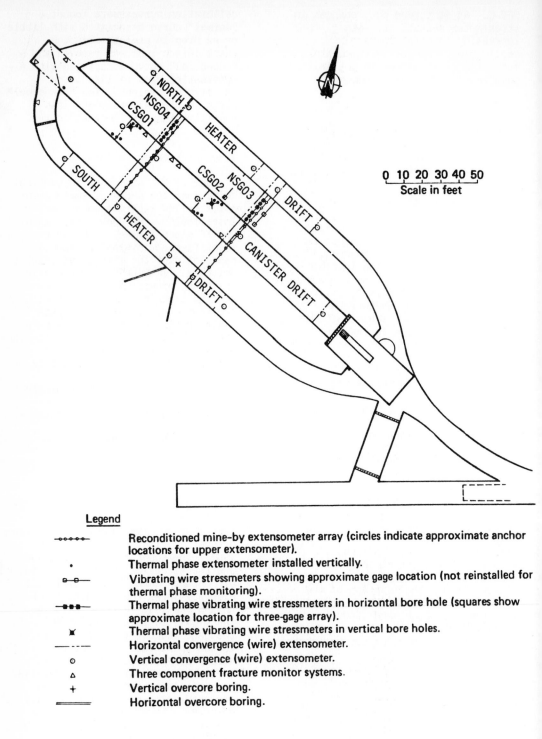

Legend

─o∘o∘o─	Reconditioned mine-by extensometer array (circles indicate approximate anchor locations for upper extensometer).
•	Thermal phase extensometer installed vertically.
─□─□─	Vibrating wire stressmeters showing approximate gage location (not reinstalled for thermal phase monitoring).
─•••─	Thermal phase vibrating wire stressmeters in horizontal bore hole (squares show approximate location for three-gage array).
✖	Thermal phase vibrating wire stressmeters in vertical bore holes.
──·──	Horizontal convergence (wire) extensometer.
o	Vertical convergence (wire) extensometer.
△	Three component fracture monitor systems.
+	Vertical overcore boring.
═══	Horizontal overcore boring.

Figure 1. Location of thermal phase instrumentation
(after Carlson et al. 1980).

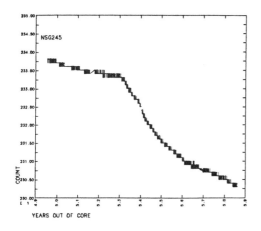

Figure 2.   Field data for NSG245.

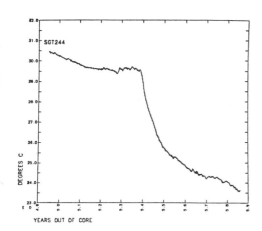

Figure 3.   Temperature data for SGT244.

Temperature has two effects on the readout. First, the readout should be corrected for temperature effect according to Eq. 3. Secondly, temperature changes will generate thermal stress in rock that is sensed by the gage.

The temperature change due to the retrieval of spent fuel at the horizontal holes was about 6°C which implies a readout temperature correction of about 9 counts according to Eq. 3. Since the vertical hole was much closer to the spent fuel canister, the temperature change was much larger. At CSG02 it was about 20°C implying a readout correction of 31 counts.

2.5 In-situ Stresses:

In-situ stress measurements in the vicinity of the SFT-C were reported by Creveling et al. (1984). The instruments used for this study included both the U.S. Bureau of Mines Borehole Deformation Gage (USBM gage) and the Australian CSIRO Hollow Inclusion Stress Cell (CSIRO cell). A total of 8 holes were drilled and tested. Among these holes ISS5 and ISS4, located in the north heater drift pillar, are 12 ft and 19 ft away from boreholes NSG03 and NSG04 which contained IRAD GAGE vibrating-wire stressmeters. Boreholes ISS6 and ISS7 are in matching positions in the south pillar.

The stress measurements at these holes began in June 1983 and were completed in September 1983 corresponding to the last leg of the vibrating-wire stressmeter data.

Stress measurements in the four pillar boreholes present a relatively consistent profile of secondary principal stresses. The major secondary principal stresses are predominantly vertical and have a maximum value of about 2000 psi (13.8 MPa) near the heater drift wall, which decreases progressively toward the canister drift wall to values in the range of 700 to 1000 psi (4.83 to 6.90 MPa). Minimum secondary principal stresses are nearly horizontal and are generally less than 700 psi (4.83 MPa).

3. OVERCORE OF STRESSMETERS

The IRAD GAGE vibrating-wire stressmeter is a very sensitive instrument which can be affected by many local irregularities. Therefore, careful calibration of the gage is the key to meaningful interpretation of the data. The calibration studies discussed previously are generic in nature. They provide many useful guidelines on the installation and operation of the gage. However, calibration of individual gages in the rock in which they were set during the SFT-C is probably the best way to take the effect of the gage-rock interface into account. In order to keep the gage-rock interface intact, we decided to overcore the gage and to calibrate the overcored gage in the laboratory.

Since it is generally very difficult to core a concentric sample with high precision in the field, we decided to have a two stage overcoring. First, we cored a 9 1/2" (24.1 cm) diameter rock with gages in place. Then we shipped the large core sample back to the laboratory and made a 5 1/2" (14 cm) core which was precisely concentric with the small 1 1/2" (3.8 cm) gage hole in the middle of the core. The 5 1/2" core with gages in place was then calibrated under uniform biaxial loading. Furthermore, the stress relief data during overcoring should also provide important information about the state of stress in-situ.

The overcoring task started on January 12, 1984 and was completed on March 19, 1984. The stressmeter overcoring was of limited success. Among the 18 gages, the stress relief data of 11 were successfully recorded during overcoring but only 8 gages and associated cabling remained intact through the field operation. Two additional gages malfunctioned after the second overcoring in the laboratory. The main problems during the field overcoring were: 1) lead wires cut by broken core rock and 2) natural fracture going through the gage area, causing it to dissociate from the core. Another problem encountered during overcoring was temperature control due to a broken thermocouple in the rock. The stress relief data for gages NSG244, NSG245, and NSG246 are shown in Figure 4. In general, the temperature corrections were small and produced little change in the plots.

4. FINAL LABORATORY CALIBRATION

Only six gages survived the two operations of overcoring. These six gages are contained in two long cores. One core contains NSG231, NSG232, and NSG233. The gage NSG231 is only about 5/8" from the end of the core which was broken from the rock at a 45° angle. The other core contains NSG244, NSG245, and NSG246. Gage NSG246 is right at the edge of the chipped end.

The laboratory calibration was carried out with the IRAD GAGE model MC-1 biaxial Modulus Chamber, which

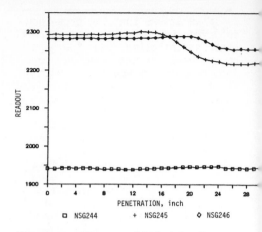

Figure 4. Stress relief data for NSG244-246.

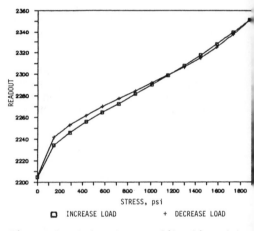

Figure 5. Laboratory calibration data for NSG245, post-test.

applied pressure over a 6" length of the core with a hand-operated jack. The overcore sample was mounted in the chamber with one gage positioned at the center. The hydrostatic load was applied to the overcore exterior via a rubber membrane. The load was cycled three times with the pressure recorded at 200 psi (1.4 MPa) increments up to 2600 psi (17.9 MPa). The equivalent uniaxial stress for the core was only 0.72 of the biaxial chamber pressure for our configuration (Dutta et al. 1981). The gage response was read from a MB6-1 vibrating-wire readout meter. The results of the biaxial calibration for NSG245 are shown in Figure 5.

504

5. DISCUSSION AND CONCLUSION

If we assume that the gage-rock interface has been the same since the gage was installed, then the gage should have the same reading under the same temperature and load condition. The temperature during the laboratory calibration of the overcored gage was about 20°C. We corrected all vibrating-wire stressmeter data to this temperature by Eq. 2 and read the corresponding stress level at 20°C from the biaxial calibration data. All data can be grouped according to the three stages of operations, i.e., the field data of the spent fuel retrieval, the data during overcoring, and the biaxial calibration data in the laboratory. These stages are indicated by the first subscript f, o, and ℓ, respectively (see Table 1). The second subscript is either 1 or 2 to indicate the values at the start and end of each stage. Thus, t_{f1}, t_{f2}, and T_{f1}, T_{f2} are the temperatures and vibrating-wire readout when the spent fuel was retrieved and at the end of the test as shown in Figure 2. T_{f1}' and T_{f2}' are the temperature corrected T_{f1} and T_{f2} at 20°C. σ_{f1} and σ_{f2} are corresponding stress levels at 20°C. The numbers in the parentheses are either extrapolated values or not temperature corrected due to lack of temperature data.

The estimated in-situ stresses (σ_{f2}) are quite consistent with those reported (Creveling et al. 1984). The largest stress (σ_{f2}), at the end of the test, was about 2015 psi (13.9 MPa) for NSG231 which is located 2.8 m from the north heater drift wall and oriented 60°CW as viewed from north heater drift wall. Both the vertically oriented gages (NSG232 and NSG245) gave stress levels between 1150 to 1296 psi (7.9 to 8.9 MPa). The other three gages all had stresses between 145 and 292 psi (1 to 2 MPa).

Thermal stress changes after retrieval of spent fuel were mainly seen by those gages oriented vertically in the horizontal holes in the pillar. The magnitude of stress drop ($\sigma_{f1}-\sigma_{f2}$) is about 300 psi (2 MPa).

The stressmeter responses due to stress relief for the gages in the two horizontal holes are somewhat different. For instance, data indicate nearly complete stress relief for NSG244, NSG245, and NSG246 but substantial residual stresses for NSG231, NSG232, and NSG233 right after overcoring. The relative gage response within a rosette for NSG231, NSG232, and NSG233 is also different from that for NSG241, NSG242, and NSG243. One possible explanation is that holes NSG03 and NSG04 are separated by a shear zone (Wilder and Yow 1981). Consequently, they are in different local stress regions.

The installation data indicate that all the six gages calibrated in the laboratory belong to the "normal" type. In Table 1, we also listed the initial and final readout ($T_{\ell1}$ and $T_{\ell2}$) during the laboratory calibration. The stress sensitivity factor (α) was calculated for each gage by calculating the wire stress according to Eq. 2 and dividing by the applied stress (1872 psi). The calculated stress sensitivity factors for NSG231 and NSG232 are 0.99 and 1.30 respectively and are much smaller than those for the other four gages (2.34 to 2.85), as shown in Table 1. All six gages had a preload above + 200 digits when they were installed. At that time, the rock was under in-situ stress loading. After overcoring, the stresses were relieved and the effective preload was much lower (all below + 150 digits). Since the stress sensitivity factor (α) is a function of preload for preload below + 175 digits (Dutta et al. 1981), we would expect some variation in the stress sensitivity factor.

A close examination of the laboratory calibration data also indicates that: 1) NSG231 has a larger hysteresis than others; 2) hysteresis is smaller at high rock stress than at low rock stress; 3) there is an initial steep change in readout for NSG244, NSG245, and NSG246. All these could be the results of low preload value. In addition, stress relief due to overcoring may generate microcracks or allow existing ones to open which in turn could change the modulus of the sample. The steep change of readout for NSG244, NSG245, and NSG246 could be due to closing of microcracks at low pressure.

Table 1. Calculated stresses at 20°C based on laboratory calibrations
(parentheses indicate either extrapolated values
or not temperature correlated).

Gage	NSG231	NSG232	NSG233	NSG244	NSG245	NSG246
Orientation	cw60°	vertical	ccw60°	ccw60°	vertical	cw60°
Values at Time of Spent Fuel Retrieval						
t_{f1} °C	29.6	29.6	29.6	29.6	29.6	29.6
T_{f1}	2308	2323	2114	1957	2333	2300
T'_{f1} (20°C)	2293	2308	2099	1942	2318	2285
σ_{f1} (20°C) psi	(2030)	1584	438	150	1470	240
t_{f2} °C	23.7	23.7	23.7	23.6	23.6	23.6
T_{f2}	2289	2300	2095	1946	2303	2288
T'_{f2} (20°C)	2283	2290	2089	1940	2297	2282
σ_{f2} (20°C) psi	(2015)	1296	292	145	1150	230
Values during Overcoring						
t_{o1} °C	----	----	----	21.6	21.6	21.6
T_{o1}	2279	2288	2086	1942	2293	2282
T'_{o1} (20°C)	----	----	----	1939	2290	2279
σ_{o1} (20°C) psi	(2000)	(1152)	(240)	120	1000	170
t_{o2} °C	----	----	----	21.9	21.9	21.9
T_{o2}	2232	2268	2091	1945	2219	2255
T'_{o2} (20°C)	----	----	----	1942	2216	2252
σ_{o2} (20°C) psi	(1008)	(680)	(360)	160	50	30
Values during Laboratory Calibration						
$T_{\ell1}$	2208	2242	2070	1927	2206	2246
$T_{\ell2}$	2266	2323	2217	2025	2351	2412
Stress Sensitivity Factor (α)	0.99	1.30	2.85	2.42	2.34	2.51

The biaxial chamber used in this study was unable to attain pressures in the range of the highest stress values recorded in situ. Since calibration of the gage is stress dependent, it is important that the calibration be conducted over the full range of stresses observed in the field. The appropriate segment of the calibration may then be used, in accordance with the range of stresses encountered in the field by a particular gage.

Rock stress changes ($\Delta \sigma_r$) may be calculated according to Eq. 4. Three sets of stress changes were calculated for each of the six gages calibrated in the laboratory. These changes are shown in Table 2 together with the changes read directly from post test calibration data as shown in Table 1. Negative values in Table 2 imply stress drop. In general stress changes estimated from post test calibration data are much larger than those calculated from Eq. 4 (with A=1.6). This implies that calculated stress changes from Eq. 4 could underestimate the magnitude of stress change as much as 75%.

The approach of calibrating overcored IRAD gages following completion of field measurements is fundamentally sound. It addresses the concerns of the unique gage/rock interactions which profoundly influence the relationship between gage reading and change in rock stress. However, the results from biaxial calibration can only be adjusted to an equivalent uniaxial case which can be somewhat different from in-situ condition of triaxial loading. Nevertheless, we believe that the error introduced by biaxial calibration may be relatively small as compared with that from the effect of gage/rock interactions. The practical matter of overcoring the gages was a limited success--only 6 of 18 gages survived both the field and laboratory coring processes. Additional fixtures must be developed and tested to provide reliable overcoring and a higher success rate of gage recovery. We found good agreement between the stress relief data obtained from the IRAD gages and the results of conventional stress-relief overcoring using USBM and CSIRO cells.

Table 2. Estimated stress changes (psi) at 20°C based on laboratory calculation and Eq. 4 (A=1.6).

Gage	NSG231	NSG232	NSG233	NSG244	NSG245	NSG246
Orientation	cw60°	vertical	ccw60°	ccw60°	vertical	cw60°
Values at Time of Spent Fuel Retrieval						
T'_{f1}	2293	2308	2099	1942	2318	2285
T'_{f2}	2283	2290	2089	1940	2297	2282
$\Delta \sigma_r$ Eq. 4	−69	−123	−90	−23	−142	−21
$\Delta \sigma_r (\sigma_{f1} - \sigma_{f2})$	−15	−288	−140	−5	−320	−10
Values during Overcoring						
T_{o1}	2279	2288	2086	1939	2290	2279
T_{o2}	2232	2268	2091	1942	2216	2252
$\Delta \sigma_r$ Eq. 4	−339	−140	45	34	−536	−192
$\Delta \sigma_r (\sigma_{o1} - \sigma_{o2})$	−992	−472	120	40	−950	−140
Values during Laboratory Calibration						
$T_{\ell1}$	2208	2242	2070	1927	2206	2246
$T_{\ell2}$	2266	2323	2217	2025	2351	2412
$\Delta \sigma_r$ Eq. 4	429	564	1239	1053	1017	1091
$\Delta \sigma_r$ (applied)	1872	1872	1872	1872	1872	1872

ACKNOWLEDGMENTS

Work performed under the auspices of the U.S. Department of Energy by the Lawrence Livermore National Laboratory under contract number W-7405-ENG-48.

I would like to thank R. Ruiz for the biaxial calibration in the laboratory. W. Patrick, R. Carlson, F. Heuze, and J. Yow, Jr. reviewed the draft and suggested many improvements.

REFERENCES

Abey, A. and H. Washington 1980. Stressmeter Placement at Climax Granite Spent Fuel Test. Lawrence Livermore National Laboratory, Livermore, CA, UCID-18629.

Brough, W. G. and W. C. Patrick 1982. Instrumentation Report #1: Specification, Design, Calibration, and Installation of Instrumentation for an Experimental, High Level, Nuclear Waste Storage Facility. Lawrence Livermore National Laboratory, Livermore, CA, UCRL-53248.

Carlson, R., W. C. Patrick, D. Wilder, W. Brough, D. N. Montan, P. Harben, L. Ballou, and H. Heard 1982. SFT-C Technical Measurement Interim Report Fiscal 1980, Lawrence Livermore National Laboratory, Livermore, CA, UCRL-53064.

Creveling, J. B., F. S. Shuri, E. M. Foster, and S. V. Mills 1984. In Situ Stress Measurements at the Spent Fuel Test--Climax Facility. Lawrence Livermore National Laboratory, Livermore, CA, UCRL-15628.

Dutta, P., R. Hatfield, and P. Runstadler 1981. Calibration Characteristics of IRAD Gage Vibrating Wire Stressmeter at Normal and High Temperature. Vols. 1 & 2, Lawrence Livermore National Laboratory, Livermore, CA, Contractor Report, UCRL-15426.

Heuze, F. E., W. C. Patrick, T. R. Butkovich, J. C. Peterson, R. V. de la Cruz, and C. F. Voss 1982. "Rock Mechanics Studies of Mining in the Climax Granite," Int. J. Rock Mechanics and Mining Science, V. 19, pp. 167-183.

Patrick, W. C., L. B. Ballou, T. R. Butkovich, R. C. Carlson, W. B. Durham, G. L. Hage, E. L. Majer, D. N. Montan, R. A. Nyholm, N. L. Rector, D. G. Wilder, and J. L. Yow, Jr. 1982. Spent Fuel Test--Climax: Technical Measurements Interim Report, Fiscal Year 1981. Lawrence Livermore National Laboratory, Livermore, CA, UCRL-53294.

Patrick, W. C., L. B. Ballou, T. R. Butkovich, R. C. Carlson, W. B. Durham, G. L. Hage, E. L. Majer, D. N. Montan, R. A. Nyholm, N. L. Rector, D. G. Wilder, and J. L. Yow, Jr. 1982. Spent Fuel Test--Climax: Technical Measurements Interim Report, Fiscal Year 1982. Lawrence Livermore National Laboratory, Livermore, CA, UCRL-53294-82.

Patrick, W. C., R. C. Carlson, and N. L. Rector 1981. Instrumentation Report #2: Identification, Evaluation, and Remedial Actions Related to Transducer Failures at the Spent Fuel Test--Climax. Lawrence Livermore National Laboratory, Livermore, CA, UCRL-53251.

Ramspott, L. D., L. B. Ballou, R. C. Carlson, D. N. Montan, T. R. Butkovich, J. E. Duncan, W. C. Patrick, D. G. Wilder, W. G. Brough, and M. C. Mayr 1979. Technical Concept for a Test of Geological Storage of Spent Reactor Fuel in the Climax Granite, Nevada Test Site. Lawrence Livermore National Laboratory, Livermore, CA, UCRL-52796.

Wilder, D. G. and J. L. Yow, Jr. 1981. Fracture Mapping at the Spent Fuel Test-Climax. Lawrence Livermore National Laboratory, Livermore, CA, UCRL-53201.

Stress relaxation monitoring prestressed hard inclusions

O. NATAU
Ch. LEMPP
G. BORM
Institute of Soil and Rock Mechanics, University of Karlsruhe, Karslruhe
Federal Republic of Germany

Abstract   The development of stress relaxation in rock salt masses according to their rheological properties is evaluated by measurements in situ and by theoretical analyses.

Hard inclusion pressure cells are embedded in a set of boreholes which are filled with a salt rock mortar. A high pressure injection of synthetic resin into the hardened mortar achieves the prestressing of the pressure cells up to the fracturing pressure of the salt rock. The overstress releases with the lapse of time and approaches monotonously the stationary stress level.

The analogous rheological model for the measured stress relaxation is a generalized Maxwell body with a highly nonlinear apparent viscosity corresponding to a hyperbolic sine creep law.

Resume   La relaxation des contraintes dans le sel gemme est mesurée sur des longues périodes in situ par des jauges précontraintes selon la méthode de l' inclusion rigide.

Les capteurs hydrauliques sont mis en place dans des puits de forage et mesurent des composantes diverses des contraintes de pression. Les puits sont remplis par un mortier ressemblant au sel. Par des injections de résine artificielle dans le mortier solidifé on obtient une précontrainte des jauges sous une pression correspondant à celle d' éclatement des puits. Cette pression retombe ensuite de façon monotone à un niveau stationaire.

Le modèle rhéologique correspondant à ce comportement est celui de Maxwell généralise avec une viscosité apparente fortement non linéaire se laissant déduire d' une fonction sinus hyperbolique.

Zusammenfassung   Die Spannungsrelaxation im Steinsalzgebirge wird in situ durch vorgespannte Spannungsmeßzellen nach der Methode des harten Einschlusses langzeitig registriert.

Die hydraulischen Druckgeber sind in einem System von Bohrlöchern eingesetzt und messen verschiedene Druckspannungskomponenten. Die Bohr löcher sind mit einem salzähnlichen Mörtel verfüllt. Durch Kunstharzinjektion im ausgehärteten Mörtel im Bereich der Druckzellen wird eine Vorspannung der Meßgeber auf einen Druck erreicht, der dem Aufreißdruck der Bohrlöcher entspricht. Dieser Druck fällt an den verschieden orientierten Meßgebern im Lauf der Zeit monoton auf ein stationäres Niveau ab.

Das dieser gemessenenen Spannungsrelaxation entsprechende rheologische Modell ist ein verallgemeinerter Maxwell Körper mit hochgradig nicht-linearer scheinbarer Viskosität, die sich aus einer hyperbolischen Sinusfunktion ableiten läßt.

Introduction

The stress distribution around underground cavities like caverns, galleries or boreholes shows typical changes during and after excavation in creeping rock masses, especially in rock salt deposits. The tangential stresses are reduced in the circumference of the underground openings, whereby the maximum tangential stresses are transferred to interior regions of the virgin rock mass (Borm 1980). The amount of stress release at the underground opening is directly related to the capability of stationary differential stresses of the surrounding rock mass.

The installation of monitoring boreholes in a folded Permian rock salt dome in NW-Germany, which are provided to measure the complete stress tensor and its changes during time (Natau et al. 1985), offered the possibility to observe the stress relaxation behaviour in situ. The basic data were obtained from a measurement system, which consists of hydraulical pressure cells. Each pressure cell forms an hard inclusion within the rock salt, installed in a defined position and prestressed by injection up to the fracturing pressure of the surrounding rock salt. The time dependent reduction of the different stress tensor components is observed during the release of the initial pressure level down to the stationary stress level at the borehole.

Measurement technique

The hydraulic pressure cells for measuring normal stress components in boreholes are attached to a cylindrical steel frame (Fig.1), the diameter of which corresponds to the diameter of the borehole. The equipment is installed and orientated at the bottom of the borehole. Rock pressures from well defined directions therefore load the hydraulic cells.

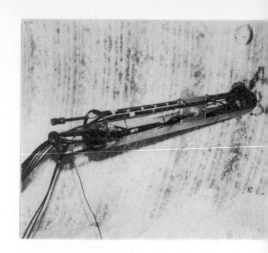

Fig.1: Hydraulic pressure cells (System Glötzl) attached to a cylindrical steel frame for positioning in a borehole

The installation of the monitoring boreholes is based on the concept of Wöhlbier & Natau(1966). The borehole is grouted with salt-like mortar pumped into the bottom of the borehole. Once the borehole is filled, all pressure cells are completely embedded in the grouting medium. The mixture of granular rock-salt (∅ 1mm-2mm), cement, and brine is tested with regard to a) pumping characteristics and b) the mechanical behaviour of the hardened mortar. The latter is adjusted properly to the mechanical behaviour of the salt rock, particularly with regard to the reloading modulus.

The filling of the borehole must be completely bubble-free to ensure perfect embedding of the hydraulic pressure cells. Flexible pipes for the supply of the pressure cells are leading from the measurement section at the bottom of the borehole to the hydraulical pump.

Together with the frame and the pressure cells a high pressure pipe system is provided. A perforated HP tube is installed within the reach of the pressure cells at the end of the borehole as injection pipe.

After hardening of the rock-salt mortar a synthetic resin is injected under high pressure resulting in a prestressing of the hydraulical pressure cells. This prestressing is further increased up to the frac stress of the borehole. In this state a hydrostatic stress field is registered at the pressure cells. In order to attain bubble-free fillings of the boreholes, downward inclinations have been approved.

Two measurement boreholes are provided for the evaluation of pressure relaxation measurements. Boreholes with inclined dipping are drilled into the walls on both sides of a gallery in approximately 750m depth. The directions of the boreholes are 344/24 (borehole I) and 084/24 (borehole II). The depths of the holes are about 20m. The pressure cells are located between 17m and 20m depth at the bottom of each borehole. With respect to the axis of each borehole the directions of the measured normal stresses are 0, 45, 90, and 135 degrees. Seven different directions of pressure (A to G) are measured in the two boreholes (Tab.1).

Borehole No.	I	II
direction of borehole axis	344/24	084/24
direction of measurement	No. of pressure cell	
A(084/24)	1,5	
B(214/55)	2	8
C(246/18)	3	
D(124/60)	4	
E(344/24)		7
F(304/60)		9
G(183/18)		10

Tab.1: Normal directions of the pressure cells

Measurement results

In order to obtain a representative set of data, the development of pressures over a period of time is studied for each pressure cell separately. The main features observed are:

- The prestressing of the measurement cells in each borehole occurs at different maximum pressures, i.e. the fracturing pressure in the two boreholes (bh) is different: (bh I: 21 MPa; bh II: 16 MPa).

Starting from this well defined pressure level in each borehole the stress tensor components release during the lapse of time. Without any further deformation of the boreholes, the induced overstress decreases with increasing time. Finally it will approach the stationary stress level, which depends on the spatial orientations of the pressure cells and the boreholes in the mine and on the virgin stress field in the salt rock.

- The reduction of pressure from the borehole-specific fracturing pressure level down to a stationary pressure level is performed within a time of about 300 days. All pressure cells with their various spatial orientations and locations in boreholes with different orientations and fracturing pressures exhibit a nearly uniform relaxation behaviour.

In order to compare all the data of the different pressure cells, the observed stress-time relationships are shown in a normalized diagram: The time dependent normal stress intensity and the initial frac stress intensity are reduced by the intensity of the final stationary stress. The ratio of these stress differences σ/σ_o is plotted vs. the dimensionless time $t^* = t/t_o$ where t is the actual time in days and the relaxation time t_o is taken as 300 days.

Fig.2 shows the data obtained from two pressure cells in equal spatial positions. Each pressure cell is located in differently orientated boreholes with different fracturing pressures. However, the slopes of both relaxation curves appear to be rather similar. The slight shift of the curves reflect small differences in relaxation times between the two boreholes.

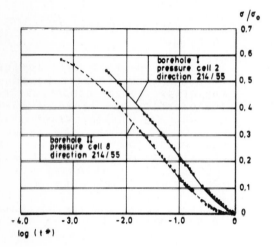

Fig.2: Stress relaxation measured in equal directions by pressure cells in different boreholes

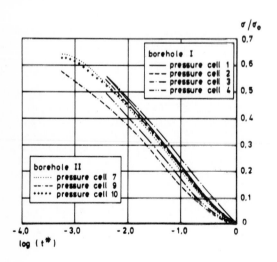

Fig.3: Stress relaxation curves from boreholes I and II

The various measurements of stress relaxation, which are observed in the boreholes (s. Tab.1) result in a nearly uniform type of stress relaxation curves, as shown in fig.3. These curves represent the stress relaxation behaviour in situ. Additional laboratory tests of rock salt relaxation (Haupt and Natau 1984) coincide well with the observations made by prestressed hard inclusion technique in the underground rock mass.

Relaxation function

Let the total strain rate of the rock salt be defined by the sum of an elastic strain rate and a creep strain rate. The elastic strain rate is proportional to the stress rate, whereas the creep strain rate is assumed to be a hyperbolic sine function of the differential stress (Nadai 1963).

In pure relaxation, the total strain is constant and its rate is equal to zero. Hence, in uniaxial compression the relaxation equation is given as:

$$a\dot{\sigma} + \sinh(b\sigma) = 0 \qquad (1)$$

Integration of eq.(1) yields

$$\int_{\sigma_o}^{\sigma} d\sigma / \sinh(b\sigma) = -t/a \qquad (2)$$

and hence

$$\left[\ln \tanh(b\sigma/2)\right]_{\sigma_o}^{\sigma} = -t^* \qquad (3)$$

where

$$t^* = at/b \qquad (4)$$

Substituting

$$\delta = \tanh(b\sigma_o /2) \qquad (5)$$

into eq.(3) and solving for σ yields

$$b\sigma = 2 \, \text{artanh}(\delta \exp(-t^*)) \qquad (6)$$

which can be converted to

$$\sigma = \frac{1}{b} \ln\left(\frac{1 + \vartheta \exp(-t^*)}{1 - \vartheta \exp(-t^*)}\right) \quad (7)$$

Let the initial differential stress be σ_0 and a new parameter α be defined by

$$\alpha = b \sigma_0 \quad (8)$$

so that the relaxation equation is given by

$$\sigma / \sigma_0 = \Phi(t^*) \quad (9)$$

where

$$\Phi(t^*) = \frac{1}{\alpha} \ln\left(\frac{1 + \vartheta \exp(-t^*)}{1 - \vartheta \exp(-t^*)}\right) (10)$$

In Fig.4, a set of relaxation curves is shown vs. time for different parameters α. Due to eq(4), the dimensionless time variable t^* in eq.(9) reflects the rheological parameters a and b. These material parameters can directly be determined by evaluation of relaxation times and functions from the pre-stress relaxation measurements in situ.

By comparison of the theoretical relaxation functions in Fig.4 with the measured curves of Fig.3 from prestressed hard inclusion soundings it is obvious, that the parameter α is about 10 and relatively invariant for every location of the pressure cells.

The relaxation times for all curves in Fig.3 were chosen to be 300 days. By slight time shiftening, the curves can be transduced into one single relaxation curve representing the rheological properties of the rock salt in situ. Through a generalization of the above relaxation function to the triaxial state of stress it can be verified that the time shift mainly eliminates the influence of the borehole diameter, the stiffness of the pressure sonde, and the intensity of the primary in situ stress.

Conclusion

Stress relaxation plays a dominant role in underground mining in salt rock. Examples are the release of supplementary stresses in the lapse of time, when former extraction chambers are filled up with goaf, the time dependent compression of cavity fillings with raw materials or special waste in saltdomes, and the relaxation of rebutment stresses in side walls, pillars, and roofs leading to a global stress redistribution in the salinar rock and to the formation of a wide span stress arch around the entire pit outlay.

In situ relaxation measurements by the prestressed hard inclusion (PHI) method offer a new technique to obtain the necessary rheological properties of salinar rock as e.g. α-values and relaxation times t_0 for the analysis and prediction of time dependent stresses and strains for solving boundary value problems according to engineering applications.

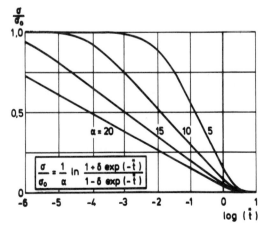

Fig.4: Theoretical relaxation diagram according to eq.(10)

References

Borm, G. 1980. Zur Analyse chroni-
scher Gebirgsdeformationen beim
Felshohlraumbau.   Veröffentli-
chungen des Instituts für Boden-
mechanik und Felsmechanik der
Universität Karlsruhe, Heft 88.

Haupt, M. and O. Natau 1984. Uniaxial Relaxation Tests on Rock
Salt. Proc.2nd Conf. on Mechanical Behaviour of Salt, Hannover.
TransTechPubl., Clausthal.

Nadai, A. 1963. Theory of Flow and
Fracture of Solids. Vol.II.
McGraw-Hill, New York.

Natau, O., Ch. Lempp and K.Baltha-
sar 1985. Monitoring System for
Stress Measurement.   Proc.Int.
Congr. IAEG on Management of
Hazardous Chemical Waste Sites.
Winston-Salem, N.C.

Wöhlbier, H. and O. Natau 1966.
Die Entwicklung einer neuartigen
Einbautechnik für Bohrlochdruck-
geber. Proc.1st Int.Congr.ISRM,
4.4: 25-30, Lisbon.

Hypothesis on rockbursts

TAN TJONG KIE
Institute of Geophysics, Academia Sinica, Beijing, China

SUMMARY
This report presents a theoretical analysis of rockbursts. Cracks, internal stresses, heterogeinity and anisotropy are fundamental features of rocks and coals. The influences of high stress concentrations, internal stresses, the conversion of potential to seismic energy, the multiple reflections of seismic waves and the local magnification of the energy and dynamic stresses are fundamental factors in the mechanism of rockbursts. An analysis of catastrophic rockbursts and some suggestions for their prevention and mitigation is presented.

RÉSUMÉ
Ce report présente un analyse theorétique des "rockbursts". Les fissures, contraints internes, le heterogeneité et l'anisotropie sont des traits fundamentaux des roches et charbons. L'influence des contraints concentrés, contraints internes, la conversion de L'energie potential en energie sismique, les reflections multiples des ondes sismiques et la magnification locale de L'energy et des contraints dynamiques sont des facteurs fundamentaux dans le mechanism des "rockbursts". L'auteur presénte un analyse des "rockbursts" catastrophiques et quelques suggestions pour leur contrôle.

ZUSAMMENFASSUNG
Diese Verhandlung bietet eine theoretishe Analyse der Gebirgschläge. Die Risze, eingefrorene Spannungen, Heterogenität und Anisotropie, sind Hauftkenmerke der Fels und Kohlen massen. Der Einflusz der hohen Spannungs-Koncentrationen, interne Spannungen, die Umverwandlung von potentiale Energie zu dynamische Energie, die vielfache Reflexionen von seismische Wellen und die lokale Vergröszerung der dynamische Energie und Spannungen sind Hauptfaktoren in das Mechanismus der Gebirgschläge. Der Schreiber gibt eine Analyse der Katastrophale Gebirgschlägen und bietet einige Vorschläge für Ihre Verhütung und Abschwächung.

1. INTRODUCTION

In China the excavation of mines, underground constructions is rapidly increasing in order to meet the big progress in industrialisation. With the ever increasing scale of mining and the deepening of mines the danger of rockbursts becomes progressively more pressing. The Chinese engineers have much experience in dealing with rockbursts, and have studied eagerly from their foreign colleagues; but as the problem is very intricate we have not yet found an efficient way to treat rockbursts. Rockbursts are known already since 1900 in the Witwatersrand (Salamon 1983) and the Kolar Gold Fields (Krishna Murti 1983). The percentage of total fatali-

ties due to rockbursts in South Africa from 1926-1975 was increasing and in the ten years from 1926-1975 rockbursts amounted to 55.7% of the total fatalities. In severe cases the mining induced seismic events can damage underground excavations, costly surface structures, haulage roadways, pumping stations etc. On the basis of his study of Chinese and foreign experiences the author is of opinion that three fundamental factors-in addition to stress concentrations, stress strain relations mode of fracturing etc-which are neglected,must be studied carefully;
1. locked in stresses and 2. conversion of potential strain energy to seismic energy 3. the multiple reflections of

seismic waves which can lead to local energy and stress magnification. Although experience is very valuable the need is pressing to study this complicated problem from more basic theories. This report is a first modest attempt to study it on the basis of rheology and dynamic fracture theory.

2. MICRO ANALYSIS OF ROCKS AND COALS

In order to get an insight into the mechanism of rock and coal bursts we now present a prelude on the microstructure of rocks and coals. Rocks are complicated materials from any aspect. They are composed of grains of various sizes, shapes and mineral compositions, which are firmly welded together, the grains having different physico chemical and mechanical properties. Generally microflaws can be easily detected as intergranular cracks extending over many grains, intragranular cracks and cracks along grain boundaries. Rock have been subjected to a series of complex processes as rock-genesis, metamorphosis, tectonics, sedimentation and erosion. The process of rock genesis was accomplished under various complex diffusional and shear transformations with changes of volume and shear. Due to the different anisotropic thermal and mechanical properties of the crystals this rock genesis resulted in a non homogeneous stress distribution which is frozen or locked in within the material. Furthermore, misfits of atoms in semi-coherent interfaces readily occured, leading to the creation of born in dislocations within the grains and grain boundaries. The motion of these dislocations along sliding surfaces could account for a partial relaxation of the intragranular and intergranular stresses. Metamorphosis lead to further recrystallisation and phase transformation and heterogeneous straining. Tectonic motion of the crust induced a further sequence of straining, resulting in additional localised stresses due to the different elastoplastic and viscous properties of the grains. In general the grains will not undergo a general strain in comformity with the applied stress and imposed constraints from the neighbouring grains. Thus incompatible straining occured which resulted in the cleavage of grainboundaries and splitting of individual grains, thus the creation of cracks and voids. In coal which are known to be brittle, cracks were created

during the tectonic history. In this way a part of the concentrated stresses was released, however a part of these stresses is retained in the form of locked in stresses. Hence born in dislocations, cracks, locked in stresses, inhomogeneity anisotropy are fundamental features inherent to rocks and coals. Therefore the mechanism of rock fracture and especially the mechanism of violent rockbursts in response to externally applied stresses are difficult to decipher from experimental data obtained during rock deformation and fracture tests, as the scale effect is an unknown factor.

3. EXTERNAL AND INTERNAL (LOCKED IN) STRESSES

We will now subdivide the stresses within a rockmass into external and internal stresses. The stresses which the engineer is usually considering in Rock Mechanics are external stresses which have their origin in external causes as forces and constraints at the outer or inner boundaries of rock masses, tectonic forces, overburden, water pressures, thermal stresses etc. This external stresses will disappear as soon as the external causes are removed. On the contrary internal stresses will persist within the medium after the external causes are removed. For example when we take a sample of rock from a deep borehole to the surface the boundaries of the samples are stressfree, yet internal stresses may remain inside in self equilibrum. It is known from solid mechanics that samples of ceramics, and rocks with high internal stresses may show brittle cracks after some lapse of time.

The concept of internal (locked in) stresses in rocks has been presented earlier (Tan 1981). The author assumes that there exist a multitude of rigid kernels within a matrix of the rock mass. When the matrix is strained plastically the gliding planes will be subjected to mutual slidings and stresses will be concentrated to the rigid kernels. The gliding planes can now be welded together by interatomic forces and cementing agents. The stresses within the kernels are now locked in and remain in self equilibrum with the shearing resistance of the many gliding planes in the matrix. In rock masses there exist an abundant multitude of such stress kernels of different dimensions, intensity, sizes and shapes and may exist for very long geological time. When an underground con-

struction is excavated, the matrix surrounding the stress kernel will be partly removed or weakened. In these cases
the internal stresses can be gradually
or abruptly released. So locked in stresses can contribute directly to rockbursts by:
1. The increase of local stress intensity due to tensorial addition of external and locked in stresses.
2. The liberation of locked in stresses
and the conversion of their potential
energy to kinetic energy.
In the following we mention some practical cases, which are related to locked
in stresses.
It is known from the Kolar Gold Fields
(Krishna Murthy 1983) that folded regions are preferred sites of rockbursts.
Here locked in stresses can easily be
accumulated. The flooding of the mine
in   such an folded area have had a
further contribution to the occurrence
of the rock-bursts. In this case the
blocking effects of the resistance in
glide planes in the matrix were reduced
and the enormous accumulated energy due
to locked in stresses were dynamically
liberated.

4. ANALYSIS OF CREEP AND FAILURE AND BURSTS OF BRITTLE ROCKS

Violent burst are known to occur in sites where the rocks and coals have been
subjected to biaxial, or uniaxial states
of stress such as the walls of underground works and pillars. In this state
of stress one or two of principal stresses are zero and the material is known
to be in the brittle state. Under maximal stresses the material collapses
suddenly after some time without any
signal of plastic flow. The typical stress strain relationships for a medium
grained granite at various values of
the hydrostatic pressures are shown in
Fig. 1, (Rummel et al 1982) axial radial
and volumetric strains as a function
of the axial deviatoric stress in Fig.2.
(Tan 1983). The response is first linear
followed by an elastic prepeak deformation occured by brittle progressive
microfracturing. The obvious onset of
inelastic volume dilatancy occurs at
rather low differential stress (f_3^*).

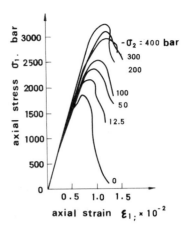

Fig. 1. Stress strain relationships
for granite (Rummel et al
1982)

This stage of initial dilatancy could be
dominated by enhanced preferred axial
crack growth. At higher differential stress f_3^* the dilatancy becomes more extensive and should be attributed to inclined
cracks which were growing and coalescing.

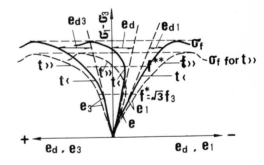

Fig. 2. Relationships between deviatoric stress $\sigma_1 - \sigma_3$ versus
axial e_1, radial e_3 and
volume strain e.

When rocks are initally loaded, previously existing microcracks grow stably
throughout the entire stress region resulting in a dilatancy. However because
of statistical variation in crack morphology as crack density distribution,
shape, orientation during durther deformation zones will develop where crack
growth, interaction and coalescence are
enhanced. While some regions may temporily
become dormant, it is the coalescence of

517

such active zones which progressively
leads to failure.

From this analysis it is clear that rock-
bursts-preluded by accoustic emissions-
may appear after the deviatoric stresses
have exceed f_3^*, and that violent rockbursts occur when f_3^* is by far exceeded.

5. VELOCITY OF CRACK DROPAGATION

A significant contribution to our understanding of rock failure has come from
single crack propagation studies in
metals, glass, ceramics and rocks. (Atkinson 1980) In these experiments specimens containing a single crack are stressed such that the crack tip advances
stably. The velocity of crack tip advance
has been found to increase exponentially
with the stress intensity and about
linearly with increasing moisture content. Further this velocity is dependent
upon many factors as moisture concentration and intrinsic material properties
such as activation energy and activation
volume.

So the rate of crack growth V can be
written as follows:

$$V = C \exp(-Q/RT) \left\{ \exp\frac{V(\sigma_c - \sigma_0)}{RT} - 1 \right\} \quad (1)$$

whereby V-activation volume and Q=activa-
tion energy and C is a material constant;
R=gas constant; T=absolute temperature;
for $\sigma_c = \sigma_0$ the crack velocity V=0; σ_c =
maximal stress at distance r_0 from crack-
tip; σ_0 =barrier stress which must be
overcome to induce crack growth. In a
two dimensional homogeneous medium including a crack with a width of 2a, and
subjected to pure shear with $\tau = \tau_0$ the
stresses are dependent on the distance
from the cracktip and the orientation,

$$\begin{matrix} \sigma_x \\ \\ \sigma_y \\ \\ \tau_{xy} \end{matrix} = \frac{K}{\sqrt{2\pi r}} \begin{cases} \sin\frac{\theta}{2}(2+\cos\frac{\theta}{2}\cos\frac{\theta}{2}) \\ \\ \sin\frac{\theta}{2}(\cos\frac{\theta}{2}\cos\frac{3\theta}{2}) \\ \\ \cos\frac{\theta}{2}(1-\sin\frac{\theta}{2}\sin3\frac{\theta}{2}) \end{cases}$$

whereby $K=\sqrt{\pi a}\ \tau_0$ (see f.i. Rice 1968)
For θ =0, the normal stresses vanish and
the shear stress attains its maximum.

$$\sigma_c = \tau_{xy} = \sqrt{\frac{a}{2\pi r_0}}\ \tau_0$$

when r_0 is the radius of a very thin
cylinder with its axis along the crack
tip.

Let us now study the case of a pillar
under uniaxial loading whereby σ_1
acts parallely to the long axis. We
have found that for stresses below the
upper yield limit f_3^* the creep proceeds
linearly with log t and that the volume
deformation is decreasing with the time.
This stage of logarithmic creep has been
attributed to the motion of dislocations
and boundary sliding, and minor microcracking; compatible deformations occur.
However for deviatoric stresses exceeding f_3^* the compatibility in the assem-
blage of grains is no longer preserved
and voids (Cracks) are generated and
mobilised. It this stage the incremental
volumetric deformations become positive
and volume dilatancy is observed. For
constant stresses exceeding f_3^* the axial
creep rate becomes first constant and
gradually increases with the time. This
may be attributed to the propagation of
cracks whereby accoustic stress waves
are emitted (Tan 1983). This process
reduces the effective load bearing contact area (see Form. 1 2) and hence
leads to the increase of the stress
transmitted through the asperites. This
in turn results into an increase of
the stress σ_c at the cracktip, and rise
in the crack propagation velocity. This
complex process is observed as an accelerated creep. The accoustic emission
increases in frequency of occurence and
intensity. As it will be shown later
in this paper the coversion of static
energy into seismic energy becomes
more efficient (formula 9).

So intense seismic energies are generate
by crack propagation and coalescence,
radiating high intensity dynamic stress
waves. When deviatoric stresses by far
exceed the upper yield value f_3^*, their
propagation at accoustic velocities,
reflection at the free boundaries of
pillars and their mutual interaction,
the impinging and reflection of waves
must lead to local intense dynamic
stress concentrations and bursts.

6. CONVERSION OF POTENTIAL ENERGY TO SEISMIC ENERGY

For physical simplicity we now first
consider the problem of a plane penny-
shaped crack in an infinite homogeneous
linear medium. When the crack grows from
the original radius a_0 to a_0 + a, then

the energy release rate following Irwin (1957) can be written

$$\mathcal{G} = -\frac{dP}{da} = -\frac{1-v^2}{E}(K_I^2 + K_{II}^2) + \frac{1}{2G}K_{III}^2 \quad (3)$$

where P=Potential Energy

$\mathcal{G}$ =Energy Release Rate when linear elasticity is considered

E,v=Elastic constants

The stress intensity factors have been found (Hartranft et al 1973);

$$K_{II} = -\frac{4}{(2-v)\pi}\sqrt{\pi a}\ \tau_o\ Sin\theta$$
$$\quad (4)$$
$$K_{III} = -\frac{4(1-v)}{(2-v)\pi}\sqrt{\pi a}\ \tau_o\ Cos\theta$$

next we consider shearing stresses, then $K_I = 0$ and

$$\mathcal{G}(a) = -\frac{1-v^2}{E}K_{II}^2 + \frac{1}{2G}K_{III}^2 \quad (5)$$

The potential energy P can now be computed by integration.

$$P = \int_0^{2\pi}\int_0^a G(r)rdr\ d\theta = \frac{8}{3}\left(\frac{1-v}{1-2v}\right)\frac{a^3}{G}\tau_o^2$$

which for v=0.25; becomes, $P = \frac{8}{7}\frac{a^3}{G}\tau_o^2$

This result has been obtained earlier (Sato et al 1973). Once a crack starts to propagate, the rate of supply of driving energy exceeds the rate of its consumption as surface energy and as strain energy. The excess is radiated in the form of kinetic energy of the parts displaced by advance of the crack. We now introduce the efficiency factor $\mathcal{G}$ for the conversion of potential to kinetic Energy.

$$E_{kin} = \mathcal{G}P = \frac{8}{3}\left(\frac{1-v}{1-2v}\right)\frac{a^3}{G}\tau_o^2\ \mathcal{G} \quad (6)$$

The kinetic energy is radiated as total wave energy which is the summation of the energy for primary waves E_p and the energy for shear waves E_s:

$$P = E_{kin} = E_p + E_s(1 + E_p/E_s) \quad (7)$$

Now the kinetic energy of an element dV increases with the velocity of crack

propagation V. Therefore the nondimensional parameter $\mathcal{G}$ must be a function of V/Cs: $\mathcal{G} = f(V/Cs)$, when Cs = shear wave velocity. When the velocity of crack propagation rises i.e. the rate of driving energy is increased such that it considerably exceeds the energy consumption as surface and strain energy and energy disipation due to plastic flow and viscous effects then it is clear that $\mathcal{G}$ will increase progressively with (V/Cs). As the kinetic energy is proportional to the square of the rate of deformation it is plausible to write

$$\mathcal{G} = f(V/c) \sim (V/Cs)^2 \quad (8)$$

Indeed rigorous mathematical computations (Sato et al 1973) have shown that this relationship is valid up to V/Cs 0.9 (for V up to the Raileigh wave velocity). So the total radiated wave energy can be written:

$$E_{kin} \sim C\frac{a^3}{G}\tau_o^2(\frac{V}{Cs})^2 \quad (9)$$

for $0 < V/Cs < 0.9$ whereby C=dimensionless constant.

Since in our analysis only the effect of shearing stresses is considered it can be inferred that the wave energy is mainly radiated in the form of shear wave energy. It has been computed (Sato et al 1973) that the ratio $E_p/E_s \sim 0.05$. As the fracturing of rocks in underground mining is mainly caused by shear stresses, excess potential energy is for the major part radiated in the form of shear waves. Now let we subject a sample with area A_o and height H to a shearing stress τ_o. Then the presence of the crack increases the strain energy by $\alpha a^3\tau_o^2/G_o$. Thus the total strain energy is

$$P = AH\frac{\tau_o^2}{2G} + \alpha a^3\frac{\tau_o^2}{2G_o} = \frac{\tau_o^2}{2G}\left(AH + \alpha a^3\right) =$$
$$\frac{\tau_o^2}{2G}V(1 + \alpha a^3/V) \quad (10)$$

where $V = A_o H$.

It is clear from the form of these equation that now the Glide modulus Go of the cracked specimen is decreased to

$$G_o/(AH + \alpha a^3) = G_o/(1 + \alpha a^3/V)V \quad (11)$$

for mutually independent mobile cracks with radius a_n, the gliding modules is

$$G_{eff} = G_0 / \left[1 + \sum_n \alpha_n a_n^3 \, \mathcal{N} \right] \nu \qquad (11a)$$

where α_n = a parameter dependent on crack orientation.

We will now give another interpretation of formula (10): for this purpose we write:

τ_q = S/A, whereby S = shearing force, and we get:

$$P = \frac{1}{2G_0} \frac{S^2}{A_0^2} \, \nu \, (1 + \alpha a^3 / \nu)$$

now we consider G_0 constant and find that the effective area is decreased to

$$A_{eff} = A_0 / \sqrt{(1 + \sum_n \alpha_n a_n^3 / V) \nu} \qquad (12)$$

with the decrease of A_{eff}, the stress τ_0 and hence σ_c will increase and the result is an accelerated tertiary creep.

7. ENERGY MAGNIFICATION, STRUCTURAL DESINTERGRATION AND ROCK BURSTS

The energy criterion for brittle fracture by extension of the 2a crack requires that the work done by the applied stress during an increment in crack length should be sufficient to supply the concurrent increase in surface energy in an elastic strain energy. For a penny shaped crack Sack (1946) obtained:

$$\sigma_f = \left(\frac{E \pi \gamma}{2(1 - \nu^2)a} \right)^{\frac{1}{2}}$$

whereby γ = surface energy. Thus when the stress is σ_f then all cracks with radius $\leq a_0$ remain immobilised, whereas all cracks with radius $> a_0$ will propagate and radiate seismic energy. In a limited volume of the rock mass f.i. a pillar the radiated waves will be subjected to multiple reflections at the free boundaries. During this process shear waves will be reflected as primary and shear waves. As the free boundaries are stress free, compressional waves will be reflected as tensional waves, and tensional waves will become compressional waves etc. The tensile strength of rocks is in the order of a few tens of kilograms/cm2 or less only and hence the reflected tensional waves will cause **fractures** parallel to the free surface.

This phenomenon is known as spalling or scabbing. The fractures are called Hophinson fractures after B. Hopkinson who first discovered the effect (1914) (Fig. 3). In the slabs kinetic energy is

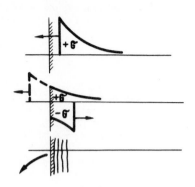

Fig. 3. Mechanism of spalling

entrapped and hence they fly away in space. This phenomenon of spalling is often experienced in underground structures. The slabs may have a few mm in thickness and an area of many tens cm2: in severe cases the slab may be more then 10 cm thick and the area in the order of 10^4 cm2. The bursts will be more violent when enormous energies are created near to the free surface. In fatal cases the outbursts have damaged underground excavations, surface structures and caused many fatalities. During the process of interaction and reflection of stress waves there may be regions to which a great part of the overall dynamic energy is transported. This is the case for example in pillars with a lozenge-shape crossection. It can be readily analysed from the multiple reflections at the free surfaces that the energy is transmitted to, concentrated and magnified at the sharp corners of the pillar (Fig. 4). As the total of static and dynamic stresses has been magnified in a very short time; the pill at these corners desintegrates dynamically and explodes in a catastrophically violent burst. In coal mining practice in China such rockbursts in lozenge shaped pillars are frequently encountere

8. CONCLUSIONS AND SUGGESTIONS

Based on the concepts and analysis presented above the following conclusion and suggestions can be made:

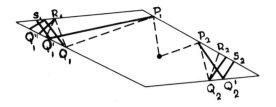

Fig. 4. Multiple reflection
of stress waves in lozenge
shaped pillars leads to
stress concentration at
the corners
---shear waves
——primary waves

1. Avoid high stress concentrations. The potential energy of a region in the rockmass increases with the square of the stress. The efficiency of conversion of potential energy into seismic energy is small for small stresses but may be 100% for high stresses. Methods of destressing must be carefully studied.

2. Avoid high stress levels. For example it must be ensured that pillars are able to support the overburden. As pillars have not the same rigidity, stress relaxation in some pillars may induce higher stresses in the more rigid ones in the group.

3. Avoid sharp edges in pillars. Dynamic energy will flow into these edges by multiple stress wave reflections and interaction leading to dynamic stress magnification.

4. A F.E. analysis based on reliable constitutive equations is helpfull in estimating the volume of the unstable region around cavities where seismic events could be triggered off. The influence of tectonic stresses must be carefully studied.

5. On the base of FE analysis, effective support systems, as steel rods (increases the tensile strength of rocks against scabbing) steelweb and shotcrete in tunnels are recommended.

6. A seismic network monitoring the distribution of Accoustic Emissions in space and time is necessary. Seismic events are preluded by accoustic emissions increasing in frequency and magnitude with the time prior to failure.

7. Features as a bend or kink in geo-

logical formations, folded regions, etc may be the sites of high locked in stresses, which in combination with the external stresses due to the overburden and tectonic force will bring the region to the brink of instability.

8. In China some succes has been obtained in the mitigation of rockbursts by means of water injection. The friction between the planes of the cracks can be lubricated and the cracks grow slowly thereby consuming potential energy; in some cases a weakening of the material is obtained. However when the stresses are high, lubrication of cracks can result into the triggering of seismic events. The destressing by water injection must be studied carefully.

REFERENCES

Atkinson, B.K. 1980: A fracture mechanics study of subcritical tensile cracking of quartz in wet environment, Pageo ph. 117: 1011-1024.
Hartanft, R.J. and Shi, G.C. 1973: Alternating method applied to edge and surface crack, problems, in C.G. Shi (Editor), Mechanics of fracture I, :234, Noordhoft Inst. Publ. Leyden.
Irwin, G.R. 1957: Analysis of stresses and strains near the end of a crack traversing a plate. J. Appl. Mech. 24: 261.
Krishna Murthy, R. 1983: Rock Mechanics studies on the problem of ground control and rockbursts in the Kolar Gold fields. Symp. Rockbursts, prediction and contral ed. by Inst. of Mining and Metallurgy. p.67-80.
Rice, J.R. 1968: Mathematical analysis in the Mechanics of Fracture in Fracture. Vol. II, P216. ed. by H. Liebowitz, Acad. Press. Ny, London.
Rummel, F. and Crohn, C. 1982: Variation of Ultrasonic velocity in granite and serpentine during dilatant fracture under general triaxial compression in W.E. Schreier (editor), High pressure researches in Geoscience: 103-111.
Sack, R.A. 1946: Proc. Phys. Soc. (London) 58: 729.
Salomon, 1983: Rockburst hazard and the fight for its alleviation in South African gold mines Symp. Rockburst: prediction and control, ed. Inst. of Mining and Metallurgy, :11-36.
Spetzler H. Mizutani, and Rummel, F. 1982: A model for time-dependent rock failure in W.E., Schreyer (editor), high pressure researches in geoscience:

85-93, Schweizerbartsche Verlagsb uch-
handlung, Stuttgart.
Tan Tjong Kie, Kang Wen Fa, 1981: Locked
in Stresses, Creep and dilatancy of rocks
and constitutive equations, Rock Mech.
13: 5-22.
Tan Tjong Kie, Kang Wen Fa, 1983: Time
dependent dilatancy prior to rock failure and earthquakes, Proc. 5th. Congress
ISRM,: 95-102, Melbourne.

A study of the bond strength in cemented epoxy solid inclusion stress cell installations

R.L. BLACKWOOD
Consultant, Sydney, Australia

S. SANDSTRÖM *
B.A. LEIJON
Luleå University of Technology, Luleå, Sweden

* now with Boliden Mineral Co, Boliden, Sweden

ABSTRACT: The radial tensile bond stress at the interface between an epoxy solid inclusion stress cell and the host rock has been examined by laboratory simulation of overcoring stress relief in an attempt to detect tensile failure. Although expected in theory, no bond failures were observed. This agrees with field experience. The reasons and significance are discussed. It is concluded that the solid inclusion method may be used with confidence in weak rocks.

RÉSUMÉ: Les tensions radiales au point de contact entre une sonde epoxyde solide et le roc ont été examinées en simulant au laboratoire un relâchement de contrainte par surcarottage afin de détecter des failles dues à la tension. Malgré les prévisions théoriques, aucune faille n'a été observée. Ceci confirme des expériences sur le terrain. Les raisons et la signification en sont discutées. On en conclut que cette méthode peut être utilisée avec confiance même dans des rocs friables.

ZUSAMMENFASSUNG: Die radiale Zugfestigkeit der Bindung bei der Grenzfläche zwischen einem epoxydischen soliden verformungsarmen Spannungsmessgeber und dem Wirtgestein wurde anhand von einer Simulation der Spannungsentlastung durch Überkernung im Labor untersucht, in einem Versuch, das Versagen in der Haltfestigkeit festzustellen. Obwohl dies nach der Theorie erwartet wurde, konnte kein solches Versagen beobachtet werden. Dies stimmt mit der Erfahrung in der Praxis überein. Die Gründe und Bedeutung werden besprochen. Die Schlußfolgerung lautet, daß die verformungsarme Methode mit Zuversicht in schwachem Gestein angewandt werden kann.

1. INTRODUCTION

The solid inclusion is an overcoring method of absolute triaxial stress measurement in rock. It essentially consists of a three-dimensional array of electrical resistance strain gauges encapsulated in an epoxy cylinder, which is cemented into a borehole in rock and so ideally acts as a "welded" elastic inclusion in an elastic host mass. Analytically the solid inclusion is a special case of a hollow cylindrical inclusion with zero internal radius, just as the Leeman/CSIR triaxial stress cell may be regarded as a hollow inclusion with zero wall thickness (Duncan Fama and Pender, 1980).

Upon relief of compressive field stresses by overcoring, the solid inclusion resists borehole deformation and induces a constant tensile stress across the diameter of the cylinder. The magnitude of this stress may be as great as the in situ stress in the rock. It

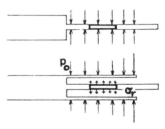

Figure 1. Overcoring stress relief causes a tensile bond stress at the epoxy/rock interface.

has often been implied that this radial, tensile stress may be sufficient to cause the rock to fail at the interface between the epoxy and the host rock: "A solid probe should not be used unless the ratio of the shear modulus of the probe to that of the rock is extremely small – or the level of in situ stress normal to probe is known to be low". (Duncan Fama and Pender, 1980, p.143).

Rock failure is not observed in practice, however. Even in highly stressed, weak coal, bond failure has not occurred (Blackwood, 1982). The elastic analytical solution does not take rock strength mechanisms into account. The present study attempts to throw light on this apparent contradiction by examining simulated stress relief in a weak rock-like host material containing bonded epoxy cylinders.

2. TENSILE BOND STRESS

The action of overcoring a solid epoxy cylinder bonded into a rock mass subjected to a compressive stress field induces a tensile bond stress as shown diagrammatically in Figure 1.

In the present case a hydrostatic pressure p_0 represents the in situ stress. It is released from the outer surface of the cylinder of "rock" which simulates the overcore annulus. The general elastic solution for the radial stress σ_r in the epoxy cylinder is given by Duncan Fama and Pender, 1980, p.146. In the hydrostatic pressure case this expression reduces to

$$\sigma_r = \frac{2\varepsilon(1 - \nu_1\nu_2)(-p_0)}{(1 - 2\nu_1 + \varepsilon)(1 + \varepsilon)} \quad \ldots \ (1)$$

where $\varepsilon = G_1/G_2$
$= E_1(1 + \nu_2)/E_2(1 + \nu_1)$
G is shear modulus
E is Young's modulus
ν is Poisson's ratio
$-p_0$ represents relaxation of the external hydrostatic pressure
and subscripts 1, 2 denote epoxy and rock respectively.

The value of σ_r in the rock annulus takes on a maximum value at the interface and reduces as a function of radius to zero at the outer surface. Thus if rock failure is to occur it is most likely to do so at the interface as long as elastic behaviour can be assumed.

The significance of ε, the ratio between the shear moduli of the two materials, is that for $\varepsilon < 0.2$ the bond stress does not present practical problems, whereas $\varepsilon > 0.4$ implies large bond stresses which theoretically lead to bond failure in low-strength rocks (Duncan Fama, 1979). In general, hard rock gives $\varepsilon \simeq 0.05$. Virtually all practical cases have $\varepsilon \ll 1$.

3. EXPERIMENTAL PROGRAMME

3.1 Summary of method (Sandström, 1986)

Low-strength, hollow concrete cylinders were subjected to external radial hydrostatic pressure in a biaxial compression cell. Axial stress is not significant in the generation of radial bond stress, and was not applied to the cylinders. Some were tested as empty

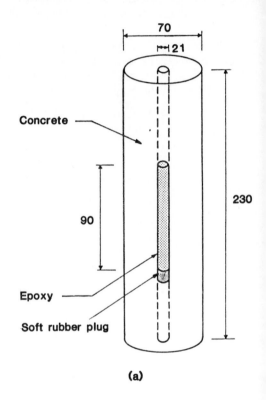

(a)

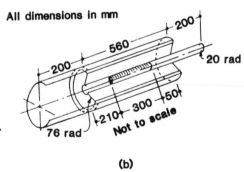

(b)

Figure 2. (a) Dimensions of test cylinders; (b) dimensions of a typical field installation of a solid inclusion cell.

cylinders for experimental control and others contained short lengths of epoxy which were cast in place while the cylinders were stressed, to simulate solid inclusion stress cell cylinders.

The cylinder configuration is shown in Figure 2, compared with the dimensions of a typical installation of the solid inclusion cell in a field overcoring operation. It can be seen that the ratio of cell diameter : outer (overcore) diameter is substantially constant; in both cases this ratio is sufficiently small that the outer diameter has negligible influence on the measured stresses.

Strain gauges were bonded to the wall of the inner hole in the axial and tangential directions prior to casting the epoxy. After the epoxy had set, the pressure was released slowly. Strain changes and acoustic emission were monitored throughout loading and unloading. After testing in this way, the cylinders were sectioned and the interface inspected for signs of fracture. The behaviour of the empty (control) cylinders was monitored in the same way.

3.2 Apparatus

The experimental arrangement is shown in

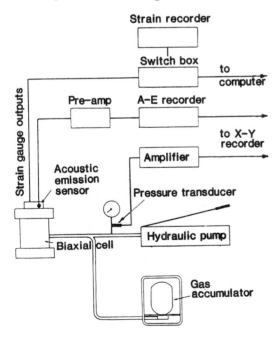

Figure 3. Experimental arrangement.

Figure 3, which is self-explanatory in general. The gas accumulator was required to maintain constant cell pressure over the experimental period, including the epoxy setting time.

Acoustic emission measurements were carried out throughout loading and unloading, incorporating an amplification of 50 to 60 dB in the frequency range 300-1000 kHz. Output was continuously recorded on an X-T plotter for later inspection.

3.3 Materials

For the purpose of this investigation it was necessary to ensure that large bond stresses would be generated. To do this, a low-strength, low-modulus concrete and high-modulus epoxy were used. These materials were designed specifically for the task.

The filled epoxy mix consisted of Araldite D resin, quartz powder CW1248KS filler and HY956 hardener, obtained from Ciba-Geigy, Sweden. A low-modulus concrete was designed as a result of tests on a number of mixes. The material properties are summarised in Table 1.

Table 1 Properties of materials in test cylinders

Property	Epoxy	Concrete
Cube strength	–	17.5 MPa
U.C.S.	7.4 MPa	17.0 MPa
Tensile strength*	–	2.8 MPa
Young's modulus	7.8 GPa	15.8 GPa
Poisson's ratio	0.32	0.17

* Brazilian test

These give a shear modulus ratio $\varepsilon = 0.44$, which lies within the range of potential tensile bond failure as discussed above. Evaluating Equation (1) with the properties in Table 1 gives a bond stress of -6.2 MPa (tensile). The tensile strength of the concrete as determined by the Brazilian test is 2.8 MPa (see below). On this basis also, rock failure would be expected; it did not occur, however, as detailed further below.

3.4 Procedure

1. Seven concrete cylinders as in Figure 2a were cored from a single block of concrete after curing for 30 days. Five were filled with epoxy as described below. Two were retained as controls.

2. Three 2-element strain gauge rosettes were bonded to the wall of the inner hole in each of the seven cylinders, positioned centrally along the length of the cylinder and equally spaced around the circumference, such that three gauges were oriented axially and three tangentially.

3. Each cylinder was placed in the biaxial cell and subjected to repeated load-unload cycles of radial pressure to ensure full consolidation and to stabilize hysteresis effects. Acoustic emission and strain recording commenced at this point.

4. Radial pressure of 7.0 MPa was then applied to each cylinder and maintained throughout step (5) below.

5. Epoxy mix was poured into the five prepared cylinders and left under load for at least 22 hours for hardening. The two empty control cylinders were subjected to radial pressure for the same period of time.

6. The radial pressure was slowly released from each of the seven cylinders.

7. A further pressure cycle $0 \rightarrow 7.0$ MPa $\rightarrow 0$ was applied to each of the seven cylinders.

8. The filled cylinders were sectioned longitudinally and the epoxy/concrete bond inspected for fracturing.

4. RESULTS

The radial bond stress was calculated from the observed strain readings in the following way.

The general form of the stress vs. tangential strain graphs for the load-unload cycles is shown in Figure 4. Actual measured values of tangential strains for all cylinders is shown in Figure 5.

These figures show non-linear strain change and a creep component. This made interpretation difficult but good approximations were possible by measuring the tangential strains (average of readings on the three rosettes in each case) at the same point in the unloading cycle for the empty cylinders (ε_a' in Figure 4) and the filled cylinders (ε_b').

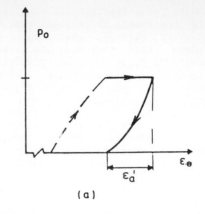

(a)

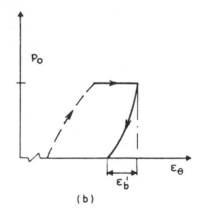

(b)

Figure 4. Form of stress-strain behaviour of concrete cylinders. (a) cylinders without epoxy (b) cylinders with epoxy.

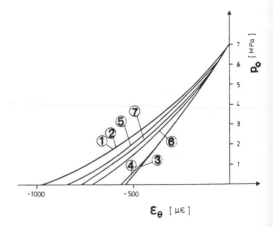

Figure 5. Observed stress-strain graphs showing the effect of the epoxy in reducing the strain in the concrete.

526

The presence of the epoxy is represented by the difference between these two values; that is, tangential strain change $\Delta\varepsilon' = \varepsilon_a' - \varepsilon_b'$. This value was used to calculate the radial stress, σ_r, at the internal boundary (i.e. the epoxy/rock interface) from the classical thick-walled cylinder analysis in the plane stress case (e.g. Obert and Duvall, 1967). Using the parameters shown in Figure 6, σ_r is given by

$$\sigma_r = \frac{\Delta\varepsilon'.E(b^2 - a^2)}{a^2(-\nu_2 - 1) + b^2(\nu_2 - 1)} \quad \ldots (2)$$

Since we are considering the unloading case (i.e. $\Delta\varepsilon'$ tensile, or negative), σ_r in Equation (2) is also tensile. The calculated values of σ_r are shown in Table 2.

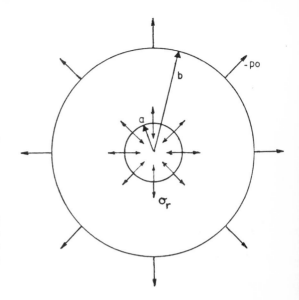

Figure 6. Thick-walled cylinder subjected to release of external pressure $-p_o$, inducing internal tensile boundary stress, $-\sigma_r$.

Table 2 Calculated bond stresses

	E_2 (GPa)	ν_2	p_o (MPa)	σ_r (Mpa)	Bond Fail?
1*	15.8	0.17	7.0	0	–
2*	15.8	0.17	7.0	0	–
3	15.8	0.17	7.0	–6.5	No
4	15.8	0.17	7.0	–6.3	No
5	15.8	0.17	7.0	–1.9	No
6	15.8	0.17	7.0	–2.4	No
7	15.8	0.17	7.0	–3.0	No

* Control cylinders (no epoxy)

In Table 2 the observed bond stresses range between –1.9 and –6.5 MPa. As shown earlier the theoretical bond stress is calculated from Equation (1) to be –6.2 MPa. The Brazilian test tensile strength of the concrete was 2.82 ± 0.50 MPa (s.d.) for 10 samples. Tensile failure would therefore be anticipated in cylinders 3, 4 and 7, with cylinder 6 being marginal; however, as noted in Table 2, failure was not detected in any of the cylinders, whether by the strain gauges, acoustic emission, or by subsequent visual inspection of longitudinally sectioned cylinders. The acoustic emission measurements, for example, did not differentiate between the empty (control) cylinders and the cylinders containing epoxy inclusions, indicating that not even incipient cracking had been initiated.

5. DISCUSSION

The radial bond stresses calculated from strain changes at the interface (Table 2) agree well with the ideal elastic case, Equation (1), which assumes linear elasticity, homogeneity, isotropy, an ideal welded bond, and an exactly cylindrical discontinuity between materials at the interface. None of these conditions is met in practice, of course, whether in the present carefully controlled set of circumstances or in the field. The agreement is therefore surprisingly good and tends to validate the experimental procedure.

When we consider concrete failure at the interface, however, clearly the observed results do not agree with the predictions based on tensile strength as estimated by the Brazilian test. On the other hand they are in complete accord with field experience of the solid inclusion cell.

Reasons for this apparent discrepancy are conjectural at this stage; three possibilities come immediately to mind.

Firstly, the Brazilian test for tensile strength may not be appropriate in this case. It is well known that apparent strengths vary with geometry, loading rate, moisture content and so on. It is suggested that nothing is known about the apparent tensile strength of a brittle material in the particular configuration being studied, that is, a cylindrical failure surface in an essentially triaxially stressed condition. This is conceptually difficult to relate to the Brazilian test mechanism of a plane stressed disc compressed diametrally to induce tensile failure along a pre-determined plane.

Alternatively the effect of epoxy entering small voids in the surface of the installation hole might lead to a smooth change of Young's modulus from the epoxy to the host material rather than the abrupt boundary of the ideal configuration.

Lastly, it is possible that some form of yielding takes place over a short radial distance at the interface, either in the epoxy or the rock, or both, so that the peak tensile stress predicted by elastic theory is not achieved. However four of the five observed bond stresses σ_r in Table 2 exceeded the Brazilian strength. If yielding of the material(s) had been the sole reason that tensile failure did not occur then it would be expected that the observed bond stresses would all be less than the Brazilian strength.

On balance it seems that the first conjecture is the best of the three: the Brazilian test tensile strength is not appropriate to a confined rock mass when the potential failure plane is cylindrical. In this configuration the tensile strength of the host rock was evidently large enough to resist failure in the circumstances of the experiments described, even although the Brazilian test strength was exceeded by a large amount.

6. CONCLUSIONS

A potentially serious limitation of the solid inclusion technique of in situ stress measurement has been investigated in a manner which simulates the overcoring stress relief action correctly. Despite the development of large tensile bond stresses in the experiments, bond failure was not detected by strain measurements, acoustic emission measurements or visual inspection of the interface following stress relief.

This finding agrees with field observations when using the solid inclusion cell in conjunction with overcoring: bond failure does not occur.

It is concluded that the solid inclusion stress cell can be used in weak rocks with confidence, since the bond stress does not appear to be sufficient to cause the bond to fail in tension even in exaggerated conditions such as the ones investigated here.

7. ACKNOWLEDGEMENTS

RLB gratefully acknowledges the opportunity to initiate this work at Luleå University of Technology, Sweden and the stimulating discussions that followed. All the authors acknowledge the assistance and advice of the technical staff at Luleå.

8. REFERENCES

Blackwood, R.L. 1982. Experience with the Solid Inclusion Stress Measurement Cell in Coal in Australia. Proc. 23rd U.S. Symposium in Rock Mechanics, Univ. California, Berkeley, 168-175.

Duncan Fama, M.E. 1979. Analysis of Solid Inclusion In Situ Stress Measuring Device. Proc. Fourth Congress Internat. Soc. Rock Mechanics Montreux, 2:113-120.

Duncan Fama, M.E. and M.J. Pender 1980. Analysis of the Hollow Inclusion Technique for Measuring In Situ Rock Stress. Internat. J. Rock Mechanics Geomechanics Abstracts 17:137-146.

Obert, L. and W.I. Duvall 1967. Rock Mechanics and the Design of Structures in Rock. Wiley, New York.

Sandström, S. 1986. Studier av Dragspänningar i Kontakten mellan Mjuk Bergarter och en Bergspänningsmätnings cell. (A Study of the Tensile Stresses at the Contact between Soft Rocks and Cell for Stress Measurements). Thesis Dept. Rock Mechanics, Luleå University of Technology, Sweden.

4. Application of rock stress measurements in mining

Ergebnisse zur Untersuchung von Gebirgsspannungszuständen und ihre Anwendung für die Hohlraum- und Ausbaudimensionierung

U. GROSS
W. MINKLEY
M. PENZEL
Institut für Berghausicherheit, Leipzig, German Democratic Republic

Zusammenfassung

Zunehmend komplizierter werdende geologische und bergtechnische Bedingungen beim Abbau von Lagerstätten erfordern zur Gewährleistung der Bergbausicherheit in der DDR unter anderem eine immer bessere Kenntnis des Gebirgsspannungszustandes in den Lagerstätten und ihrer Umgebung.
Aus langjährigen Untersuchungsergebnissen werden Einflüsse von Teufe, geologischer Struktur des Gebirges sowie regionaler Tektonik abgeleitet und dargestellt. Durch Verwendung einfacher Modelle kann die Wirkung von rezenten tektonischen Spannungsfeldern auf den Gebirgsspannungszustand sichtbar gemacht werden.
Für eine Vielzahl von Untersuchungsgebieten ergeben sich deutliche Unterschiede für den Einfluß rezenter tektonischer Spannungen auf die Gebirgsspannungszustände in mesozoischen Sedimenten und älteren Methamorphiten sowie Magmatiten.

Abstract

For the guarantee of mining safty in the GDR more and more complicated geological conditions in the mining of deposits require among other things a better and better knowledge of the rock stress state in the deposits and their environment. The influence of depth, geological rock structure as well as regional tectonics are being derived and described from long lasting research. The effect of rezent tectonical stress fields on the rock stress state can be shown by the application of simple models. For quite a number of observation districts there are significant distinctions for the influence of rezent tectonical stresses on the rock stress state in mesozoical sedimantary rocks and ground mass rocks.

Résumé

A cause des conditions géologiques de plus en plus compliquées lors de l'exploitation des gisements, il est entre autres nécessaire de connaitre toujours mieux l'état de tension du terrain afin d'assurer la sécurité de l'exploitation miniére en R.D.A..
Des résultats obtenus au cours de longues années d'études, on peut déduire et représenter les influences de la profondeur, de la structure géologique du terrain ainsi que de la tectonique régionale.
En se servant de modéles simples, on peut rendre visible l'effet des champs de tension actuels produit sur l'état de tension du terrain.
Dans beaucoup de domaines étudiés, on a constaté des différences sensibles dans l'effet produit par les tensions tectoniques actuelles sur les états de tension du terrain qui existent dans des sédiments mésozoiques et du soubassement plus ancien.

1. Einleitung

Die Bearbeitung von geomechanischen Standsicherheitsproblemen, die Bewertung der Gebirgsschlaggefährdung von Grubenbauen, und viele andere geomechanische Aufgabenstellungen in der Bergbaupraxis setzen Kenntnisse bzw. begründete Annahmen über Beträge und Richtungen der im Gebirge wirkenden Spannungen voraus. Einhergehend mit der Entwicklung der geomechanischen Meßtechnik werden vom Institut für Bergbausicherheit Leipzig zunehmend Messungen der Gebirgsspannungszustände für die Lösung praktischer geomechanischer Aufgaben hinzugezogen.

Diese Herangehensweise ist um so mehr erforderlich, als die internationalen Erfahrungen wie auch die in der DDR durchgeführten Spannungsmessungen zeigen, daß aus Materialgesetzen für bestimmte Bedingungen abgeleitete konventionelle Lastannahmen den realen geomechanischen Verhältnissen nicht entsprechen. Vielmehr können vor allem die Horizontalspannungen, z. B. verursacht durch das Wirken rezenter tektonischer Kräfte im oberen Teil der Erdkruste, die Vertikalspannungen erheblich übersteigen.

In der vorliegenden Arbeit wird sich auf die Auswertung von Meßergebnissen für den Grundspannungszustand des Gebirges, d. h. für den vom Bergbau nicht beeinflußten Bereich des Gebirges, beschränkt. Die Messungen sind an verschiedenen Stellen des Territoriums der DDR durchgeführt worden. Dabei wurden unterschiedliche stratigraphische und lithologische Einheiten des Gebirges im Teufenbereich von wenigen Dekametern bis zu einigen tausend Metern untersucht. Zur Ermittlung der Komponenten des Gebirgsspannungszustandes und ihrer Orientierung werden am Institut für Bergbausicherheit Leipzig

- die Bohrlochendflächen-Entlastungsmethode,
- die hydraulische Aufreißmethode in Bohrungen von untertägigen Auffahrungen aus sowie
- die hydraulische Aufreißmethode in Bohrungen von der Tagesoberfläche aus

angewendet.
Über die Verfahren ist ausführlich in der Literatur berichtet worden (KNOLL u. a., 1977; MENZEL u. a., 1982; GROSS u. a., 1982).
Zur Erhöhung der Zuverlässigkeit der Meßergebnisse wird bei gegebenen Bedingungen angestrebt, diese Verfahren kombiniert anzuwenden.

2. Ergebnisse von Spannungsmessungen

Um eine übersichtliche Darstellung der Ergebnisse der Spannungsmessungen zu ermöglichen, wird im weiteren angenommen,

daß von den drei Komponenten des Gebirgsspannungszustandes eine Komponente vertikal und zwei Komponenten horizontal orientiert sind, obwohl häufig in Abhänigkeit von Oberflächenrelief und Gebirgsstruktur diese Annahme nicht zutrifft. Bei der Untersuchung des Zusammenhanges von Spannungszustand und Verformungseigenschaft des Gebirges wird aus den gleichen Gründen auf die Verwendung von anisotropen Materialgesetzen verzichtet und von isotropem, linearelastischem Verhalten ausgegangen. Unter Komponenten des Gebirgsspannungszustandes werden die drei senkrecht aufeinander stehenden Hauptnormalspannungen verstanden, wobei gelten soll:

$$\sigma_1 \geqq \sigma_2 \geqq \sigma_3 \qquad (1)$$

Druckspannungen werden mit positivem Vorzeichen versehen.
Die Mehrheit der durchgeführten Messungen bestätigte, daß die vertikale Spannungskomponente dem lithostatischen Druck der überlagernden Gebirgssäule entspricht und als Betrag

$$\sigma_V = \bar{\varrho} \cdot g \cdot H \qquad (2)$$

$\bar{\varrho}$ – mittlere Dichte des überlagernden Gebirges
g – Erdbeschleunigung
H – Teufe
aufweist.
Die ermittelten Horizontalspannungen sind im allgemeinen anisotrop,

$$\sigma_H \geqq \sigma_h \qquad (3)$$

wobei unter entsprechenden geologischen Bedingungen für die größeren Horizontalspannungskomponenten maximal die zwei- bis dreifachen Beträge gegenüber den kleineren Horizontalspannungskomponenten und etwa die zweifachen Beträge bezogen auf die Vertikalspannungen auftreten können. Viele Autoren erklären derartige Spannungsverhältnisse mit rezenten tektonischen Spannungen und im Gebirge verbliebenen Restspannungen. Wie die weitere Bewertung der Meßergebnisse zeigt, könnte der Haupteinfluß auf den Gebirgsspannungszustand für einige Gebiete der DDR, in denen die größeren Horizontalspannungen die Vertikalspannungen übersteigen, mit dem Wirken eines fast einachsigen rezenten tektonischen Spannungsfeldes erklärt werden, für das folgende Beziehung gilt

$$\sigma_H = \sigma_H^S + \sigma_H^T \qquad (4)$$

σ_H^S — lithostatischer Spannungsanteil

σ_H^T — rezenter tektonischer Spannungsanteil

Damit soll nicht ausgeschlossen werden, daß auch Restspannungen im Gebirge vorhanden sind und wirken. Entsprechende Hinweise ergaben die meßtechnischen Untersuchungen z. B. hinsichtlich der teufenabhängigen Änderung der Orientierung der Horizontalspannungen in einem Untersuchungsgebiet. Der Einfluß von Restspannungen in den untersuchten Gebieten scheint aber viel geringer als der tektonische Anteil zu sein. Zur Darstellung der Ergebnisse der durchgeführten Untersuchungen des Gebirgsspannungszustandes werden im folgenden wegen der besseren Vergleichbarkeit, als Seitendruckbeiwerte zu bezeichnende Parameter verwendet:

$$\lambda_H = \frac{\sigma_H}{\sigma_V} \ , \qquad \lambda_h = \frac{\sigma_h}{\sigma_V} \qquad (5)$$

(BROWN, HOEK, 1978) haben Mittelwerte für Seitendruckbeiwerte von 120 in verschiedenen Gebieten der Erde durchgeführten Spannungsmessungen zusammengestellt und entsprechende teufenabhängige Grenzwerte für dieses Datenmaterial ermittelt. Die auf Abbildung 1 dargestellten Werte von 15 auf dem Territorium der DDR durchgeführten Untersuchungen zeigen keine Abweichung von diesen angegebenen Grenzen. Bei den dargestellten Werten handelt es sich um Mittelwerte, die überwiegend aus einer Reihe von Messungen in etwa gleicher Teufenlage, in einem Untersuchungsgebiet und einer lithologischen bzw. stratigraphischen Einheit gewonnen worden sind. Zugrunde liegen etwa 200 Einzelmessungen mit den oben genannten unterschiedlichen Verfahren. Die durchgeführten Messungen zeigen, daß es für das Territorium der DDR keinen in Betrag und Richtung einheitlichen Grundspannungszustand gibt. Eine Erhöhung der größeren Horizontalspannung σ_H über die Vertikalspannung ist überwiegend an die in den Mittelgebirgen zutage tretenden bzw. für Beckenbereiche, daß Fundament bilden Grundgebirgseinheiten gebunden. Einbezogen sind häufig auch die auf dem Grundgebirge lagernden Sedimentfolgen des Subsalinars.

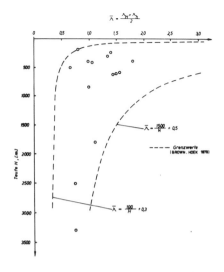

Abb. 1: Verhältnisse von gemessenen Horizontalspannungen zu Vertikalspannungen; Grenzwerte nach (BROWN, HOEK, 1978)

In den Salinarschichten, vor allem des Zechstein, wurde, wie auch von (MENZEL u.a., 1982) angegeben, bisher stets isotrope Spannungszustände mit Beträgen in der Größenordnung des lithostatischen Überlagerungsdruckes ermittelt.
Im Erzgebirgsraum ist die Richtung der größeren Horizontalspannungen σ_H vorwiegend NW-SE orientiert. Im Bereich des nördlichen Thüriger Waldes und im Thüringer Becken bis zum südlichen Harzrand überwiegt die NE-SW-Richtung.
An Meßorten im norddeutschen Tiefland ist für die größere Horizontalspannung σ_H die NW-SE-Richtung in postsalinaren Triasschichten gefunden worden, während im Subsalinar eine NE-SW-Richtung für die größere Horizontalspannung ermittelt wurde.
Zusammenfassend läßt sich feststellen, daß scheinbar die Beträge der größeren Horizontalspannungen σ_H hauptsächlich vom lithologischen Bau des Gebirges bzw. von seiner Fähigkeit rezente tektonische Spannungen zu übertragen und damit sicher sehr wesentlich vom Verformungsverhalten des Gebirges abhängen. Die Hauptrichtungen

der Horizontalspannungen scheinen dagegen mehr von den tektonischen Bedingungen, zum Beispiel von als Schwächeflächen wirkenden geologischen Störungen, beeinflußt zu werden.

3. Zusammenhänge zwischen Verformungseigenschaften des Gebirges und Spannungszustand

Einen großen Einfluß auf den Gebirgsspannungszustand hat zweifellos die Relaxationsfähigkeit des Gebirgsmaterials. In Gebirgsschichten mit ausgeprägtem Relaxationsverhalten, wie Salinargesteinen und auch Tonsteinen, bestätigten die Meßergebnisse die Ausbildung eines isotropen Spannungszustandes mit allseitig gleichem Druck, der dem lithostatischen Überlagerungsdruck entspricht.

$$\sigma_H \approx \sigma_h \approx \sigma_V \qquad (6)$$

Das Relaxationsverhalten der Schichten ist wahrscheinlich auch der Grund für den Stockwerkscharakter des Gebirgsspannungszustandes in Beckengebieten mit Salinarhorizonten. Durch die Salinarschichten erfolgt offensichtlich unter bestimmten Bedingungen eine "Abkopplung" des Postsalinar vom Subsalinar und vom Grundgebirge. Die gegenüber den tiefer gelegenen Stockwerken z. T. wesentlich geringeren Horizontalspannungen im Postsalinar weisen auf einen verminderten Einfluß regional wirkender rezenter Spannungsfelder hin. Der Einfluß tektonischer Spannungsfelder wirkt vor allem in kompetenten Gebirgsschichten des Grundgebirges.
Nimmt man behinderte Querdehnung an, wird der lithostatische Anteil an der größeren Horizontalspannung entsprechend Beziehung

$$\sigma_H^S = \frac{\nu}{1-\nu}\,\sigma_V \qquad (7)$$

bzw. $\lambda^S = \dfrac{\nu}{1-\nu}$

ν – Querdehnungszahl
(mit $0 \leqq \nu \leqq 0,5$)

Setzt man weiterhin isotropes Materialverhalten voraus, gilt außerdem:

$$\lambda_H^S = \lambda_h^S \qquad (8)$$

Mit diesen Beziehungen läßt sich bei Annahme des Wirkens eines einachsigen, horizontalen tektonischen Spannungsfeldes die Größe des tektonischen Anteils an den gemessenen Gebirgsspannungen abschätzen. Es soll gelten:

$$\lambda_h^T = \nu \cdot \lambda_H^T \qquad (9)$$

somit wird:

$$\lambda_H = \lambda_H^T + \frac{\nu}{1-\nu} \qquad (10)$$

$$\lambda_h = \nu \cdot \lambda_H^T + \frac{\nu}{1-\nu}$$

Die Querdehnungszahl ν ist in einfacher Weise aus der quadratischen Gleichung

$$\nu^2 - \frac{(\lambda_H + \lambda_h + 1)}{(\lambda_H + 1)} \cdot \nu + \frac{\lambda_h}{(\lambda_H + 1)} \qquad (11)$$

zu bestimmen.
Damit läßt sich mit Beziehung (7) der tektonische Anteil an der größeren Horizontalspannung errechnen.

$$\lambda_H^T = \lambda_H - \lambda_H^S \qquad (12)$$

Für die kleinere Horizontalspannung gelten die Beziehungen sinngemäß. In Abbildung 2 sind für die durchgeführten Messungen errechnete tektonische Anteile der größeren Horizontalspannung σ_H dargestellt.
Es sei darauf hingewiesen, daß für die Mehrheit der ausgewerteten Messungen, die nach (11) errechneten Querdehnungszahlen plausible Beträge angenommen haben, z. B. für Granit 0,23 für Anhydrit 0,38 und für metamorphe Schiefer 0,32. Für einige Messungen erscheinen die Querdehnungszahlen zu hoch, was nahelegt, daß an den entsprechenden Meßorten u. U. ein mehrachsiger tektonischer Spannungszustand wirkt und die Annahme (9) nicht zutrifft.
Die dargestellten tektonischen Anteile zeigen, zumindest nach dem gegenwärtigen Kenntnisstand, keine Teufenabhängikeit. Deutlich ist jedoch der wesentlich höhere tektonische Anteil an den im Grundgebirge ermittelten Spannungszuständen.
Als Näherungen für den größeren und kleineren Seitendruckbeiwert können aus den auf dem Territorium der DDR durchgeführten Messungen abgeleitet werden.

für das Grundgebirge: $\lambda_H = 1,1 + \dfrac{\nu}{1-\nu}$

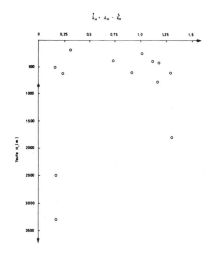

Abb. 2: Tektonischer Anteil an der größeren Horizontalspannung

für postsalinare
Sedimente:

$$\lambda_H = 0,2 + \frac{\nu}{1-\nu}$$

Ausdrücklich sei darauf hingewiesen, daß mit diesen Beziehungen nicht das Ziel verfolgt wird, eine Vorausberechnung von Lastannahmen zu ermöglichen. Deren Ermittlung sollte möglichst immer durch in-situ-Messungen erfolgen.

5. Schlußfolgerungen für die Lösung geomechanischer Probleme

Die aufgezeigten Zusammenhänge fordern für die Lösung von geomechanischen Aufgabenstellungen, wie z. B. Standsicherheitsbewertungen von Grubenhohlräumen in der Phase der Projektierung oder auch für die Einschätzung der Gebirgsschlaggefährdung beim Fortschreiten des Abbaus in die Teufe, den Einfluß von Verformungsverhalten und Schwächeflächen auf den Spannungszustand des Gebirges richtig einzuschätzen. Besonders wichtig ist das im Hinblick auf den beschriebenen möglichen Stockwerkcharakter des Spannungszustandes, mit dem verbunden sich die geomechanischen Bedingungen für vertikale Aufschlüsse nicht nur im Salinar entscheidend ändern können. Auf-

grund der häufig ausgeprägten Anisotropie der Horizontalspannung, vor allem im Grundgebirge, kann es mit größer werdenden Abbauteufen in kompetenten Gesteinen erhebliche Vorteile für die Standsicherheit der Auffahrungen bringen, die Orientierung des Spannungszustandes zu beachten. Günstig ist es z. B. horizontale Grubenbaue parallel zum Streichen der größeren Horizontalspannung anzuordnen, um die Spannungskonzentration in den Konturbereichen möglichst gering zu halten. Entsprechende praktische Erfahrungen bestätigten die Richtigkeit dieser Aussage.

Speziell für die Bewertung der hydrologischen Gefährdung von Grubenbetrieben ist die Kenntnis von potentiellen Schutzschichten im Hangenden wichtig. Die für die Schutzschichtfunktion günstige Relaxationsfähigkeit drückt sich letzlich auch in einem Spannungszustand, den allseitig gleichen Druck charakterisiert, aus. Randbedingungen des Spannungszustandes zu beachten, kann auch für die Abbauführung und weitere Aufgaben wichtig sein.

Die Wirksamkeit von tektonischen Spannungsfeldern, die auch im Gebiet der DDR erheblichen Einfluß auf die Horizontalspannung, im Grundgebirge größenordnungsmäßig 110 Prozent der Vertikalspannung, ausüben, wie auch von Verformungseigenschaften und Schwächeflächen gestalten den Spannungszustand des Gebirges relativ inhomogen. Um sichere Aussagen zu ermöglichen, sollten deshalb immer meßtechnische Untersuchungen, wobei eine Kombination verschiedener Verfahren günstig ist, durchgeführt werden.

Literatur

BROWN, E. T. und E. HOEK. 1978
Trends in Relationships between measured In-Situ-Stresses and Depth. Int. J. Rock Mech. Min. Sci. 15: 211 – 215.

GROSS, U. und KNOLL, P. 1982.
Hydraulische Aufreißmessungen in Tiefbohrungen und Bestimmung des Gebirgsspannungszustandes in oberen Teil der Erdkruste.
in: Application of Analytical Methods to Mining Geomechanics.
ed. by M. BORECKT & M. KWASNIEWSKI, A. A. Baldema, Rotterdam.

KNOLL, P.; VOGLER, G. und SCHMIDT, M. 1977.

Bisherige Ergebnisse von Spannungsmessungen mit Hilfe der Bohrlochentlastungs-
methode.
Freiberger Forschungsheft A 569: 29 - 45.

KNOLL, P.; GROSS, U. und MENZEL, W. 1982.
Bestimmung, Interpretation und geomechanische Bewertung von Gebirgsspannungszu-
ständen in Bergbaugebieten der DDR.
Rock Mech. Suppl. 12: 215 - 226

MENZEL, W. und WEBER, D. 1982.
Ergebnisse von Aufreißversuchen im Salzgebirge.
in: Application of Analytical Methods to
Mining Geomechanics.
ed. by M. BORECKI & M. KWASNIEWSKI,
A. A. Balkema, Rotterdam.

Spannungssondierungen in Salzpfeilern und ihre numeriche Modellierung

W. HÜLS
W. MENZEL
D. WEBER
Institut für Bergbausicherheit, Leipzig, German Democratic Republic

ABSTRACT: Knowledge of stress states in the ground and in pillars is an essential prerequisite both for the design of consistent underground cavities an the application of efficient exploitation methods. It is shown that reproducable results are obtained from the measurements of stress components by the borehole fracturing method. A sufficient conformity of stress values measured and those calculated by the finite element method permits safe statements on the stress state within the domains explored.

RESUME: La connaissance de l'état de contrainte dans le massif et dans les piliers d'exploitation est une condition essentielle non seulement pour les études des cavités souterraines stables mais aussi pour l'utilisation des procédés d'exploitation performants. Il est évident que la méthode de fracture des sondages fournit des résultats reproductibles en cas de mesure des composantes de contrainte. Par suite d'une conformité suffisante des contraintes mesurées et calculées par l'emploi de la méthode des éléments finis, il est possible de proposer des données assurées relatives à l'état de contrainte dans les domaines étudiés.

ZUSAMMENFASSUNG: Die Kenntnis des Spannungszustandes im Gebirge und in Abbaupfeilern ist sowohl für die Projektierung standsicherer unterirdischer Hohlräume als auch für die Anwendung effektiver Abbauverfahren eine wesentliche Voraussetzung. Es zeigt sich, daß die Bohrloch-Aufreißmethode bei der Sondierung von Spannungskomponenten reproduzierbare Ergebnisse liefert. Infolge einer ausreichenden Übereinstimmung von sondierten und mittels der Methode finiter Elemente berechneten Spannungen können gesicherte Aussagen zum Spannungszustand in den sondierten Bereichen gemacht werden.

1 EINLEITUNG

Die Kenntnis des Spannungszustandes im Gebirge ist sowohl für die Projektierung und Anlage jeglicher unterirdischer Hohlräume als auch für die Entwicklung effektiver Abbauverfahren eine wesentliche Voraussetzung. Neben der Spannungssondierung durch Messung der elastischen Rückverformung beim Entlasten des Gesteins und dem Einsatz der Ultraschallmethode werden in jüngster Zeit zur Ermittlung wirkender Spannungen sogenannte Aufreißversuche in Bohrlöchern durchgeführt. Diese Methode wurde aus dem bekannten Verfahren des Aufreißens von Bohrlöchern im Speichergestein von Erdöl- und Erdgaslagerstätten abgeleitet.

Sie kommt am Institut für Bergbausicherheit zum Einsatz, um die für die Anwendung effektiver Abbauverfahren im Kali- und Steinsalzbergbau und die Senkung der Abbauverluste notwendigen Kenntnisse über den Grundspannungszustand im Salzgebirge und dessen Veränderung durch den Abbau zu erweitern.

Die Spannungssondierungen sind von wesentlicher Bedeutung bei der Bestätigung der Ergebnisse von nichtlinearen numerischen Rechenverfahren zur Modellierung von Spannungs- und Deformationsfeldern.

Das Finite-Element-Verfahren der "variablen Elastizität" verwendet direkt die triaxialen Versuchsergebnisse aus dem Labor und ist in der Lage, mit ausreichender Approximationsfähigkeit den

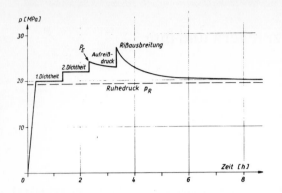

Bild 1 Aufreißversuch im Salzgebirge

sondierten in situ Spannungszustand nach-
zu bilden.

2 THEORIE DER RISSBILDUNG

Bei der theoretischen Behandlung der Rißbildung im dichten Gestein wird davon
ausgegangen, daß Risse um ein druckbeauf-
schlagtes Bohrloch im Gebirge dann ent-
stehen und sich ausbreiten, wenn das aus
Gebirgsdruck und Innendruck im Bohrloch
superponierte Spannungsfeld an der Bohrlochkontur in tangentialer oder axialer
Richtung die Zugfestigkeit des anstehen-
den Gesteins überschreitet.

Vereinfacht soll die Richtung einer
Hauptspannung σ_3 im Gebirge mit der
Bohrrichtung übereinstimmen, so daß die
Hauptspannungen σ_1 und σ_2 in einer
Ebene senkrecht zur Bohrlochachse lie-
gen. An der Bohrlochkontur ergibt sich
dann die Spannungsverteilung

$$\sigma_r = p_i$$

$$\sigma_\theta = \sigma_1 + \sigma_2 - 2(\sigma_1 - \sigma_2)\cos 2\theta - p_i$$

$$\sigma_z = \sigma_3 - 2\nu(\sigma_1 - \sigma_2)\cos 2\theta$$

$$\tau_{r\theta} = 0$$

mit p_i = Innendruck, θ - auf die Richtung von σ_1 bezogene Winkelkoordinate
und ν - Poissonzahl.

Für das Minimum der Tangentialspannung
($\theta = 0, \pi$) an der Bohrlochkontur gilt

$$\sigma_\theta = 3\sigma_2 - \sigma_1 - p_i$$

Bild 2 Aufreißsonde

Bei axialer Rißbildung, d. h. die Rißbildung verläuft in Richtung der Bohrlochachse, muß ein Innendruck p_i erzeugt
werden, bei dem die tangentiale Zugspan-
nung σ_θ die Zugfestigkeit des Gesteins
senkrecht zur Richtung der größeren
Hauptspannung σ_1 überschreitet.

Damit gilt für den Aufreißdruck (Hubbert, 1957) die Beziehung

$$p_E = (\sigma_z)_A + 3\sigma_2 - \sigma_1$$

wobei $(\sigma_z)_A$ die axiale Zugfestigkeit
des Gesteins ist.

Die Bedingungen für eine Rißbildung
normal zur Bohrlochachse treten nur bei
einem durch Packer oder Bohrlochsohle be-
grenzten Bohrlochabschnitt auf (Kehle,
1964). Für eine derartige Rißbildung gilt
näherungsweise die Beziehung

$$p_E = \frac{(\sigma_z)_N + \sigma_3}{0,94}$$

wobei $(\sigma_z)_N$ die Zugfestigkeit in der
Ebene normal zur Bohrlochachse darstellt

Nach der Rißbildung an der Bohrlochkontur breitet sich der Riß senkrecht
zur Richtung der minimalen Hauptspannung
aus. Das Modell eines dünnen Schlitzes
(Haimson, 1968) gibt eine gute experimen-
tell untermauerte theoretische Darstellung.

Wird nach der Rißbildung und Ausbrei-
tung des Risses aus dem Bohrlochbereich
hinaus das Einpumpen des Druckmediums
beendet, stellt sich im dichten homogenen Gestein ein konstanter Druck ein
(Bild 1). Dieser sogenannte Ruhedruck
p_R ist annähernd gleich der Größe der
senkrecht zur Rißebene wirkenden minima-

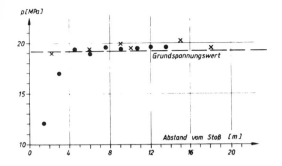

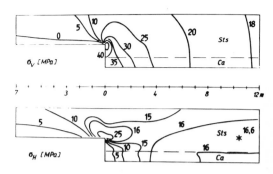

Bild 3 Sondierung des Grundspannungswertes

Bild 4 Spannungsverteilung im Pfeiler

len Hauptspannung. Damit ergibt sich bei axialer Rißbildung

$$p_E > p_R \geqq \sigma_1$$

und bei normaler Rißbildung

$$p_E > p_R \geqq \sigma_3$$

Für die Auswertung der Aufreißversuche ist somit die Kenntnis der Rißausbreitung erforderlich.

3 VERSUCHSTECHNIK

Die Aufreißsonde des Institutes für Bergbausicherheit für das Salzgebirge (Bild 2) ist als ein starr verbundenes Doppelpackersystem aus zwei Hydraulikpackern für Bohrlöcher zwischen 37 bis 75 mm Durchmesser ausgebildet. Die aufblähbaren Gummipacker befinden sich an den Enden eines starren Grundkörpers und begrenzen bzw. dichten den dazwischenliegenden Aufreißraum ab. Im Aufreißraum besteht unmittelbarer Kontakt zwischen Druckflüssigkeit und Gebirge.

Die Länge der Aufreißsonde beträgt je nach Durchmesser zwischen 600 und 800 mm, wobei der Aufreißraum 300 bis 500 mm Länge besitzt. Damit wird es möglich, ein Bohrloch in Abschnitten von 1,0 bis 1,5 m Länge zu sondieren.

Die hydraulische Druckbeaufschlagung der Packer und des Aufreißraumes erfolgt getrennt. Die zur sicheren Abdichtung des Bohrloches erforderlichen Packerdrücke liegen im Salzgebirge bei etwa 1 bis 2 MPa über dem im Aufreißraum erzeugten Druck. Die Meßdaten werden über Feinmeßmanometer in jeder Druckleitung di-

rekt angezeigt und durch automatische Druckbandschreiber ständig aufgezeichnet.

4 UNTERSUCHUNGSERGEBNISSE

4.1 GRUNDSPANNUNGSZUSTAND

Der Spannungszustand im ungestörten Gebirgsmassiv wird durch die Beziehung

$$\sigma_V = \gamma \ (T - y)$$
$$\sigma_H = \lambda \gamma \ (T - y)$$

unter der Nebenbedingung

$$\frac{\nu}{1 - \nu} = \lambda \leqq 1$$

gekennzeichnet, wobei γ die mittlere Dichte des Gebirges und T die Teufe bedeuten. Um eine kreisförmige Strecke, die im homogenen und isotropen Gebirge aufgefahren ist, bildet sich ein ebener Spannungszustand aus. Sowohl bei elastischer als auch bei zeitabhängiger Lösung der Spannungsverteilung ist der Hohlraumeinfluß in einer Entfernung von etwa 4 Radien von der Kontur theoretisch auf den Grundspannungszustand abgeklungen (Savin, 1956).

Aus einer Strecke in 840 m Teufe im unverritzten Steinsalz mit einem Streckenquerschnitt von 3,5 m Höhe und 8 m Breite werden 3 Meßbohrlöcher von 20 m Länge sondiert. In Tiefen zwischen 4 und 18 m (Bild 3) liegen die ermittelten Ruhedrücke zwischen 18,6 und 19,8 MPa. Die Meßwerte korrespondieren gut mit dem Grundspannungswert entsprechend dem petrostatischen Teufendruck von 19,3 MPa. Es ist bemerkenswert, daß der Hohlraumeinfluß wesentlich eher abklingt als es

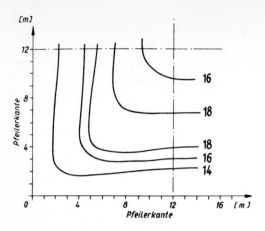

Bild 5 Isolinien der Horizontalspannungen

die theoretische Voraussage angibt.

4.2 SPANNUNGSAUFBAU IN PFEILERN

Im Kammer-Pfeiler-Abbau bei einer Teufe
von 520 m besitzen die Quadratpfeiler
24 m Kantenlänge und 4 m Höhe. Die Kammer-
breiten sind mit 14 m aufgefahren.
  Für den ebenen Mittelschnitt eines Pfeilers wird die Spannungsverteilung mittels
der Methode finiter Elemente berechnet.
Das Modell besteht im Hangenden und im
oberen Drittel des Pfeilers aus Steinsalz,
sonst aus Trümmercarnallitit. Die Stoff-
parameter sind aus Triaxialversuchen ab-
leitet.
  Im Bild 4 ist zu erkennen, daß im Pfeilerkern, ab etwa 5 m vom Stoß entfernt,
eine gleichmäßige vertikale Spannung zwischen 20 und 18 MPa herrscht, die zur
Pfeilermitte leicht abnimmt. Der Pfeiler-
bereich, der bis etwa 2 m in den Pfeiler
reicht, ist den größten Spannungsumlage-
rungen ausgesetzt. An der Schichtgrenze
zwischen Steinsalz und Carnallitit treten sowohl in der Vertikalspannung als
auch in der Horizontalspannung keine
Spannungssprünge auf.
  In der Horizontalkomponente deutet sich
eine etwas größere entspannte Zone im
Pfeilerrandbereich bei Carnallititausbil-
dung als bei Steinsalz an. Ab etwa 4 m
besitzt die horizontale Spannungskomponente im Pfeiler ein annähernd gleichmä-
ßiges Niveau von 16 MPa, wobei in einer
Entfernung von 5 bis 7 m vom Stoß eine
leichte Spannungserhöhung nicht auszu-
schließen ist.
  In diesem Pfeiler wurde mittels 7 Hori-
zontalbohrungen, die parallel zum Stoß
in 2; 4; 5,5; 7; 9,5; 11 und 13 m Ent-

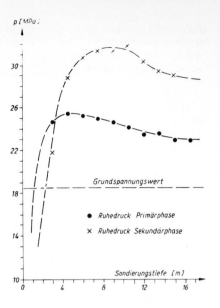

Bild 6 Änderung der Horizontalspannung
im Pfeiler

fernung von der Kontur sondiert wurden,
systematisch der horizontale Spannungsaufbau untersucht. Im Bild 5 sind die E
gebnisse der Messungen in Form von Li-
nien gleicher Horizontalspannung dargestellt. Das Bild zeigt, daß sich der
Spannungsaufbau im Pfeiler annähernd sy
metrisch zum Pfeilerrand vollzieht. Ein
Entspannung, bezogen auf den Grundspannungszustand von 12 MPa, tritt nur im
konturnahen Bereich bis 2 m vom Stoß en
fernt auf. Der Anstieg der Horizontalspannung reicht bis etwa 4 m Tiefe. Dor
wird ein Wert von 18 MPa gemessen. Dahi
ter stellt sich bis etwa 7 m ein konsta
tes Niveau ein. Zum Pfeilerkern setzt e
leichter Spannungsabfall bis auf 16 MPa
ein.
  Der Vergleich der Spannungssondierung
mit den theoretischen Ergebnissen ergib
eine befriedigende Übereinstimmung für
die horizontale Spannungskomponente. Un
ter weiterer Hinzuziehung von Pfeiler-
querdehnungs- und Kovergenzmessungen wi
die Schlußfolgerung gezogen, daß der th
retisch ermittelte Vertikalspannungsauf
bau das in situ-Spannungsfeld abbildet.

4.3 SPANNUNGSÄNDERUNG IN PFEILERN

Eine im Kalibergbau typische Abbaugesta
tung ist der Mehrphasenabbau. Eine primäre Abbauphase wird mit wesentlich übe
dimensionierten Parametern gestaltet un

gleichzeitig eine geologische Detailer-
kundung durchgeführt, um dann in einer
nachfolgenden sekundären Abbauphase eine
optimale Lagerstättenausbeute zu errei-
chen.

Der zu untersuchende Pfeiler liegt in
einer Teufe von 810 m. Die Kantenlänge
des quadratischen Pfeilers beträgt 36 m,
die Kammerbreite 10 m und die gebaute
Mächtigkeit 4 m. Die geometrischen Verhältnisse ergeben eine mittlere Pfeilerbelastung von 30 MPa. In der Folgezeit
wurden am Meßpfeiler und den benachbarten
Pfeilern sekundäre Abbaumaßnahmen durchgeführt. Dadurch erhöhte sich die theoretische mittlere Pfeilerbelastung von
30 auf 40 MPa.

Das numerische Modell wird als ebener
Mittelschnitt durch den Pfeiler aufgestellt. Als Berechnungsvariante wird die
finite Element-Methode der variablen Elastizität verwendet. In 4 inkrementellen
Belastungsschritten mit den Laststufen
40, 30, 20 und 10 % werden die Spannungs-
wege des primären und sekundären Abbau-
standes berechnet.

Im Bild 6 ist für die Mittellinie des
Pfeilers die berechnete Horizontalspannung aufgetragen. In der primären Abbauphase verlaufen berechnete und gemessene
Spannungswerte auf ein Maximum von etwa
25 MPa in 5 m Entfernung vom Stoß und
klingen im Pfeilerinnern bis auf 23 MPa
ab.

Für die sekundäre Abbauphase weisen berechnete und gemessene Werte gleicherma-
ßen auf die Veränderung des Spannungsauf-
baus im Pfeiler hin. Der Pfeilerrandbereich vergrößert sich. Das horizontale
Spannungsmaximum verlagert sich unter Erhöhung auf etwa 32 MPa 8 m hinter die
Kontur. Eine Spannungsumverteilung erfaßt
den gesamten Pfeiler. Das horizontale
Spannungsniveau sinkt auch im Pfeilerkern
nicht unter 28 MPa.

Die theoretisch ermittelten Spannungen
stimmen weitgehend mit den gemessenen
Werten überein. Mit Hilfe der aus Triaxialversuchen abgeleiteten Grenztragfähig-
keiten für Steinsalz und Carnallitit ist
eine weiterführende Beurteilung des Pfeilers möglich.

5 ZUSAMMENFASSUNG

Aus den bisher im Salzgebirge durchgeführten Untersuchungen mit der Aufreißmethode können die folgenden grundsätzlichen Ergebnisse abgeleitet werden:
Die Untersuchungen zum Spannungszustand

zeigen, daß mit der Aufreißmethode wesentliche Fortschritte bei der Bestimmung des
Spannungszustandes erzielt werden können.
Die Methode liefert qualitativ und quan-
titativ gut reproduzierbare Ergebnisse.
Die in unterschiedlichen Salzlagerstätten
in Teufen zwischen 450 bis 850 m ermittelten Ruhedrücke außerhalb der Einflußzonen
von Grubenbauen korrespondieren gut mit
dem aus der mittleren Dichte des Deckgebirges berechneten petrostatischen Teufendruck. Der mittels der Aufreißmethode in
Salzpfeilern ermittelte Verlauf der minimalen Spannungskomponenten ergibt eine
gute Übereinstimmung mit den theoretischen
Spannungsfeldern, die mit Hilfe der Methode finiter Elemente und Laborstoffpara-
metern berechnet wurden.

Zur Bestimmung des vollständigen Spannungszustandes im Gebirge sind Messungen
in drei, möglichst senkrecht zueinander
orientierten Bohrlöchern erforderlich.
Diese Bedingungen können im Bergbau nur
selten realisiert werden. Deshalb ist es
erforderlich, die Aufreißmethode mit anderen Untersuchungsmethoden zu ergänzen
und aus den bestätigten theoretischen Modellen Aussagen zur Bewertung des Spannungszustandes abzuleiten.

LITERATUR

Haimson, B. C. 1968. Hydraulic Fracturing
in Porous and nonporous Rock and its
Potential for Determining In-Situ-
Stresses at Greath Depth. Technical Re-
port 4-68. Missouri River Division
Corps of Engineers, Omaha.

Hubbert, M. K. 1977. Mechanics of Hydraulic Fracturing. Trans. AIME 210: 153 pp.

Hüls, W. and Lindert, A. 1986. Numerical
modelling of stress transfer at room
and pillar mining. Proc. 2nd Int. Conf.
Numerical Models in Geomech. Ghent,
in press.

Hüls, W., Menzel, W. und Schreiner, W.
1980. Ergebnisse geomechanischer Untersuchungen beim Abbau von Carnallitit in
großen Teufen. Neue Bergbautechnik 10
(4): 203-209.

Kehle, O. R. 1964. Determination of Tectonics Stresses through Analysis of Hydraulic Well Fracturing. J. of Geophysical Research 69: 259 pp.

Menzel, W. und Weber, D. 1981. Ergebnisse
von Aufreißversuchen im Salzgebirge.
Proc. Int. Büro für Gebirgsmechanik,
Katowice.

Savin, G. N. 1956. Spannungserhöhung am
Rande von Löchern, Verlag Technik,
Berlin.

Measurement of in situ stress in coal

K.W. MILLS
Consulting Engineer, Applied Rock Mechanics, Auckland, New Zealand

M.J. PENDER
University of Auckland, Auckland, New Zeeland

D. DEPLEDGE
New Zealand State Coal Mines, New Zealand

ABSTRACT   The results of in situ stress measurements made at four sites in the underground coal mines at Huntly, New Zealand, are presented and discussed. Measurements were made in the coal seam by overcoring a flexible hollow inclusion instrument developed for use in soft, jointed rock.   The measured stresses are characterised by a near vertical principal stress equal to the overburden pressure, and two horizontal stresses of different magnitudes both less than the vertical stress (except at very shallow depths).   Alignment of measured stresses with cleat in the coal, local and regional faulting, and regional geodetic surveys of earth deformation is examined.

RESUME   Les résultats de mesures de constraintes en place effectuées à quatre emplacements à la mine de charbon souterraine de Huntly, Nouvelle Zélande, sont présentés et discutés.   Les mesures ont été faites dans le filon de charbon par "overcoring" un instrument développé pour ce type de roche molle et fracturée. L'instrument est constitué d'une inclusion creuse.   Les contraintes mesurées sont caractérisées par une tension principale proche de la verticale égale à la pression des roches surjacentes, et par deux tensions horisontales de valeurs inégales et toutes deux moindres que la contrainte verticale (excepté à des profondeurs très faibles).   L'alignement des tensions mesurées avec les fissures dons le charbon, et avec les failles locales et régionales et les déformations géodésiques réginales révèléss par les études disponibles est examiné.

ZUSAMMENFASSUNG   Die Resultate von Spannungsmessungen vor Ort die an vier verschiedenen Messpunkten in den Untertage-Kohlemienen in Huntly, Neuseeland durchgefuehrt wurden sind praesentiert und diskutiert.   Die Messungen wurden durch Kernbohrung eines weichen, hohlen Einschliessungsinstruments im Kohle-Floez, welches fuer die Anwendung in weichem, gefuegtem Gestein entwickelt wurde, erhalten.   Die gemessenen Spannungen sind characterisiert durch eine nahezu vertikale Hauptspannung gleich gross als der Druck des Hangenden, und zwei horizontale Spannungen (ausser bei sehr niedrigen Tiefen).   Die Ausrichtung der gemessenen Spannungen zu Schlechten in der Kohle, lokalen und regionalen Sprungbildungen und geodaetischen Vermessungen von Erdverformungen ist untersucht.

1 INTRODUCTION

In this paper the results of tests to measure the in situ stresses in the Waikato coal field are presented. The instrument and technique used to make the measurements are described elsewhere in these proceedings, Mills and Pender (1986).

The Waikato coal field is located 100 km south of Auckland (Figure 1). The coal field exists within a large depression formed on a basement graben and horst structural regime. The countryside is low lying with surface features rising to a maximum height of approximately 50 m above the general level. A pattern of two sets of normal faults extend throughout the basin, one in a north easterly direction and the other at approximately right angles to this.

The coal reserve is divided between two seams. The lower seam averages 6 m thick, ranging from 2 m to 12 m, and is of most significance for mining. The upper seam is less persistent and will

only be mined in localised areas. Both seams dip gently to the northwest.

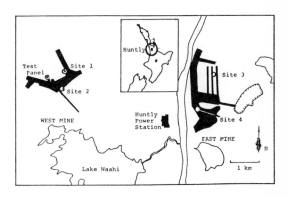

Figure 1 : Locality and Site Location Plan

The coal is being worked from two underground mines, Huntly West and Huntly East, as well as from several opencasts in the south (Figure 1). In the underground mines, overburden ranges from 80 m in the south and east to greater than 300 m in the north.

Coal tends to exhibit two well defined joint sets that are perpendicular to each other and to the seam horizon. The more dominant joint set is called the major or face cleat and the secondary joint set the minor or butt cleat. At Huntly, the face cleat has a regional strike of approximately 070° GN, but is observed to change direction to align with faults. In some localised areas, the butt cleat becomes the more dominant cleat.

It has long been recognised by the mining industry at Huntly, that conditions there are somewhat different to those typically encountered in Australia or the United Kingdom. In 1980, work was started to try to establish which factors were contributing to these unusual conditions.

As part of this work, a series of in situ stress measurements were undertaken in the East Mine using CSIRO Hollow Inclusion cells. These measurements were unsuccessful because of tensile failure of the coal adjacent to the interface. Measurements were confined to the coal seam because roof and floor materials are composed of relatively soft mudstones unsuitable for overcoring.

A second study involved tunnel monitoring in an area of the West Mine called the Test Panel. Material properties were determined by testing core samples and conducting in situ pressuremeter tests. The in situ stress field was measured and was found to be unusual in that one of the horizontal stresses was only 0.3 times the vertical overburden stress. Deformations and stress changes were monitored during excavation of a full scale roadway. Later finite element modelling confirmed that the only in situ stress field capable of reproducing the observed displacement pattern had a low horizontal stress across the opening (Mills 1986).

Following the Test Panel study, a third investigation was initiated involving a series of further in situ stress measurements at other locations in both underground mines to see if the unusually low horizontal stress field was typical of the Waikato coal field.

The results of the initial series of stress measurements in the Test Panel and the subsequent series in both mines are discussed in this paper.

2 STRESS MEASUREMENTS

The five stress measurement sites are shown in Figure 1. No successful measurements were made at site 2 because of excessive methane gas pressures which deflated the instrument and prevented satisfactory bonding.

Best core recovery was generally obtained when holes were drilled perpendicular to the main cleat. At other orientations, there is a tendency for the core to split or for wedges to fall out and jam in the barrel.

Cleat spacing in Huntly coal is typically 1-2 cm. It was not unusual to get at least one of the three strain gauge rosettes on any one instrument interacting with a joint. Only very seldom did all the rosettes give the expected stress relief curves.

At each site, three successive measurements were made in each of two near parallel boreholes at a distance of approximately one tunnel diameter from the rib. The boreholes were horizontal and oriented perpendicular to the main cleat. In some overcoring tests, there were sufficient strain measurements for the in situ stress field to be calculated without additional information. For others, reliable strain measurements from several tests in the same borehole could be combined to generate synthetic sets of strain relief data. Combination was only possible because tests were conducted in close proximity to one another in an area of relatively uniform stress.

It was found that best results were obtained if gauges were located away from the 0° or 180° positions (Figure 2). Gauges in these positions seldom worked as well as gauges between 45° and 135° or 225° and 315°. This phenomenon is thought to be a result of excessive overbreak in the top of hole caused by the presence of butt cleat.

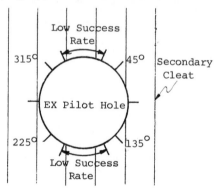

Figure 2 : Cross-section of an EX pilot hole showing positions where there is a high probability of strain gauge malfunction.

3 RESULTS

Pressure test and stress relief curves for tests T307 and 4A2 are shown in Figure 3. The core of T307 was closely jointed, perhaps partly due to discing, with the result that the transition phase of the stress relief is much shorter than in 4A2. In test 4A2, the core remained essentially intact.

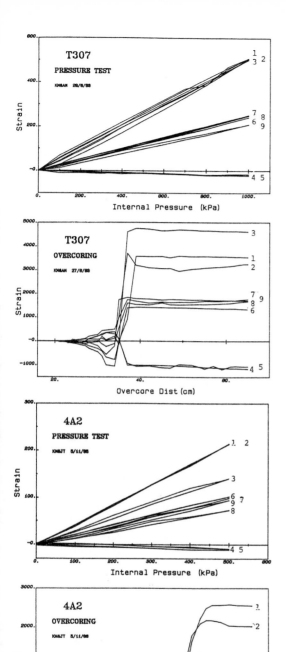

Figure 3 :   Pressure Test Results and Stress Relief Curves for T307 (Test Panel) and 4A2 (Site 4).

Pressure tests, and where possible biaxial tests, indicate that the properties of the coal are approximately constant at all the measurement sites despite the marked difference in joint intensity and core recovery. Values of 2.7 GPa for Young's modulus and 0.36 for Poisson's ratio were used throughout the analyses.

Figure 4 shows the principal stress directions at each site plotted on stereonets. The directions and magnitudes of the horizontal stresses and the faults observed underground are also shown. These faults are all normal faults typically of 3-5 m displacement.

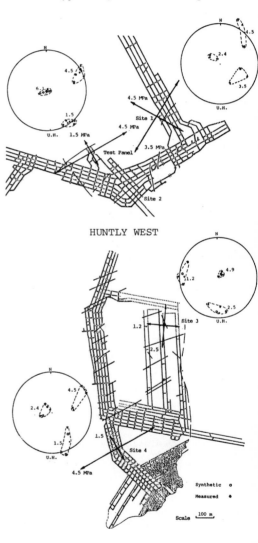

HUNTLY WEST

HUNTLY EAST

Figure 4 : Plan of East and West Mines showing faults observed underground, the directions of the measured horizontal principal stresses and, on stereonets, the calculated principal stresses for each successful test.

4   DISCUSSION

4.1   Vertical Stress

In Figure 5, the near vertical stress measured at each site is plotted against overburden pressure. At all the sites except site 1, the magnitude of the measured vertical stress equals the overburden pressure. This correlation is consistent with the flat even surface topography of the area and gives confidence in the accuracy of the stress measurements.

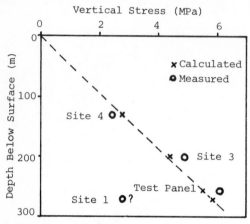

Figure 5 : Comparison of near vertical stresses calculated from overburden densities and measured in situ.

Site 1 is located beneath a fault plane. The stresses measured there are aligned with the fault plane. The near vertical stress is equal to the overburden pressure generated by material beneath this fault plane suggesting the possibility of a shielding or arching mechanism.

4.2   Horizontal Stresses

Figure 4 shows the direction and magnitude of the horizontal stresses. At all the sites, there is close alignment of horizontal stresses with nearby faults and with the major cleat in the coal.

This correlation is also illustrated in Figure 6 which shows a stereonet of all the fault planes and measured stresses. Close correlation appears to be regional, apart from the horizontal stresses measured at site 3 and several irregular faults. As well as aligning with the faults, the ratios of the two horizontal stresses to the vertical stress and to one another are consistent with the nature of faulting and the predominant fault direction. All faults in the region are normal faults which is consistent with the observations of stress ratios (vertical to horizontal) of less than 1.0. The lowest horizontal stress acts across the predominant fault direction. This is consistent with the stress conditions required to form the faults.

Upper Hemisphere

Figure 6 : A stereonet showing alignment of principal stress envelopes for each site with the normal faults observed at Huntly.

The directions and magnitudes of horizontal stresses measured at site 4 and in the Test Panel are the same, despite the fact that site 4 is approximately half the depth of the Test Panel. Such an observation suggests the horizontal stresses do not change appreciably with depth and therefore that the stress ratio will decrease with depth. A similar phenomenon has been observed by Hoek & Brown (1980) over a larger range of depths and for generally harder rocks (Figure 7). It is apparent from these observations that the stress ratios measured at Huntly are lower than those measured elsewhere at the same depth.

4.3   Site 3 Anomaly

The horizontal stresses measured at site 3 are anomalous in terms of a regional pattern, although they are consistent with other irregularities in that area. Both horizontal stresses are less than elsewhere, they do not align with the regional pattern and the difference between them is not as great as at other measurement sites. Site 3 is unusual in some other repects as well:

(i)   A boundary fault which cuts across the regional pattern runs close to the site. The measured stresses align with this fault.

(ii) The butt cleat has become the dominant cleat in the area.

(iii) The intensity of faulting has increased, particularly perpendicular to the predominant fault direction.

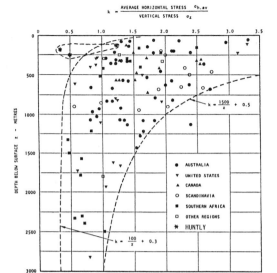

Figure 7 : Stress ratios measured at various depths (after Hoek & Brown 1980) superimposed with the stress ratios measured at Huntly.

These observations are generally consistent with a higher stress ratio (more faulting) and less difference between the horizontal stresses (more dominant secondary faulting and butt cleat). The close proximity of the boundary fault which itself does not reflect regional trends, may explain the stress anomalies at this site.

4.4 Tectonic Mechanism

Considerations of rock strength suggest that the current stress levels at Huntly are not sufficient to generate faults. However, at some time in the geologic past overburden pressures are estimated to have reached a maximum of 40 MPa, equivalent to 1800 m of cover (Suggate 1982). At some time sufficient shear stress must have been present to cause the observed faulting.

Alignment of faults with the stress field suggests that either the existing faults constrain the horizontal stress to act in given directions or the tectonic mechanism operating at the time of fault formation is similar to that operating at present.

New Zealand is located on an active plate margin, with the Pacific Plate being subducted beneath the North Island area. Kamp (1984) suggests that progress of the subduction zone beneath the Australian Plate can be charted from the migration of a volcanic front from Whangarei in the north (18 million years) to the currently active Taupo volcanic zone and that the basic tectonic mechanism has not changed over this period. Such a tectonic model is consistent with the alignment of existing faults and existing horizontal stresses.

The regional faulting pattern for the whole Waikato basin is shown in Figure 8. The directions of regional faults are consistent with the smaller faults observed underground, and with the stress field measured.

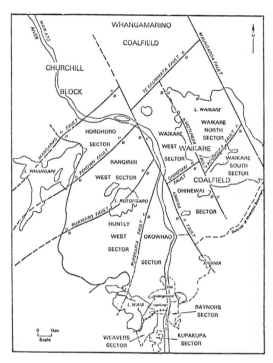

Figure 8 : Regional Faulting in the Waikato Basin (courtesy of New Zealand DSIR Geological Survey).

Fault directions are a good indicator of stress direction at the time of fault formation. However once the faults have formed, it is possible that the tectonic mechanism may change, and with it the stress direction (although the extent to which the stress directions can change may be limited by the shear stress sustainable by the fault plane).

The current tectonic mechanism is reflected in deformation of the earth's crust. Figure 9 shows the strain directions inferred from recent geodetic earth deformation surveys for the Waikato region. Two hundred kilometres to the southeast, the Taupo rift zone is widening, a process which gives rise to the geothermal activity associated with the Rotorua area (Sissons 1979). Closer to Huntly, directions of relative strain have been inferred from survey information and are shown as deformed squares (Bibby 1984). Determination of absolute movements is not possible here because of the poor quality of available data. Hochstein et al (1984) infer a relative stretching of the Hauraki Graben in the direction shown.

547

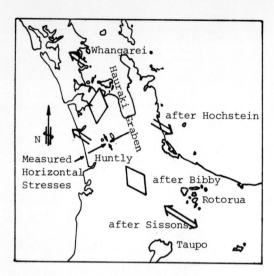

Figure 9 : Directions of earth deformation in the region around Huntly
inferred from various sources.

The horizontal stress directions measured at Huntly at site 4 and in the
Test Panel correlate well with the earth
strain measurements.. This very good
correlation suggests that the stresses
measured at Huntly do reflect the current tectonic mechanism and that the
tectonic mechanism which is now operating in New Zealand is similar to that
which was operating when the faults
formed.

4.5   Application to Mining

Since the introduction of mechanised
mining to Huntly, mining has been possible at greater depths than was previously possible.   Mining techniques and
equipment similar to those used in Australia have been imported.   However, as
depth has increased, problems with roof
stability have been encountered.   These
have generally been attributed to the
weak roof strata consisting of interbedded carbonaceous mudstones.   It is
interesting to examine the problems in
terms of stress conditions.

In Australian coal mines, horizontal
stresses are often several times higher
than overburden pressure.   In difficult
areas, best roadway performance is attained in drivages parallel to the maximum horizontal stress ie: where the
difference between the horizontal stress
acting across the opening and the vertical stress is a minumum (Gale 1986).
Underground roadways are typically
driven 5-6 m wide by 2-3 m high.   In
terms of the stream flow analogy suggested by Hoek & Brown (1980), this
opening profile is close to optimum in
these conditions.

Stress ratios measured at Huntly
range from 0.3 (site 3 and Test Panel at

190-230 m depth) to 1.5 (site 2 at 120 m
depth).   At shallow depths, the rectangular openings have performed satisfactorily.   At greater depths however,
problems of roof instability are more
frequent.   In the context of the measured stress ratios decreasing with
depth, it is not suprising that these
problems have occurred.   Hoek & Brown's
streamline analogy clearly illustrates
the large disturbance that such a profile will have in a low horizontal
stress environment Figure 10.

There is a significant difference in
the horizontal stress magnitudes at
Huntly suggesting the possiblity of a

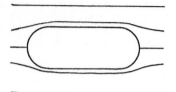

High Horizontal Stress

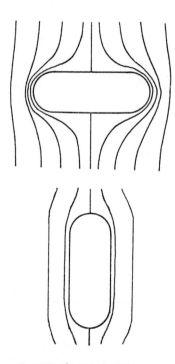

Low Horizontal Stress
(High Vertical Stress)

Figure 10 :   The streamline analogy
discussed by Hoek & Brown (1980)
showing the different orientation of
openings required for different stress
fields.   The upper orientation is more
appropriate for Australian conditions,
the lower one for conditions at Huntly.

548

preferred mining direction. Such a direction has been identified (O'Beirne & Shepherd 1985) as perpendicular to the major cleat direction and therefore to the largest horizontal stress. As in Australia, the best drivage direction has the difference between the horizontal stress acting across the opening and the vertical stress, at a minimum.

As a result of the in situ stress measurements, it has been recommended that panels are oriented to take advantage of the difference in horizontal stress magnitudes, and roadway profiles are matched to the in situ stress conditions, by reducing the width of openings and increasing their height. Where implemented, these changes have led to significant improvements in roadway performance. Despite anticipated minor rib buckling problems, high narrow openings should give considerable economic advantages in the thick seam environment at Huntly.

5 CONCLUSIONS

The stress field measured at Huntly is consistent with overburden pressure, cleat orientations within the coal seam, regional fault patterns, and the current tectonic mechanism inferred from surface strain measurements.

Stress ratios measured range from 0.3 to 1.5 and for the depth range 120-250 m represent unusually low horizontal stress conditions.

Identification of low horizontal stress as a critical factor in roadway performance has allowed some significant improvements to be made.

6 ACKNOWLEDGEMENTS

The authors wish to acknowledge the support and funding provided for this work by New Zealand State Coal Mines and the New Zealand Energy Research and Development Committee.

7 REFERENCES

Bibby, H.M. 1984. Personal Com.

Gale, W.J. 1986. Personal Com.

Hochstein, M.P., Tearney, K., Rawson, S., Davey, F.J., Davidge, S., Henrys, S. and Blackshall, D. 1984. Geophysical Structure of the Hauraki Rift (North Island, N.Z.). Proceedings of the International Symposium on Recent Crustal Movement of the Pacific Region, Victoria University, New Zealand. Royal Society of New Zealand Bulletin 24.

Hoek, E. and Brown, E.T. 1980. Underground Excavations in Rock. Institute of Mining and Metallurgy, London.

Kamp, P.J.J. 1984. Neogene and Quaternary Extent and Geometry of the Subducted Pacific Plate beneath Noth Island, New Zealand: Implications for Kaikoura Tectonics. Tectonophysics, 108:241-266.

Mills, K.W. 1986. In Situ Mechanical Behaviour of Huntly Coal. PhD thesis, University of Auckland, New Zealand.

Mills, K.W. and Pender, M.J. 1986. A Soft Inclusion Instrument for In Situ Stress Measurement in Coal. Proceedings of International Symposium on Rock Stress and Rock Stress Measurement, Stockholm.

O'Beirne, T.J. and Shepherd, J. 1984. The Failure of Coal Pillar Ribs and Possible Methods of Control. Fourth Australia - New Zealand Conference on Geomechanics,Perth 2:661-667.

Sissons, B.A. 1979. The Horizontal Kinematics of the North Island of New Zealand. PhD Thesis, Victoria University, New Zealand.

Suggate, P.R. 1982. Personal Com.

Proceedings of the International Symposium on Rock Stress and Rock Stress Measurements/Stockholm/1-3 September 1986

The application of stress measurements to the optimisation coal mine roadway driveage in the Illawarra coal measures

W.J. GALE
CSIRO, Division of Geomechanics, Wollongong, N.S.W., Australia

ABSTRACT

Difficult mining conditions are commonly experienced during underground road-way driveage in the Southern Coalfield, Australia. Rock failure occurring in roof strata at the mining face is commonly experienced together with high loading of roof support and reinforcement.

The type of rock failure surrounding a mine roadway and the subsequent opening stability are significantly influenced by the orientation of the face with respect to the in-situ principal stresses.

Mine layouts and roof reinforcement procedures have been developed on the basis of an anticipated mode and geometry of rock failure occurring at or ahead of the mining face.

RESUME

Les conditions difficiles minieres sont rencontre pendant tracage des voies souterraines dans la region sud du Bassin Houiller de Sydney en Australie. L'occurrence de cassure des roches dans les strates du toit au chantier minier est rencontre ordinairement avec les charges lourds du soutenement et renforcement du toit.

Le type de cassure de roches environnant une voie miniere et la stabilite suivante du chantier sont influence significativement par les directions comparatifs de la orientation de la face et les pressions principales de terrain in situ.

Les plans des mines et les procededes de renforcement du toit ont ete developpe sur la base d'une mode et d'une geometrie anticipee de cassure de roche qui se presente a ou en avant de la face miniere.

ZUSAMMENFASSUNG

Schwierige Bergbau umstande sind oft aus Erfahrung entstanden wahrend des abbaus untertag strecken vortrieb in den Sudlichen Kohlfedern in Australien. Die erfahrung hat ergeben das das hohe gewicht der geschteinsmassen so schwer ist, das gesteinsrisse vorkommen in den gesteinschichten beim Abbaustoss, zusammen mit hohe beanspruchung der Abstutzungen und verstarkungen.

Die art des Gesteinsbruch in der umgebung der Vortriebstrecke sind die folgen der offnung stabilitat hat ein bedeutenden einfluss auf die orientierung von dem Abbaustoss mit hinsicht auf die haupt spannungen (stress).

Grubenauschnitt und Deckenverstarkungen verfahren, sind so Konstruiert worden wegen dem vorrausschende quantitative mineralogische zusammensetzung und das geometrie des Gesteinsbruch.

1. INTRODUCTION

Underground coal mining is being undertaken at increasing depth and within highly stressed rock masses. Mining developments are subject to the effects of virgin stressfields and gross stress redistributions occurring about extraction panels.

Many coal measure rocks are weak engineering materials which require artificial support or reinforcement to maintain opening stability.

High production mining operations require rapid and stable roadway development with minimum obstruction.

The magnitude and orientation of stresses are major factors influencing underground roadway stability in mining areas within weak strata and high virgin stressfields (Gale et al., 1984, Gale and Blackwood, in press).

This paper presents an overview of the application of stressfield data to the optimisation of roadway driveage in the Bulli coal of the Illawarra coal measures, N.S.W., Australia.

2. LOCATION AND GEOLOGY

The Illawarra coal measures are located in the southern portion of the Sydney Basin, a broad basin structure containing extensive coal reserves Permian Age (Fig. 1).

The coal measure strata are gently dipping between 0-5°. Dominant structural features within the coal measures are broad folds, minor monoclinal flexures and normal faults with displacements up to 100 m. Igneous dykes, sills and volcanic plugs intersect the coal measures. The stratigraphy and structure of the coal measures has been discussed in greater detail by Bunny (1972) and Wilson (1975).

The Bulli Seam is the upper seam of the coal measures and is enclosed by roof and floor sections of siltstone, sandstone, mudstone and shales. Finely interbedded sequences of these rock types are referred to as laminite, and commonly occur in the immediate mine roof section.

The typical strength properties of strata above the Bulli seam are presented in Table 1.

TABLE 1. TYPICAL ILLAWARRA COAL MEASURE ROCK STRENGTH PROPERTIES.

Rock Type	Mean UCS (MPa)	Range	Mean E (GPa)	Range
Sandstone (Medium grained)	96.5	79-133	18.0	15.6-25.16
Sandstone (Fine grained)	91	40-128	19.0	13.7-27.0
Siltstone	74	58-95	22	19.0-30.0
Mudstone	40	21-53	15	13.0-17.0
Laminite	53	33-71	16	13.0-20.0

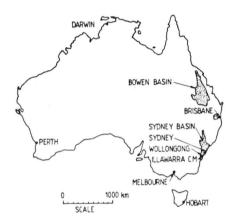

FIGURE 1. LOCATION OF THE SYDNEY BASIN AND ILLAWARRA COAL MEASURES.

3. VIRGIN STRESSFIELD MEASUREMENTS

Stress measurements conducted in the coal measures, and the Sydney Basin in general (Enever et al, 1980, Walton, 1983; Gale, 1983; Gale et al., 1984 (a), and 1984 (b)) delineate the existence of high and anisotropic lateral stress components.

In situ stress measurements have been made at 13 sites in the Southern Sydney Basin using the CSIRO HI stress cell and the overcore technique (Worotniki and Walton, 1976). Stress measurements were made at distances of 6.5 - 12.5 m from development roadways in collieries and represent the virgin stress environment into which roadways are driven.

Results from the in situ stress measurements indicated that the maximum principal stress, σ_1, was effectively horizontal and that the virgin stressfields were often oriented with respect to local and regional structural features. Stress measurements above the Bulli seam at depths between 400 and 500 m revealed that σ_1, typically had magnitudes between 18 - 27 MPa. The vertical stress components varied between 10-17.5 MPa and were often significantly greater than vertical stresses attributable to overburden alone.

The in situ stresses measured in the coal measures are consistent with near surface stress measurements reported elsewhere (Hoek and Brown, 1980) for which horizontal stress components exceed vertical stress components. Locally, ratios of maximum horizontal stress to vertical stress are variable between (1.5-1.8):1 and an anisotropy of (1.3-2):1 exists between the horizontal stress components. Overall, the ratio of maximum horizontal stress : minimum horizontal stress : vertical stress can be expressed in the range of (1.3-2) : 1 : (0.82-1.3).

4. EFFECT OF STRESS GEOMETRY ON ROADWAY STABILITY

The effect of virgin stress distributions on roof behaviour is a complex function dependent upon the strength and stiffness of the strata, the magnitude of the principal stresses, the distribution of discontinuities and the orientation of the roadway.

An overview of some gross effects of stress magnitude and geometry typical in coal mining developments can be gained from an examination of two "end member" situations;
a) where rock material strength is not exceeded or in low lateral stress conditions and;
b) where rock material strength is exceeded or in high lateral stress conditions.

The effect of stress geometry for case (a) is presented in Figure 2. where a number of factors influencing stability are plotted relative to angle of between the maximum lateral stress component and the roadway axis, (Θ_{SR}). The lateral stresses and bending moments are normalised relative to the maximum values obtained. The results indicate that factors which enhance roof stability of roadways increase as Θ_{SR} tends to 90°. The stability is enhanced as a result of
i) the stress redistribution about the opening creating a bending moment which resists roof displacement into the opening. The bending moment increases as Θ_{SR} tends to 90°.
ii) the lateral stress component across the roof increases the stability of steeply dipping discontinuities (e.g. joints, coal cleat) oriented parallel to the roadway and reduces the likelihood of rock dropout.

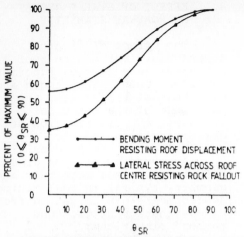

FIGURE 2. NORMALISED VALUES OF LATERAL STRESS AND BENDING MOMENT DEVELOPED ABOVE A MINE ROADWAY PLOTTED RELATIVE TO ΘSR.

The effect of stress geometry for case (b) has been studied by Gale and Blackwood (in press), and Gale et al., 1984 a,b). These studies show that the incidence of rock failure in the roof strata is a function of the opening geometry and the orientation of the opening to the in-situ stressfield.

It was found that for rectangular shaped mine roadways the factors of safety against roof rock shear failure reduce as the angle between σ_1 and the roadway axis (Θ_{SR}) increases to 90°. This response is summarised in Figure 3. which presents the effect of Θ_{SR} upon factors of safety against coulomb shear fracture in the vicinity of a mining face. The factors are normalised as a percentage of the maximum value obtained. The results indicate that the occurrence of rock shear failure increases as Θ_{SR} tends to 90°.

In the Illawarra Coal Measures roof rock failure is commonly experienced at the roadway face during driveage under laminite and closely interbedded roof sections (Figure 4.). Rock failure takes the form of shear and

tensional fracture through the rock material.

Roadways driven in the Bulli coal are affected by high lateral stresses and exhibit behaviour typical of case (b) above. Under these conditions the prediction and control of rock failure is a major consideration in the roadway driveage and reinforcement optimisation strategies employed.

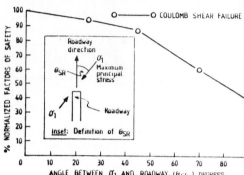

FIGURE 3. NORMALISED FACTORS OF SAFETY AGAINST SHEAR FRACTURE THROUGH THE ROCK MATERIAL ABOVE THE FACE OF A MINE ROADWAY PLOTTED RELATIVE TO ΘSR.

FIGURE 4.   FRACTURED ROOF STRATA ABOVE A MINE ROADWAY.
SHEAR FRACTURES OCCUR AT THE FACE DURING ADVANCE.

5.   OPTIMISATION OF ROADWAY LAYOUT

Optimisation of roadway driveage requires characterisation of the stressfield in workings and predictability of the rock stability about the roadways.

5.1. Stressfield Characteristation

Stressfield characterisation is undertaken by the use of overcore stress measurement using the CSIRO HI stress cell (Worotnicki and Walton 1976) and by observational techniques (Gale et al., 1984 a; Gale and Stone, in prep.).   The observational techniques employed resolve the direction of σ_1 from rock failure which occurred during roadway driveage.

Observational techniques allow a rapid appraisal of the direction and variability of the lateral stress components over a colliery.   Overcore measurements are conducted to quantify the stressfield in key locations defined from the observational surveys.   An example of the approach is given in Figure 5. where observational and overcore stress data are presented.

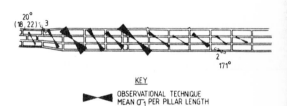

KEY

◄► OBSERVATIONAL TECHNIQUE
    MEAN σ_1 PER PILLAR LENGTH

▭✕▭ C.S.I.R.O. STRESS CELL OVERCORE SITE

FIGURE 5.   COMPARISON OF OBSERVATIONALLY DETERMINED STRESS DIRECTIONS AND OVERCORE RESULTS FROM A MINE PANEL.

The stressfield delineated in the workings can be assessed with respect to local or regional structures.   A regional assessment of the stressfield is important with regard to predictability of the stressfield on the basis of proximity to structural features.   The regional nature of the stressfield geometry in a number of collieries affected by a broad fold structure is presented in Figure 6.   It is apparent that the stresses measured reflect the stresses associated with folding of the strata.   This type of analysis indicates the structural influences on the stressfield and allows an appraisal of the persistence of such influences.

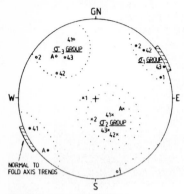

NORMAL TO
FOLD AXIS TRENDS

PRINCIPAL STRESS ORIENTATIONS

KEY
• MAXIMUM STRESS (σ_1)
× INTERMEDIATE STRESS (σ_2)
○ MINIMUM STRESS (σ_3)
⋯ STRESS GROUPING

LOWER HEMISPHERE STEREOGRAPHIC PROJECTION
FIGURE 6. STERBOGRAPHIC PROJECTION OF PRINCIPAL STRESS AXIS OBTAINED FROM OVERCORE STRESS MEASUREMENTS AT TWO COLLIERIES TOGETHER WITH THE REGIONAL FOLD TREND.

5.2 Prediction of Development Roadway Behaviour

The effect of virgin stresses on roadway performance can be assessed by back analysis and correlation with predicted responses. Driveage within the Bulli coal under laminite is significantly influenced by stress orientation and magnitude.

The extent of the influence is presented in Figure 7. which shows the percentage of driveage affected by rock shear failure relative to the angle between σ_1 and roadway axis (Θ_{SR}). The factors of safety against shear fracture of the rock obtained from computational modelling (Gale and Blackwood, in press) are also plotted as a percentage of the maximum value. The results show that the occurrence of driveage affected by significant rock shear fracture correlates with

the reduction in factors of safety modelled and that the roadways affected can be predicted for operational planning.

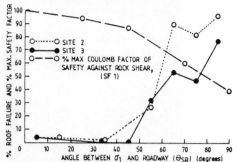

FIGURE 7. FIELD SURVEY OF THE PERCENTAGE OF ROADWAY DRIVEAGE AFFECTED BY SHEAR FRACTURE OF ROOF STRATA PLOTTED RELATIVE TO ΘSR. NORMALISED FACTORS OF SAFETY AGAINST SHEAR FRACTURE ARE ALSO PLOTTED (AFTER FIG.3).

The practical application of this is delineated in Figure 8. where the percentage of driveage having a stable and visibly undeformed roof condition is plotted relative to Θ_{SR}.

The results show that good stable driveage conditions occur when roadways are driven at small angles to σ_1. Roadways driven at angles greater than 45° to σ_1 ($\Theta_{SR} > 45$) exhibit rock failure as described above.

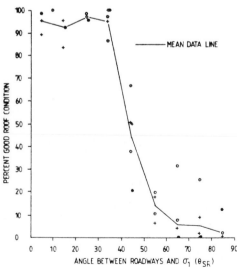

FIGURE 8. FIELD SURVEY OF THE PERCENTAGE OF ROADWAY DRIVEAGE HAVING GOOD (STABLE, UNDEFORMED) ROOF CONDITIONS RELATIVE TO ΘSR.

The occurrence of rock failure about the opening has a significant and detrimental influence on roadway advance rates.

A case example of the percentage of good roof and its effect on roadway driveage rate is presented in Figure 9. The driveage rate is normalised as a percentage of the maximum.

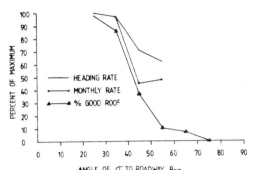

FIGURE 9. A CASE EXAMPLE OF THE EFFECT OF Θ_{SR} ON THE INCIDENCE OF GOOD ROOF AND ROADWAY DRIVEAGE RATE.

The results indicate that advance rates significantly reduce when driveage is oriented at high angles to σ_1. The greatest driveage rate was achieved when roadways were oriented at small angles to σ_1. The reduction in advance rates shown is related to delays caused by the necessity to place additional reinforcement or support.

These stressfield conditions play a significant role in the layout of longwall retreat panels where gateroads are required to be stable and rapidly developed. Under high lateral stress conditions gateroad driveage is optimised when driven parallel to σ_1.

This type of analysis shows that roadway driveage can be significantly optimised and that the gross rock response about roadway can be predicted by the use of stress measurement based analyses.

6.   STRESS CONTROL METHODS

Although optimisation layout procedures can be accomplished on a mine-wide scale, panel or roadway driveage is still required in directions for which roadways are subject to significant rock deformation. Such roadways are typified by Θ_{SR} values between 70° and 90°. Considerable rock failure or softening occurs in the roof and floor strata of these roadways when driven into virgin ground.

The lateral stress redistribution which occurs about the softened roof and floor zones allows practical "ground destressing" to occur up to 30 m from the softened roadway.

The generalised phenomenon is depicted in Figure 10. which shows the geometry of softened zones together with the associated extent of destressing in an elastic medium.

This type of approach allows the utilisation of a softened roadway to provide lateral stress relief for subsequent roadways driven in close proximity. Roadways driven in the stress relieved ground are typified by good driveage conditions, long term stability and reduced reinforcement requirements.

Panel layouts are designed to maximise the effect of local stress control strategies for driveage under high lateral stress conditions.

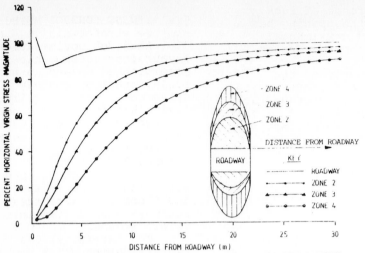

FIGURE 10.   REDUCTION OF HORIZONTAL STRESS AT ROADWAY ROOF HEIGHT ADJACENT
TO ROADWAYS FOR VARIOUS ZONES OF ROOF AND FLOOR SOFTENING.

7.   ROCK REINFORCEMENT DESIGN

The predictability of rock failure on the basis of stressfield data allows predetermined rock reinforcement strategies to be applied.   Rock bolt reinforcement patterns can be placed to provide reinforcement against specific rock failure modes where the location and height of rock failure can be anticipated.

Research conducted (Gale et al., 1984 a; Gale and Blackwood, in press) has shown that the location of rock failure occurring at the face of roadways could be predicted on the basis of Θ_{SR}.   It has been found that for roadways driven with 40< Θ_{SR} <70 shear fracturing was biassed to one roof side.   The position of shear fracture relocated toward the roadway centre as Θ_{SR} increased to 90°.

The effect of biassed roof failure on rock bolt loads developed during face advance is shown in Figure 11.   The forces developed in bolts per M^2 across the roadway show a very biassed distribution.

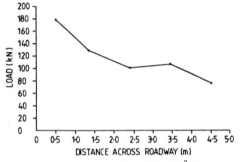

FIGURE 11.   ROOF BOLT LOAD DISTRIBUTION PER M^2 ACROSS A ROADWAY
SUBJECT TO SHEAR FAILURE ON THE LEFT HAND SIDE (0.0 M).

Bolts on the left hand roofside were often excessively loaded or broken under these driveage conditions.   A modified bolt pattern was trialled which minimised the forces developed in the bolts on left-hand roofside to levels at which roof stability was significantly improved.

The height to which rock failure progresses has a significant impact on the length and type of reinforcement required to stabilise roadways driven at high Θ_{SR} angles.   The type of reinforcement employed is dependent upon the intended use of the roadway and is discussed elsewhere (Gale, 1986).

This type of predictive analysis is coupled with detailed site monitoring of the height and mode of rock failure and the forces developed in the reinforcement (Gale and Fabjanczyk, 1986). Monitoring of reinforcement performance allows a reinforcement system to be designed on the basis of a predictable rock response.

8.   CONCLUSION

The application of stress measurements to underground coal mining operations is widespread. In high stress conditions of the Illawarra coal measures the stability, and advance rate, and layout of mine roadways are significantly affected by stressfield geometry.

The reinforcement used in the roadways is designed with regard to the predictability of stress related rock failure during driveage.

Stress measurements and stress based analyses allow mine planning in Bulli coal mining operations on the basis of advance rate optimisation and roadway stability.

9.   REFERENCES.

Bunny, M.R. 1972. Geology and coal resources of the southern catchment coal reserve, Southern Sydney Basin, N.S.W. Geol. Survey of N.S.W. Bull. No.22, 146 p.

Enever, J.R., Shepherd, J., Cook, C.E., Creasy, J.W., Rixon, L.K., Crawford, G., Dean, A. and White, A.S. 1980. Analysis of factors influencing roof stability at Wallsend Borehole Colliery. CSIRO Aust., Div. Applied Geomech., Geomech. Coal Mining Rep. No. 15, 82 pp.

Hoek, E. and Brown, E.T. 1980. Underground excavation in rock. I.M.M. Publication, London, pp 532.

Gale, W.J. 1983. Measurements of the stressfield in Appin and Corrimal Collieries N.S.W., Australia. CSIRO, Aust., Division of Geomechanics, Site Investigation Report No.11.

Gale, Winton J. 1986. Design considerations for reinforcement of coal mine roadways in the Illawarra Coal Measures. Proc. Aus. I.M.Metal. Symp. on Ground Control in Coal Mines. Wollongong, Australia.

Gale, W.J., Rawlings, C.D., Cook, E.E., Stone, I., Rixon, L.K., Enever, J.R., Walton, R.J., and Litterbach, N. 1984 a. An investigation of in-situ stressfield and its effect on mining conditions at Tahmoor Colliery N.S.W. Australia. CSIRO Aust., Division of Geomechanics, Geomechanics of Coal Mining Report No. 49.

Gale, W.J., Enever, J.R., Blackwood, R.L. and McKay, J. 1984 b. An investigation of the effect of a fault/monocline structure on the in-situ stressfield and mining conditions at Nattai Bulli Colliery, N.S.W., Australia. CSIRO, Aust., Division of Geomechanics, Geomechanics of Coal Mining Report No.48.

Gale, W.J. and Blackwood, R.L. (in press). Three dimensional computational modelling of stress and rock failure distributions about the face of a rectangular underground opening and its correlation with coal mine roadway behaviour. Int. J. Rock. Mech. and Mining Sci.

Gale, W.J. and Fabjanczyk, M.W. 1986. Application of Field Measurement Techniques to the Design of Roof Reinforcement Systems in Underground Coal Mines. 13th Congress of Council of the Mining and Met. Inst. Singapore, pp. 135-141.

Gale, W.J. and Stone, I.
Observational methods of
determining maximum principal
stress direction in underground
coal mines and their
correlation with the CSIRO
overcore technique. (In
preparation.).

Walton, R.J. 1983. A Study of
the Behaviour of a Bolted Coal
Mine Roof Subject to
Medium/High Horizontal Stress.
Part 1. 2.1 Metre Long Resin
Anchored Bolts. CSIRO Aust.,
Div. of Geomechanics,
Geomechanics of Coal Mining
Report No.46.

Wilson, R.G. 1975. Southern
coalfield. In, Economic
geology of Australia and New
Guinea, E. Traves and King,
Aus. I.M.M. Monograph No. 6.
pp 206-218.

Worotnicki, G. and Walton, R.J.
1976. Triaxial `Hollow
Inclusion' gauges for
determination of rock stresses
in situ. Proc. Symp. on
Investigation of Stress in Rock
- Advances in stress
measurement, Inst. Eng. Aust.,
Nat. Conf. Public No. 76/4, pp.
1-8).

In-situ stress measurements of rock by stress relief method at some locations in Korea

HAN-UK LIM
Kangweon National University, Chunchon, Korea
CHUNG-IN LEE
Seoul National University, Seoul, Korea

Abstract

Three sites of mines and one site of underground powerhouse at depths of 150m to 802m in Korea were chosen as testing sites to get informations on the initial rock stresses.

Three directional borehole deformation gage was used to take a large number of strain-relief measurements, from which three dimensional stresses for each site were calculated.

Attempts have been made to determine the state of absolute stresses, the influence of surface topography on the stresses and the changes of stresses in the magnitude with depth.

Résumé

Trois endroits des mines et un endroit de la centrale électrique souterraine à la profondeur de 150m à 802m en Corée ont été choisis comme l'endroit d'essai pour obtenir les informations sur l'effort initial de roche.

La jauge de déformation de trou percé de trois orientations a été emploiée pour effectuer un bon nombre de mesure de contrainte-détante, d'où les efforts de trois dimensions à chaque endroit ont été calculees.

L'essai a été fait de determiner l'état des efforts absolus, l'effet de la topographie superficielle sur les efforts et la variation de l'intensité de l'effort avec la profondeur.

Zusammenfassung

Die Durchführung der In-situ-Spannungsmessungen erfolgte in drei verschiedenen Bergbaugebieten und einer unterirdischen Kraftwerke in Teufe von 150m und 802m in Korea.

Es werden drei Bohrlöcher von unterschiedlicher Achsrichtung gebohrt, wobei die Messung nach dem Überbohrverfahren ausgeführt wird. Mit den so gewonenen Daten wird der vollständige räumliche Spannungszustand errechnet.

Der absolute Spannungszustand, der Einfluß der Gebirge auf den Spannungszustand und entsprechend variierenden Werte mit der Teufe werden näher erläutert.

1. INTRODUCTION

The determination of the local state of stress at depth in rock masses is important in both the design of mining excavations and the understanding of the mechanism of geologic structures.

If the stress is determined in the rock in an area of a prospective underground opening, it is possible to predict the stresses that will act around openings. It will then be possible to choose the orientation and shape of the opening so as to minimize tensile stresses and extreme concentrations of compressive stresses in its boundary surfaces.

For such purposes, in-situ measurements have been made in different geologic formations and at different depths.

This paper presents current information on stress measurements in Korea. We have studied the variation of average horizontal and vertical stresses with depth in various geologic conditions and calculated the ratio of maximum to minimum principal stresses. We also discussed the relation between the principal stresses and shear stresses in rock.

The results are compared with the analyses of other data reported by Brown (1) etc.

2. PROCEDURE

The in-situ stress measurements were made by U.S.B.M. borehole deformation gage method. The overcoring procedure of making in-situ stress measurement is well known and described here briefly.

As practised by the U.S.B.M., a 38mm diameter borehole is drilled in rock mass and the gage is inserted at a proper location in hole. The gage is overcored with a 15,24 cm diameter bit. As the stresses are removed from the core, the hole deformation is monitored by the gage.

To calculate the absolute stress from the strainrelief measurements at each site, it is necessary to know the elastic constants and Poisson's ratio of the rocks in which the measurements are made.

These constants were determined from uniaxial loading in laboratory test and biaxial loading in the in-situ test. The components of stresses were reduced by using the plane strain solution(2).

By means of the least square method, it is possible to estimate the values of the principal stresses, of their directions and of their confidence levels.

3. MEASUREMENTS AND RESULTS

More than 70 measurements for determining the natural stesses in the undisturbed rocks have been made at six testing sites in four different localities and at depths ranging from 150m to 802m(Fig. 1).

The measurements were performed continuously in several horizontal boreholes of which length is up to 15m and strainrelief deformations were taken at a distance about 2-3 times radius of the tunnel from the tunnel wall. All testing sites were more than 400m distant from areas of mining and could be considered to be free of stress concentration eff-

ects due to mining.

Table. 1 Provides data about the full stress tensors, i, e. the three principal stresses and their directions, and six stress components in the vertical (σ_z), east(σ_x), and north(σ_y) coordinate systems.

4. DISCUSSION

Despite of limited number of stress measurements. We have studied the effects of topographic irregularities, the variations of vertical and average horizontal stresses with depth and the relation between principal stresses.

4.1 Influence of topography on vertical stress.

The calculated average stress components are considered to represent the natural stress fields that existed prior or to excavation because the measurements were made at a distance far away from the influence zone due to the opening. The natural stress field is consisted of gravitational(current) and tectonic(current, residual) stresses(4). The surface topography overlying the testing sites is mountainous.

Therefore, gravitational stresses are influenced by nearby mountain peaks as well as direct overburden depth. The influence of topography on stress can be evaluated by using a two or three dimensional finite element model(5) or distributed load(6) in the area sur-

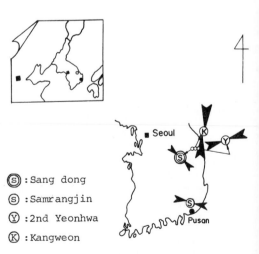

Ⓢ : Sang dong
ⓢ : Samrangjin
Ⓨ : 2nd Yeonhwa
Ⓚ : Kangweon

Fig. 1 Locations of Measurements and directions of Max. principal stress.

Table.1 Initial Stresses of Rock Masses at Testing Site.

Site	Depth (m)	Rock	No. of measure-ment	Principal stress (MPa)						Ave. Stress Components (MPa)					
				S_1	S_2	S_3	α_1/β_1	α_2/β_2	α_3/β_3	σ_x	σ_y	σ_z	τ_{xy}	τ_{yx}	τ_{zx}
Samrangjin	150	rhyolite	5	-6.85	-5.3	-3.08	110.8/96.4	16.9/143.8	10.5/98.8	-6.37	-3.41	-5.20	-0.59	-0.78	-0.27
2nd Yeonhwa	200	limestone	7	-12.17	-5.3	-3.20	71.0/106.5	37.7/35.7	180.4/123.1	-10.24	-4.80	-5.63	-0.62	+0.63	-0.74
	440	limestone	4	-39.12	-18.33	-13.41				-25.78	-24.59	-20.47	-11.3	+3.32	-4.0
Sangdong	285	limestone	4	-10.72	-6.83	-2.721	313.3/104.3	37.2/30.9	128.6/92.3	-5.82	-7.25	-7.19	-1.34	-0.53	-0.57
	594	slate	3	-22.43	-14.78	-10.69	132.3/73.1	262.2/25.2	219.1/103.5	-14.83	-12.7	-15.28	-2.29	-2.87	-0.69
Kangweon	802	sandstone	3	-51.87	-30.82	-17.16	182/88	84/63	92/122	-22.03	-50.92	-25.9	-4.0	+2.45	-6.60

α/β =bearing of direction/inclination.

* 1. Inclinations are referred to vertical, downward as being 0°, horizontal as 90° and upward as 180°
* 2. A negative sign for principal stresses S_1 (maximum principal), S_2 (intermediate principal stress) S_3 (minimun principal stress) and normal components of rock stresses σ_x, σ_y, σ_z indicates that these stresses are compressive.
* 3. A negative sign for shear stresses τ_{xy}, τ_{yz}, τ_{zx} indicates the direction of stresses are opposite to the those of axes.

rounding the proposed site.

In this study, the effect of topography was estimated by considering the mountain as distributed load acting on the boundary of a semi-infinite plate(6). The results for each site are as follows (table 2).

The influence of the local topography on the overburden vertical stress appears to be 7.0-12.3% of the measured stress but the effect decreases with depth.

At the Samrangiin(relatively shallow depth) and the Kangweon, the measured vertical stresses are greater than calculated ones by 12-18%, while at the sangdong and the 2nd Yeonhwa smaller by 5-14%.

4.2 Changes of Stresses with Depth

Though there have been a few studies in which stresses were measured at the same location, trend of stress changes with depth could be established. The determination of average horizontal

stress($\frac{\sigma_x + \sigma_y}{2}$) are indicated in table 3.

The regression equations for the vertical and average horizontal stresses obtained from data are respectively as follows :

$$\sigma_z = 1.36 + 0.0233 \ Z(MPa) \quad \text{(confidence limit } r = 0.97) \quad (1)$$

$$\sigma_{hav}= 2.78 + 0.0183 \ Z(MPa) \quad \text{(confidence limit } r = 0.86) \quad (2)$$

Where, Z is in meters,

Both equations show a non-zero stress intercept at zero depth. Herget, Brown, Worotnicki(7), Hast, Haimson and many other researchers (1) have assembled informations about stress at different depths in different locations and analysed it statistically to establish the most probable common trend in the change of stress with depth (Fig. 2, Fig. 3).

Table. 2 Magnitude of vertical Stress and Topographic Effect on Stress

Site / Items	Samrangjin (branch3)	Sang dong site 1	site 2	2nd Yeon-hwa (site 1)	Kangweon
Depth (m)	150	285	594	200	802
Measured stress (MPa)(a)	5.2	7.2	15.3	5.63	25.9
Calculated stress (MPa) (b = c + d) (b)	4.42	8.32	17.60	5.96	23.0
(c) : $\sigma_z = r \cdot h$	3.78	7.51	15.72	5.34	21.17
(d) : stress due to topographic effect	0.64	0.81	1.88	1.62	1.83
a/b (%)	117.7	86.5	86.9	94.4	112.6
d/a (%)	12.3	11.3	12.3	11.0	7.0
Change of inclination due to topography	35°	10°	8°	12°	6°

Table. 3 Magnitude of Horizontal Stesses

Site	Depth (m)	Hor. stress (measured) (MPa) σ_x	σ_y	Ia	Ave. hor. stress (MPa) measured(a)	calculated(b)	Differ- ence (a-b)	Excess hor. stress (difference/ 100m depth)
Samrangjin	150	6.37	3.41	1.86	4.89	1.21	3.68	2.45
2nd Yeonhwa	200	10.24	4.80	2.13	7.52	1.80	5.72	2.86
Sangdong (site 1)	285	5.82	7.25	1.24	6.53	3.52	3.01	1.05
(site 2)	594	14.83	12.7	1.17	13.78	5.90	7.88	1.32
Kangweon	802	23.03	50.92	2.21	36.98	5.76	31.22	3.89

1) Ave. hor. stress (measured) = $(\sigma_x + \sigma_y)/2$

2) calculated stress was considered the topographic effect. $(\sigma_h = \frac{\nu}{1-\nu} \cdot \sigma_z)$

3) Ia (horizontal stress anisotropy) = $\dfrac{\sigma_h \, max}{\sigma_h \, min}$

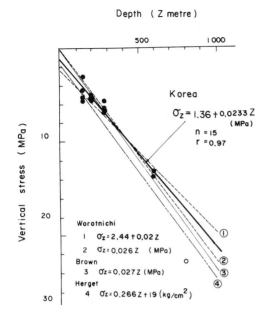

Fig.2 Variation of Vertical Stresses
With Depth.

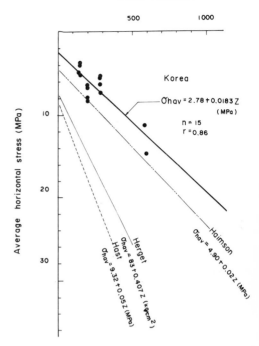

Fig.3 Change of Average Horizontal
Stresses with Depth.

As compared with those data, both vertical and average horizontal stresses with depth in Korea appear to be substantially lower than other data.

The ratio of maximum to minimum horizontal stress, which is also listed in table 3, varies from 1.17 to 2.21 depending on different localities. The horizontal stress exhibits a stress anisotropy clearly in most cases.

In order to make a comparison among the values of the tectonically most important horizontal stresses, the excess horizontal stress(8) was calculated by the difference between the measured horizontal stress and the theoretical horizontal stress considering the lithostatic stress is caused by weight of overburden in areas such as the Kangweon and the 2nd Yeonhwa. The high horizontal stresses are presumed as the result of lateral compression from the geologic structures such as the Cheolam fault, the Cheolam syncline, and the Baiksan thrust etc (Fig. 4).

4.3 The ratio of horizontal to vertical
stress

The ratio of average horizontal to vertical stress is one of the important factors in the design of underground openings. The results obtained from the measuring data were presented in table. 4.

The values of K in Korea appear to be 0.90-0.94 except the 2nd Yeonhwa and the Kangweon site.

In south Africa and U.S.A., this ratio tends to have a value of less than one at depths of greater than one kilometer while in Canada it tends to be greater than one (9).

4.4 Relation between principal stresses

In a rock mass containing several group of discontinuities it can be conceived that the most likely equilibrating process would be movements along the discontinuities. The equilibrium would be controlled by shear resistance on the discontinuities.

The relation between the principal stress components and the maximum shearing stress was given in table 5.

The ratio between maximum and minimum principal stesses varies within a wide range : For most cases, however, they fall within a range of 2.1 - 3.95. By assuming a 30° friction angle and the

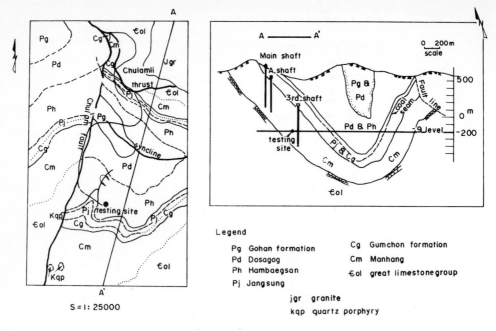

Legend

Pg	Gohan formation	Cg	Gumchon formation
Pd	Dosagog	Cm	Manhang
Ph	Hambaegsan	€ol	great limestone group
Pj	Jangsung		

jgr granite

kqp quartz porphyry

S = 1 : 25000

Fig. 4 Geologic Map of Kangweon Coal Mine

absence cohesion, the value of the ratio could drop to 3.0.

The similar results for principal stress ratios were reported by Gay for south Africa, Haimson for U.S.A., Worotnicki and Deham for Australia(1), and Sbar et al for north America(10).

Table 5 shows the mean bearing and inclination of maximum principal stress at the testing sites. It appears that the inclination of maximum principal stress is nearly subhorizontal, and it should be noted that the maximum shear stress is about one-third of the maximum principal stresses in magnitude.

5.   CONCLUSION

In-situ strain measurements performed in the southeastern part of Korean peninsula show a recent state of stress in rock masses. Despite of studying limited data, the results are summarized as follows.

(1) Vertical stresses are in close agreement with the calculated values considering the overburden depth and the influence of local topography. The ratio of measured to calculated stresses is from 86.4 to 117.7%. The regression equation obtained for the vertical stress components (σ_z, MPa) as a function of depth(z. meter) is σ_z = 1.36 + 0.0233z.

The influence of surface topography on theorientation and the magnitude of stress has been calculated by using a distributed vertical stresses appears to be 7.0 - 12.3 % of the measured stress but the effect decreases with depth.

(2) The regression equation for the average horizontal stress (σ_{hav} , MPa) is σ_{hav} = 2.78 + 0.0183z.

The ratio of horizontal to vertical stress at the testing sites varies from 0.90 to 1.42. The state of stress of the Kangweon area is believed to have been affected by the tectonic structure such as the Cheoloam fault, the Cheoloa syncline, and the Baiksan thrust etc.

(3) The ratio of the maximum to the minimum principal stress widely varies. For most cases, however, it varies from 2.10 to 3.95. The maximum principal stress acts nearly in the subhorizontal direction at all sites.

(4) The two horizontal stress σ_x and σ also show considerable differences and the ratio ranges from 1.17 to 2.21. To understand about the natural state of stress in Korea, it will be necessar to carry out the more measurements.

Table 4. The Relation between K and Depth

Site	Depth(m)	Ave. hor. stress (MPa)	ver. stress (MPa)	K ($\frac{\sigma\text{hav}}{\sigma v}$)
Samrangjin	150	4.89	5.20	0.94
2nd Yeonhwa	200	7.52	5.63	1.33
Sang dong(1)	285	6.53	7.19	0.91
Sang dong(2)	594	13.78	15.28	0.90
Kangweon	802	36.98	25.9	1.42

Table. 5. The Relation between Stress Components

Site	Depth (m)	S_1/S_2	Max.shearing stress(MPa)	max/S_1 (%)	bearing inclination of S_1	Remarks
Samrangjin	150	2.23	- 1.89	27.6	110.8/96.4	at branch 3
2nd Yeonhwa	200	3.81	- 4.48	36.8	71.0/106.5	at site 1
Sangdong	285	3.95	- 4.0	37.3	313.3/104.3	at site 2
2nd Yeonhwa	440	2.91	- 12.85	32.8	134.4/76.5	measured at fault zone
Sangdong	594	2.1	-15.86	26.2	132.3/73.1	at site 2
Kangweon	802	3.02	- 17.35	33.4	182/88	
ave. value		3.0		32.3		

S_1 : max. principal stress.

S_2 : intermediate principal stress.

S_3 : min. principal stress.

$$\tau_{max} = \frac{S_1 - S_3}{2}$$

REFERRENCES

1. Brown,E.T., and Hoek, E., 1978, Trends in relationships between measured in-situ stresses and depth : Int. J. Rock Mech. Min. Sci., v. 15, pp. 211-215.

2. Obert,L., and Duvall, W.I., 1967, Rock mechanics and the design of structures in rock : john Wiley & sons, 650 p.

3. Schmitt,T.J., 1981. The west European stress field : new data and interpretation : J. of structural Geo., V.3, No.3, pp. 309 - 315.

4. Voight, B., 1966. Interpretation of in situ stress measurements : proc. 1st Congr. lnt. soc. Rock mech., Lisbon, V.3, p. 332 - 348.

5. Sturgul, J.R., and Grinshpan, A., 1975, Finite-element model for

    possible isostatic rebound in the
    Grand Canyon : Geology, V.3, pp.
    169 - 172.

6. Hooker, V.E., Bickel, D.L., and Agg-
    son, J.R., 1972, In-situ determi-
    nation of stress in mountain top-
    ography : U.S.B.M., R.I. 1654,
    19 p.

7. Worotnicki, G., and Denham, D., 1976,
    The state of stress in the upper
    part of the earth's crust in Aus-
    tralia according to measurements
    in mines and tunnels and from se-
    ismic observations : symp. lnv.
    of stress in rock advances in st-
    ress measurements. sydney., pp.
    71 - 85.

8. Greiner, G., and Lohr, T., 1980,
    Tectonic stresses in the northern
    foreland of the Alpine system.
    measurements and interpretation:
    Rock Mech., Suppl. 9, pp. 5 - 16.

9. Gay, N.C., 1982, The state of stress
    in the plates :

10. Sbar, M.L., Sykes, L.R., 1973, Con-
    temporary compressive stress and
    seismicity in easterm north Amer-
    ica, and example of intraplate
    tectonics : Geol. Soc. Am. Bull.,
    V.84, pp. 1861 - 1883.

Application of the LUT triaxial overcoring technique in Swedish mines

B.A. LEIJON
Division of Rock Mechanics, Luleå University of Technology, Luleå, Sweden

ABSTRACT: A brief presentation of the Luleå University of Technology (LUT) triaxial overcoring technique is given, and the field applications of this technique in Swedish mines are summarized. Data from stress measurements at two locations, selected so as to represent different geological conditions, are analysed to obtain statistical measures of data confidence. It is shown that the local rock conditions have a major influence on the confidence of results from individual stress measurements, as well as on results from groups of measurements. It is also found, however, that the most significant uncertainties encountered when introducing stress data into geomechanical analysis related to mining, are the variations of the stress field that often occurs within the large volumes of rock typically considered in such analysis.

RÉSUMÉ: Une courte présentation de la méthode de surcarottage développée à Luleå (adaptée de la technique CSIR bien connue) est faite, ainsi que de ses conditions d'application aux secteurs miniers Suédois. Des mesures de contraintes ont été effectuées sur deux sites, choisis de manière à représenter des contextes géologiques différents. Les données obtenues ont été analysées afin de déterminer leur intervalle de confiance statistique. L'interprétation des résultats est menée dans une optique minière. On montre que le contexte géologique local a une influence prédominante sur l'intervalle de confiance des rfsultats, qu'il s' agisse de mesures de contrainte groupées ou isolées. On montre également, cependant, que les incertitudes de mesures les plus significatives que l' on rencontre en traitant les données par analyse géomecanique minière, sont les variations du champ de contrainte à grande échelle, qui apparaissent fréquemment dans les volumes de roche habituellement pris en compte pour ce genre d'étude.

ZUSAMMENFASSUNG: Das Referat enthält eine kurzgefasste Beschreibung der LUT-Überkerntechnik, einer Weiterentwicklund der bekannten CSIR-Technik, und eine Zusammenfassung des Aussendienst-Einsatzes dieser Technik in Schwedischen Gruben. Daten von Spannungsmessungen an zwei Orten, die zur Darstellung verschiedener geologischer Verhältnisse zusammengestellt wurden, werden zum Erhalt statistischer Messwerte mit Datenwürdigkeit analysiert. Die Ergebnisse werden mit dem Schwergewicht aug für das Bergbauwesen wichtige Gesichtspunkte analysiert. Es wird nachgewiesen, dass die örtlichen Gesteinsverhältnisse einen massgeblichen Einfluss auf die Vertrauenswürdigkeit des Ergebnisse individueller Spannungsmessungen und von Messgruppen haben. Es wird auch festgestellt, dass die hervortretendsten Unsicherheiten, denen man bei der Einführung von Spannungsdaten in auf den Bergbau bezogene geomechanische Analysen begegnet, die grossmasstäblichen Schwankungen des Spannungsfeldes sind, die oft in den bei solchen Analysen betrachteten Gesteinsvolumina auftreten.

1 THE LUT TRIAXIAL OVERCORING TECHNIQUE

The first efforts in rock stress measurements made by the Luleå University of Technology took place at the Näsliden Mine in 1977 (Leijon et al., 1981). Three dimensional overcoring technique, in the form of the well known CSIR-cell (Leeman, 1968), was used. From the experience gained at the Näsliden Mine, it was concluded that the principle utilized by this technique, i.e. the recording of core relaxation by means of a soft-type of instrument and strain gauges glued to the wall of the pilot hole, was appropriate with respect to the applications foreseen. It was also discovered that the equipment suffered from certain technical shortcomings that made it unsatisfactory in terms of reliability and convenience. A decision was therefore made to develop a device operating according to the CSIR-principle but of a new construction, with emphasis put on its applicability in mining environments. The LUT system, including a new strain cell, was developed and taken into the field in 1979. The strain cell has alternately been referred to as "the LUH-Gauge" and "the LUT-Gauge". The proper name is "the LUT-Gauge", "LUT" being an abbrevation for "Luleå University of Technology".

Figure 1 shows the major components of the equipment. Basically, it includes a number of LUT-Gauges, various tools for borehole preparation and gauge installation, a computerized system for recording and processing of data, a device for bi-axial loading of overcored rock cylinders and laboratory equipment for reconditioning of strain cells. The LUT-Gauge is shown in some more detail in Figure 2. It consists of a hallow aluminum cylinder, nose- and tail guides, a connector with gold-metallized connection pins and

three radially operating pistons. The pistons are moulded in a soft epoxy material and act as carriers for the strain gauges. Four, 5 mm long gauge elements are placed on each piston, and thus the cell incorporates in total twelve strain gauges. Three of those are identically oriented (parallel to the hole axis) and thus the strain gauge array represent ten spatially different orientations. The remote control of the pistons required for gluing the strain gauges to the hole wall is accomplished pneumatically by pressurizing the gauge body.

The gauge is designed for a pilot hole diameter of 38 mm (EX-size). The auxiliary devices permits a minimum overcoring diameter of 86 mm and a maximum depth of the measuring hole of about 30 m. The technique is intended for use in drained holes, which in practice means that the hole orientation is choosen so as to allow self drainage.

The data reduction procedures appropriate for the present type of overcoring measurements is a well documented subject. The theoretical basis was developed by Leeman (1968). The rock is assumed to be a linear elastic, isotropic and homogeneous continuum with known elastic constants. The design of the LUT-Gauge includes an inherent redundancy in each overcoring test, since the number of independent strain readings (in total ten) exceeds the six independent observations required to solve the stress tensor. The multiple regression technique is therefore applied to obtain the stress tensor best fitting the measured strain data.

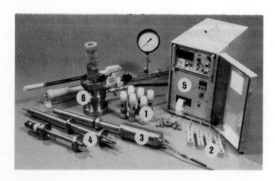

Figure 1. Components of the triaxial stress measurement equipment. 1) LUT-Gauges, 2) Moulds for manufacturing of epoxy pistons, 3) Installing tool, 4) Tools for borehole preparation, 5) Field data logger, 6) Biaxial load chamber with pressure generator and manometer.

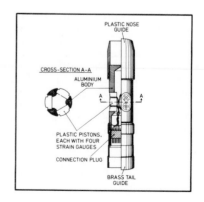

Figure 2. Schematic drawing of the LUT-Gauge.

The computer code currently used to process data obtained with the LUT-Gauge
prescribes isotropic rock. Closed form
solutions applicable to overcoring stress
measurements in anisotropic rock have
recently been presented by Amadei (1982).
A new code based on these solutions is
currently being implemented.

2   CURRENT APPLICATIONS AND EXPERIENCE

Since 1979, the LUT-technique has been
applied at the following sites in Sweden
and in the United States:
- LKAB's iron ore mines in Kiruna and
Malmberget (Leijon, 1981).
- Viscaria Mine, Kiruna.
- Luossavaara Mine, Kiruna (Stillborg
and Leijon, 1982).
- Björka Mine (Leijon, 1982).
- Zinkgruvan Mine (Borg et al., 1984).
- Stripa Test Site (Doe et al., 1983).
- Hanford Test Site, Washington (Leijon,
1983).
- CSM/OCRD Test Site, Colorado.
- Bolmen tunnel (Bjarnason et al., 1985).

The work at the Stripa, Hanford and CSM/
OCRD test sites was related to the U.S.
research programme on final storage of
nuclear waste in crystalline rock formations. The bulk of the field work, however, has been done in the mines. By far
the most extensive bank of data stems
from the Kiruna Mine, where the technique
has been used on a more or less continuous basis for five years.

From the point of view of instrument
performance, we can summarize our experiences of the LUT-technique as follows:
- The mechanical and electrical reliability of the instrumentation is very good.
- Field comparisons with other overcoring
techniques and with hydraulic fracturing
have generally shown good agreement in
results.
- The LUT-technique has proved to be
relatively convenient to use, owing to
the simple measuring procedure and to
the fact that the gauges are reusable.
These advantages are of practical importance, but are gained at the price of
not having the ability to monitor stress
relief during the overcoring sequence.
- Computerized data recording, and the
resulting ability to perform on-site
data reduction, is beneficial.

3   AN EXAMINATION OF TWO SETS OF FIELD
RESULTS

When applied in the context of underground mining, stress measurements usually constitutes a part of a larger programme of data collection. The stress
data together with data on other parameters such as strength, deformability
and geometrical features, are aimed to
provide the information required to perform geomechanical analysis related to
the design or operation of the mine. Most
of the stress measurements conducted in
mines with the LUT-technique are examples
of such applications, in that they were
done to provide input data for numerical
modelling efforts.

The mining engineer who is in charge of
the analysis effort usually has to work
with limited resources. His key task during the data collection phase is therefore to put priority on those data that
are the most relevant ones with respect
to the final outcome of his particular
analysis. As regards his attitude towards
stress measurements, he focuses more on
the role of the stress data in his specific problem than on the technical mat-
ters associated the measurements. Important questions that he must address are:
1) are stress measurements justified, or
are estimates based on existing data compilations sufficient, in view of the uncertainties attached to other input data?
2) What confidence can be placed in the
stress measurements, and to what extent
can the results be generalized?
3) How can the stress measurement programme be optimized?

It is important to realize the scale
problem that enters into the picture
whenever data from stress measurements
are interpreted for the purpose of geomechanical analysis. This is illustrated
in Figure 3. Moving from left to right
in the figure, we first notice that a
single overcoring test is indeed a point
observation, involving about 10^{-3} m^3 of
rock. In fact, we have to consider even
smaller volumes, since the strain gauges
of the instrument operate over lengths
of a few millimeters. The common practice is to repeat the overcoring operation a number of times, in one or several boreholes drilled at the location
selected for measurements. This is done
to ensure the experimental quality and
to verify data consistency. Data from

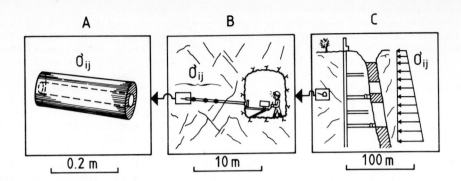

Figure 3. Scales involved in the interpretation of stress measurements in mines.
A) Derivation of the stress tensor from a single overcoring test. B) Combination of
results from several tests to an average result representing that particular location.
C) Combination of all data into a global result that can be applied in analysis of
mine design and stability.

all tests that are considered valid are
then combined to yield a result representing that particular location. This
intermediate scale typically involves
rock volumes of the order of $10^2 \, m^3$. Proceeding finally to the scale of the mining engineers' analysis, this could range
from the size of single pillars or drifts
up to the whole mine. On this scale, we
usually have to combine results from a
number of locations and generalize them
to form an overall picture.

In the following an attempt is made to
address some of the problems outlined
above, by examining two sets of data
originating from two different locations
in the Malmberget Mine. The two locations
selected are:
Location L1: Hanging wall of the Dennewitz ore body, depth 460 m. The rock is
a foliated and jointed biotitic leptite
(fine grained feldspatic rocks). In total
11 experimentally successful overcoring
tests were done within an 11 m long section of the nearly horizontal hole
drilled.
Location L2: Hanging wall of the Hens
ore body, depth 460 m. The rock is a
homogeneous, sparsely jointed granite.
In total 9 experimentally successful
tests were done within a 7 m long section of the nearly horizontal hole
drilled.

Figure 4 shows the measuring locations
in a plan view of the mine. Summarized
results from the measurements at L1 are

given in Table 1 and Figure 5. The corresponding data from L2 are shown in Table
2 and Figure 6.

The motive for selecting these two sets
of data for study was that the rock cond-
tions were drastically different at the
two locations, whilst all other experimental variables were as close to identical as practically attainable. All
field work was done within a time period
of four weeks by the same crew, using
exactly the same equipment and adopting
exactly the same experimental routines
throughout. The depths were identical,
and the state of stress at both locations was virgin and free from any disturbances caused by excavations. The roc
types, in turn, represent two extremes:
The very uniform granite at L2 exhibited
nearly ideal mechanical characteristics,
whilst the leptite at L1 was obviously
very non-ideal due to fractures, high
porosity and local variations in mineral
composition. Analysis of the data could
therefore provide bound estimates of the
level of confidence that is to be expected when applying the LUT-technique
in different geological environments.

3.1 Confidence of individual test
     results

We first consider an individual overcoring test, cf. Figure 3. There is a
variety of errors that may affect the
confidence of such a test, and attemptin

572

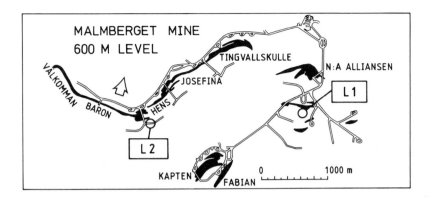

Figure 4. Plan view of the Malmberget Mine, 600 m level (460 m below surface), showing locations of measurements.

to quantify them one by one does not appear promising. However, the redundancy built into the measuring method offers some help to assess the data confidence in statistical terms. As mentioned, the standard regression technique is used to find the stress tensor best fitting the redundant number of strain readings resulting from the overcoring test. The regression also produces the standard statistical information required to calculate confidence intervals for individual stress components. It is our experience that the type of errors that influence the so calculated confidences are largely attributable to the local rock conditions and not to the instruments or experimental procedures used. This can be illustrated by a comparative calculation performed for the L1 - L2 data. 90 % confidence intervals were calculated for the three components of normal stress, as derived for each overcoring test and with reference to an arbitrarily choosen coordinate system. In summary, the relative confidence intervals calculated for the L1-data averaged ± 26 %, corresponding to an average absolute figure of ± 5.7 MPa. The variation in confidence intervals between different tests was considerable. For the L2-data, the same calculation yielded averages of ± 8 % and ± 1.2 MPa respectively, and little variation between the different tests. Possible errors related to the instrumentation and the experimental procedures, i.e. affecting the ability to correctly measure the strain occurring at the locations in the borehole where

the strain gauges are glued, must be equally present in both cases. Hence, this category of errors is in total less than, or equal to the uncertainty derived for the L2-data.

Another, and it is believed, more important finding as regards statistical analysis based on the regression treatment of the data on a pointwise scale, is that the outcome of such analysis is usually of limited value in the final scrutinization of the results. It can not alone be relied upon as the basis for acceptance or rejection of a test, but must be complemented by more subjective engineering judgement. One reason for this is that the regression is based on certain assumptions as regards the statistical nature of the input data. These assumptions may not been met. An example of a consequence of this is the inability to detect and reject single, "wild outliers" in the strain data, which are not seldom encountered in practice. The use of more sophisticated statistical methods could probably mitigate this problem. Another important shortcoming is the fact that the statistical analysis can only account for errors of a nonsystematic nature, while systematic errors remain undetected. The systematic errors can only be assessed by means of controlled testing or comparative measurements. From the comparisons of the present technique that have been made with others (Doe et al., 1983, Stillborg and Leijon, 1982), it can be concluded that the systematic errors originating from

Table 1. Principal stress magnitudes calculated from 11 overcoring tests at Location L1 (Dennewitz, Malmberget Mine).

Test No.	Principal stress [MPa]		
	σ_1	σ_2	σ_3
1	25.2	13.8	8.3
2	45.0	19.7	15.3
3	22.8	17.4	7.3
4	42.4	27.0	19.0
5	22.0	20.1	11.2
6	30.9	17.6	13.9
7	33.9	30.3	13.3
8	29.5	21.6	15.7
9	38.8	16.4	12.8
10	31.3	19.0	9.4
11	24.5	22.1	18.3
Mean	31.5	20.5	13.1

Table 2. Principal stress magnitudes calculated from 9 overcoring tests at Location L2 (Hens, Malmberget Mine).

Test No.	Principal stress [MPa]		
	σ_1	σ_2	σ_3
1	17.2	11.4	5.0
2	18.7	17.1	8.3
3	16.4	15.2	7.1
4	17.7	12.6	6.8
5	19.3	14.1	8.4
6	21.0	15.7	7.4
7	25.3	20.1	11.9
8	22.0	16.3	9.0
9	16.0	12.6	7.3
Mean	19.3	15.0	8.0

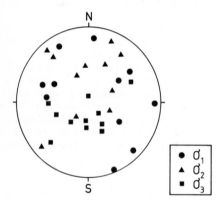

Figure 5. Principal stress directions calculated from overcoring tests at Location L1 (Wulff-net, lower hemisphere).

Figure 6. Principal stress directions calculated from overcoring tests at Location L2 (Wulff-net, lower hemisphere).

the instrumentation are of little significance. Non-ideal rock behaviour can, however, also introduce systematic error components. Our experience is that the most important factor in this respect is nonlinear and/or inelastic deformation characteristics of the rock. This factor can impose significant errors in the determination of the elastic properties, implying a corresponding error in the calculated stress magnitudes.

3.2 Confidence of locationwise results

We now expand the discussion to the intermediate scale, i.e. we consider the confidence that can be attached to the results from one location. We choose to study principal stresses, since they are the representation of the stress tensor that can best be visualized, and since this allows magnitudes and directions to be treated separately. Depending on the type of application, magnitudes and directions may not of equal importance to the engineer. However, he would still

574

have to look at both magnitudes and directions to be able to properly design
his analysis and derive the stress components that are relevant in his case.
With regard to optimization of measuring
programmes it is of considerable interest
to know the number of tests that for a
given confidence level should be conducted at each location. Hence, we should
study how the confidence develops as a
function of number of tests included.
For this purpose it is useful to do a
simple statistical analysis of the L1 and
L2 data on a step-by-step basis, adding
one test for each step. We take advantage
of the fact that the measurements at both
L1 and L2 were done in areas where exca-
vation-induced stress disturbances can be
neglected. This means that we can consider all tests made at each location as
independent observations of the same set
of variables. We ignore the result of the
pointwise analysis referred to in the
previous section. This means that we do
not distinguish if the variation found
within the two groups of tests are due
to uncertainty in each test, or if it is
a consequence of actual variations in
the state of stress along the borehole
in question.

Considering first the principal stress
magnitudes, they can be assumed to be
independent observations on normal distribution with unknown means and variances. 90 % confidence intervals are obtained using Students' t-distribution.
Figure 7 shows the results of the analysis of L1-data. Estimates (sample means)
for the principal stress magnitudes, and
the associated confidence intervals, are
given as functions of the number of tests
conducted. The corresponding quantities
as calculated from the L2-data are presented in Figure 8. Two tests is taken to
be the minimum nimber of observations
required for calculation of sample means,
and three for calculation of confidences.
Some irregularities and strange characteristics of the confidence intervals
are apparent from the figures. The best
example is the top curve in Figure 8,
which in fact indicates an increasing
width of the confidence interval with
increasing number of observations. These
pecularities are simply consequences of
the low number of observations, and the
order in which these observations happen
to enter into the calculation. Random-
ization, repeated calculations and averaging procedures would produce smoother

curves. We can thus neglect the irregularities, and look only at the general
trends. We can then observe significant
differences between the two sets of data.
It appears that 4-5 tests in the granite
at L2 (Figure 8) allows determination of
the principal stress magnitudes with an
accuracy of about ± 3 MPa (on average
14 %). This confidence is not improved
by conducting additional tests. The same
amount of tests in the leptite at L1
yields an average uncertainty of about
± 8 MPa (35 %). This figure can be somewhat improved by doubling the number of
tests.

To derive confidence limits for the principal stress orientations, we apply the
statistical theory for directional data
developed by Fisher (1953), (Fisher-dis-
tribution, small-sample solution) and
more completely explained by Mardia
(1972). This distribution is unimodal,
and the confidence limit for the direction is defined by a symmetrical cone
around the best-estimate. The opening of
the cone is defined by its opening angle,
2Θ. The radius angle, Θ, hence describes,
to 90 % probability, the maximum angular
deviation between the true and the estimated average direction. Applying this
technique to the L1 and L2 data produces
the the curves shown in Figure 9. The
three principal stresses were treated
separately. Since the results were similar, they have been averaged to condense
the presentation. Independent analysis
is, of course, not entirely correct since
the principal stress directions are dependent. It is, however, relevant if the
results are considered to be confidence
estimates for the direction of one of
the principal stresses, irrespective of
the two others. The shaded areas in the
diagrams shown in Figure 9 are the respective radius angles (Θ) of the cones
of confidence for each set of data, which
can thus be considered as "half width
confidence intervals". The solid lines
show the angular change in direction
estimate as tests are successively added,
i.e. the angular "travelling" that the
best-estimate undergoes as tests are
successively added. The "travelling" has
been referred to the direction obtained
when taking all available tests into
account (11 and 9 respectively).

The outcome of the analysis of directions
as shown in Figure 9 is similar to that
for the magnitudes. The uncertainty in

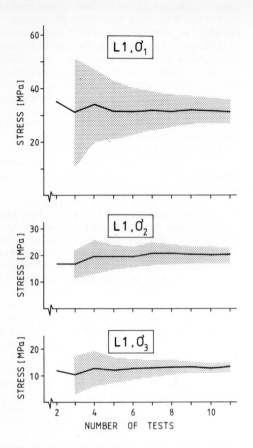

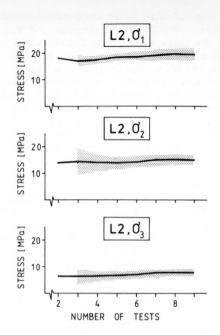

Figure 7. Principal stress magnitudes as functions of number of tests conducted, Location L1. Lines show sample means. Shaded areas show 90 % confidence intervals.

Figure 8. Principal stress magnitudes as functions of number of tests conducted, Location L2. Lines show sample means. Shaded areas show 90 % confidence intervals.

direction estimate after 5 tests at L2 is about 15°. It is interesting to note also that the total angular "travelling" that the best-estimate undergoes when expanding the data base from 2 tests to 9 is less than 6°. For L1, in turn, the uncertainty in direction after 5 tests is 40°. This can be visualized as a cone with an opening angle of 80°, which is indeed not a very satisfying result in most engineering applications. The degree to which the principal stress directions can be determined also increases with increasing mutal differences between the magnitudes. In the present case, the magnitude differences ranges between 4 MPa and 11 MPa. If two principal stresses are equal or nearly equal in magnitude, the present type of analysis is, of course, not relevant.

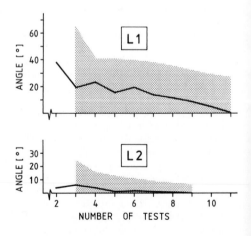

Figure 9. Confidence of principal stress directions as a function of number of tests. L1-data (upper), and L2-data (lower). Shaded area shows the radius angle, Θ, of the cone defining the 90 % confidence limit. Line shows angular deviation between the direction estimate after the corresponding number of tests, and the estimate including all tests.

It should finally be observed that the above, locationwise analysis, is similar to the pointwise analysis in that it can not account for any type of systematic errors. Thus, the comments given in this regard in connection with the discussion of pointwise confidence applies equally well on the locationwise scale.

4   IMPLICATIONS OF LARGE-SCALE VARIATIONS

The analysis above was restricted to the small and intermediate scale but did not consider the large scale, i.e. the scale where the mining engineer usually is operating. The reason is that the two sets of data looked at would be inappropriate for comparison in this respect. The general experience from our measurements in mines is, however, that quite significant variations in the state of stress are common on a scale of say hundreds of meters. These large scale variations seems to be larger for the directions of stress than for the magnitudes, and are not readily explained on the basis of the geological framework. The extensive bank of stress data available

from the Kiruna Mine could serve to illustrate this. Figure 10 shows a schematic plan view of the 795 m level of this mine. This level corresponds to a depth of about 650 m, which is well below the current mining depth. The very large body of iron ore has a tabular shape and dips about 65°. Stress determinations have been made at a total of eight locations at, or close to this level. The figure displays average, locationwise stress results. As can be seen, there is a considerable variation between the different locations. This variation can not be explained by uncertainty in the locationwise averages. It is, to say the least, difficult to extract an overall result that we could claim is representative for the state of stress at the 795 m level or parts thereof from the information given. It may be argued that the understanding of the results could be improved by introducing the relevant geological information, primarily on major structures into the analysis. A common result from such analysis is the prediction that the principal stresses are directed respectively perpendicular and parallel to the major geological features in the area. As has been

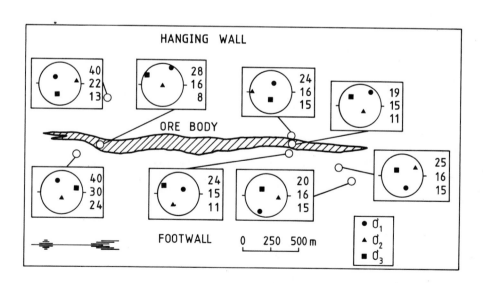

Figure 10. Horizontal section of the Kiruna Mine, 795 m level, showing average results from stress measurements at 8 locations. Directions of principal stresses are shown in stereographic projections (Wulff-net, lower hemisphere). Numbers indicate magnitudes of principal stresses. From Johansson (1986).

shown by Stillborg and Leijon (1982), this is, however, not an assumption that can be generally applied. It is, in fact, believed that it would be difficult to explain the results given in Figure 10 on the basis of geological information. It is also felt that attempts to predict the state of stress at other locations in the mine would have limited success. The implication is that extrapolation of stress data over longer distances can not generally be done with satisfying accuracy.

To the engineer, this would suggest that stress determinations should be done at locations where he really needs to know the stresses, and that he pays less attention to the global stress situation. These locations would be the critical components of the mine structure such as pillars and roofs. With regard to his analysis, this would imply that the stress data are used for model calibration, verification of results and perhaps even establishment of failure criteria, rather than for initial establishment of boundary conditions.

5   CONCLUSIONS

- The practicality and field reliability of the LUT overcoring device is found to be satisfactory.
- The confidence that can be attached to the results of single overcoring tests or to sets of tests is to a major extent governed by the local rock conditions. When the LUT-technique is applied in rock types which closely meet the assumptions of linear elasticity, homogeneity and isotropy, a field accuracy of ± 3 MPa in magnitude and 15° in principal stress direction, can be attained. These figures refers to stress levels of 10-30 MPa and differences between principal stresses of 4 MPa or more. Deficiencies in the rock quality can amplify the figures given for the accuracy by a factor of 2 or 3.
- All values above exclude the effects of systematic measuring errors. Non-ideal mechanical behaviour can impose significant errors of this category.
- 4-5 overcoring test at each location is an optimum number if rock conditions are favourable. More tests do not improve the confidence of the results, and less tests is undesireable due to the then poor protection against single out-

liers.
- Measurements in Swedish mines have shown the existence of significant stress variations on a scale of hundreds of meters. These large scale variations impose difficulties in the interpretation and application of in-situ stress data i analysis related to mine design.

6   ACKNOWLEDGEMENTS

The contributions made by several staff members at the Luleå University of Technology during the development of the LUT technique are gratefully acknowledged. Further acknowledgements goes to the LKA Mining Company for financial support and allowance to use field data. The manuscript of this paper was reviewed and significantly improved by Professor O. Stephansson and Professor W.A. Hustrulid The study was financially supported by the Swedish National Science Research Foundation.

7   REFERENCES

Amadei, B. 1982. The Influence of Rock Anisotropy on Measurement of Stresses In-Situ. Ph. D. Thesis. University of California, Berkeley, Ca. 475 p.

Bjarnason, B., Leijon, B. and Stephansso O. 1985. The Bolmen Project; Rock Stre Measurements Using Hydraulic Fracturin and Overcoring Techniques. Project Report, Swedish Rock Engineering Foundation, Stockholm. (in press).

Borg, T., Leijon, B., Röshoff, K. and Stephansson, O. 1984. Stability Prediction for the Zinkgruvan Mine, Central Sweden. Proc. ISRM Symp. on Desig and Performance of Underground Excavations, Cambridge, U. K., 113-122.

Doe, T.W., Ingevald, K., Strindell, L., Leijon, B., Hustrulid, W.A., Majer, E. and Carlsson, H. 1983. In Situ Stress Measurements at the Stripa Mine. Technical Report LBL-15009, SAC-44, Lawrence Berkeley Laboratory, Ca. 251 p

Fisher, R. 1953. Dispersion on a Sphere. Proc. Royal Society of London, Ser. A, 217:295-305.

Johansson, B. 1986. Pers. comm.

Leeman, E.R. 1968. The Determination of the Complete State of Stress in a Single Borehole - Laboratory and Under ground Measurements. Int. J. Rock Mech Min Sci., 5:31-56.

Leijon, B., Myrvang, A. and Carlsson, H.

1980. Stress Measurements in Näsliden Mine. Proc. Application of Rock Mechanics to Cut and Fill Mining, Luleå, 162-168.

Leijon, B. 1980. Rock Stress Measurements at the Björka Mine. Technical Report 1980:61 T, Luleå University of Technology, Luleå, 25 p. (in swedish).

Leijon, B. 1981. Rock Stress Measurements at LKAB Mines, 1979-1980. Technical Report 1981:67 T, Luleå University of Technology, Luleå, 74 p. (in swedish).

Leijon, B. 1983. Rock Stress Measurements with the LUH-Gauge at the Near-Surface Test Facility, Hanford Test Site. Research Report TULEA 1983:18, Luleå University of Technology, Luleå. 62 p.

Mardia, K. 1972. Statistics of Directional Data. Academic Press, New York. 275 p.

Stillborg, B. and Leijon, B. 1982. A Comparative Study of Rock Stress Measurements at Luossavaara Mine. Report FB 8217. Swedish Mining Research Foundation, Kiruna. 108 p.

5. Application of rock stress measurement in underground construction

Rock stress measurements for the design of a 965 metre head unlined pressure shaft

J. BERGH-CHRISTENSEN
A/S Geoteam, Oslo, Norway

ABSTRACT

The paper describes investigations for a 965-metre head unlined pressure shaft at the Nyset-Steggje Hydropower Project in Western Norway.

Site investigations have included in-situ rock stress measurements and hydraulic fracturing tests to verify the safe siting of the shaft.

RESUMÉ

L'article décrit les reconnaissances menées pour le projet hydroénergétique de Nyset-Steggje, dans la Norvège de l'ouest. Le projet comporte un puits non-revétu destiné à des pressions de 965 metres d'eau.

Les reconnaissances effectuées en chantier ont inclus les mesures du condition de contrainte in situ et les expérience de fracture hydraulique pour confirmer le certitude du puits.

ZUSAMMENFASSUNG

Die Voruntersuchungen für eine unverbaute Druckschacht von 965 meter Druckhohe bei der Wasserkraftanlage Nyset-Steggje in West-Norwegen werden beschrieben.

In situ Felsspannungsmessungen sowohl wie hydraulische Spaltungsversuche wurden durchgeführt um die Sicherheit des Schachtes zu bestätigen.

INTRODUCTION

The Nyset-Steggje hydropower project presently under construction in Sogn, Western Norway, includes a 1300 metre long unlined pressure shaft. With a static head of 965 metres, the shaft will imply a new world record in water pressure on unlined rock.

A basic design criterium for siting of an unlined pressure shaft is that the minimum in situ rock stress should be higher than the water pressure at all points along the shaft, in order to avoid the risk of failure by hydraulic fracturing.

At the design stage, siting of the Nyset-Steggje shaft was selected on the basis of finite-element models of stress distribution in the shaft site area, as well as on empirical data from the more than 70 unlined high-pressure shafts and tunnels presently in operation in Norway.

During construction of the power plant, rock stress measurements have been performed at 4 locations and hydraulic fracturing tests at 9 locations in the power station and shaft area to investigate in situ rock stress conditions.

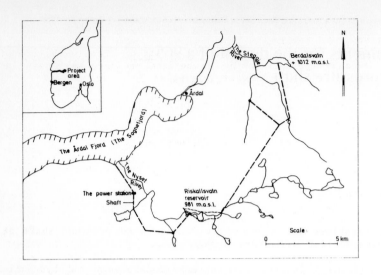

FIG. 1: LOCATION MAP OF THE NYSET-STEGGJE PROJECT

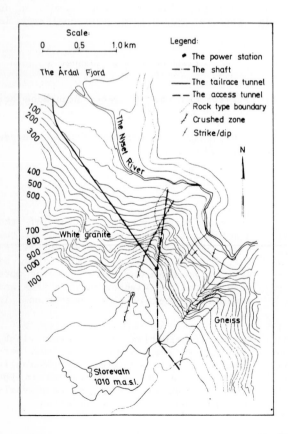

FIG. 2:

THE POWER
STATION AREA

The measurements show good correlation with the design calculations, and verify that the selected shaft siting gives an acceptable factor of safety against hydraulic fracturing failure.

THE HYDROPOWER PROJECT

Fig. 1. shows the main layout of the project, which includes a 12 km tunnel leading water from the northern cachment areas into the main reservoir at elevation 980.3 metre, and then a 5.6 km long 16m^2 headrace tunnel leading to the top of the pressure shaft. The shaft, with a length of 1300 metres and a diameter of 3.2 metres, has been excavated by full face Tunnel Boring Machine (TBM). From the power station situated in rock, a 2,5 km long tailrace tunnel leads out into the Årdal fjord.

The motive for selecting an unlined pressure shaft for the plant is primarily economic. By omitting the conventional steel lining – a saving of the' order of 4 million US dollars can be achieved.

Client and main engineer for the Nyset-Steggje hydropower development is Årdal og Sunndal Verk A/S. A/S GEOTEAM is engineering geological and rock mechanics consultant for the project, with full responsibility for design and commissioning of the pressure shaft. Main Contractor for the development is the norwegian AIVE-group (joint venture of Astrup-Høyer A/S, A/S Veidekke and H.Eeg-Henriksen A/S).

THE SHAFT AREA

The topography of the power station and pressure shaft area is characterized by a plateau at elevation 1100 metres, with very steep, incised valley slopes towards the Nyset River, as illustrated in fig. 2.

The rocks in the shaft area are sparsely jointed gneiss, gneiss-granite and granite of Paleozoie age.

DESIGN CRITERIA

A basic design criterium for siting of an unlined shaft is that the minimum in situ rock stress should be higher than the water pressure at all points along the shaft, in order to avoid the risk of

failure by hydraulic fracturing.

At the design stage, the feasibility of using an unlined pressure shaft was investigated based on:

- empirical design criteria
and
- rock mechanics calculations by means of finite-dement models.

During construction the design assumptions have been checked and verified, by means of in situ rock stress measurements and by hydraulic fracturing tests.

EMPIRICAL CRITERIA

As of today, more than 70 unlined pressure shafts and pressure tunnels with heads exceeding 150 metres are in operation in Norway.

A few but serious failures of such shafts in the past have clearly illustrated the importance of rock cover – the shaft must have a sufficient rock cover so that the in-situ stresses at any point along the shaft prevents large seale deformations or hydraulic fracturing failure.

Bergh-Christensen and Dannevig (1971) presented in 1971 an empirical "rule of thumb" for shaft siting based on the accumulated experiences with unlined shafts up to that time. The "rule of thumb" indicates a minimum rock cover requirement of

$$L \geq \frac{\gamma_w \cdot H}{\gamma_r \cdot \cos\beta}$$

where:

L = minimum distance from the shaft out to the valley slope rock surface

β = valley slope angle

H = water pressure (metres)

γ_w, γ_r = unit weight of water and rock respectively.

Fig. 3. shows a section through the valley slope indicating the provisionally selected siting of the foot of the pressure shaft.

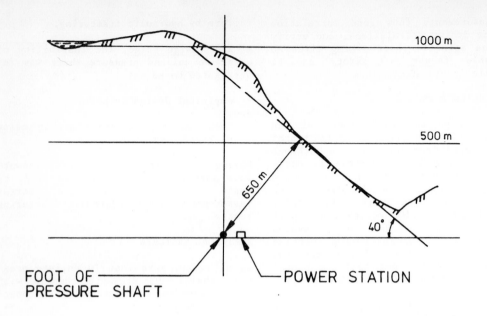

FIG. 3: SECTION THROUGH THE SHAFT AREA

With an overburden to pressure head
ratio (L/H) of 0.68, this indicates a
factor of safety of the order of 1.3
relative to the limit equilibrium indicated by the "rule of thumb"

FINITE ELEMENT MODELS

For finite element calculations, a
smoothed topographical model of the
shaft area was developed as shown in
fig. 4, and FEM calculations of stress
distribution was carried out for three
sections (A-A, B-B, C-C) intersecting
the middle and lowest part of the shaft
respectively. Fig. 5 shows the geometry
and rock distribution, and fig. 6 the
division of the FEM model in
substructures.

The relation between the calculated
minor principal stress and static water
pressure at the three shaft inter-
sections is the critical factor.

The ratio of minor principal stress to
water head – indicating the factor of
safety against hydraulic failure – is:

Section A-A: 1.44
Section B-B: 1.56
Section C-C: 1.50

The FEM calculations confirmed that th
provisionally selected shaft siting wa
feasible for detailed design of th
powerplant.

IN SITU MEASUREMENTS FOR VERIFICATION O
DESIGN CALCULATIONS

Excavation of the 1000 metre long acces
tunnel to the power station started i
february 1984.

For verification of rock stress conditi
ons and documentation of shaft safety,
programme of in situ rock stress mea
surements and hydraulic fracturing test
were performed during construction.

If these measurements were to indicat
more adverse conditions than expected,
fallback alternative for steel-lining o
the lower part of the pressure shaf
might be implemented.

Fig 7 shows locations of the in sit
rock stress measurements performe
during construction. The measurements
were performed by the SINTEF departmen
of rock mechanics, employing a three-
dimensional rock stress gauge.

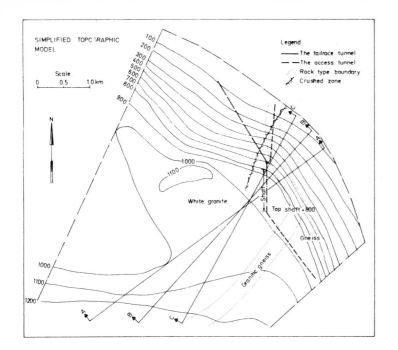

SIMPLIFIED TOPOGRAPHIC MODEL

Scale
0   0.5   1.0 km

Legend
— The tailrace tunnel
— — The access tunnel
Rock type boundary
Crushed zone

N

White granite

Shaft

Top shaft +800

Gneiss

Granitic gneiss

FIG. 4

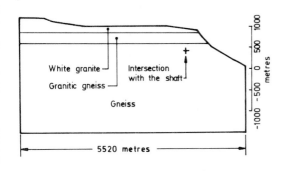

White granite
Granitic gneiss
Intersection with the shaft
Gneiss

5520 metres

FIG. 5

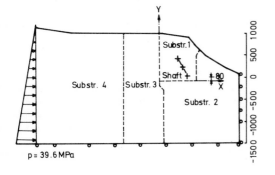

Y

Substr.1
Shaft
80
X

Substr. 4   Substr. 3   Substr. 2

p = 39.6 MPa

FIG. 6

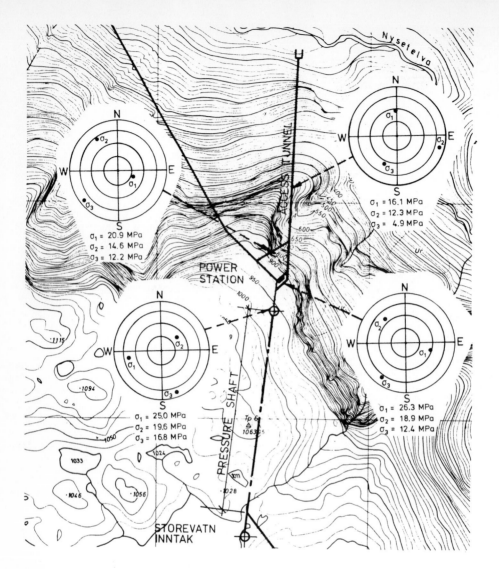

FIG. 7: ROCK STRESS MEASUREMENTS IN THE POWER STATION AREA

The first measurement was carried out 590 metres into the access tunnel, and gave the first indication of the stress conditions. As can be seen from fig. 7, the principal stress directions corresponds to what might be expected from gravity-induced rock stresses beneath a valley slope.

However, the high magnitude of the intermediate stress σ_2 = 12.3 MPa indicates the existence of geologically induced stresses superimposed on the gravitational stress field. This was also verified by the occurrence of rock burst problems in the access tunnel. Additional in situ rock stress measurements were carried out in the power station area and at the foot of the pressure shaft, as indicated in fig. 7.

Even if the lower value of minor principal stress σ_3 = 12.4 MPa measured adjacent to the power station is taken into account, this still indicates a factor of safety against hydraulic fracturing of 12.4/9.64 = 1.3.

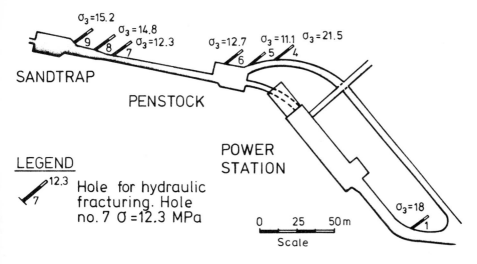

FIG. 8: HYDRAULIC FRACTURING TESTS IN THE POWER STATION AREA

HYDRAULIC FRACTURING

In addition to rock stress measurements, a series of hydraulic fracturing tests were performed in the area immediately downstream of the pressure shaft as an additional direct verification of the safety against hydraulic fracturing failure.
The tests were performed by the Norwegian Geotechnical Institute with their dedicated equipment.

The basic principle of hydraulic fracturing is that a section of a borehole is sealed off by a special packer and pressurized until a crack is initiated in the surrounding rock. The crack will be oriented normal to the least principal stress σ_3. By continued injection of fluid, the crack will propagate further away from the borehole. By shut-off of the injection pump, the pressure will drop to a level giving equilibrium between the minor principal stress σ_3 and the fluid pressure. By performing repeated pressurizing cycles, all fairly reliable measurement of the minor principal stress is obtained.

Fig. 8 shows locations and measured values of σ_3 for the hydraulic fracturing tests.

The sandtrap shown on the left side of the figure is situated at the foot of the pressure shaft, and represents the section with highest water pressure on unlined rock.

If the lowest value of σ_3 = 12.3 MPa measured in hole no. 7 adjacent to the sandtrap is taken into account, this indicates a ratio between minor principal stress and water pressure of 12.3/9.64, corresponding to a factor of safety of the order of 1.3. As can be seen, this is in good correspondance with the values obtained from the rock stress measurements.

DESIGN CALCULATIONS VERSUS IN SITU MEASUREMENTS

A comparison of the calculations performed at the design stage with the in situ measurements undertaken during construction shows the following relations - expressed as factor of safety against hydraulic fracturing failure:

	Safety factor
Empirical "rule of thumb" =	1.3
Finite element calculations =	1.4-1.5
In situ rock stress measurements =	1.3
In situ hydraulic fracturing tests =	1.3

It may be concluded that there is a satisfactory consistency between design assumptions and verified in situ conditions.

ROCK STRESS MEASUREMENTS - A USEFUL TOOL
BY THE DESIGN OF PRESSURIZED ROCK
CAVITIES

As mentioned initially, Norway has a
unique world record of utilizing unlined
pressure tunnels and shafts, with more
than 70 plants of water pressure heads
from 150 metres up to 880 metres
currently in operation.

The Nyset-Steggje shaft will be put into
operation early in 1986, hopefully
constituting another world record for
Norwegian tunnelling technology.

Another Norwegian innovation is the use
of unlined air-cushion surge chambers in
connection with pressure tunnels. Nine
plants are presently in operation, with
compressed air volumes ranging from
1.200 to 88.500 m^3 and air pressures
from 18 to 78 Bars.

Unlined rock chambers of containment of
pressurized fluids and gases are also in
use and under planning for bulk storage
of hydrocarbons.

For all the above types of projects
there are two main problems to take into
consideration.

- fluid and/or gas leakage
and
- safety against hydraulic or pneumatic
  fracturing failure.

During recent years both theoretical and
semiempirial calculation models, as well
as in situ testing procedures have been
developed and extensively tested in
Norway for design of unlined, highly
pressurized rock cavities.

As illustrated by the present paper, in
situ rock stress measurements and
hydraulic fracturing tests, are invaluable tools for safe and rational design
of such constructions.

The cost of typical triaxial stress
measurement will usually be of the order
of US$ 7000-8000 plus travelling
expences. This includes approximately
10 measurements in a 10-15 m deep borehole, laboratory investigations of rock
properties, and reporting.

As for hydraulic fracturing tests, the
total programme executed at Nyset-

Steggje power plant amounted to a cost
of approximately US$ 10.000.

These figures can be compared to the
estimated US$ 4 million saved by
omitting steel lining of the pressure
shaft, indicating that site investigations may indeed be a good investment.

REFERENCES:

BERGH-CHRISTENSEN, J., and DANNEVIG,
N.T. 1971.
Ingeniørgeologiske vurderinger ved-
rørende uforet trykksjakt ved Mauranger
kraftverk (Engineering geological
evaluations of the unlined pressure
shaft at the Mauranger hydropower
plant). A/S Geoteam Report 2398.03,
Oslo, Norway.

BERGH-CHRISTENSEN; J., and KJØLBERG, R.
1982.
Investigations for Norway's longest
unlined pressure shaft. Water Power and
Dam Construction 34:4, 31-35.

BERGH-CHRISTENSEN, J. 1985.
Design of unlined pressure shaft at
Nyset-Steggje Hydro-Power Project. Pro-
ceedings, Norwegian Soil and Rock
Engineering Association, Annual Con-
ference 1985.
Tapir Publishers, Trondheim.

BROCH, E., 1985.
Development of unlined pressure shafts
and tunnels in Norway.
Norwegian Hydropower Tunnelling. Publi-
cation no. 3.
Norwegian Soil and Rock Engineering
Association.
Tapir, Trondheim.

SELMER-OLSEN, R., 1985.
Experience gained from unlined high
pressure tunnels and shafts in hydro-
electric power stations in Norway.
Norwegian Hydropower Tunnelling. Publi-
cation no. 3.
Norwegian Soil and Rock Engineering
Association.
Tapir, Trondheim.

Hydraulic fracturing – a simple tool for controlling the safety of unlined high pressure shafts and headrace tunnels

G. VIK
L. TUNDBRIDGE
Norwegian Geotechnical Institute, Oslo, Norway

ABSTRACT

This article describes a simplified method of determining the in situ stress by hydraulic fracturing to evaluate the safety of pressurized tunnels and shafts. Test data from four hydropower plants in South Norway are presented, the interpretation of the stresses discussed and the results compared with those from overcoring tests.

RESUME

Cet article fait une description de la méthode de la fracture hydraulique pour evaluer la sécurité des puits et tunnels pressurisés relative á la fracture hydraulique. Les résultats d'éssais de quatre centrales hydroélectriques du sud de la Norvége sont présentés avec les résultats de mesures de pression rocheuse dans un forage sur dimensionné.

ZUSAMMENFASSUNG

Dieser Artikel beschreibt eine vereinfache Form der "hydraulic fracturing" Methode um die Sicherheit von Druckschächten gegen "hydraulic fracturing" abschätzen zu können. Messungen von vier Wasserkraftanlagen in Sud-Norwegen wirt presentiert, und mit andere Bergdrucsmessungen vergleichert.

1. INTRODUCTION

Recent Norwegian hydro-electric power projects have been utilizing high water heads in unlined pressure tunnels and shafts. In situ stress measurements were required to determine the risk of hydraulic fracturing occurring in these excavations.

The Norwegian Geotechnical Institute (NGI) in collaboration with the Norwegian consultants Berdal A/S have developed a simplified hydraulic fracturing technique to determine the minimum in situ stress. The results from this method are directly applicable to determining the likelihood of hydraulic fracturing occuring in the excavations during operation.

The tests can be carried out in a relatively short time. The preparation work can be done by a contractor and the actual testing of the hole accomplished in a couple of hours. The cost of such tests can be as low as 10 - 15000 NOK (1 US$ = 7.5 NOK, June 1986).

2. TEST METHOD

The tests are conducted in boreholes drilled in the wall of an underground excavation. High pressure steel tubes are grouted in the test holes using a rubber disc to separate the grout from a test section of about 5 m. The length to the test section is generally about twice the tunnel diameter. A sketch of the test set-up is presented on Figure 1.

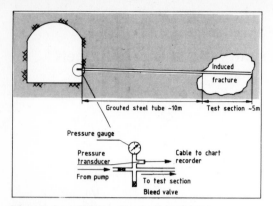

Figure 1. Test set up for hydraulic fracturing.

A high pressure pump is used to
pressurise this test section with
water. Pressure in the test section
is measured by a transducer at the
mouth of the borehole and recorded
on a strip chart. The test section
is first pressurized until rupture, indicated by a sudden drop in
pressure, when the pump is shut off
and the pressure in the borehole
observed to determine the shut-in
pressure. The test zone is later
vented and then repressurised to
determine the refracture
pressure and further values of the
shut-in pressure. A typical record
of the pressure variations in the
test section during a test is shown
on Figure 2.

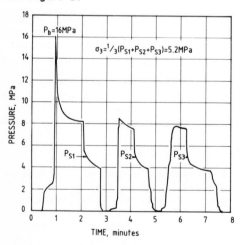

Figure 2. Typical pressure - time
graph from simple hydraulic fracture
test.

The pressure-time diagrams generally
indicate a clear shut-in pressure as
shown on this example. In other
cases, however, leakage of water
from the system may cause the
pressure-time curve after shut-in to
look smooth and the shut-in pressure
is ambiguous (Figure 3).

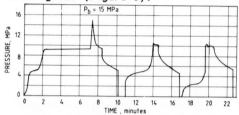

Figure 3. Pressure - time graph
with smooth ambiguous shut-in curve.

3. INTERPRETATION

The breakdown pressure is determined
from the highest pressure attained

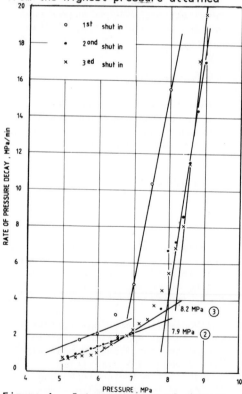

Figure 4. Interpretation of shut-in
pressure on graph of rate of pressure
decay vs. pressure-

in a test before rupture. The shut-in pressure is determined at the point of inflection on the pressure time curve following shut off of the pump. In the cases where there is no obvious inflection in the curve a graphical method must be used to determine the shut-in pressure. Many such methods have been proposed. The use of log-log and semi-log plots of pressure and time, and squareroot time and time ratio plots have been described (1). Similarily the Muskat method (2) and tangent intersection and tangent divergence analyses (3) may be used. However, a simple method involving the plotting of rate of pressure decay against pressure (4) was found to give unambiguous and consistent results. A typical plot taken from the shut-in curve in Figure 3 is shown on Figure 4.

The most relevant parameter to the design of pressure tunnels and shafts is the minimum stress determined directly from the shut-in pressure. The values of the minimum stress reported, are the mean values of 3 (occasionally 2) shut-in values determined from breakdown and refracture tests in a borehole. Generally 2 to 3 holes in the same area are tested, and the results combined to give a mean minimum principal stress for the area.

The method does not permit inspection of the borehole after fracturing to determine the orientation of the fracture and thereby orientation of the principal stresses.

4. SITES

The sites tested by these methods are shown on the map, Figure 5. Stress orientations determined by overcoring tests at each site are shown on the appropriate figures in upper hemispherical polar diagrams. The overcoring tests reported here have been carried out by The Foundation for Scientific and Industrial Research of the Norwegian Technical University, Trondheim, Norway (SINTEF).

Figure 5.   Location plan

4.1 Tjodan power plant

The plant is at the head of the Lysefjord near Stavanger. The maximum water head is close to 900 m and the 1250 m long shaft, inclined at 41° was drilled with a TBM-machine at a diameter of 3.1 m.

The layout of the project is outlined on Figure 6. The hydrofracture measurements were carried out at two locations in two holes each. An overcoring test was carried out 250 m away. The results are summarised on Table 1.

The results from the overcoring tests show predictable orientations, but the value of the maximum principal stress, which is nearly vertical, is a little high for the depth of cover. In comparison the minimum stress determined by the hydrofracture method is much higher than the minimum principal stress measured by overcoring. The ratio of stresses was very high at around 4.5:1.

4.2 Kvilldal power plant

The Kvilldal plant is part of the Ulla-Førre scheme near Stavanger. The maximum water head is about 420 m with a cross-section area of 150 m² at the headrace (Figure 7).

This plant has an air-cushion surge chamber with an air volume of 88500 m³ at 4.1 MPa pressure instead of a

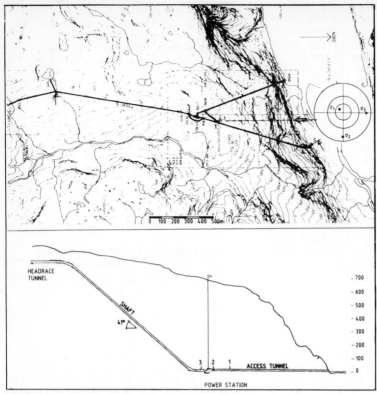

Figure 6. Plan and section of Tjodan power plant

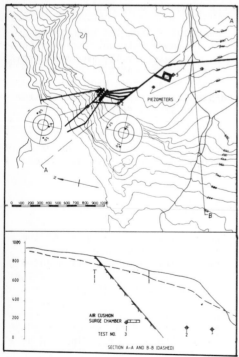

Figure 7. Plan and section of
Kvilldal power plant.

surge shaft to surface. Before
start-up of the power plant, NGI had
estimated an air leakage rate of 1
to 10 m³ min. though it was considered more likely to be closer to
1 than to 10. The owner, the State
Power Board of Norway, chose the
refill compressor capacity to be 3
m³/min. After one year of operation
the leakage rate was close to 4
m³/min. Instead of increasing the
compressor capacity, NGI's advice
was to construct a water curtain
above the surge chamber.

To estimate the maximum pressure in
the water curtain to avoid hydraulic
fracturing a measurement of the
minimum principal stress was
required. The mean value from four
holes with three pressurization
cycles in each hole was 4.6 MPa.
The results of the hydrofracturing measurements and overcoring
stress measurements are presented on
Table 1. A maximum waer curtain
pressure of 5.1 MPa (water head + 1
MPA) was used to cause a flow gradient towards the chamber and

594

subsequent air leakage has been negligible.

The results of the overcoring tests again show predictable principal stress orientations, but variable values for the nearly vertical maximum principal stress in comparison with the overburden depth. The minimum stress determined by the hydraulic fracturing tests are very close to the minimum principal stress determined by overcoring. The ratio of stresses was between 2:1 and 3:1.

4.3 Naddevik power plant

The Naddevik power plant is south of Sognefjorden on the west coast of Norway. This plant is currently under construction and is planned to be in operation by late 1986. It has a TBM drilled unlined pressure shaft with a diameter of 3.2 m and maximum water head of 964 m (Figure 8).

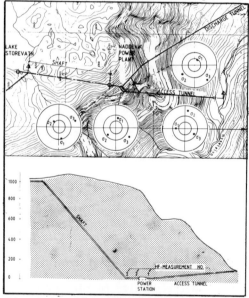

Figure 8. Plan and section of Naddevil power plant.

To provide data for the design at this extreme head, a total of 4 overcoring and 7 hydrofracture stress determinations have been made. Three of the holes are in a group near the end of the shaft, location

3 in the section in Figure 8. Two other holes, at location 2, were too near the tunnel walls so only a single value is reported. The results are presented on Table 1.

Orientations of the principal stresses determined by overcoring are very variable, but the values are roughly consistent with the depth of cover. The ratio of stresses was around 2:1 except at shallow depths where it increased to 3:1- The values of minimum stress determined by hydraulic fracture are very close to the minimum principal stress determined by overcoring.

4.4 Jostedalen power plant

The Jostedalen power plant is situated in a north-south trending valley, 20 km north of Sognefjorden on the west coast of Norway.

This plant is presently under construction. A sloping headrace tunnel, 31 km long, leads to an inclined shaft, excavated by drilling and blasting, down to the power station. The maximum water head is about 1200 m. To provide

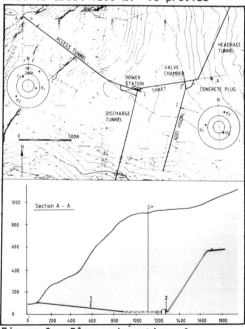

Figure 9. Plan and section of Jostedalen power plant.

data, to enable a decision to be made on whether the shaft should be lined, a total of two overcoring and 5 hydrofracturing stress measurements have been made. The boreholes are located in the access tunnel to the power station and the valve chamber (Figure 9). The results are shown on Table 1. The profiles on the figure were drawn by NGI's digital terrain model system. This system can also produce 3 dimensional drawings (Figure 10).

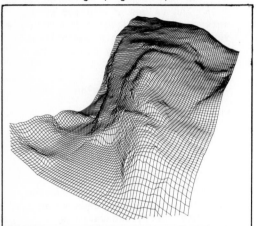

Figure 10. Terrain model of Jostedalen power plant.

The orientations of the stresses determined by overcoring are quite variable. In the access tunnel the values indicate a very high ratio of stresses (about 7:1). In the Vigdalen adit the minimum stress determined by both methods are very close in value and consistent with the depth of cover. The overcoring tests indicated that the minimum principal stress was near vertical and that the ratio of stresses was about 2.5:1.

5. DISCUSSION

Comparison of the stresses determined by the hydrofracture and overcoring methods are in good agreement (Table 1) at the Kvilldal and Naddevik power plants and in the Vigdalen adit at the Jostedalen power plant. At these locations the overcoring measurements indicate credible orientations, values and ratios of the principal stresses.

Table 1. Summary and comparison of rock stress measurements for the four sites.

SITE	Method HF/OC (1)	Hole/loc. No.	Break down pressure P_b, MPa	Stresses, MPa σ_1	σ_2	σ_3	Overburden m	Ref. Fig. No. Remarks
Tjodan powerplant	OC	1	-	21.9	6.2	4.7	640	
	HF	2	15.5	-	-	7.9	660	2)
	HF	3	23.5	-	-	13.1	700	Fig. No. 6
Kvilldal powerplant	OC	1	-	11.8	7.5	2.8	320	
	OC	2	-	9.9	6.4	4.8	500	Fig. No. 7
	HF	3	16.2	-	-	4.6	600	2)
Naddevik powerplant	HF	1	31.0			18.0	880	3)
	HF	2	21.0	-	-	12.7	900	
	HF	3	21.5	-	-	14.2	930	2)
	OC	3	-	16.1	12.3	4.9	450	Fig. No. 8
	OC	4	-	20.9	14.6	12.2	750	
	OC	2	-	26.3	18.9	12.4	900	
	OC	3	-	25.0	19.6	16.8	930	
Jostedalen powerplant access tunnel	HF	1	21.0	-	-	7.8	570	2)
	OC	1	-	28.2	15.1	3.7	570	
	HF	2	30.2	-	-	12.5	900	2)
Vigdalen adit	HF	1	9.3	-	-	2.0	250	Fig. No. 9
	OC	2	-	16.7	14.6	6.2	360	
	HF	2	19.2	-	-	6.0	360	2)
	HF	3	22.8	-	-	9.9	440	2)

1) HF – hydrofracturing test
   OC – overcoring measurement, Leeman method

2) Values reported are the mean σ_3 measured in a group of holes

3) The measured value is very high, probably because of the test section is near the tunnel wall with high tangential stresses

In the access tunnel to the Jostedalen plant and the Tjodan power plant the stress ratios were very high and the values of minimum stress determined by overcoring and hydrofracture were not in good agreement. Poor rock conditions for the overcoring tests leading to unreliable results could be one explanation for these discrepancies.

The very high stress ratios measured by the overcoring method do not appear credible though the orientations are reasonable. The discrepancies might also be due to an anisotropic rock mass. If the orientation of the weakness plane in the rock mass was not parallel to the plane perpendicular to the least principal stress, then a hydraulic fracturing test might open up this plane of weakness and the measured normal stress would then be greater than the least principal stress.

The results from the hydraulic fracturing tests have been very useful in measuring the minimum stress even though the orientation is not determined. The value obtained is a direct measure of the minimum

direct measure of the minimum
pressure required to cause hydraulic
fracturing or open up existing
discontinuities in the rock mass.

6. REFERENCES

(1) Doe, T.W., Ingevald, K., Strin-
     dell, L. Haimson, B. and Carleson, H.
     "Hydraulic fracturing and over-
     coring stress measurements in a
     deep borehole at the Stripa
     Test Mine, Sweden".
     Proc. 22nd U.S. Symposium on
     Rock Mechanics, M.I.T.
     373-378, 1981.

(2) Aamodt, L. and Kuriyagawa, M.
     "Measurement of instantaneous
     shut-in pressure in crystalline
     rock".
     Proceedings of the Workshop on
     Hydraulic Fracturing Stress
     Measurements, U.S. Nat. Comm.
     on Rock Mech., Washington,
     D.C., 394-402, 1982.

(3) Enever, J.R. and Wooltorton,
     B.A.
     "Experience with hydraulic
     fracturing as a means of esti-
     mating in situ stress in
     Australian Coal Basin
     sediments". Proceedings of the
     Workshop on Hydraulic Frac-
     turing Stress Measurements,
     U.S. Nat. Comm. on Rock
     Mech., Washington, D.C.,
     62-102, 1982.

(4) Tunbridge, L.W., Cooling, C.M.
     and Haimson, B.C
     "Measurement of rock stress
     using the hydrofracturing
     method in Cornwall, U.K. Part
     1: Field measurement."
     Int. J. Rock Mech. Min. Sci. &
     Geomech. Abstr. in press.

Definition of the use of steel liners based on hydraulic fracturing tests. A case history

A. MARULANDA
C. ORTIZ
R. GUTIERREZ
INGETEC S.A., Bogota, Colombia

Abstract

For many years the decision for using steel liners in a pressure tunnel was fundamented on empirical criteria, evaluating the stress level based on vertical and horizontal overburden. During the last years the hydraulic fracturing test has been developed as a fundamental tool for taking this decision.

Minor geological characteristics of the rock mass can introduce an appreciable influence in the in-situ stress level, that ought to be taken in account when using these test criteria.

This article illustrates how a systematic use of hydraulic fracturing tests reveals the presence of such influence in the stress state for determining the required steel lining length.

Résumé

Pendant de nombreuses années, la décision d'utiliser des blindages en acier dans les tunnels à pression, se basait sur des critères empiriques qui évaluaient le niveau des contraintes à partir de la couverture verticale et horizontale. Dans les dernières années, on a développé l'essai de fracturation hydraulique comme un instrument fondamental pour prende cette décision.

Des caractéristiques géologiques mineures de la masse de roche, peuvent influencer appréciablement le niveau des contraintes in-situ et dôivent être prises en considération au moment d'utiliser les resultats des essais.

Cet article indique comment l'emploi systématique des essais de fracturation hydraulique, révèle la présence de ces effets dans l'état des contraintes, permettant ainsi de déterminer la longueur nécessaire de blindage en acier.

Zusammenfassung

Für viele Jahre, die Benutzung von Stahlverkleidung in Hochdruchsrohren war nur im empirische Kriterium begründet, welche in vertikalen und horizontalen Spannkraftüberladungsniveau abschätz. In den letzten Jahre, hat sich die hydraulische Abbruchsprobe, als ein grosser Werkzeug entwickelt, um diese Entscheidung zu nehmen.

Wirkungen, die infolge säkundaeren geologischen Bezeichnungen den Gesteinmasse davon haben, dass ein wichtiger Einfluss in den in-situ Spannkraftüberladungsniveau einführen können, Probleme entwickeln, die gegenwertig halten müssen, wenn diese zur Abbruchsprobe benutz wird.

Dieser Artikel erklärt, wie eine systematische Benutzung, von hydraulischen Abbruchsproben die Anwesenheit dieser Einflusses in Spannkraft, um die Länge der Stahlverkleiderung zu entscheiden, enthüllt.

1. INTRODUCTION

The design of a pressure tunnel has to consider three fundamental aspects: Structural stability during operation; avoid excessive leakage due

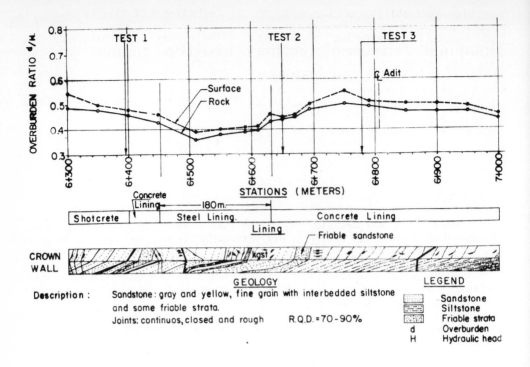

FIG. 1.- OVERBURDEN RATIO, LINING AND GEOLOGY

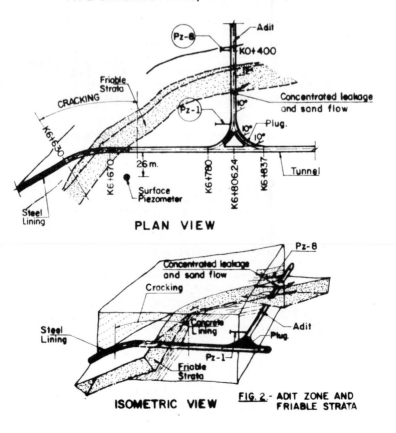

PLAN VIEW

ISOMETRIC VIEW

FIG. 2.- ADIT ZONE AND FRIABLE STRATA

to high permeability of the mass of rock, and avoid excessive leakage due to hydraulic fracturing when the stress level in the mass of rock is not high enough.

The only alternative to guarantee that the phenomena of hydraulic fracturing do not occur is the use of a steel liner. This paper illustrates the criteria used to design a section of a long pressure tunnel where the vertical overburden was low with relation to the operating water pressure. In this same sector a construction adit was designed to reduce the required length of the excavation phases.

The tunnel was totally excavated in sedimentary rock of cretaceous age composed mainly by sandstones with in-terbedded hard siltstones.

From the stand point of hydraulic fracturing this sector particularly critic due to low overburden as shown in figure 1.

2. ADOPTED OVERBURDEN CRITERIA

Initially, the criterion adopted to avoid hydraulic fracturing was to use a steel liner whenever the vertical overburden ratio is less than 0.4 (relationship between the internal pressure in the tunnel and the rock cover above as defined by (Kieser 1960), (Selmer-Olsen 1970), (Dann - Hartwig 1964) and (Broch 1982). The topography in this section of the tunnel is relatively flat, and

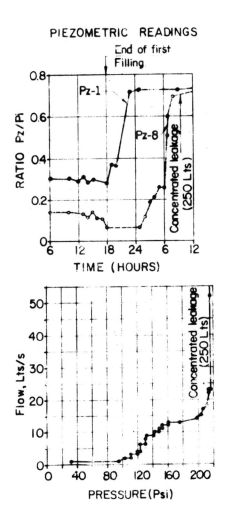

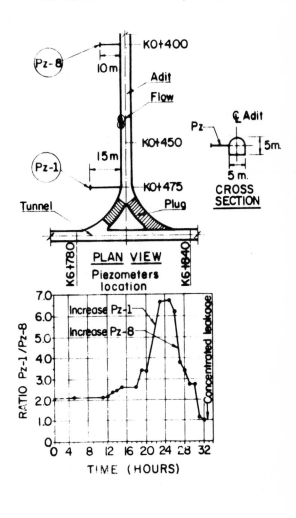

FIG. 3- PIEZOMETRIC READINGS

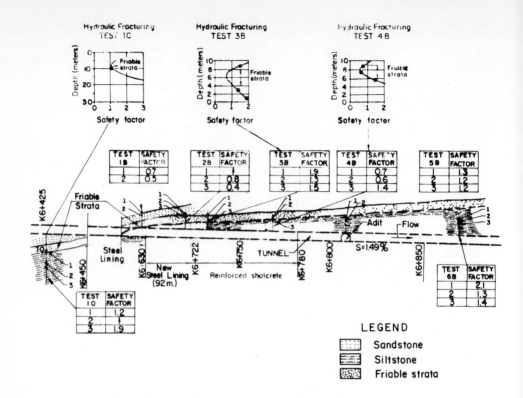

FIG. 4. HYDRAULIC FRACTURING TESTS

therefore the horizontal overburden was not important. Additionally, after excavation a program of hydraulic fracturing tests was envisioned with the purpose of determining if the adopted criteria of overburden ratio of 0.4 was related to the real in-situ state of stress. The tests were performed in stations K6+395, K6+350 and K6+779. The results of these tests show that the minimum stress in the area, corresponded basically to the one that could be calculated by the rock overburden with a rock density of 2.8 Tn/m3.

Based on these results, a 180 m. steel liner was defined between stations K6+450 and K6+630, considering that the minimum overburden ratio would be 0.43, wich corresponds to a factor of safety of 1.20. Figure 1 shows how the overburden ratio varies along the section of the tunnel and the location of the hydraulic fracturing tests. -Geology and adopted final lining is also shown.

3. HYDRAULIC FRACTURING PHENOMENA

During the first filling of the tunnel the maximum pressure of 15 Kg/cm2, was reached at this sector. The recorded phenomena showed very dramatically that hydraulic fracturing developed in the tunnel. Leakage into the adit, that had reached during the tunnel filling a value of the order of 20 l/s, increased in a very short period of time up to 250 l/s that also brought a large amount of material into the adit. This leakage was concentrated in one station of the adit.

The behavior of the piezometers installed from the adit, described also how the phenomena developed, showing how the ratio between the pressure in the mass rock with respect to the internal pressure in the tunnel varied with time. Before the hydraulic fracturing developed, this ratio was about 0.3 along many of the places where the pressure was being recorded along the tunnel. As the phenomena developed, the ratio increased very rapidly up to a point of 70% of the internal pressure. Also piezometers PZ-1 and PZ-8, that were located very close to where the erosion developed, showed how the waterflow was occurring with very little pressure drop, in spite of the fact that the piezometers were located more that 80 m. away from the tunnel; therefore the pressure from the tunnel had developed along a major area that produced the fracture and the uplifting of the rock. The phenomenon was also checked by the behavior of a hole drilled from the surface very close to the tunnel alignment that was done for the purpose of installing a piezometer; the instrument at that time was not yet installed and a water jet 5 m. above the surface was observed in the ground, coming from this drilled hole.

The tunnel was immediately unwatered and during the first inspection it was obvious that the concrete lining downstream of the steel lining suffered heavy cracking especially between stations K6+630 and K6+710 with longitudinal cracks concentrated mainly among the crown of the tunnel, with large displacements in the concrete lining. Scratch plates installed before filling the tunnel showed vertical movements up to 3.0 cm, which have clear evidence of the general uplift that occurred in the area. Evidently once the hydraulic fracturing of the rock developed, water under pressure had easy access to a friable sandstone bed that existed in this area, as shown in Figure 2. Leakage developed into the adit with very little loss of pressure and therefore with great piping capacity producing a large amount of eroded material. Fig. 2 shows a plan and an isometric view of the damaged area.

4. NEW HYDRAULIC FRACTURING TEST

The events previously described and the results of the available instrumentation show very clearly that a very dramatic hydraulic fracturing phenomenon had developed in the mass of rock. It apparently started in a local point where due to minor defects in the mass of rock, the state of stress was less than the one previously envisioned, and specifically

inside a softer friable stratum along which an erosion problem developed later and extended down to the adit.

Due to the uncertainty that existed with respect to this phenomenon and the conditions that developed in order to design the repair works, it was decided to obtain, by means of hydraulic fracturing, the principal stress value, (Haimson 1978), (Howar 1970), Hubbert 1975), in order to carry out the analysis of what had ocurred. The results of these new tests are shown in Fig. 4.

The new series of tests performed in the area, show how the stress level in the friable stratum is lower than the surrounding stress level in the harder rock, as if an arching effect had been produced, by which the harder rock absorbed a higher portion of the overburden stress.

Based on the results of the hydraulic fracturing tests and due to the shortage of lining in the country and the time required for additional supplies, it was decided to extend the lining only in the length that would be considered absolutely essential to avoid a new hydraulic fracturing phenomenon to develop. The steel lining was extended up to station K6+722, where the distance between the tunnel and the friable strata was at least one diameter. Downstream of the new steel liner a reinforced shotcrete lining was designed to take the full internal pressure. Additionally, several drainage holes were done from the adit in order that if any leakage came out from the tunnel in the concrete lined area, the pressure would be dissipated avoiding the creation of a larger pressure along an extended area.

5. NEW FILLING

After the repair works were finished the tunnel was filled again with maximum pressure for more than a week. In this time the leakage in the adit was no more than 14 l/s, about the same amount that was measured during the excavation of the adit itself. The piezometers showed that the ratios between the pressure and the rock with respect to the internal pressure, were at a maximum value of 40%.

All the observations and the piezometers records showed that the phenomena of hydraulic fracturing had been
adequately controlled.

A new inspection of the tunnel was
performed and the reinforced shotcrete
did not suffer any cracking at all.

7. REFERENCES

Broch, E. 1982. The Development of Unlined Pressure Shafts and Tunnels in
    Norway.   ISRM Symposium on Rock Mechanics: Caverns and Pressure Shafts.
    Aachen.
Dann, H.E., Hartwig, W.P. and Hunter, J.R. 1964.   Unlined Tunnels of the Snowy
    Montains Hydroelectric Authoroty.   Journal of Power Division. Proceedings of
    the ASCE. Vol. 90 (PO3). Austria.
Haimson, B.C.   1978.   The Hydrofracturing Stress Measurement Method and recent
    field results. Inst. J. Rock. Mech. Vol. 15 (4): 167 - 178.
Howard, G.L. and Fast, C.R. 1957. Hydraulic Fracturing. AIME Soc. Petr. Eng.
    New York, Dallas.
Hubbert, G.C. and Fast, C.R. 1957.   Mechanics of Hydraulic Fracturing.
    AIME: 153.
Kieser, A. 1960. Druckstollenbau. Wien. Springer Vellag.
Selmer-Olsen, R. 1970.   Experience with Unlined Pressure Shafts in Norway.
Proceedings Int. Symposium on Large Underground Openings. Orlo.

Initial rock stresses around the Vietas headrace tunnels nos. 2 and 3, Sweden

J. MARTNA
Swedish State Power Board, Stockholm, Sweden

L. HANSEN
VLF - Geo, Uppsala, Sweden

ABSTRACT

The headrace tunnels 2 and 3 at the Vietas hydro power station, Lapland, Sweden penetrate the middle and lower nappes of the Swedish Caledonides, sedimentary Cambrian rocks as well as the Precambrian basement. The latter rocks are cut by several faults. In the tunnels 134 rock stress measurements were carried out. In the downstream part of the tunnel, rock bursting and high horizontal stresses perpendicular to the tunnel have been common. Owing to the large number of measurements, observation of rock bursting and a detailed geological mapping, a fair picture of the stress levels in and between the tunnels has been obtained.

RESUME

Les galeries d'amenée 2 et 3 de l'usine hydroélectrique de Vietas, en Laponie suédoise pénètrent dans les nappes moyennes et basses des Calédonides suédoises aussi bien que dans des roches sédimentaires et dans le socle autochtones. Les roches autochtones sont coupées par plusieurs failles. Dans les tunnels, 134 mesures de contrainte de la roche ont été effectuées et ont permis de constater que les ruptures de roches par éclatement et les contraintes horizontales élevées perpendiculaires aux tunnels étaient courantes dans la partie aval de ces derniers. Grâce au grand nombre de mesures, à l'observation des ruptures de roche par éclatement et à une cartographie géologique détaillée, on a pu obtenir une bonne image des niveaux de contrainte dans et entre les tunnels.

ZUSAMMENFASSUNG

Die Druckstollen 2 und 3 des Wasserkraftwerks Vietas in Lappland, Schweden durchstossen sowohl die mittleren und tieferen Decken der in Schweden im Paläozoikum entstandenen Auffaltungen als vorkommenden sedimentäre Schichten und das Grundgebirge. Das Grundgebirge und die sedimentäre Gesteine wird von mehreren Verwerfungen durchschnitten. In dem Druckstollen wurden 134 messungen der Spannungen im Gestein durchgeführt. Im unteren Teil der Druckstollen waren Abbrüche und starke waagerechte, rechtwinklig zum Stollen verlaufende Spannungen üblich. Zufolge der hohen Anzahl von Messungen, Beobachtung von Abbrüchen und der Erstellung einer detaillierte geologische Karte gewann man ein zuverlässiges Bild der Spannungsverhältnisse in und zwischen den Druckstollen.

1   INTRODUCTION

The Vietas Hydro Power Station is situated
on the River Lule Älv in the mountains of
the far north of Sweden, more than a
hundred kilometres north of the Arctic
Circle (Figs. 1 and 2). The installed
capacity is 320 MW and the average annual
energy production is 1160 GWh. The power
station utilizes the water from Lakes
Akkajaure and Satihaure. The gross head
between these two lakes and Lake Langas is
78 and 82 metres respectively. The power
station with appurtenant dams and tunnels
has been designed and constructed by the
Swedish State Power Board. The power
station with headrace tunnels 1 and 2
(Fig. 3) was taken into operation in 1972.
Tunnel 2 is 7.4 km long and has a square
area of 190 m^2 with a width of 12.5 m and
a height of 16.5 m.

Fig. 1. Location of the Vietas Hydroelectric
Power Station.

Fig. 2. Topography of Mt. Nieras above the downstream part of the Suorva-Vietas
headrace tunnels, as seen from southwest of Vietas.

Headrace tunnel 3 was designed and
excavated by the Swedish State Power Board
during the years 1982-1985 and was taken
into operation in December 1985. The
purpose of this tunnel is to increase the
area of tunnel 2 in order to minimize flow
losses due to friction. It is also
possible that another unit will be added
to the power station in the future and be
supplied with water via tunnel 3. The
tunnel is roughly parallel to tunnel 2 and
the tunnels are situated about 100 metres
apart.

Tunnel 3 is 5.6 km long and has a square
area of 212 m^2, divided into a top heading
of 96 m^2 and a bench of 116 m^2. The width
of the tunnel is 14.5 m and the height
16 m. As can be seen in Fig. 3, tunnel 3
lies north of tunnel 2 at Suorva and south

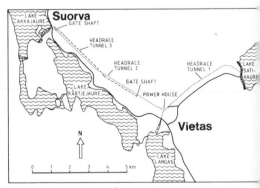

Fig. 3. Vietas Hydroelectric Power Station. General
layout.

of it at Vietas. Thus, the the two tunnel
cross each other at about chainage 4+000

606

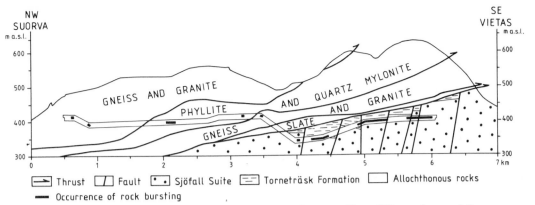

NW
SUORVA
m a.s.l.

SE
VIETAS
m a.s.l.

GNEISS AND GRANITE
PHYLLITE AND QUARTZ MYLONITE
GNEISS SLATE AND GRANITE

➡️ Thrust ⬜ Fault ⋅⋅ Sjöfall Suite ☰ Torneträsk Formation ⬜ Allochthonous rocks
— Occurrence of rock bursting

Fig. 4. Vietas Headrace Tunnel 3. Longitudinal section showing an outline of the geology and the occurrence of rock bursting in tunnel 3. Note the graben structure in the middle of the section. Geological mapping by O Kulling, M Moberg, L Björklund and the authors. Vertical scale / horizontal scale = 5 : 1

As shown in Fig. 4, tunnel 3 features a slope at about 4+000 m. This feature (which tunnel 2 also has) was designed for geological reasons, to give the tunnels the shortest possible transit through the crushed graphitic slates of the Lower Allochthon. In the slope, tunnel 3 also turns southwards, passes under tunnel 2 and climbs thereafter again to elevation 400 m.

2   GEOLOGY

2.1   General

An outline of the complex geology of the Suorva-Vietas area is shown in Fig. 4. The rocks can be divided into three main units. The oldest one consists of Precambrian quartzites and metavolcanics formed 1000-2000 million years ago and is named the Snavva-Sjöfall Formation (Lundqvist, 1979) or the Sjöfall Suite (Ödman 1957). Later on these rocks have been folded and were also subject to subsequent erosion.

Upon these rocks the Torneträsk Formation was deposited during early Cambrian (Kulling 1964, Thelander 1982). In the tunnel this formation is represented by a horizontally bedded, greenish grey siltstone with a basal conglomerate. Together the Sjöfall Suite and the Torneträsk Formation compose the autochthonous bedrock beneath the mountain chain, and the downstream parts of the tunnels lie in these rocks.

The third main unit of rocks was also formed during the Precambrian and early Palaeozoic, but far to the west of the tunnel site. In the middle Palaeozoic they were thrust over the earlier mentioned rocks and now form the Scandinavian Caledonide Mountains. During the thrusting these originally sedimentary and magmatic rocks were strongly deformed and metamorphosed into mylonites, phyllites, slates and gneisses. In the tunnel four main thrust sheets can be defined. The lowest one is built up of slates belonging to the Lower Allochthon (Gee & Zachrisson, 1979). These slates are often strongly deformed and crushed. Particularly the graphite bearing ones have caused problems and standstills during excavation.

The three other sheets all belong to the Akkajaure Nappe Complex of the Middle Allochthon (Björklund 1985). These sheets consist of alternating granite gneiss, quartz mylonite, mylonite and phyllite (Fig. 4), and the upstream parts of the tunnels lie in these rocks.

2.2   Geology of the High-Stress Sections

Since most of the high stresses occur within the autochthonous rocks in the downstream parts of the tunnels, the geology of these parts is elucidated in Fig. 6, which shows the tunnel passages through the complex rocks in section 4+500 - 6+200. As can be seen from the figure, tunnel 2 passes from the grey and black slates of the Lower Allochthon down into the greenish grey Upper Siltstone of the autochthonous Torneträsk Formation at about 4+500. Further downstream, from about section 4+900, it enters the grey metaarkose of the Sjöfall Suite. Thereafter tunnel 2 lies entirely in rocks of the Sjöfall Suite. Downstream of 4+900 the Basal Conglomerate of the Torneträsk Formation forms the roof in parts of tunnel 2. Due to faulting this conglomerate suddenly disappears at 5+275.

The corresponding part (4+500 - 4+900) of tunnel 3 lies at a lower level, and entirely within the autochthon. However, the lithology alters between rocks belonging to the Sjöfall Suite and those of the overlying Torneträsk Formation. For example, tunnel 3 abruptly passes from siltstone into the metaarkose at 4+600, and then back into the siltstone, the roof at 4+800 and the floor at 4+900.

Downstream from section 4+900 tunnel 3 lies at a higher level than tunnel 2, and consequently the Basal Conglomerate with a one metre thick bed of sandstone upon it lies in the middle of the bench. The bottom and the lower part of the bench lies in metaarkose, and the rest of the bench as well as the top heading lies entirely in siltstone. This succession is suddenly cut off by a fault at 5+320 (Figs. 4 & 6), where the tunnel passes into a violet Sjöfall rock, probably of volcanic origin.

The main reason for these sudden changes in lithology within and between the two tunnels is the occurrence of several faults in the area (Figs. 4 and 6). These faults displace the Basal Conglomerate between one and thirty-five metres each and altogether more than one hundred metres, forming a graben structure (Fig. 4). However, the faults do not seem to influence the Allochthon (Martna & Hansen 1986b, 1986c).

The faults appear as drag structures in the siltstone beds or as zones of fractured and crushed rock. Most of the fracture zones seem to be healed with extremely fine-grained (perhaps glassy) material. Several of them, however, feature slickensides or are filled with clay and rock fragments, indicating that some of the faults have been re-activated although no larger movements have been traced. The effect of the faulting on the lithology in the tunnels can be seen in Figs. 4 and 6.

3 ROCK STRESSES

3.1 Rock Stress Measurements

Sixty-six rock stress measurements have been carried out in tunnel 2, using the two-dimensional "doorstopper"-method. The measurements and their results are published in Hiltscher 1969, 1972 and Hiltscher & Ingevald 1971. In tunnel 3 sixty-eight measurements were carried out by the three-dimensional overcoring method, using the Hiltscher probe developed by the Swedish State Power Board (Hiltscher et al. 1979). These results are presented in Martna & Hansen 1986b. Fig. shows the magnitude of the highest principal stress (σ_1) along tunnel 2 and 3, and Fig. 6 shows more detailed the measuring results at chainage 4+900 - 6+200.

Most of the measurements in tunnel 3 have been made between the chainages 4+900 and 5+900 because of the stress manifestation and practical problems occurring during the excavation. The areas with high stresses are thus over-represented in the

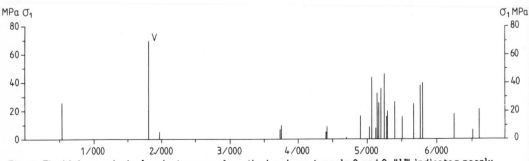

Fig. 5. The highest principal rock stresses along the headrace tunnels 2 and 3. "V" indicates nearly vertical stress, all other stresses are almost horizontal.

measurements. In the areas where rock bursting occurs, the approximately horizontal stresses attain a value of 40-50 MPa. The vertical stresses have more or less the value expected from the thickness of the overburden, generally less than 10 MPa.

In general the initial rock stress around the tunnel has a magnitude of 10 - 20 MPa, is practically uniaxial, almost horizontal and perpendicular to the tunnel axis, plunging gently (10-20°) towards the SSW. There is one notable exception. In the overthrusted rocks at section 1+800, the initial stress is almost vertical and reaches a magnitude of about 70 MPa whilst the expected value is less than 10 MPa.

There are also sections in the tunnel where the rock stress is considerably lower than 10 MPa, and crushed rocks seem to be more or less de-stressed.

3.2   Rock Stress Manifestations

Within sections with high rock stresses, mainly between 4+000 and 6+000, rock bursting, rock instability and a variety of sound phenomena have occurred. Fig. 4 shows the occurrence of these phenomena in tunnel 3. The most intensive rock bursting occurred on the stretches 4+950-5+270 and 5+700 - 5+950. Such manifestations of stress have been practically absent in the slates, phyllites, gneisses and mylonites in the upstream part of the tunnel. An exception was a stretch around 2+100, where the rock (a quartz mylonite) is extremely brittle and minor rock falls were common during the excavation, possibly due to vertical stress.

Rock bursting and related phenomena have also been described from the excavation of the headrace tunnel 2 (Martna 1970, 1971, 1972). The rock bursting often resulted in rock-falls causing overbreaks (Martna 1972) but fortunately no serious personal injuries. Rock bursting was often accompanied by sound effects of variable intensity. A rather subjective classification has been made up for the noise, as perceived by an observer in the tunnel. Level 0 represents no sound effects, 1 corresponds to the sound of a typewriter, 2 to a hammer blow on rock, 3 to a gunshot and finally, at level 4 the noise is comparable with shooting a round, and has often been accompanied by shaking of the tunnel (Martna 1970). This

classification has also been used during the mapping of tunnel 3, and daily observations have been recorded in the high-stress areas of both tunnels.

There were three rather well defined high stress zones in tunnel 2, all of them situated in the hard and brittle rocks of the Sjöfall Suite at chainages 4+950 - 5+275, 5+500 - 5+865 and 6+350 - 6+400. In each of these zones, the observed stress manifestations and the measured stresses were highly variable (Fig. 6). They all started, however, gradually in the upstream (western) part and ended abruptly towards the east in the hanging wall of a fault (Fig. 6).

Outside these zones there were only a few and insignificant observations of rock stress manifestations, such as sounds and rock instability. This applies to the autochthonous Sjöfall Suite as well as to the allochthonous slates, gneisses etc. The stress related phenomena were practically absent in the allochthonous rocks because there the stresses were low. When, as an exception, such phenomena occurred, higher stresses were also present. This was, for instance, the case in the quartz mylonite in which exceptional high vertical stresses of about 70 MPa were measured at chainage 1+800 in tunnel 3.

In tunnel 3 the rock stress effects have, despite equal stresses, been less intense than in tunnel 2, although falls of rock and shotcrete have occurred, usually in connection with blasting. Only in one case (at 5+260) has level 4 been reached, although without shaking of the tunnel. Elsewhere, reports of levels 2 and 3 in tunnel 3 have corresponded to levels 3 and 4, respectively in reports from tunnel 2. Rock-falls have often resulted in overbreaks and, together with influence of rock structure, they have determined the shape of the tunnel (Martna & Hansen 1986a).

4   DISCUSSION

The topography along and across the tunnels is shown in Figs. 4, 7 and 8. The theoretical rock pressure due to the load of the rock mass of Mt. Nieras (Fig. 7) and its slopes has been calculated using the FEM method (unpublished). This theoretical stress plunges about 55 degrees to the south and does not exceed

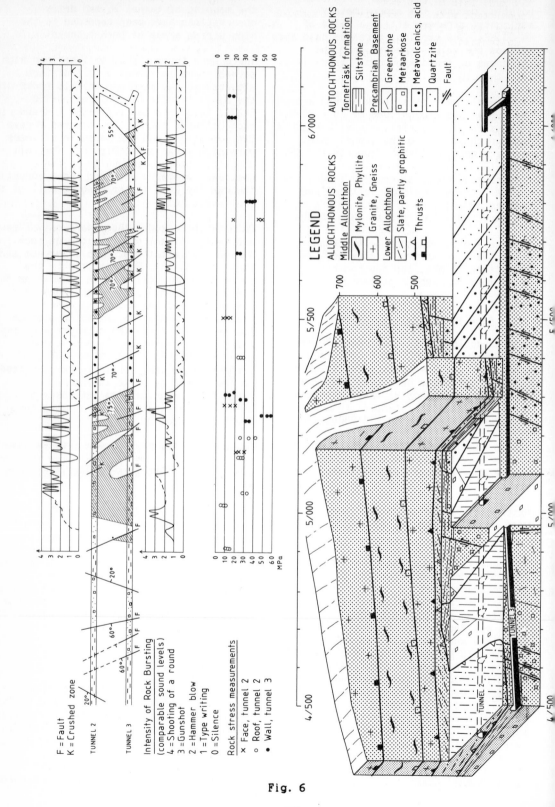

F = Fault
K = Crushed zone

TUNNEL 2

TUNNEL 3

Intensity of Rock Bursting
(comparable sound levels)
4 = Shooting of a round
3 = Gunshot
2 = Hammer blow
1 = Type writing
0 = Silence

Rock stress measurements
× Face, tunnel 2
○ Roof, tunnel 2
● Wall, tunnel 3

LEGEND

ALLOCHTHONOUS ROCKS

Middle Allochthon

Mylonite, Phyllite

Granite, Gneiss

Lower Allochthon

Slate, partly graphitic

Thrusts

AUTOCHTHONOUS ROCKS

Torneträsk formation

Siltstone

Precambrian Basement

Greenstone

Metaarkose

Metavolcanics, acid

Quartzite

Fault

Fig. 6

10 MPa. This stress level is fairly well consistent with the measured stresses in those parts of the tunnels where no stress manifestations have occurred. On the other hand this calculated stress level is far from the measured ones in those tunnel-sections where rock bursting and other stress effects were common.

The weak rock masses encountered in the tunnels seem to be de-stressed. There are no observations of stress manifestations in weak rock such as tunnel convergence or undue loosening of rock which could be ascribed to high rock stress.

The high stresses in the Vietas tunnels occur essentially in certain parts of the autochthonous bedrock beneath the mountain chain. This is especially true concerning

the north-to-south striking and gently southwards plunging almost uniaxial stresses. These stresses occur in connection with faults which probably do not pass into the allochthon (Martna & Hansen 1986b, 1986c). Cf. Figs 4 & 6.

The distribution of the intensity of the stresses is highly variable and has been recorded by stress measurements and daily observations of stress manifestations. Correspondence between the two tunnels regarding the distribution of stress manifestations as well as lithology and faults is quite good and a tentative correlation has been attempted. The shadowed area in and between the tunnels in Fig. 6 indicates the distribution of stress manifestation intensities of level 2 or more. This figure also shows how the

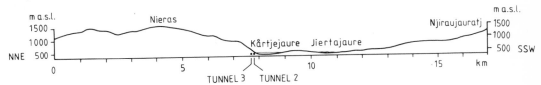

Fig. 7. SSW – NNE section across the headrace tunnels 2 and 3. Vertical scale = horizontal scale.

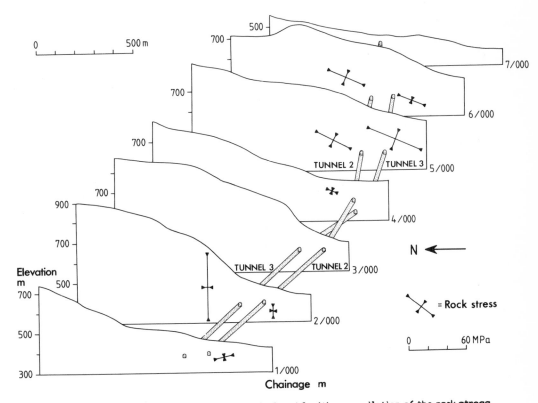

Fig. 8. N – S sections across headrace tunnel tunnels 2 and 3 with a compilation of the rock stress measurements of the nearby chainages.

stress manifestation zones often decrease or disappear abruptly in the footwalls of the faults.

As mentioned in Chapter 3.2, the tunnels differ with respect to the intensity of the rock stress manifestations. For the section 4+900 - 5+250 this could be due to the difference in lithology: tunnel 2 lies in metaarkose and tunnel 3 was, after borehole investigations (Moberg 1986), designed to lie mainly in the less brittle siltstone in order to reduce rock bursting effects. On the other hand, this is not the case with regard to the other stretch (5+700 - 6+000) where rock falls were common in tunnel 2 but not in tunnel 3. In this section both tunnels lie in red and violet Sjöfall quartzite with beds of metavolcanics. The structures are similar, and the measured rock stresses are equal, although the effects are less in tunnel 3.

This comparison between the tunnels indicates that the intensity of stress manifestations is partly dependent on the type of rock and may also partly depend on the elevation of the tunnel. The more brittle metaarkose causes more spectacular effects than the siltstone. It is also possible that the difference in rock structure may play a role. The bedding of the metaarkose is almost parallel to the faults, while the siltstone is horizontally bedded which causes another type of rock fall (Martna & Hansen 1986a).

In tunnel 3 there have been rock bursts in section 4+000 - 4+500 (Fig. 4), but not in tunnel 2. The reason for this seems to be that tunnel 3 in this section lies in the autochthon, while tunnel 2 lies in allochthonous slate, where the stresses for some reason usually are considerably lower than in the autochthonous metaarkose and siltstone (Fig. 6).

The highest stress in the downstream part of tunnel 3 (about 50 MPa) was measured at chainage 5+260-70 (Fig. 6), about 50 metres from a fault. Stress measurements were also carried out on both sides of this fault. The results are shown in Fig. 9. As can be seen from the figure, the stress plane strikes parallel to the fault and the stresses are rather high (25 MPa) in the hanging wall. As soon as the fault has been passed, the vertical stress disappears and the horizontal stress decreases to about 10 MPa and changes direction (into ENE-WSW). Thereafter they gradually increase while they revert to the north-south direction.

As mentioned in Chapter 2.2 the faults form a graben structure. The rapid changes of stress levels and directions near the faults and the crushed, unhealed material in several of them indicate that the fault zone may still be active. It may be noted that the gradient of the present-day uplift is very steep in the northern part of the Swedish Caledonides (Pettersson 1969, Mörner 1981). It is suggested that there exists a correlation between the uplift and the rock stresses met with in the fault zone in the Vietas tunnels.

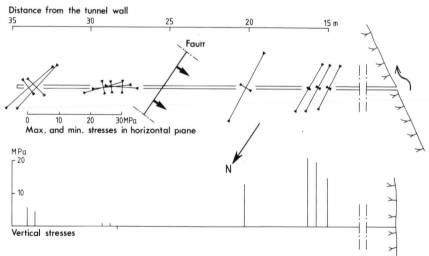

Fig. 9. Rock stresses around the fault at section 5+320 (tunnel 3). Arrows on fault indicate downthrow direction. Note the difference in stress direction and level between the hanging and foot wall of the fault.

Acknowledgements

Stress measurements were carried out by K. Ingevald, L. Strindell, T. Öhman and M. Andersson, all of the Swedish State Power Board. FEM-calculations were made by M. Andersson. The figures were drawn by C. Wernström, Uppsala. With R. Hiltscher, L. Hallbjörn and M. Andersson the authors have had fruitful discussions concerning the interpretation of the stress measurements. The authors wish to express their sincere thanks to all these persons.

References

Björklund, L., (1985). The Middle and Lower Allochthons in the Akkajaure-Tysfjord area, Northern Scandinavian Caledonides. The Caledonide Orogen: Scandiavia and related areas. Ed. by Gee D & Sturt B. Wiley, Chichester.

Gee, D. & Zachrisson, E., 1979. The Caledonides in Sweden. SGU, ser. C, 769. Uppsala.

Hiltscher, R., 1969. Bergtryck och spänningsfördelning omkring tilloppstunneln Suorva-Vietas. Bergmekaniskt diskussionsmöte, IVA-rapport nr 18, 229-34. Stockholm.

Hiltscher, R., 1972. Anwendung der Gebirgsspannungsmessung bei der Schwedischen Staatlichen Kraftwerksverwaltung. Int. Symp. Untertagbau, 555-560. Luzern.

Hiltscher, R & Ingevald, K., 1971. Bergmekaniska undersökningar beträffande smällbergszonens inverkan vid pallsprängning i tilloppstunneln Suorva-Vietas. (Summary: Rock-mechanical investigations concerning the influence of a rock-burst zone on the bench excavation in the headrace tunnel at Suorva-Vietas hydro power plant). IVA-rapport nr 38, 153-164. Ingenjörsvetenskapsakademin, Stockholm.

Hiltscher, R., Martna, J. & Strindell, L., 1979. The Measurement of triaxial rock stresses in deep boreholes and the use of rock stress measurements in the design and construction of rock openings. Proc. 4. Int. Congr. Rock Mechanics, vol 2, 227-234. Montreux.

Kulling, O., 1964. Översikt över norra Norrbottensfjällens kaledonberggrund. SGU ser Ba, 19. Stockholm.

Lundqvist, T., 1979. The Precambrian of Sweden. SGU ser C, 768. Uppsala.

Martna, J., 1970. Rock bursting in the Suorva-Vietas headrace tunnel. 1st Int.Congr. Int.Ass.Eng.Geol., vol 2, 1134-1139. Paris.

Martna, J., 1971. Geologiska synpunkter på smällberget i Suorva-Vietastunneln (English summary: Geological aspects on rock bursting in the Suorva-Vietas tunnel). Bergmekaniskt diskussionsmöte, IVA-rapport nr 38, 141-151, Stockholm.

Martna, J., 1972. Selective overbreak in the Suorva-Vietas tunnel caused by rock pressure. Int. Symposium on Underground Openings, 141-145. Luzern.

Martna J & Hansen L, 1986a. The influence of rock structure on the shape and the supports of a large headrace tunnel. Int. ITA Congr. Large Underground Openings, Firenze.

Martna, J. & Hansen, L., 1986b. Vietas kraftstation, tilloppstunnel 3. Dokumentation av geologiska förhållanden och tunnelns drivning. Swedish State Power Board, Stockholm.

Martna, J. & Hansen, L.,1986c (in preparation). Vietas hydro power station, headrace tunnel 3. Documentation of geology and excavation. Swedish State Power Board, Stockholm.

Moberg, M., 1986 (in: Martna & Hansen 1986b). Vietas Kraftstation. Tilloppstunnel 3, lm 3+000-6+047. Kärnborrning och bergprognos. Swedish State Power Board, Stockholm.

Mörner, N. A., 1981. Crustal movements and geodynamics in Fennoscandia. Tectonophysics, 71 (1981), 241-251. Elsevier, Amsterdam.

Pettersson, L., 1969. Topografisk höjdbestämning: Precisionsavvägningar och nytt höjdsystem i Sverige. Teknisk Tidskrift vol. 99:19, 407-412. Stockholm

Swedish State Power Board, 1981. Vietas. Tekniska uppgifter. Technical data. Stockholm.

Thelander, T., 1982. The Torneträsk Formation of the Dividal Group. Northern Swedish Caledonides. SGU ser C, 789. Uppsala.

Ödman, O. H., 1957. Beskrivning till berggrundskarta över urberget i Norrbottens Län (Summary: Description to map of the Precambrian rocks of Norrbotten County, N. Sweden). SGU ser Ca, 41. Stockholm.

Proceedings of the International Symposium on Rock Stress and Rock Stress Measurements/Stockholm/1-3 September 1986

High horizontal stresses at Niagara Falls, their measurement, and the design of a new hydroelectric plant

B.C. HAIMSON
University of Wisconsin, Madison, Wisconsin, USA

C.F. LEE
J.H.S. HUANG
Ontario Hydro, Toronto, Ontario, Canada

ABSTRACT: Several underground hydroelectric plants in the Niagara Falls region are showing signs of structural distress as a result of preexisting high horizontal stresses and time-dependent rock deformation upon stress relief. Thus, a major emphasis in the feasibility and preliminary design studies toward the construction of a new power plant has been the measurement of the in-situ stress using both overcoring and hydrofracturing. This paper reports the results of the first comprehensive stress measurements in the area, confirming that high horizontal stresses prevail, but also showing that substantial jumps in stress magnitudes exist between rock units, and that stress changes, especially with respect to direction, may occur along the route of the planned power tunnels. These results have been incorporated in the design analysis of the power plant underground components.

RESUME: Fortes contraintes horizontales à Niagara Falls, leur mesure, et la conception d'une nouvelle generatrice hydro-electrique. Plusieurs génératrices hydro-electriques souterraines dans le région de Niagara Falls montrent des signes de de'tresse de structure résultant de fortes contraintes horizontales et de la déformation de la roche causée par le reláchement de ces contraintes. Par conséquent, les études préliminaires de faisabilite et de conception pour la construction d'une nouvelle génératrice ont mis l'accent sur la mesure des contraintes en place, par le sur-carottage et la fracturation hydraulique. Cette communication rapporte les resultats des premières mesures d'ensemble dans la région, lesquels confirment que les contraintes horizontales sont en général éleveés, mais aussi demontrent qu il existé des variations substantielles dans l'intensité de ces contraintes dans les diverses roches, et que des variations de contraintes peuvent done survenier le long des tunnels proposés. Ces resultats furent incorpores dans l'analyse de tous les composants sous-terrains du groupe electrogène.

ZUSAMMENFASSUNG: Einige Untergrund - Wasserkraftwerke im Gebiet der Niagara-Fälle zeigen Anzeichen der Baufälligkeit als Resultat der vorgegebenen hohen horizontalen Spannungen und der zeitabhangigen Felsdeformation in Folge des Spannungsabbaus. Daher wird bei vorläufigen Design - Studien bei der Konstruktion eines neuen Kraftwerks der Messung der in-situ Spannung unter Benutzung von "overcoring" und "hydrofracturing" besondere Beachtung geschenkt. In diesem Artikel wird über die ersten vergleichenden Spannungsmessungen berichtet, welche bestätigen, daß hohe horizontale Spannungen vorherrschen und außerdem zeigen, daß große Unterschiede in der Höhe der Spannungen verschiedener Felseinheiten bestehen und richtungsabhängige Spannungsanderungen entlang der geplanten Druck-tunnel aufreten können. Diese Ergebnisse wurden in die Designanalyse der Untergrundkomponenten des Kraftwerkse ingebaut.

1. INTRODUCTION

The Niagara Falls region has long been recognized for its scenic attractions and hydroelectric resources. A number of power plants were completed at the turn of the century. Of those owned by Ontario Hydro - the provincial electric utility - the Toronto Power Generating Station has already been retired, and the Ontario Power Generating Station is coming close to retirement. To make efficient use of the available water, Ontario Hydro is currently evaluating the feasibility of building a new hydraulic plant in the region known as Sir Adam Beck Niagara Generating Station No. 3 (SAB #3).

Similar to the 1400 MW SAB #2 plant built in the 1950's, the proposed SAB #3 project will involve a system of hydraulic tunnels and canal. The SAB #2 project included twin 9 km long tunnels, each with 15.5 m excavated and 13.7 m finished diameters. As illustrated in the geologic section in Figure 1, the twin tunnels were excavated in horizontally bedded sandstone, shale, dolomite and limestone units of the Silurian age. The new tunnels for the proposed SAB #3 project will likely be excavated in the underlying Queenston shale formation, with the Whirlpool sandstone as the roof. The reference scheme favours a twin tunnel system with a finished diameter of 10.7 m. Alternatively, a single 15 m diameter tunnel could also be contemplated, the limiting factors being excavation cost and machine tunnel technology.

Figure 2 shows the layout of the existing SAB #2 as well as the proposed layout schemes for the SAB #3.

2. ROCK ENGINEERING DESIGN CONSIDERATIONS

Rock structure performance in the region over the years clearly suggested that there are two major rock mechanics factors in the design of the underground openings for the SAB #3. The first is the state of high horizontal stresses in the sedimentary units, the second being the time-dependent deformation properties of some shale and shaly limestone units.

It has been recognized that high horizontal stresses exist in many of the bedrock units in Southern Ontario and adjacent areas (Haimson and Lee 1980; Lee 1981; Lo 1978). The magnitude of these horizontal stresses would typically be in the range of 5-15 MPa in near-surface bedrock formations. The orientation of the maximum horizontal stress varies considerably within the region, being affected locally by topographic as well as geological features (Lee 1981). In general, the maximum and minimum horizontal stresses approximate to the major and intermediate principal stresses

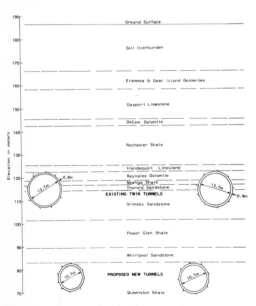

Figure 1 - Typical section in the Niagara Falls area, showing existing and planned pressure tunnels.

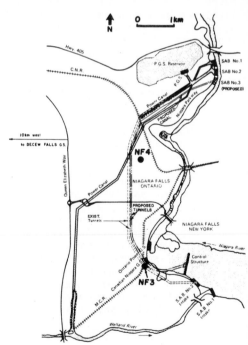

Figure 2 - General plan of the Ontario Hydro power station complex at Niagara Falls, showing the planned SAB No. 3 plant and the two test holes NF3 and NF4.

respectively. The vertical stress, which correlates with the overburden pressure, is often the minor stress.

The existence of high horizontal stresses generally leads to stress concentration effects in the roof and floor of an underground excavation. In some instances, this may lead to localized buckling failure, as observed in the SAB #2 twin tunnels and the SAB #1 canal (Lee 1978a; Lee et al 1975; Lo 1978). Buckling failure may also occur in some quarry floors and rock outcrops (Lee 1981). The origin of this state of stress is not well defined. A number of mechanisms have been postulated, including viscoelastic deformation under glacial loading, changes in the Earth's curvature due to continental glaciation, erosion, and plate tectonics (Lee 1978b; Lee and Asmis 1979; Asmis and Lee 1980). The second rock mechanics factor pertains to the tendency for some shale and shaly limestone units to move progressively into underground excavations with time. The direction of movement is largely horizontal, reflecting a long-term relief of horizontal stresses in these units. This stress relief could not be explained in terms of the hydration of swelling minerals or known physiochemical effects. Rather, it appears to be related to a gradual release of locked-in strain energy in some shaly units (Lo et al 1975).

This progressive inward movement often results in the build-up of loads on support structures and linings. It could lead to the buckling or crushing of support structures (as observed in the turbine pits of the Toronto Power and Canadian Niagara Generating Stations) and the cracking of tunnel linings (e.g. the Thorold Tunnel and the Heart Lake Tunnel (Lee and Lo 1976; Lee 1978c; Lo et al 1975; Lo and Yuen 1981). In light of the significance of in-situ stresses and stress relief on underground structures in the Niagara region, a comprehensive in-situ stress measurement program was therefore carried out as an integral part of the SAB #3 feasibility study.

3. HYDROFRACTURING STRESS MEASUREMENTS

3.1 Test Holes, Equipment and Procedures

The hydrofracturing technique was used to conduct ten stress measurements ·each in two NQ (76 mm) drillholes, NF3 (130 m deep) and NF4 (117 m deep), which are located some 3 km apart along the proposed pressure tunnel route (Figure 2). Both holes penetrate the rock units given in Figure 1. The formations tested were those between the Irondequit limestone and the Queenston shale, since they were considered to be the most probable host rocks to the underground components of the proposed SAB #3 Project.

Both testholes were continuously cored, and the core carefully logged for natural fractures. Based on these logs ten segments that appeared least affected by discontinuities were selected in each hole for hydrofracturing stress measurements.

A drilling rig and AQ (45 mm OD) drill rod were used to lower a borehole assembly, consisting of two 90 cm long inflatable packers straddling a 75 cm injection interval, to the predetermined testing depth. The drill rod was also used as a high pressure tubing conveying water to the straddled interval. The packers were inflated through a separate slim high-pressure hose strapped to the outside of the AQ rod. Each of the two hydraulic lines were fed by a high-pressure air-activated pump, aided by an accumulator used to eliminate pressure surges. The packers were first pressurized to a level sufficient to inflate them into the borehole wall and provide a sealed interval. During the test the packer pressure was always maintained at a level higher by at least 2 MPa than the interval pressure so as to avoid leaks past the packers. The hydrofracture pressure in the straddled interval was raised while maintaining a uniform flow rate until a critical value (P_c) was reached and a hydrofracture occurred causing a sudden drop in pressure. Pumping was stopped immediately in most cases so as to obtain the shut-in pressure value (P_s). The pressurization cycle was repeated several times.

The inclination and direction of the induced hydrofractures at the borehole wall were obtained using an impression packer and a magnetic orienting instrument. The impression packer, consisting of an inflatable element covered with a 0.9 m long sleeve of soft rubber, was lowered on a graduated wireline to precisely the depth of the previously hydrofractured interval. The

Table 1 - Hydrofracturing Test Results - Holes NF3 and NF4

Depth m	Rock Type	P_o MPa	P_{c1} MPa	P_{c2} MPa	P_s MPa	P_s^h MPa	Vert. Frac. I Direct.	Vert. Frac. II Direct.	No. of Horiz. Fracs	σ_v^{wt} MPa	σ_v MPa	σ_h MPa	σ_H MPa	σ_H Direction
NF3														
60.6	Ir. Ls.	0.4	11.6	3.7	3.8	3.0	ND	ND	1	1.6	3.0	3.8	7.3	
62.0	Re. Dol.	0.4	5.5	4.1	3.5		N44°W	S04°E	1	1.6		3.5	6.0	N24°W
67.7	Th. Ss.	0.5	8.3	3.9	2.6		N11°E	S11°W	4	1.7		2.6	3.4	N11°E
71.5	Gr. Ss.	0.5	10.5	3.3	2.4		N09°W	ND	ND	1.8		2.4	3.4	N09°W
86.6	P.G. Sh.	0.7	16.2	3.0	4.7		N85°E	S42°W	1	2.2		4.7	10.4	N64°E
94.4	Wh. Ss.	0.8	11.6	5.3	4.1	3.1	S74°W	N89°E	1	2.4	3.1	4.1	6.2	N80°E
98.0	Wh. Ss.	0.8	13.5	8.3	5.3		N60°E	S60°W	ND	2.5		5.3	6.8	N60°E
105.0	Qu. Sh.	0.9	17.3			3.4	Not Measured			2.7	3.4			
110.8	Qu. Sh.	0.9	16.3	5.1	4.4	3.5	S23°W	ND	1	2.9	3.5	4.4	7.3	N23°E
123.8	Qu. Sh.	1.0	15.1	7.1	5.5	3.8	ND	ND	1	3.2	3.8	5.5	8.4	-
NF4														
64.0	Gr. Ss.	0.5	14.4	2.5	3.1		N56°E	ND	2	1.7		3.1	6.3	N56°E
67.7	Gr. Ss.	0.5	10.6			2.3	Not Measured			1.8	2.3			
73.1	P.G. Sh.	0.6	16.6	7.7	6.5	2.4	N06°E	ND	1	1.9	2.4	6.5	11.2	N6°E
82.3	Wh. Ss.	0.7	6.7	3.0	3.3		N15°E	S54°W	3	2.1		3.3	6.2	N31°E
84.4	Wh. Ss.	0.7	16.3	7.2	6.6		N38°E	S69°W	1	2.2		6.6	11.9	N51°E
86.6	Wh. Ss.	0.7	17.6	6.1	5.2		N58°E	S74°W	2	2.2		5.2	8.8	N66°E
93.9	Qu. Sh.	0.8	13.7			3.1	ND	ND	1	2.4	3.1			
98.5	Qu. Sh.	0.8	12.7			3.4	ND	ND	2	2.6	3.4			
106.1	Qu. Sh.	0.9	13.3	6.0	4.5	3.5	S42°W	ND	2	2.7	3.5	4.5	6.6	N42°E
110.3	Qu. Sh.	0.9	15.9	7.6	5.9	3.6	S30°W	ND	1	2.8	3.6	5.9	9.2	N30°E

ND - Not detected on the impression sleeve
All other symbols are defined in the text. Rock types abbreviated from Figure 1.

impression packer was held under pressure for about 1 hour to enable the soft rubber to penetrate the fracture and set permanently. During this period a magnetic orienting tool which was lowered on the same wireline produced a picture of a scribe line aligned with a marker on the packer. From it the orientation with respect to magnetic north of the hole and the fracture impression were readily obtained. The fracture(s) impressions were immediately inspected and marked over with an indelible paint for later recording of fracture inclination and orientation.

Two surface pressure transducers were used during hydrofracturing to continuously monitor packer pressure and interval pressure. In addition the hydrofracture interval flow rate was monitored through a flow meter installed in the hydraulic line. The two pressures and the flow rate were simultaneously recorded on a three channel time-base continuous plotter.

3.2 Field Data and Stress Calculations

The vertical stress was obtained in two ways: (a) from the weight of the overlying rock (σ_v^{wt}), and (b) from shut-in pressures corresponding to the initiation of horizontal hydrofractures (σ_v).

The density of the rock was obtained from the measurement of representative weight and volume of the local shales, dolomites, limestones, and sandstone (ten core specimens). The mean density of (2.62 ± 0.08) g/cm^3 translates to a weight gradient of 0.026 MPa/m. Thus

$$\sigma_v^{wt} = 0.026 \times D \qquad (1)$$

where D is depth in meters and the stress σ_v^{wt} is in MPa (1 MPa = 145 psi). The vertical stress was independently established directly from hydrofracturing tests in six tests in NF4 and five tests in NF3 (see Table 1). The typical signature of the pressure-time record for opening horizontal fractures in bedded rock is one in which the pressure drop following shut-in is stopped rather abruptly and the curve turns almost horizontal. In cases where such signatures occurred and where only horizontal fracture impressions were obtained, σ_v was calculated as follows:

$$\sigma_v = P_s^h \qquad (2)$$

where P_s^h is the mean shut-in pressure at test horizon corresponding to horizontal hydrofracturing. Table 1 presents the values of both σ_v^{wt} and σ_v in holes NF3 and NF4.

In a number of tests (see Table 1) two dominant shut-in pressures were obtained, and both vertical and horizontal hydrofractures were traced on the impression packers. The vertical stress σ_v was calculated using equation (2) as in the case where only P_s^h was

618

recorded.

The horizontal principal stresses (σ_h and σ_H) were calculated based on the relationships (Haimson, 1980):

$$\sigma_h = P_s \qquad (3)$$

$$\sigma_H = 3P_s - P_{c2} + P_0 \qquad (4)$$

where P_s is the shut-in pressure required to keep open a vertical hydrofracture, P_{c2} is the secondary breakdown pressure required to reopen the fracture, and P_0 is the pore pressure at the depth of testing determined from the water table in the testhole. The use of P_{c2} in equation (4) implies that $P_{c2} = P_{c1} - T$, where P_{c1} is the initial breakdown pressure which causes the rock to fracture and T is the field hydrofracturing tensile strength of the rock.

The two values obtained directly from the pressure-time records were P_{c2} and P_s. Pressure P_{c2} is the level at which the induced hydrofracture (obtained in the first pressurization cycle) reopens at the testhole wall and starts accepting fluid. This pressure is taken as the point in subsequent pressurization cycles where the injection pressure curve departs from that in the first cycle provided the

same flow rate is maintained (Haimson, 1980; Zoback and Haimson, 1982).

The shut-in pressure, P_s, was obtained as the point of inflection in the decaying pressure-time curve after shut-in. In some tests this value was easily picked directly from the record. In others, the curving of the decaying pressure was more gradual and pressure versus log-time replotting of the period immediately following shut-in (about 1 minute) was carried out. This yielded two straight lines, the intersection of which was taken as P_s. An independent verification of the shut-in pressure was obtained by a cycle of very low pressurization. The value of constant pressure reached was taken as the upper limit of P_s. A typical pressure-time record is shown in Figure 3.

In a number of cycles in which pumping was continued past the breakdown point a "stick-slip" type of behavior was observed. This behavior is not clearly understood but appears to be related to the way in which the hydrofacture extends in some shales: the fracture appears to resist extension during pressurization until a critical pressure is reached at which it abruptly grows, thus bringing about a sharp pressure drop. As pressurization is continued

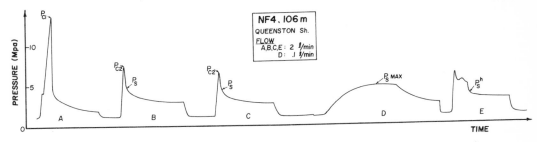

Figure 3 - Typical pressure time-record yielding two shut-in pressures, one corresponding to a vertical hydrofracture and the other to a horizontal bedding-plane opening.

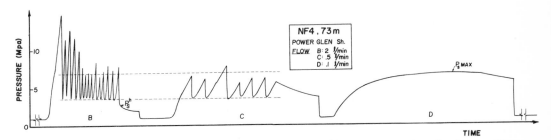

Figure 4 - "Stick-slip" phenomenon during hydrofracture extension in Power Glen shale. The two horizontal dashed lines approximate the locus of the upper and lower peaks. These appear to be limited by the two shut-in pressures P_s and P_s^h.

the phenomenon repeats itself. Thus, the fracture appears to grow not continuously but rather in discrete steps (Figure 4). It also appears that the peaks of the stick-slip cycles are limited by the P_s and P_s^n values (see two dashed lines in Figure 4).

Impression packer tests revealed only vertical and/or horizontal hydrofractures. The interpretation of the vertical hydrofracture directions is that they are parallel to the direction of the largest horizontal principal stress:

$$\sigma_H \text{ direction} = \text{Direction of vertical hydrofracture} \quad (5)$$

The values given for σ_H direction in Table 1 are based on equation (5).

3.3 Discussion of Hydrofracturing Results

Generally, the sandstones and dolomites produced mainly vertical hydrofractures, while the shales yielded both vertical and horizontal fractures, and sometimes only horizontal. Using the results in Table 1 we plotted stress magnitudes versus depth in Figures 5 and 6. We note that the vertical stresses obtained from the tests (σ_v) are typically higher than those calculated from rock density (σ_v^{wt}) by an average of 0.7 MPa. This is consistent with previous cases in which σ_v was obtained directly from test results (e.g., Haimson and Lee, 1980). The horizontal stresses are not as consistent as we expect them to be when all tests are conducted in one rock type. It is well known from the petroleum industry experience that in sedimentary rocks the horizontal stresses may vary substantially from formation to formation. A similar situation occurs in NF3 and NF4. Moreover, since within a single formation there may be complications such as shale bands in sandstones, and sandstone interbeds in shales, we have cases where the stresses appear to be rather scattered within the same rock type.

With respect to hydrofracture impressions we note that in tests in which vertical fractures were obtained their length was quite variable. Long fractures, covering most or all of the injection interval, occured in non highly bedded rocks such as the Whirlpool sandstone and the Reynales dolomite. Shorter vertical fractures obtained in shales were apparently stopped by horizontal bedding planes. The directions of the vertical hydrofractures were again quite scattered, although some relative consistency was noted in testhole NF4 (averaging N40°E ± 20°). In NF3, however, the upper three tests within the depth of 60-72 m averaged N7°W ± 17°, while the hydrofractures in the 86-111 m zone averaged N57°E ± 24°. We speculate that the directions of the horizontal principal stresses in the upper zone of NF3 are affected by the nearby North-South trending Niagara River Gorge. The north-south free surface would favor σ_h direction to be generally east-west which is in accord with our results. The directions of the horizontal stresses at depths below 86 m appear to have rotated back to the regional NE trend which also dominates in NF4.

The degree of uncertainty in our test results cannot be determined

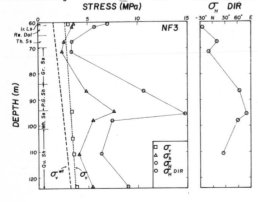

Figure 5 - Stress-depth profile in hole NF3.

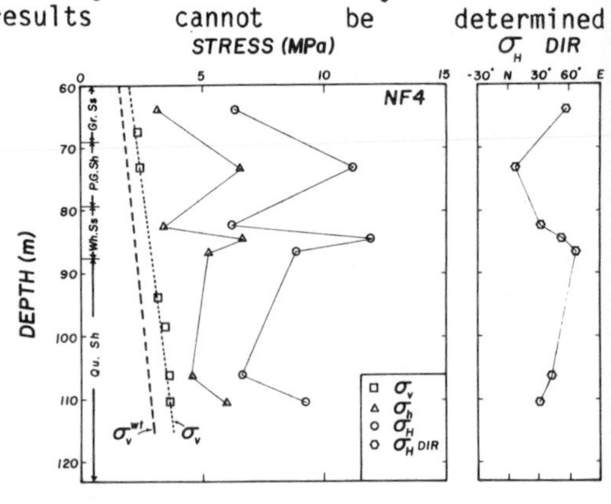

Figure 6 - Stress-depth profile in hole NF4.

accurately. Based on the quality of field data and previous experience with hydrofracturing we estimate that the uncertainty in the calculated values is no more than ±10% for σ_h and σ_v, and ±25% for σ_H. Similarly an uncertainty of ±10% is estimated for σ_H direction.

One way of summarizing our results in both testholes is by averaging each principal stress over the entire test range of approximately 60 m:

$$\sigma_v = 3.2 \pm 0.5$$

$$\sigma_h = 4.5 \pm 1.3$$

$$\sigma_H = 7.5 \pm 2.4 \qquad (6)$$

Equations (6) as well as the individual test results indicate that the stress regime in the shallow crust of Niagara Falls area is compressive ($\sigma_v < \sigma_h < \sigma_H$) and could lead to thrust faulting under favorable conditions. This regime is in accord with many surface and near-surface observations described in section 2 above.

The ratio between the major and the minor principal stresses, a helpful parameter in assessing opening stability, is roughly 2.5:1 if the mean values given in equations (6) are used. However, if the vertical stresses based on gravitational forces (σ_v^{wt}) are employed the ratio exceeds 3:1.

Equations (6) reveal that despite the obvious scatter of results the standard deviation of the mean is not excessive. However, for the purpose of design in any of the tested formations it is suggested that the worst stress conditions within the formation as determined by our tests be taken as the representative one.

It is useful to compare the hydrofracturing results with previous overcoring tests in the area (Table 2). A direct comparison is not possible

because the two methods were employed at different locations and depths, and mostly in different formations. Overall, however, the results obtained by the two methods agree in the relative magnitudes of the stresses, and in the characteristic scatter of results. Specifically, in the two formations in which both overcoring and hydrofracturing were conducted (Whirlpool sandstone and Queenston shale) Tables 1 and 2 reveal close agreement with respect to σ_H, and a much lower σ_h in the overcoring tests. The latter is probably a result of the testhole being very close to the free vertical surface of the Niagara River gorge.

4. DESIGN IMPLICATIONS

For underground openings such as the proposed SAB #3 twin tunnels, the state of stress has an impact on both fracture-induced instability and stress-induced instability. Fracture-induced instability refers to that created by fractures in the rock mass, enhanced by blasting and loosening. In general, mechanical support systems such as rockbolts, shotcrete and steel sets are targeted for reducing or alleviating this mode of instability. Stress-induced instability results from a gross or localized overstressing of the rock mass. In a high horizontal stress field, the predominant mode of stress-induced instability consists of the buckling of the floor and/or the roof. Some shear failure may also occur in the haunch, resulting in the spalling of surficial layers of rock. However, these types of compressive and shear failure are often localized in character, primarily because of the variability of in-situ stress magnitude and orientation. This variability is clearly illustrated by the results of the in-situ measurements reported in the present paper.

From the viewpoint of alleviating fracture-induced instability, the state of high horizontal compressive stress should be considered as a positive factor. This is because the high horizontal stresses, enhanced by the stress concentration effect in the roof tend to produce a clamping (and therefore stabilizing) effect on joint blocks, rock wedges or slabs in the roof which may otherwise become unstable upon

Table 2 - Summary of Overcoring Test Results at Niagara Falls

Rock Type	Location	No. of Tests	σ_h MPa	σ_H MPa	σ_H Dir.
Lock. Dol.	OPGS	9	1.7±1.5	12.7±6	N20°E
	Th.T	10	8.2±2	11.1±6	N60°E
D.C. Dol.	OPGS	1	6.8	10.5	N20°E
		1	9.4	19.2	
Roch. Sh.	OPGS	1	1.9	11.1	N20°E
Wh. Ss.	SAB No. 1	3	2.0±1	10.1±5	N55°W
Qu. Sh.	SAB No. 1	1	1.0	5.3	N55°W
		1	2.0	8.5	

OPGS - Ontario Power GS (See Figure 2 for location).
Th.T - Thorold Tunnel.
SAB No. 1 - Location in Figure 2.
Rock types abbreviated from Figure 1.

excavation. Experience has indicated that properly oriented tunnels in a high horizontal field are typically self-supporting, requiring only nominal support. This generally applies to the range of tunnel span and geological conditions in Southern Ontario.

To determine the potential impact of high horizontal stresses on stress-induced instability, stress analyses are generally required, based on the results of in-situ stress measurements and measured mechanical properties. The stress analyses would help to identify the size of the overstressed zone as well as the degree and mode of overstressing. Such analyses could be carried out for the various layout schemes under consideration.

In the present case of the proposed SAB #3 project, the layout of the new tunnel system will likely be governed by cost minimization requirements and hydraulic design considerations. Moreover, the variations in in-situ stress orientation and magnitude would probably not lead to a clearly preferred tunnel alignment from the in-situ stress point of view. The results of in-situ stress measurement are, however, useful in identifying the extent of any overstressing that may possibly occur. Along with the time-dependent deformation properties of the rock units of interest, they also enable

predictions and evaluations to be made on the long-term effects of stress relief on the proposed tunnels and their linings (Lee and Klym 1976).

Figure 7 illustrates an application of the in-situ stress measurement results to the identification of overstressed zone around a 15 m diameter tunnel excavated in Queenston shale, with the tunnel crown located at 1 m below the Whirlpool sandstone. The results of a finite element stress analysis using SAP4 program (Huang and Semec, 1985) is presented in the form of strength to stress ratio contours, based on the Hoek and Brown (1980) empirical failure criterion. The overburden pressure and the maximum value of measured in-situ horizontal stress in each formation were employed as boundary conditions. The predicted overstressed zone is quite small, occurring as a thin layer in the floor of the tunnel. There is hence no major instability forecasted for the tunnel, other than some minor localized floor buckling and heaving. This type of local failure also occurred during the construction of the SAB #2 twin

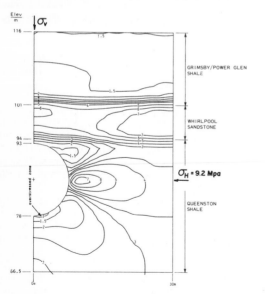

Figure 7 - Strength/stress contours around proposed 15 m. diameter circular tunnel, showing overstressed zone.

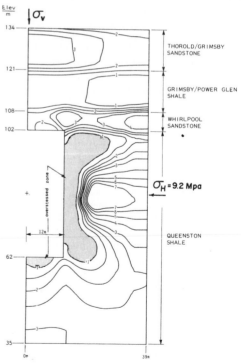

Figure 8 - Strength/stress contours around proposed powerhouse cavern with its length perpendicular to σ_H, showing extensive overstressed zones.

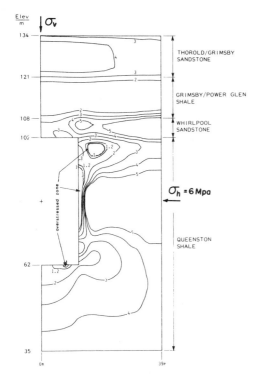

Figure 9 - Strength/stress contours around proposed powerhouse cavern with its length perpendicular to σ_h, showing overstressed zones.

tunnels in the 1950's, resulting in little or no problems once the shallow failure zone was mucked out.

One of the schemes being considered for the SAB #3 project is an underground powerhouse in Queenston shale, with the stronger Whirlpool sandstone as the roof rock. Finite element analyses were carried out for two distinct cases of cavern orientation, again using program SAP4. The first case consisted of a maximum horizontal in-situ stress of 9.2 MPa acting perpendicularly to the longitudinal axis of a rectangular cavern for the underground powerhouse. Figure 8 shows the size of the overstressed zone to be quite large, primarily due to tensile failure in the walls and compressive failure in the floor. Figure 9 shows the corresponding results with the longitudinal axis of the cavern perpendicular to the direction of the minimum horizontal stress (6 MPa). The size of the predicted overstressed zone is much reduced. These case studies clearly illustrate the importance of in-situ

stresses in the final design of the underground cavern. It is intended that additional measurements and analyses be carried out before an optimal layout of the SAB #3 underground openings is selected.

5. ACKNOWLEDGEMENTS

This project was sponsored by Ontario Hydro. Mr. Moo Y. Lee provided considerable assistance with equipment design and test performance.

6. REFERENCES

ASMIS, H. W. and C. F. Lee, 1980, Mechanistic modes of stress accumulation and relief in Ontario rocks, Proceedings, 13th Canadian Rock Mechanics Symposium, Toronto, pp. 51-55.

HAIMSON, B., 1980, Near surface and deep hydrofracturing stress measurements in the Waterloo quartzite, Int. J. Rock Mech. Min. Sci. and Geomech. Abstr., vol. 17, pp. 81-88.

HAIMSON, B. C. and C. F. Lee, Hydrofracturing stress determinations at Darlington, Ontario, Proceedings, 13th Canadian Rock Mechanics Symposium, Toronto, pp. 42-50.

HOEK, E. and E. T. Brown, 1980, Underground excavations in rock, Institution of Mining and Metallurgy, London.

HUANG, J.H.S. and B. P. Semec, 1983, Sir Adam Beck Niagara GS No. 3 - 1983 Geotechnical Investigation, Ontario Hydro Report No. 83511, Toronto.

HUANG, J.H.S. and B. P. Semec, 1984, Sir Adam Beck Niagara GS No. 3 - 1984 Geotechnical Investigations and Evaluations, Ontario Hydro Report No. 84478, Toronto.

HUANG, J. H. S. and B. P. SEMEC, 1985, Sir Adam Beck Niagara GS No. 3 - 1985 Geotechnical Investigations and Evaluation, Ontario Hydro Report No. 85403, Toronto.

LEE, C. F., 1978a, Stress-induced instability in underground excavations, Proceedings, 19th US Symposium on Rock Mechanics, vol. 1, pp. 165-173.

LEE, C. F., 1978b, A rock mechanics approach to seismic risk evaluation, Proceedings, 19th US Symposium on Rock Mechanics, vol. 1, pp. 17-88.

LEE, C. F., 1978c, Stress Relief and cliff stability at a power station near Niagara Falls, Engineering Geology, vol. 12, pp. 193-204.

LEE, C. F., 1981, In-situ stress measurements in Southern Ontario, Proceedings, 21st US Symposium on Rock Mechanics, vol. 1, pp. 435-442.

LEE, C. F. and H. W. Asmis, 1979, An interpretation of the crustal stress field in northeast North America, Proceedings, 20th US Symposium on Rock Mechanics, Austin, vol. 1, pp. 655-622.

LEE, C. F. and T. W. Klym, 1978, Determination of rock squeeze potential for underground power projects, Engineering Geology, vol. 12, pp. 181-192.

LEE, C. F. and K. Y. Lo, 1976, Rock squeeze study of two deep excavations at Niagara Falls, Proceedings ASCE Specialty Conference on Rock Engineering, Boulder, vol. 1, pp. 116-140.

LO, K. Y., 1978, Regional distribution of in-situ horizontal stresses in rocks of Southern Ontario, Canada Geotechnical Journal, vol. 15, pp. 371-381.

LO, K. Y. and C. M. K. Yuen, 1981, Design of tunnel lining in rock for long term time effects, Canadian Geotechnical Journal, vol. 18, pp. 24-39.

LO, K. Y., C. F. Lee, J. H. L. Palmer and R. M. Quigley, 1975, Stress relief and time-dependent deformation of rocks, Final Report to National Research Council of Canada, Special Project S-7307.

ZOBACK, M. D. and B. C. Haimson, 1982, Status of the hydraulic fracturing method for in situ stress measurement, Proceedings 23rd U.S. Symposium on Rock Mechanics.

Rock stresses and rock stress effects in the Kobbelv area, northern Norway

T.H. HANSSEN
SINTEF, Division of Rock and Mineral Engineering, Trondheim, Norway

A. MYRVANG
Norwegian Institute of Technology, Division of Mining, Trondheim, Norway

Abstract

The regional stress distribution has been established for the Precambrian Tysfjord Culmination in Northern Norway. The major and intermediate principal stresses are trending near E and N respectively, while the minor principal stress is vertical. Mainly tunnels heading near N - S, exhibit severe spalling in roof and floor. Mapping of exfoliation show that intensity of exfoliation is depending on stress level, orientation and stress anisotropy.

Resume

La distribution regionale des tensions a été établie pour la région précambrienne de la culmination de Tysfjord dans le nord de la Norvège. Les tensions principales et intermediaires sont orientées est - ouest et nord - sud respectivement, tandis que la tension verticale est mineure. Uniquement des tunnels orientés nord - sud sont soumis à des problèmes de chute des roches sevères, meme à faible profondeur. Des cartes sur l'exfoliation montrent que l'intensité des problemes dépend du nivau des tensions, l'orientation et l'anisotropie des tensions.

Zusammenfassung

Die regionale Spannungsverteilung ist in das Prekambrische Gebiet Tysfjord, Nord - Norwegen bestimmt. Die grösste und mittlere Hauptspannungen sind beziehungsweise ungefährlich Ost und Nord orientiert, weil die kleinste hauptspannung wertikal ist. Nur Tunnels die ungefähr in Richtung Nord gehen, zeigen intense Gebirgsschläge im Firste und Sohle. Kartierung von Exfoliation auf der Überfläche zeigt dass der Intensität des Exfoliations vom Spannungsniveau, Orientierung der Spannungen und Spannungsanisotropie abhengig ist.

1. Introduction

The Kobbelv area is located in the county of Nordland, Northern Norway, figure 1. During the last years many tunnels have been constructed in the area in connection with highway and hydro power projects. This includes both conventional drill & blast and TBM driven tunnels. Both types of tunnels have in many cases experienced severe rock bursts and spalling problems, which were not anticipated during planning.

With financial support from the Norwegian State Power Board, the Norwegian Road Authorities, the Royal Norwegian Council for Scientific and Industrial Research and the Foundation for Scientific and Industrial Research at the Norwegian Institute of Technology (SINTEF), the SINTEF Division of Rock and Mineral Engineering has carried out an extensive rock mechanics investigation in the area to reveal the reasons for the problems.

The investigation has included mapping of rock stress effects on the surface and in the tunnels, in-situ rock stress measurements at several sites and extensive laboratory testing of the rock.

Based on the investigation results, it has been possible to make rock stress problem forecasts for the remaining tunnels to be driven in the area.

The investigations in the Kobbelv area is part of a larger program, the aim of which is to map the general rock stress pattern in Norway.

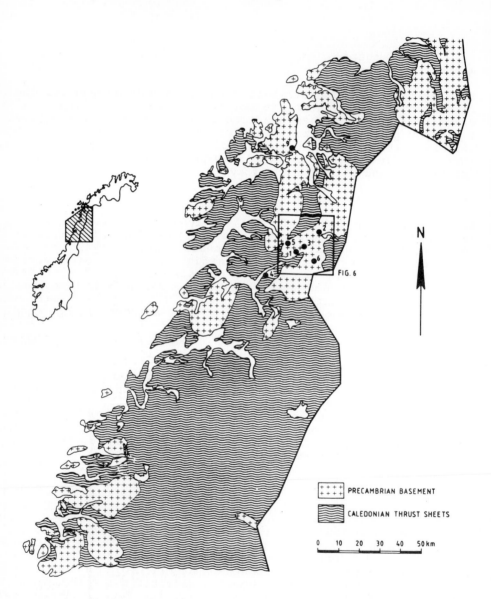

Figure 1 The Precambrian windows of the northern Nordland area (Sigmond et al 1984 and Gustavsen 1973). Rock stress measurement sites are marked, refer also to table 3 and figure 5.

2. Geological Environment

2.1. Tectonic History

The Kobbelv area is situated in the Tysfjord Culmination, which consist of Precambrian granitic rocks. Locally these rocks have been remobilized and are found in the cores of large recumbent folds, especially in the Svartisen - Glomfjord area (Rutland & Nicholson 1965). These rocks have been overthrusted during the Caledonian orogeny. The nappes consist of metamorphic rocks of different age and origin. Both allochtone and autochtone are polymetamorphic (Oftedahl 1980).

The epicentre of small earthquakes are situated just off the coast of the Svartisen - Glomfjord area, approximate 150 km SW of the Kobbelv area. Earthquakes are small and regular, but no damages have been reported. The earthquakes may be related to faults running parallel to the coast, which divide the older mainland rocks from the younger continental shelf rocks.

2.2. Structural interpretation

Continental drift have given rise to the stresses that lead to the Caledonian orogeny and associated thrusting and faulting. It must be anticipated that these stresses have been reoriented over time. The last thrusting phase is supposed to have trended ESE. From this, remanent compressional stresses would be anticipated in both WNW and NNE direction, where the first would be the major stress direction. Depending on the creep effect of the rocks, the horizontal stresses may be anticipated to be higher than the vertical stress.

The measured in-situ rock stresses seem to coincide with these orientations, figure 5.

3. Field mapping

3.1. Surface mapping

Systematic registration of the intensity of exfoliation and surface spalling, has shown an increase in exfoliation for mountain slopes with certain orientations. A relative scale of intensity has been introduced to describe the exfoliation:

1 Low intensity
2 Middle intensity
3 High intensity

Hence, the class of intensity in one area may not necessarily correspond to that of another.

Large scale spalling or exfoliation has even been recorded on flat surface in the valleys as shown in figure 2.

Figure 2 Spalling on flat surface (Kildemo 1985).

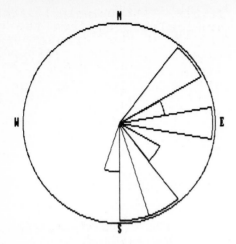 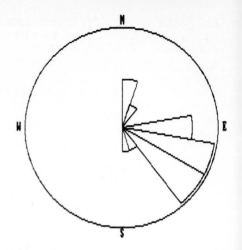

Figure 3 Orientation of mountain slopes with high (left) and low (right) spalling intensity. Max. radial is 12 at left and 8 at right. Class size is 20°.

The results of such mapping for the Reinoksvatnet area are given in figure 3. Certain distinct orientations exhibit low intensity of exfoliation and vice versa.

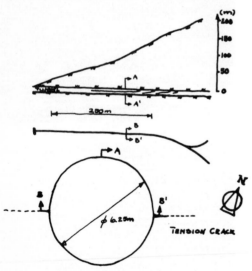

Figure 4 Vertical, horizontal and cross section of TBM driven tunnel shoving tension cracks.

3.2. Tunnel mapping

Most of the tunnels have been mapped with regard to stress induced effects. Spalling in the walls have not been registered to any extent in the Kobbelv-area. Severe spalling in roof and floor usually occur in areas with low overburden. Blockfalls from the walls in some of the tunnels are believed to be caused by low tangential stresses combined with jointing.

In the southern part of the Kobbelv Hydro Power Scheme, spalling has occurred in the tunnel roof with an overburden of only 10 - 20 m.

Remarkable are also the horizontal tension cracks that have been observed in one of the TBM tunnels in a low overburden area, figure 4.

4. Material properties

The basement rocks are uniform with regard to mineralogy, although the degree of schistosity may vary. Mineralogical composition is shown in table 1.

The grain size varies from 5 to 30 mm for the basement rocks of the Tysfjord culmination.

The material properties also exhibit low variation over considerable distances. In table 2 the results of 72 parallel tests on rocks from different locations are shown. The tests were performed on cores with diameter d = 61.5 mm, with in situ water content.

Table 1   Mineralogic composition of the Precambrian granitic rocks

Quartz	30 %
K - feldspar	45 %
Plagioclase	15 %
Mica	7 %
Amphibole	1 %
Other minerals	2 %

Table 2   Material properties. (Standard deviation is given in same units as mean value.)

Property		Mean	S.dev.
Uniaxial compressive strength	(MPa)	89.0	30.1
Failure angle	(°)	17.0	4.8
Tensile strength	(MPa)	9.3	1.7
Youngs modulus	(GPa)	18.5	2.8
Poisson ratio		0.13	0.04
Unit weight	(kN/m^3)	25.4	0.94
Sonic velocity	(m/s)	2982	133

Creep testing are being conducted at time of writing. So far, the tests show that the rock exhibit a considerable creep tendency. The stress has to be higher than 75-80 % of uniaxial compressive strength before secondary and tertiary creep develope.

Experiences from the tunnels show that a considerable time delay in the spalling may occur. This may be due to creep effects.

5. Virgin stress measurements

5.1. In-situ stress measurements

The triaxial state of stress has been measured using a modified Leeman triaxial cell. Normally 8 - 10 single measurements are taken at approximately 0.5 m intervals in the borehole. The first measurement is taken about one diameter away from the tunnel to avoid influence from the tunnel

itself. The principal stresses are calculated from the mean values of the corresponding 9 strains measured in each point, and the mean values of Young's modulus and Poissons ratio. If possible the elastic constants are determined from uniaxial loading of the overcored hollow cylinder containing the triaxial cell, using the strain gauges of the cell. This will simultaneously give a check of the strain gauge / rock surface bond.

18 years of experience with this procedure from more than 100 different sites has shown a reasonable accuracy at reasonable costs in most cases.

The measuring crew consisting of two technicians will normally use 1 - 3 working shift to complete 8 - 10 single measurements in a 10-12 m measuring hole (Myrvang 1983)

5.2. Summary of results

Rock stress measurements have been conducted at 7 different sites. Each site have been carefully selected with regard to jointing etc. The results are based on 6-11 single measurements at each site, totalling 79 measuring points.

Based on the measured strains and the calculated elastic properties from laboratory testing of the overcored gauges, the stresses have been calculated. The results are presented in table 3, together with relevant mechanical properties.

6. Discussion

The Precambrian basement rocks outcrop in several areas in the county of Nordland. The rocks in the western part are more influenced by the metamorphosis than those in the eastern culminations. In the western parts anatexis have been dominant, and the original stresses may have been released through this.

Table 3 Rock stresses and related information

Site		1	2	3	4	5	6	9
σ_1	(MPa)	20.3	17.1	24.7	9.2	26.4	26.8	9.0
dipd.	(°)	215	109	104	149	263	053	095
dip	(°)	34	16	03	01	10	08	04
σ_2	(MPa)	16.3	8.0	17.5	6.4	15.7	14.8	6.8
dipd.	(°)	349	017	194	059	357	323	186
dip	(°)	46	10	04	03	18	02	11
σ_3	(MPa)	9.7	3.5	12.1	4.1	11.5	5.1	3.3
dipd.	(°)	107	256	339	258	147	219	344
dip	(°)	24	72	85	87	69	81	79
σ_v	(MPa)	17.7	4.7	12.3	4.1	12.3	5.3	3.5
$\sigma_h$max	(MPa)	20.3	13.3	24.4	9.2	26.1	24.6	8.1
$\sigma_h$min	(MPa)	11.5	10.6	17.6	6.5	17.5	16.8	7.6
h	(m)	680	90	450	30	620	250	35
σ_v (theor)	(MPa)	17.0	2.2	11.4	0.7	15.4	6.5	1.0
σ_h (theor)	(MPa)	2.8	0.4	2.0	0.2	2.9	1.4	0.2
Rock type		G	G	G	G	G	G	Q
Youngs m. (GPa)		24.1	24.2	26.9	27.2	27.3	24.0	32.0
Poissons r.		0.14	0.16	0.13	0.18	0.16	0.18	0.14
Unit weight (kN/m^3)		25.0	24.4	25.4	24.7	-	26.1	-
Remark		-	1	1	2	-	-	3

Abbreviations:

$\sigma_1,\sigma_2,\sigma_3$ - Principal stresses

Dip direction (dipd.) and dip of stressvectors are related to lower hemisphere charts.

σ_v,σ_hmax,$\sigma_h$min - measured vertical, max. and min. horizontal stresses

h,σ_v(theor),σ_v(theor) - Vertical overburden and related theoretical vertical and horizontal stresses

Rock type:

G - Gneiss   Q - Quartz

Remarks:

1   Measured stresses are influenced by valley side

2   The measuring hole is drilled from the surface in a road cutting, and is influenced by valley side stresses
3   Measurements are conducted in the pegmatitic quartz.

Measurement sites:

1 Lower part of penstock, near Kobbelv hydropower station.
2 Diversion tunnel, Reinoksvatnet.
3 Junction headrace tunnels, Litletind.
4 Highway tunnel opening, Berrflågan.
5 Highway tunnel, Kobbskar south.
6 Diversion tunnel, Langvatn.
9 Quartz - mine, Drag.

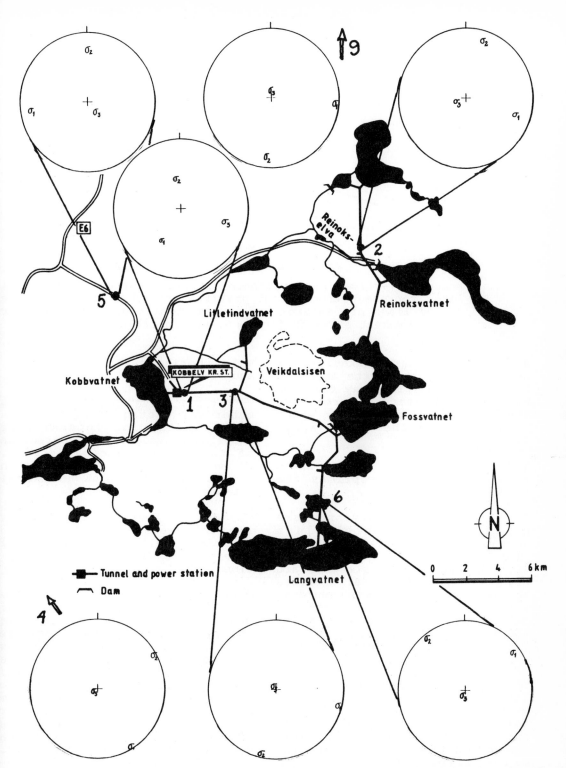

Figure 5 Stereographic representation of stress distribution in the
Kobbelv area. Each stereogram refer to site-numbers in table
3. For observation no 4 and 9, refer to figure 1.

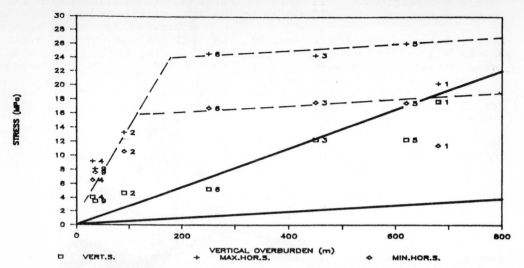

Figure 7 Measured vertical and horizontal stresses versus depth. Full
lines represent theoretical gravity induced stresses, while
dashed lines are interpreted stress relations. Numbers refer
to measurement sites in figure 6, and in table 3.

However, the earthquakes in the southwestern part of the area are stress-induced. They may therefor be related to stresses released through shearing or faulting which originate from the Mid-Atlantic Ridge.

The measured stresses in all sites show with a few exceptions the following trend:

I   The principal stresses are oriented approximately in a vertical - horizontal configuration.
II   The horizontal stresses are higher than the vertical stresses at least down to 700 m overburden.
III   The major horizontal principal stress is trending E - W and the intermediate N - S.
IV   The overall results indicate a regional pattern.

The mapping of exfoliation also indicate regional features. In areas where the horizontal stress-field is high and anisotropic, such as in the Reinoksvatnet area, the exfoliation is related to the orientation of the mountain slopes. Relatively high intensity of exfoliation occur in mountain slopes oriented parallel to the

major horizontal stress-vector, and vice versa.

Generally, it cannot be stated the other way around, that mountain slopes with high intensity of exfoliation indicate the direction of the major principal stress. However the degree of exfoliation always indicates high horizontal stresses.

The measured vertical stress is linearly related to depth, and coincides well with theoretical gravity stresses with minor exceptions.

Measurements conducted near the surface and in the vicinity of major zones deviate from this theory.The measurements indicate that the horizontal stresses consist of two components, one gravitational and one tectonic. The tectonic components increase to a constant level at 100 - 150 m below the surface. Further increase in horizontal stresses are governed by gravity which superpose the tectonic components.

The constant horizontal tectonic components seem to be:

632

```
E - W direction..... 23 MPa
N - S direction..... 15 MPa
```

From the tunnel mapping it can be stated that stress induced problems almost exclusively occur in tunnel roof and floor. Outfall from the walls are interpreted as caused by stress relief because of zones crossing the tunnels.

Due to spalling, extensive rock bolting in the roof is necessary. Because of floor heave, the rails in some of the TBM tunnels must regularly be removed in the most afflicted areas, and loose material taken away.

The tension cracks in the TBM tunnel and the spalling in the roof in shallow tunnels, are clear indications of high horizontal stresses.

The tunnel mapping also show that spalling in roof and floor are dependent of the tunnel direction.

The spalling do not always occur instantaneously with excavation. The "stand-up time" may be several days and even weeks. This can be interpreted as high stresses acting in conjunction with high creeping ability of the rock. As mentioned above, ongoing laboratory creep tests support this hypothesis.

7. Conclusion

The rock stress pattern in the Kobbelv area is dominated by high horizontal tectonic stresses. The major principal stress is oriented approximately E - W, while the intermediate is trending N - S. The horizontal stresses are higher than the gravitational vertical stress at least down to a depth of 800 - 1000 m.

The granitic rock is coarse-grained and has a comparatively low strength, Young's modulus and seismic velocity.

Especially tunnels running N - S, ie. normal to the major principal stress, at shallow depth exhibit heavy spalling in both tunnel roof and floor. This can be seen both in conventional drill & blast and TBM tunnels, and must be anticipated in similar future tunnels.

Surface spalling and exfoliation intensity is connected to the horizontal stresses. In some cases surface spalling orientation in the valley sides may indicate the direction of the major horizontal stress. Nevertheless, surface spalling and exfoliation in general indicate geological stresses.

Acknowledgments

The authors cordially thank the Royal Norwegian Council for Scientific and Industrial Research (NTNF), the Norwegian State Power Board (NVE), the Norwegian Roads Authorities (Statens Vegvesen), the Foundation for Scientific and Industrial Research at the Norwegian Institute of Technology (SINTEF) for their financial and practical support, without which this work had not been possible.

References

Gustavson,M. 1973: "Geological Map of Norway - Narvik Sc.1:250.000", The Geological Survey of Norway, Trondheim

Kildemo, G. 1985: "En Bergmekanisk Undersøkelse av Kobbskaret Vegtunnel", M.Sc.-thesis at The Norwegian Institute of Technology, Department of Mining Engineering, unpublished, Trondheim

Myrvang, A.M. 1983: "Practical use of rock stress and deformation measurements", in: Norwegian Tunneling Technology Publication no.2, eds: Bergh-Christensen, J., Broch, E. & Lien, R., Tapir Publishers, Trondheim

Oftedahl, C. 1980: "Geology of Norway", in: Norges geo. Unders. 356, p.61, Univeritetsforlaget, Oslo

Rutland, R.W.R. & Nicholson, R. 1965: "Tectonics of the Caledonids of part of Nordland, Norway" Qt. J. Geol. Soc. Lond. 121, pp. 73 -109.

Sigmond,E.M.O., Gustavson,M. & Roberts,D. 1984: "Bedrock map of Norway - Sc. 1:1 million", The Geological Survey of Norway.

Stress changes near the face of underground excavations

P.K. KAISER
D. KORPACH *
University of Alberta, Department of Civil Engineering, Edmonton, Canada
* now with Hardy Assiciates Ltd, Calgary, Canada

ABSTRACT

An innovative approach for the determination of the in situ stress field during the construction of a shaft and a tunnel is evaluated. The stress changes that resulted during face advance were recorded by stiff inclusions measuring uniaxial stress changes. From these stress change measurements it was possible to calculate the in situ stress field. Two case histories and the data interpretation are discussed together with an evaluation of the optimum instrument locations. Some longterm measurements are also presented.

RÉSUMÉ

Une approche nouvelle pour la détermination du champ des contraintes in situ durant la construction d'un puite et d'un tunnel est évaluée. Les changements de contrainte résultant de la progression de la face ont été enregistrés par des inclusions rigides qui mesurent les modifications de la contrainte uniaxiale. Il a été possible de calculer le champ des contraintes in situ à partir des changements notés dans ces mesures. Deux cas documentés et l'interprétation de leurs résultants sont présentés. La localisation optimale des instruments est évaluée. Quelques mesures à long terme sont aussi présentées.

ZUSAMMENFASSUNG

Eine neue Methode zur Spannungszustandsmessung im Fels während dem Bau eines Schachtes und eines Tunnels wurde untersucht. Einaxiale Spannungsänderungen während dem Vortrieb wurden mit steifen Messzellen gemessen und der Spannungszustand im Fels durch Rückrechnung bestimmt. Messungen von zwei Beispielen werden interpretiert und die optimale Anordnungen von Messtellen diskutiert. Einige Resultate von Langzeitmessungen sind auch erläutert.

1. INTRODUCTION

The design of underground openings requires knowledge of the in situ stress field, the ground water conditions, the deformation and strength behaviour of the rock mass and the properties of the support system.

Because it is normally impossible to predict conclusively the in situ state of stress in rocks, stresses are measured by one of two techniques:

a) **Hydraulic fracturing** (e.g., Zoback and Haimson (1982)); and

b) **Stress relief methods** (e.g., Hooker and Bickel (1974)).

The basic principles of the second approach were adopted to measure the in situ stress field during two projects described later. Instead of overcoring an inclusion, the change in stress was recorded during 'undercoring' or, more accurately, during excavation of an opening between stress change gauges. From these measurements it was possible to determine the in situ stress field and to observe the stress redistribution near the excavation face.

The latter is of practical significance because the magnitude of stress change and deformation ahead of the face is largely unknown. Because of the large stress gradient near the excavation face, it is likely that the assumed stress change and, hence, the deformation moduli back-calculated from extensometer or convergence measurements may be significantly misjudged. Only by combining displacement measurements with stress change observations can the accuracy of back-calculated rock mass deformation properties be improved (Kaiser and Mackay, 1982).

This paper presents briefly two field instrumentation studies and discusses problems related to the data interpretation. Factors affecting the selection of the best location for positioning stress change gauges for the purpose of in situ stress field determination are also discussed. Results from the first investigation and an evaluation of the support - ground interaction were already presented by Kaiser and Mackay (1982).

2.PROJECT I: INSTRUMENTATION OF A SHAFT

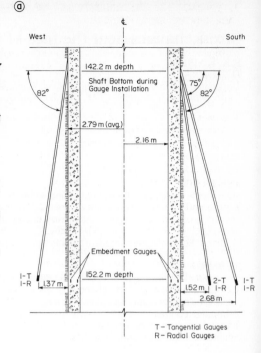

In 1980, a 4.32 m finished diameter concrete lined shaft was sunk to a depth of 235 m at a coal mine site near Lethbridge, Alberta. The shaft was sunk by Thyssen Mining Construction of Canada Ltd. using conventional shaft sinking methods (Kaiser and Mackay (1982); Kaiser et al. (1982); and Mackay (1982)). The lining generally followed one to two shaft diameters behind the shaft bottom. The rock was seldom unsupported for more than 16 to 20 hours.

The shaft penetrated about 60 m of glacial clay till underlain by about 6 m of saturated basal sands and gravels, and the Upper Cretaceous marine Bearpaw Formation composed of clay shales, siltstones and mudstones. The non-marine Oldman Formation was reached at a depth of about 200 m. It consists of interbedded sandstones and shales with frequent coal seams in the uppermost member.

At three levels of the shaft multi-point borehole extensometers, vibrating wire embedment strain gauges in the concrete liner, piezometers behind the liner, and 3 radial and 4 tangential vibrating wire borehole stress change gauges were installed and monitored.

An attempt was made to determine the in situ stress field at a depth of 91 m by overcoring. Due to time limitations, testing was restricted to one single horizontal borehole. The two tests, considered to be reliable, indicated that the vertical stress was slightly less than the overburden pressure and that the maximum horizontal stress was about 1.5 times the vertical stress.

Fig.1 shows the location of eight strain gauges embedded in the concrete liner and seven IRAD stress change gauges placed at the 152 m level. The stress change gauges were installed 10 m ahead of the shaft bottom from a depth of 142 m in steeply inclined boreholes drilled into the shaft wall. The stress change gauges were orientated radially and tangentially with respect to the shaft perimeter.

Piezometers placed at the rock-liner interface recorded no significant water pressure build-up. Even though some water seepage through the liner was observed in the upper portion of the bedrock, it is believed that little or no water pressure acted at the test section.

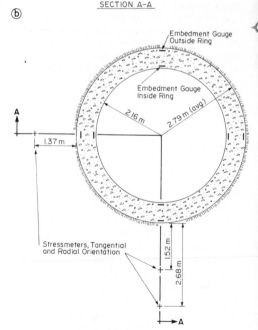

Fig.1. Section and plan view of instrumentation at 152 m depth (Kaiser and Mackay, 1982).

3. PROJECT II: INSTRUMENTATION OF A TUNNEL FACE DURING BREAK-TROUGH

In 1983, the deformations and stress changes near the tunnel face were measured during construction of the Wolverine Tunnel (British Columbia, Canada). The tunnel was horseshoe-shaped; 5.4 m wide and 8.4 m high. It penetrated primarily sedimentary rocks, triassic limestones, dolomites, calcareous sandstones and siltstones, and quartzites. The rock quality was generally classified as good to excellent (Kaiser et al. (1986)). The tunnel was driven simultaneously from two headings using conventional full-face dill and blast technique.

The west heading was completed in April 1983, approximately one month before break-through. This difference in completion time provided an excellent opportunity to install instruments ahead of the west face for the purpose of monitoring stress changes during break-through.

Seven stress change gauges were installed 9 m ahead of the face as shown on Fig.2.a; radial and tangential gauges in Boreholes 1 and 2, and tangential gauges only in Boreholes 3 and 4. Hole 2 was drilled directly ahead of the west face and one vertically orientated gauge was positioned. Several borhole extensometers were installed as shown in Fig.2.b. Monitoring commenced when the east heading was almost 50 m from the plane of measurement and continued until break-through when all stressmeters were destroyed.

4. IRAD GAGE VIBRATING WIRE STRESSMETER

The Irad Gage stressmeter consists of a hollow steel cylinder with a vibrating wire strain gauge. It is activated diametrically across a 38.1 mm diameter borehole by steel wedges. The soft and hard rock models have platens with a maximum contact angle of 112° and 20°, respectively. For a linear elastic material, the relationship between the uniaxial rock stress change in the direction of the loading axis of the gauge and the wire tension (Hawkes and Hooker (1974)) is:

$$\Delta\sigma_R = \Delta\sigma_w/a \qquad (1)$$

where: a is the uniaxial gauge sensitivity factor and $\Delta\sigma_R$ and $\Delta\sigma_w$ are

the changes in rock stress and wire stress, respectively. The sensitivity factors reported by Hawkes and Bailey

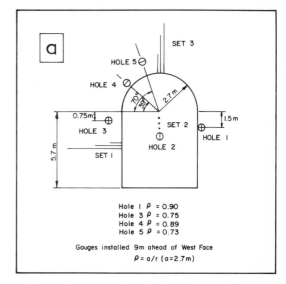

Hole 1 ρ = 0.90
Hole 3 ρ = 0.75
Hole 4 ρ = 0.89
Hole 5 ρ = 0.73

Gauges installed 9m ahead of West Face
$\rho = a/r$ (a=2.7m)

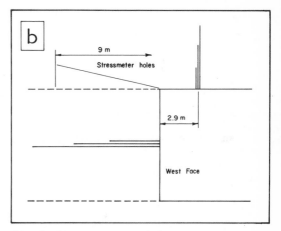

Fig.2. Stressmeter and extensometer installation at Wolverine Tunnel.

(1973) were verified and confirmed by Korpach (1983) for this study.

5. APPLICATION OF STRESS CHANGE GAUGES TO DETERMINE IN SITU FIELD STRESSES

Assuming plane stress conditions, the radial and tangential stress changes induced by excavation of a circular opening in linear elastic rock are:

$$\Delta\sigma_r=(S/2)[(1+N)(-\rho^2)+(1-N)(3\rho^4-4\rho^2)\cos2\theta]$$

$$\Delta\sigma_t=(S/2)[(1+N)(\rho^2)-(1-N)(3\rho^4)\cos2\theta] \qquad (2)$$

where:
S = principal biaxial stress (horizontal for shaft);
NS = minor or major principal biaxial stress perpendicular to S (assumed horizontal for shaft);

θ = angle measured from direction of S (clockwise) to point of interest;
ρ = a/r (a = radius of opening and r = distance to point of stress determination).
(Positive values indicate a stress increase).

Vibrating wire stress gauges placed near an underground opening, however do not record these stress changes directly. They record an 'equivalent uniaxial stress' that is affected by changes in both principal stresses. In determining the relationship between the equivalent stress and the principal stresses it is assumed that the force on the stressmeter platens is proportional to the deformation that would have occurred if the gauge had not been present (Hawkes and Bailey (1973)). Merrill and Peterson (1969) provide a detailed derivation of the relationship between the radial displacement of the borehole wall and the magnitude of the two principal stresses in the plane of the borehole in an elastic medium. From this it follows (Korpach, 1983) that, for plane stress condition, the uniaxial stress changes recorded by radial and tangential gauges are:

$$\Delta\sigma_{rG} = S[(-2\rho^2/3)(1+N) + (2\rho^4-2\rho^2)\cos2\theta(1-N)]$$

and

$$\Delta\sigma_{tG} = S[(2\rho^2/3)(1+N) + (2\rho^2/3 - 2\rho^4)\cos2\theta(1-N)] \tag{3}$$

where:
$\Delta\sigma_{rG}$ = uniaxial stress change recorded by a radial gauge; and
$\Delta\sigma_{tG}$ = uniaxial stress change recorded by a tangential gauge.

From Eqns.3 the original field stress can be back-calculated from the stress change measured by the radial or tangential gauge.

For gauges placed parallel to one of the principal stress directions (θ = 0° and 90°) the principal stress S in a nonuniform stress field can be found from the following equations:

$$S=\Delta\sigma_{rG}/[(1+N)(-2\rho^2/3)\pm2(1-N)(\rho^4-\rho^2)]$$

or

$$S=\Delta\sigma_{tG}/[(1+N)(2\rho^2/3)\pm2(1-N)(\rho^2/3 -\rho^4)] \tag{4}$$

Two measurements are theoretically sufficient to determine S and N.

For the most general case (N, S and θ unknown) at least three measurements are required. Fortunately, because of the insensitivity of (cos 2θ) for angles of θ = (0 or 90) ±15°, errors of less than about 10% result if the gauges are not placed exactly in the direction of the principal stresses and Eqns.4 can be applied.

5.1 Optimum Instrument Location

For a field monitoring project, it is important to determine an optimum gauge location to achieve most accurate result For the following, it will be assumed th the rock mass surrounding the opening behaves in a linear elastic manner and t orientation of the principal stresses is known or can be estimated, i.e., the gauges are installed on the principal stress axis (θ is 0° or 90°). These axes are assumed to be parallel or perpendicular to the axis of a circular opening.

The optimum instrument location in terms of gauge orientation (radial or tangential), location (θ = 0° or 90°) an position (ρ describing distance from opening wall) can best be evaluated by varying individual parameters separately and by comparing various combinations. Th principal stress S can then be expressed in terms of the stress change recorded by a radial or tangential gauge. It depends only on the stress ratio N and the gauge position ρ. From Eqn.4 it follows for gauges at θ = 0°:

$$S = \Delta\sigma_{tG} / [A + NB]$$

or

$$S = \Delta\sigma_{rG} / [NA + C]$$

and for gauges at θ = 90°: (5

$$S = \Delta\sigma_{tG} / [AN + B]$$

or

$$S = \Delta\sigma_{rG} / [A + NC]$$

where: $A = 2[(2\rho^2/3) - \rho^4]$
$B = 2\rho^4$
$C = 2[\rho^4 - 4\rho^2/3]$.

By equating any two of these equations i$\ast$ is possible to calculate the stress ratio N in terms of a **stress change ratio SCR** for various gauge positions ρ. For example, using two tangential gauges at 90° to each other the stress ratio N is:

$$N = (A_1 - SCR_{12} B_2)/(SCR_{12} A_2 - B_1) \tag{6}$$

where:
A_i = A of gauge i; i = 1 or 2;
B_i = B of gauge i; i = 1 or 2; and
$SCR_{12} = \Delta\sigma_{tG1}/\Delta\sigma_{tG2}$ = ratio of two stress change measurements. The first subscript refer to the gauge orientation and the third subscript i refers to the gauge number.

ρ-values in excess of 0.85 are seldom practical because of stress redistribution in zones of rock damage near the opening walls. The accuracy of stress change measurements is affected by many factors, such as local stress variations in a discontinuous rock mass, variations in contact angle of platens, etc. Consequently, the stress change ratio becomes increasingly inaccurate if it approaches zero or infinity. Our experience shows that stress change ratios of $0.20 < SCR < 5$ can only be used reliably for in situ stress determinations.

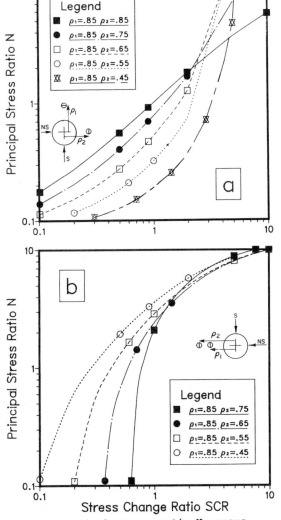

Fig.3. Principal stress ratio N versus stress change ratio SCR for: (a) two tangential gauges at $\theta = 0°$ and $90°$; and (b) two tangential gauges at $\theta = 90°$.

Figs 3 to 5 show double logarithmic plots of principal stress ratio N versus stress change ratio SCR generated for various combinations of gauge locations, orientations and positions.

• Fig.3.a presents results for two tangential gauges at 90° to each other. From Eqn. 6, it follows that N = SCR for $\rho_1 = \rho_2 = 0.816$. This combination of gauges can be used effectively to measure (N) over a relatively wide and practical range of $0.2 < N < 5$. Arrangements with gauges placed further ouside, e.g., at $\rho < 0.8$, are less appropriate.

• Fig.3.b presents results for two tangential gauges on the same side perpendicular to the principal stress S ($\theta = 90°$). For this arrangement to be beneficial for predicting N, the gauges should be placed as far apart as possible and one gauge should be located close to the opening, i.e., $\rho = 0.85$. The range of stress ratios N that can be determined reliably at $\rho_2 = 0.55$ is about 0.5 to 5.

• Fig.4.a presents the case of a pair of radial gauges at 90° to each other. Because of the relatively flat curves, these radial gauges can be used to determine a relatively wide range of stress ratios provided they are positioned close to the opening or relatively far apart. However, the measurements are extremely sensitive to the gauge position. This sensitivity can be eliminated with small ρ-values but the range of the stress ratio N is then severely restricted.

• Fig.4.b presents results for one radial and one tangential gauge on the same side ($\theta = 90°$). This arrangement was found to be desirable for N values from 0.4 to 2.5 but only if placed close to the opening, i.e., $\rho_1 = 0.85$.

• Fig.5.a demonstrates the sensitivity to variations in the gauge location relative to the axis of principal stresses. The cases of two tangential gauges at 90° to each other is presented. It can be seen that deviations of ±15° from the principal stress direction will not introduce significant errors for stress ratios N between 0.3 and 3.0.

• Fig.5.b demonstrates the importance of accurate determination of the gauge position ρ, particularly when relatively small stress change ratios (i.e, SCR<1) are measured. At SCR = 0.5, a variation of ρ_1 from 0.85 by about ±6% to 0.8 or 0.9, changes (N) from 3.2 to 2.3 or 6.1. This sensitivity decreases rapidly if measurements are made further away from the opening.

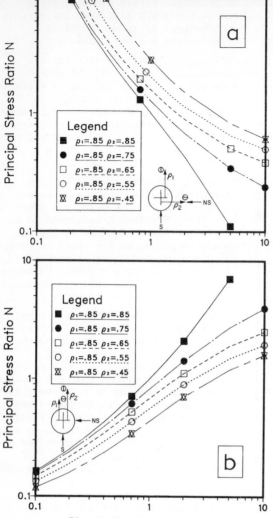

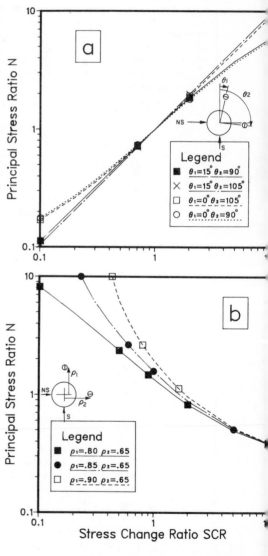

Fig.4. Principal stress ratio N versus stress change ratio SCR for: (a) two radial gauges; and (b) one radial and one tangential gauge.

In summary, both radial and tangential gauges located on the principal stress axes at either $\theta = 0°$ or $90°$ and placed at strategic positions can be used effectively to determine the stress ratio N and the magnitude S. The best combination for intermediate N-values is two tangential or two radial gauges set at $90°$ to each other at $\rho_1 = \rho_2 = 0.82$. However, large stress ratios (N) cannot be determined reliably with this method.

Arrangements with one radial and one tangential gauge, on the same side, was found to be undesirable for stress ratios significantly different from unity.

Fig.5. Principal stress ratio N versus stress change ratio SCR to demonstrat effect of variation of: (a) gauge orientation; and (b) gauge position.

5.2 In situ Stress near Lethbridge, Alberta

In the following some of the conclusions from previous work (Mackay (1982); Kaiser and Mackay (1982); and Kaiser et al. (1982)) are summarized and a reevaluation of the in situ stress field, calculated from the stress change gauge measurements, is presented.

Kaiser **et al.** (1982) predicted the in situ stress field from stress change gauge measurements based on the assumption that the stress change measured by a gauge was independent of the stress normal to the gauge. They found that the best results are achieved when the tangential and radial stress change data were considered independently. The radial gauge data were disregarded and the in situ stress field at 152 m depth was estimated from the tangential measurements only:

$\sigma_{h(max)}$ = 4.25 MPa; N = 0.6; θ = East-West. Mackay (1982) also assumed that the gauge response was not affected by stress changes normal to the gauge loading axis but considered tangential and radial gauges together because he found that the tangential gauges alone were of limited value for the determination of the orientation of the principal stresses. He then predicted:

$\sigma_{h(max)}$ = 4.25 ± 0.5 MPa;
N = 0.5 to 0.8; θ = S40°W ± 20°.

The stress change data from the Kipp shaft was now re-evaluated employing the method described earlier. The radial and tangential gauges together and the influence of the stress changes normal to the gauge axis were considered.

Numerous variations of the three parameters, θ, N, and S, were investigated. As θ moved outside the range of 55 to 65°, the measured data could not be matched. Thus, θ could be determined with a relatively high degree of confidence.

However, as shown by the theoretical stress change distribution in Fig.6, several combinations of widely differing parameters, N and S, fit the field data equally well. This must be attributed to the uncertainty in the stress ratio N which cannot be determined accurately from the gauge locations selected for this project. The tangential gauge in the west wall gave consistently poorly fitting readings.

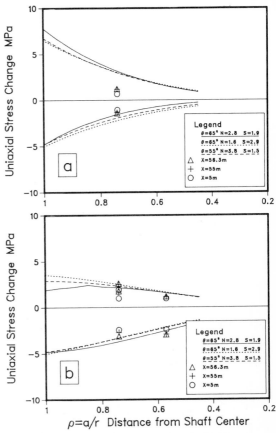

Fig.6. Theoretical uniaxial stress distribution (for different N, θ, and S) compared with measurements: (a) West wall; (b) South wall (X = Distance from shaft bottom).

Nevertheless, the results from this analysis have been used to establish an improved estimate of the in situ field stress at a depth of 152 m for the mine site near Lethbridge:

$\sigma_{h(max)}$ = 5.1 ± 0.6 MPa;
N = 0.45 ± 0.2; θ = S30°W ± 10°.

The larger value for the maximum principal stress results from including the effects of the stress normal to the gauges.

Both the re-evaluated results and those of Mackay (1982) are in good agreement with the interpretation from oilwell breakout measurements presented by Gough and Bell (1981).

5.3 Longterm Stress Change Measurements in Shaft

The longterm stress changes inside the rock mass surrounding an underground opening are of interest for two main reasons: (a) for the support evaluation and (b) for the interpretation of convergence and extensometer records.

(a) **Support evaluation:** As soon as the liner is activated the radial stresses at the wall will increase and cause a proportional radial stress increase at the gauge location. Simultaneously, the tangential stresses will decrease as load is transferred to the lining. This latter tangential stress decrease may, however, be dominated by creep of the highly stressed rock near the stress change gauges.

(b) **Interpretation of monitoring data and determination of the rock mass deformation properties:** Most in situ measurements of displacements inside or near underground openings are only possible during a limited time period. Extrapolations are necessary to determine the displacements that accumulate ahead of the face and after support installation. The reliability of such extrapolations can be significantly increased by stress change measurements. This aspect will be covered in more detail in another paper.

Fig.7 presents the longterm stress change development over a 830-day period for seven gauges. It is of interest to note that a major portion of the stress change occurred ahead of the face (42 to 59% of the total tangential stress change). Only a relatively small stress change (6 to 21%) could actually be recorded during the extensometer monitoring period (X = 0R to 2R). The radial stresses changed even more rapidly with between 74 and 85% occurring ahead of the shaft bottom and only an additional 4 to 11% before the installation of the liner at 2R. (Note: one radial gauge (Fig.7.a) dropped below the base level after 36 days; hence, subsequent measurements are unreliable.)

The more or less steady decrease in radial stress supports the conclusion presented by Kaiser and Mackay (1982) that the liner is under negligible stress at the test section. The slight, temporary radial stress increase between 100 and 300 days may indicate that some load buildup might have occurred due to subsidence during coal mining. The tangential stress decrease after 40 to 100 days may not reflect a true stress change in the rock mass but rather a relaxation of the rock near the gauges.

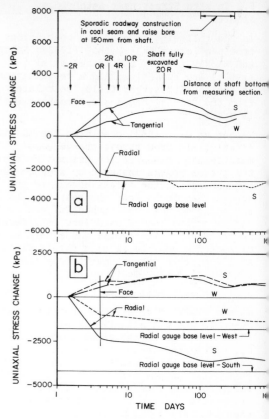

Fig.7. Long term uniaxial stress change for: (a) Stressmeters at $\rho = 0.65$; (b) Stressmeters at $\rho = 0.51$ (S) and $\rho = 0.67$ (W); S = South and W = West wall.

The time-dependent stress change can be separated into two stress change components: (a) due to advancement of the shaft, and (b) due to time-dependent rock mass properties. From laboratory tests on small tunnels (Kaiser et al. (1983)) it was concluded that the wall convergence rate in relatively soft rock (E = 1 to 3 GPa) was dominated by the advance rate until the face has advanced 10 to 20 radii beyond the test section. After this point rock mass creep prevailed in the cases analysed. While these conclusions cannot be generalized Fig.7 demonstrates that tangential stresses increase and radial stresses decrease until excavation was stopped at 20 radii from the test section. Time-dependent stress redistribution continued in the rock surrounding the shaft after the excavation process was stopped.

5.4 Stress Change near Excavation Face

Fig.8 summarizes the stress change measured by gauges located at 1.5 to 1.55R in radial and tangential directions from the west and south wall of the shaft. The stress changes predicted for an axisymmetric opening in a linear elastic medium are shown for two cases: Case 1 – unlined opening; and Case 2 - unlined opening excavated one radius further (shift of curve by 1R) to simulate the influence of heavily damaged rock due to blasting of the shaft floor during double bench excavation.

From Fig.8, it can be seen that the predicted radial and, particularly, the tangential stress change exceeds the observed average stress change. The maximum measured values are, however, only slightly exceeded at the south wall. The discrepancy in magnitude must be attributed to the difference between the assumed and actual stress ratio N.

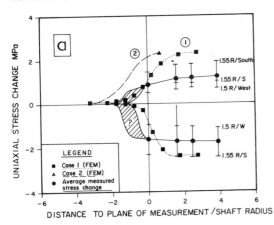

Fig.8. Uniaxial stress change measured near shaft bottom by five gauges at a distance of 1.5 to 1.55R from the shaft center.

The tangential and radial stress change occurred much earlier than predicted. Better correspondence in timing can be achieved if the predicted stress change is shifted by one radius ahead (Case 2). Redistribution of stresses from damaged to undamaged zones causes this translation of the stress change curves. As indicated by the shaded area, the exact shape of the real stress change curve is not known, but it appears that the stress change was shifted by about one radius ahead of the shaft bottom due to blast damage at the bottom of the shaft. For the determination of the rock mass modulus, this shift is of great importance.

5.5 Stresses during Tunnel Break-Through

All stressmeters were installed relatively close to the tunnel at less than 1 m from the wall (some as close as 0.3 m). Little stress change was measured until the tunnel was within less than 5 m of the plane of measurment. All gauges, including the tangentially orientated gauges, recorded a reduction in stress as the excavation reached and moved past the gauges (see Fig.9).

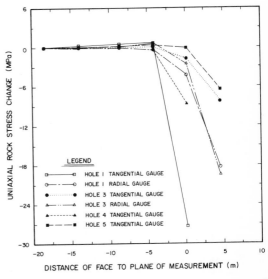

Fig.9. Uniaxial stress changes near tunnel face during break-through (for gauge location see Fig.2).

This suggests that a blast damaged zone in excess of 1 m was created during excavation. Two dimensional and axisymmetric finite element analyses , conducted to aid in the interpretation of the data, were employed to calculate the theoretical stresses around the opening for various in situ stress conditions and various assumptions for the extent of the damage zone (Korpach, 1983). By comparison of predicted with measured stress changes it was possible to come up with an estimate of the in situ stress field at the site. The damage zone was treated as a softened zone (modulus reduction). In this manner, the in situ stress field was found to be approximately described by:

$$\sigma_1 = 30 \pm 8 \text{ MPa}; \quad \theta = 0°;$$
$$N = 1.4 \pm 0.6 \text{ (i.e., } \sigma_h > \sigma_v)$$

for a ratio of deformation modulii of the intact rock to the softened rock of 5. The stress releaved zone due to blast damage was estimated to be 2 m at the crown and 1 m at the springlines. This is in good agreement with results obtained from the particle velocity method for assessing blast damage (Stimpson (1982)).

The in situ stress field could not be predicted accurately because all gauges were positioned inside the blast damaged zone. In future projects, stressmeters should be installed both inside and outside the expected damage zone to provide sufficient data for a better estimate. Nevertheless, the collected data helped to determine a reasonable model for describing the rock mass behaviour, the stress field and the stress changes near the tunnel face.

Results from one extensometer are presented in Fig.10. It provides further evidence (rock compression near the wall) that an extensive damage zone must have existed and in this manner supports the findings of the analyses. That relatively high horizontal stresses might exist in this area was also evident from some popping of the roof rock in other sections of the Tumbler Ridge Tunnels.

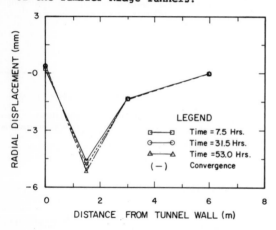

Fig.10. Radial displacement relative to deepest anchor point for springline (North wall).

6. CONCLUSIONS

The stress monitoring program described and evaluated in this paper provides a rational approach to determine the in situ stress field. Stress change gauges can be used effectively to back-calculate the in situ stress field from the stress change that is caused by the excavation of an underground opening (if the ground responds essentially in an elastic manner during the measuring period and if the stress ratio (N) is not excessive). While the optimum gauge position is at $\rho = 0.82$,

some stressmeters should be placed far enough from the opening to ensure they are outside a possible damage zone.

For the data interpretation it is paramount that the gauges are located accurately at positions where unique and sensitive measurements are possible. Several dominating factors have been discussed and it was found that, in general for elastic behaviour without softening, at least two sets of gauges, at 90° to each other should be installed at a distance of 1.2 to 1.25 times the opening radius. A redundancy factor of at least 2 to 3 will be necessary to guarantee sufficient data for a conclusive interpretation.

7. ACKNOWLEDGEMENTS

This research project was funded by Petro Canada Exploration Inc., Calgary, the B.C.Railway Comp. and was supplemented by funds from the National Sciences and Engineering Research Council of Canada. The execution of the field instrumentation program was successful only because of excellent cooperation of the contractors and because of the dedication of our field engineer, C. Mackay, and our senior technician, G. Cyre.

8. REFERENCES

Hawkes, I. and V.E.Hooker, 1974. The vibrating wire stressmeter. 3rd Congress of the International Society of Rock Mechanics, Denver, 2B, pp.439-444.

Hawkes, I. and W.V.Bailey, 1973. Low Cost Cylindrical Stress Gauge. Report prepared for U.S. Bureau of Mines, NTIS No. PB243347, 142 p.

Hooker, V.E. and D.L.Bickel, 1974. Overcoring Equipment and Techniques used in Rock Stress Determination. U.S. Bureau of Mines, IC 8618, 32 p.

Kaiser, P.K. and C.Mackay, 1982. Development of rock mass and liner stresses during sinking of a shaft in clay shale. 1st International Conference on "Stability in Underground Mining", Vancouver, Ch.36, pp.790-809.

Kaiser, P.K., C.Mackay and A.D.Gale, 1986. Evaluation of rock classification at B.C.Rail Tumbler Ridge Tunnels. Rock Mechanics and Rock Engineering, (in press).

Kaiser, P.K., C.Mackay and
    N.R.Morgenstern, 1982. Performance of
    a shaft in weak rock (Bearpaw Shale).
    **ISRM Symposium on Caverns and Pressure
    Shafts**, Aachen, 2, pp.613-622.

Kaiser, P.K., S.M.Maloney and
    N.R.Morgenstern, 1983. Time-dependent
    behaviour of tunnels in highly
    stressed rock. **5th Congress of the
    International Society of Rock
    Mechanics**, Melbourne, pp. D329-D336.

Mackay, C.H.R., 1982. Performance of a
    Shaft in Weak Rock. **M.Sc.thesis,
    Department of Civil Engineering,
    University of Alberta**, 257 p.

Merrill, R.H. and J.R.Peterson, 1969.
    Deformation of a borehole in Rock.
    U.S.Bureau of Mines, RI 5881, 32p.

Stimpson, B., 1982. Tunnel Drilling and
    Blasting. **Review paper presented at
    Short Course on Tunnelling**, University
    of Alberta, 33pp.

Zoback, M.D. and B.C. Haimson, 1982.
    Status of the hydraulic fracturing
    method for in-situ stress
    measurements. **23nd U.S. Symposium on
    Rock Mechanics**, Berkeley, Ch. 15,
    pp.143-156.

The importance of in situ rock stress in repository design

C.M. COOLING
Geotechnics Division, Building Research Establishment, Garston, Watford, United Kingdom

J.A. HUDSON
*Department of Mineral Resources Engineering, Imperial College of Science and
Technology, London, United Kingdom*

Abstract

For the design of a radioactive waste repository, the in situ stress is
one vital component of the rock mass structure - in situ stress - water
flow - construction coupled model. The model is required basically for
radionuclide migration calculations. In this paper, the results of a
comparative study of in situ stress measurement techniques are described. The work was conducted within the context of developing the
necessary site assessment procedures for candidate sites.

Resumé

Pour le design des dépots de déchets radioactifs, les contraintes en
place constituent l'un des pôles du modèle d'étude qui couple la
structure du massif rocheux, les contraintes en place, les mouvements
d'eau et la construction, et dont le but principal est l'étude de la
migration des particules radioactives. Ce papier presente les resultats d'une étude qui compare les differentes techniques de mesure des
contraintes en place et qui se situe dans le cadre du dévelopement des
moyens nécéssaires à l'évaluation des différents sites candidats.

Zusammenfassung

In der Planung einer Felskavernenanlage für die Endlagerung radio-
aktiver Abfallstoffe ist die in situ Spannung ein wesentlicher Bestand-
teil des Modells; hier werden Folgende zusammengebracht - Gesteinmasse,
in situ Spannung, Wasserlauf, Konstruktion. Das Modell ist grundsätz-
lich für die Kalkulation der Kernteilchenwanderung wichtig. In diesem
Bericht werden Resultate einer vergleichenden Untersuchung verschiedener Messungsmethoden für in situ Spannung beschrieben. Diese
Arbeit wurde im Kontext der Entwicklung nötiger Einschätzungsmethoden
für Kandidatstellen durchgeführt.

1. INTRODUCTION

The UK Department of the Environment has completed a series of
stress measurement tests within
the general context of its research programme on the geotechnical aspects of radioactive waste
disposal. The background to the
work was described in Hudson
(1983) and has involved a co-
ordinated study of rock mass properties, permeability, in situ
stress, excavation, support and
backfilling. The effect of heat
flow was not emphasized because
the work was mainly directed towards the disposal of intermediate
level waste. In this paper, we
describe a hydraulic fracturing
system and the results of several
sets of measurements, using both
hydraulic fracturing and overcoring techniques, made in the Carnmenellis granite in Cornwall,
south west England.

The basic design criterion for a radioactive waste repository is that unacceptable quantities of radionuclides should not be carried back to the biosphere by groundwater flow. The in situ stress is normally regarded as an input parameter for considerations of rock failure around underground excavations. In the case of radioactive waste disposal, however, (where engineering stability may have to be replaced by geological stability), the crucial importance of in situ stress is related to the radionuclide migration modelling through the effect of the stress on rock mass permeability. In other words, the interaction between the stress tensor and the permeability tensor must be known – and each tensor depends on rock structure.

Both the stress tensor and the permeability tensor are complex entities, especially when inhomogeneous, discontinuous rock is involved. Some of the factors relating to the stress tensor are described in an associated paper (Hyett et al., 1986); many of the factors relating to the permeability tensor are very well described and analyzed in Long, 1983. The next and most difficult research step is the coupling of the two tensors, because principal permeability directions in a rock mass are a function of the stress state.

We concentrate here on reporting the results of a suite of rock stress measurements. These measurements were made to clarify the nature of in situ stress and the measurement techniques, but the interpretation and significance of the measurements must eventually be considered within the general background of rock mass permeability, radionuclide migration modelling and site assessment methodologies.

2. SITE LOCATION AND ROCK MASS DESCRIPTION

In order to assess the importance of these parameters and to establish, if possible, the interaction

and relation between them in practice, the Building Research Establishment under the aegis of the DOE's radioactive waste management programme established a collaborative research programme on a test bed site in the Carnmenellis granite in Cornwall (Fig. 1). The site comprised a shallow drift mine, with tunnels at right angles and a series of boreholes, up to 700 m deep, in an adjacent quarry.

The in situ stress measurements were, therefore, carried out in conjunction with a detailed exploration of a variety of rock mass assessment methods including scanline measurements, statistical techniques (including geostatistics), geophysics and consideration of the regional and local structural geology. This enabled

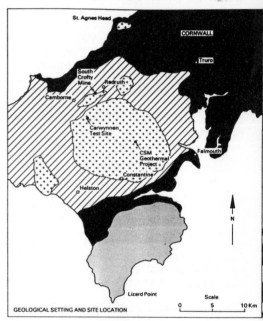

GEOLOGICAL SETTING AND SITE LOCATION

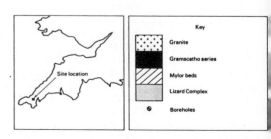

Figure 1(a). Geological setting and site location.

648

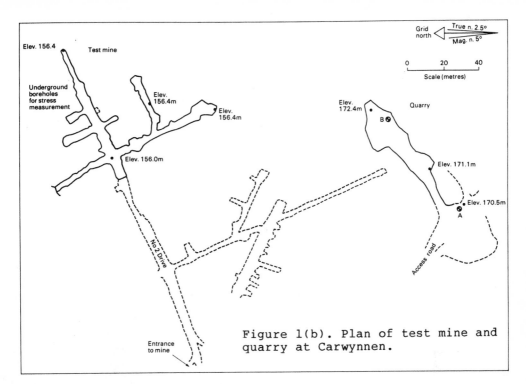

Figure 1(b). Plan of test mine and quarry at Carwynnen.

the results of the stress measurements to be analyzed in the context of a detailed knowledge of
the characteristics of the local
rock mass.

The Carnmenellis granite is part
of the Cornubian granite batholith
which underlies most of Cornwall.
It is thought to be late Carboniferous (310-300 Ma) in age and
intruded during the Hercynian orogeny. The discontinuity survey
within the mine complex and the
nearby borehole cores demonstrated
one major sub-vertical joint set
striking approximately 025° - 205°
with additional sub-vertical sets
striking at 065° - 245° and 095° -
275°. Sub-horizontal joint sets
were present throughout and appear
related to the surface contours.
Study of the borehole cores indicated, as anticipated, that the
spacing of the joints increased
with depth. A contoured plot of
pole concentrations is given in
Fig. 2. The granite was generally
fresh to slightly weathered with
local zones of moderate weathering, particularly in association
with master joints and mineralized
zones.

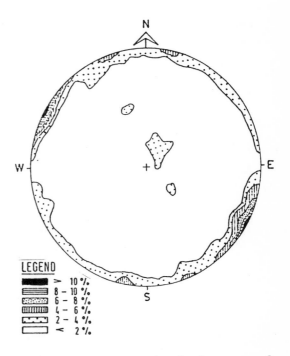

LEGEND
▰ > 10 %
▤ 8 - 10 %
▦ 6 - 8 %
▥ 4 - 6 %
⬚ 2 - 4 %
☐ < 2 %

Figure 2. Lower hemisphere equal
area projection contours of pole
concentrations, from Golder Associates (1985).

3. STRESS MEASUREMENT PROGRAMME AND RESULTS (1982-84)

3.1 Overcoring

The in situ stress measurements on site comprised both overcoring and the hydraulic fracturing techniques. In the mine, which allowed man access, three commercially available overcoring devices were employed. The performances of the United States Bureau of Mines (USBM) borehole deformation gauge, the Commonwealth Scientific and Industrial Research Organization's (CSIRO) hollow inclusion cell and the Interfels triaxial probe were evaluated and compared. An attempt was also made to obtain a series of hydraulic fracture stress measurements in the same boreholes for the purpose of comparison.

The results obtained are summarized in Table 1. Broadly, the major principal stress had a magnitude of 5.6 MPa, was sub-horizontal and trended in a direction of 312° (relative to true north); whilst the minor principal stress was approximately vertical and was measured as 1.4 MPa. The high ratio (3.9:1) between these stresses in this near-surface environment is accounted for by the low value of the vertical stress.

TABLE 1: COMPARISON OF OVERCORING RESULTS

Magnitude (MPa)	Trend (Degrees)	Plunge (Degrees)
CSIRO HOLLOW INCLUSION CELL		
σ_1 = 5.9	331	01
σ_2 = 4.9	241	09
σ_3 = 2.2	055	81
INTERFELS TRIAXIAL PROBE		
σ_1 = 5.3	308	19
σ_2 = 3.9	040	06
σ_3 = -0.6	146	70
USBM BOREHOLE DEFORMATION GAUGE		
σ_1 = 5.9	317	09
σ_2 = 2.2	224	17
σ_3 = -0.2	075	71

The exact location of the test zone within the mine was selected on the basis of a relative absence of major discontinuities, distance from other mine workings and the greatest available depth of overburden; it is, however, important to note that this was only about 34 m, so that the tests were conducted in a near surface, relatively low stress environment an close to the resolution limits o the measurement devices.

3.2 Hydraulic Fracturing

In locations where man-access i possible within 10-30 m, the em placement of devices capable o measuring changes in the stres field during overcoring by mean of a rosette of strain gauges ma be the most efficient method o stress measurement. In deep bore holes, however, only the hydrauli fracturing method is practicabl and it may indeed be the more versatile and effective genera method. Its rugged nature and th relative size of the test is a advantage in heterogeneous rock since it tests a zone of roc rather than a small section (poss ibly based on a 38 mm borehole which is the case in overcoring Its very robustness enables it t over-ride local perturbations which may obscure the overal stress pattern despite the greate resolution achieved by overcoring and the measured values are likel to be on a scale more relevant t designing a large structure under ground (cf. Hyett et al., 1986 Fig. 4).

It was important, in view of the paucity of existing data on i situ stress in the UK (Klein an Brown, 1983), to obtain informa tion on stress directions an magnitudes in a range of rock types at various locations withi the UK. It was, therefore, de cided that BRE, together wit Golder Associates, should develo a mobile hydraulic fracturing sys tem capable of measuring in sit stress as a part of the DOE re search programme and that the

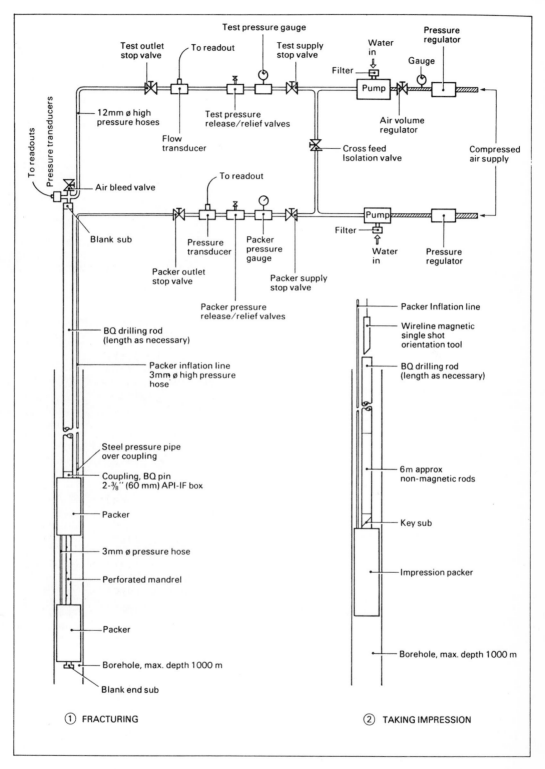

Figure 3.   Schematic layout of hydraulic fracture system for the measurement of in situ stress, from Tunbridge et al. (1986).

system should be proved by a series of tests in deep boreholes on this site.

The system was designed to be as simple as possible in order to ensure mobility, robustness and reliability in use and to minimize costs. A schematic layout of the system developed is shown in Fig. 3 and detailed descriptions are reported in Golder Associates, 1985 and Tunbridge et al., 1986, so only a brief outline will be given here. A straddle packer system, comprising two inflatable rubber packer elements on a perfo-rated hollow mandrel, isolates a section of the borehole in which there are no existing fractures (Fig. 4). Two compressed air-powered pumps provide hydraulic pressure
(i) to inflate the packers via a high pressure hose and
(ii) to pressure the test zone via the drill string and perfor-ated mandrel.
Data are measured and recorded using a system consisting of tran-sducers, chart recorder and auto-matic data logger (Fig. 5).

The usual hydraulic fracturing test procedures and interpretation methods were adopted. Following the initial fracture and observa-tion of the resulting pressure decay, the test zone was repress-urized to determine the refracture pressure and another value of the shut-in pressure. Further cycles of pressurization and decay beh-aviour were studied. The orienta-tion of the borehole fracture was established with an impression packer (Fig. 3) and used to deter-mine the principal stress orienta-tion.

Principal stress results obtained at three depths using the hydraulic fracturing method are given in Table 2 and shown graphically in Fig. 6 together with other results. It can be seen that the results given in Table 2 are in agreement with the overall trends of the overcoring data presented in Table 1.

Figure 4. Straddle packer system being lowered into borehole.

Figure 5. Hydraulic control con-sole and data recording system.

3.3 Comparison of Results

Other information concerning the stress in the Carnmenellis granite is available from the geothermal programme ,Pine et al. 1983, and is summarized in Table 3 below.

TABLE 2:   IN SITU PRINCIPAL STRESS MAGNITUDES AND ORIENTATIONS DETER-
MINED BY HYDRAULIC FRACTURE TESTS.

Depth (m)	σ_V (MPa)	σ_H (MPa)	σ_h (MPa)	Trend, σ_H (degrees, grid N)	Trend σ_h (degrees, grid N)
74	2.0	16.5	6.5	141	51
122	3.3	16.7	7.2	145	55
642	16.7	34.9	12.3	145	55

These data, together with those presented in the previous two sub-sections are all plotted on the stereographic projection in Fig. 7.

4. DISCUSSION AND CONCLUSIONS

At the beginning of the paper, it was noted that the in situ stress was one of the vital pieces of information required for the de-sign of a radioactive waste rep-ository, not only for the usual aspects of underground construc-tion stability but also because of the need to predict radionuclide migration with a rock mass struc-ture, in situ stress, water flow and construction coupled model. From the results of the stress programme presented here, let us consider to what extent the in situ stress field can be estab-lished for input to such models.

From Figure 7, it can be seen that the results of all the separate stress measurement methods have

TABLE 3:   PUBLISHED DATA ON STRESS IN THE CARNMENELLIS GRANITE.

Magnitude (MPa)	Trend (Degrees)	Plunge (Degrees)

OVERCORING AT SOUTH CROFTY, 790 M DEPTH
(from Pine et al, 1983a)

σ_1 = 37.7	130	05
σ_2 = 18.5	347	84
σ_3 = 11.3	220	03

HYDRAULIC FRACTURING, 2000 M DEPTH
(from Pine et al, 1983b)

σ_1 = 70	130*	00*
σ_2 = 52*	-*	90*
σ_3 = 30	040*	00*

[* estimated]

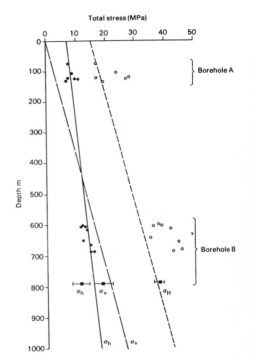

Figure 6.   Graph of principal stress magnitudes versus depth for the hydraulic fracturing results from Boreholes A and B (see also Figure 1(b)) and data from Table 3

provided consistent results for the directions of the principal stresses.   All the overcoring re-sults and hydraulic fracturing test results indicate similar principal stress directions, close to NW-SE and NE-SW horizontally, with the other principal stress vertical (although this latter direction was assumed in the hyd-raulic fracturing).   These prin-cipal stress orientation results

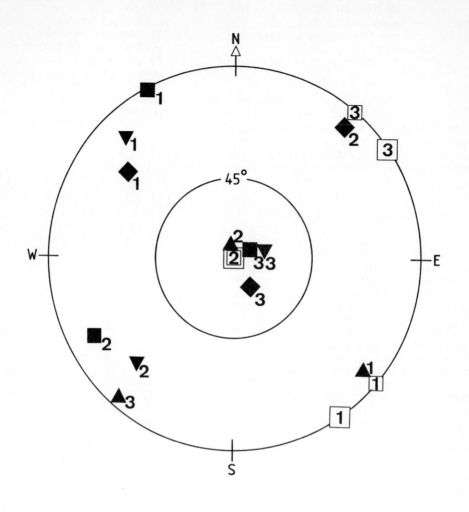

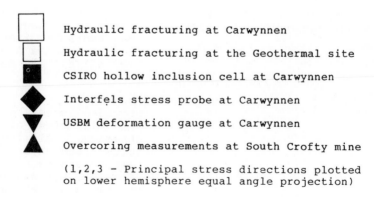

Hydraulic fracturing at Carwynnen

Hydraulic fracturing at the Geothermal site

CSIRO hollow inclusion cell at Carwynnen

Interfels stress probe at Carwynnen

USBM deformation gauge at Carwynnen

Overcoring measurements at South Crofty mine

(1,2,3 - Principal stress directions plotted
on lower hemisphere equal angle projection)

Figure 7.   Orientations of the principal stresses listed in Tables 1-3.

also agree with other tests conducted in the Carnmenellis granite. Thus, we can conclude that the evidence from these tests supports the idea that the directions of principal stresses can be reliably established.

This, in itself, is most important when the inter-relation between the in situ stress tensor and the rock mass permeability tensor are being studied. Moreover, the identity of the principal stresses with respect to direction was also established. The maximum principal stress was measured as sub-horizontal and in the NW-SE direction by all the test methods. The apparant inconsistency in the directions of the second and third principal stresses as shown in Figure 7 is because results obtained from different depths have been plotted on the same diagram. Near the surface, the vertical stress is the lowest principal stress; whereas at depth the NE-SW sub-horizontal stress is the lowest principal stress. Again, this accords with many other stress measurement results, and the fact that the vertical stress must be zero at the ground surface.

The fact that the directions and identities of the principal stresses can be established reliably is of great importance - and, especially in the context of water flow, the knowledge of the direction of the lowest principal stress is most important.

However, the magnitudes of the principal stresses were not as consistent as the directions. There was general agreement within the tests concerning the overall values, but for studying the influence of the in situ stress on permeability one would like more enhanced confidence in the magnitude values.

From these results, it is recommended that further work be conducted in the UK to improve the in situ rock stress data base on a country wide basis and that em-

phasis is placed on
a) establishing the distribution of principal stress directions in the UK, and
b) conducting further work on developing instrumentation and/or interpretation procedures that will enable the magnitudes of the principal stresses to be measured with greater confidence.

ACKNOWLEDGEMENTS

The work reported in this paper was supported by the Radioactive Waste Professional Division of the UK Department of the Environment. The project was co-ordinated by the Building Research Establishment and the paper is published with the permission of the Director of the Building Research Establishment. The results of this work will be used in the formulation of Government policy but at this stage they do not necessarily represent Government policy.

The authors would like to thank all those who contributed to the collaborative rock mass assessment and stress measurement programme, particularly L.W. Tunbridge and B. Monaghan of Golder Associates and R.A. Irvin and P. Garritty now of Ian Farmer Associates who supported BRE with the in situ stress measurements on site.

REFERENCES

Golder Associates 1985. Final Report on Geotechnical Site Assessment Methodology. UK DOE Report DOE/RW/85.148.

Hudson, J.A. 1983. UK Rock Mechanics Research for Radioactive Waste Disposal. Proc. 5th ISRM Congress held in Melbourne, Australia, Vol 2, E 161-165.

Hyett, A.J., Dyke, C.G. and J.A. Hudson 1986. A Critical Examination of Basic Concepts Associated with the Existence and Measurement of In Situ Stress. Proceedings of the International Symposium on Rock Stress and Rock Stress Measurements held in Sweden, September, 1986. Centek Publishers.

Klein, R.J. and E.T. Brown 1983. The State of Stress in British Rocks. UK DOE Report DOE/RW/83.060, 73pp.

Long, J.C.S. 1983. Investigation of Equivalent Porous Medium Permeability in Networks of Discontinuous Fractures. PhD thesis, University of California at Berkeley.

Tunbridge, L.W., Cooling, C.M. and B. Haimson 1986. Measurements of Rock Stress Using the Hydraulic Fracturing Method in Cornwall, UK - Part I: Field Measurements. In preparation.

Characterization of the state of in situ stress by hydraulic fracturing for a nuclear waste repository in basalt

K. KIM
S.A. DISCHLER
Basalt Waste Isolation Project, Rockwell Hanford Operations, Richland, Washington, USA
J.R. AGGSON
M.P. HARDY
J.F.T. Agapito and Associates, Inc., Grand Junction, Colorado, USA

ABSTRACT

Hydraulic fracturing tests designed to characterize the state of in situ stress were conducted in four deep boreholes. These tests are part of a site investigation program to assess the feasibility of constructing a nuclear waste repository in a basalt formation underneath the Hanford Site in southeastern Washington State, U.S.A. The results of these tests are examined in light of stress indicator data, which include core disking, borehole wall spalling, and fault plane solution data obtained at the site.

RESUME

Des tests de fracturation hydraulique conçus pour determiner les caractéristiques des contraintes in situ ont été effectués dans quatre trous de sonde profonds. Ces tests font partie d'un programme d'etudé de site destiné à évaluer la possibilité de construire un dépôt de déchets nucléaires dans une formation basaltique sous le site Hanford dans la région sud-est de l'État de Washington, aux États-Unis. Les résultats de ces tests sont anaylsés à la lumière de données d'indicateurs de contraintes, y compris des données relatives à la rupture des carottes en disques, a l'effritement des parois des trous de sonde et des données de resolution de plan de faille obtenues sur le terrain.

ZUSAMMENFASSUNG

Für die Charakterisierung von Untertage-Spannungszuständen ausgelegte Hydrafrac-Tests wurden in vier tiefen Bohrungen durchgeführt. Diese Tests sind Teil eines Standort-Untersuchungsprogramms, das die Durchführbarkeit des Baus einer Deponie für kerntechnischen Abfall in einer Basaltformation unter der Hanford-Anlage im Südosten des Staates Washington in den U.S.A. erfassen soll. Die Ergebnisse dieser Tests werden im Hinblick auf spannungsanzeigende Daten wie Bohrkern-Scheibenzerfall, Bohrungswand-Abblätterung und Verwerfungsebenenlösung untersucht, die am Standort gewonnen wurden.

1. INTRODUCTION

The Hanford Site is one of several sites being considered by the U.S. Department of Energy for terminal storage of commercial high-level radioactive wastes in an underground repository. The site investigation to assess the feasibility of constructing a repository in a deep basalt formation beneath the Hanford Site was initiated in 1976 and is continuing. The importance of understanding in situ stress state has been recognized since the inception of the Basalt Waste Isolation Project (BWIP) due to its direct influence on waste emplacement density and, thus, the areal requirement for the repository.

In 1981, the U.S. Nuclear Regulatory Commission issued Title 10 of the Code of Federal Regulations, Part 60, (10CFR60; NRC 1981). Sections 60.10 and 60.21 of this Federal Regulation mandated the measurement of in situ stresses in the site before and during the construction of a repository. One year later, the U.S. Congress enacted the Nuclear Waste Policy Act of 1982 (NWPA; NWPA 1983), which specifies site identification process and sets the schedule for site selection, licensing, and construction of the repository with an objective to have an operating repository available for commercial high-level nuclear wastes before the end of the century. The formalization of the site selection process highlighted the need to obtain in situ geoengineering data before underground access is available. Therefore, attention has been focused on the acquisition of in situ stress data at the Hanford Site.

The need for a comprehensive stress measurement program at the Hanford Site was recognized long before the enactment of the NWPA and the release of 10CFR60 because the site data obtained from early exploratory drillings revealed disking of cores from deep holes, suggesting the presence of high horizontal stress at depth. Frequent microseismic swarms observed near the site were also considered an indication of high-stress conditions at the candidate repository depth. An evaluation of these stress indicators generated

a consensus that quantification of the state of stress at the candidate horizon was necessary and this need could be met by hydraulic fracturing tests in existing boreholes.

A hydraulic fracturing test plan was prepared to characterize the state of in situ stress at the candidate horizon within the reference repository location. The prime objective of the hydraulic fracturing tests was to obtain an engineering estimate of the magnitudes and directions of the principal stresses. The first series of tests were initiated in 1981 and completed in 1984. During the course of the investigation, improvements and innovations were made in test methods and equipment.

A detailed analysis of data obtained from the tests provided a reasonably coherent preliminary understanding of the state of in-situ stress at the candidate repository horizon. These data were used in the repository conceptual design, which was an ongoing activity parallel with this study. A description of the work performed, information gathered, and impact of the new information on repository design is presented in the following sections.

2. GEOLOGIC BACKGROUND OF THE SITE

The Hanford Site is located in southeastern Washington State near the center of the Columbia Plateau, a flood basalt underlain by Miocene tholeiitic basalts that erupted from northnorthwest-trending linear vent systems exposed in southeastern Washington, northeastern Oregon, and west-central Idaho. These highly fluid lavas spread over great distances from their source vents and flowed generally westward along a gentle slope before consolidating in a basin between the ancestral Cascade and Rocky Mountain ranges in the interval of 16.5 to 6 million years ago. The Columbia River basalts encompass $\sim 200,000$ km^2 and reach a maximum known thickness of > 3 km in the Pasco Basin.

The location where construction of a repository is being considered is called the reference repository location and is in the axial region of the western part of the southeast-trending Cold Creek syncline, one of several synclines rising more gently to the north on the south limb of the Umtanum Ridge/Gable Mountain structure and more steeply on the buried extension of the Yakima Ridge to the south (Fig. 1).

During the preliminary site investigation and exploration drilling, large amounts of data were accumulated that serve as stress indicators. These include microseismic swarms, core disking, and borehole-wall spalling. Further descriptions of these data are presented below.

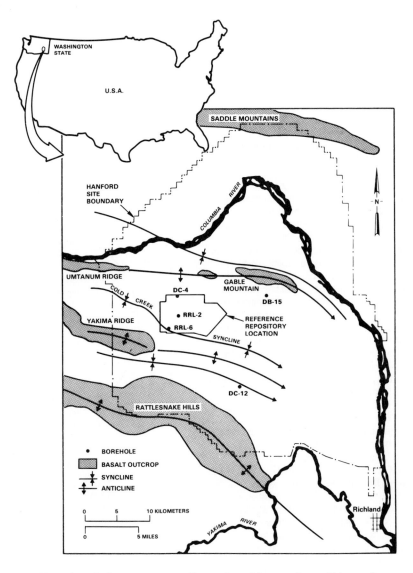

Fig. 1. Reference repository location and position of boreholes used for hydraulic fracturing tests on the Hanford Site.

Microseismic Swarms: Swarms of small-magnitude earthquakes, typically 3 on the Richter scale, have been considered a predominant characteristic of the Columbia Plateau seismicity. Earthquake sequences typically last from a few days to several months and occur in a volume of rock with typical dimensions of 5 km. During a swarm, there is no distinctively large event that is followed by a generally decreasing level of seismicity, as is typical of a main-shock/after-shock sequence. Swarm earthquakes tend to gradually increase and decay in frequency but not in magnitude. Focal-mechanism solutions (Fig. 2) of earthquakes in the central Columbia Plateau indicate a response to a nearly horizontal maximum stress oriented north-south, and minimum stress oriented vertically (Malone and others 1975; Rohay and Davis 1983).

Core Disking: Core disking, which is a tendency for cylindrical core samples to break into saddle-shaped disks (Fig. 3), has been observed in a number of deep boreholes at the Hanford Site (Moak 1981). This phenomenon has been known to occur under the combined effects of in situ stress, rock properties, and drill-bit/rock interaction. Numerical modeling of the phenomenon revealed that the saddle-shaped disking is the result of nonaxisymmetric horizontal stresses, and that the ratio of average horizontal stress to vertical stress is predicted to be in the range of 1.6:1 to 2.0:1 at a depth of 1,130 m (Lehnhoff and others 1983).

Borehole Wall Spalling: Spalling of deep boreholes was first revealed by fracture impressions taken during hydraulic fracturing operations and was later confirmed by a downhole acoustic teleview (ATV) survey (Fig. 4).

The ATV log indicated a consistent east-west orientation of borehole-wall spalling in all boreholes surveyed. The extent of core disking and borehole-wall spalling in three boreholes in which hydraulic fracturing tests were conducted have been compared, and a relatively good correlation between the two was found (Fig. 5). It was also revealed that the disking and spalling are confined to the interiors of individual flows (Paillet and Kim 1986).

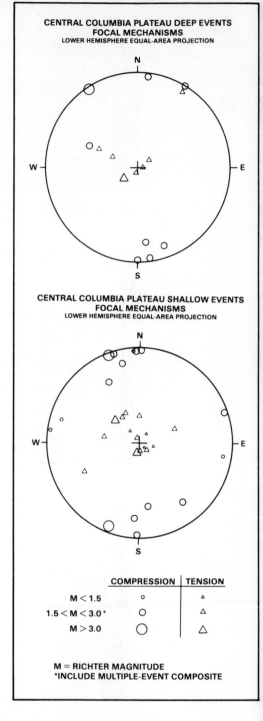

Fig. 2. Focal mechanisms of eastern Washington (lower hemisphere, equal area projection of compression and tension axes derived from focal-mechanism solutions).

Fig. 3. Saddle-shaped core disk (5-cm dia.).

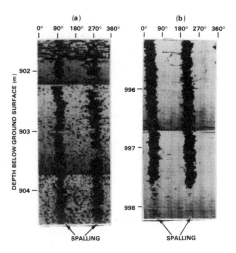

SPALLING   SPALLING

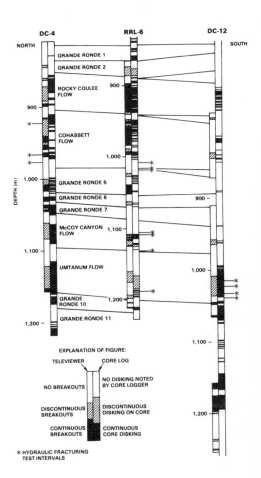

Fig. 5. Correlation of core disking with borehole-wall spalling in
boreholes DC-4, RRL-6, and DC-12.

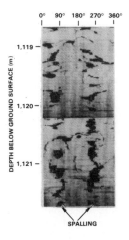

SPALLING

Fig. 4. Examples of borehole wall
breakouts observed in the dense
interior by a downhole acoustic
televiewer in borehole RRL-6.

The stress indicators discussed above
suggest consistently that in-situ
stresses at the candidate horizon are
high, and the maximum stress is acting
in a north-south horizontal direction.
However, these stress indicators provide only qualitative indications regarding the magnitudes of the stresses.

3. TEST PROGRAM

A comprehensive test program was
designed to obtain quantitative data
needed for engineering and design calculations. Initial tests were conducted in a shallow borehole, DB-15, to
demonstrate the feasibility of the test

method in the basalt formation and to develop appropriate test procedures (see Fig. 1 for borehole locations).

The next series of tests was carried out in four deep boreholes, DC-12, RRL-2, DC-4, and RRL-6, within and around the reference repository location at depths of ~1,000 m, the candidate repository horizon depth. In one borehole, RRL-2, hydrologic tests were conducted in a zone encompassing the hydraulic fracturing test intervals in order to assess the influence of the hydraulic fracturing operations on hydraulic conductivity.

Test intervals were determined after examining cores, core photos, ATV logs obtained from proposed test boreholes, or a combination of the above. In selecting intervals, consideration was given to avoid spalled, extensively disked, or fractured zones to ensure adequate seating of the straddle packer system in the borehole. Every effort, was made to obtain a maximum amount of information from each test.

4. TEST RESULTS

4.1 Hydraulic Fracturing Results

The test results obtained from 40 test intervals within the four deep holes in the candidate horizon have been rigorously examined and exhaustively analyzed (Kim and others 1986). The boreholes are located in an area covering ~15 km in diameter. Test depths range from 921 to 1,195 m. A set of typical test results, obtained from a depth of 927.7 m in borehole RRL-2, and a fracture impression are presented in Figs. 6 and 7.

A number of tests yielded indistinct shut-in pressures and fracture-reopening pressures as shown in Fig. 6. In order to identify the shut-in pressures in a consistent and technically defensible manner, the pressure-time curves from one borehole, RRL-2, were analyzed by five methods described by Zoback and Haimson (1982). This analysis showed that the shut-in pressures determined, using these five methods, varied as much as 14% and the resulting maximum horizontal stresses

varied by as much as 23% (Aggson and Kim 1986). It was determined that the "inflection point method" described by Gronseth and Kry (1983) provides relatively conservative results (i.e., high-stress magnitudes). This method of determining shut-in pressure has produced acceptable results in laboratory tests and was used in the analysis of all data obtained.

The fracture-reopening method described by Bredehoeft and others (1976) was used to determine the borehole rupture strength. Pore pressure was assumed to be equal to hydraulic head at the test depth and was assumed to act in the fracture interval prior to fracture reopening.

Most fracture impressions revealed well-defined vertical fractures with a minimal degree of inclined fracturing, branching and/or spalling. Some intervals showed extensive spalling. Test results obtained from spalled intervals were considered suspect and unsatisfactory for further analysis. A summary of the results analyzed by the foregoing methods is given in Table 1.

The mean maximum and minimum horizontal stresses from all tests are 61.1 and 33.8 MPa, with standard deviations of 5.4 and 2.7 MPa, respectively. Both maximum and minimum horizontal stresses were normally distributed about the mean values. Within the reference repository location, the mean maximum and minimum horizontal stresses are 61.1 and 33.4 MPa with standard deviations of 4.9 and 2.7 MPa, respectively. Mean fracture orientation is N. 02° E. ± 17°.

4.1.1 Hydrologic tests before and after hydraulic fracturing. One of the concerns raised during the course of study was the extent of perturbation that hydraulic fracturing tests will cause to the integrity of the basalt formation. Although the potential effect was considered minimal, it became necessary to quantify the extent of the effect.

Constant head injection tests and over-pressure pulse tests were conducted in borehole RRL-2 before and after

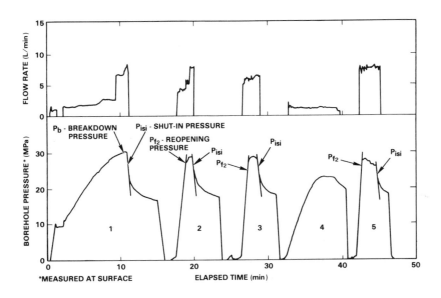

Fig. 6. Typical flow rate and pressure versus time curves (borehole RRL-2--test depth of 927.7 m).

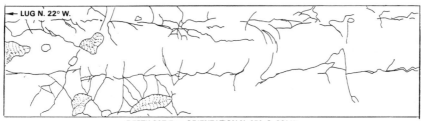

DEPTH 927.7 m, ORIENTATION N. 05°, S. 02° W.

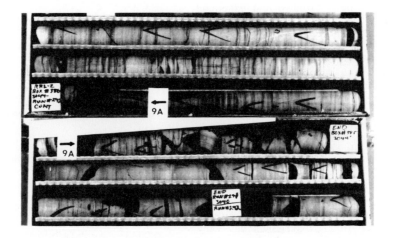

Fig. 7. Fracture impression and core photograph from the test interval.

Table 1. Summary of mean stress values (±1 standard deviation) obtained in each test borehole.

Borehole	Number of tests	Mean depth, m	Mean minimum horizontal principal stress, σ_h, MPa	Mean maximum horizontal principal stress, σ_H, MPa	Mean vertical stress, σ_v, MPa	Mean fracture orientation
DC-4	1	976	30.8	59.9	24.4	N. 12° E.[a] ± 16°
DC-12	6	1,024 ± 15	34.8 ± 2.7	61.2 ± 6.8	26.2 ± 0.4	N. 23° E.[b] ± 21°
RRL-2	5	1,047 ± 119	34.5 ± 2.7	60.6 ± 5.3	26.3 ± 3.1	N. 03° W.[c] ± 14°
RRL-6	7	1,174 ± 74	33.0 ± 2.4	61.6 ± 5.4	27.8 ± 1.9	N. 05° E. ± 22°
All RRL holes combined, DC-4, RRL-2, and RRL-6	13	1,074 ± 96	33.4 ± 2.7	61.1 ± 4.9	26.9 ± 2.5	N. 02° E.[d] ± 17°

[a]Mean orientation based on three impression tests.
[b]Mean orientation based on four impression tests.
[c]Mean orientation based on 11 impression tests.
[d]Mean orientation based on 21 impression tests.

hydraulic fracturing tests in a test interval covering 21.65 m of the dense interior. The results indicated an increase of hydraulic conductivity as a result of the hydraulic fracturing tests. Average hydraulic conductivities before and after the hydraulic fracturing tests were 2.0×10^{-8} and 1.1×10^{-6} m/d, respectively (Strait and Spane 1983).

4.1.2 Discussion. The tests reported in this paper were planned and executed to minimize the uncertainties associated with data interpretation and test methods. Although it is difficult to quantify the degree of uncertainty, the data obtained to date were consistent within and between test holes. The data show minimal variations of stress with depth between test hole locations or between basalt flows. The profile of minimum and maximum horizontal stresses within test intervals covering ~300 m exhibit no substantial gradient (Fig. 8). These results should not be extrapolated with confidence beyond the study area. An analysis of core disking data suggests, however, that the magnitudes of in-situ stresses may vary more within the Hanford Site than within the reference repository location.

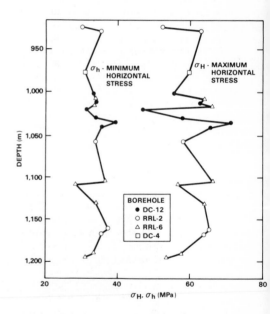

Fig. 8. Hanford Site minimum and maximum horizontal stress versus depth.

664

The orientations of the principal stresses determined by hydraulic fracturing tests show an excellent correlation with those of stress indicators. The direction of minimum stress obtained from impression packer testing is subparallel to the axis of the Cold Creek syncline, which is the dominant structure in the general study area. Focal-mechanism solutions of earthquakes in the central Columbia Plateau indicate a response to a nearly horizontal maximum stress oriented north-south and minimum stress oriented vertically (Malone and others 1975; Rohay and Davis, 1983, see Fig. 2). Orientations of borehole-wall spallings surveyed by an ATV are also aligned in a general east-west direction.

Some tests were conducted in severely disked zones and others in relatively disk-free zones as indicated in Fig. 5. Overall test results do not suggest any appreciable differences between the results from severely disked and disk-free zones. It can be deduced from this observation that the stress magnitude is not the only dominant factor affecting disking. Figure 5 also indicates a relatively close correlation between the distribution of borehole-wall spalling and the incidence of core disking. Differences in the distribution of breakouts and disking are attributed to the differences in failure mechanisms. Breakouts are related to high or unequal horizontal principal stresses that bring about stress concentrations exceeding the shear strength of the rocks, and disking is associated with high ratios of horizontal-to-vertical stresses that cause strain relief upon coring under influence of drill-bit/rock interaction.

Tests conducted in spalled zones were rejected in the data analysis process due to the considerations that test zones may not have been adequately sealed during pressurization of the test interval, and the standard data analysis method assumes circularity of the borehole. All pressure-time and flow-time histories and fracture impressions obtained from these zones can be analyzed if acceptable methods of analysis are derived.

All information obtained to date show reasonable correlations with each other and provide a reasonably coherent explanation on the state of in-situ stress in the candidate horizon at the Hanford Site. These also provide credence to the hydraulic fracturing test results, although uncertainties regarding data accuracy and representativeness still exist. Some of these uncertainties originate from an incomplete understanding of factors such as (1) the effect of pore pressure, (2) the inaccuracy associated with the determination of borehole rupture strength, (3) the influence of pumping rate, and (4) the effect of branching of fractures. Efforts are being made to enhance our understanding of these fundamental aspects in order to characterize the site accurately enough to make an informed decision on selecting the site and on designing and engineering a repository that has to last thousands of years.

5. REPOSITORY DESIGN CONSIDERATIONS

In-situ stress data obtained to date have influenced the repository conceptual design. Prior to measuring high horizontal stresses that exceed twice the vertical stress, the basic opening configuration for the conceptual repository was horseshoe-shaped with vertical waste emplacement holes (Ritchie 1980). This opening configuration was changed to an elliptical (a vertically compressed horseshoe) shape with long, horizontal emplacement holes after numerical and empirical analyses of the opening's stability (RKE/PB 1983). The long, horizontal emplacement hole concept was further changed to a short, single-canister hole concept primarily because of the consideration of retrievability in which the high horizontal stress played a substantial role (RKE/PB 1985).

6. CONCLUSIONS

Hydraulic fracturing tests have played a significant role in characterizing the Hanford Site since the candidate repository horizon is not accessible except through boreholes. Of all the information obtained in the past several years of study, only hydraulic fracturing has provided quantitative data on the state of in-situ stress at the proposed repository location. Some fundamental questions still need to be answered regarding the accuracy of the hydraulic fracturing data. The BWIP's effort to resolve these questions will be continued until defensible answers are derived. Alternate stress-measurement techniques, namely, strain-relief methods including overcoring planned at the Exploratory Shaft Facility, are expected to help verify the accuracy and representativeness of the hydraulic fracturing data at the Hanford Site.

The repository design will advance as more site data are obtained from the exploration and characterization activities. The opening configuration may undergo further changes to take into account new findings of the site characteristics and the refinement of analysis methods. Emphasis will remain on the accurate determination of representative in-situ stress data at the Hanford Site.

7. ACKNOWLEDGEMENT

We gratefully acknowledge the contribution of the following individuals. Professor B. C. Haimson of the University of Wisconsin-Madison conducted tests at borehole DC-12 during the early stage of the program, thus contributing significantly to the establishment of the BWIP hydraulic fracturing capability. Messrs. T. Rundle, D. J. Moak, T. M. Wintzack, C. T. Webster, and R. L. Jones of the BWIP provided invaluable assistance during field tests.

8. REFERENCES

Aggson, J. R., and K. Kim 1986. Analysis of Hydraulic Fracturing Pressure Histories: A Comparison of Five Methods Used to Identify Shut-In Pressure, RHO-BW-SA-571. Rockwell Hanford Operations, Richland, Washington.

Bredehoeft, J. D., R. G. Wolff, W. S. Keys, and E. Shutter 1976. Hydraulic Fracturing to Determine the Regional In-Situ Stress Field in the Piceance Basin, Colorado. Geological Society of American Bulletin 87:250-258.

Gronseth, J. M., and P. R. Kry 1982. Instantaneous Shut-In Pressure and its Relationship to the Minimum In Situ Stress. Proceedings of the Workshop on Hydraulic Fracturing Stress Measurements, Open-File Report 82-1075, U.S. Geological Survey, Washington, D.C., pp. 147-167.

Kim, K., S. A. Dischler, J. R. Aggson, and M. P. Hardy 1986. The State of In-Situ Stresses Determined by Hydraulic Fracturing at the Hanford Site, RHO-BW-ST-73 P. Rockwell Hanford Operations, Richland, Washington.

Lehnhoff, T. F., B. Stefansson, K. Thirumalai, and T. M. Wintczak 1982. The Core Disking Phenomenon and its Relation to In-Situ Stress at Hanford, SD-BWI-TI-085. Rockwell Hanford Operations, Richland, Washington.

Malone, S. D., G. H. Rothe, and S. W. Smith 1975. Details of Microearthquake Swarms in the Columbia Basin, Washington. Bulletin of the Seismological Society of Ameria 65(4): 855-864.

Moak, D. J. 1981. Borehole Geologic Studies. In C. W. Myers, and S. M. Price (Eds.), Subsurface Geology of the Cold Creek Syncline, RHO-BWI-ST-14, Rockwell Hanford Operations, Richland, Washington.

NRC 1981. Disposal of High-Level Radioactive Wastes in Geologic Repositories: Licensing Procedures. Title 10, Code of Federal Regulations, Part 60, U.S. Nuclear Regulatory Commission, Washington, D.C.

NWPA 1983. Nuclear Waste Policy Act of 1982, Public Law 97-425, 42 USC 10101-10226.

Paillet, F. L., and K. Kim 1986. The Character and Distribution of Borehole Breakouts and Their Relationship to In-Situ Stresses in Deep Columbia River Basalts, RHO-BW-SA-548. Rockwell Hanford Operations, Richland, Washington.

Ritchie, J. S. 1980. Description of a Nuclear Waste Repository in Basalt, RHO-BWI-80-100. Rockwell Hanford Operations, Richland, Washington, pp. VI-8 through VI-31.

RKE/PB 1983. Conceptual System Design Description, Nuclear Waste Repository in Basalt, Engineering Design, Vol. 1, SD-BWI-SD-005. Raymond Kaiser Engineers, Inc./Parsons Brinckerhoff Quade & Douglas, Inc., for Rockwell Hanford Operations, Richland, Washington.

RKE/PB 1985. Task V, Engineering Study No. 9, Underground Repository Layout, SD-BWI-ES-023. Raymond Kaiser Engineers, Inc./Parsons Brinckerhoff Quade & Douglas, Inc., for Rockwell Hanford Operations, Richland, Washington.

Rohay, A. C., and J. D. Davis 1983. Contemporary Deformation in the Pasco Basin Area of the Central Columbia Plateau. In J. A. Caggiano, and D. W. Duncan (Eds.), Preliminary Interpretation of the Tectonic Stability of the Reference Repository Location, RHO-BW-ST-19 P. Rockwell Hanford Operations, Richland, Washington, pp. 6-1 through 6-11.

Strait, S. R., and F. A. Spane Jr. 1983. Preliminary Results of Hydrologic Testing in the Middle Sentinel Bluff Basalt Colonnade Entablature at Borehole RRL-2, SD-BWI-TI-109. Rockwell Hanford Operations, Richland, Washington.

Zoback, M. D., and B. C. Haimson 1982. Status of the Hydraulic Fracturing Method for In-Situ Stress Measurements. Proceedings 23rd U.S. Symposium on Rock Mechanics, University of California, Berkeley, California, pp. 143-156.

Large silo for waste material in Forsmark, Sweden

H. STILLE
Royal Institute of Technology and Skanska AB, Stockholm, Sweden

A. FREDRIKSSON
ADG Grundteknik, Stockholm, Sweden

H. LARSSON
Swedish State Power Board, Stockholm, Sweden

Abstract

A central repository for low and medium level radioactive waste from the Swedish
nuclear power plants is under construction at Forsmark, Sweden. The most active
waste will be disposed of in a rock cavern, designed as a silo 69 m in height and
30 m in diameter. The rock stability requirements are high. Pre-investigations were
very extensive. The initial rock stresses were measured at several points. Based on
these investigations, an analysis of the behaviour of the silo was performed using
the Finite Element Method. During construction, the behaviour of the rock mass
around the silo was monitored with extensometers. Very small deformations of a few
millimeters were measured which were comparable with the calculated results.

Résumé

On construit actuellement à Forsmark, en Suède, un dépôt central pour les déchets
radioactifs de radioactivité basse ou moyenne des centrales nucléaires suédoises.
Les déchets les plus actifs seront placés dans une caverne creusée dans la roche,
en forme de silo de 69 m de hauteur et 30 m de diamètre. Les exigences de stabilité
de la roche sont très sévères. Les études préliminaires furent très importantes.
Les contraintes initiales de la roche furent mesurées en plusieurs endroits. A
partir de ces études, on entreprit une analyse des fonctions du silo à l'aide de la
méthode élémentaire finie. Lors de la construction, le comportement de la roche
autour du silo fut contrôlé à l'aide d'extensomètres. On constatat des déformations
minimes de quelques millimètres correspondant aux valeurs calculées.

Zusammenfassung

Ein Zentrallager für die Verwahrung von Atomabfall niedriger und mittlerer Strah-
lungsstärke aus schwedischen Kernkraftwerken wird zur Zeit in Forsmark, Schweden,
gebaut. Der strahlungsaktivste Abfall soll in Felsgestein in einer unterirdischen
Kaverne zur Verwahrung kommen, die in der Form eines Silos von 69 m Höhe und 30 m
Durchmesser konstruiert wird. In bezug auf Felsstandfestigkeit werden hohe Anfor-
derungen gestellt. Sehr gründliche Voruntersuchungen wurden durchgeführt. Der
anfängliche Gebirgsdruck wurde an mehreren Punkten gemessen. Auf Basis dieser
Untersuchungen wurde dann eine Analyse über das Verhalten des Silos erstellt unter
Verwendung der endlichen Elementmethode. Während der Bauarbeiten wurde das Verhal-
ten der Gesteinsmassen um das Silo herum mit Hilfe von Extensometern überwacht.
Sehr kleine Verschiebungen von wenigen Millimetern konnten gemessen werden.
entsprechend den berechneten Ergebnissen.

1 INTRODUCTION

In June 1983, the Swedish Government
granted the Swedish Nuclear Fuel and
Waste Management Company (SKB) a
licence to build and operate a facility called SFR for the final disposal
of low and medium-level reactor waste
from all the Swedish nuclear power
plants.

The Swedish nuclear utilities have de-
legated to their jointly-owned company, SKB, the responsibility for the

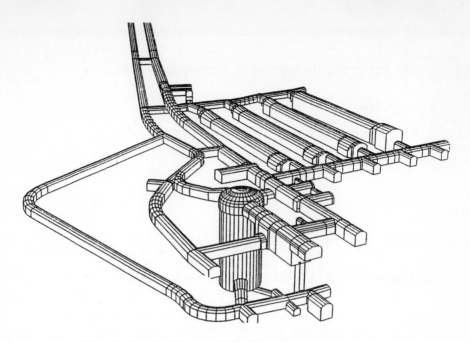

Fig. 1 General layout of the repository.

design, construction and operation of the waste facilites. SKB has commissioned the Swedish State Power Board to plan, design and build SFR.

The underground complex consists of two access tunnels, communication tunnels and rock chambers, and a large silo for the waste material.

In this article the rock mechanical considerations, calculations and measurements of the silo will be presented.

The project has been described from different aspects in papers presented at several different congresses.

The tunnelling work has been described by Carlsson and Hedman (1986). The rock mechanical aspects of the intersection of the tunnels by the Singö fault have been described by Carlson, Olsson and Stille (1985).

A general description of the excavation of the silo has been given by Larsson and Christiansson (19869.

Data on the rock stress situation and geological structures in the area of the repository will be given by Carlsson and Christiansson at this symposium.

Two access tunnels have been excavated under the sea to the area chosen for the repository. The very complex system of the tunnels, chamber and the large silo for the first construction phase can be seen in Fig. 1

The silo is one of the larger rock caverns excavated in Sweden with a height of 69 m and a diameter of 30 m. The rock cover above the silo is about 60 m. In the upper part there are two connecting tunnels, a construction tunnel and a tunnel for transportation during the operation period. A construction tunnel and a drainage tunnel have been excavated at the bottom of the silo.

The excavation sequence is shown in Fig. 2. The first phase includes excavation of the dome. After the excavation of the dome and the tunnel to the base of the silo, work started on the long-hole drilling of the central pole, which had a diameter of 14 m. The central hole was then blasted from the bottom to the top in benches.

The remaining rock between the central hole and the silo wall was then excavated by conventional bench blasting. The rock support of the silo consists of shotcrete and rock bolting, and the support work was carried out after

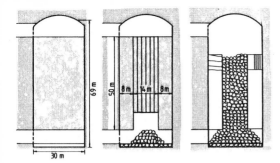

Fig. 2 The excavation sequence of the
silo.

each excavation sequence.

2   DESCRIPTION OF THE ROCK MASS

2.1 Geology

The rock in the area is a gneiss granite. Bands and small blocks of older,
supracrusted sediments occur. Dikes of
amphibolites and pegmatites intersect
the rock mass. The mechanical properties of the rock are given in table 1.

Three dominant joint sets can be found
with two vertical systems orthogonal
to each other and a subhorizontal
one. The joints give the rock mass a
blocky and sometimes schistose structure. The joint surfaces are rough.
Most of the joints are filled with a
thin coating of chorite, calcite or
laumontite. The joint frequency is
around 5-6 joints per meter.

The RQD value calculated on cores
drilled just above the dome of the
silo was found to be 60-80.

The initial stress field was measured
in three boreholes. One hole, Kb7 was

drilled from the sea level and 300 m
southeast of the silo. The other two,
Kb20 and 21 were drilled from the tunnels into the site of the silo before
excavation. The results of the stress
measurements are given in Table 2.

For the purposes of the calculation,
the following stress field was therefore assumed:

-    Maximum horizontal stress 10 MPa
-    Minimum horizontal stress 5 MPa
-    Vertical stress   overburden
                                2 - 3 MPa

2.2 Rock Mass Properties

The rock mass properties have been
evaluated from empirical relations
based on the rock mass quality estimated according to different classi-
fications systems. The well-known Rock
Mass Rating system, (RMR) and Q-factor
were used, which gave a RMR value of
60 - 72 and a Q-factor of 5 - 10.

And according to Bieniawski's terminology, the rock mass may be described
as good rock.

The different empirical relations for
evaluation of the properties can give
widely differing results. The decision
on the design values must therefore be
based on engineering judgement of the
relevance of the different relations.

The Young's Modulus, E_m, was estimated
from the relation given by Bieniawski
(1979) and Barton (1980). The results
are given in Table 3, together with
the value chosen for the design.

The evaluation of the rock mass strength is much more difficult. The presence of three joint sets means that

Table 1. Mechanical properties of the rock

	Gneiss granite	Amphibolite	Pegmatite
Unconfined compressive strength	241 MPa	148 MPa	157 MPa
Young's Modulus	76 GPa	88 GPa	69 GPa

Table 2. Initial stress measurements

Level	Horizontal stress σ_1 MPa	σ_3 MPa	Direction of σ_1	Vertical stress σ_z MPa
Kb7 +460	11.9	3.2	131°	6.2
+430	16.7	8.3	117°	6.3
+400	17.0	7.6	134°	2.9
+360	17.1	11.5	54°	3.7
Kb21 +430	5.2	2.3	162°	1.4
+435	5.7	1.9	129°	0.6
+440	21.1	5.0	156°	0.9
+445	7.9	3.0	144°	- 1.4
Kb22 +425	8.3	3.2	157°	- 2.3
+430	7.3	4.2	159°	0.7

the rock mass can be treated as iso-tropic material, provided that the overall behaviour for an approximately 2 m large part of the rock mass is studied.

The unconfined compressive strength of the rock mass has been estimated from relations given by Bieniawski (1979), Hoek and Brown (1981) and Stille et al (1982). The results are given in Table 4 together with the value chosen for the design.

The scatter of the results is very wide and obviously another design value can equally well be chosen.

3   ROCK MECHANICAL ANALYSIS

3.1   Models

A number of rock mechanical calcula-tions have been carried out in order to form the basis of the decision on rock stability and rock support. The calculations were performed with JOBFEM, a 2-D finite element program developed at the Department of Soil and Rock Mechanics, KTH, see Fredriksson (1985).

Three different models were used, based on 2-D conditions in order to study the behaviour of the silo.

The first model is a vertical section through the silo with axial symmentric

conditions, see Fig. 3. The initial horizontal stress field was chosen at the mean value, 7.5 MPa, of the meas-ured values. The load cases in the calculations followed the excavation procedure described and are illus-trated in Fig. 4.

The estimated rock support from the preliminary design was incorporated in the model. A 15 cm thick shotcrete layer, and rockbolts of a length of 3.65 to 6.0 m and spacing of 1.75 m, were applied to the dome.

Table 3. Deformation Modulus of the Rock Mass

Method	E_m, GPa
RMR-Bieniawski (1979) Q - Barton (1980)	20 - 44 2 - 43
Design value	20

Table 4.   Unconfined compression strength of the rock mass

Method	Strength, MPa
Bieniawski Hoek & Brown Stille et al	1 - 1.5 7 - 29 5 - 11
Design value	10

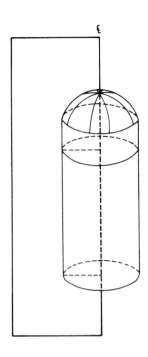

Fig. 3   Model I, Axial symmetrical
          case.

The second and third models were used
in order to study the effect of the
anistropic stress field on the silo.

The second model was used to study the
deformations and stresses in the high
walls, see Fig. 5. The ratio between
the height and the diameter is large
enough to imply a decision on plane
strain conditions at the middle part
of the walls. A horizontal section was
therefore studied with the axis along
the direction of the horizontal principal stresses.

The third model was used in order to
study an upper limit of stresses and
strains in the crown. A plane strain
condition was assumed, with horizontal
stresses equal to maximum stresses of
10 MPa, see Fig. 5. The axial symmetric calculations had shown that the
stresses and strain in the crown would
not change significantly when the excavation depth exceeded 20 m. The
third model with the plane strain condition was therefore only excavated
down to a depth of 20 m.

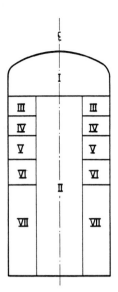

Fig. 4   Load cases for the excavation
          sequence.

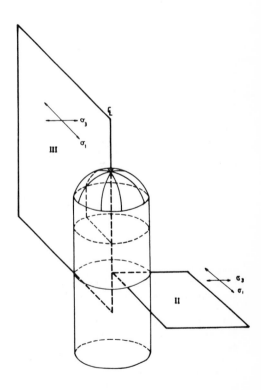

Fig. 5   Model II, Planar case and
          Model III, Plane strain case.

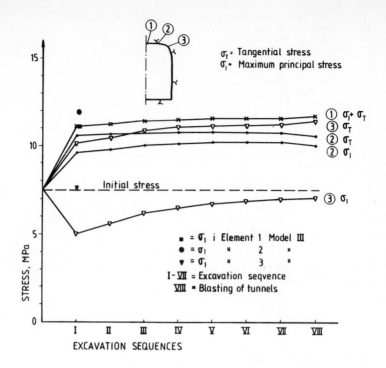

Fig. 6 Calculated stresses in the dome.

3.2 Calculation results

The stress situation in the dome and the stress changes due to the excavation sequences are illustrated in Fig. 6. The stresses in three elements are given, the first in the crown, the second situated 7.5 m away from the central line, and the last in the abutment. In the figure, the results from the analysis of models I and III are given. The results do not differ very much, which is quite natural since plastic strains occur and therefore the stresses are governed by the strength value.

The unfavourable assumption for model III means that the plastic zone is much deeper, about 3.5 m instead of less than 1 m in model I. The conclusion was that a bolt length of about 4 m should be sufficient, even if the worst conditions should occur. The calculated vertical deformations in the crown were very small, less than 1 mm. The load in the rock support was low. The stresses in the shotcrete layer were up to 4 MPa and

the load on the bolts was around 10 to 20 kN.

The stress situation in the walls is shown in Fig. 7.

The figure shows that the stress situation depends on the anisotropic stress field. The stresses calculated from model I lie just between the results from model II. The plastic zone is about 1.5 m in model I and in the case of model II, the zone varies between 0 and 3 m depending on the orientation. The deformations in model II varied between 2 and 11 mm. The maximum value occurred in the wall against the maximum horizontal initial stress. the deformation of the walls was 16 mm in model I.

The degree of utilization of the rock mass strength after excavation of the complete silo is shown in Fig. 8.

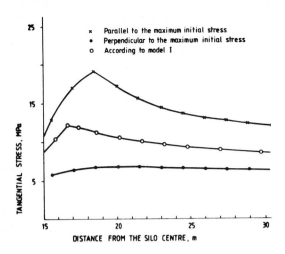

Fig. 7   Calculated stresses in the
          walls.

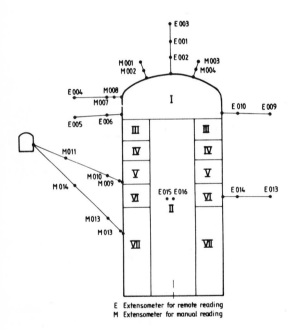

E Extensometer for remote reading
M Extensometer for manual reading

Fig. 9   Location of the extensometers
          around the silo.

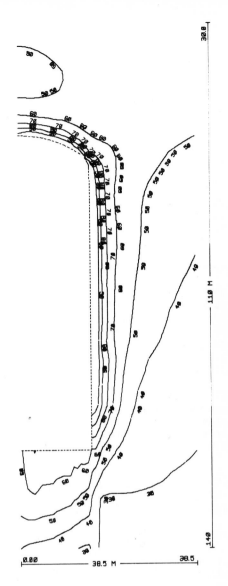

Fig. 8   Degree of utilization of the
          rock mass strength.

4   MONITORING SYSTEM

A monitoring system with extensometers
was installed in order to follow the
deformations in the rock during the
excavation, and also to study the
long-term behaviour. The very large
dimensions of the silo implied that

remote reading of most of the extensometers was necessary. The location and
system for notation of the extensometers are shown in Fig. 9. The monitoring system was designed by the Royal
Institute and ADG Grundteknik. Some
problems occurred in connection with
the electric system for the remote
reading due to moisture, salinity in
the groundwater and damage from the
excavation work, and involved some repair work.

The extensometers in the dome were installed from a pilot tunnel. The extensometers in the walls were installed from the bench when the excavation passed by alongside the 50 m long extensometers which were installed from a transportation tunnel before the excavation of the benches started.

5 Comparison between measured and calculated deformations

The results from the measurements indicated very small deformations of up to 5 mm. The measured deformations are presented in Fig. 10 - 15 as a function of the different excavation sequences given in Fig. 4. Positive values correspond to deformations inwards in the silo. In the figures, the corresponding calculated deformations are also presented. In general, there is very close agreement between calculated and measured deformations both as regards magnitude and trend, even if some disparity may be found.

The deformations of the crown were some millimeters bigger than calculated. Nearly all of the deformations in the dome occurred in connection with the excavation of the dome.

The deformations of the walls followed the calculated results more closely. The deformations were also more dependent on the excavation depth.

The electrical measuring device for extensometer E 005 had to be changed between excavation sequences II and III, which may explain the divergent result.

The disparity between measured and calculated deformations for the 50 m long extensometers indicates problems in connection with measurement accuracy. Even a small amount of friction between the steel rod and the surrounding plastic tube may be sufficiently large to prevent the very long extensometers from working properly for deformations as small as a couple of millimeters.

The extensometers in the walls were installed in different directions in order to study the effect of stress anisotrophy on the wall displacements.

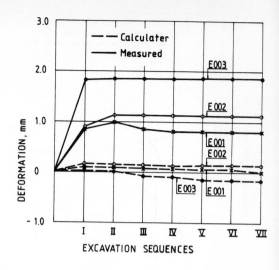

Fig. 10   Deformations in the crown of the dome.

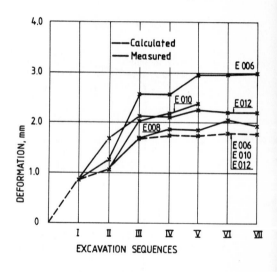

Fig. 11   Deformations in the 5 m long extensometers in the abutment.

The measured deformation pattern in the walls cannot be interpreted unambiguously as being a result of the stress situation.

6 CONCLUSION

The excavation of the large silo has been carried out without any significant rock engineering problems. The

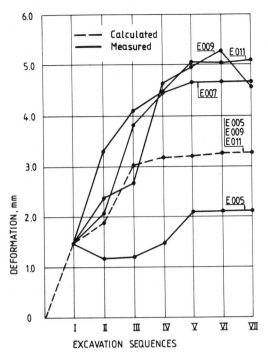

Fig. 12   Deformations in the 15 m long
extensometers in the abutment.

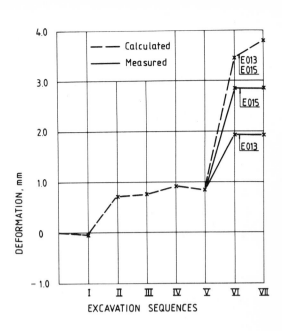

Fig. 14   Deformations in the 15 m long
extensometers in the walls.

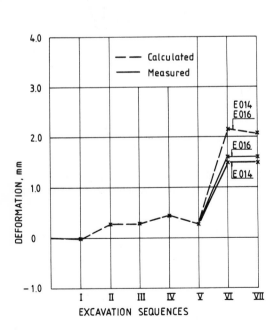

Fig. 13   Deformations in the 5 m long
extensometers in the walls.

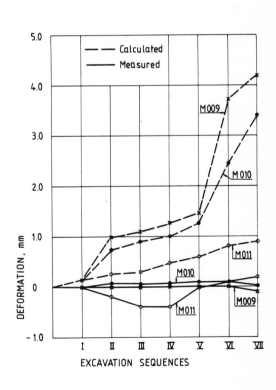

Fig. 15a Deformations in the 50 m long
extensometers in the walls.

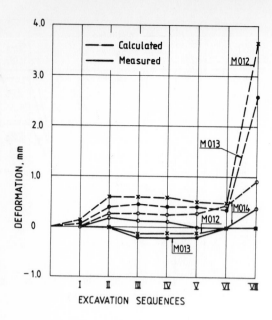

Fig. 15b Deformations in the 50 m long
  extensometers in the walls.

roof of the dome was supported by
means of 3.6 m long untensioned rock
bolts with 1.75 m spacing, and an approximately 10 cm thick layer of
steel-fibre-reinforced shotcrete. In
the walls of the silo mainly 3 m long
bolts were used with an average spacing of 2 m. The walls were protected
with a 3-5 cm thick layer of shotcrete. The behaviour of the silo was
analysed by means of the Finite Element Method and followed up by
measurements during the excavation.
Close agreement was obtained between
the measured and calculated
deformations.

REFERENCES

1. Barton N. et al, (1980). Appli-
    cation of Q-system in design de-
    cisions concerning dimensions and
    appropriate support for under-
    ground installations. Proc. Rock-
    store '80 Symp., Stockholm,
    Sweden, Vol. 2, pp. 553-561.
    Pergamon Press, Oxford.
2. Bieniawski Z. T. (1979). The geo-
    mechanics classification in rock
    engineering applications. Proc.
    4th Congr. Int. Soc. Rock Mech.,
    Montreux, Switzerland, Vol. 2,
    pp. 41-48.
3. Carlsson A., Christiansson R.,
    (1986). Rock stress and geological
    structures in the Forsmark area
    (to be published in this sym-
    posium).
4. Carlsson A., Hedman T., (1986).
    Tunnelling of the Swedish undersea
    repository for low and inter-
    mediate reactor waste. Seikan
    Colloquium, Japan Tunnelling
    Association, Tokyo (in press).
5. Carlsson A., Olsson T. and Stille
    H. (1985). Submarine Tunnelling in
    poor rock. Tunnelling 85. Proc of
    the fourth Int. Symp., the Insti-
    tution of Mining and Metallurgy,
    149-157, Brighton.
6. Fredriksson A. (1985). Analysis of
    geotechnical problems with Finite
    Element Method. Ph.D thesis. Royal
    Institute of Technology, Stock-
    holm. (In Swedish).
7. Larsson H., Christiansson R.,
    (1985). A silo in bedrock for
    nuclear waste. Int. symposium of
    Large Caverns. Helsinki. (To be
    published).
8. Stille H., Groth T., Fredriksson
    A. (1982). FEM analysis of rock
    mechanical problems with JOBFEM.
    BeFo No. 307:1/82, Stiftelsen
    Bergteknisk Forskning, Stockholm.
    (In Swedish).

Initial stress back analyzed from displacements due to underground excavations

S. SAKURAI
N. SHIMIZU
Kobe University, Department of Civil Engineering, Kobe, Japan

ABSTRACT: This paper describes a back analysis method for determining the initial stress and elastic constants of the ground, using the displacements measured during the excavation of underground openings. This method is formulated by the three dimensional boundary element method, so that the three dimensional state of initial stress can be obtained. A case study is presented here to demonstrate the applicability of this method.

1 INTRODUCTION

In the design of underground openings, initial stress as well as mechanical characteristics of rock masses must first be determined by in-situ tests. The overcoring stress relief method and hydrofracturing tests are commonly applied for determination of initial stress. However, the validity of the initial stress determined by these methods is limited to the immediate vicinity of the testing points in the ground, and in general, is not uniformly distributed throughout the ground. In addition, determination of the distribution of initial stress all over the region under consideration is restricted by technical and financial difficulties. Therefore, initial stress obtained at some local points cannot directly be used in the design of underground openings. The average value of initial stress evaluated throughout the surrounding ground in relation to the size of the underground opening is of uppermost importance.

One of the most promising ways to determine the average value of initial stress is to back analyze the field measurements taken of the deformations of underground openings. Displacement measurements such as convergence and multi-point borehole extensometer measurements are desirable because of the simplicity of instrumentation, and the reliability of data obtained. Initial stress and material properties can then be determined by so-called back analysis of these measured displacements.

Back analysis for determining initial stress and elastic constants from the displacements measured during the excavation of tunnels has been proposed (Sakurai and Takeuchi, 1983; Sakurai and Shinji, 1984). It was formulated by the finite element method, and its computer programme is called "Direct Back Analysis Programme (DBAP)". This method has already been used in various projects dealing with underground openings (Sakurai, 1983a ; Sakurai, Hongoh and Tanigawa, 1986).

Plasticity constants such as cohesion and friction angle can also be determined from measured displacements of the ground (Gioda and Maier 1980 ; Sakurai,1983b ; Sakurai, Shimizu and Matsumuro, 1985).

Although the principle of each method mentioned above is the same for both two and three dimensional problems, the methods are only applicable to the two dimension cases.

Therefore, this paper describes three dimensional back analysis that is based on "DBAP", but formulated by the three dimensional boundary element method. A case study demonstrating the applicability of this method to a practical problem is presented.

2 ASSUMPTIONS

The objective of the back analysis method described herein is to determine the average initial stress and Young's modulus of the ground materials from displacements measured during the excavation of underground openings.

The following assumptions are made ;

1.The mechanical behaviour of the ground is idealized by an isotropic

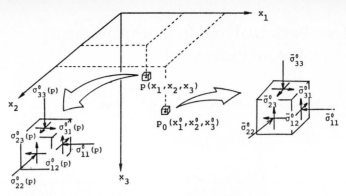

Fig. 1 Initial state of stress

linear-elastic model, so that the material constants reduce to Young's modulus and Poisson's ratio. Since Poisson's ratio has less influence on the results of an analysis, an appropriate value can be assumed.

2. The vertical component of initial stress is approximately equal to the overburden pressure, and the principal direction of initial stress does not change all over the region under consideration. This assumption leads to the initial stress at a point $p(x_1, x_2, x_3)$ representing as follows,

$$\sigma_{ij}^0(\mathbf{p}) = \lambda(\mathbf{p}) \bar{\sigma}_{ij}^0 \; ; \; \lambda(\mathbf{p}) = x_3/x_3^0 (1)$$

where $\bar{\sigma}_{ij}^0$ is the initial stress at the datum point $\mathbf{p}_0$ (see Fig.1).

3 OUTLINE OF THREE DIMENSIONAL BACK ANALYSIS

This back analysis is formulated by the three dimensional boundary element method. Since the detailed formulation of this back analysis will be presented elsewhere (Sakurai and Shimizu, 1986), only a brief description is given here.

Displacement due to the excavation at a point $\mathbf{p}$ in the ground (see Fig.2) is derived from the well-known Somigliala's identity as follows,

$$u_i(\mathbf{p}) = \int_S U_{ki}(\mathbf{q}, \mathbf{p}) t_k(\mathbf{q}) dS_{\mathbf{q}}$$
$$- \int_S T_{ki}(\mathbf{q}, \mathbf{p}) u_k(\mathbf{q}) dS_{\mathbf{q}} \quad (2)$$

where $U_{ki}(\mathbf{p}, \mathbf{q})$ is the Kelvin solution, corresponding to a concentrated force acting at the point $\mathbf{p}$ in the infinite elastic space.

$$U_{ij}(\mathbf{q}, \mathbf{p}) = (1+\nu)/[8\pi E(1-\nu)r] \cdot$$
$$\cdot [(3-4\nu)\delta_{ij} + r_{,i} r_{,j}]$$

where, δ_{ij} is Kronecker's delta, r is the distance between points $\mathbf{p}$ and $\mathbf{q}$, and E and ν denote Young's modulus and Poisson's ratio, respectively. $T_{ij}(\mathbf{p}, \mathbf{q})$ is the fundamental solution of traction, corresponding to the Kelvin solution. Traction vector $t_i(\mathbf{q})$ is given as follows,

$$t_i(\mathbf{q}) = -n_j(\mathbf{q}) \sigma_{ji}^0(\mathbf{q}) \quad (3)$$

where $n_j(\mathbf{q})$ denotes the normal unit vector at point $\mathbf{q}$ on the surface of the underground opening.

The following linear relationship between displacements {u} and initial stress can be derived from eqns. (1)-(3).

$$\{u\} = \frac{1}{E} [F]\{\sigma^0\} = [F] \{\sigma_0^*\} \quad (4)$$

where $\{\sigma_0^*\}$ is defined as $\{\bar{\sigma}_{11}^0/E$ $\bar{\sigma}_{22}^0/E \; \bar{\sigma}_{33}^0/E \; \bar{\sigma}_{23}^0/E \; \bar{\sigma}_{31}^0/E \; \bar{\sigma}_{12}^0/E \}^T$, and is called the "normalized initial stress". E denotes Young's modulus of the ground. It should be noted that matrix [F] is only a function of Poisson's ratio and the location at which the displacements are measured.

Equation (4) consists of the same number of equations as the number of data of displacement measurements, and contains six unknown values of the normalized initial stress. If the number of measurements is six, eqn.(4) gives a simultaneous equation to solve the normalized initial stress, and if greater than six, the normalized initial stress can be determined by an optimization procedure. When adopting the least squares method, eqn.(4) yields,

$$\{\sigma_0^*\} = ([F]^T[F])^{-1}[F]^T \{u_m\} \quad (5)$$

where $\{u_m\}$ is a vector of the measured

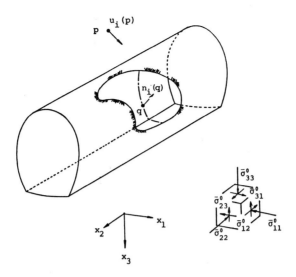

Fig. 2 Displacements due to excavation of an underground opening

displacements. This equation gives the normalized initial stress uniquely determined from the measured displacements by assuming Poisson's ratio. It is noted that in eqn.(4) the measurement of relative displacement between two measurement points as well as absolute displacements can be used as input data (Gioda and Jurina, 1981; Sakurai and Takeuchi, 1983). It follows that simple convergence measurements alone carried out at the surface of underground openings are sufficient for this method.

The components of initial stress and Young's modulus can be separated from the normalized initial stress by assuming that vertical stress is equal to the overburden pressure, i.e.,

$$\bar{\sigma}_{33}{}^0 = \gamma \cdot x_3{}^0 \qquad (6)$$

where $x_3{}^0$ and γ denote the overburden at the datum point and the specific weight of the ground, respectively.

4 ILLUSTRATIVE EXAMPLE

To demonstrate the applicability of the proposed back analysis for engineering practices, a case study of an underground powerhouse is shown here.

The underground powerhouse is located with an overburden of about 200 m. The cavern is shaped like the head of bullet and is 28.6 m high, 16.5 m wide and 25.1 m long, as shown in Fig.3 together with the arrangement of the measurements.

The back analysis was conducted using

the measured displacements at the period of completion of the 4th excavation stage (see Table 1). Assumption of $\nu = 0.3$ leads immediately to the normalized initial stress.

$$\bar{\sigma}_{11}{}^0/E = 0.90E\text{-}03$$

$$\bar{\sigma}_{22}{}^0/E = 0.72E\text{-}03$$

$$\bar{\sigma}_{33}{}^0/E = 0.40E\text{-}03$$

$$\bar{\sigma}_{23}{}^0/E = -0.15E\text{-}03$$

$$\bar{\sigma}_{31}{}^0/E = 0.65E\text{-}03$$

$$\bar{\sigma}_{12}{}^0/E = 0.69E\text{-}03$$

The normalized initial stress obtained may now be split into initial stress and Young's modulus by assuming the vertical component of initial stress.

$$\bar{\sigma}_{33}{}^0 = \gamma \cdot x_3{}^0$$

$$= 23.5(kn/m3) \ast 200(m) = 4.70 \text{ MPa}$$

and

$$E = 11.75 \text{ GPa}$$

$$\bar{\sigma}_{11}{}^0 = 10.58 \text{ MPa}$$

$$\bar{\sigma}_{22}{}^0 = 8.46 \text{ Mpa}$$

$$\bar{\sigma}_{23}{}^0 = -1.76 \text{ MPa}$$

$$\bar{\sigma}_{31}{}^0 = 7.64 \text{ MPa}$$

$$\bar{\sigma}_{12}{}^0 = 8.11 \text{ MPa}$$

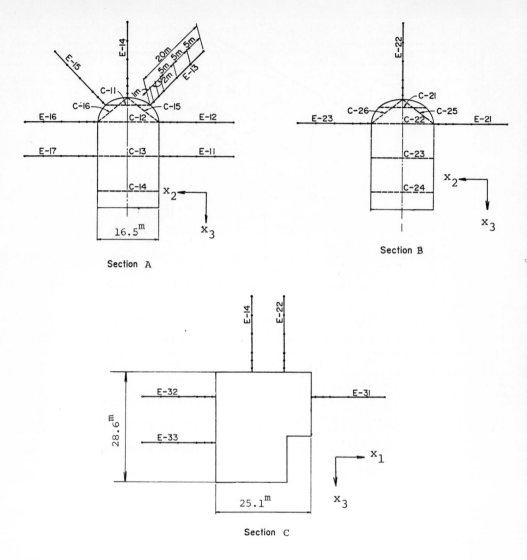

Fig. 3 Shape of cavern and arrangement of instruments

Displacement distribution in the surrounding ground is now computed by means of an ordinary boundary element analysis utilizing the initial stress and Young's modulus as input data. The corresponding results are illustrated in Fig.4. One can see the computed and measured displacements agree fairly well. The only large discrepancy appears at the extensometer E-14 installed at the arch crown. This may be due to the separation of discontinuous geological formations, which is caused by the gravitational force.

5 CONCLUSION

In this paper the authors have described the method of back analysis used to determine initial stress and Young's modulus of the ground, from displacements measured during excavation of underground openings. Since this method is based on the three dimensional boundary element method, the sequence of steps for excavation and the period for installation of measuring instruments can easily be considered in the back analysis. In order to verify the applicability of the methods, a case study has been presented.

Table 1　Installation of measuring instruments and sequence of excavation step

Stage	Excavation　step	Installation of extensometers	convergence lines
Arch 3		E-14　E-22 E-15　　E-13	section A & B C-11 C-21
Lift 1		E-12 E-16　　E-21 E-23　　E-31	section A & B C-16　　C-15 C-26　　C-25 C-12 C-22
Lift 4			

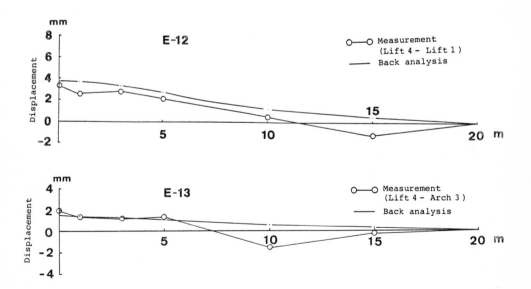

Fig. 4　Comparison between measured and back analyzed displacements

(to be continued)

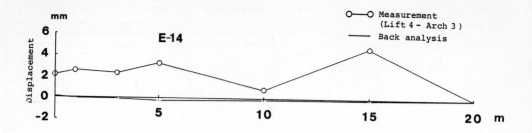

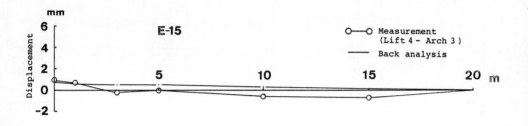

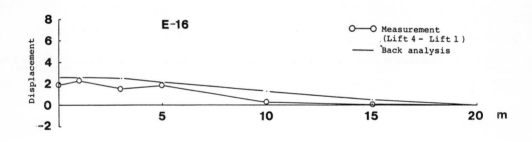

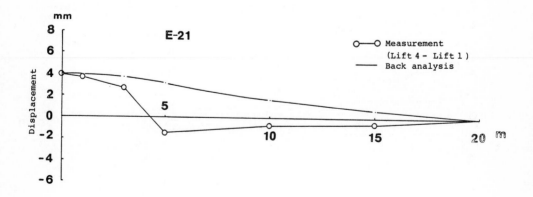

Fig. 4 (to be continued)

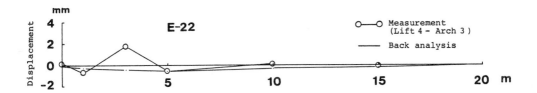

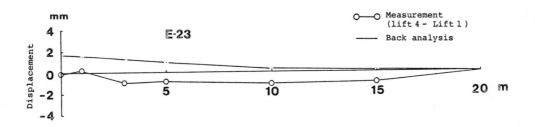

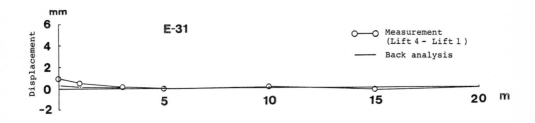

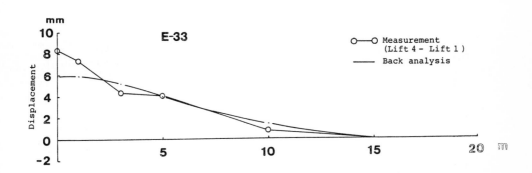

Fig. 4   (to be continued)

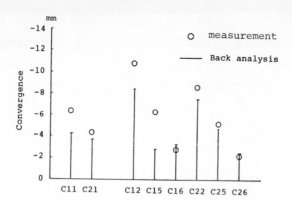

Fig. 4

ACKNOWLEDGEMENTS

The authors are much obliged to Kansai Electric Power Company and New Japan Engineering Consultants Inc. for their valuable contribution to various aspects of the case study reported.

The authors are also grateful to former graduate student Mr. Tsubouchi for his assistance in the numerical computation.

REFERENCES

Gioda, G. and G. Maier 1980. Direct Search Solution of an Inverse Problem in Elasto-plasticity: Identification of Cohesion, Friction Angle and In Situ Stress by Pressure Tunnel Test. Int.J.Numer.Methods in Engineering 15: 1823-1848.

Gioda, G. and L. Jurina 1981. Numerical Identification of Soil Structure Interaction Pressures. Int.J.Numer. Anal. Methods in Geomechanics 5: 33-56.

Sakurai, S. and K. Takeuchi 1983. Back Analysis of Measured Displacements of Tunnels. Rock Mechanics and Rock Engineering 16: 173-180.

Sakurai,S. 1983a. Field Measurements for the Design of the Washuzan Tunnel in Japan. Proc.Int.Congress on Rock Mechanics, Melbourne, A: 215-218.

Sakurai, S. 1983b. Displacement Measurements Associated with the Design of Underground Openings. Proc. Int.Sympo. on Field Measurements in Geomechanics, Zurich: 1163-1178.

Sakurai, S. and M. Shinji 1984. A Monitoring system for the Excavation of the Underground Openings based on Microcomputers. Proc.ISRM Sympo. Cambridge: 471-476.

Sakurai, S., N. Shimizu and K.Matsumuro 1985. Evaluation of Plastic Zone around Underground Openings by Means of Displacement Measurements. Proc. 5th Int.Conf. on Numer.methods in Geomechanics, Nagoya, 1: 111-118.

Sakurai, S., T. Hongoh and M. Tanigawa 1986. Excavation Control of Underground Powerhouse Cavern. Int.Sympo. on Large Rock Caverns, Helsinki, (to appear)

Sakurai, S. and N. Shimizu 1986. Three Dimensional Back Analysis of Measured Displacements of Underground Openings by Means of the Boundary Element Method. (in preparation)

Proceedings of the International Symposium on Rock Stress and Rock Stress Measurements/Stockholm/1-3 September 1986

The effect of residual stress and drill holes size on the in situ stress determined by overcoring

P.A. LANG
P.M. THOMPSON
L.K.W. NG
Atomic Energy of Canada Ltd, Pinawa, Manitoba, Canada

ABSTRACT

Concentric overcoring tests with first 200-mm-, then 150-mm- and finally 96-mm-diameter overcoring bits were conducted to determine the effect of residual stress and of overcore diameter on the in situ stress measurement results obtained by the overcoring method. The tests were conducted in unfractured granite at the 240-m depth in the Underground Research Laboratory, Manitoba, Canada. The results indicate that: 1) the residual stress at the test site is small (1.5 to 2.5% of the applied stress) and its effect can be neglected in determining the in situ stresses by the overcoring method, 2) if careful test procedures are used, the results obtained from overcoring with a 96-mm diameter are not significantly different from results with a 150-mm or a 200-mm diameter, 3) the best overall assessment of the in-situ state of stress is obtained by overcoring with the 96-mm-diameter overcore bit because of the larger number of tests (larger statistical sample) that can be performed for a given cost. These conclusions may be site specific.

RÉSUMÉ

On a mené des essais de surcarottage d'abord au trépan de 200 mm de diamètre, ensuite au trépan de 150 mm de diamètre eet enfin au trépan de 96 mm de diamètre de surcarottage sur les résultats de mesure de la contrainte in situ obtenus avec la technique de surcarottage. On a effectué less assais en Recherches Souterrain, à Lac du Bonnet, Manitoba, Canada. Les résultats indiquent que: 1) la contrainte résiduelle au lieu des assais est faible, (1,5 à 2,5% de la contrainte appliquée) et on peut négliger son effet lors surcarottage; 2) avec des techniques d'essai rigoureuses, la différence obtenus par surcarottage à un diamètre de 96 mm et ceux obtenus par surcarottage à des diamètres de 150 ou 200 mm est insignifiante; 3) la meilleure évaluation globale de l'état de containte in situ est par d'essais (carotte statistique plus grande) qu'il est possible d'exécuter pour un coût donné. Ces conclusions pourraient être particulières au lieu des essais.

ZUSAMMENFASSUNG

Es wurden konzentrische Doppelkernbohrungen mit einem Bohrerdurchmesser von 200 mm, 150 mm und 96 mm durchgeführt, um den Einfluß der residualen Spannung sowie den des Durchmessers der Doppelkernbohrung auf die Ergebnisse der in situ Spannungsmessung mit der Methode der Doppelkernborhrung zu ermitteln. Die Untersuchungen wurden in bruchfreiem Granit in einer Tiefe von 240 m im Untergrund Forschungslabor in Manitoba, Kanada, durchgeführt. Die Ergebnisse zeigen daß: 1) die residuale Spannung am Messort klein ist (1,5 bis 2,5% der angewandten Spannung), und daß ihr Einfluß bei der Bestimmung der in situ Spannung mit der Doppelkernmethode vernachläßigt werden kann, 2) wenn sorgfältig gemessen wird, sind die Ergebnisse mit der konzentrischen Doppelkernmethode mit dem Bohrdurchmesser von 96 mm nicht wesentlich unterschiedlich, verglichen mit den Ergebnissen für Bohrungen mit Durchmessern von 150 mm und 200 mm, 3) die beste Gesamtabschätzung der in situ Spannung wurde mit der Bohrung von 96 mm Bohrdurchmesser bestimmt, da eine größere Anzahl von Untersuchungen (eine größere statistische Menge) für einen fest vorgegebenen Preis durchgeführt werden kann. Die Ergebnisse können vom Ort der Bohrung abhängen.

INTRODUCTION

The natural state of stress in a rock mass is made up of two components; the applied stress and the residual stress (Friedman 1972, Bielenstein and Barron 1971). The applied stress is due to tectonic, gravitational or other applied forces. When a piece of rock is removed from its environment (e.g., by overcoring) the applied stresses are removed. The piece of rock relaxes accordingly. However, the piece of rock still contains residual stress. This is stress locked into the piece of rock within the grains and along grain boundaries. The effect of the residual stress can be measured by cutting the piece of rock into successively smaller pieces (Friedman 1972, Nicols 1975). Each time a piece is cut off, some residual stress is removed and the piece of rock deforms accordingly.

Leijon (1983) suggested that, at the Basalt Waste Isolation Project at Hanford, Washington, residual stress may be a significant component of the stress relieved during overcoring. We conducted the tests described in this paper to determine the magnitude of the residual stress in the granite at the Underground Research Laboratory (URL)*, and to see if it was a factor that needed to be considered in the analysis of the overcore tests at the URL.

A second factor that may have an effect on the overcore results is the diameter of the overcore. Investigators in the USA, Canada and the United Kingdom generally prefer to use a 150-mm-diameter because:

· the core is less likely to break in weak rock,
· heat generated by the overcoring bit has less effect on the results,
· small-scale inhomogeneities have less effect on the results.

Investigators in Sweden prefer to use a 88-mm diameter because:

· it is more economical
· there is less residual stress left in the sample.

The 96-mm diameter has been used extensively in the Canadian Shield

---
* see next section for details.

(Herget 1973) largely because about twice as many 96-mm-diameter tests can be conducted as 150-mm-diameter tests for the same cost. At the URL we decided to use 96-mm diameter because core breakage is not a problem in the excellent rock conditions at the URL, and the heat problem is largely overcome by accurately controlling the drill water temperature. Most importantly, it was felt that, because of the natural variation of the in situ stresses in a rock mass, the larger number of tests possible with the 96-mm diameter were needed to reduce the uncertainty in the results (Doe, Hustrulid and Leijon 1981). It was believed that the errors due to insufficient tests were greater than the errors created by using the 96-mm diameter instead of the 150-mm diameter. However, before we embarked on a program of some 300 overcore tests over a period of a year (Thompson, Baumgartner and Lang 1984), we decided to conduct the tests described in this paper to determine whether using the 96-mm size would have a significant effect on the results.

This paper describes the tests conducted at the URL to determine the effect of residual stress and of overcore diameter on the in-situ stresses determined by the overcoring method.

DESCRIPTION OF THE TEST SITE

Atomic Energy of Canada Limited's URL is being constructed in a previously undisturbed granite pluton of the Canadian Shield (Simmons and Soonawala 1982; Davison and Simmons 1983; Thompson, Baumgartner and Lang, 1984; Lang and Thompson 1985). The site is 100 km east of Winnipeg, Manitoba. The URL is being constructed as part of a comprehensive program to evaluate the concept of nuclear fuel waste disposal deep in stable rock formations.

At present the URL consists of a 4.9 m by 2.8 m rectangular shaft to a 255-m depth, with shaft stations at the 130-m and 240-m depths.

The tests described in this paper were conducted in the rock around Room 206, a 15-m long, 3.5-m high by 3-m wide heading off the lower shaft station. The test hole locations are shown on Figure 1.

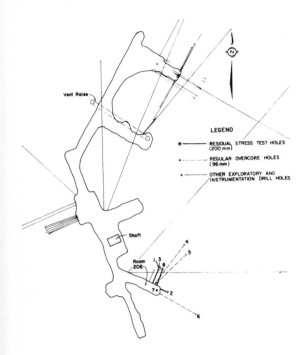

FIG. 1 Plan of Lower Shaft Station showing drill holes

The geology of the heading is shown on Figure 2 (Everitt, Pers. Comm.). The rock in the test area is a homogenous to slightly gneissic, medium grained (1 – 5 mm) grey granite. No natural fractures intersect the 15-m long drift or any of the drill holes within 15 m of the drift. Because of the uniform rock conditions and the lack of any natural fractures this area is considered an ideal site for these tests.

The average far field in-situ stresses in the test area are shown on Figure 3. These were obtained from 22 USBM tests in three 96-mm diameter, 15-m long, nearly orthogonal drill holes (see Figure 1).

TEST PROCEDURE

The general principle was to install either a USBM borehole deformation gauge (Hooker and Bickel 1974; Hooker, Aggson and Bickel 1974) or a modified* CSIR triaxial strain cell

* The CSIR cell has been modified by AECL to allow strains and temperature to be monitored during overcoring.

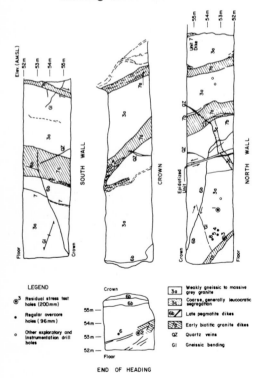

FIG. 2 Geology of walls and crown of Room 206 (view from outside)

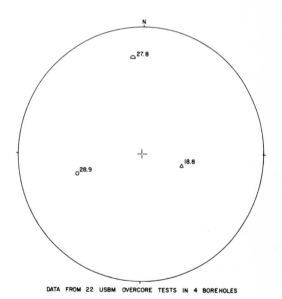

DATA FROM 22 USBM OVERCORE TESTS IN 4 BOREHOLES

		σ (MPa)	SE	DIP	AZ.
O	σ_1	28.9	0.3	33	253
D	σ_2	27.8	0.2	16	354
Δ	σ_3	18.8	0.3	53	105

FIG. 3 Stereoplot of far field in situ stresses in Room 206 area

(Leeman 1969; CSIR 1973; Thompson, Lang and Snider 1986) in a 38-mm-diameter drill hole, then overcore the gauge (or cell) with concentric drill holes (see Figure 4). The gauge (or cell) was overcored first with a 200-mm-, then with a 150-mm-, and finally with a 96-mm-diameter drill bit. (The actual inside and outside dimensions are listed in Table 1.) The concept was that the 200-mm-size overcore would relieve all the applied stress. Any additional stress relief during overcoring with the 150-mm and 96-mm sizes would be due to release of residual stress locked in the rock. Furthermore, significant differences between the results from the 150-mm and 96-mm sizes would indicate that the results are drill-hole size dependent and that the more economical 96-mm size may not be suitable.

The testing was done in two stages. In the first stage, two holes in different directions were used so that if there was any orientation dependency, it could be detected. Three USBM tests were done in each hole. This number of tests was considered necessary to ensure a conclusive result, allowing for the natural variation of stresses that occurs in a rock mass. A third hole was added later because of various problems with the tests in one of the first holes, and

TABLE 1: Drill Bit Dimensions

NOMINAL SIZE (mm)	HOLE DIAMETER (mm)	CORE DIAMETER (mm)
200	204.5	195.1
150	152.9	144.5
96	96.0	86.7
38	37.7	21.5

because no triaxial testing had been done in the first holes. Two CSIR and one USBM test were conducted in the third hole.

The tests started at about 2 m and continued to about 5 m from the excavation wall. The fact that the tests were done within the zone of stress perturbation around the excavation is not important because we are interested only in the amount of residual stress. It does not matter that the applied stress is perturbed by the proximity of the excavation*.

---

*   This may not be strictly correct (see Billenstein and Barron 1971) but any effect would be much smaller than is measureable with the instruments used for this study.

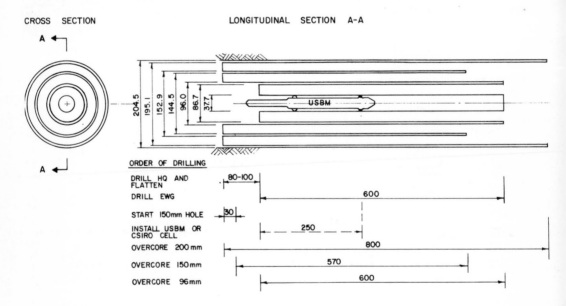

FIG. 4   Sections showing drill hole dimensions, and lengths drilled, for the residual strain tests

The temperature of drill water entering and exiting the drill hole was monitored throughout the tests. For the CSIR tests only, the temperature at the cell was also monitored. The temperature of the water entering the drill hole was maintained, within $\pm$ 0.2°C, at 0.5°C below the in situ rock temperature. For the USBM tests the outlet temperature was maintained within 2°C of the in-situ rock temperature by controlling the flow rate. For the CSIR tests the cell temperature was maintained within 2°C of the in-situ rock temperature by controlling the flow rate.

Time-dependent stress relaxation was monitored for up to two hours after each overcore test.

RESULTS

Example overcore plots from a USBM and a CSIR test are shown in Figures 5 and 6. The calculated stress changes for each overcore size for the seven USBM tests are listed in Table 2 and for the two CSIR tests in Table 3.

The data in Table 2 show that, for the USBM tests, the maximum residual stress relieved during the second or third overcoring, i.e., with the 150- and 96-mm diameters, is about 1 MPa. This is less than 5% of the stress relieved by the first overcoring. On average, the residual stress (that relieved by the 150-mm and 96-mm diameters) is about 1.3% of the applied in-situ stress at the test location (i.e., that relieved by the 200-mm diameter).

Table 3 shows that the conclusions from the two CSIR overcore tests are similar to those from the USBM tests but the average residual stress relieved during the second and third overcorings is slightly higher than with the USBM tests. For the two CSIR tests the average residual stress relieved by the second and third overcorings was 2.5% of the average stress relieved by the first overcoring.

The small response recorded as the 150- and 96-mm bits passed over the

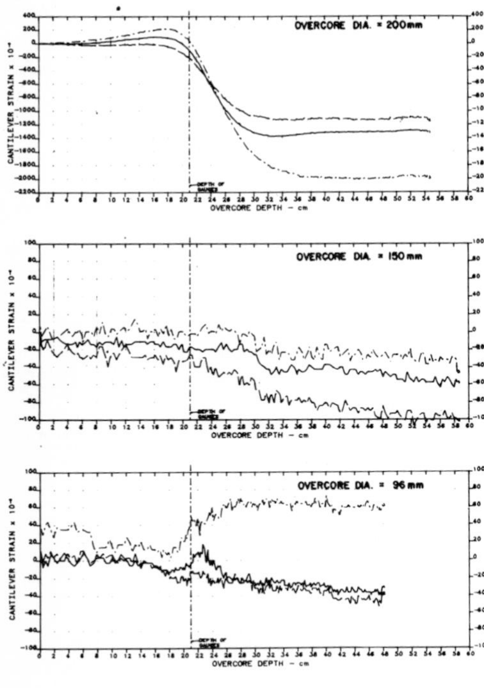

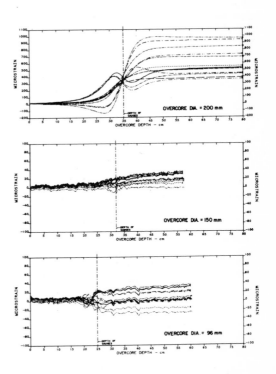

FIG. 5 Typical USBM residual stress overcore test series

FIG. 6 Typical CSIR residual stress overcore test series

gauge (or cell) (see Figures 5 and 6) was within the noise level for these instruments. When the response is interpreted in terms of stress relief the results are quite variable from one test to another. More sensitive instruments and better controlled test conditions would be required to determine the magnitude and direction of the residual stress.

In Figures 7 and 8, the stresses determined from the 200-mm overcore tests are plotted together with the results from standard 96-mm-diameter overcore tests in nearby, similarly oriented, drill holes. There appears to be no significant difference between the stresses determined from 200-mm- and 96-mm-diameter overcoring.

Tables 2 and 3 and Figures 7 and 8 show that the difference between the results of overcoring with the 200-mm, 150-mm or 96-mm size is insignificant at this particular test site.

Time-dependent stress relaxation for the 2 hours following overcoring occurred at the rate of 0.33 µε/min after the 200-mm-diameter overcoring and 0.7µε/min after the 96-mm-diameter overcoring.

TABLE 2:   Results of USBM Residual Strain Overcore Tests

DRILL HOLE NUMBER	TEST DEPTH (m)	DIP DIR. (Az)	200 mm O/C			150 mm O/C			96 mm O/C			NOTES
			P (MPa)	Q (MPa)	DIP OF P	P (MPa)	Q (MPa)	DIP OF P	P (MPa)	Q (MPa)	DIP OF P	
1	2.14	294	22.98	14.60	53	0.24	0.22	-55	0.71	0.44	70	
	3.04		24.61	14.77	46	0.17	-0.09	-80	0.11	-0.50	-65	
	3.63		23.30	14.39	34	0.55	0.37	-29	0.39	-0.45	-57	
			23.63	14.59	44	0.32	0.17	-54	0.40	-0.17	-17	MEAN
			0.41	0.09	4	0.09	0.11	12	0.14	0.25	36	STE.
			3	3	3	3	3	3	3	3	3	n
2	2.31	024	24.75	19.22	15	0.41	-0.64	-27	<0.40	<1.0	-41	1
	3.51		23.79	18.83	26	0.26	-0.24	57	-0.36	-0.52	-55	2
	4.14		20.99	18.85	-13	1.08	0.79	-71	0.00	0.00	0	3
			23.18	18.97	18	0.31	-0.03	-13	-0.36	-0.52	-55	MEAN
			0.92	0.10	3	0.35	0.35	31	—	—	—	STE.
			3	3	3	3	3	3	1	1	1	n
3	3.73	291	22.3	12.26	50.78	0.00	-0.11	-1.9	0.30	-0.45	-77.12	

NOTES:

1. Water pressure fluctuated up to 500 kPa during 96 mm overcore test causing irregular readings. However, even with these fluctuations, changes were less than 1.0 MPa.

2. Gauge moved (settled in) during 200 mm overcore test while overcoring from 3 to 6 cm into test, and it moved again after about 40 cm into test. However, enough information was collected between 6 cm and 40 cm to obtain a reasonable result.

3. Gauge moved during 150 mm overcore test. Stress changes should be less than those indicated. No measureable change was recorded on any channel during the 96 mm overcore test.

LEGEND:

Az - azimuth of dip direction
P - secondary major principal stress in the test plane.
Q - secondary minor principal stress in the test plane.
DIP OF P - in the test plane direction.
STE - standard error
n - number of samples (tests).

TABLE 3:   Results of CSIR Residual Strain Overcore Tests

DRILL HOLE NUMBER	TEST DEPTH (m)	OVERCORE DIA (mm)	σ_1			σ_2			σ_3		
			σ (MPa)	AZ (deg)	DIP (deg)	σ (MPa)	AZ (deg)	DIP (deg)	σ (MPa)	AZ (deg)	DIP (deg)
3	2.08	200	30.34	334	24	27.67	229	30	16.57	96	50
	2.94	200	29.24	197	10	25.94	293	35	17.05	93	54
3	2.08	150	0.65	17	3	0.39	110	45	0.31	284	45
	2.94	150	0.93	2	3	0.58	94	46	0.21	269	44
3	2.08	96	1.79	216	19	0.26	105	44	-0.10	322	40
	2.94	96	0.97	186	11	-0.39	286	43	-0.15	85	46

LEGEND:

Az - Azimuth (direction) of principal stress

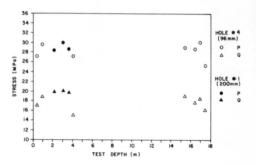

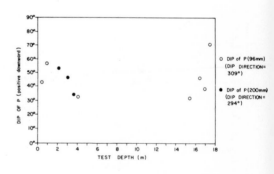

FIG. 7   Comparison of USBM overcore tests from nearby 86-mm- and 200-mm-diameter drill holes. Top: stress magnitude vs. test depth. Bottom: dip of P vs. test depth.

For conventional engineering of underground constructions (for design lives less than about 100 years) the residual stress in this rock mass is insignificant. However, for very long term stability of underground excavations, especially where the rock will be heated, the residual stress and time-dependent relaxation of residual stress may be significant. The residual stress is certainly of interest in working out the geologic history of the site. Therefore, further studies will be conducted to investigate the residual stress and time-dependent stress relief at the URL.

The results reported here may be site specific so the tests should be conducted at other sites to confirm their general applicability.

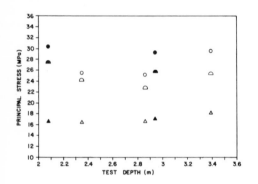

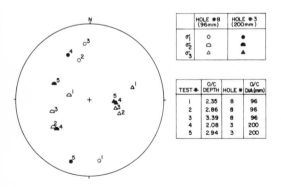

FIG. 8 Comparison of CSIR overcore tests from nearby 86-mm- and 200-mm-diameter drill holes. Top: stress magnitude vs. test depth. Bottom: principal stress orientations

CONCLUSIONS

1. The residual stress in the rock is less than 1 MPa at the URL test site. The average residual stress is about 1.5 to 2.5% (depending on test method used) of the applied stress at this location. The error due to ignoring residual stress in overcoring tests at the URL is considered insignificant compared with the other errors inherent in the overcoring test method.

2. The results from overcoring with 96-mm do not appear to be significantly different from those from the 150-mm or 200-mm sizes.

3. Because of the inherent variability of results of stress measurement in rock, it is considered that, where rock conditions permit, best value is obtained by using the 96-mm diameter and, hence, obtaining a larger number of tests than can be obtained for the same cost using the 150-mm size.

4. These conclusions may be site specific. The tests should be conducted at other sites to confirm their general applicability.

ACKNOWLEDGEMENT

We would like to thank Dr. A. Brown for alerting us to the possible problem of residual stress in the first place and thank Dr. A. Brown, Dr. G. Herget and P. Baumgartner for their helpful suggestions and constructive criticism of this paper.

REFERENCES

Bielenstein, H. V. and K. Barron 1971. in-situ Stresses. In Proceedings of the 7th Canadian Rock Mechanics Symposium, Ontario Mines Branch, Department of Energy, Mines and Resources, Edmonton, Alberta, 1971 March, 25-27.

CSIR, 1973. Instruction manual for the use of the CSIR triaxial rock stress measuring equipment, Report MEG ME 1214, National Mechanical Engineering Research Institute, Pretoria.

Davison, C. C. and G. R. Simmons 1983. The research program at the Canadian Underground Research Laboratory. Proceedings of the Nuclear Energy Agency Workshop on Geological Disposal of Radioactive Waste and in-situ Experiments in Granite. Stockholm, Sweden, 1982, October 25-27, 197-219.

Doe, T., W. A. Hustrulid and B. Leijon 1981. Determination of the state of stress at the Stripa Mine, Sweden. Presented at the USGS Conference on Hydraulic Fracturing Stress Measurements, Monterey, CA., 1981 December 3-5.

Friedman, M. 1972. Residual elastic strain in rocks. Tectonophysics, Vol. 15, No. 4, 297-330.

Herget, G. 1973. First experiences with the CSIR triaxial strain cell for stress determinations. Int J Rock Mech Min Sci & Geom Abstr; Vol 10, pp. 509-522.

Hooker, V. E., J. R. Aggson and D. L. Bickel 1974. Improvements in the borehole deformation gauge and overcoring techniques. U. S. Bureau of Mines. Report of Investigation 7894 (1974), 29 p.

Hooker, V. E. and D. L. Bickel 1974. Overcoring equipment and techniques used in rock stress determination, USBM, IC. 8618, 32 p.

Lang, P. A. and P. M. Thompson. Geomechanics experiments during excavation of the URL shaft. 20th Nuclear Fuel Waste Management Information Meeting, Winnipeg, Manitoba, 1985. Atomic Energy of Canada Technical Record* TR-375.

Leeman, E. R. 1969. The CSIR "Doorstopper" and triaxial rock stress measuring instruments. Proceedings of the International Symposium on the Determination of Stresses in Rock Masses, Lisbon.

Leijon, B. A. 1983. Rock stress measurements with the Luh-gauge at the near surface test facility, Hanford Test Site. Research Report TULEA 1983:18. University of Lulea, Sweden.

Nichols, T. C. 1975. Deformations associated with relocation of residual stresses in a sample of Barre Granite from Vermont. U.S. Geological Survey Professional Paper #875, U.S. Government Printing Office.

Simmons, G. R. and N. Soonawala 1982. Underground Research Laboratory Experimental Program. Atomic Energy of Canada Limited Technical Record, TR-153*.

Thompson, P. M., P. Baumgartner and P. Lang 1984. Planned construction phase geomechanics experiments at the Underground Research Laboratory. Proceedings of the CEC/NEA Workshop on the Design and Instrumentation of In-Situ Experiment in Underground Laboratories for Radioactive Waste Disposal, Brussels, 15-17 May (1984).

Thompson, P. M., P. A. Lang and G. R. Snider 1986. Recent improvements to in-situ stress measurements using the overcoring method. For presentation at the 39th Canadian Geotechnical Conference, Ottawa, August, 1986.

---

* Unrestricted, unpublished report, availble from SDDO, Atomic Energy of Canada Limited Research Company, Chalk River, Ontario K0J 1J0

*Proceedings of the International Symposium on Rock Stress and
Rock Stress Measurements/Stockholm/1-3 September 1986*

ML

#142912 47

ROCK STRESS

AND ROCK STRESS MEASUREMENTS

EDITOR
OVE STEPHANSSON
LULEÅ UNIVERSITY OF TECHNOLOGY, SWEDEN

CENTEK PUBLISHERS

ORGANIZATION

The Symposium was organized by the Swedish National Group of the International Society for Rock Mechanics – ISRM, the Swedish Rock Engineering Research Foundation – Befo and the Luleå University of Technology, Sweden.

HONOURABLE COMMITTEE

PROFESSOR L.A. ENDERSBEE, Monash University, Australia
PROFESSOR C. FAIRHURST, University of Minnesota, USA
PROFESSOR A.E. SCHEIDEGGER, Technical University Vienna, Austria
DOCTOR R. HILTSCHER, Stockholm, Sweden
PROFESSOR N. HAST, Stockholm, Sweden

ORGANIZING COMMITTEE·

STEN BJURSTRÖM, Swedish Nuclear Fuel and Waste Management Co (chairman)
TOMAS FRANZÉN, Swedish Rock Engineering Research Foundation – Befo
TUULA KYRÄS, Centek Congress, (Conference Secretariat)
ARNE MYRVANG, Norwegian Technical University (Nordic representative)
ANNICA NORDMARK, Swedish Rock Engineering Research Foundation – Befo
OVE STEPHANSSON, Luleå University of Technology
PEKKA SÄRKKÄ, Helsinki Technical University, (Nordic representative)

SPONSORSHIP:

The symposium is sponsored by
ISRM
Swedish Nuclear Fuel and Waste Management Co
Swedish State Power Board
City of Stockholm
National Swedish Board for Technical Development

© Centek
Printed by: TECE TRYCK, Luleå, Sweden
Centek Publishers 1986
ISBN 91-86998-17-X

Postal address: S-951 87 Luleå
Phone: +46-920-910 00
Telex: 80207 Centek S